AS YOU EXAMINE

HOLT ALGEBRA 2 WITH TRIGONOMETRY

Please Notice   HOLT ALGEBRA 2 WITH TRIGONOMETRY provides a complete, balanced course designed to be mastered by all second-year algebra students. All of the basic concepts usually studied in a second-year algebra course, along with the fundamental concepts of trigonometry, are found in HOLT ALGEBRA 2 WITH TRIGONOMETRY.

Format   HOLT ALGEBRA 2 WITH TRIGONOMETRY'S four-part lesson format represents a significant innovation in facilitating student learning:

- Lesson objectives on the pupil page
- Worked-out examples demonstrate solution process
- Hints, suggestions, and comments on the pupil page make learning difficult skills and concepts easier
- Graded exercises provide for continuous skill development

Contents

1. The course begins with a review of fundamental algebraic concepts of linear equations and inequalities (see pp. 1–3, 5–6).

2. Worked-out examples focus on teaching the solution process without complicated explanations (see pp. 115–116).

3. Suggestions, hints, and comments encourage students to attempt more difficult skills and concepts (see pp. 264–265).

4. Oral exercises appear before written exercise sets so that the teacher can quickly test understanding and readiness (see page 252).

5. Exercises are plentiful and are graded according to three levels of difficulty. Also, exercises within each level are graded from easiest to most challenging. Examples presented in the lesson match every type of exercise in levels Ⓐ and Ⓑ (see pp. 118, 127, 287).

6. Reading instruction helps students analyze and better understand the language of algebra.

7. Each chapter ends with a Chapter Review and a Chapter Test. The Review is diagnostic and

keys items to lesson pages on which skills and concepts necessary to solve the item are taught.

8. Special topics pages vary the pace and enrich the course. They include practical applications of algebra in the real world, as well as an introduction to careers that use mathematics (see pp. 23, 138, 181, 275).

9. Flow charts guide students through calculator and computer activities and familiarize them with accepted methods of diagramming logical thought processes (see p. 576).

10. Answers to selected exercises are provided in the back of the pupil edition (see pp. 611–632). Worked-out solutions to every problem in the text are available in the separate Solutions Manual.

11. A Teacher's Edition with teaching suggestions and lesson commentary, an Assignment Chart with pacing suggestions for three levels of difficulty, and a complete set of answers makes teaching HOLT ALGEBRA 2 WITH TRIGONOMETRY easy.

Supplementary Materials on Duplicating Masters

- **HOLT ALGEBRA 2 Skillmasters** provide 48 pages of additional exercises and cumulative reviews.
- **HOLT ALGEBRA 2 Tests** provide an alternative form of the Chapter Test.
- **HOLT ALGEBRA 2 Management System** provides assignment sheets, placement tests, and record-keeping forms to aid in individualizing instruction.

Holt Algebra 2
with Trigonometry

Teacher's Edition

About the Authors

Egene D. Nichols
Dinguished Professor of Mathematics Education
at Lecturer Mathematics Department
Flda State University
Tahassee, Florida

Mrvine L. Edwards
Clrman of Mathematics Department
Sh Regional High School
W(Long Branch, New Jersey

E.nry Garland
He of the Mathematics Department
Deopmental Research School
DRofessor
Flo State University
Talssee, Florida

Syr A. Hoffman
Rese Consultant in Mathematics
Illinate Board of Education
Sta Illinois

Alk Mamary
AssiSuperintendent of Schools for Instruction
JohCity Central School District
JohCity, New York

Wil F. Palmer
Profnd Chairman
Depnt of Education
CatCollege, and
Matlcs Consultant
Salisty Schools
Salisorth Carolina

Consulting Author for uter Strand

Barbara L. Kurshan
Assistant Professor, and
Director of Academic Comp
Hollins College
Hollins College, Virginia

Holt Algebra 2 with Trigonometry

Teacher's Edition

Eugene D. Nichols
Mervine L. Edwards
E. Henry Garland
Sylvia A. Hoffman
Albert Mamary
William F. Palmer

HOLT, RINEHART AND WINSTON, PUBLISHERS
New York • Toronto • London • Sydney

Staff Credits

Editorial Development Eleanor R. Spencer, Everett T. Draper, Dennis P. Rogan, Earl D. Paisley, Arlene Grodkiewicz

Editorial Processing Margaret M. Byrne, Regina Chilcoat, Holly L. Massey, Elizabeth Santiago

Art and Production Vivian Fenster, Fred C. Pusterla, Robin M. Swenson, Russel Dian, Annette Sessa-Galbo, Susan Woolhiser, Anita Dickhuth, Ellen Lokiec, Donna Bogdanowich, Richard Haynes

Product Manager John W. M. Cooke

Advisory Board Robert Wolff, Patricia M. Cominsky, Jose Contreras, Roy V. Eliason, C. Paul Moore, Randolph Ragsdale, Kenneth C. Scupp

Consultant Patricia M. Cominsky

Researchers James R. George, Erica S. Felman

ISBN: 0-03-053921-8
 2345   032   98765432

TEACHER'S EDITION

CONTENTS

HOLT ALGEBRA 2 WITH TRIGONOMETRY

Benefits

1. Emphasizes skill development and practical application

2. Frequent worked-out examples guide students through the solution process

3. Algebra-related reading instruction helps students understand mathematical language better

4. Concrete approach to problem solving gives students clear directions in finding solutions

5. College prep tests in each chapter help prepare students for standardized tests

6. Graded exercises promote continuous growth

7. Frequent evaluation keeps students and teachers aware of progress

8. Optional computer activities extend students' experience in this application of technology

9. Optional calculator activities are related to chapter concepts

10. The pupil edition and the teacher edition provide a complete program for Holt Algebra 2

11. A complete solutions manual is available

12. A single management system helps to evaluate Algebra 1 and Algebra 2 student progress

OVERVIEW

Philosophy

Every student can perform optimally with a simple series of feedback/correction procedures. Research and the experience of teachers, supervisors, and administrators across the country support this idea. This is what HOLT ALGEBRA 2 WITH TRIGONOMETRY is all about.

HOLT ALGEBRA 2 WITH TRIGONOMETRY contains all of the major algebra concepts students need to successfully meet the testing demands in your school. In addition to feedback materials, which include tests at the end of each unit with items keyed to lesson objectives, HOLT ALGEBRA 2 WITH TRIGONOMETRY provides materials to supplement basic course work. To challenge gifted and able students, this course includes units and activities on the use of computers and calculators and practice for standardized college admissions tests. Supplementary instructional materials are also available to help those students who need to overcome learning problems.

The instructional advantages of Holt's approach are clear and well documented. First, frequent evaluation—minicumulative reviews after every few lessons, chapter reviews and tests at the end of units, and cumulative reviews after every four chapters—provides continuous feedback for both you and the student. Second, a varied instructional technique provides more students with the opportunity to participate actively in learning and to find an instructional method that best suits their needs. Some students, those who learn more quickly and can work independently, need the challenge provided by

supplements and extensions to the basic course material. Others benefit from experiencing success by solving selected problems that challenge their own levels of competence. HOLT ALGEBRA 2 WITH TRIGONOMETRY addresses the needs of both types of students.

Mathematics teachers generally agree that students need to experience a variety of problems in the same problem-solving context if they are to become adept at using algebraic skills in finding solutions. HOLT ALGEBRA 2 WITH TRIGONOMETRY helps students recognize a wide variety of opportunities to apply skills and concepts from the very first chapter. Using the Read-Plan-Solve-Interpret pattern, students are encouraged to become flexible thinkers who attack problems logically and who recognize the wide application of their algebra skills. As students become more accustomed to flexibility in applying their algebra skills, they are challenged with increasingly difficult problems. This pattern of instruction is characteristic of the approach used throughout HOLT ALGEBRA 2 WITH TRIGONOMETRY.

You need only the Teacher's Edition and the Pupil Edition to have a complete, carefully graded course in Algebra 2. The textbook format makes learning easier for students and allows you to make the best use of your time. Students who learn quickly and who can work independently can get most of the direction they need from the textbook. This allows you to provide more structure and give more direction to students who need it. All of this combines to assure success for you and each of your students.

COURSE CONTENT ORGANIZATION

The contents of HOLT ALGEBRA 2 WITH TRIGONOMETRY provide the teacher with a complete course in second-year algebra skills and concepts and with fundamental concepts of trigonometry.

Chapter 1: A review of fundamental algebraic concepts; introduction to problem solving

Chapter 2: Properties of exponents; addition, subtraction, multiplication of polynomials, problem solving

Chapter 3: Factoring, solving quadratic equations, solving quadratic inequalities, problem solving using quadratic equations

Chapter 4: Operations with rational expressions and simplifying

Chapter 5: Problem solving using equations with rational expressions, division of polynomials, synthetic division

Chapter 6: Operations with radicals and simplifying; operations with rational number exponents

Chapter 7: Quadratic formula in problem solving; Radical equations

Chapter 8: Complex numbers, solving quadratic equations

Chapter 9: Coordinate geometry—slopes of parallel and perpendicular lines

Chapter 10: Solving systems of two or three linear equations; determinants; matrices

Chapter 11: Relations and functions, direct and inverse variations

Chapter 12: Fundamentals of analytic geometry—concepts of the parabola, circle, ellipse, and hyperbola; conics

Chapter 13: Solving systems of equations— linear-quadratic, quadratic-quadratic; solving systems of inequalities

Chapter 14: Arithmetic and geometric progressions, arithmetic and geometric series, binomial expansion

Chapter 15: Logarithms, logarithms of products, quotients, powers, and radicals; logarithms to any base; exponential equations

Chapter 16: Introduction to the counting principle, permutations and combinations, probability of simple and compound events

Chapter 17: Fundamentals of trigonometry— sine, cosine, tangent, cotangent, secant, cosecant functions; functions of negative angles; using the trigonometric tables, including interpolation

Chapter 18: Graphing trigonometric functions, amplitude, periodicity, solving quadratic trigonometric equations, proving trigonometric identities, the radian measure of angles, solving problems using the radian measure of angles

Chapter 19: Law of sines; law of cosines; deriving formulas for sine, cosine, and tangent of the sum and difference of two angle measures

LESSON FORMAT

OBJECTIVES

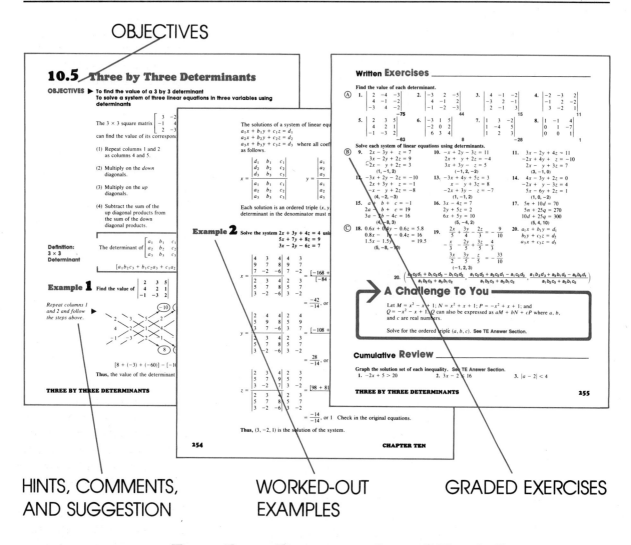

10.5 Three by Three Determinants

OBJECTIVES ▶ To find the value of a 3 by 3 determinant
To solve a system of three linear equations in three variables using determinants

Four-Part Presentation of Each Lesson

1. **Objective** states expected performance in the language of the student.

2. **Worked-Out Examples** demonstrate the solution pattern for the student.

3. **Hints, Comments, and Suggestions** guide the student through the solution process.

4. **Graded Exercises** (levels Ⓐ, Ⓑ, and Ⓒ) provide challenge and promote continuous development for students of all abilities.

HINTS, COMMENTS, AND SUGGESTION

WORKED-OUT EXAMPLES

GRADED EXERCISES

LESSON FEATURES

Definition: Relation	A *relation* is a set of ordered pairs of real numbers.
Domain	The *domain* of a relation is the set of all first coordinates of the ordered pairs.
Range	The *range* of a relation is the set of all second coordinates of the ordered pairs.

Example 1 Factor $3x^2 - 8x + 5$ into two binomials.

$$3x^2 - 8x + 5 = (3x \quad \underset{?}{})(x \quad \underset{?}{})$$

The first terms of the binomial factors are $3x$ and x. The last terms are either $+1$ and $+5$ or -1 and -5. Since the middle term of the trinomial is negative, $(-8x)$, try -1 and -5.

Possible Factors	Middle Term	
$(3x - 1)(x - 5)$	$-15x - x = -16x$	
$(3x - 5)(x - 1)$	$-3x - 5x = -8x$	◀ *Correct middle term:* $-8x$

Thus, $3x^2 - 8x + 5 = (3x - 5)(x - 1)$.

Oral Exercises

Factor each trinomial into two binomials.

1. $x^2 - 7x + 12$
2. $x^2 - 13x + 12$
3. $x^2 + x - 12$
4. $x^2 - x - 12$
5. $x^2 + 8x + 12$
6. $x^2 - 4x - 12$
7. $x^2 + x + 3$
8. $x^2 - 5x + 6$
9. $x^2 - 5x - 6$

Written Exercises

Factor each trinomial into two binomials.

(A)
1. $7x^2 - 12x + 5$
2. $5y^2 - 36y + 7$
3. $5y^2 + 14y - 3$
4. $7n^2 + 4n - 11$
5. $5a^2 - 54a - 11$
6. $3x^2 - 10x - 13$
7. $6x^2 - 7x - 2$
8. $8n^2 + 14n + 3$
9. $2a^2 + a - 10$
10. $2x^2 - 11x + 14$
11. $5x^2 - 28x + 15$
12. $3y^2 + 11y + 6$
13. $9a^2 + 18a + 8$
14. $6t^2 - 11t - 10$
15. $4c^2 - 15c + 9$
16. $15n^2 + 7n - 4$
17. $x^2 + 4xy - 12y^2$
18. $x^2 + 13xy + 36y^2$
19. $x^2 - xy - 12y^2$
20. $8a^2 - 2ab - b^2$
21. $15c^2 - 8cd + d^2$
22. $21m^2 + 10mn + n^2$
23. $x^4 - 9x^2 + 14$
24. $n^4 + 8n^2 + 15$
25. $a^4 - 3a^2 - 18$
26. $10c^4 + 3c^2 - 1$
27. $15a^4 + 16a^2 - 7$
28. $21d^4 - 8d^2 - 5$
29. $x^2 - 14x - 72$
30. $72x^2 + 21x - 1$
31. $64y^2 - 12y - 1$
32. $8a^2 - 5a - 10$
33. $y^2 + 30y - 64$

(B)
34. $10x^2 + 23x + 12$
35. $12n^2 - 17n + 6$
36. $12y^2 - 8y - 15$
37. $18a^2 - 35a + 12$
38. $24x^2 - 46x - 35$
39. $16n^2 + 10n - 21$
40. $20c^2 - 48c + 27$
41. $24a^2 - 5a - 36$
42. $6y^2 + yz - 12z^2$
43. $5x^2 + 4xy - 12y^2$
44. $36m^2 - 7mn - 15n^2$
45. $24c^2 + 17cd - 20d^2$
46. $15x^4 - 8x^2 - 12$
47. $12x^4 - 23x^2 + 10$
48. $18y^4 + 9y^2 - 20$
49. $6y^4 - 23y^2 - 18$
50. $10n^4 - 31n^2 + 24$
51. $9a^4 + 24a^2 - 20$
52. $2x^4y^4 - 7x^2y^2 + 6$
53. $3a^4b^4 - a^2b^2 - 10$
54. $5m^4n^4 + 4m^2n^2 - 12$

CHAPTER FEATURES

Chapter Openers focus on problems in logical thinking, historical and biographical facts, practical problem solving, and careers to motivate students for class discussions of ideas and work in the chapter.

8 COMPLEX NUMBERS
Maria Gaetana Agnesi

Maria Gaetana Agnesi was born in 1782 into a wealthy family of Milan, Italy where her father was a professor of mathematics at the university. She was educated privately and showed outstanding ability at a very early age. At age nine she published a paper defending the right of women to have a liberal arts education, and by the age of thirteen, she knew seven languages.

In her early adult life, much of Maria's time was spent in the study of mathematics. She is most famous for an equation and its corresponding graph that she formulated in her work in analytic geometry. The graph, or curve, is known as "the witch of Agnesi."

Applications of the skills and concepts taught appear in each chapter to help students recognize the importance of practical problem solving.

Applications

Formulate → Plan → Solve → Interpret

1. The frequency of a string under constant tension is inversely proportional to its length. If a string, 40 cm long, vibrates 680 times per second, what length must the string be to vibrate 850 times per second under the same tension? **32 cm**

2. The frequency of a radio wave is inversely proportional to its wavelength. If a radio wave, 30 m long, has a frequency of 1,200 kilocycles per second, what is the length of a wave with a frequency of 900 kilocycles per second? **40 m**

3. Boyle's Law states that the volume of a given mass of gas varies inversely as the absolute pressure, provided the temperature remains constant. If the volume of a gas is 40 in.^{3} when the absolute pressure is 50 lb/in.^{2}, what will be the volume when the pressure is 70 lb/in.^{2}? **28$\frac{4}{7}$ in.^{3}**

4. The kinetic energy, E, of a body varies jointly as its weight, w, and the square of its velocity, V. If a 10-lb body moving at 6 ft/s has 3 ft-lb of kinetic energy, what will the kinetic energy be of a 4-T truck traveling at 50 mi/h? **3.585 × 10^5**

5. The load, l, that a beam of fixed length can support varies jointly as its width, w, and the square of its depth, d. A beam with $w = 4$ and $d = 2$ can support a load of 1,760 kg. Find l when $w = 4$ and $d = 8$.

6. The pressure, P, of a gas varies directly as the temperature, T, and inversely as the volume, V. If $P = 50$ when $T = 25$ and $V = 2$, find P when $T = 40$ and $V = 4$. **40**

7. The force of attraction, F, between two objects varies jointly as their masses, m_1 and m_2, and inversely as the square of the distance, d, between them. When $m_1 = 1$ g, $m_2 = 500$ g, and $d = 5$ cm, then $F = 1.33 \times 10^{-6}$ dynes. Find F when $m_1 = 2$ g, $m_2 = 600$ g, and $d = 6$ cm. **2.216 × 10^{-6} dynes**

8. Refer to Exercise 7. What is the effect on the force of attraction between the two objects if the mass of each is doubled and the distance between them is halved? **force is multiplied by 16**

9. The speed, V, at which a motorcycle must travel on the inside cylinder in order not to fall varies as the square root of the radius of the cylinder. If the motorcycle must travel at least 45 km/h to stay on the side of the cylinder with a radius of 12 m,

10. A conservationist can approximate the number of deer in a forest. Suppose 650 deer are caught, tagged and released. Suppose later 216 deer are caught and 54 of them were tagged. How many deer are in the forest? Assume that the number of

T-12

Reading In Algebra

Determine whether each statement is true or false.

1. $4x^2 - 8x = 0$ is a quadratic equation. **T**
2. $5x - 15 = 0$ is a quadratic equation. **F**
3. A quadratic equation may have two solutions. **T**
4. A fourth degree equation may have four solutions. **T**
5. If $x(x - 5) = 0$, then $x = 0$ or $x - 5 = 0$. **T**
6. If $(x - 1)(x - 3) = 8$, then $x - 1 = 8$ or $x - 3 = 8$. **F**
7. If $(n - 6)(n - 2) = 0$, then $n + 6 = 0$. **F**
8. If $(y - 5)(y - 5) = 0$, then $y = 5$. **T**

Algebra-Related Reading Instruction appears regularly since reading ordinary English effectively does not imply equally effective reading in the language of mathematics. Holt provides students with help in learning the technical language of algebra and trigonometry.

A Challenge To You

Let $M = x^2 - x + 1$; $N = x^2 + x + 1$; $P = -x^2 + x + 1$; and $Q = -x^2 - x + 1$. Q can also be expressed as $aM + bN + cP$ where a, b, and c are real numbers.

Solve for the ordered triple (a, b, c). **See TE Answer Section.**

A Challenge To You provides gifted and able students with problems and activities to challenge them.

In Example 3, you saw the four major steps in solving a word problem.

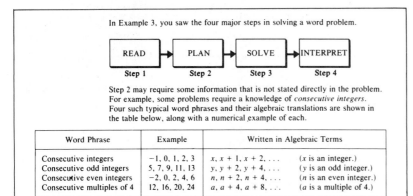

| READ | PLAN | SOLVE | INTERPRET |
| Step 1 | Step 2 | Step 3 | Step 4 |

Step 2 may require some information that is not stated directly in the problem. For example, some problems require a knowledge of *consecutive integers*. Four such typical word phrases and their algebraic translations are shown in the table below, along with a numerical example of each.

Word Phrase	Example	Written in Algebraic Terms	
Consecutive integers	$-1, 0, 1, 2, 3$	$x, x + 1, x + 2, \ldots$	(x is an integer.)
Consecutive odd integers	$5, 7, 9, 11, 13$	$y, y + 2, y + 4, \ldots$	(y is an odd integer.)
Consecutive even integers	$-2, 0, 2, 4, 6$	$n, n + 2, n + 4, \ldots$	(n is an even integer.)
Consecutive multiples of 4	$12, 16, 20, 24$	$a, a + 4, a + 8, \ldots$	(a is a multiple of 4.)

A word problem about consecutive odd integers is solved in Example 4.

Problem solving which appears in each chapter of HOLT ALGEBRA 2 with Trigonometry, encourages students to approach problem solving in a logical, step-by-step way using a logo.

COLLEGE PREP TEST

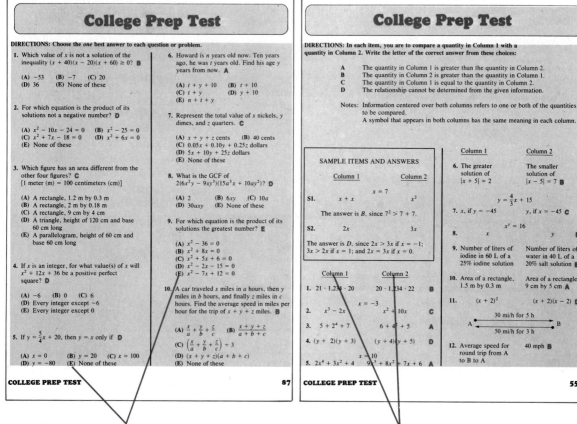

College Prep Test

DIRECTIONS: Choose the *one* best answer to each question or problem.

1. Which value of x is not a solution of the inequality $(x + 40)(x - 20)(x + 60) \geq 0$? **B**
   (A) -53 (B) -7 (C) 20
   (D) 36 (E) None of these

2. For which equation is the product of its solutions not a negative number? **D**
   (A) $x^2 - 10x - 24 = 0$ (B) $x^2 - 25 = 0$
   (C) $x^2 + 7x - 18 = 0$ (D) $x^2 + 6x = 0$
   (E) None of these

3. Which figure has an area different from the other four figures? **C**
   [1 meter (m) = 100 centimeters (cm)]
   (A) A rectangle, 1.2 m by 0.3 m
   (B) A rectangle, 2 m by 0.18 m
   (C) A rectangle, 9 cm by 4 cm
   (D) A triangle, height of 120 cm and base 60 cm long
   (E) A parallelogram, height of 60 cm and base 60 cm long

4. If x is an integer, for what value(s) of x will $x^2 + 12x + 36$ be a positive perfect square? **D**
   (A) -6 (B) 0 (C) 6
   (D) Every integer except -6
   (E) Every integer except 0

5. If $y = \frac{5}{4}x + 20$, then $y = x$ only if **D**
   (A) $x = 0$ (B) $y = 20$ (C) $x = 100$
   (D) $y = -80$ (E) None of these

6. Howard is n years old now. Ten years ago, he was t years old. Find his age y years from now. **A**
   (A) $t + y + 10$ (B) $t + 10$
   (C) $t + y$ (D) $y + 10$
   (E) $n + t + y$

7. Represent the total value of x nickels, y dimes, and z quarters. **C**
   (A) $x + y + z$ cents (B) 40 cents
   (C) $0.05x + 0.10y + 0.25z$ dollars
   (D) $5x + 10y + 25z$ dollars
   (E) None of these

8. What is the GCF of $2(6x^2y - 9xy^3)(15a^3x + 10ay^2)$? **D**
   (A) 2 (B) $6xy$ (C) $10a$
   (D) $30axy$ (E) None of these

9. For which equation is the product of its solutions the greatest number? **E**
   (A) $x^2 - 36 = 0$
   (B) $x^2 + 8x = 0$
   (C) $x^2 + 5x + 6 = 0$
   (D) $x^2 - 2x - 15 = 0$
   (E) $x^2 - 7x + 12 = 0$

10. A car traveled x miles in a hours, then y miles in b hours, and finally z miles in c hours. Find the average speed in miles per hour for the trip of $x + y + z$ miles. **B**
    (A) $\frac{x}{a} + \frac{y}{b} + \frac{z}{c}$ (B) $\frac{x+y+z}{a+b+c}$
    (C) $\left(\frac{x}{a} + \frac{y}{b} + \frac{z}{c}\right) \div 3$
    (D) $(x + y + z)(a + b + c)$
    (E) None of these

COLLEGE PREP TEST 87

College Prep Test

DIRECTIONS: In each item, you are to compare a quantity in Column 1 with a quantity in Column 2. Write the letter of the correct answer from these choices:

A The quantity in Column 1 is greater than the quantity in Column 2.
B The quantity in Column 2 is greater than the quantity in Column 1.
C The quantity in Column 1 is equal to the quantity in Column 2.
D The relationship cannot be determined from the given information.

Notes: Information centered over both columns refers to one or both of the quantities to be compared.
A symbol that appears in both columns has the same meaning in each column.

SAMPLE ITEMS AND ANSWERS

Column 1	Column 2
	$x = 7$
S1. $x + x$	x^2

The answer is B, since $7^2 > 7 + 7$.

S2. $2x$	$3x$

The answer is D, since $2x > 3x$ if $x = -1$; $3x > 2x$ if $x = 1$; and $2x = 3x$ if $x = 0$.

Column 1	Column 2
1. $21 \cdot 1{,}234 \cdot 20$	$20 \cdot 1{,}234 \cdot 22$ **B**
	$x = -3$
2. $x^3 - 2x$	$x^2 + 10x$ **C**
3. $5 + 2^4 + 7$	$6 + 4^2 + 5$ **A**
4. $(y + 2)(y + 3)$	$(y + 4)(y + 5)$ **D**
	$x = 10$
5. $2x^4 + 3x^2 + 4$	$9x^3 + 8x^2 + 7x + 6$ **A**

Column 1	Column 2
6. The greater solution of $|x + 5| = 2$	The smaller solution of $|x - 5| = 7$ **B**
	$y = \frac{4}{3}x + 15$
7. x, if $y = -45$	y, if $x = -45$ **C**
	$x^y = 16$
8. x	y **D**
9. Number of liters of iodine in 60 L of a 25% iodine solution	Number of liters of water in 40 L of a 20% salt solution **B**
10. Area of a rectangle, 1.5 m by 0.3 m	Area of a rectangle, 9 cm by 5 cm **A**
11. $(x + 2)^2$	$(x + 2)(x - 2)$ **D**

A —— 30 mi/h for 5 h —— B
50 mi/h for 3 h

Column 1	Column 2
12. Average speed for round trip from A to B to A	40 mph **B**

COLLEGE PREP TEST 55

Students practice choosing the best answer from among five possible answers.

Students practice determining the relationship between two pieces of information.

Standardized tests measure the mathematical reasoning abilities students need for success in college work. Scores on standardized tests can improve as mathematical abilities develop. Experts suggest that long-term study can have a great effect on scores. It is also believed that taking practice tests can familiarize students with the kinds of questions they can expect.

At the end of each chapter, students have the opportunity to practice taking a test similar to the standardized tests they will see in the future. This practice, along with discussion and analysis, can improve students' abilities to reason through standardized test questions.

ENRICHMENT LESSONS

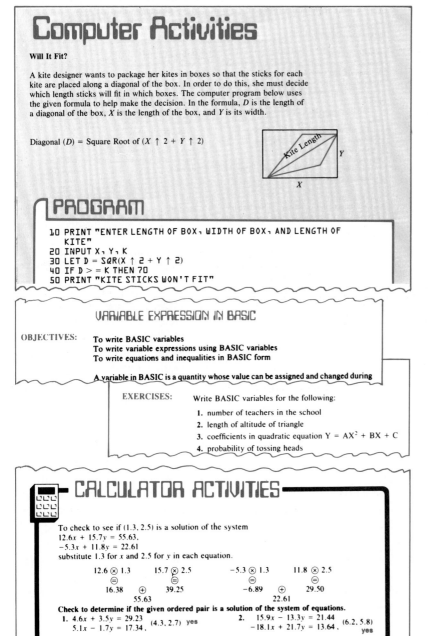

Computer Activities

Will It Fit?

A kite designer wants to package her kites in boxes so that the sticks for each kite are placed along a diagonal of the box. In order to do this, she must decide which length sticks will fit in which boxes. The computer program below uses the given formula to help make the decision. In the formula, D is the length of a diagonal of the box, X is the length of the box, and Y is its width.

Diagonal (D) = Square Root of ($X \uparrow 2 + Y \uparrow 2$)

PROGRAM

```
10 PRINT "ENTER LENGTH OF BOX, WIDTH OF BOX, AND LENGTH OF
   KITE"
20 INPUT X, Y, K
30 LET D = SQR(X ↑ 2 + Y ↑ 2)
40 IF D > = K THEN 70
50 PRINT "KITE STICKS WON'T FIT"
```

VARIABLE EXPRESSION IN BASIC

OBJECTIVES:

To write BASIC variables
To write variable expressions using BASIC variables
To write equations and inequalities in BASIC form

A variable in BASIC is a quantity whose value can be assigned and changed during

EXERCISES: Write BASIC variables for the following:

1. number of teachers in the school
2. length of altitude of triangle
3. coefficients in quadratic equation $Y = AX^2 + BX + C$
4. probability of tossing heads

CALCULATOR ACTIVITIES

To check to see if (1.3, 2.5) is a solution of the system
$12.6x + 15.7y = 55.63$,
$-5.3x + 11.8y = 22.61$
substitute 1.3 for x and 2.5 for y in each equation.

$12.6 \otimes 1.3$	$15.7 \otimes 2.5$	$-5.3 \otimes 1.3$	$11.8 \otimes 2.5$
$\ominus$	$\ominus$	$\ominus$	$\ominus$
16.38	39.25	-6.89	29.50

$$55.63 \qquad\qquad 22.61$$

Check to determine if the given ordered pair is a solution of the system of equations.

1. $4.6x + 3.5y = 29.23$
    $5.1x - 1.7y = 17.34$, (4.3, 2.7) **yes**

2. $15.9x - 13.3y = 21.44$
    $-18.1x + 21.7y = 13.64$, (6.2, 5.8) **yes**

Computer Activities appear throughout the chapters, providing a continuous strand of well-structured developments and problems for students with access to a computer.

A Computer Chapter at the end of Holt Algebra 2 offers students an opportunity to learn the fundamental statements of BASIC computer programming language.

Calculator Activities provide students with a selection of exercises for which use of the calculator is both logical and helpful. The use of calculators has become so widespread in recent years that many schools have introduced them into the classroom.

FEATURES OF THE TEACHER'S EDITION

Vocabulary identifies algebra terms on which to focus students' attention.

Background explains algebraic concepts.

Suggestions offer proven teaching approaches.

For Additional Chalkboard Work offers problems for further class analysis and discussion.

Enrichment provides additional challenges for able and gifted students.

1.2 Linear Inequalities (page 5)

Vocabulary
order of an inequality: $<$, $>$

Background
Lessons 1.1 and 1.2 illustrate that, in this textbook, the language and symbolism associated with sets is used only when there is a definite advantage in doing so. For example, (1) in Lesson 1.1 we say that
"The *solution* of $78 = 22 - 8t$ is -7" rather than
"The solution *set* of $78 = 22 - 8t$ is $\{-7\}$."
However, (2) in Lesson 1.2 we say that
"The *solution set* of $8 - 5x \le 28$ is $\{x \mid x \ge -4\}$" rather than
"The *solutions* of $8 - 5x \le 28$ are -4 and all numbers greater than -4."

Suggestions
Students should think of solving a linear inequality in the same way they solve a linear equation, with one exception:
Multiplying (or dividing) each side by the same *negative* number reverses the order of the inequality.
Many students believe erroneously that the graph of "$a > x$" is a ray to the *right* of a because they see

---

1.3 Absolute Value (page 8)

Vocabulary
absolute value, $|x|$

Suggestions
Some students have trouble with the part of the definition of absolute value that states

$$|x| = -x, \text{ if } x < 0.$$

The "$-$" in "$-x$" should not be thought of as "negative"; $-x$ can be read (thought of) as:
1. the opposite of x,
2. the additive inverse of x, or
3. -1 (negative one) times x.
The use of a frame as a variable can help some students:

$$\left| \boxed{} \right| = -\boxed{}, \text{ if } \boxed{} < 0.$$

Substitute a negative number for $\boxed{}$:

$$\left| \boxed{-5} \right| = -\boxed{-5}, \text{ if } \boxed{-5} < 0.$$

For Additional Chalkboard Work
Display the following on the chalkboard to help the students see the relationships of the three

---

1.4 Problem Solving: Number Problems (page 11)

Vocabulary
consecutive integers, even integers, odd integers

Background
Problem solving is a central theme in this book. This lesson and the next two provide a simple introduction to solving word problems by using algebra. The exercises lend themselves readily to the five steps in solving a word problem:
Step 1   *Represent the data in terms of one variable.*
Step 2   *Write an equation.*
Step 3   *Solve the equation.*
Step 4   *Check in the problem.*
Step 5   *Answer the question.*
   Step 5 is necessary, as shown in Example 3 in which the solution (7) of the equation is not the solution (7, 21 and 23) of the problem.

Suggestions
Stress the translation of "less than" where "a less than b" is "$b - a$" rather than "$a - b$." This should not be confused with "a decreased by b," which translates to "$a - b$."
   Students often wonder which quantity should be represented by x in a word problem. Example 2 provides an answer to this question. The quantity that is mentioned second is usually represented by x since the quantity mentioned first is described in

---

1.5 Problem Solving: Perimeter Problems (page 16)

Background
Step 1 in problem solving is to *represent the data*. Lessons 1.4, 1.5, and 1.6 show three different ways to organize the data represented in terms of a variable.
1. In Lesson 1.4, the data was organized in paragraph form. For example: Let x = the first number. Then $3x$ = the second number and $3x + 2$ = the third number.
2. In this lesson (1.5), the data is organized by sketching and labeling a geometric figure.
3. In Lesson 1.6, the data will be organized in the form of a table.

Suggestions
Encourage the students to represent the data by sketching and labeling a geometric figure as shown in Examples 1 and 2.
   This is an appropriate lesson in which to review the units of length and area in the metric system. The authors encourage students to think of these units in terms of common objects. Students should be able to match the items in the two columns below when the items in one column are scrambled.

1. centimeter (cm)
2. square centimeter (cm^2)
3. meter (m)

A. width of the nail on your little finger
B. one face of a dime
C. width of an ordinary

Cumulative Review provides additional items to test students understanding of skills and concepts previously taught.

Lesson Plans are complete in one column for easy reference.

Errors that Students Make identifies common difficulties students have and suggests approaches for correcting those difficulties.

Solutions Manual provides teachers with worked-out solutions to every problem and exercise in the text.

COMPLETE EVALUATIVE TOOLS

Mini-Cumulative Reviews appear after every two or three lessons to review skills and concepts taught in preceding lessons. Two-page Cumulative Reviews appear after every four chapters and in the Skillmasters.

Chapter Reviews and Chapter Tests measure students' understanding of all major skills and concepts. Items in the Reviews are keyed to pages on which skills are taught for re-study. Chapter Tests parallel the Chapter Reviews in form.

Cumulative Review (Chapters 1–8)

DIRECTIONS: Choose the *one* best answer to each question or problem. (Exercises 1–12)

1. Factor $3x^3 - 4x^2 + 15x - 20$ completely by grouping pairs of terms. **D**

   (A) $(3x^2 + 5)(x - 4)$ (B) $(x^2 - 4)(3x + 5)$
   (C) $(3x^2 - 4)(x + 5)$ (D) $(x^2 + 5)(3x - 4)$

2. If $x^2 - 5x - 14 > 0$, then **B**

   (A) $-2 < x < 7$ (B) $x < -2$ or $x > 7$
   (C) $-7 < x < 2$ (D) $x < -7$ or $x > 2$

7. Solve $a(bx - c) = x - 2(x + c)$ for x. **C**

   (A) $\dfrac{ac - 2c - x}{ab}$ (B) $\dfrac{ac - 2c}{ab}$
   (C) $\dfrac{ac - 2c}{ab + 1}$ (D) $\dfrac{2c - ac}{ab + 1}$

8. Use synthetic division to find the value of $3x^4 + 20x^3 - 2x + 20$ if $x = -6$. **A**

   (A) -400 (B) 32
   (C) 104 (D) $8,216$

Cumulative Review

Find the solution set of each inequality. Graph the solutions on a number line.

1. $-3x < 2x + 35$
   $\{x \mid x > -7\}$

2. $|x - 2| < 5$
   $\{x \mid -3 < x < 7\}$

3. $|x + 3| > 7$
   $\{x \mid x < -10 \text{ or } x > 4\}$

70

CHAPTER THREE

Chapter One Review

Vocabulary
absolute value [1.3]
consecutive integers [1.4]
linear equation [1.1]
linear inequality [1.2]
perimeter [1.5]

Solve each equation.
1. $5a + 8 - 3a = 4a - 5 - 6a$ **–3.25** [1.1]
2. $12 + \frac{3}{5}x = \frac{2}{5}x - 3$ **–75**
3. $7.2c + 2.3 = 1.4c - 0.6$ **–0.5**
4. $0.05 + 2.7(3n - 0.3) = 4.3n$ **0.2**
5. $-2x - (4 - 5x) = x - 3\frac{1}{3}$
6. $4c - 2(4c - 3) = 3(2c - 5)$ $2\frac{1}{10}$
7. $\frac{2}{3}(6x - 9) + \frac{3}{4}(8x + 4) = 28 - 4x$ $2\frac{3}{14}$
★ 8. $12 - 7[6(2x + 5) - 3(7x + 8)] = 0$ $\frac{18}{91}$

9. $|3x - 15| = 6$ **3, 7** [1.3]
10. $|4y + 3| = 9$ **–3, $1\frac{1}{2}$**
★ 11. $|n + 4| + |3 - 2n| = 16$ **–5$\frac{2}{3}$, 5**

Find the solution set of each inequality. Graph the solutions on a number line.
12. $-5n - 3 \le 17$ $\{n \mid n \ge -4\}$ [1.2]
13. $2x - 15 > 6x$ $\{x \mid x < -3\frac{3}{4}\}$
14. $|y + 4| < 6$ $\{y \mid -10 < y < 2\}$ [1.3]
15. $|5z - 15| \ge 30$ $\{z \mid z \le -3 \text{ or } z \ge 9\}$
★ 16. $|x - 4| < 6$ or $|x - 4| > 12$
    $\{x \mid -2 < x < 10 \text{ or } x < -8 \text{ or } x > 16\}$

Find the solution set of each inequality.
17. $8 - 3y \ge 2y - 2$ $\{y \mid y \le 2\}$ [1.2]
18. $2(3a + 1) > 3(4a - 5) - 2a$ $\{a \mid a < 4\frac{1}{4}\}$
★ 19. $\frac{4(y - 6)}{-3} > 12 - 2y$ $\{y \mid y > 6\}$

Solve each problem.
21. Twice the sum of a number and 3 is the same as 24 less than 7 times the number. What is the number? [1.4] **6**

22. The sum of three consecutive even integers is 20 more than twice the second integer. Find the three integers. [1.4] **18, 20, 22**

23. Side a of a triangle is 3 times as long as side b and side c is 2 cm shorter than side a. Find the length of each side if the perimeter is 26 cm. [1.5] **a: 12 cm, b: 4 cm, c: 10 cm**

24. Paul is 7 years younger than Carol. Three years from now, she will be twice as old as he will be. How old is each now? [1.6] **Carol: 11, Paul: 4**

25. An oak tree is 6 times as old as a pine tree and a spruce tree is 20 years younger than the oak tree. Three years ago, the age of the oak was 3 times the sum of the ages of the pine and the spruce. Find the present ages of the trees. [1.6] **pine: 5, oak: 30, spruce: 10**

26. Find p in dollars if $A = \$7,623$, $r = 8\frac{1}{2}\%$, and $t = 4$ yr 3 mo. Use the formula $A = p + prt$. [1.7] **\$5,600**

27. Find r_2 in ohms if $R = 8.4$ ohms and $r_1 = 12$ ohms. Use the formula $R(r_1 + r_2) = r_1 \cdot r_2$. [1.7] **28 ohms**

28. Find the initial velocity needed for a missile, launched upward, to reach a height of 4,875 m at the end of 15 s. Use the formula $h = vt - 5t^2$. [Applications] **400 m/s**

★ 29. The length of a rectangle is 6 cm more

Chapter One Test

Solve each equation.
1. $8 + 5c - 6 = 9c - 22 - 12c$ **–3**
2. $6 + \frac{3}{5}n = 14 - \frac{1}{5}n$ **10**
3. $3 + 5(2y - 1) = 2y - 4(y + 1)$ **–$\frac{1}{6}$**
4. $2.5(6y - 1.2) = 22.8 - 2.2y$ **1.5**
5. $\frac{1}{2}(16x + 24) + \frac{2}{3}(6x - 9) = 42$ **3**
6. $|2a - 7| = 15$ **–4, 11**

Find the solution set of each inequality. Graph the solutions on a number line.
7. $3 - 4n \ge 19$ $\{n \mid n \le -4\}$
8. $|y + 2| < 5$ $\{y \mid -7 < y < 3\}$

Find the solution set of each inequality.
9. $4(y - 2) + 1 \ge 3(2y + 1)$ $\{y \mid y \ge -5\}$
10. $|2a + 3| > 11$ $\{a \mid a < -7 \text{ or } a > 4\}$
11. $\frac{2}{5}(15n + 25) < \frac{2}{3}(12n - 6)$ $\{n \mid n > 7\}$

Represent each number in terms of one variable.
12. A third number is 7 less than a first number. A second number is 5 times the first number. **1st: x, 2nd: $5x$, 3rd: $x - 7$**

Solve each problem.
13. The sum of three consecutive integers is 40 less than 4 times the third integer. Find the three integers. **35, 36, 37**

14. Room A has twice as many chairs as room B. Room C has 20 more chairs than room

16. Sides a and b of a triangle have the same length. Side c is 12 cm less than 3 times the length of b. Find the length of each side if the perimeter is 23 cm. **a: 7 cm, b: 7 cm, c: 9 cm**

17. Find p in dollars if $A = \$5,620$, $r = 9\%$, and $t = 4$ yr 6 mo. Use the formula $A = p + prt$. **\$4,000**

18. Find r_2 in ohms if $R = 4.8$ ohms and $r_1 = 8$ ohms. Use the formula $R(r_1 + r_2) = r_1 \cdot r_2$. **12 ohms**

19. Building A was built 10 years before building B and 5 years after building C. In 20 years, the combined ages of buildings A and C will be 3 times that of building B. What is the present age of each building? **A: 15, B: 5, C: 20**

20. If an object is sent upward, what initial velocity is required to reach a height of 200 m at the end of 3.2 s? Use the formula $h = vt - 5t^2$ [Applications] **78.5 m/s**

★ 21. Solve. $5[4(6x - 3) - 7(5x - 2)] = 12(1 - 5x)$ $\frac{2}{5}$

★ 22. Find and graph the solution set of $|x + 7| \le 3$ or $|x - 7| \le 3$. $\{x \mid -10 \le x \le -4 \text{ or } 4 \le x \le 10\}$

HOW TO USE THE BOOK

HOLT ALGEBRA 2 WITH TRIGONOMETRY presents information in a way that facilitates understanding for all high school students. Able and gifted students who can work independently will enjoy HOLT ALGEBRA 2 WITH TRIGONOMETRY because they can find motivating extensions and enrichment activities after they complete the course work in a lesson or chapter. Students who require more structure and direction will enjoy HOLT ALGEBRA 2 WITH TRIGONOMETRY because of the frequency of worked-out examples that show solution patterns in a clear, step-by-step way.

Because of HOLT ALGEBRA's approach to presenting content, many more students can successfully perform in a complete and rigorous course in algebra. Your own particular teaching style and the ability of your students will determine whether you present lesson material as part of large-group or small-group instruction or have students work on lesson content individually.

Each lesson guides students to develop skills and concepts by means of numerous worked-out examples. A check using **Oral Exercises** can help you assess students' understanding before you assign the Written Exercises. **Written Exercises** are graded (A), (B), and (C), according to level of difficulty, and are further arranged by degree of difficulty within each level. There are simple practice exercises provided in each level to facilitate learning and later review. **Additional Practice** exercises appear in the Teacher's Edition. The **Assignment Chart** can serve as a guide for projecting a reasonable pace for individuals or groups.

Chapter Openers provide a solid basis for promoting group interest and discussion of the chapter contents. **Special Features** provide enrichment activities and extensions for students who perform lesson objectives successfully. **Mini-Cumulative Reviews** after every two or three lessons, **Chapter Reviews and Tests** after each unit, and two-page **Cumulative Reviews** after every four chapters provide both student and teacher with continuous feedback so that you can direct students to appropriate lessons or drill materials for practice and restudy.

INDIVIDUALIZING THE COURSE

The approach of HOLT ALGEBRA 2 WITH TRIGONOMETRY makes it easy to develop a program to fit individuals or small groups. There are two basic ways to individualize HOLT ALGEBRA 2 WITH TRIGONOMETRY:

BY LESSON: The Written Exercises for each lesson are graded according to difficulty. Those labeled (A) are the easiest; those labeled (B) are of average difficulty; those labeled (C) are challenging. Items within each section are further graded, so that those with lower exercise numbers are easier than those with higher numbers.

Students taking the basic course might work exercises labeled (A) and some of the first exercises labeled (B). Students pursuing a rigorous course might work some of the last few exercises labeled (A) and those labeled (B). Students pursuing a challenging course should work exercises at the end of (B) and then concentrate on exercises labeled (C).

BY COURSE: The Assignment Chart provides a guide for individualizing the course on a continuous basis. It divides the course into three levels of difficulty and prescribes assignments for Level A (the minimum course), Level B (the average course), and Level C (the above-average enriched course). Using the Assignment Chart, each student can complete the course by the end of the school year.

SUPPLEMENTARY MATERIALS

The following supplementary materials for HOLT ALGEBRA 2 WITH TRIGONOMETRY provide additional resources for students as they pursue their study of algebra at a level consistent with their abilities and styles of learning:

HOLT ALGEBRA 2 SKILLMASTERS Each of the Skillmasters can be used for individual or group instruction. Each Skillmaster, with two parallel forms (A and B), can be used as a pre- or post-test, as a diagnostic tool, as extra practice for skill mastery, or as a regular assignment. There are also two parallel forms of a cumulative review at the bottom of each Skillmaster that test skills and concepts previously taught.

HOLT ALGEBRA 2 TESTS Testmasters provide you with an alternate form of Chapter Tests found in the textbook. These alternate chapter tests can be used to retest students who need or want to improve their performances before they proceed. In continuous progress individualization, the Chapter Test in the textbook might be used as a pre-test and the alternate Testmaster as a post-test.

There are also five additional Cumulative Tests included in the Testmaster packet that can be used for semester or trimester courses.

HA2 Lessons 1.1–1.3 Form A

[After p. 4]

Solve each equation.
1. $9x - 12 - 7x - 15 + 4x - 9$ -9
2. $9.2y - 45 = 6.4y + 3.3$ 17.25
3. $8 + \frac{2}{3}n = \frac{1}{3}n - 2$ -25
4. $5(8 + 3x) - (9x - 2) = x$ $-8\frac{2}{3}$
5. $y - 5.7 = 2.7 - 1.4y$ 3.5
6. $1.4(5x - 0.3) = x + 0.06$ 0.08
7. $\frac{2}{3}(15x - 20) - \frac{2}{3}(18 - 6x) = -3(x - 4)$ $2\frac{1}{4}$

[After p. 7]

Find the solution set of each inequality.
8. $-3x > 6$ $\{x \mid x < -2\}$
9. $21 - 6y \le 8 + 4y$ $\{y \mid y \ge 6\frac{1}{2}\}$
10. $6(2n - 4) \ge 5(3n - 4) - 10$ $\{n \mid n \le 2\}$
11. $\frac{3}{4}a < 24$ $\{a \mid n < 32\}$

[After p. 10]

HA2 Lessons 1.1–1.3 Form B

[After p. 4]

Solve each equation.
1. $12x + 27 - x = 14 + 16x - 22$ 7
2. $8.2y - 38 = 4.7y + 6.1$ 12.6
3. $7 + \frac{4}{5}n = \frac{2}{3}n - 3$ -25
4. $12x - (10x \div 6) = 5(x + 1)$ $-3\frac{2}{3}$
5. $y - 7.8 = 7.5 - 2.4y$ 4.5
6. $1.5(4x - 0.5) = 2x + 0.09$ 0.21
7. $\frac{3}{4}(8x - 24) - \frac{2}{3}(15 - 9x) = -4(2 - x)$ $2\frac{1}{2}$

[After p. 7]

Find the solution set of each inequality.
8. $-4x < 12$ $\{x \mid x > -3\}$
9. $23 - 7y \ge 6 - 4y$ $\{y \mid y \le 5\frac{2}{3}\}$
10. $2(2x + 5) < 3(2x - 6) + 12$ $\{x \mid x > 8\}$
11. $\frac{2}{3}y \le 16$ $\{y \mid y \ge 24\}$

[After p. 10]

Name _____

Chapter 1 Test

Solve.
1. $n - 17 - 3n = 8 + 3n - 35$ 2

2. $12 + \frac{2}{3}x = 18 - \frac{1}{5}x$ 10

3. $5(2y - 3) - 3(3y - 2) = 9 - (2 - 3y)$ -8

4. $2.5(8a - 1.6) = 29.3 - 2.2a$ 1.5

5. $\frac{1}{3}(12x - 6) + \frac{3}{4}(8x + 12) = 22$ $1\frac{1}{2}$

6. $|5y - 1| = 9$ $-1\frac{3}{5}$

Find and graph the solution set.
7. $12 - 2x \le 4$ $\{x \mid x \ge 4\}$

8. $|a + 3| < 5$ $\{a \mid -8 < a < 2\}$

Find the solution set.
9. $2(7y - 3) \ge 3(2y + 3) + 1$ $\{y \mid y \ge 2\}$

Solve each problem.
12. Find three consecutive even integers so that their sum is 18 less than 4 times the third integer. 8, 10, 12

13. Box A has 3 times as many oranges as box B, and box C has 12 fewer oranges than Box A. Find the number of oranges in each box if box A has 4 more oranges than the total number in boxes B and C. A: 24, B: 8, C: 12

14. Betty is 10 years older than Alex and, 4 years from now, she will be twice as old as he will be. Find their ages now. Alex: 6 years, Betty: 16 years

15. Side a of a triangle is 4 m shorter than side b, and the length of side c is 1 m more than twice the length of side a. Find the length of each side if the

Reference Chart for Algebra 2 Skillmasters

LESSON PAGES	SKILLMASTER NUMBER	LESSON PAGES	SKILLMASTER NUMBER
1, 5, 8	1	291, 294	29
11, 16	2	303, 306, 310	30
18, 20	3	314, 317, 321	31
31, 34, 37	4	323, 327	32
41, 44, 49	5	338, 341	33
57, 60, 62	6	346, 349	34
65, 68, 71	7	357, 361, 364	35
74, 78	8	368, 372, 375	36
89, 91	9	379, 382	37
94, 96	10	390, 392, 394, 397	38
98, 102, 107	11	402, 404, 406	39
115, 119	12	410, 415	40
122, 125	13	424, 428, 431	41
128, 130	14	433, 435	42
139, 142, 145	15	438, 441, 445	43
148, 152, 155, 157	16	454, 455	44
165, 169, 172	17	462, 466	45
175, 178	18	470, 473, 475	46
187, 190, 193	19	477, 481, 483	47
195, 198	20	486, 489	48
209, 212	21	497, 500, 503	49
216, 220, 223	22	506, 509, 512	50
226, 228, 231	23	515, 518, 521	51
240, 243, 247	24	523, 526, 529	52
250, 253, 256	25	539, 542, 544	53
259, 263, 267	26	546, 549, 552	54
276, 279, 282	27	556, 560	55
285, 288	28	563, 566	56

Acknowledgements

Holt is grateful to thousands of teachers and to hundreds of thousands of students who have used our algebra texts in the past and who have contributed their comments and constructive criticism to help make the teachable textbooks of the past even more teachable and enjoyable.

We are also grateful to teachers, supervisors, and administrators across the country who have participated in systematic surveys so that Holt can give America's high school students the kind of materials that best facilitate their learning.

1
Chapter and Lesson Commentaries

Chapter 1   Linear Equations and Inequalities

Chapter Objectives

To solve a linear equation in one variable
To find the solution set of a linear inequality
To graph the solutions of a linear inequality
To solve an equation involving absolute value
To find the solution set of an inequality involving absolute value
To graph the solutions of an inequality involving absolute value
To write a word phrase in algebraic terms
To solve word problems

Chapter Overview

Problem solving is introduced in this chapter through a series of word problems separated into four types. The last lesson provides problems in which the types are mixed. Solving linear equations is extended to inequalities and absolute value equations.

Special Features

Four Steps in Problem Solving   p. x
*Calculator Activities   pp. 4, 22
Applications   pp. 23, 24
College Prep Test   p. 29
Computer Activities   p. 28
Chapter Review   p. 26
Chapter Test   p. 27
Cumulative Review   p. 10
Reading in Algebra   pp. 7, 10, 13, 18

*Calculator Activities in this book are designed so that only the simplest four-function minicalculator (with a floating decimal point) is needed. Each answer can be found without the use of a memory function.

1.1   Linear Equations (page 1)
Vocabulary
distributive properties

Suggestions
In Example 2, the simplified equation, $\frac{4}{5}y = 11$, is solved by using the *property of reciprocals*: $\frac{a}{b} \cdot \frac{b}{a} = 1$ for all nonzero numbers a and b.

$$\frac{5}{4} \cdot \frac{4}{5}y = \frac{5}{4} \cdot \frac{11}{1}$$
$$y = \frac{55}{4}, \text{ or } 13\frac{3}{4}$$

Basic skills are maintained in this lesson and throughout the book by including expressions that contain decimals or common fractions. Some students may need to review the rule for placing the decimal point in a product of two decimal numbers.

Enrichment
Some linear equations, often called identities, have every real number as a solution, and some linear equations have no solution.
1. Solve $8x + 3(4x - 5) = 15 - 5(6 - 4x)$.
$$8x + 12x - 15 = 15 - 30 + 20x$$
$$20x - 15 = 20x - 15$$
1. Every number is a solution:
   $20x - 15 = 20x - 15$, for each x.
2. Solve $6(2x + 5) = 3x + 3(9 + 3x)$.
$$12x + 30 = 3x + 27 + 9x$$
$$12x + 30 = 12x + 27$$
2. There is no solution:
   $12x + 30 > 12x + 27$, for each x.

Errors Students Make
They may solve equations of the form $ax = b$ or of the form $c = dx$ by dividing the greater number by the smaller number when the greater number is the coefficient of the variable. For example,
1. $12x = 3$; wrong solution: $\frac{12}{3}$, or 4
2. $10 = 15y$; wrong solution: $\frac{15}{10}$, or $\frac{3}{2}$.

Cumulative Review
1. Compute $-18 + 12 - (-15) - 19$. -10
2. Compute $8 - 2 \cdot 5 - (-4)(-3)$. -14
3. Simplify $-14x + y - x - 15y$. $-15x - 14y$

1.2 Linear Inequalities (page 5)

Vocabulary
order of an inequality: $<$, $>$

Background
Lessons 1.1 and 1.2 illustrate that, in this textbook, the language and symbolism associated with sets is used only when there is a definite advantage in doing so. For example, (1) in Lesson 1.1 we say
   "The *solution* of $78 = 22 - 8t$ is -7" rather than
   "The solution *set* of $78 = 22 - 8t$ is $\{-7\}$."
However, (2) in Lesson 1.2 we say that
   "The *solution set* of $8 - 5x \le 28$ is $\{x \mid x \ge -4\}$" rather than
   "The *solutions* of $8 - 5x \le 28$ are -4 and all numbers greater than -4."

Suggestions
Many students believe erroneously that the graph of "$a > x$" is a ray to the *right* of a because they see the symbol $>$. These students should rewrite "$a > x$" as "$x < a$" (rewrite "$b < x$" as "$x > b$") so that the variable is on the left side. This is shown in Example 2.

For Additional Chalkboard Work
Write the following on the chalkboard and practice reading the expressions below.

   1. $\{x \mid x > 4\}$
   "the set of"   "$x > 4$"
         "all x"   "such that"
   2. $\{y \mid y < -2\}$ **3.** $\{a \mid a \ge 5\}$
   4. $\{n \mid n \le -3\}$ **5.** $\{c \mid c \ne 6\}$

Errors Students Make
1. They draw the graph of $a \le x$ (e.g., $7 \le x$) as a ray to the left of a because of the symbol "$<$."
2. They solve $-ax < b$ as $x < -\dfrac{b}{a}$ where $-a < 0$.

Cumulative Review
   1. Compute: $\dfrac{-16 - 4 \cdot 3 - 22}{9 - 7 \cdot 7}$.
   2. Solve: $1 - \dfrac{3}{5}x = 7$.
   3. Simplify: $-4(2x - 3) - (7 - 12x)$.
   1. $\dfrac{5}{4}$ 2. -10 3. $4x + 5$

1.3 Absolute Value (page 8)

Vocabulary
absolute value, $|x|$

Suggestions
Some students have trouble with the part of the definition of absolute value that states
$$|x| = -x, \text{ if } x < 0.$$
The "$-$" in "$-x$" should not be thought of as "negative"; $-x$ can be read (thought of) as:
1. the opposite of x,
2. the additive inverse of x, or
3. -1 (negative one) times x.
The use of a frame as a variable can help.
$$\left| \;\square\; \right| = - \;\square\;, \text{ if } \square < 0.$$

Substitute a negative number for $\square$:
$$\left| \;\boxed{-5}\; \right| = - \boxed{-5}, \text{ if } \boxed{-5} < 0.$$

For Additional Chalkboard Work
Display the following on the chalkboard to help the students see the relationships of the three properties in this lesson.
  A. $|x| = k$; $x = -k$ or $x = k$
  B. $|x| < k$; $-k < x < k$
  C. $|x| > k$; $x < -k$ or $x > k$

The Reading in Algebra Exercises 7–9 serve as a hint for the Written Exercises 37–40.

Errors Students Make
They may write $a < x < b$ (e.g., $5 < x < 2$) instead of $b < x < a$ ($2 < x < 5$), where $b < a$.

Cumulative Review (Needed for Lesson 1.7)
   1. Write $12\frac{1}{2}\%$ as a decimal and as a common fraction.
   2. Write $\frac{6}{5}$ as a decimal and as a percent.
   3. Find 8 less than 3 times the sum of -4 and 6. -2
   4. Find $2\frac{1}{2}\%$ of 80.   2

   1. 0.125 and $\frac{1}{8}$ 2. 1.2 and 120%

1.4 Problem Solving: Number Problems (page 11)

Vocabulary

consecutive integers, even integers, odd integers

Background

Problem solving is a central theme in this book. This lesson and the next two provide a simple introduction to solving word problems by using algebra. The exercises lend themselves readily to the five steps in solving a word problem:

Step 1   *Represent the data in terms of one variable.*

Step 2   *Write an equation.*

Step 3   *Solve the equation.*

Step 4   *Check in the problem.*

Step 5   *Answer the question.*

Step 5 is necessary, as shown in Example 3 in which the solution (7) of the equation is not the solution (7, 21 and 23) of the problem.

Suggestions

Stress the translation of "less than" where "*a* less than *b*" is "$b - a$" rather than "$a - b$." This should not be confused with "*a* decreased by *b*," which translates to "$a - b$."

Students often wonder which quantity should be represented by x in a word problem. Example 2 provides an answer to this question. The quantity that is mentioned second is usually represented by x since the quantity mentioned first is described in terms of the one mentioned second. This hint should be emphasized in this lesson and repeated in the next two lessons.

Errors Students Make

They may translate "*x less than y*" as $x - y$ instead of $y - x$.

Cumulative Review (Needed for Lesson 1.5)

1. Represent the perimeter of a rectangle whose length is $5x - 6$ and whose width is $9 - x$.
2. Represent the perimeter of an isosceles right triangle where one leg is $6x$ feet long and the hypotenuse is $(2x + 40)$ feet long.

1. $8x + 6$ 2. $14x + 40$ ft

1.5 Problem Solving: Perimeter Problems (page 16)

Background

Step 1 in problem solving is to *represent the data.* Lessons 1.4, 1.5, and 1.6 show three different ways to organize the data represented in terms of a variable.

1. In Lesson 1.4, the data was organized in paragraph form. For example: Let $x = $ the first number. Then $3x = $ the second number and $3x + 2 = $ the third number.
2. In this lesson (1.5), the data is organized by sketching and labeling a geometric figure.
3. In Lesson 1.6, the data will be organized in the form of a table.

Suggestions

Encourage the students to represent the data by sketching and labeling a geometric figure as shown in Examples 1 and 2.

This is an appropriate lesson in which to review the units of length and area in the metric system. The authors encourage students to think of these units in terms of common objects. Students should be able to match the items in the two columns below when the items in one column are scrambled.

1. centimeter (cm)	**A.** width of the nail on your little finger
2. square centimeter (cm^2)	**B.** one face of a dime
3. meter (m)	**C.** width of an ordinary door
4. square meter (m^2)	**D.** surface of a door on a sports car

In Exercise 14, students will need to recall that the ratio of $2:3:5:6$ can be represented by $2x:3x:5x:6x$.

Errors Students Make

They represent the perimeter of a rectangle, x units by $3x$ units, as $x + 3x$ instead of $2x + 2 \cdot 3x$.

Cumulative Review

1. Solve $4t + 10 = 3[(t + 6) + (5t - 12)]$.   2
2. Find the solution set of
$$3x - (9x - 5) \le 15 - 4(7 - 3x).$$
$\{x \mid x \ge 1\}$

1.6 Problem Solving: Age Problems (page 18)

Background

In this lesson, the data is organized in the form of a table. This method of organizing data will be used with many other types of word problems.

Suggestions

Continue to encourage students to follow the five steps in solving a word problem. A simpler opening example is given below.

> "Carol is 6 times as old as Howard and Betty is 22 years younger than Carol. One year ago the sum of their ages was 27. How old is each now?"

	Howard	Carol	Betty
Age Now →	x	$6x$	$6x - 22$
Age 1 yr ago →	$x - 1$	$6x - 1$	$6x - 22 - 1$

$$(x - 1) + (6x - 1) + (6x - 23) = 27$$
$$13x - 25 = 27$$
$$13x = 52$$
$$x = 4$$

Howard is 4, Carol is 24, and Betty is 2.

Enrichment (A Contest-Type Problem)

A grocer bought some apples at 3 for 26¢. He bought the same number of apples at 5 for 40¢. To "break even" (no profit and no loss), the grocer must sell all of the apples at **A** 8 for 60¢, **B** 4 for 30¢, **C** 5 for 38¢, **D** 11 for 80¢, **E** 12 for $1. **E**

Errors Students Make

They multiply the wrong age. For example, they may write $3(x + 4) = x - 12 + 4$ instead of $x + 4 = 3(x - 12 + 4)$ as the equation to be solved, in "*she* is x years old, *he* is 12 years younger, and in 4 years *she will be 3 times as old as he will be*."

Cumulative Review (Needed for Lesson 1.7)

Evaluate each expression for the given values of the variable.
1. $445xy$ if $x = 0.08$ and $y = 2.5$ 89   1190
2. $x + xyz$ if $x = 800$, $y = 0.15$, and $z = 3.25$
3. Change $9\frac{3}{4}\%$ to a decimal.   0.0975
4. Change 0.0825 to a percent. $8\frac{1}{4}\%$

1.7 Problem Solving: Using Formulas (page 20)

Vocabulary

principal, simple interest, rate of interest

Background

Two formulas involving simple interest and one formula involving resistances in an electrical circuit are used to show applications of algebra to problem solving. Compound interest is in an applications lesson on pages 400–401.

Suggestions

The formula $A = p + prt$ can lead to an expression like $p + 0.16p$. If a student cannot combine these like terms, suggest that it be rewritten as $1p + 0.16p$, or as $1.00p + 0.16p$.

In Exercises 21 and 22, notice that $1,000 and $700, respectively, must be added to the principal in order to answer the questions.

A hand-held calculator can be used to advantage in all of the exercises.

Applications (page 23)

The Applications pages in this book serve to answer students' questions, such as:
1. Where is algebra used in the real world?
2. How is algebra used in the real world?
3. Who uses algebra in the real world?
These pages are also a part of the problem solving theme of this book. These pages may be used as lessons.

Enrichment (A Contest-Type Problem)

If a waiter receives a 25 percent cut in wages, he will return to his original pay with a raise of
A. 25 percent.   **B.** $29\frac{1}{6}$ percent.
C. $33\frac{1}{3}$ percent.   **D.** $25   **E.** $33.33.   **C**

Cumulative Review

Compute.
1. 7^2 **2.** 2^5 **3.** $(-10)^3$
1. 49   2. 32   3. −1,000

1.8 Problem Solving: Mixed Types (page 25)

Background

A student's problem solving ability will increase as he or she solves series of problems, each of which contains a variety of types. Such collections of word problems appear at intervals in this book.

The teacher can easily construct similar collections of problems of mixed types by using problems, previously unassigned, from several different lessons in the book.

Suggestions

This page has several possible uses:

1. A regular lesson, which may be assigned any time after Lesson 1.6.
2. A 4-item quiz made up of the even-numbered exercises. (Odd-numbered answers are in the pupil edition.)
3. An 8-item test.
4. An example of mixed types that the teacher can construct by selecting previously unassigned exercises from several lessons on problem solving.

Enrichment (A Contest-Type Problem)

Mrs. Jones invested $10,000 with $4,000 at 10% and $3,500 at 8%. At what rate did she invest the remainder in order to have a yearly income of $1,000?

A. 12%   **B.** 12.2%   **C.** 12.4%
D. 12.6%   **E.** 12.8%   **E**

Cumulative Review

1. Solve $|3x + 9| = 6$. $-5, -1$
2. Find the solution set of $|3x + 9| < 6$.
3. Find the solution set of $|3x + 9| > 6$.
2. $\{x \mid -5 < x < -1\}$ 3. $\{x \mid x < -5 \text{ or } x > -1\}$

Computer Activity (page 28)

This program demonstrates the use of arrays and data statements. The arrays L, W & C are used to store the data. Special attention should be given to the criteria for lot selection used in lines 160 and 170.

2 Chapter and Lesson Commentaries

Chapter 2   Polynomials and Problem Solving

Chapter Objectives

To simplify expressions containing integral exponents
To solve an exponential equation
To evaluate a polynomial
To add polynomials
To multiply two or more polynomials
To solve a word problem involving a collection or mixture of items
To solve problems involving two objects in motion

Chapter Overview

Properties of positive integer exponents are reviewed and then extended to include zero and negative integer exponents such as x^{-3} and y^0.

Simple exponential equations are solved.

Polynomials in one or more variables are evaluated, added, subtracted, and multiplied.

Problem solving is extended to include mixture problems as a category that includes 1. coin problems, 2. dry-mixture problems, 3. wet-mixture problems, and 4. miscellaneous mixture problems. 5. two objects moving in either the same or opposite directions.

Special Features

2.1 Properties of Exponents (page 31)

Vocabulary
base, exponent, power, exponential equation

Background
Five properties of positive integer exponents are reviewed. These properties will be extended to include all integer exponents in the next lesson. Simple exponential equations are introduced. Other types of exponential equations are studied in Chapters 6 and 15.

Suggestions
Some students do not distinguish between look-alike expressions such as $4(a^2)^3$ and $(4a^2)^3$. List the following expressions on the chalkboard and ask for the base with respect to the exponent 3.

$$5x^3 \qquad (5x)^3 \qquad 4(a^2)^3 \qquad (4a^2)^3$$

The exponential equations in this lesson are solved by using the following property.

$$\text{If } y^a = y^b, \text{ then } a = b.$$

Enrichment (A Contest-Type Problem)
Find the value of $x + x^x + x(x^x)$ if $x = 2$.
A. 6   B. 10   C. 14   D. 18   E. 22
C

Errors Students Make
1. They confuse $x^4 \cdot x^3$ with $(x^4)^3$; wrong answers: $x^{4 \cdot 3}$, or x^{12}, for $x^4 \cdot x^3 [= x^7]$; and x^{4+3}, or x^7, for $(x^4)^3 [= x^{12}]$.
2. They treat $5(a^2)^3$ as $(5a^2)^3$; wrong answer: $125a^6$ for $5(a^2)^3 [= 5a^6]$.
3. They divide exponents in a quotient of powers; wrong answer: $x^{\frac{12}{4}}$, or x^3, for $\dfrac{x^{12}}{x^4} [= x^8]$.
4. They treat $(2x^3)^2$ as $[(2x)^3]^2$; wrong answer: $(8x^3)^2$, or $64x^6$, for $(2x^3)^2 [= 4x^6]$.

Cumulative Review
Find the solution set of each inequality.
1. $8x - \frac{2}{3}(9x + 15) < 12x$ $\{x \mid x > -2\}$
2. $|2x - 5| > 11$ $\{x \mid x < -3 \text{ or } x > 8\}$
3. $|x + 7| < 2$ $\{x \mid -9 < x < -5\}$

2.2 Zero and Negative Integral Exponents (page 34)

Background
The zero exponent and negative integer exponents are defined by extending two properties of positive integer exponents as shown on page 34.

Suggestions
The definition of the zero exponent leaves 0^0 undefined. This can be explained to a student as follows: $0^0 = 0^{n-n} = \dfrac{0^n}{0^n} = \dfrac{0}{0}$ and $\dfrac{0}{0}$ is undefined since division by zero is undefined.

Students should interpret the definition of negative exponents loosely as: A negative exponent in the numerator (denominator) becomes a positive exponent in the denominator (numerator).

Some students confuse expressions of the form ax^n with expressions of the form $(ax)^n$. Notice that this contrast is shown in the exercises.

Enrichment (Contest-Type Problems)
1. $0.000000025 \neq$
    A. 2.5×10^{-8} B. 25×10^{-9}
    C. 0.25×10^{-7} D. $\dfrac{1}{40000000}$
    E. None of these E
2. If $16 \cdot 2^x = 6^{y-8}$ and $y = 8$, then $x =$ B
    A. -8.   B. -4.   C. -3.   D. 0.   E. 8.
3. $[7 - 2(5 - 7)^{-1}]^{-1} =$ B
    A. 8   B. $\frac{1}{8}$ C. 11   D. $\frac{1}{11}$ E. -8

Errors Students Make
1. They might confuse $10a^{-3} \left[= \dfrac{10}{a^3} \right]$ with $(10a)^{-3} \left[= \dfrac{1}{1000a^3} \right]$.
2. They might confuse $\dfrac{3}{2c^{-5}} \left[= \dfrac{3c^5}{2} \right]$ with $\dfrac{3}{(2c)^{-5}} [= 96c^5]$.

Cumulative Review
1. Alex is 15 years younger than Carol and 2 years from now she will be 4 times as old as he will be. How old is Alex now?
                    3 years old

2.3 Polynomials (page 37)

Vocabulary
descending order of exponents, monomial, binomial, trinomial, degree of a polynomial, linear, quadratic

Background
Polynomials are evaluated, added, subtracted, and multiplied in this lesson. They are classified in two ways: by degree and by number of terms.

Suggestions
List several polynomials on the chalkboard. Identify the degree of each, those that are linear, and those that are quadratic. For example:

$$x^5 + 6x^3 - 7x + 4 \quad \text{5th degree}$$
$$5x^2 - 6 \quad \text{2nd degree: quadratic}$$
$$-x + 3 \quad \text{1st degree: linear}$$
$$7x^2 \quad \text{2nd degree: quadratic}$$
$$8m^2n - 3mn^2 + mn - 5 \quad \text{3rd degree}$$
$$5m^2 + 6mn - 8n^2 \quad \text{2nd degree: quadratic}$$
$$4mn \quad \text{2nd degree: quadratic}$$
$$8m + 4n - 3 \quad \text{1st degree: linear}$$
$$-2m \quad \text{1st degree: linear.}$$

Students should use the words "linear" and "quadratic" fluently. This vocabulary is tested by the Reading in Algebra Exercises 7–12. Notice the following.
1. Every monomial is a polynomial.
2. Every real number is both a monomial and a polynomial.

For students who wonder as to the degree of a real number such as 7:

Since $7 = 7 \cdot 1 = 7x^0$, 7 is of degree 0.

In examples 3–5, the like (or similar) terms are combined by using the distributive property,

$$ac + bc = (a + b)c.$$

Cumulative Review
1. Multiply $-2a^2(a^3 - 4a + 2)$.
2. Simplify $4m^2 \cdot 5m^3n(-3mn^5)$.
3. Simplify $6t(4t^3v^4)^2$. $96t^7v^8$

1. $-2a^5 + 8a^3 - 4a^2$ 2. $60m^6n^6$

2.4 Multiplying Polynomials (page 41)

Vocabulary
FOIL method

Background
The FOIL method for multiplying two linear bionomials in one variable is reviewed and then extended to:
1. binomials in more than one variable
2. binomials of degree greater than one, and
3. the product of a monomial and a pair of binomials.

Suggestions
It should be emphasized that the FOIL method can only be applied to finding the product of two binomials. Have students try to apply it to the product of a monomial and a binomial or a trinomial and a binomial.

Example 4, the product of a binomial and a trinomial, does not lend itself to the FOIL method. The only difference in the two methods shown for finding the product in this example is the way in which the partial products are listed. The second method can be abbreviated as follows.

$$(3x + 2)(5x^2 - x - 4)$$
$$(15x^3 - 3x^2 - 12x) + (10x^2 - 2x - 8)$$
$$15x^3 + 7x^2 - 14x - 8$$

Enrichment (A Contest-Type Problem)
Mrs. X owns an auto worth $6,000. She sells it to Mr. Y at a 10 percent profit. Then Mr. Y sells it back to Mrs. X at a 10 percent loss.
A. Mrs. X comes out even.
B. Mrs. X makes $600.
C. Mrs. X makes $60.
D. Mr. Y loses $600.
E. None of these is true.   C

Cumulative Review
Find three consecutive multiples of 4 for which the second number, decreased by 3 times the third number, is 56 less than the first number.
12, 16, 20

2.5 Problem Solving: Mixture Problems (page 44)

Suggestions

In Example 1, the data may also be represented in the form of a table as follows.

	Number	Value in ¢
nickels	n	$5n$
dimes	$n - 4$	$10(n - 4)$
quarters	$3(n - 4)$	$25 \cdot 3(n - 4)$

In Example 2, emphasize that: x kg and $20 - x$ kg (*not* $x - 2$) make 20 kg of the mixture.

The Chapter 3 opener, page 56, provides a good introduction to wet-mixture problems and may be studied in connection with Example 3 on page 45.

In Example 3, the equation is based on the facts that

1. an alcohol *solution* is part water and part alcohol and
2. the amount of alcohol is *not changed* as water is removed.

A diagram in which the alcohol and the water are "separated" may help the student.

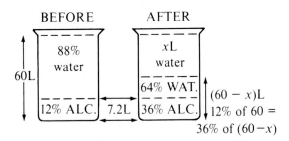

In Example 4, the equation is based on the fact that

$$\frac{\text{Iodine}}{\text{before}} + \frac{\text{Iodine}}{\text{added}} = \frac{\text{Iodine}}{\text{after}}$$

$$0.16(20) + 0.80x = .30(20 + x)$$

Errors Students Make

They use $x - 20$, instead of $20 - x$, to represent the number of kilograms of a brand B that must be added to x kilograms of a brand A in order to form a 20-kg mixture of brands A and B.

Cumulative Review

1. Solve $|3 - 2x| = 21$. **2.** Find the solution set of $-5(x + 2) > 4 - 7x$.

1. −9 and 12   2. $\{x \mid x > 7\}$

2.6 Problem Solving: Motion Problems (page 49)

Background

This lesson covers a first type of motion problem: two objects moving in either the same or opposite directions. A second type of motion problem, a round trip, is studied in Chapter 5.

Suggestions

"Vector diagrams," as used in Examples 1 and 2, can assist the student in deciding whether to add two distances or to set them equal.

This lesson (2.6) and the previous lesson (2.5) can occupy 3 class periods by assigning previously unassigned exercises from the two lessons for the third class period.

Enrichment (Contest-Type Problems)

1. How many hours will it take a car, averaging 80 km/h between stops, to travel x kilometers if it is to make k stops of n minutes each? **A**

   A. $\dfrac{3x + 4kn}{240}$ **B.** $3x + 4kn$

   C. $\dfrac{3x + 4kn}{24}$ **D.** $\dfrac{x + kn}{80}$

2. You have a choice between three successive discounts of 10%, 10%, and 5% and two successive discounts of 20% and 5% on an order of $1,000. How much can you save by taking the better offer?

   A. no saving   **B.** $250
   C. $190   **D.** $50
   E. $9.50 **E**

Cumulative Review

1. Solve $\frac{1}{5}x - 18 = 14 - \frac{3}{5}x$. **40**
2. Solve $x + 1.2(0.5x - 3) = 0.4(x + 3)$. **4**

Computer Activity (page 54)

This program makes use of the INPUT command to obtain data from the users' response to the PRINT statements. Careful attention should be given to the results and the accuracy of the answers. Answers can be rounded to two decimal places by adding a line 145. To round W to hundredths with the INTEGER function: 145 LET W = INT (W*100 + .5)/100.

3

Chapter and Lesson Commentaries

Chapter 3 Factoring and Special Products

Chapter Objectives

To factor a polynomial completely
To multiply a pair of related polynomials
To factor a difference of two squares
To factor a perfect square trinomial
To factor a sum or difference of two cubes
To solve a quadratic equation by factoring
To find the solution set of a quadratic inequality
To graph the solutions of a quadratic inequality
To solve a word problem that leads to a quadratic equation

Chapter Overview

Trinomials are factored into binomials by reversing the FOIL method for finding products. Trinomials of degree 4, 6, and 8 are included. Factoring is extended to factors of some special products:
1. difference of two squares, $a^2 - b^2$
2. perfect square trinomial, $a^2 \pm 2ab + b^2$
3. sum or difference of two cubes, $a^3 \pm b^3$.
Common monomial factors are introduced and factoring is extended to include factoring *completely* and factoring by *grouping* pairs of terms.

Special Features

Formulating A Problem-Solving Situation p. 56
Reading in Algebra pp. 64, 67, 70, 73
Cumulative Review pp. 59, 70, 77
A Challenge to You p. 82
Calculator Activities pp. 77, 82
Applications p. 83
Computer Activities p. 86
College Prep Test p. 87
Chapter Review p. 84
Chapter Test p. 85

3.1 Factoring Trinomials into Two Binomials (page 57)

Background

This chapter assumes familiarity with the meaning of *factor, prime factor, greatest common factor,* etc. The teacher may wish to introduce the chapter by reviewing the following vocabulary and skills.
1. Factor 15 as the product of two prime numbers.
2. Write the prime factorization of 72.
3. Factor 400 completely.
4. Find the greatest common factor (GCF) of 18, 24, and 36.
5. Find the GCF of x^4, x^2, and x.
6. Find the GCF of x^3y^2, x^2y^3, and xy^4.

Suggestions

Trinomials of the form $ax^2 + bx + c$ in which $a = 1$ are found in the Oral Exercises. Additional practice to accompany each example is given below.
Example 1:
   1. $2x^2 - 3x - 5 = (2x - 5)(x + 1)$
   2. $11x^2 + 4x - 7 = (11x - 7)(x + 1)$
Example 2:
   3. $8y^2 - 6y - 9 = (4y + 3)(2y - 3)$
   4. $24y^2 + 5y - 14 = (8y + 7)(3y - 2)$
Example 4:
   5. $15x^2 + 26xy + 8y^2 = (3x + 4y)(5x + 2y)$
   6. $20a^2 - 9ab - 18b^2 = (5a - 6b)(4a + 3b)$
Example 5:
   7. $n^4 + 7n^2 - 18 = (n^2 + 9)(n^2 - 2)$
   8. $3p^4 + 5p^2 - 2 = (3p^2 - 1)(p^2 + 2)$
Fourth degree polynomials that can be factored into three or four binomials are delayed until Lesson 3.4, which involves factoring completely.

Cumulative Review

Multiply.
1. $(3x^2 - 4y)(3x^2 + 4y)$
2. $(8a + 5)(8a + 5)$
3. $(n - 5)(n^2 + 5n + 25)$
1. $9x^4 - 16y^2$ 2. $64a^2 + 80a + 25$
3. $n^3 - 125$

3.2 Special Products (page 60)

Background
Three special products are introduced.
1. $(a + b)(a - b) = a^2 - b^2$
2. $(a + b)^2 = a^2 + 2ab + b^2$ and
   $(a - b)^2 = a^2 - 2ab + b^2$
3. $(a + b)(a^2 - ab + b^2) = a^3 + b^3$
   and $(a - b)(a^2 + ab + b^2) = a^3 - b^3$

These three formulas will be reversed in Lesson 3.3 and called special factors.

Suggestions
The teacher may want the Level A students to omit this lesson and continue to use the FOIL method for $(a + b)(a - b)$ and $(a \pm b)^2$. In such a case, emphasize that $(a + b)^2$ should be written as $(a + b)(a + b)$ as a first step.

Cumulative Review
Some 50-cent paper tablets are mixed with some 30-cent tablets to make a package worth $14.40. If the number of 30-cent tablets is 4 more than twice the number of 50-cent tablets, how many tablets of each kind are in the package?
12 50-cent tablets, 28 30-cent tablets

3.3 Special Factors (page 62)

Vocabulary
difference of two cubes, difference of two squares, perfect square trinomial, sum of two cubes

Suggestions
Additional practice to accompany Example 5.

1. $x^2 - y^2 - 8y - 16$

   $x^2 - (y^2 + 8y + 16)$

   $x^2 - (y + 4)^2$

   $[x + (y + 4)][x - (y + 4)]$

   $(x + y + 4)(x - y - 4)$

2. $a^2 - 2am - 10a + m^2 + 10m + 25$

   $a^2 - 2a(m + 5) + (m^2 + 10m + 25)$

   $a^2 - 2a(m + 5) + (m + 5)^2$

   $x^2 - 2xy + y^2\colon x = a, y = m + 5$

   $(x - y)^2$

   $[a - (m + 5)]^2$

   $(a - m - 5)^2$

Errors Students Make
They may not recognize perfect cubes: 1, 8, 27, 64, 125, 1000, x^6, x^9, x^{12}, ...

Cumulative Review
1. Factor 180 into prime factors.
2. Simplify $\dfrac{-10x^{-6}y^{-4}z^3}{25x^2y^{-6}z^{-5}}$.
3. Find the GCF of 18, 24, and 36.   6

1. $2 \cdot 2 \cdot 3 \cdot 3 \cdot 5$ 2. $\dfrac{-2y^2z^8}{5x^8}$

3.4 Combined Types of Factoring (page 65)

Vocabulary
Common monomial factor, common binomial factor, factor completely

Suggestions
Emphasize throughout the remainder of the chapter that the first step in factoring is to seek a common factor of the terms.

After factoring out the greatest common monomial factor, if any, the students may use the following hints according to the number of terms in the remaining polynomial.
1. Two terms: Look for difference of squares, sum or difference of cubes.
2. Three terms: Look for perfect square trinomial.
3. Four or more terms: Look for ways to group the terms to fit one of the patterns.

For Additional Chalkboard Work
(Additional Practice for Example 7)
1. $ax + bx - ay - by$
   $(a + b)x - (a + b)y$
   $(a + b)(x - y)$
2. $3x^2 + 9xy + 2x + 6y$
   $3x(x + 3y) + 2(x + 3y)$
   $(3x + 2)(x + 3y)$

Cumulative Review
Solve.
1. $5^{2x+3} = 625$ $\frac{1}{2}$
2. $|2x + 15| = 37$ 11 and -26
3. $x - 3.4 = 0.2x$ 4.25

3.5 Quadratic Equations (page 68)

Vocabulary
Standard form of a quadratic equation

Suggestions
For the remainder of the chapter, continue to stress the *Procedure for Solving Quadratic Equations by Factoring:*
Step 1   *Write the equation in standard form.*
Step 2   *Factor the polynomial.*
Step 3   *Set each binomial factor equal to zero.*
Step 4   *Solve both linear equations.*

Call attention to the fact that both $0 = ax^2 + bx + c$, and $ax^2 + bx + c = 0$, are in standard form. In other words, if a quadratic equation is in standard form, then either the left or the right side is zero (0) and the other side is a quadratic (second degree) polynomial with descending order of exponents.

For Additional Chalkboard Work
(Additional Practice for Example 4)
1. $y^4 = 20 - y^2$
   $y^4 + y^2 - 20 = 0$
   $(y^2 - 4)(y^2 + 5) = 0$
   $(y + 2)(y - 2)(y^2 + 5) = 0$
   $y = -2$ or $y = 2$ or $y^2 + 5 = 0$
   -2 and 2 $[y^2 + 5 > 0$ for each $y]$
2. $y^4 - 10y^2 + 9 = 0$
   $(y^2 - 1)(y^2 - 9) = 0$
   $(y + 1)(y - 1)(y + 3)(y - 3) = 0$
   $-1, 1, -3, 3$

Cumulative Review
Find the solution set of each inequality. Graph the solutions on a number line.
1. $4 - 5x \leq 2(x + 9)$
2. $|x - 5| < 7$
3. $|x + 3| > 8$
1. $\{x \mid x \geq -2\}$ The set of all real numbers greater than or equal to -2.
2. $\{x \mid -2 < x < 12\}$ The set of all real numbers between -2 and 12.
3. $\{x \mid x < -11$ or $x > 5\}$ The set of all real numbers less than -11 and all real numbers greater than 5.

3.6 Quadratic Inequalities (page 71)

Suggestions

Examples 1 and 2 suggest the following steps for solving a quadratic inequality in one variable.

Step 1 Solve the related equation for the two values of x, $x = r$ or $x = s$ where $r < s$.

Step 2 Plot r and s on a number line, separating the number line into three parts.

Part I: $x < r$
Part II: $r < x < s$
Part III: $x > s$

Step 3 Substitute a point from each part into $(x - r)(x - s)$ to determine whether the solution set is
$\{x \mid r < x < s\}$ or
$\{x \mid x < r$ or $x > s\}$.
Add an equal sign if the original inequality had one.

For Additional Chalkboard Work

(Additional Practice for Examples 1 and 2)

1. $x^2 + 3x - 10 < 0$
$(x + 5)(x - 2) < 0$
$\{x \mid -5 < x < 2\}$

2. $x^2 + 3x - 10 > 0$
$(x + 5)(x - 2) > 0$
$\{x \mid x < -5$ or $x > 2\}$

(Additional practice for Example 3)

3. $x^3 \leq 20x - x^2$
$x^3 + x^2 - 20x \leq 0$
$x(x^2 + x - 20) \leq 0$
$x(x + 5)(x - 4) \leq 0$

```
←—•    •———•—→
  -5  0    4
```
$\{x \mid x \leq -5$, or $0 \leq x \leq 4\}$

Cumulative Review

1. Find three consecutive odd integers such that the second integer, decreased by twice the third, is the same as 20 less than the first.

2. Each type A box contains a dozen oranges and each type B box holds 18 oranges. A truck is loaded so that the number of type A boxes is 50 less than the number of type B boxes. The truck contains 7,200 oranges. How many boxes of each type are in the truck?

1. 7, 9, 11   2. A: 210 boxes, B: 260 boxes

3.7 Problem Solving: Number Problems (page 74)

Background

Many word problems lead to quadratic equations that can be solved by factoring. Since a quadratic equation may have two distinct solutions, these solutions need to be interpreted in the problem.

1. In Example 1, $x = -5$ or $x = 10$ and there are two sets of answers: $(-5, 0, 5)$ and $(10, 15, 20)$.

2. In Example 2, $x = -6$ or $x = 10$ where x is the number of boxes/carton. In this case, -6 cannot be the number of boxes in a carton so there is only one answer.

Suggestions

After studying Example 1, use one of the Written Exercises 1–4 or 13–16 as a practice example. Use one of the Exercises 5–8 as a practice example after studying Example 2.

Enrichment (A Contest-Type Problem)

$x + yz$ and $(x + y)(x + z)$ are equal, if and only if,

A. $x + y + z = 0$.   **B.** $x + y + z = 1$.
C. $x = y = z = 0$.   **D.** $x = y = 1$.
E. $x^2 = 0$.   **B**

Cumulative Review

1. The length of a rectangle is 8 units more than the width. Represent the area of the rectangle in algebraic terms.

2. The lengths of the sides of a right triangle are x, $x + 1$, and $x + 2$ units. Represent the area of the triangle in terms of x.

1. $x(x + 8)$ square units
2. $\frac{1}{2}x(x + 1)$ square units

3.8 Problem Solving: Geometric Problems (page 78)

Vocabulary
Pythagorean relation

Suggestions
This lesson contains enough material for two full class periods and may be covered in the following way.

Period 1   Examples 1–3   Selected Exercises from 1–10 and 15–18

Period 2   Example 4   Selected Exercises from 11–14 and 19–22

In Example 3, each side is multiplied by 2 *before* expanding the product, base times height. This avoids introducing the fractional equation

$$\tfrac{3}{2}b^2 - 3b = 36.$$

In Example 4, stress the need to begin by sketching and labeling the two figures whose areas are to be added or subtracted.

Cumulative Review
Simplify.

1. $-5x^{-2}y^4z^0 \cdot 3xy^{-1}z^{-2}$ 2. $(-2x^{-2}y^4)^3$

3. $\dfrac{16x^{-5}yz^4}{12xy^{-3}z^{-2}}$ 1. $\dfrac{-15y^3}{xz^2}$ 2. $\dfrac{-8y^{12}}{x^6}$ 3. $\dfrac{4y^4z^6}{3x^6}$

Computer Activities (page 86)

This program makes use of a simple FOR Loop. This type of FOR loop can be applied to other sums and products. Exercise 2 can be used in class and then altered to search for additional numbers that are triangular and square.

4 Chapter and Lesson Commentary

Chapter 4   Rational Expressions

Chapter Objectives

To show that a given number is a rational number
To evaluate a rational expression for given values of its variables, if possible
To determine the values of the variables for which a rational expression is undefined
To simplify a rational expression
To multiply and divide rational expressions
To add and subtract rational expressions
To simplify a complex rational expression

Chapter Overview

Rational numbers are identified as decimals that either terminate or repeat. Then, rational expressions are evaluated and simplified. Products and quotients of rational expressions are simplified using the multiplicative inverse for quotient problems. Addition and subtraction is handled in two lessons. The first lesson deals with rational expressions with the same denominator. Finally, complex rational expressions are simplified.

Special Features

4.1 Rational Numbers and Decimals (page 89)

Suggestions

Emphasize that the student is already familiar with many types of rational numbers:

Integers: $-3 = \frac{-3}{1}$

Common fractions: $\frac{7}{4}$

Mixed numbers: $5\frac{2}{3} = \frac{17}{3}$

Terminating decimals: $6.39 = \frac{639}{100}$.

Repeating decimals, such as $0.333\ldots$, or $\frac{1}{3}$, must now be added to the list of familiar rational numbers.

Students may wonder if there are decimals that are nonterminating and nonrepeating. These are the irrational numbers and they are studied in Chapter Six. An example of a nonterminating nonrepeating decimal is $2.6161161116\ldots$.

Emphasize the importance of the restriction $b \neq 0$ in the definition of a rational number. For example: $\frac{8}{2} = 4$ because $4 \cdot 2 = 8$, but $\frac{8}{0}$ is undefined since no number times 0 is equal to 8. This concept is important in lesson 4.2.

Enrichment

Which of the following are names (numerals) for $2\frac{3}{4}$?

A. $\frac{11}{4}$ **B.** 2.75   **C.** $2.74999\ldots$
D. $2.75000\ldots$ **E.** all of these   **E**

Cumulative Review

1. A spruce tree is 1 year older than twice the age of a pine tree, and an oak tree is 1 year older than twice the age of the spruce tree. In 3 years, the oak tree will be 2 years older than the sum of the ages of the pine and the spruce. How old is the oak tree now?   15 years old
2. Three brands of canned soup are placed in 12 boxes so that there are twice as many cans of brand A as brand B and 6 dozen more cans of brand C than brand A. If brands A, B, and C are worth 60¢, 75¢, and 80¢ per can, respectively, and if the 12 boxes of soup are worth $185.40, how many cans of each brand are in the boxes?
2. A: 36 cans, B: 72 cans, C: 144 cans

4.2 Simplifying Rational Expressions (page 91)

Background

A rational expression is the quotient $\frac{P}{Q}$ of two polynomials P and Q, $Q \neq 0$. Thus, the following expressions *are* rational expressions.

1. $\frac{5x^2 - 10xy + 5y^2}{6x - 6y}$, where $P = 5x^2 - 10xy + 5y^2$ and $Q = 6x - 6y$

2. $x + 3$, or $\frac{x + 3}{1}$, where $P = x + 3$ and $Q = 1$

3. $\frac{0}{4n}$, or 0, where $P = 0$ and $Q \neq 0$

In contrast, the following expressions are *not* rational expressions.

4. $\frac{\sqrt{x + 3}}{2x}$ is not a rational expression, since $\sqrt{x + 3}$ is not a polynomial.

5. $\frac{8x + 4}{0}$ is not a rational expression, since the denominator is zero (0).

Suggestions

List expressions, like the five above, on the chalkboard and have the students identify those that are rational expressions.

Emphasize that it is common *factors*, not *terms*, that are divided out (canceled) when simplifying a rational expression.

Students should be aware that a rational expression cannot be simplified if the numerator and the denominator cannot be factored.

Errors Students Make

They "cancel" a term or a factor of a term in the numerator and denominator of a rational expression.

1. $\frac{\cancel{5}x + 15y}{\cancel{10}} = \frac{x + 15y}{2}$ 2. $\frac{3x + 9y}{\cancel{3}x + 10} = \frac{9y}{10}$

Cumulative Review

1. At 7 A.M. a car left city A and headed toward city B at 70 km/h and at 8 A.M. another car left city B at 60 km/h and headed toward city A. If the two cities are 265 km apart, at what time did the cars pass each other?   9:30 AM
2. Factor $x^3 + 8y^3$. $(x + 2y)(x^2 - 2xy + 4y^2)$

4.3 Products and Quotients (page 94)

Suggestions
Additional practice examples:

Example 1: $\dfrac{-3a^2}{10b^2} \cdot \dfrac{15c}{7a^5} \cdot \dfrac{28b^6}{-9c^5}$

$$\dfrac{-3 \cdot 15 \cdot 28a^2b^6c}{10 \cdot 7(-9)a^5b^2c^5}$$

$$\dfrac{2b^4}{a^3c^4}$$

Example 2: $\dfrac{3x^2 - 75}{5x + 35} \cdot \dfrac{7x + 49}{2x^2 + 4x - 30}$

$$\dfrac{3(x+5)(x-5) \cdot 7(x+7)}{5(x+7) \cdot 2(x-3)(x+5)}$$

$$\dfrac{21(x-5)}{10(x-3)}$$

Example 3: $\dfrac{5x - 30}{x^2 + 4x} \div \dfrac{x^2 - 4x - 12}{x^2 - 2x - 24}$

$$\dfrac{5(x-6)}{x(x+4)} \cdot \dfrac{(x+4)(x-6)}{(x-6)(x+2)}$$

$$\dfrac{5(x-6)}{x(x+2)}$$

Enrichment (Contest-Type Problems)

1. $\dfrac{x^{-2}y^{-2}}{x^{-3} - y^{-3}} =$

   A. $\dfrac{xy}{y^2 - x^2}$ **B.** $\dfrac{xy}{y^3 - x^3}$ **C.** $\dfrac{1}{x - y}$

   D. $\dfrac{x^2y^2}{x^3 - y^3}$ **E.** $\dfrac{x^3 - y^3}{x^2y^2}$ **B**

2. The equation $\dfrac{3}{x - 3} = \dfrac{1}{x - 1}$ is satisfied by

   A. either $x = 1$ or $x = 3$.
   B. only $x = 1$.   **C.** only $x = 3$.
   D. only $x = 0$.   **E.** no value for x.   **D**

Cumulative Review
1. Solve $2^{3-2x} = 16$.
2. Simplify $(3x^2y^{-3})^{-2}$.

1. $-\dfrac{1}{2}$ 2. $\dfrac{y^6}{9x^4}$

4.4 Sums and Differences: Common Denominator (page 96)

Background
Rational expressions are combined (added or subtracted) in this lesson where the denominators are the same and in the next lesson (4.5) where the denominators are different.

Suggestions
In Example 4, emphasize the need for parentheses where $-\dfrac{2x + 5}{6x + 12} = \dfrac{-(2x + 5)}{6x + 12} = \dfrac{-2x - 5}{6x + 12}$.
A common *error* with a binomial numerator is to write

$$-\dfrac{2x + 5}{6x + 12} \text{ as } \dfrac{-2x + 5}{6x + 12}.$$

Additional practice for Example 4:

$$\dfrac{5a}{2a + 6} - \dfrac{a - 12}{2a + 6} = \dfrac{5a}{2a + 6} + \dfrac{-(a - 12)}{2a + 6}$$

$$= \dfrac{5a - a + 12}{2a + 6}$$

$$= \dfrac{4a + 12}{2a + 6}$$

$$= \dfrac{4(a + 3)}{2(a + 3)}$$

$$= 2$$

Enrichment (A Contest-Type Problem)

$\dfrac{x^{-2} - y^{-2}}{x^{-4} - y^{-4}} =$

   A. $x^2 + y^2$ **B.** $x^2 - y^2$ **C.** $x^{-2} - y^{-2}$

   D. $x^{-2} + y^{-2}$ **E.** $\dfrac{1}{x^{-2} + y^{-2}}$ **E**

Cumulative Review
A second number is 7 less than a first number. If the second number is multiplied by 3 times the first number, the product is -30. Find both numbers. $(5, -2)$ and $(2, -5)$

Errors Students Make
They may write $\dfrac{a}{5} - \dfrac{3a - 7}{4}$ as $\dfrac{a}{5} + \dfrac{-3a - 7}{4}$

instead of $\dfrac{a}{5} + \dfrac{-(3a - 7)}{4}$, or $\dfrac{a}{5} + \dfrac{-3a + 7}{4}$.

4.5 Sums and Differences: Different Denominators (page 98)

Suggestions

Review the concept of least common multiple (LCM) before beginning the lesson. The LCM of 90, 36, and 72 is 18 since the LCM of $3 \cdot 3 \cdot 2 \cdot 5$, $3 \cdot 3 \cdot 2 \cdot 2$, and $3 \cdot 3 \cdot 2 \cdot 4$ is $3 \cdot 3 \cdot 2$. The LCM of $x^2 y^5$, $x^3 y^2$, and xy^3 is xy^2. Notice that the LCM in each case contains each factor the greatest number of times it appears in any one term.

Simpler alternate examples with answers are listed below.

Example 1:
$$\frac{5x}{9} - \frac{x+3}{6} = \frac{2 \cdot 5x}{2 \cdot 9} + \frac{-3(x+3)}{3 \cdot 6}$$
$$= \frac{7x - 9}{18}$$

Example 2:
$$\frac{1}{xy^2} + \frac{2}{xy} - \frac{3}{x^2}$$
$$\frac{1x}{x \cdot xy^2} + \frac{2xy}{xy \cdot xy} + \frac{-3y^2}{x^2 \cdot y^2}$$
$$\frac{x + 2xy - 3y^2}{x^2 y^2}$$

Example 3:
$$\frac{5}{2x+8} - \frac{2x}{3x+12}$$
$$\frac{3 \cdot 5}{3 \cdot 2(x+4)} + \frac{-2x \cdot 2}{3(x+4) \cdot 2}$$
$$\frac{15 - 4x}{6(x+4)}$$

Example 4: $5 - \dfrac{x}{3} = \dfrac{5 \cdot 3}{3} - \dfrac{x}{3} = \dfrac{15 - x}{3}$

Example 5:
$$\frac{5}{2n-6} - \frac{2-n}{n^2 - 9}$$
$$\frac{5(n+3)}{2(n-3)(n+3)} + \frac{-2(2-n)}{2(n+3)(n-3)}$$
$$\frac{7n + 11}{2(n+3)(n-3)}$$

Example 6:
$$\frac{x}{n-5} + \frac{y}{5-n} = \frac{x}{n-5} + \frac{-y}{-(5-n)}$$
$$= \frac{x-y}{n-5}$$

Cumulative Review

Find the solution set.
1. $x^2 - 3x - 10 < 0$ $\{x \mid -2 < x < 5\}$
2. $x^2 > 9$ $\{x \mid x < -3 \text{ or } x > 3\}$

4.6 Complex Rational Expressions (page 102)

Suggestions

In Example 1, notice that $5x^2 y$ is the *LCM* of the denominators x, xy, x^2, and 5 and $5x^2 y$ is also the *LCD* of the fractions $\dfrac{2}{x}$, $\dfrac{3}{xy}$, $\dfrac{3}{x^2}$, and $\dfrac{1}{5}$.

An alternate method for Example 1 is the following:

$$\frac{\dfrac{2}{x} + \dfrac{3}{xy}}{\dfrac{3}{x^2} + \dfrac{1}{5}} = \frac{\dfrac{2y+3}{xy}}{\dfrac{15+x^2}{5x^2}} = \frac{2y+3}{xy} \cdot \frac{5x^2}{15+x^2}$$
$$= \frac{5x^2(2y+3)}{xy(x^2+15)} = \frac{5x(2y+3)}{y(x^2+15)}$$

This alternative method requires more steps than the original method. It becomes even more complicated if the terms of the fractions are binomials or trinomials.

Enrichment (Contest-Type Problems)

1. If $\dfrac{1}{a} = \dfrac{1}{b} - \dfrac{1}{c}$, then a equals

   A. $b - c$.   **B.** $c - b$.   **C.** $\dfrac{c-b}{bc}$.

   D. $\dfrac{bc}{c-b}$.   **E.** $\dfrac{bc}{b-c}$.   **D**

2. If you replace each x in $\dfrac{x-1}{x+1}$ with $\dfrac{n-1}{n+1}$ and evaluate the result for $n = \frac{1}{2}$, the value is

   A. 2   **B.** -2 **C.** $\frac{1}{2}$ **D.** $-\frac{1}{2}$ **E.** -1
   B

3. The average (mean) of $\dfrac{x+y}{x}$ and $\dfrac{x-y}{x}$ is

   A. 2   **B.** 1   **C.** x **D.** $2x$ **E.** y
   B

Cumulative Review

Simplify.
1. $\left(\dfrac{-2x^{-2}y}{3a^3 b^{-3}} \right)^4$ $\dfrac{16b^{12}y^4}{81a^{12}x^8}$
2. $-4x^2(-2x^3 yz^4)^3$ $32x^{11}y^3 z^{12}$

Factor completely.
3. $8x^3 - 125$ $(2x - 5)(4x^2 + 10x + 25)$
4. $6x^3 + 15x^2 y - 9xy^2$
   $3x(x + 3y)(2x - y)$

4.7 Problem Solving: Mixed Types (optional) (page 107)

Background

Word problems of mixed types from Chapters 1–3 are presented to improve or to test the students' problem solving ability.

Suggestions

This page may be used in a variety of ways.

1. A lesson
2. A quiz or test by assigning the even-numbered exercises. (Answers to odd-numbered exercises are in the pupil edition of this book.)
3. A model list of mixed types of word problems. The teacher can construct a similar list at any time by selecting exercises from previous chapters.

Cumulative Review

Find the solution set. Graph the solutions on a number line.

1. $x^2 - 16 < 0$ **2.** $|x| < 4$
3. $x^2 - 9 > 0$ **4.** $|x| > 3$
5. $x^2 - 6x - 16 \leq 0$ **6.** $|x - 3| \leq 5$

1. and 2. $\{x \mid -4 < x < 4\}$
3. and 4. $\{x \mid x < -3 \text{ or } x > 3\}$
5. and 6. $\{x \mid -2 \leq x \leq 8\}$

Computer Activities (page 110)

This program uses nested FOR loops. A clear explanation of the order of computation in the loops should be reviewed with pencil and paper before running the program. Special note should be given to the statement in line 80, P = P + I where P is being accumulated and replaced with the new value during each iteration of the Q & Y loop. Exercise 2 uses variables from INPUT in the FOR loops.

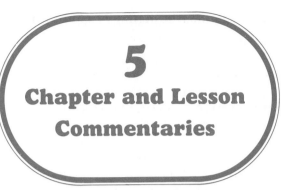

5

Chapter and Lesson Commentaries

Chapter 5   Using Rational Expressions

Chapter Objectives

To solve a fractional equation
To solve a work problem that leads to a fractional equation
To solve a motion problem that leads to a fractional equation
To divide a polynomial of two or more terms by a binomial
To divide a polynomial by a binomial, using synthetic division
To determine if a binomial is a factor of a given polynomial, using synthetic division
To evaluate a polynomial for a value of its variable, using synthetic division

Chapter Overview

Operations with rational expressions are applied to solving fractional equations and literal equations. Three types of word problems that lead to fractional equations are solved. Polynomials are divided by binomials. Synthetic division is used to evaluate a polynomial and to determine whether a binomial of the form $x - a$ is a factor of a given polynomial.

Special Features

Zero   p. 114
Reading in Algebra   pp. 118, 123, 132
A Challenge to You   p. 118
Cumulative Review   pp. 124, 129
Calculator Activities   pp. 127, 133
Computer Activities   p. 136
College Prep Test   p. 137
Chapter Review   p. 134
Chapter Test   p. 135

5.1   Fractional Equations (page 115)

Vocabulary
extraneous solution, proportion, extremes and means of a proportion

Background
If a variable appears in a denominator, as in Example 3

$$\frac{2n - 9}{n - 7} + \frac{n}{2} = \frac{5}{n - 7},$$

the equation is called a *fractional equation*. When solving a fractional equation, the "possible" solutions must be checked to see if any is (are) an extraneous solution(s).

An extraneous solution may be introduced if each side of an equation is multiplied by the same expression containing a variable. This is illustrated below.

Example A: 1. $x - 3 = 4$
2. $(x - 3)(x - 3) = 4(x - 3)$
$x^2 - 6x + 9 = 4x - 12$
$x^2 - 10x + 21 = 0$
$(x - 7)(x - 3) = 0$
$x = 7$, or $x = 3$

The solution of equation (1) is 7. If each side of (1) is multiplied by $x - 3$, the derived equation (2) has two solutions: 7 and 3.
NOTE: For all numbers a, b, and c, $a = b$ *if and only if* $ac = bc$ and $c \neq 0$. In Example A above, $c = x - 3$ and $c = 0$ if $x - 3 = 0$, or $x = 3$.

Suggestions
In checking for extraneous solutions to a fractional equation, it is sufficient to substitute the possible solutions in only the *denominators*. If the value of a denominator is zero, then the possible solution is extraneous. See Example 3 on page 116.

Cumulative Review
Factor completely.
1. $24x^2 + 44x - 140$ **2.** $75x^2y - 48y$
3. $9x^4 + 30x^3 + 25x^2$ **4.** $2n^3 + 16$
1. $4(3x - 5)(2x + 7)$ 2. $3y(5x + 4)(5x - 4)$
3. $x^2(3x + 5)^2$ 4. $2(n + 2)(n^2 - 2n + 4)$

5.2   Problem Solving: Work Problems (page 119)

Background
This lesson (5.2) and the next (5.3) are problem solving lessons in which three types of word problems lead to fractional equations.

Suggestions
Encourage students to represent the data in a table as shown in Examples 1 and 2 where the first row shows
"the part done in *1* unit of time" and the second row shows
"the part done in ☐ units of time" where ☐ is the time needed to complete the job.

Enrichment (A Contest-Type Problem)
If $xy = n$ and $\dfrac{1}{mx^2} + \dfrac{1}{my^2} = 1$,
then $(x + y)^2 =$
A. $(m + 2n)^2$ **B.** $m^2 + n^2$ **C.** $n(mn + 2)$
D. $mn(n + 2)$ **E.** $\frac{1}{m} + 2n$ C

Cumulative Review
1. Solve $3^{2-3x} = 243$ for x. -1
2. Factor $9x^2 - 12xy + 4y^2 - 25$.
2. $(3x - 2y + 5)(3x - 2y - 5)$

5.3 Problem Solving: Round Trips (page 122)

Suggestions

The students will be familiar with the formula $d = rt$. Have them solve this formula for t $\left(t = \frac{d}{r}\right)$, since the equations needed to solve the problems will be based on either

1. $t_1 + t_2 = t$ round trip, or
   $$\frac{d_1}{r_1} + \frac{d_2}{r_2} = t \text{ round trip, or}$$
2. $t_1 = t_2$, or
   $$\frac{d_1}{r_1} = \frac{d_2}{r_2}.$$

Some of the exercises will involve an airplane flying with a tailwind or against a headwind. This is analogous to Example 2 where a boat travels downstream (with the current) or upstream (against the current). The following example may be used after Example 2 to illustrate travel with or against a wind.

Example: A certain plane can fly at 400 km/h in still air. It can fly 126 km with a certain tailwind in the same time it could fly 114 km in the opposite direction (against the headwind). Find the rate of the tailwind.

Let w = the rate of the tailwind.

$$\frac{126}{400 + w} = \frac{114}{400 - w}$$
$$126(400 - w) = 114(400 + w)$$
$$50{,}400 - 126w = 45{,}600 + 114w$$
$$4800 = 240w$$
$$20 = w$$

Thus, the rate of the tailwind is 20 km/h.

Cumulative Review

Solve.
1. $3c^2 = 5c + 28$ 2. $4x^2 = 8x$
3. $4n^4 - 17n^2 + 4 = 0$
1. $-2\frac{1}{3}, 4$ 2. $0, 2$ 3. $-\frac{1}{2}, \frac{1}{2}, 2, -2$

5.4 Literal Equations and Formulas (page 125)

Suggestions

After Example 1, help the students to understand that solving a literal equation for one variable in terms of the other variables does not provide a *unique* expression but does provide an expression that is equivalent to other correct responses. A helpful type of exercise is to have the class create other expressions that are equivalent to a given rational expression, such as

$$\frac{x - a}{-y - b}.$$

Some appropriate answers are:

$$-\frac{x - a}{y + b}, \quad \frac{-x + a}{y + b}, \quad \frac{a - x}{y + b}.$$

Example 4 and Exercises 16–21 provide a type of equation that will occur in Chapter 9 when the point-slope form of the equation of a line is developed.

In Exercises 22–25 and 36–41, the student should solve for the specified variable before finding the value of the variable. These exercises can be facilitated with the use of a calculator.

Enrichment (A Contest-Type Problem)

If $x^{-2} - 1$ is divided by $x - 1$, the quotient is

A. $\frac{1}{x}$. **B.** $\frac{-x^2}{x + 1}$. **C.** $-x - 1$.

D. $-\frac{1}{x^2}$. **E.** $-\frac{x + 1}{x^2}$. **E.**

Cumulative Review

Simplify.

1. $-3c(-5a^{-2}bc^2)^3$

2. $\left(\dfrac{-2x^{-2}y^3}{3mn^{-3}}\right)^4$ $\dfrac{16y^{12}n^{12}}{81x^8m^4}$

3. $\dfrac{5}{2x - 8} - \dfrac{3x + 2}{x^2 - 7x + 12}$ $\dfrac{-x - 19}{2(x - 3)(x - 4)}$

4. $\dfrac{\dfrac{1}{x} - \dfrac{2}{y}}{x - \dfrac{1}{y}}$ $\dfrac{y - 2x}{x^2y - x}$ 1. $\dfrac{375b^3c^7}{a^6}$

5.5 Dividing Polynomials (page 128)

Background

In reporting the quotient of two polynomials, some teachers prefer to use the polynomial quotient. In Example 1, $4x + 7$ is the *polynomial quotient* (and the remainder is -9).

Suggestions

Review the meaning of *divisor, dividend, quotient,* and *remainder.*

The division work can be checked as follows: (divisor) × (polynomial quotient) + remainder = dividend. This is analogous to checking division with whole numbers.

Example 1 may be followed by the example below where the dividend is of a degree greater than 2.

Example

Divide: $(15x^3 - 2x^2 - 7x - 3) \div (3x - 1)$.

$$
\begin{array}{r}
5x^2 + x - 2 \\
3x - 1 \overline{)15x^3 - 2x^2 - 7x - 3} \\
\underline{15x^3 - 5x^2} \\
3x^2 - 7x \\
\underline{3x^2 - 1x} \\
-6x - 3 \\
\underline{-6x + 2} \\
-5
\end{array}
$$

Thus, the quotient is $5x^2 + x - 2 + \dfrac{-5}{3x - 1}$.

In Example 2, the dividend needs to be arranged in descending order of exponents.

Example 3 illustrates the need to examine the dividend for any missing terms. In this example, the missing term may be written as either 0 or $0x^2$.

Cumulative Review

1. Simplify $\dfrac{16x^{-4}y^6(3x^2 - 108)}{10x^{-1}y^{-2}(2x^2 - 14x + 12)}$.

2. Factor $16x^3 - 2y^3$ completely.

3. Find three consecutive even integers such that the product of the second and the third integers is 168.

1. $\dfrac{12y^8(x + 6)}{5x^3(x - 1)}$ 2. $2(2x - y)(4x^2 + 2xy + y^2)$

3. $(10, 12, 14)$ and $(-16, -14, -12)$

5.6 Synthetic Division (page 130)

Vocabulary

synthetic division

Suggestions

Some students are confused about the sign of a in the divisor: $a \rfloor$. The following summary may be helpful.

To *divide* a polynomial, P
1. by $x - a$, use: $a \rfloor$
2. by $x + a$, use: $-a \rfloor$.

To *evaluate* a polynomial, P, if $x = a$, use $a \rfloor$.

Explanation of Calculator Activity Procedure

$5x^4 - 17x^3 + 23x^2 - 49x + 90$, if $x = 7$,
$= 5 \cdot 7^4 - 17 \cdot 7^3 + 23 \cdot 7^2 - 49 \cdot 7 + 90$
$= 7(5 \cdot 7^3 - 17 \cdot 7^2 + 23 \cdot 7 - 49) + 90$
$= 7[7(5 \cdot 7^2 - 17 \cdot 7 + 23) - 49] + 90$
$= 7\{7[7(5 \cdot 7 - 17) + 23] - 49\} + 90$
$= \{[(5 \times 7 - 17) \times 7 + 23] \times 7 - 49\} \times 7 + 90$
7048

Above, $x > 0$ and there are no missing terms. If terms *are* missing, evaluate as follows:

Example

Evaluate $4x^5 - 6x^3 + 7x$, if $x = 2$.

$4x^5 + 0x^4 - 6x^3 + 0x^2 + 7x + 0$, if $x = 2$,
$= 4 \otimes \underbrace{2 \otimes 2}_{0x^4} \ominus 6 \otimes \underbrace{2 \otimes 2}_{0x^2} \oplus 7 \otimes 2 \oplus 0 \ominus 94$

Enter $\otimes$ 2 for each missing term.

For Additional Chalkboard Work

Evaluate each polynomial for the given datum.
1. $2n^5 - 6n^4 - 12n^2 - 15$, if $n = 4$ 305
2. $3x^3 + 22x^2 + 10x + 20$, if $x = -10$ -880

Cumulative Review

One leg of a right triangle is 3 cm longer than the other leg and 3 cm shorter than the hypotenuse. Find the lengths of the three sides.
9 cm, 12 cm, 15 cm

Computer Activities (page 136)

This program can be used to supplement the synthetic division lessons in the book. Homework assignments can be checked with the program.

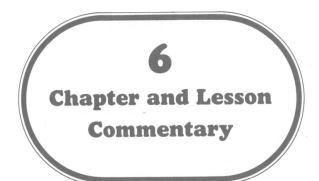

6 Chapter and Lesson Commentary

Chapter 6 Radicals and Rational Number Exponents

Chapter Objectives

To solve a quadratic equation by using the definition of square root

To approximate a square root to the nearest hundredth by using a square root table

To determine whether a given real number is rational or irrational

To simplify a product or quotient of nth roots

To simplify radical expressions containing sums, differences, products, or quotients

To write a radical expression in exponential form

To write an exponential expression in radical form

To evaluate an expression containing rational number exponents

To simplify an expression containing rational number exponents

To solve an exponential equation using properties of rational number exponents

Chapter Overview

Radicals are introduced as solutions of equations like $x^2 = 8$, $x^3 = 16$, and $x^4 = 32$. Operations with square roots are studied as a means of simplifying radical expressions containing nth roots. Properties of exponents are extended to include rational number exponents. Irrational numbers are introduced to complete the system of real numbers. Additional types of exponential equations are solved.

Special Features

6.1 Square Roots (page 139)

Vocabulary
approximately equal to ($\doteq$), irrational number, real number, square root ($\sqrt{k}$), radical, radical sign, radicand

Suggestions
Review the process of finding the square root of a number as the *inverse* of squaring the square root, as shown in the following examples.

$$4^2 = 16 \text{ and } \sqrt{16} = \sqrt{4^2} = 4$$
$$7^2 = 49 \text{ and } \sqrt{49} = \sqrt{7^2} = 7$$
$$\text{In general, } \sqrt{x^2} = x, \text{ for } x \geq 0.$$

Some students confuse these situations.

1. The equation $x^2 = 7$ has *two* solutions, $\sqrt{7}$ and $-\sqrt{7}$.
2. The radical $\sqrt{9}$ has but *one* value, 3.

Emphasize that an *equation* like $x^2 = 16$ has two solutions. The solutions of $x^2 = 16$ are $\sqrt{16}$ and $-\sqrt{16}$, or 4 and -4, where $\sqrt{16} = 4$ and $-\sqrt{16} = -4$.

Stress the terms *radical*, *radicand*, and *radical sign*. The word *radicand* will be used widely in this chapter.

The nonterminating decimal $4.3231131113\ldots$ is also nonrepeating since it cannot be written with a bar above a single block of digits as in $9.887887887\ldots = 9.88\overline{7887}$.

Enrichment
In *n* is any integer, then $n^2(n^2 - 1)$ is always divisible by

A. 12.   **B.** 24.   **C.** 12 and 24.
D. every multiple of 12.
E. no unique number greater than 1.   **A**

Cumulative Review
Solve each problem.
1. A triangle's height is 5 cm less than twice the length of its base. Find the height if the area of the triangle is 44 cm².
2. The length of a rectangle is 3 m more than 3 times its width. Find the length if the area of the rectangle is 60 m².
1. 11 cm   2. 15 m

6.2 Simplifying Radicals (page 142)

Background
This is the first of three consecutive lessons in which expressions containing square roots are simplified, added, multiplied, and divided. In Lesson 6.5, these properties are extended to cube roots, fourth roots, fifth roots, etc.

The first condition for *simplest radical form* is introduced. More conditions are added in the next few lessons. These conditions are listed below for $\sqrt[n]{k}$.

1. No radicand contains a perfect *n*th power.
2. No denominator contains a radical.
3. No radicand contains a fraction.

Suggestions
Students should memorize a list of the perfect squares through 169: 4, 9, 16, 25, 36, 49, 64, 81, 100, 121, 144, 169.

Emphasize that when computations with approximate data are involved, no rounding should occur until all other computations have been done. In Example 1, if 4.583 was rounded to 4.58 and then multiplied by 3, the result would be 13.74 which is in error by 0.01.

Example 2 shows that a radicand may contain more than one perfect square factor. Each factor of a radicand should be inspected to determine whether it contains a perfect square factor. For example,

$$\sqrt{72} = \sqrt{4 \cdot 18} = \sqrt{4 \cdot 9 \cdot 2} = 2 \cdot 3\sqrt{2}$$
$$= 6\sqrt{2} \text{ and } \sqrt{72} = \sqrt{9 \cdot 8} = \sqrt{9 \cdot 4 \cdot 2}$$
$$= 3 \cdot 2\sqrt{2} = 6\sqrt{2}.$$

A classroom set of the table of square roots on page 592 can be duplicated (dry copied) for student use on tests and quizzes.

Cumulative Review
Factor completely.
1. $x^2 y - y^2 + 5x^2 - 5y$
2. $36 - 4x^2 + 4xy - y^2$
3. $5x^3 - 40y^3$
1. $(x^2 - y)(y + 5)$ 2. $(6 + 2x - y)(6 - 2x + y)$
3. $5(x - 2y)(x^2 + 2xy + 4y^2)$

6.3 Sums, Differences, and Products of Radicals (page 145)

Vocabulary
like radicals

Suggestions
Stress the importance of the quantifier: If $x \geq 0$ and $y \geq 0$, in the property of the product of square roots, $\sqrt{x} \cdot \sqrt{y} = \sqrt{x \cdot y}$. If $x = -4$ and $y = -9$, notice that $\sqrt{-4}$ and $\sqrt{-9}$ are not real numbers

$$\text{and } \sqrt{-4} \cdot \sqrt{-9} \neq \sqrt{-4(-9)}$$
$$\text{since } \sqrt{-4(-9)} = \sqrt{36}, \text{ or } 6,$$
$$\text{while } \sqrt{-4} \cdot \sqrt{-9} = 2i \cdot 3i = 6i^2, \text{ or } -6.$$

Level C Exercises 51–58 require students to factor polynomials with integer coefficients over the set of real numbers. Previously, students factored polynomials with integer coefficients over the set of integers. Exercises 51–58 introduce a skill that is required in a first course in calculus.

Enrichment
Farmers A and B had equal amounts of hay for their cows. The herd of farmer A consumed its hay in 4 h while the herd of farmer B consumed its hay in 3 h. If each herd ate at a constant rate and the two herds began eating at the same time, in how many hours was A's amount of hay twice B's amount of hay?

A. $\frac{3}{4}$ h **B.** $1\frac{1}{3}$ h **C.** 2 h

D. $2\frac{2}{5}$ h **E.** $2\frac{1}{2}$ h **D.**

Cumulative Review
Machine A can do a certain job in 12 h. If Machine B works at the same time, the job is done in 8 h. How long would the job take Machine B working alone?
24 h

6.4 Quotients of Radicals (page 148)

Vocabulary
conjugates

Suggestions
In simplifying $\dfrac{\sqrt{5}}{3\sqrt{2}}$, notice that you can multiply by $\dfrac{\sqrt{2}}{\sqrt{2}}$ rather than $\dfrac{3\sqrt{2}}{3\sqrt{2}}$. This saves one step, as shown below.

$$\frac{\sqrt{5}}{3\sqrt{2}} \cdot \frac{\sqrt{2}}{\sqrt{2}} = \frac{\sqrt{10}}{6} \text{ compared to } \frac{\sqrt{5}}{3\sqrt{2}} \cdot \frac{3\sqrt{2}}{3\sqrt{2}}$$
$$= \frac{3\sqrt{10}}{18} = \frac{\sqrt{10}}{6}.$$

Example 3 shows that it is better to simplify each radical *before* rationalizing the denominator.

Compare the methods of simplifying $\dfrac{5a}{\sqrt{8x^6y^5}}$:

Method 1	*Method 2*
$\dfrac{5a}{\sqrt{8x^6y^5}}$	$\dfrac{5a}{\sqrt{8x^6y^5}} \cdot \dfrac{\sqrt{8x^6y^5}}{\sqrt{8x^6y^5}}$
$= \dfrac{5a}{2x^3y^2\sqrt{2y}} \cdot \dfrac{\sqrt{2y}}{\sqrt{2y}}$	$= \dfrac{5a \cdot 2x^3y^2\sqrt{2y}}{8x^6y^5}$
$= \dfrac{5a\sqrt{2y}}{4x^3y^3}$	$= \dfrac{5a\sqrt{2y}}{4x^3y^3}$

Enrichment
Rationalizing the *numerator* rather than the denominator of an expression is a skill that is used in calculus. Rationalize the *numerator*:

1. $\dfrac{3\sqrt{5x}}{7\sqrt{6y}}$ **2.** $\dfrac{9\sqrt{x} - 2\sqrt{y}}{\sqrt{xy}}$

3. $\dfrac{10\sqrt{m} + 4\sqrt{n}}{3}$ **4.** $\dfrac{\sqrt{c} - \sqrt{c+d}}{-2\sqrt{c}}$

1. $\dfrac{15x}{7\sqrt{30xy}}$ **2.** $\dfrac{81x - 4y}{9x\sqrt{y} + 2y\sqrt{x}}$

3. $\dfrac{50m - 8n}{15\sqrt{m} - 6\sqrt{n}}$ **4.** $\dfrac{d}{2c + 2\sqrt{c^2 + cd}}$

Cumulative Review
Solve.

1. $2^{3x} = 64$ **2.** $\dfrac{y+1}{y+2} - \dfrac{y-3}{3} = \dfrac{y-1}{y+2}$

1. 2   2. 4, −3

6.5 Other Radicals (page 152)

Vocabulary
index for a radical, nth root of k ($\sqrt[n]{k}$)

Background
Properties for square roots are extended to cube roots, fourth roots, fifth roots, and nth roots in general.

Suggestions
The students should memorize third, fourth, and fifth powers of some bases, as shown in the table on page 152.

This lesson deals with *odd* numbered indexes for $\sqrt[n]{k}$, where k is *any* real number, and *even*-numbered indexes for $\sqrt[n]{k}$, where k is a *positive* number or zero. Some students may ask how to deal with $\sqrt[n]{k}$ where n is even and k is a negative number, for example, $\sqrt{-9}$ and $\sqrt{-25}$. Explain that expressions such as these will be defined and used in Chapter 8, where $\sqrt{-1}$ is defined so that $\sqrt{-1} = i$ and $i^2 = -1$.

Notice that if $x < 0$, then $\sqrt{x^2} \neq x$, since $\sqrt{(-3)^2} \neq -3$. Instead, $\sqrt{x^2} = |x|$, if $x < 0$, since $\sqrt{(-3)^2} = |-3| = 3$. Similarly, $\sqrt{x^6} = |x^3|$, $\sqrt[4]{x^4} = |x|$, and $\sqrt[4]{x^{12}} = |x^3|$ if $x < 0$. In general, if n is even, then $\sqrt[n]{k^n} = |k|$. This use of absolute value is avoided by the statement made at the top of page 143, ''In the remainder of this chapter, all variables represent positive real numbers or zero.''

Enrichment (A Contest-Type Problem)
$$2 - \frac{1}{2 + \sqrt{3}} + \frac{1}{2 - \sqrt{3}} =$$
A. $2 + 2\sqrt{3}$ **B.** $2 - 2\sqrt{3}$
C. $2\sqrt{3}$ **D.** $-2\sqrt{3}$ **E.** $\sqrt{3}$ **A.**

Cumulative Review
Brands A, B, and C of peanuts are worth \$1.20, \$1.50, and \$1.80 per kilogram, respectively. If 3 kg of brand A are added to twice as much brand C as brand B to form a mixture that is worth \$24.00, how much brand C is in the mixture?   8 kg

6.6 Rational Number Exponents (page 155)

Vocabulary
rational number exponent ($x^{\frac{m}{n}}$)

Background
Rational number exponents are defined in terms of radicals.

Suggestions
After $x^{\frac{1}{n}}$ is defined as $\sqrt[n]{x}$, the Power of a Power Property can be used to show that
$(x^{\frac{1}{n}})^m = x^{\frac{m}{n}}$ and $(x^{\frac{1}{n}})^m = (\sqrt[n]{x})^m$, thus, $x^{\frac{m}{n}} = (\sqrt[n]{x})^m$. The student should associate the *denominator* n in $x^{\frac{m}{n}}$ with the *index* n in $(\sqrt[n]{x})^m$ and the *numerator* m in $x^{\frac{m}{n}}$ with the *exponent* m in $(\sqrt[n]{x})^m$. The student should note also that the base x can be raised to the power either *before* or *after* the root is taken, since $x^{\frac{m}{n}} = \sqrt[n]{x^m}$ and $x^{\frac{m}{n}} = (\sqrt[n]{x})^m$.

For Additional Chalkboard Work
You may wish to assign these Level C exercises. Write in simplest radical form.

49. $(x^2 y^3)^{\frac{5}{n}}$ **50.** $(x^a y^b)^{\frac{c}{n}}$

51. $(x^n y^{3n})^{\frac{1}{n}}$ **52.** $(x^{5n} y^n)^{\frac{a}{n}}$

53. $(x^{n+1} y^{2n+2})^{\frac{1}{n}}$ **54.** $(x^{4n} y^{4n+3})^{\frac{k}{n}}$

49. $\sqrt[n]{x^{10} y^{15}}$ 50. $\sqrt[n]{x^{ac} y^{bc}}$ 51. xy^3

52. $x^{5a} y^a$ 53. $xy^2 \sqrt[n]{xy^2}$ 54. $x^{4k} y^{4k} \sqrt[n]{y^{3k}}$

Enrichment
$$(\sqrt{\sqrt[4]{a^6}})^8 \cdot (\sqrt[4]{\sqrt{a^6}})^8 = \underline{}\quad a^{12}$$

Cumulative Review
Simplify.

1. $\dfrac{2a^2 - 50}{15 - 3a}$ **2.** $\dfrac{6 - \dfrac{3}{x}}{6 + \dfrac{3}{y}}$

3. $\dfrac{4x - 3}{x - 6} + \dfrac{2x + 5}{6 - x} - \dfrac{x - 1}{x - 6}$

1. $-\dfrac{2(a + 5)}{3}$ 2. $\dfrac{2xy - y}{2xy + x}$ 3. $\dfrac{x - 7}{x - 6}$

6.7 Expressions With Rational Number Exponents (page 157)

Background

In the previous lesson, rational number exponents were defined in terms of radicals. In this lesson, the properties for integer exponents are extended to rational number exponents.

Suggestions

Examples 1–4 illustrate the extension of all of the properties for integer exponents to expressions containing rational number exponents. Emphasize that an expression containing rational number exponents is *not* in simplest form if an exponent is a *negative* number.

The solution of exponential equations is extended to cover two additional types in Example 5, which lead to rational number solutions.

Enrichment

1. $1 + \sqrt{3} + \dfrac{1}{1 - \sqrt{3}} + \dfrac{1}{1 + \sqrt{3}} =$

   A. $\sqrt{3}$. **B.** $1 + \sqrt{3}$. **C.** $1 - \sqrt{3}$.
   D. $2 + \sqrt{3}$.   **E.** $2 + 2\sqrt{3}$. **A**

2. If $4^{2x} = 25$, then $4^{-x} =$

   A. $\frac{1}{5}$.   **B.** $\frac{1}{25}$.   **C.** $\frac{1}{125}$.
   D. $\frac{1}{625}$.   **E.** $-\frac{1}{5}$. **A**

Cumulative Review

Solve.

1. $\dfrac{a - 26}{a^2 - 16} + \dfrac{3}{a - 4} = \dfrac{6}{a + 4}$ 5
2. $x^2 + 7x = 0$ $0, -7$
3. $\frac{3}{4}x - 2 = 7$ 12

Computer Activities (page 164)

This program uses the BASIC functions SQR (square root) and INT (integer). These functions should be explained before running the program. The program can be used with other related lessons in the chapter.

7
Chapter and Lesson Commentaries

Chapter 7   Quadratic Formula

Chapter Objectives

To solve a quadratic equation by completing the square
To solve a quadratic equation by using the quadratic formula
To solve word problems with irrational solutions by using the quadratic formula
To solve a radical equation

Chapter Overview

The quadratic formula is developed and applied to solving quadratic equations and to solving word problems that lead to quadratic equations with irrational solutions. The nature of the solutions of a quadratic equation is delayed until the next chapter, where complex (imaginary) numbers are introduced. Radical equations are solved.

Special Features

7.1 Completing the Square (page 165)

Vocabulary

completing the square

Background

An equation of the form $ax^2 + bx + c = 0$, $a \neq 0$, is called a *quadratic equation* in standard form. In Chapter 3, quadratic equations, such as $3x^2 + 10x - 8 = 0$, $5x^2 - 15x = 0$, and $4x^2 - 9 = 0$, were solved by factoring the quadratic polynomial. In this lesson quadratic equations are solved by completing the square. The method is generalized in the next lesson and results in the quadratic formula. The skill of completing the square has immediate application to maximum value, an optional topic found on pages 167–168 and extensive application in Chapter 12, where equations of conic sections are rewritten in standard form.

Suggestions

Leave a space for the third term when completing the square, as shown in Examples 1–3. The symbol "$\pm$" is introduced to represent the abbreviated form of the two square roots of a positive number. Students should demonstrate understanding of the symbol, $\pm$, in exercises such as Oral Exercises 1–6.

For Additional Chalkboard Work

The alternate examples listed below may be used in place of, or in addition to, the examples in the text. Solve each equation by completing the square.
1. $y^2 - 12y = -7$ 2. $n^2 + 5n = 24$
3. $16x^2 - 24x + 7 = 0$

1. $6 \pm \sqrt{29}$ 2. $3, -8$ 3. $\dfrac{3 \pm \sqrt{2}}{4}$

Cumulative Review

1. Simplify: $\dfrac{3}{x-9} + \dfrac{7}{9-x} - \dfrac{2}{x-9}$. $\dfrac{-6}{x-9}$

2. Solve: $\dfrac{3x+5}{2x-3} = \dfrac{2x+7}{x-1}$. $2, -8$

3. Evaluate by using synthetic division:
   $2x^4 + 10x^3 - 11x^2 - 40$ if $x = -6$ -4

7.2 The Quadratic Formula (page 169)

Vocabulary

quadratic formula

Suggestions

Encourage the B- and C-level students to study the derivation of the quadratic formula on page 169 in preparation for a future quiz.

Point out to students that a pair of irrational solutions can be written in either of two ways. For example, either $\dfrac{1 \pm 2\sqrt{3}}{2}$ or $\dfrac{1 + 2\sqrt{3}}{2}$, $\dfrac{1 - 2\sqrt{3}}{2}$ is an acceptable answer in Example 2. However, a pair of rational solutions, such as $\dfrac{9 \pm 9}{10}$, must be listed separately as $\dfrac{9}{5}$, 0, as shown in Example 3.

For Additional Chalkboard Work

You may wish to use this as a B- and C-level quiz. Solve $mx^2 + nx + p = 0$, $m \neq 0$, by completing the square.
$$x = \dfrac{-n \pm \sqrt{n^2 - 4mp}}{2m}$$

The examples below are alternate forms for the exercises included in Examples 1–3. They may be used as additional practice or as a quiz.

Solve. Use the quadratic formula.
1. $4x^2 - 7x + 2 = 0$ 2. $9x^2 = 12x - 1$
3. $6x^2 + 5x = 0$ 4. $72 - x^2 = 0$

1. $\dfrac{7 \pm \sqrt{17}}{8}$

2. $\dfrac{12 \pm \sqrt{108}}{18} = \dfrac{12 \pm 6\sqrt{3}}{18} = \dfrac{2 \pm \sqrt{3}}{3}$

3. $0, -\dfrac{5}{6}$ 4. $\pm 6\sqrt{2}$

Cumulative Review

1. Factor $x^3 - 125$.
2. Factor $ax^2 - nx - amx + mn$.
3. A second number is 1 more than twice a first number. The product of the second number and 3 less than the first number is 30. Find both numbers. $-3, -5; \frac{11}{2}, 12$

1. $(x - 5)(x^2 + 5x + 25)$
2. $(x - m)(ax - n)$

7.3 Problem Solving: The Quadratic Formula (page 172)

Background

In Chapter 3 the students solved word problems that led to quadratic equations with rational solutions. The equations were solved by factoring. In this lesson and in the next lesson, the students will solve problems that lead to quadratic equations with irrational solutions.

Suggestions

In some of the exercises, answers are to be given to the nearest tenth (0.1). Emphasize that rounding to the nearest tenth should be delayed until all other operations have been done. The reason for this is shown below.

Correct Way	Wrong Way
$\dfrac{3 + 6\sqrt{17}}{2}$	$\dfrac{3 + 6\sqrt{17}}{2}$
$\dfrac{3 + 6(4.123)}{2}$	$\dfrac{3 + 6(4.1)}{2}$
$\dfrac{3 + 24.738}{2}$	$\dfrac{3 + 24.6}{2}$
13.869	13.8
13.9	

Notice that the answers differ by 0.1.

Emphasize that the irrational solutions in simplest radical form rather than the "rounded" decimal solutions should be used to check the solutions, as shown in Example 2.

Cumulative Review

1. Simplify $\dfrac{-16x^{-3}y^2z^{-4}}{24x^6y^{10}z^{-12}} \cdot \dfrac{-2z^8}{3x^9y^8}$
2. Simplify $3x^2(-5xy^4)^3$. $-375x^5y^{12}$
3. Solve $3^{4-x} = 243$. -1
4. Find the value of 8.76×10^{-3}.
4. 0.00876

7.4 Problem Solving: Irrational Measurements (page 175)

Suggestions

The most difficult part of this lesson is representing the data in exercises such as Example 2. Use the chalkboard and complete the diagram in Example 2 step by step.

Represent the data on diagrams for Exercises 3 and 7 during the class discussion. Then, assign the parallel Exercises 4 and 8. The diagrams for Exercises 3 and 7 are shown below.

3.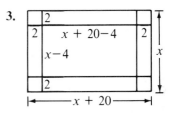

7.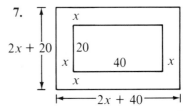

Cumulative Review

Find the solution set. Graph the solutions on a number line.
1. $x^2 - 3x - 10 < 0$ 2. $x^4 - 10x^2 + 9 > 0$
3. $|3x - 6| > 12$
1. $\{x \mid -2 < x < 5\}$
2. $\{x \mid x < -3 \text{ or } -1 < x < 1 \text{ or } x > 3\}$
3. $\{x \mid x < -2 \text{ or } x > 6\}$

7.5   Radical Equations (page 178)

Vocabulary

extraneous solution, radical equations

Background

The students encountered extraneous solutions in Chapter 5 when they solved fractional equations. A radical equation is solved by raising each side of the equation to the same power. This step can introduce an extraneous solution, as shown below:

$$x + 1 = 3 \text{ (the solution is 2)};$$
$$(x + 1)^2 = 3^2$$
$$x^2 + 2x + 1 = 9$$
$$x^2 + 2x - 8 = 0$$
$$(x - 2)(x + 4) = 0$$
$$x = 2 \text{ or } x = -4 \text{ (the solutions are 2 and } -4).$$

Suggestions

Stress, as shown in all of the examples, that the ''apparent'' solutions of a radical equation must be checked in the original equation to identify any extraneous solutions.

Notice that Exercises 28 and 30 have no solution. They can be solved as the other radical equations and an extraneous solution will appear. Some students should notice that an equation such as $\sqrt{2t + 5} = -3$ has no solution since $\sqrt{2t + 5} \geq 0$ for each t, but $-3 < 0$.

Cumulative Review

Simplify.

1. $\sqrt{50} + 3\sqrt{8} - \sqrt{32}$ $7\sqrt{2}$
2. $(2\sqrt{x} - 5\sqrt{y})^2$ $4x - 20\sqrt{xy} + 25y$
3. $\left(\dfrac{16x^8}{81y^{-12}} \right)^{\frac{3}{4}}$ $\dfrac{8x^6 y^9}{27}$

Computer Activities (page 184)

This program is an example of how a quadratic equation can be applied to a manufacturing problem. Students can develop other applications that apply the quadratic formula.

8

Chapter and Lesson Commentaries

Chapter 8   Complex Numbers

Chapter Objectives

To solve an equation whose solutions are imaginary numbers
To add, subtract, multiply, and divide complex numbers
To find the three cube roots of a nonzero integer
To determine the nature of the solutions of a quadratic equation by examining its discriminant
To find the sum and the product of the solutions
To write a quadratic equation, given its solutions

Chapter Overview

Imaginary numbers are introduced and classified as the real number system is extended to the complex number system. Operations with complex numbers are studied and practiced. The discriminant of a quadratic equation is related to the nature of the solutions of the equation. The coefficients of a quadratic equation are related to the sum and the product of the solutions of the equation. The three cube roots of a nonzero integer that is a perfect cube are found as one real number and a pair of conjugate imaginary numbers. Given the solution set of a quadratic equation, the equation is written in standard form.

Special Features

Maria Gaetana Agnesi   p. 186
Reading in Algebra   pp. 188, 192, 197
Cumulative Review   pp. 189, 206–207
Problem Solving   p. 201
A Challenge to You   pp. 197, 200
Computer Activities   p. 204
College Prep Test   p. 205
Chapter Review   p. 202
Chapter Test   p. 203

8.1 Sums and Differences of Complex Numbers (page 187)

Vocabulary
complex number, imaginary number, pure imaginary number

Suggestions
In Example 1, point out that we write $i\sqrt{7}$ rather than $\sqrt{7}\,i$ to avoid confusion with $\sqrt{7i}$.

Have students complete the following table after they study pages 187–188.

Number	Com-plex	Imag-inary	Pure Imag.	Real	Ra-tional	Irrat.
-8	*			*	*	
$3i$	*	*	*			
$5 - 2i$	*	*				
0	*			*	*	
$3 - 2\sqrt{5}$	*			*		*
i^2	*			*	*	

Enrichment
1. The solutions of $ax^2 + bx + c = 0$, $a \neq 0$, will be a pair of reciprocals if
   A. $a = b$ **B.** $b = c$ **C.** $a = c$
   D. $a = bc$ **E.** $ab = c$ **C**
2. The sum of three numbers is 49. The ratio of the first number to the second number is $\frac{2}{3}$ and the ratio of the second number to the third number is $\frac{5}{8}$. The second number is **C**
   A. 1 **B.** 10 **C.** 15 **D.** 20 **E.** 24

Cumulative Review
Samuel is 6 years older than Tina and Renée is 4 years younger than Samuel. Three years ago, 3 times the sum of the two younger ages was 4 times the oldest age. Find their present ages.
Tina, 12 Renée, 14 Samuel, 18

8.2 Products and Quotients of Complex Numbers (page 190)

Vocabulary
conjugate complex numbers

Suggestions
In Example 1, stress that $\sqrt{-6} \cdot \sqrt{-3}$ is *not equal* to $\sqrt{-6(-3)}$. Introduce Examples 5 and 6 by showing the analogy to dividing by an irrational number in the real number system. For example,

$$\frac{7}{3 + 4\sqrt{2}} = \frac{7}{3 + 4\sqrt{2}} \cdot \frac{3 - 4\sqrt{2}}{3 - 4\sqrt{2}}$$
$$= \frac{7(3 - 4\sqrt{2})}{9 - 32} = \frac{21 - 28\sqrt{2}}{-23}$$
$$\frac{7}{3 + 4i} = \frac{7}{3 + 4i} \cdot \frac{3 - 4i}{3 - 4i}$$
$$= \frac{7(3 - 4i)}{9 - 16i^2} = \frac{21 - 28i}{25}$$

In simplifying expressions involving complex numbers, all answers should be expressed in the form $a + bi$. For example, $5 + \sqrt{-4}$ should be changed to $5 + 2i$. An expression such as $\frac{3}{7i} = \frac{3}{7\sqrt{-1}}$ is not in simplest radical form.

$\frac{3}{7i}$ is simplified to $\frac{3i}{-7}$ to remove the radical in the denominator.

Some standardized tests require the student to simplify large integral powers of i such as i^{98} and i^{100}. Present similar examples that can be simplified as integral powers of i^2 as follows:

$$i^{98} = (i^2)^{49} = (-1)^{49} = -1 \text{ and}$$
$$i^{100} = (i^2)^{50} = (-1)^{50} = 1.$$

Point out that consecutive powers of i take on the values i, -1, $-i$, 1, and repeat in cycles of four:

$$i^1 = i, \, i^2 = -1, \, i^3 = -i, \, i^4 = 1;$$
$$i^5 = i, \, i^6 = -1, \, i^7 = -i, \, i^8 = 1; \text{ and so on.}$$

Cumulative Review
Machines A, B, and C can each complete a certain job in 45 min, 1 h, and 90 min, respectively. How long will the job take if the machines work at the same time? 20 minutes

8.3 Equations with Imaginary Number Solutions (page 193)

Suggestions
Point out that although every quadratic equation can be solved by using the quadratic formula, it is sometimes more convenient to solve the equation by another method. For example, the equations $x^2 + 4 = 0$ and $2x^2 - 5 = 0$, in Example 2 could have been solved as follows.

$$x^2 + 4 = 0$$
$$x = -\frac{0 \pm \sqrt{0^2 - 4 \cdot 1 \cdot 4}}{2}$$
$$= \frac{\pm\sqrt{-16}}{2} = \pm\frac{4i}{2} = \pm 2i$$

$$2x^2 - 5 = 0$$
$$x = 0 \pm \sqrt{0^2 - 4 \cdot 2(-5)}$$
$$= \pm\sqrt{\frac{40}{4}}$$
$$= \pm\frac{2\sqrt{10}}{4} = \frac{\pm\sqrt{10}}{2}$$

For Additional Chalkboard Work
An alternate example for each of the three examples in the text is provided below. Students may find these simpler to solve.
1. Solve. $x^2 + 2x + 3 = 0$.
2. Solve. $x^4 + 8x^2 - 9 = 0$.
3. Find the three cube roots of 1.

1. $x = \dfrac{-2 \pm \sqrt{4 - 12}}{2} = \dfrac{-2 \pm \sqrt{-8}}{2}$
$= \dfrac{-2 \pm 2i\sqrt{2}}{2}$
$= -1 \pm i\sqrt{2}$
2. $(x^2 + 9)(x^2 - 1) = 0$; $x^2 + 9 = 0$,
   or $x^2 - 1 = 0$; $x^2 = -9$, or $x^2 = 1$; $\pm 3i$, ± 1
3. $x^3 = 1$ $x^3 - 1 = 0$; $(x - 1)(x^2 + x + 1) = 0$
   $x - 1 = 0$, or $x^2 + x + 1 - 0$;
   $\dfrac{-1 \pm \sqrt{1 - 4}}{2}$; 1, $\dfrac{-1 \pm i\sqrt{3}}{2}$

Cumulative Review
Compute.
1. $16^{-\frac{3}{2}}$ $\dfrac{1}{64}$ 2. 9.72×10^{-2} 0.0972
3. $\dfrac{4.73 \times 10^2}{1.1 \times 10^{-3}}$ 430,000   4. $\dfrac{6^{-2}}{5^{-3}}$ $\dfrac{125}{36}$

8.4 The Discriminant (page 195)

Vocabulary
discriminant, nature of solutions

Suggestions
Stress that determining the *nature* of the solutions of a quadratic equation means all of the following where a, b, and c are rational numbers.
1. Determine whether the solution(s) is (are):
   A. two real numbers ($b^2 - 4ac > 0$),
   B. two imaginary numbers ($b^2 - 4ac < 0$), or
   C. one rational number ($b^2 - 4ac = 0$); and
2. if the solutions are real numbers, then determine whether they are:
   A. rational numbers ($b^2 - 4ac$ is a perfect square), or
   B. irrational numbers ($b^2 - 4ac$ is not a perfect square).

For Additional Chalkboard Work
After Example 3, have students complete this chart.

Equation	$b^2 - 4ac$	Predicted Number and Nature of Solutions
$x^2 + 6x + 9 = 0$	0	1, rational
$x^2 + 2x + 2 = 0$	-4	2, imaginary
$x^2 - 3x + 1 = 0$	5	2, irrational
$x^2 - 3x - 10 = 0$	49	2, rational

Enrichment (A Contest-Type Problem)
For the equation $x^2 + x\sqrt{2} - 4 = 0$, the nature of the solution(s) is (are)
A. two irrational solutions.
B. two rational solutions.
C. two imaginary solutions.
D. one rational solution.
E. one irrational solution.   A.

Cumulative Review
Simplify.
1. $4m^2n\sqrt{75m^8n^7p^3}$ 2. $\dfrac{5t}{\sqrt{18t^3}}$
3. $\dfrac{x^3 + 125}{2x^2 - 10x + 50} \cdot \dfrac{14x}{3x + 15}$
1. $20m^6n^4p\sqrt{3np}$ 2. $\dfrac{5\sqrt{2t}}{6t}$ 3. $\dfrac{7x}{3}$

8.5 Sum and Product of Solutions (page 198)

Suggestions

In Example 2, point out that *in standard form* means *integral coefficients*. Thus $12x^2 + x - 6 = 0$, not $x^2 + \frac{1}{12} x + -\frac{1}{2} = 0$, is the correct equation.

After studying Examples 1 and 2, show that the two lesson objectives are inverses of each other. This can be done as follows:

Find $r + s$ and $r \cdot s$ for $3x^2 - 2x - 1 = 0$.
$$3x^2 - 2x - 1 = 0$$
$$x^2 - \frac{2}{3} x - \frac{1}{3} = 0$$
$$r + s = \tfrac{2}{3} \text{ and } r \cdot s = \tfrac{-1}{3} \ .$$

Write an equation for which $r = -\frac{1}{3}$ and $s = 1$.

$$r + s = \tfrac{2}{3} \text{ and } r \cdot s = -\tfrac{1}{3}$$
$$x^2 - \tfrac{2}{3}x - \tfrac{1}{3} = 0$$
$$3x^2 - 2x - 1 = 0$$

For Additional Chalkboard Work

Following is an alternate example for each of the examples in the lesson.
1. Find the sum and the product of the solutions of $3x^2 - 5x - 2 = 0$.
2. Write a quadratic equation whose solutions are -5 and 3.
3. Write a quadratic equation whose only solution is 3.
4. Write a quadratic equation whose solutions are $3 \pm \sqrt{2}$.

1. sum, $\frac{5}{3}$; product, $-\frac{2}{3}$
2. $x^2 + 2x - 15 = 0$
3. $r + s = 6$, $rs = 9$; $x^2 - 6x + 9 = 0$
4. $r + s = 6$, $rs = 7$; $x^2 - 6x + 7 = 0$

Computer Activities (page 204)

This program shows how a simple program can be used to deal with advanced mathematical numbers. This program can be used in conjunction with the entire chapter on complex numbers.

8.6 Problem Solving: Mixed Types (page 201)

Suggestions

Here is an alternate example you may wish to use to illustrate the basic problem solving steps.

Earl is four years older than Arlene. Five years ago the sum of their ages was forty-eight. How old are they now?

Step 1   READ carefully. What is the number you are asked to find?

Step 2   PLAN You are asked to find two numbers.
REPRESENT the numbers algebraically.

	Age Five Years Ago	Age Now
Earl	$(x + 4) - 5$	$x + 4$
Arlene	$x - 5$	x

Now use the second sentence to write an equation.

''Five years ago the sum of their ages was 48.''

$$(x - 1) + (x - 5) = 48$$

Step 3   SOLVE.
$$(x - 1) + (x - 5) = 48$$
$$2x - 6 = 48$$
$$2x = 54$$
$$x = 27$$

Step 4   INTERPRET Look back at the statement of the problem and be sure you give a full answer: not just ''27.'' ''Arlene is 27, Earl is 31.'' Stress that checking involves more than just checking the equation. The equation could be solved correctly, but an error could have been made in the original interpretation of the word problem.

Students should read the problems and write down the four problem solving steps for each.

9 Chapter and Lesson Commentaries

Chapter 9 Coordinate Geometry

Chapter Objectives

To find the slope of a line
To graph a line
To write an equation of a line
To determine whether a point lies on a line
To determine the distance between any two points
   in a plane
To determine whether two lines are parallel or
   perpendicular, given their slopes
To find the slope of a line parallel to or
   perpendicular to a given line
To write an equation of a line parallel to or
   perpendicular to a given line
To apply the slope, distance, and midpoint formulas

Chapter Overview

Finding the slope, graphing, and writing an
equation of a line are taught in this chapter.
Writing an equation of a line parallel or
perpendicular to a line and determining whether two
lines are parallel or perpendicular are also taught.
Determining distance between two points and
finding the coordinates of the midpoint or
endpoints of a line segment are included. The
chapter concludes with applications.

Special Features

Careers: Computer Programming   p. 208
Applications   p. 234; Computer   p. 235
Reading in Algebra   pp. 211, 215, 219
Cumulative Review   pp. 215, 225, 230
A Challenge to You   p. 222
College Prep Test   p. 238
Chapter Review   p. 236
Chapter Test   p. 237

9.1   The Coordinate Plane (page 209)

Vocabulary

cartesian coordinate plane, quadrant, abscissa,
ordered pairs, ordinate

Background

The word *Cartesian* is derived from the last
name of the brilliant mathematician René
Des*cartes* (1596–1650). It was Descartes who
determined that every point in a plane can be
determined by a pair of numbers (scalars) and,
conversely, every point in a plane determines
a pair of numbers.

Suggestions

The idea of locating points in a quadrant and
graphing an equation is not new to the students and
will be used throughout the text. When other methods
fail, graphing using a table of values will often yield
results.

   It is important to use correct terminology in
referring to graphs. One does not graph a line or
graph a point. A line or a point is a *graph*. An
ordered pair of numbers or an equation *is graphed*.

   Students should not always call the horizontal
axis the x-axis and the vertical axis the y-axis.
You may wish to have students graph ordered pairs
(s, t) or other such pairs.

For Additional Chalkboard Work

Draw the graph of the line described by each
equation.

1. $s = -2t + 3$ **2.** $s = 3t - 1$
3. $4t - 3s = 9$ **4.** $2t + 4s = -5$

Errors Students Make

Students frequently do not choose values for the
abscissa judiciously when formulating a table of
values. In Example 2 we chose 0, 2 and 4 for x in
order to reduce unnecessary calculations.

Cumulative Review

1. Simplify. $\dfrac{\frac{3}{4} + \frac{1}{5}}{\frac{4}{5} + \frac{1}{2}}$. $\frac{19}{26}$

2. Simplify. $2(3 - 2a) + 3(4a - 2)$. $8a$
3. Find the solution set of $|3x - 7| \le 2$.
$\{x \mid \frac{5}{3} \le x \le 3\}$

9.2 Slope of a Line (page 212)

Vocabulary
slope, 0-slope, positive slope, undefined slope, negative slope

Background
The concept of a slope is one of the most important ones in mathematics, especially in differential calculus. In differential calculus two major types of problems involving slope emerge. They are problems involving rate, speed, velocity and acceleration, and those involving finding the slope of a tangent line at any given point on a curve.

Suggestions
Students can be guided to discover that lines that slant up to the right have a positive slope and those that slant down to the right have a negative slope. Emphasize that a vertical line has no slope. It is incorrect to say that a vertical line has a slope of infinity.

The concept of the slope of a line can also be taught through a discussion of the ratio of vertical change to horizontal change $\left(\dfrac{\text{rise}}{\text{run}}\right)$, or $\dfrac{\Delta y}{\Delta x}$. Either approach leads to the same definition of slope,

$$m = \frac{y_2 - y_1}{x_2 - x_1}.$$

Students should understand that when finding the slope of a line, the change in y-coordinates and change in x-coordinates can be accomplished in either direction, i.e., either of the points can have coordinates of (x_1, y_1).

For Additional Chalkboard Work
Are points P, Q and R on the same straight line? Verify.
1. $P(6, -3)$, $Q(0, 0)$, $R(-2, 1)$ Yes
2. $P(-1, 2)$, $Q(7, 4)$, $R(11, 5)$ Yes
3. $P(-3, -4)$, $Q(2, 5)$, $R(6, 12)$ No

Errors Students Make
A puzzling point to students is that a vertical line has an undefined slope not an infinite slope. Students sometimes will subtract the y's in one direction and the x's in another when using

$$m = \frac{y_2 - y_1}{x_2 - x_1}.$$

9.3 Equation of a Line (page 216)

Vocabulary
point-slope, slope-intercept, y-intercept, standard form, x-intercept

Background
Descartes stated that every point on a coordinate plane can be represented by an ordered pair. Since a line is a set of points, the obvious question is, can a line be described by an equation? An equation of a line does precisely that.

It is not necessary to use $y - y_1 = m(x - x_1)$ to write an equation of a line. The slope-intercept form $y = mx + b$ is sufficient to write an equation, given any of the examples and exercises in this lesson. But, it is often easier to write equations using the point-slope form of an equation.

Suggestions
When finding the equation of a line in which the coordinates of two points are given, the coordinates of either point can be used to substitute in the point-slope form. In Example 4, let $x_1 = 5$ and $y_1 = -4$.
$y + 4 = -\frac{5}{8}(x - 5); 8y + 32 = -5x + 25;$
$5x + 8y = -7$. This yields the same results.

The equation of a horizontal line is of the form $ax + by = c$, where $a = 0$ and $b \neq 0$. Thus, $by = c$ is an equation of a horizontal line. The equation of a vertical line is of the form $ax + by = c$, where $a \neq 0$ and $b = 0$. Thus, $ax = c$ is an equation of a vertical line.

For Additional Chalkboard Work
Write an equation, in standard form, of each line. First use $y - y_1 = m(x - x_1)$ and then $y = mx + b$.
1. $P(-4, -3)$, $Q(5, 6)$ $y = x + 1$
2. $P\left(-\frac{2}{3}, \frac{5}{2}\right)$, $Q\left(-4, +\frac{2}{3}\right)$ $y = \frac{11}{20}x + \frac{172}{60}$
3. $P\left(-3, \frac{1}{2}\right)$, $m = \frac{2}{3}$ $y = \frac{2}{3}x + \frac{5}{2}$
4. $P(6, -1)$, $Q(0, 3)$ $y = -3x + 3$

Cumulative Review
Find the solution.
1. $-6 < 3x + 3 < 12$ 2. $|x| \leq 4$
3. $|3n| > 12$ $n > 4$, or $n < -4$
1. $-3 < x < 3$ 2. $-4 \leq x \leq 4$

9.4 Slope-Intercept Method of Drawing Graphs (page 220)

Background

To graph any linear equation it is sufficient to use only the slope-intercept method of drawing graphs. However, it is not always convenient or wise to do so. Therefore, other methods of graphing lines should be discussed. Other approaches such as plotting points and using tables should continue to be encouraged. Another method of graphing lines is to find both intercepts.

Suggestions

The approach used to draw graphs of equations of lines in this lesson is to find the slope and y-intercept of the line. Students should first graph the coordinates of the y-intercept and then use the numerator and denominator of the slope to locate another point on the line.

You may also wish to have students use a calculator to determine whether a given point is on a line described by a given equation.

Enrichment

Find n so that $\dfrac{3^{n+1} - 3^n + 6}{3^n + 7}$ equals an integer.

$$\frac{3^{0+1} - 3^0 + 6}{3^0 + 7} = \frac{3 - 1 + 6}{1 + 7} = \frac{8}{8}, \text{ or } 1.$$

For Additional Chalkboard Work

Have students discuss the graph of the equation $y = mx + b$ for different values of x, y, m and b. For example, if $x = 0$, $y = b$. If $b < 0$, the line crosses the y-axis below the origin. Consider positions of the line when $b = 0$ and m assumes different values.

Errors Students Make

Students sometimes have difficulty determining which part of the fraction representing the slope determines the horizontal distance and direction and which determines the vertical distance and direction. The expression $\dfrac{\text{rise}}{\text{run}}$ may help to clarify. The sign of the slope can go with either the numerator or the denominator.

9.5 The Distance Between Two Points (page 223)

Vocabulary

Pythagorean relation, converse of the Pythagorean relation

Suggestions

Review for the students the definition of length of a horizontal and vertical line segment. These two definitions are important for the understanding of the distance formula.

The distance formula can be used for any two points even if these points happen to form a horizontal or vertical line segment. However, the methods developed earlier for finding the length of a horizontal and vertical line segment would probably be easier to use.

In deciding which of the three given lengths is the length of the hypotenuse, students may need to use the square root table in the back of the book. You also may encourage them to use a calculator.

For Additional Chalkboard Work

Find the coordinates of vertex C, the vertex of the right angle of $\triangle ABC$ where A and B are given.   1. $(5, 8)$ 2. $(1, 9)$
1. $A(-3, 5)$, $B(6, 8)$ 2. $A(3, 1)$, $B(9, 4)$
3. $A(2, 8)$, $B(5, 3)$ 4. $A(-3, 9)$, $B(6, -4)$
3. $(8, 5)$ 4. $(9, 6)$

Errors Students Make

Students sometimes have difficulty finding the coordinates of point C, the intersection of the perpendicular segments from A and B. You may wish to use some numerical examples to help remove this difficulty.

Cumulative Review

1. Factor $5x^3 - 14x^2 - 3x$.
2. Factor $8a^2 - 50$.
3. Solve $x^2 + 2x - 15 = 0$.
1. $x(5x + 1)(x - 3)$ 2. $2(2a + 5)(2a - 5)$
3. $-5, 3$

9.6 The Midpoint of a Segment (page 226)

Vocabulary
midpoint of a segment, endpoint of a segment

Suggestions
You may wish to develop the formula for finding the midpoint of a line segment by determining the midpoints of horizontal and vertical line segments. Draw right triangle PQR with T, S, and M as Midpoints,

Midpoint $\overline{PR}$ is $T(5, 2)$, or $\left(\dfrac{9 + 1}{2}, 2\right)$.

Midpoint $\overline{QR}$ is $S(9, 4)$, or $\left(9, \dfrac{6 + 2}{2}\right)$.

Thus midpoint $\overline{PQ}$ is $(5, 4)$.

In general, M has coordinates $\left(\dfrac{x_1 + x_2}{2}, \dfrac{y_1 + y_2}{2}\right)$. Exercise 42 leads to the generalization that the segments joining the midpoints of any quadrilateral in order form a parallelogram.

For Additional Chalkboard Work
Determine the coordinates (x, y) of M, the midpoint of the segment joining P and Q.
1. $P(2, 1)$, $Q(8, 7)$ $(5, 4)$
2. $P(-6, -2)$, $Q(4, -6)$ $(-1, -4)$
3. $P(4, -1)$, $Q(-6, 5)$ $(-1, 2)$
4. $P(3, -3)$, $Q(6, 4)$ $\left(\frac{9}{2}, \frac{1}{2}\right)$

Errors Students Make
Students sometimes subtract coordinates when finding the midpoint. Show some examples on the chalkboard to avoid this difficulty.

Cumulative Review
Simplify.

1. $\dfrac{\dfrac{3a}{a^2 - 4} + \dfrac{2}{a - 2}}{\dfrac{4}{a + 2} + \dfrac{5}{a - 2}}$ $\dfrac{5a + 4}{9a + 2}$

2. $\dfrac{1 - \dfrac{9}{a^2}}{\dfrac{1}{a} - \dfrac{3}{a^2}}$ $a + 3$

9.7 Parallel and Perpendicular Lines (page 228)

Background
Two lines may be perpendicular to each other with one of the lines having undefined slope. For example, a vertical line and a horizontal line are always perpendicular, yet the slope of the vertical line is undefined.

Another way to show that two lines are perpendicular is to show that the product of their slopes is -1 (no vertical lines) and the converse is true. If the slope of one line is $-\frac{3}{2}$ then the slope of a line perpendicular to it is $\frac{2}{3}$. Hence, $\left(-\frac{3}{2}\right)\left(\frac{2}{3}\right) = -1$.

Suggestions
In this lesson the point-slope form of an equation is used to write an equation of a line. The slope-intercept form can also be used. In Example 1, $m = \frac{3}{2}$ and the line passes through the point $P(4, 2)$. Use $y = mx + b$ and find b.

$$2 = \tfrac{3}{2}(4) + b; b = 2 - 6 = -4$$

Thus, $y = \frac{3}{2}x - 4$, or $3x - 2y = 8$.

This form is a good alternative of the development in the lesson.

Write an equation in standard form at the line that passes through the point $A(-3, -2)$ and is perpendicular to the line whose equation is $-4x - 3y = 10$.

$m = -\frac{4}{3}$; the slope of the line perpendicular to it is $\frac{3}{4}$. Use $y = mx + b$;

$$-2 = \tfrac{3}{4}(-3) + b; -8 = -9 + 4b;$$

$$4b = 1; b = \tfrac{1}{4}.$$

Thus, $y = \frac{3}{4}x + \frac{1}{4}$ is an equation of the line. In standard form, $3x - 4y = -1$ is the equation.

Cumulative Review
Solve each equation.
1. $-4a - 3 + 5a = 7 - 2a + 2$ 4
2. $-3x - (6 + 2x) = -2(x - 3)$ -4
3. $|2x - 3| = 5$ $-1, 4$

9.8 Using Coordinate Geometry (page 231)

Vocabulary

collinear, trapezoid, parallelogram, median, quadrilateral, rectangle, isosceles triangle, rhombus, equilateral triangle, diagonals

Suggestions

Many of the concepts developed in this chapter are applied in this lesson. It might be appropriate to review some geometric definitions and properties.

To show a triangle is a right triangle, students can show either that two sides have negative reciprocal slopes or that the converse of the Pythagorean relation is true. That is, if $c^2 = a^2 + b^2$, then $\triangle ABC$ is a right triangle.

For Additional Chalkboard Work

Show that the lines joining the points $A(-3, -4)$, $B(2, 5)$ and $C(-5, 3)$ form a right triangle. Use the converse of the Pythagorean relation.

$$
\begin{aligned}
d(\overline{AB}) &= \sqrt{(-3-2)^2 + (-4-5)^2} \\
&= \sqrt{25 + 81} = \sqrt{106} \\
d(\overline{BC}) &= \sqrt{(5-3)^2 + (2+5)^2} \\
&= \sqrt{4 + 49} = \sqrt{53} \\
d(\overline{AC}) &= \sqrt{(-3+5)^2 + (-4-3)^2} \\
&= \sqrt{4 + 49} = \sqrt{53} \\
&\quad (\sqrt{106})^2 = (\sqrt{53})^2 + (\sqrt{53})^2 \\
&\quad 106 = 53 + 53
\end{aligned}
$$

Cumulative Review

1. Three times the sum of a number is 3 more than twice the product. What is the number?
2. Find p in dollars if $A = \$9,350$, $r = 10\frac{1}{2}\%$, and $t = 3$ years 3 months. Use the formula $A = p + prt$.

1. 32   2. \$6971.11

Computer Activities (page 235)

This program is an application of the distance formula. Four variables are INPUT at the start of the program. Exercises 4 and 5 show two other applications of coordinate geometry.

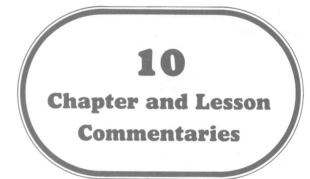

10 Chapter and Lesson Commentaries

Chapter 10 Linear Systems, Matrices, and Determinants

Chapter Objectives

To solve a system of two linear equations graphically and algebraically
To solve a system of three linear equations
To find the value of a 2 by 2 and 3 by 3 determinant
To solve systems of linear equations using determinants
To solve a system of three linear equations using matrix transformations
To find sums and products of matrices

Chapter Overview

The purpose of this chapter is to introduce students to several methods for solving systems of linear equations.

Some matrix algebra is introduced, since it is an important topic in the fields of mathematics, science, computer science, economics, and engineering.

Special Features

Reading in Algebra   pp. 241, 249
Cumulative Review   pp. 255, 262
A Challenge to You   p. 255
Calculator Activities   p. 242
Computer Activity   p. 271
College Prep Test   p. 274
Chapter Review   p. 272
Chapter Test   p. 273

10.1 Solving Linear Systems Graphically (page 240)

Vocabulary
consistent system, dependent system, inconsistent system, independent system, linear system

Background
Since the intersection of the lines represented by a system of linear equations is the solution of the system, students should understand and have sufficient experience in graphing equations in order to understand algebraic solutions.

Suggestions
You may wish to give an overview of the lesson by reviewing that, given two lines, they may: be parallel and have no points in common, intersect and have exactly one point in common, or coincide and have all their points in common. You may also want your students to use slopes and y-intercepts to determine, without graphing, whether the lines for a given system of equations: are parallel and therefore form an inconsistent system, coincide and therefore form a dependent system, or intersect in exactly one point and therefore form an independent system.

The greater the number of squares used to represent one unit, the easier it is to estimate solutions to the nearest tenth of a unit.

Errors Students Make
Students sometimes have difficulty in reading the solutions from their graphs. Emphasizing careful drawing of graphs will help to remove this difficulty. Some students also have difficulty with classifying solutions. It is more important that students are able to find solutions than to classify them.

Cumulative Review
Simplify. Write each expression with positive exponents.

1. $\dfrac{-2a^4b^4}{a^2b^4}$ **2.** $\dfrac{-12a^{-4}b^6c^{-3}}{6a^{-2}b^{-4}c^5}$ **3.** $\left(\dfrac{2x^{-2}y^3}{6xy^{-5}}\right)^4$

1. $-2a^2$ 2. $\dfrac{-2b^{10}}{a^2c^8}$ 3. $\dfrac{y^{32}}{81x^{12}}$

10.2 Solving Linear Systems Algebraically (page 243)

Suggestions
In solving systems of equations by substitution, students should be reminded that they can solve for either variable in either equation. However, students should be encouraged to solve for the variable that is easier to isolate. Emphasize that after the value of one variable is found, the other variable's value can be found by substituting in either of the original equations, but to check the solution both values must be substituted in both of the original equations.

You may wish to note that the addition method is based on the *Addition Property of Equality*.

Another method for solving linear systems of equations involves solving both equations for the same variable, then using the *Transitive Property of Equality* to write an equation in one variable. This process is often easier to use than either the substitution or addition method. You may wish to apply to the system in Example 1:

$y = 2x - 5$ and $y = x - 3$; then $2x - 5 = x - 3$; $x - 5 = -3$ $x = 2$; $y = -1$.

Errors Students Make
Students often need to be reminded that a solution for one equation may not be a solution for both equations. Students need to be reminded also that they must check in the original equations, since errors may cause false solutions to satisfy the derived equations.

For Additional Chalkboard Work
You may wish to point out the advantage of solving an equation for the variable that is easier to isolate when solving a system of equations such as
$\begin{aligned} 2x - y &= 4 \\ 3x + 2y &= 1 \end{aligned}$ by substitution.

Cumulative Review
Solve each equation.
1. $5^{x-2} = 125$ **2.** $81 = 3^{3x-2}$ **3.** $2^{4x-2} = 64$
1. 5 2. 2 3. 2

10.3 Solving Systems of Three Linear Equations (page 247)

Vocabulary
ordered triple

Background
Two planes may: coincide, be parallel, or intersect in a line. Three planes may: be parallel, intersect, or intersect in a point. For example, two walls and a ceiling intersect in a point at a corner of a room. If this were put on a coordinate system, the point of intersection would be an ordered triple, as shown.

Suggestions
A system of three linear equations in three variables is: an independent system if its solution is an ordered triple of real numbers, an inconsistent system if it has no solution, or a dependent system if it has more than one solution. Be sure that students understand that $(2, -1, 3) \neq (3, 2, -1)$

Errors Students Make
Students forget which equations they were working with and which variable was eliminated. Numbering the equations and eliminating variables in some specific order, for example, first the third variable, then the second, will help.

For Additional Chalkboard Work
Solve the system: $2x - y + z = 5$ (1)
$$x + 2y - z = 0 \ (2)$$
$$4x + 2y + 5z = 6 \ (3).$$
$$(2, -1, 0).$$
In the second equation, $z = x + 2y$. Substitute in equations (1) and (3): $2x - y + (x + 2y) = 5$
$4x + 2y + 5(x + 2y) = 6$

Cumulative Review
Find the solution set. Graph the solution set.
1. $-3n + 5 \leq -13$ **2.** $3a - 12 > 5a$
3. $|x + 5| < 8$
1. $\{n | \geq 6\}$ 2. $\{a | a < -6\}$ 3. $\{x | -13 < x < 3\}$

10.4 Two by Two Determinants (page 250)

Vocabulary
determinant, matrix, square matrix, 2×2 determinant

Background
The method for solving a system of linear equations by determinants is known as Cramer's rule.

Suggestions
Distinguish between a matrix and a determinant. A matrix is any array of elements or numbers arranged in rows and columns. A determinant is a real number assigned to the matrix. For example, $\begin{bmatrix} 1 & 2 \\ -3 & -5 \end{bmatrix}$ is a matrix and $\begin{vmatrix} 1 & 2 \\ -3 & -5 \end{vmatrix}$ is the determinant assigned to the matrix. Thus, the number assigned to the matrix is $(-5) - (-6)$, or 1. Emphasize that all equations must be put in standard form before determinants can be used to solve them.

Errors Students Make
Students are sometimes careless with signs. Using parentheses freely can help avoid such errors. For example, $\begin{vmatrix} 2 & -2 \\ -3 & -4 \end{vmatrix} = 2(-4) - (-3)(-2)$.

For Additional Chalkboard Work
1. Solve for x.   **2.** For what values of x is
$$\begin{vmatrix} -3 & 2 \\ x & 4 \end{vmatrix} = 6 \qquad \begin{vmatrix} x & 3 \\ 27 & x \end{vmatrix} > 0?$$

1. $-12 - 2x = 6$ 2. $x^2 - 81 > 0$
     $-2x = 18$ $x^2 > 81$
       $x = -6$ $x < -9$ or $x > 9$

Cumulative Review
Evaluate each polynomial for the given values of the variables.
1. $-2xy^2 + 3x^3y^3 - 4$; $x = -2$ and $y = 3$
2. $4x^3y^2 - 2xy^3$; $x = 4$ and $y = 5$
3. $1.3a^2 - 4.2b$; $a = 0.2$ and $b = 1.3$
1. 356   2. 5,400   3. -5.408

10.5 Three by Three Determinants (page 253)

Background

Some of the many properties associated with determinants are listed below. You may wish to have some students prove these properties.

1. Corresponding elements of rows and columns of a determinant can be interchanged and the value does not change.

$$\begin{vmatrix} a_1 & a_2 & a_3 \\ b_1 & b_2 & b_3 \\ c_1 & c_2 & c_3 \end{vmatrix} = \begin{vmatrix} a_1 & b_1 & c_1 \\ a_2 & b_2 & c_2 \\ a_3 & b_3 & c_3 \end{vmatrix}$$

2. If each element of a row or column is 0, the value of the determinant is 0.

$$\begin{vmatrix} a_1 & a_2 & a_3 \\ 0 & 0 & 0 \\ c_1 & c_2 & c_3 \end{vmatrix} = \begin{vmatrix} 0 & a_2 & a_3 \\ 0 & b_2 & b_3 \\ 0 & c_2 & c_3 \end{vmatrix} = 0$$

3. If any two rows or columns are reversed, the sign of the determinant is reversed.

$$\begin{vmatrix} a_1 & a_2 & a_3 \\ b_1 & b_2 & b_3 \\ c_1 & c_2 & c_3 \end{vmatrix} = -\begin{vmatrix} c_1 & c_2 & c_3 \\ b_1 & b_2 & b_3 \\ a_1 & a_2 & a_3 \end{vmatrix}$$

4. If any two rows or columns of a determinant are identical, the value of the determinant is

$$\begin{vmatrix} a_1 & a_2 & a_3 \\ b_1 & b_2 & b_3 \\ a_1 & a_2 & a_3 \end{vmatrix} = 0.$$

Suggestions

This alternative method for finding the value of the determinant in Example 1 may save time.

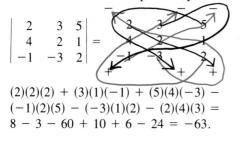

$$\begin{vmatrix} 2 & 3 & 5 \\ 4 & 2 & 1 \\ -1 & -3 & 2 \end{vmatrix} =$$

$(2)(2)(2) + (3)(1)(-1) + (5)(4)(-3) -$
$(-1)(2)(5) - (-3)(1)(2) - (2)(4)(3) =$
$8 - 3 - 60 + 10 + 6 - 24 = -63.$

10.6 Matrix Addition (page 256)

Vocabulary

additive identity matrix, dimension of a matrix, equal matrices, matrix addition

Background

Matrices form a *commutative (Abelian) group* under addition. More specifically, if A, B, and C are any three matrices, then: $A + B$ is a matrix, Closure Property; $A + B = B + C$, Commutative Property; $(A + B) + C = A + (B + C)$, Associative Property; $A + I = I + A = A$, Identity Property; and $A + (-A) = I$, Inverse Property.

Suggestions

You may wish to discuss the difference of two matrices. If $A = \begin{bmatrix} a_{11} & a_{12} \\ a_{21} & a_{22} \end{bmatrix}$ and $B = \begin{bmatrix} b_{11} & b_{12} \\ b_{21} & b_{22} \end{bmatrix}$, then $A - B = \begin{bmatrix} a_{11} - b_{11} & a_{12} - b_{12} \\ a_{21} - b_{21} & a_{22} - b_{22} \end{bmatrix}$; thus, if $A = \begin{bmatrix} -3 & 5 \\ 6 & -2 \end{bmatrix}$ and $B = \begin{bmatrix} 8 & -3 \\ -2 & 7 \end{bmatrix}$, then

$$A - B = \begin{bmatrix} -3 - (8) & 5 - (-3) \\ 6 - (-2) & -2 - (7) \end{bmatrix} = \begin{bmatrix} -11 & 8 \\ 8 & -9 \end{bmatrix}.$$

In general, each element of a matrix can be written a_{ij}, where i is the row and j the column.

If each element of a matrix is a real number, the matrix is called a *real matrix*.

Errors Students Make

Students may have to be reminded that two matrices can be added only if the two matrices have the same dimension.

Enrichment

If A, B, and C are 3×3 matrices, show that A, B, and C form a commutative group under addition.

Cumulative Review

1. Add $(4ab + 2ab^2 - 3a^2b) + (-3ab^2 + 6a^2b - ab)$.
2. Subtract $(10xy^2 - 3x^2y) - (2xy - 2xy^2)$.
3. Multiply $(2x - 5)(4x + 3)$.
1. $3ab - ab^2 + 3a^2b$ 2. $12xy^2 - 3x^2y - 2xy$
3. $8x^2 - 14x - 15$

10.7 Matrix Multiplication
(page 259)

Vocabulary
matrix multiplication, multiplicative identity matrix, multiplicative inverse matrix, scalar

Background
Matrices do not form a group under multiplication. The commutative property does not hold nor does every square matrix have a multiplicative inverse. The set of square matrices is closed under multiplication and the associative property holds. Thus, the set of square matrices forms a semigroup under multiplication.

Suggestions
Emphasize that a product of two matrices is defined if the second dimension of the first matrix is the same as the first dimension of the second matrix. Matrices do not necessarily have to be square matrices for multiplication.

The following example can be used to show that not every square matrix has an inverse. Given $\begin{bmatrix} -3 & 4 \\ 0 & 0 \end{bmatrix}$, let $\begin{bmatrix} a_{11} & a_{12} \\ a_{21} & a_{22} \end{bmatrix}$ be its multiplicative inverse. Then,

$$\begin{bmatrix} -3 & 4 \\ 0 & 0 \end{bmatrix} \cdot \begin{bmatrix} a_{11} & a_{12} \\ a_{21} & a_{22} \end{bmatrix} = \begin{bmatrix} 1 & 0 \\ 0 & 1 \end{bmatrix};$$

$$\begin{bmatrix} -3a_{11} + 4a_{21} = 1 & 0a_{11} + 0a_{21} = 0 \\ -3a_{12} + 4a_{22} = 0 & 0a_{21} + 0a_{22} = 1 \end{bmatrix};$$

but $0a_{12} + 0a_{22} = 0$, *not* 1. Thus, no multiplicative inverse exists. A necessary and sufficient condition that A^{-1} exists for square matrix A is that the determinant associated with A is not 0.

Cumulative Review
1. How many milliliters of a 30% iodine solution should be added to 70 mL of a 55% iodine solution to obtain a 40% iodine solution?
2. The number of dimes in a coin holder is 12 more than the number of quarters and the number of nickels is twice the number of dimes. Find the number of each kind of coin if their total value is $9.15.

1. 105 mL   2. n, 54; d, 27; q, 15

10.8 Matrix Transformations
(page 263)

Vocabulary
matrix transformations, triangular form

Background
An alternate method for finding the multiplicative inverse of a 2 × 2 matrix follows: Interchange the first and fourth elements, find the additive inverses of the second and third elements, and multiply this matrix by $\dfrac{1}{\text{determinant}}$.

Suggestions
To provide an overview of this lesson: Show that linear systems can be written as a product of matrices involving coefficients (called *the matrix of detached coefficients*) as one matrix, the variables as a second matrix, and the constants as a third matrix. Show that the first transformation is one that transforms three equations in standard form to one in triangular form. Show that it is sufficient to represent coefficients and constants as one matrix (called the *augmented matrix*).

Errors Students Make
The major difficulty occurs in the elementary transformation of the augmented matrix. Encourage students to establish a procedure. For example, get 1 in a_{11}, then 0 in a_{21}, then 0 in a_{31}, then 1 in a_{22}, then 0 in a_{32}, etc.

Enrichment
Solve:
$$\begin{aligned} x + 2y - 3z &= 10 \\ -4x + y - z &= -10 \\ 3x - 7y + 2z &= 5. \end{aligned}$$

Cumulative Review
Solve. Express answers to the nearest tenth.
1. $5x^2 - 8x - 3 = 0$ 2. $-3x^2 + 7x = -2$
3. $x^2 - 3x - 8 = 0$

Computer Activities (page 271)
This program uses a series of arrays to store the data and results. The output arrangement should be studied and lines 220 to 250 reviewed for table and title formatting.

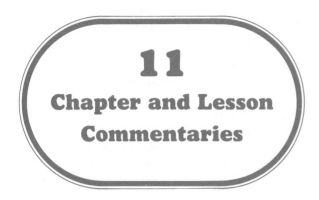

11 Chapter and Lesson Commentaries

Chapter 11 Functions

Chapter Objectives

To determine the domain and the range of a relation and of a function

To determine whether a relation is a function

To find the value of a function and of a composition of functions

To determine whether a given function is a linear function or a constant function, given either an equation of the function or a graph of the function

To draw the graphs of some special functions

To find the inverse of a relation

To draw the graph of a function and its inverse

To determine whether the inverse of a function is a function

To determine whether a relation expresses a direct variation, an inverse variation, a joint variation, or a combined variation

Chapter Overview

A function is defined as a special kind of relation. The distinction between a relation and a function and the distinction between an inverse of a function and inverse function are made. Two different checks, *the definitions* and *the vertical line test*, are used to determine whether a relation is a function and whether the inverse of a function is a function. Evaluating functions and the composition of functions precede identifying and drawing graphs of special functions. The chapter concludes with a discussion of the different types of variations.

11.1 Relations and Functions (page 276)

Vocabulary

domain, function, range, relation

Background

A relation is defined as a set of ordered pairs of real numbers. This definition is preferable to one that defines a relation in terms of a rule or a correspondence. However, a rule or a correspondence is usually associated with a set of ordered pairs of real numbers. Frequently the complete set of ordered pairs of real numbers is generated by a rule.

Suggestions

In this lesson, the two major points are: determining the domain and the range of a relation and determining whether a relation is a function. Students should be able to use both the definition of a function and the vertical-line test to determine whether a relation is a function.

Errors Students Make

Students sometimes confuse the domain and the range of a function, but the real problem often occurs with the definition of a function. To help remove this difficulty, you may wish to use this alternate definition: A *function* is a set of ordered pairs of real numbers such that for each first element there exists *one and only* one second element. In other words, no first element can have more than one second element.

Cumulative Review

Write each expression in simplest radical form.

1. $3a^{\frac{4}{3}}$ **2.** $(2x)^{\frac{4}{5}}$ **3.** $-2^{\frac{3}{2}}$

1. $3a\sqrt[3]{a}$ 2. $\sqrt[5]{16x^4}$ 3. $-2\sqrt{2}$

11.2 Values and Composition of Functions (page 279)

Background
Composition of functions is an important topic in mathematics. Almost all derivatives involve composition of functions. Exercises such as Exercises 49–52 are used in defining a derivative in the study of calculus.

Suggestions
When a function, denoted by f, g, or any other letter, is described by a rule, it may be necessary to remind students that a function is a set of ordered pairs of real numbers. Letters such as f and g refer to sets of ordered pairs, but $f(x)$ and $g(x)$ refer to function values; that is, $f(x)$ and $g(x)$ refer to the range, or the elements of the set of second coordinates, or f and g, respectively. Thus, every ordered pair of f and g has the form $(x, f(x))$ and $(g, g(x))$, respectively. Point out that finding a function value means finding the value of the function for a given element in the domain.

For a composition such as $f(g(x))$, point out that this is an ordered pair $(g(x), f(g(x)))$ which was derived from the ordered pair $(x, g(x))$. Note that $g(x)$ is an element from the range which then becomes an element in the domain of the function f.

In Example 5, emphasize that 0 and 2 are nonpermissible elements of the domain because the function would not be defined for these values.

For Additional Chalkboard Work
Let $g(x) = \sqrt{x - 1}$ and $h(x) = x^2 + 1$. Find each of the following.
1. $g(1) - h(3)$ **2.** $h(2) + g(5)$ **3.** $h(g(2))$
4. $g(h(3))$
1. -10 2. 7 3. 2 4. 3

Cumulative Review
Simplify.
1. $\dfrac{\sqrt{2}}{3 - \sqrt{3}}$ **2.** $\dfrac{\sqrt{3}}{\sqrt{2} - \sqrt{5}}$ **3.** $\dfrac{\sqrt{27a^5 b^6}}{\sqrt{3ab^3}}$
1. $\dfrac{3\sqrt{2} + \sqrt{6}}{6}$ 2. $\dfrac{\sqrt{6} + \sqrt{15}}{-3}$ 3. $3a^2 b\sqrt{b}$

11.3 Linear and Constant Functions (page 282)

Vocabulary
constant function, linear function

Background
Because the mathematical ideas of slope, rate of change, maximum, and minimum are often defined in terms of intervals and increasing and decreasing functions, you may wish to discuss special classes of functions, such as: (1) A function f is an *increasing function* in some interval *if and only if* for all $x_1 < x_2$ in the interval, $f(x_1) \leq f(x_2)$. (2) A function f is a *decreasing function* in some interval *if and only if* for all $x_1 < x_2$ in the interval, $f(x_1) \geq f(x_2)$. (3) A function h is called an *even function if and only if* $h(-x) = h(x)$ for all x in the domain. (4) A function g is called an *odd function if and only if* $g(x) = -g(-x)$ for all x in the domain. (5) A function g is called a *periodic function if and only if* there is some real number p such that $g(x + p) = g(x)$ for all x in the domain.

Suggestions
The special functions discussed in this lesson include: functions whose graphs are not continuous, functions that have a restricted domain, and functions that are defined in two or more different domains. The graphs in Example 4 and Exercises 25, 27–32 illustrate *step functions*.

Errors Students Make
Distinguishing between a linear and a constant function and the fact that a vertical line does not represent any function may be the most confusing part of this lesson.

Enrichment
$f = \{(x, y) | f(x) = x^2\}$ in the interval $-4 \leq x \leq 4$. Where is f decreasing? Where is f increasing? Prove your answer by using the definitions above.

Cumulative Review
Simplify. Write each with positive exponents.
1. $\dfrac{27x^4 y^{-7} z^2}{-3x^2 y z^{-3}}$ **2.** $\dfrac{-25a^4 bc^{-3}}{5a^2 b^3 c^4}$ **3.** $\dfrac{81mn^4 p^{-2}}{27m^2 n^{-2} p^{-4}}$
1. $\dfrac{-9x^2 z^5}{y^8}$ 2. $\dfrac{-5a^2}{b^2 c^7}$ 3. $\dfrac{3n^6 p^2}{m}$

11.4 Inverse Relations and Functions (page 285)

Vocabulary
inverse function, inverse relation, inverse of a function, inverse of a relation

Background
Three different ideas emerge: Finding the inverse of a relation, or a function, by reversing the order of the elements in the set; finding the inverse of a function, given the formula that describes the function; and graphing the inverse of a function by finding the set of ordered pairs of the function, then reversing the order of the function, and finally reversing the elements of each ordered pair.

Suggestions
Careful terminology must be used to distinguish between an inverse of a function and an inverse function. When the inverse of a function is a function, it is called an *inverse function*.

Exercise 28 states that the graph of a function and its inverse are reflections through the line described by $y = x$. This line is the axis of symmetry. The exercise implies that the graph of an inverse can be formed by graphing the function on a sheet of paper, rotating the paper 90° counterclockwise, flipping the paper over bottom to top, and then tracing the graph.

Errors Students Make
Solving for y after the domain and the range are interchanged may cause problems.

Enrichment
1. Show that the inverse of a linear function is a linear function. Start with $y = mx + b$.
2. Show that if $f(x) = x + 3$ and $f^1(x)$ is its inverse, then $f(f^1(x)) = f^1(f(x))$.

1. $y = mx + b$; $x = my + b$; $y = \frac{1}{m}x - \frac{b}{m}$; $y = m_1x - b_1$ 2. $f(f^1(x)) = (x - 3) + 3 = x$; (note $f^1(x) = x - 3$); $f^1(f(x)) = (x + 3) - 3 = x$

Cumulative Review
Simplify.
1. $\sqrt{24a^8b^9}$ 2. $xy^2\sqrt{36x^4y^5z^{13}}$ 3. $xy^2\sqrt{162x^{20}y^{31}}$
1. $2a^4b^4\sqrt{6b}$ 2. $6x^3y^4z^6\sqrt{yz}$ 3. $9x^{11}y^{17}\sqrt{2y}$

11.5 Direct Variation (page 288)

Vocabulary
constant of proportionality, direct variation

Suggestions
The graph of a direct variation is a line that passes through the origin. Therefore, you may wish to have students plot the ordered pairs of a relation to see whether its graph passes through the origin. Students may observe that the slope of the line is the constant of variation (proportionality). Since the constant of variation depends on the order in which the variables are compared, the answers to Exercises 1–13 can be the reciprocals of those given.

Emphasize that a direct variation is *always* a linear function, but a linear function *does not necessarily* yield a direct variation.

Example 4 and the narrative preceding it present an alternate approach, one that does not involve the constant of proportionality, to teach direct variation. Both methods are useful.

For Additional Chalkboard Work
1. The number of liters of gasoline used by an automobile traveling at a constant speed is directly proportional to the distance traveled. At 60 km/h, a certain automobile uses 8 L of gasoline. How many liters of gasoline will the automobile use if it travels 560 km?
   9.3 L, to the nearest tenth of a liter
2. The amount of money a person earns varies directly as the number of hours worked or the number of units completed. If a person earns $280 in a 40–h wk, how many weeks would the person have to work in order to earn enough money to buy a used car, if the car costs $3,800? Assume that 60% of the earnings are set aside for the car.
   22.6 wk, to the nearest tenth of a week

Cumulative Review
Solve each equation by completing the square.
1. $x^2 + 8x = 2$ 2. $n^2 + 6n - 6 = 0$
1. $4 \pm 3\sqrt{2}$ 2. $-3 \pm \sqrt{15}$

11.6 Inverse Variation (page 291)

Vocabulary
constant of variation, inverse variation

Suggestions
In inverse variation, an increase in one variable causes a decrease in the other variable. Moreover, inverse variation is characterized by the concept that when one variable doubles, the other is halved; when one variable triples, the other is divided by three, and so fourth. Contrast this type of variation with direct variation.

Emphasize that an inverse variation is *never* linear and that the graph of an inverse variation is *never* a straight line.

Two different methods for solving inverse variation problems are presented. Both methods are acceptable.

Errors Students Make
Students sometimes confuse the two types of variations. Emphasizing that for an inverse variation the product of the two variables is a constant, while for a direct variation the quotient of the two variables is a constant may help remove this difficulty.

For Additional Chalkboard Work
1. If y varies inversely as x and x is multiplied by c, how is y affected?
2. If y varies inversely as the square of x and x is doubled, how is y affected?
3. The time it takes to travel a given distance varies inversely as the average speed. If it takes 45 min to drive a certain distance at 60 km/h, how long would it take to drive the same distance at 50 km/h?

1. y is divided by c. 2. y is divided by 4.
3. 54 min

Cumulative Review
Solve each equation.
1. $3\sqrt{2x - 1} = 4$ 2. $2\sqrt{x + 4} = 7$

1. $\frac{25}{18}$ 2. $\frac{33}{4}$

11.7 Joint and Combined Variation (page 294)

Vocabulary
combined variation, joint variation

Suggestions
Indicate the similarities between joint variation and direct variation. A joint variation is a function in which one variable varies directly as the product of two other variables. Combined variation is a function in which direct and inverse variation are combined. Joint and combined variations usually yield quadratic equations, but these simplify to linear equations after substitution.

Errors Students Make
Initial substitution for a joint or a combined variation may cause difficulty. Also, some students may become confused if they are required to use both methods for solving variation problems.

For Additional Chalkboard Work
1. The formula, V, of a given mass of a gas varies directly as the absolute temperature, T, and inversely as the pressure, P. If $V = 300$ L when T is 400° and P is 16 lb/in.^{2}, what is the volume when T is 468° and P is 18 lb/in.^{2}? 312 L
2. The simple interest on a given amount of money varies jointly as the rate and the time. If the interest is $1,320 when the rate is 11% and the time is 2 yr, find the rate when the interest is $1,710 and the time is 3 yr. What amount of money was invested? 9.5%; $6,000

Cumulative Review
Find the value of each expression.
1. $27^{\frac{2}{3}}$ 2. $8^{\frac{4}{3}}$ 3. $25^{\frac{3}{2}}$ 4. $64^{\frac{2}{3}}$
1. 9 2. 16 3. 125 4. 16

Computer Activities (p. 300)
This program takes a complicated concept and formula and simply computes the results. Exercise 4 allows the student to solve for different variables in the formula. Exercise 5 applies the table formatting and titles explained previously.

12

Chapter and Lesson Commentaries

Chapter 12 Conic Sections

Chapter Objectives

To determine a pair of points that are symmetric with respect to the *x*-axis, the *y*-axis, or the origin

To draw the graphs of the equations of the conic sections—the parabola, circle, ellipse and hyperbola

To find the coordinates of the vertex and the *x*-intercepts of a parabola and to determine an equation for its axis of symmetry

To find an equation of a circle, an ellipse, and a hyperbola whose center or vertex is at the origin

To find the radius of a circle

To determine the equation of a circle whose center is not at the origin

To find the equations of the asymptotes of a hyperbola and to determine the hyperbola's intercepts

To use translations in the graphing of an equation of an absolute value function or a conic section whose vertex or center is not at the origin

Chapter Overview

The text does not provide derivations of all the general equations of conic sections. The parabola is simply presented as the graph of a quadratic equation. However, the text *does* explain how to derive the general equation for a circle and the equations for the ellipse and the hyperbola are derived for a specific example and then generalized. This approach will help students understand some

Chapter Overview (cont.)

of the theory without being overwhelmed with tedious algebraic derivations. It is advised however, that the student, does see a formal derivation. Some are included in the Theory of Conics Lesson. The students should be able to draw the graphs of the equations of the conic sections as well as write the equations, given certain conditions. The correspondence between the solutions to the equations and the coordinates of the graph should be stressed throughout the chapter.

An understanding of concepts such as intercepts, vertices, asymptotes and latus rectum will eliminate the need for the use of a table of values for graphing.

The concept of symmetry is presented in Lesson 1. Symmetric points on a circle will be used in the study of trigonometry and will be discussed later in this Teachers Edition. The second lesson introduces the parabola, the first of the conic sections. However, the actual term conic section is not introduced until Lesson 6. The parabola, circle, ellipse and hyperbola are each covered separately before any mention of a cone.

Special Features

Reading in Algebra   p. 313
Cumulative Review   p. 322
A Challenge to You   p. 326
Computer Activity   p. 331
College Prep Test   p. 334
Chapter Review   p. 332
Chapter Test   p. 333
Cumulative Review (Chapters 1–12)   pp. 335–336

12.1 Symmetric Points in a Coordinate Plane (page 303)

Vocabulary
symmetric, line of symmetry, axis of symmetry, point of symmetry

Background
To determine whether a function is even, that is, symmetric with respect to the y-axis, replace x by $-x$ and if no change occurs in the equation, the function is even. Show that $y = x^2$ is an even function. Similarly, to determine whether the graph of a relation is symmetric with respect to the y-axis, replace y by $-y$ and if no change occurs in the equation, the graph is symmetric with respect to the y-axis. To determine whether a function is odd, that is, symmetric with respect to the origin, replace x by $-x$ and y by $-y$ and if no change occurs in the equation, the function is odd. Show that $y = \frac{3}{x}$ is odd.

Suggestions
If the graph of an equation is symmetric with respect to the x-axis, it is sufficient to graph the equation in the first and second quadrants and then reproduce it in the 3rd and 4th quadrants. Similarly, a graph symmetric with respect to the y-axis reflects itself from the first and fourth quadrants into the second and third quadrants. If the graph of an equation is symmetric with respect to the origin, then it is sufficient to graph the equation in two adjacent quadrants and then reproduce it in the diagonally opposite quadrants.

Enrichment
Determine which of the following are even, odd, symmetric with respect to the y-axis or none of the former.

1. $\dfrac{x^2}{16} + \dfrac{y^2}{4} = 1$ **2.** $xy = -3$ **3.** $|y| = x$
4. $y = |x|$ **5.** $x^2 - y^2 = 6$ **6.** $x^2 + y^2 = 36$
7. $y = |x - 3|$

Cumulative Review
Solve each system by substitution.
1. $3x + 5y = 2$ **2.** $x + 7y = -9$
    $4x - y = -5$ $-5 + 3y = 7$
1. $(-1, 1)$ 2. $(-2, -1)$

12.2 The Parabola (page 306)

Vocabulary
parabola, vertex or turning point

Background
The parabola can be flat or steep. For $y = ax^2$, if $a = \dfrac{1}{100,000}$, then the parabola is quite flat.

Suggestions
In the equation of the parabola $y = ax^2 + bx + c$, if $a > 0$, the graph opens upward, and if $a < 0$, the graph opens downward. Thus, when $a > 0$, the parabola's vertex is a minimum point. When $a < 0$, the vertex is a maximum point.

If the graph crosses the x-axis, the two roots are real and unequal. If the graph of a parabola is tangent to the x-axis, the two roots of x-intercepts are real and equal. If the graph does not cross the x-axis, there are no x-intercepts, hence no real roots. In this case the roots are imaginary numbers. Roots, solutions, or x-intercepts are also called zeros of a quadratic function since these values make the function value (y-value) zero.

Errors Students Make
Students might have some difficulty choosing appropriate values of x when constructing a table of values. Determining the axis of symmetry first is one way to alleviate this problem. Larger-square graph paper will help students better estimate solutions to the nearest tenth.

Enrichment
Have students determine why transmitting reflectors and receivers, and car headlights are shaped in the form of a parabola.

Cumulative Review
Solve each system by addition.
1. $3x - 4y = 2$ **2.** $4x - 2y = -12$
    $-5x + 6y = -2$ $-3x + 5y = 23$
1. $(-2, -2)$ 2. $(-1, 4)$

12.3 The Circle (page 310)

Vocabulary
circle

Background
The equation of a circle does not yield a function. Solving $x^2 + y^2 = r^2$ for y, $y = \pm\sqrt{r^2 - x^2}$. Thus, for each value of x there are two values for y. However, a circle has x-axis, y-axis, and origin symmetry. Notice from $y = \pm\sqrt{r^2 - x^2}$ that $y = \pm r$ when $y = 0$. Similarly, $x = \pm r$ when $y = 0$. The extent of the circle is $-r \leq x \leq r$ and $-r \leq y \leq r$.

Suggestions
Students are expected to write an equation of any circle whose center is known, given a point through which the circle passes or given the radius of the circle. Students should also be able to graph the equation of a circle without using a table of values. Emphasize that each of the ordered pair of coordinates of the points on the circle is a solution of the equation of the circle.

It.is advisable to review the method of finding the distance between two points before the start of the lesson.

Errors Students Make
Formulas for finding the radius and distance between two points will need reinforcement. Sometimes students interchange the values for x and y.

Enrichment
Cut a string of desired radius. Attach a tack at one end and a pencil on the other. Tack it at the origin and, holding the string taut, trace a circle. Explain how this illustrates the definition of a circle.

Cumulative Review
Find the value of each determinant.

1. $\begin{vmatrix} 4 & -1 \\ 6 & 3 \end{vmatrix}$
2. $\begin{vmatrix} 3 & -1 & 2 \\ -1 & 2 & 1 \\ 3 & 2 & -1 \end{vmatrix}$

1. 18 2. -30

12.4 The Ellipse (page 314)

Vocabulary
ellipse, focus (foci) of an ellipse

Background
When $a^2 > b^2$, in the general equation of an ellipse whose center is at the origin, the major axis of the ellipse is on the x-axis. When $b^2 > a^2$, the major axis is on the y-axis. When $a^2 = b^2$, the ellipse is a circle.

The extent of an ellipse can be determined by first solving the equation of the ellipse for y, then for x, and observing permissible values. You get

$$y = \pm\frac{b}{a}\sqrt{a^2 - x^2} \text{ and } x = \pm\frac{a}{b}\sqrt{b^2 - y^2}.$$ To avoid a negative under the radical, $x \leq a$ and $y \leq b$. The extents, or limiting values, of x and y are $-a \leq x \leq a$ and $-b \leq y \leq b$. You may also wish to derive the formula for the length of the latus rectum, $\dfrac{2b}{a}\sqrt{a^2 - c^2}$.

Suggestions
The length of the latus rectum, which is introduced in the C exercises of Lesson 8, will contribute to a more accurate graph of an ellipse. Lesson 8 also formally derives the equation of an ellipse, whereas this lesson enables students to derive an equation in a specific example, given the coordinates of the foci.

Errors Students Make
When the intercepts are fractions, as in Example 3, convert $\dfrac{6x^2}{27} + \dfrac{9y^2}{27} = 1$ to $\dfrac{x^2}{\frac{27}{6}} + \dfrac{y^2}{\frac{27}{9}} = 1$ to avoid difficulty in determining a and b.

Cumulative Review
Solve each system of equations.

1. $2x - 3y + z = -9$
   $-2x + y - 32 = 7$
   $x - 2y + 32 = -8$

2. $2x - 3y = 7$
   $4x + 5z = 13$
   $-2y - 3z = -1$

1. $(-1, 2, -1)$ 2. $(2, -1, 1)$

12.5   The Hyperbola (page 317)

Vocabulary
hyperbola, foci of a hyperbola, asymptotes, rectangular hyperbola

Background
The asymptotes of the hyperbola whose equation is $\frac{x^2}{a^2} - \frac{y^2}{b^2} = 1$ are $y = \pm \frac{b}{a}x$.

If a is very large, the slope $\frac{b}{a}$ approaches 0, hence the arms of the hyperbola get very close together and, conversely, the arms spread out when a is very small. This illustrates that a limiting position of a hyperbola is either an axis or a straight line.

The extent of a hyperbola can be determined by solving the equation of an hyperbola for y.

$$y = \pm \frac{b}{a}\sqrt{x^2 - a^2}, \text{ thus } x \geq a \text{ or } x \leq -a$$

For Additional Chalkboard Work
Additional work may be necessary to overcome the difficulty of determining the equations of the asymptotes. Tell orally the equations of the asymptotes.

1. $\frac{x^2}{25} - \frac{y^2}{9} = 1$ **2.** $\frac{x^2}{36} - \frac{y^2}{100} = 1$

Errors Students Make
Additional chalkboard work may be necessary to overcome the difficulty of determining the equations of the asymptotes.

Cumulative Review
Find the sum, if possible.

1. $\begin{bmatrix} 3 & -1 \\ -4 & 6 \end{bmatrix} + \begin{bmatrix} 6 & -2 \\ 3 & 9 \end{bmatrix}$

2. $\begin{bmatrix} 3 & 4 & 3 \\ 2 & -1 & 1 \\ -1 & 2 & 2 \end{bmatrix} + \begin{bmatrix} 2 & 5 \\ 4 & 2 \\ -1 & -2 \end{bmatrix}$

1. $\begin{bmatrix} 9 & -3 \\ -1 & 15 \end{bmatrix}$ 2. not possible

12.6   Identifying Conic Sections (page 321)

Vocabulary
cone, conic section

Background
One way to identify a conic section, given its equation, is to examine the general formula $Ax^2 + Bxy + Cy^2 + Dx + Ey + F = 0$. If $A = C = D = E = F = 0$, then $Bxy = -F$. This is an equation of a rectangular hyperbola. If $B = 0$, then $Ax^2 + Dx + Cy^2 + Ey = -F$ is an equation of a conic section whose center is not at the origin. If $B = D = E = 0$, then $Ax^2 + Cy^2 = -F$ is an equation of a conic section whose origin is at the center. Note, $-F$ may or may not be negative. Let $G = -F \neq 0$, neither A nor C being 0. So, $Ax^2 + Cy^2 = G$. If $A = C$ and A, C, and G have the same sign, the equation represents a circle. If $A \neq C$ and A, C and G have the same sign, the equation represents an ellipse. If A and C have different signs, the equation represents a hyperbola. Finally, if Bxy is present with the other terms, the graph of the conic is rotated.

Suggestions
The standard form of the equations of the conics presented are for an ellipse and circle whose center is at the origin and for a hyperbola whose foci are on one of the axes. While there are other ways to identify a conic, in this lesson students are asked to put the equation in standard form before deciding which conic is represented by the equation. Some exercises in Part B do not have the center at the origin. This is covered more extensively in 12.8.

For Additional Chalkboard Work
Identify the conic section $x^2 + 8x + y^2 - 4y = 26$. By completing the square, you get $x^2 + 8x + 16 + y^2 - 4y + 4 = 26 + 16 + 4$. $(x + 4)^2 + (y - 2)^2 = 46$. This is an equation of a circle whose center is at $(-4, 2)$ and whose radius is $\sqrt{46}$.

Cumulative Review
Let $g(x) = -x^2 + 4x - 1$. Find each of the following function values.

1. $g(0)$ **2.** $g(-1)$ **3.** $g(a)$
1. -1 2. -6 3. $-a^2 + 4a - 1$

12.7 Translations (page 323)

Vocabulary

translation

Background

By completing the square of $y = ax^2 + px + q$, you get $y = a(x - b)^2 + c$. The equation of the axis of symmetry is $x = b$, and (b, c) are the coordinates of the turning point. The turning point is a maximum if $a < 0$ and a minimum point if $a > 0$. The graph of $y = a(x - 3)^2 - 4$ has the same shape as $y = ax^2$ but is translated 3 units to the right and 4 units down.

Suggestions

The graphs of $y = |x - 2|$ and $y = |x + 2|$ on page 323 suggest a translation called a horizontal translation. In general, if f is a function such that $g(x) = f(x + b)$, where b is any constant, the graph of g has the same shape as that of f, but is translated b units to the left if $b > 0$ and $|b|$ units to the right if $b < 0$. Example 1 suggests a translation called a vertical translation. In general, if f is any function and $g(x) = f(x) + c$, where c is any constant, the graph of g has the same shape as that of f, but is translated c units up if $c > 0$ and $|c|$ units down if $c < 0$.

Errors Students Make

To overcome the difficulty in Examples 4–6 of drawing the graph after finding the new center, construct a new set of axes through the new center and then graph the basic function on the new axes.

Enrichment

Complete the square for each of the following. State the equation of the axis of symmetry and the coordinates of the maximum or minimum point. Then graph the functions using horizontal and vertical translations.

1. $y = x^2 + 8x + 3$ **2.** $y = x^2 - 10x - 4$
3. $y = -2x^2 + 12x - 3$ **4.** $y = 4x^2 - 16x + 1$

Cumulative Review

Let $f(x) = x + 2$ and $g(x) = x^2 - 3$. Find each of the following.

1. $f(g(2))$ **2.** $g(f(2))$ **3.** $f(g(-a))$
1. 3 2. 13 3. $a^2 - 1$

12.8 Equations of Conic Sections (page 327)

Background

As stated earlier, a useful aid in sketching graphs of the equations of conic sections is to determine the length of the latus rectum, the perpendicular segment through a focus terminating on the graph.

For the parabola $y^2 = 4px$, let $x = p$ (the x-coordinate of a focus). Then $y^2 = 4p^2$. Thus the length of the latus rectum is $2y = |4p|$. For an ellipse, Exercise 31 asks the student to find the length of the latus rectum. Let $x = c$ with $(\pm c, 0)$ as the coordinates of the foci, then $\dfrac{c^2}{a^2} + \dfrac{y^2}{b^2} = 1$

or $\dfrac{y^2}{b^2} = 1 - \dfrac{c^2}{a^2}$, $y = \pm \dfrac{b}{a} \sqrt{a^2 - c^2}$. But it was learned that $a^2 - c^2 = b^2$. Thus, $y = \dfrac{b}{a} \cdot b$

or $y = \dfrac{b^2}{a}$, $2y = \dfrac{2b^2}{a}$. Note that $b^2 = a^2 - c^2$ is an equation that connects the intercepts and foci.

Another useful aid in graphing conics is to determine the eccentricity of the conic. The eccentricity, e, of an ellipse is $e = \dfrac{c}{a}$ where $c = \sqrt{a^2 - b^2}$. Hence, $e = \dfrac{\sqrt{a^2 - b^2}}{a}$. When $a \to b$, $e \to 0$ and the ellipse approximates a circle when $b \to 0$, $e \to 1$. When b is very small the hyperbola approaches a horizontal line; when b is very large the hyperbola approaches a vertical line.

Suggestions

Derive the equation $\dfrac{x^2}{a^2} + \dfrac{y^2}{b^2} = 1$ to clarify the relationship between the intercepts and the foci. You may also wish to formally derive the equation of a hyperbola.

Computer Activities (page 331)

This program applies print techniques to creating a graph. It is an excellent program to use for lessons on manipulating the parabolic function. If the microcomputer you are using has graphic functions, compare the BASIC commands to create a parabola with the advanced function with this program.

13

Chapter and Lesson Commentaries

Chapter 13 Linear Quadratic Systems

Chapter Objectives

To find the real-number solutions of a system composed of one quadratic equation and one linear equation through graphing

To solve a system made up of two quadratic equations both graphically and algebraically

To find the real-number solutions of a system of two linear inequalities, two quadratic inequalities and one linear and one quadratic inequality graphically

To draw the graph of a linear inequality in two variables

To draw the graph of a quadratic inequality

Chapter Overview

In this chapter students are expected to:
1. solve systems of linear-quadratic equations
2. solve quadratic equations both algebraically and graphically.

Some examples should be done both algebraically and graphically to show that both methods do arrive at the same solutions. Use the graphing method first, having students estimate the answers, and then solve algebraically. This will give students confidence in estimating, yet will also reinforce the fact that at times graphing gives only an estimation of the solution.

Chapter Overview (cont.)

The lesson goes on to cover linear inequalities. Simple linear inequalities are introduced first, followed by systems of different combinations of inequalities. The systems include two linear inequalities, a linear-quadratic inequality and two quadratic inequalities. Students are expected to solve these systems graphically. Emphasize that each pair of coordinates of the infinite number of points in the cross-hatched region is a solution to both inequalities. Encourage students to utilize all the aids in graphing the conic sections—asymptotes, extents, latus rectum, and so forth, to enable them to draw smooth, accurate curves. This is important if you wish them to find points of intersection to estimate solutions.

Special Features

13.1 Solving Linear-Quadratic Systems of Equations (page 338)

Vocabulary
linear-quadratic systems

Background
From symbolic logic, the word *conjunction* is the connective "and" that is used to join two simple sentences into one compound sentence. For the compound sentence to be true, both simple sentences must be true. When it is stated that students should solve a system of equations like $\frac{x^2}{16} + \frac{y^2}{9} = 1$, $2x - 3y = 6$, it is implied that students should find values for x and y such that $\frac{x^2}{16} + \frac{y^2}{9} = 1$ and $2x - 3y = 6$. Thus, the solution would be $\left\{ (x,y) \mid \frac{x^2}{16} + \frac{y^2}{9} = 1 \wedge 2x - 3y = 6 \right\}$.

Suggestions
Review the standard forms of the equations of the conic sections. Also remind the students that the coordinates of every point on the graph is a solution of the equation. By substituting the coordinates of each point in the equation, the equation checks. In this lesson the system is first solved graphically. This approach does not give the accuracy that one would get algebraically, but it is believed that students will get a better understanding by this visual approach.

Remind students that the purpose of this lesson is to find coordinates of points that solve both the quadratic and linear equations.

Students should substitute into the linear equation to find the second coordinate after finding the first coordinate. There is a possibility of introducing extraneous roots if they don't. For example, solving $x^2 + y^2 = 10$ and $x - 2y = 1$ algebraically yields an extraneous root when you substitute into the quadratic equation instead of into the linear equation.

Cumulative Review
Solve each of the following.
1. $-3x + 6 \le -9$ **2.** $|x - 4| \le 14$
3. $|x + 1| > 3$ 3. $x > 2$ or $x < -4$
1. $x \ge 5$ 2. $-10 \le x \le 18$

13.2 Solving Quadratic Systems of Equations (page 341)

Vocabulary
quadratic systems

Suggestions
This lesson illustrates the intersection of the graphs of two quadratic equations. It is shown that there may be no, one, two, three, or four common points of intersection. Therefore, there may be no, one, two, three, or four solutions.

The ordered pairs obtained by graphing or estimating are approximate solutions and may not check exactly. You may wish to have students use a calculator in checking solutions.

Errors Students Make
Example 3 shows a system solved algebraically where there are four solutions. Students should be careful to include all of them.

For Additional Chalkboard Work
Solve the system $x^2 + y^2 = 10$ algebraically.
$$xy = 3$$
$y = \frac{3}{x}$; $x^2 + \left(\frac{3}{x}\right)^2 = 10$; $x^2 + \frac{9}{x^2} = 10$; $x^4 + 9 = 10x^2$; $x^4 - 10x^2 + 9 = 0$
Factor.
$(x^2 - 9)(x^2 - 1) = 0$; $x^2 = 9$; $x = \pm 3$; $x^2 = 1$; $x = \pm 1$
So $x = 3, -3, 1, -1$, and $y = 1, -1, 3, -3$; thus, $(3, 1)$, $(-3, -1)$, $(1, 3)$ and $(-1, -3)$ are solutions. They check.

Enrichment
Solve the following systems algebraically.
1. $x^2 + xy + y^2 = 19$ **2.** $3y^2 + 2xy = 7$
$ xy = 6$ $ -2y^2 + 3xy = 4$
1. $(3, 2)$, $(-3, -2)$, $(2, 3)$, $(-2, -3)$
2. $(2, 1)$, $(-2, -1)$

Cumulative Review
Solve.
Fred mixed some brand A cereal worth \$1.30/lb and some brand B cereal worth \$1.94/lb to make a 10-lb package that was worth \$15.54. Find the amount of each brand used.
6.03 lbs of brand A and 3.97 lbs of brand B

13.3 Solving Linear Inequality Systems (page 346)

Vocabulary
linear, inequality systems

Background
While it is sometimes tempting to describe the solution set as the double-shaded region, it is not correct to do so. The double-shaded region is the graph of the solution set and not the solution set itself. The solution set is the set of all ordered pairs for the points in the double-shaded region. Distinguish between finding the solution set and graphing the solution set. Graphing the solution set yields the double-shaded region.

Suggestions
Testing with a checkpoint is not so much used as a check but as a method to determine which half-plane is to be shaded. To check after shading is only a verification check.

Whenever the equation of a line is graphed, the plane is separated into three regions; the region above the line, the region below the line, and the line itself. Discuss the use of dashed lines and solid lines when graphing inequalities.

Some students may wish to use colored pencils to show the double-shaded region. Others may wish to draw horizontal lines for one space and vertical lines for another. The graph of the solution set would be the intersection of the vertical and horizontal lines or the cross-hatched space.

Errors Students Make
Difficulty might arise when students try to represent the region graphing the solution set. Colored pencils will help avoid problems.

Whether to include or exclude the line may also cause difficulty. Emphasize that a solid line is generated by $\leq$, $\geq$ or $=$ and a dashed line is used with $<$ or $>$.

Cumulative Review
Solve.

How many liters of 32 percent alcohol solution must be added to 24 L of a 58 percent alcohol solution to obtain a 48 percent alcohol solution?
15 L

13.4 Solving Linear-Quadratic Inequality Systems (page 349)

Vocabulary
linear-quadratic inequality

Suggestions
Review graphs of the equations of the conic sections. Whenever the equation of a conic is graphed, the plane is divided into three regions: the region within the conic, outside the conic, and on the conic. Students should graph the inequalities as though they were equations and then use two checkpoints, one point within, and one point outside the graph of the conic. The inequalities using $\leq$ or $\geq$ will include all points on the curve. Thus the curve is solid. The inequalities with $<$ or $>$ will have a dashed curve.

For Additional Chalkboard Work
Solve each system of inequalities graphically.

1. $\dfrac{x^2}{16} + \dfrac{y^2}{9} \leq 1$

   $\dfrac{x^2}{9} + \dfrac{y^2}{4} \geq 1$

2. $\dfrac{x^2}{25} - \dfrac{y^2}{4} \leq 1$

   $x^2 + y^2 \geq 4$

3. $\dfrac{x^2}{36} + \dfrac{y^2}{25} \leq 1$

   $\dfrac{x^2}{9} - \dfrac{y^2}{4} \geq 1$

4. $\dfrac{x^2}{4} + \dfrac{y^2}{9} \geq 1$

   $x^2 + y^2 < 16$

5. $\dfrac{(x-3)^2}{9} + \dfrac{(y+2)^2}{4} \leq 1$

   $(x-3)^2 + (y+2) \geq 4$

Cumulative Review
Solve.

One leg of a right triangle is 7 m longer than the other leg and 1 m shorter than the hypotenuse. Find the area of the triangle. $30\ \text{m}^2$

Computer Activities (page 354)
This program applies a series of logic commands to determine the intersections. Students should flow chart the program and go through each of the cases with paper and pencil before running it. Exercise 6 can be adapted to determine the intersections of other figures.

14

Chapter and Lesson Commentaries

Chapter 14 Progressions, Series, and Binomial Expansions

Chapter Objectives

To write several consecutive terms of an arithmetic progression (A.P.) or a geometric progression (G.P.)

To find a specified term of a given A.P. or a given G.P.

To find arithmetic means or geometric means between two given numbers

To find the arithmetic mean or the geometric mean of two numbers

To find the sum of the first n terms of an arithmetic series or a geometric series

To write an arithmetic series using Σ-notation

To find the sum, if it exists, of an infinite geometric series

To write a repeating decimal as an infinite geometric series or an infinite indicated sum

To write a repeating decimal in the form $\frac{x}{y}$ where x and y are integers

To expand a positive integral power of a binomial

To find a specified term of a binomial expansion

Chapter Overview

Arithmetic and geometric progressions, or sequences, are introduced with emphasis on finding the nth term for a given counting number n. Arithmetic and geometric means between two given numbers are found. Arithmetic and geometric *series* are related to their corresponding A.P. and G.P. with emphasis on finding the sum of the first n terms of a series. The sum of an *infinite* geometric series is included.

Σ-notation is introduced as an abbreviation for the expanded form of a series. Pascal's triangle and the Binomial Theorem are used to expand positive integral powers of a binomial.

In this chapter there is much arithmetic computation. You may wish to let students use inexpensive pocket or mini-calculators. This will save time and increase accuracy.

An interesting paperback book to have on hand is *Games Calculators Play* by Wallace Judd, published by Warner Books, Inc., New York, NY 10019. The book contains many games, patterns, puzzles, and tricks to be done with a mini-calculator. One section shows pictures of the interior parts of a calculator and describes their functions.

Special Features

Reading in Algebra   pp. 359, 370, 377, 384
Calculator Activities   pp. 360, 371, 378
Cumulative Review   pp. 363, 371
Computer Activities   p. 385
Chapter Review   p. 386
Chapter Test   p. 387
College Prep Test   p. 388
Blaise Pascal   p. 356

14.1 Arithmetic Progressions
(page 357)

Vocabulary
arithmetic progression (or sequence), common difference

Background
An arithmetic progression with its common difference d and nth term l provides the background for the study of arithmetic means and arithmetic series.

You might have a few students do some research on the mathematicians mentioned in the text and present it to the class. This helps to "humanize" mathematics. Encourage the researchers to find out something about Gauss, Pascal, or Fibonacci, the times they lived in and their occupations. Students are often surprised at how young some mathematicians were at the time of their important mathematical discoveries.

When presenting such topics as Pascal's triangle or the sum of an arithmetic series, it is a good idea to lead up to the formula or pattern by asking "what do you notice here?" along the way. Having the students discover the outcome, rather than just giving them the answer, will make for a more interesting lesson and achieve better retention for students.

Suggestions
You may wish to introduce and use the term *sequence* as a synonym for *progression*, since some students will meet it in their continuing mathematical studies.

Before Example 4, you can use a simpler example:
Find the 21st term of $8, 3, -2, -7, \ldots$.
$$a = 8 \qquad n = 21 \qquad d = -5$$
$$l = a + (n - 1)d = 8 + (21 - 1)(-5) =$$
$$8 + 20(-5) = -92$$

Cumulative Review
1. Find the slope of $\overrightarrow{AB}$ for $A(-2, 4)$, $B(3, 3)$.
2. Solve $x^2 + 3x - 1 = 0$.
3. Simplify $\dfrac{x^5}{x^{-3}}$.

1. $\dfrac{-1}{5}$ 2. $\dfrac{-3 \pm \sqrt{13}}{2}$ 3. x^8

14.2 The Arithmetic Mean
(page 361)

Vocabulary
arithmetic means, *the* arithmetic mean

Suggestions
Encourage students to draw the appropriate number of blanks between the two given numbers when finding two or more means, as shown in Example 1. When finding exactly one mean between two numbers x and y, students should use the formula $\dfrac{x + y}{2}$. Example 2 is used only to introduce "the arithmetic mean of x and y."
Example 1 can follow a simpler example: Find the two arithmetic means between 29 and 8.

$$29, \underline{\quad}, \underline{\quad}, 8$$
$$a = 29 \quad n = 4 \quad l = 8$$
$$l = a + (n - 1)d$$
$$8 = 29 + (4 - 1)d$$
$$d = -7$$

The A.P. is 29,22,15,8 and the means are 22 and 15.

You may wish to mention the use of the term *mean* in statistics. Given a list of data, one may wish to find the mode, median, or the mean of the data. The mode is the number that occurs most often in the list. The median is the number for which there are the same amount of numbers on the list greater than it and less than it. And finally, the mean is the average of the numbers on the list. For instance, if the scores on a test were 98 72 63 90 22 88 84 83 87 78 87: the *mode* is 87. The *median* is 84 (there are 5 numbers > 84 and 5 numbers < 84). The *mean* is 77.45, the sum of the numbers on the list divided by 11, the amount of numbers on the list.

Cumulative Review
1. Find the slope and the y-intercept of the line with equation $6x + 2y = 8$.
2. Multiply $(3 + 2i)(2 + i)$.

1. $-3; 4$ 2. $4 + 7i$

14.3 Arithmetic Series And Σ-Notation (page 364)

Vocabulary

arithmetic series, summation, index of summation, sigma, sigma notation

Suggestions

Emphasize the differences and the similarities between an arithmetic progression and an arithmetic series. For each progression: $x_1, x_2, x_3, \ldots$, there is a series, or indicated sum: $x_1 + x_2 + x_3 + \ldots$. The series is arithmetic if the progression is arithmetic. An arithmetic series and an arithmetic progression have the same first term, the same common difference, and the same nth term.

Students should know that there are two sum formulas and also understand when to use each of them. Use $S = \frac{n}{2}(a + l)$ if the values of n, a, and l are given and use $S = \frac{n}{2}[2a + (n - 1)d]$ if the values of n, a, and d are given.

You may wish to tell the old story about the German mathematician Carl Gauss (1777–1855) who was asked as a child in elementary school to do some busywork. The assignment was to add up the integers 1 to 100. While the other children were adding up the numbers two at a time, Gauss was finished in a few minutes. He had figured out that if you add 1 2 3 4 . . . 99 100
to 100 99 98 97 . . . 2 1
you get 101 101 101 101 . . . 101 101
so you get 100(101). Thus the sum in question must be $\frac{100(101)}{2}$ since you added up the series twice. The formula in the text is derived from this line of reasoning.

Cumulative Review

Given $f(x) = 5x - 4$, find the following.
1. $f(6)$ **2.** $f(-3)$ **3.** $f(f(2))$
4. $f(c) - f(h)$ **5.** $\dfrac{f(c + h) - f(c)}{h}$

1. 26   2. −19   3. 26
4. $5c - 5h$ 5. 5

14.4 Geometric Progressions (page 368)

Vocabulary

geometric progression (or sequence), common ratio

Background

A geometric progression with its common ratio r and nth term l provides the background for the study of geometric means and geometric series.

Suggestions

Powers of 2 and powers of $\frac{1}{2}$ are used frequently in this lesson. Students should learn to use shortcuts like the following:
1. To find 2^{10}, use $2^5 = 32$ and $2^{10} = 2^5 \cdot 2^5 = 32 \cdot 32 = 1024$.
2. To find 2^9, use $2^{10} = 1024$ and $2^9 = 2^{10} \div 2 = 1024 \div 2 = 512$.
3. To find $\left(\frac{1}{2}\right)^{10}$, use $2^{10} = 1024$ and $\left(\frac{1}{2}\right)^{10} = \frac{1^{10}}{2^{10}} = \frac{1}{1024}$.
4. To find 2^{10} using a pocket calculator, depress ② once, ⊗ once, and then ⊜ $10 - 1$, or 9, times.

Before Example 4, you can use a simpler example. Find the 10th term of the G.P.

$$\frac{1}{4}, \frac{1}{2}, 1, \ldots$$

$$r = \frac{1}{2} \div \frac{1}{4} = 2 \qquad a = \frac{1}{4} \qquad n = 10$$

$$l = a \cdot r^{n-1} = \frac{1}{4} \cdot 2^{10-1} = \frac{2^9}{4} = \frac{512}{4} = 128$$

For the calculator activity ($l = a \cdot r^{n-1} = 12.5x3^6$), suggest the following alternative: 3 ⊗ ⊜ ⊜ ⊜ ⊜ ⊜ ⊗ 12.5 ⊜ 9112.5.

Cumulative Review

1. Find the distance between $P(1, -1)$ and $Q(-2, 3)$.   **2.** Simplify $6 - 5\sqrt{-12}$.
3. Find the solution set of $|x| < 7$.
1. 5   2. $6 - 10i\sqrt{3}$ 3. $\{x \mid -7 < x < 7\}$

14.5 The Geometric Mean
(page 372)

Vocabulary
geometric means, *the* geometric mean, mean proportional

Suggestions
Encourage students to draw the appropriate number of blanks between the two given numbers when finding two or more means, as shown in Examples 1 and 2. When finding exactly one mean between two numbers x and y, students should use the formula: $\sqrt{xy}$ or $-\sqrt{xy}$.

Emphasize that there are two sets of n real geometric means between two numbers if n is an odd number.

You might mention the mean proportional in relation to a direct variation. $y = kx$ represents a direct variation. Since $k = \dfrac{y}{x}$, then for any ordered pair in the linear variation $\dfrac{y_1}{x_1} = \dfrac{y_2}{x_2} = k$, x_1 and y_2 are called the means, while y_1 and x_2 are called the extremes. The product of the means equals the product of the extremes. If $a = x_1 = y_2$ then $\dfrac{y_1}{a} = \dfrac{a}{x_2}$ and a is called the mean proportional. Therefore, $y_1 x_2 = a^2$, $a = \sqrt{y_1 x_2}$. This formula for geometric mean or mean proportional is mentioned on page 373.

Cumulative Review
1. Write $\sqrt[3]{5x}$ in exponential form.
2. Write $5\sqrt[3]{x}$ in exponential form.
3. Write $2y^{\frac{3}{4}}$ in radical form.
4. Write $(2y)^{\frac{3}{4}}$ in radical form.

1. $(5x)^{\frac{1}{3}}$ 2. $5x^{\frac{1}{3}}$ 3. $2\sqrt[4]{y^3}$
4. $\sqrt[4]{(2y)^3}$, or $\sqrt[4]{8y^3}$

14.6 Geometric Series
(page 375)

Vocabulary
geometric series

Suggestions
Students should know that there are two sum formulas and also understand when to use each of them. Use $S = \dfrac{a - rl}{l - r}$ if a, r, and l are given and use $S = \dfrac{a(1 - r^n)}{1 - r}$ or $\dfrac{a - a \cdot r^n}{1 - r}$ if a, r, and n are given.

Give special attention to Exercises 41 and 42. In Exercise 41, there are 8 descents (128 m, 64 m, 32 m, . . .) and 7 upward flights (64 m, 32 m, 16 m, . . .), which can be summed separately and then combined.

The second Calculator Activity, $\dfrac{2(1 + 3^7)}{4}$, can be done in an alternate way as follows.

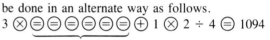

You might suggest a hypothetical choice to the students. Within a few seconds have them decide whether they would choose between $100,000,000 or a chessboard with $1 on the first square, $2 on the second, $4 on the third, $8 on the fourth, $16 on the fifth, and so on until all 64 squares are covered. They might be surprised to learn that the chessboard is a far better choice. Have them find on their calculators the value of the highest power of 2 that is permissible on the calculator. Our calculator shows that $2^{26} = 67,108,864$, which would be the amount of money on only the 27th square.

You may also wish to show how the concept of a geometric series applies to the study of the half-life of substances.

Cumulative Review
1. Solve the system. $\begin{array}{l} 3x + 2y = 8 \\ 5x - 3y = 7 \end{array}$ for (x, y).

2. Simplify. $\dfrac{x}{x^2 - 5x + 6} + \dfrac{4}{3x - 6}$.

1. $(2, 1)$ 2. $\dfrac{7x - 12}{3(x - 2)(x - 3)}$

14.7 Infinite Geometric Series
(page 379)

Vocabulary
limit

Suggestions
Notice that Examples 2 and 3 provide a new approach to the problem of writing a repeating decimal in the form $\frac{x}{y}$ where x and y are integers.

Stress that an infinite geometric series like $3 + 6 + 12 + 24 + \ldots$ does not have a sum, and that $r = 2$ (r is not between -1 and 1) in this case.

Cumulative Review
Rationalize the denominator. Simplify.

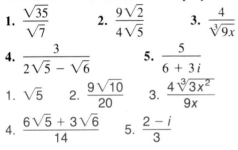

1. $\dfrac{\sqrt{35}}{\sqrt{7}}$ **2.** $\dfrac{9\sqrt{2}}{4\sqrt{5}}$ **3.** $\dfrac{4}{\sqrt[3]{9x}}$

4. $\dfrac{3}{2\sqrt{5} - \sqrt{6}}$ **5.** $\dfrac{5}{6 + 3i}$

1. $\sqrt{5}$ 2. $\dfrac{9\sqrt{10}}{20}$ 3. $\dfrac{4\sqrt[3]{3x^2}}{9x}$

4. $\dfrac{6\sqrt{5} + 3\sqrt{6}}{14}$ 5. $\dfrac{2 - i}{3}$

14.8 Binomial Expansions
(page 382)

Suggestions
You can use the following procedure to write and simplify a binomial expansion. Example: Expand $(x^2 - 5y)^4$. Simplify. First, write only the coefficients:

$1 \underline{\quad} + 4 \underline{\quad}\,\underline{\quad} + 6 \underline{\quad}\,\underline{\quad} + 4 \underline{\quad}\,\underline{\quad} + 1 \underline{\quad}.$

Second, write the descending powers of x^2 using parentheses:

$1(x^2)^4 + 4(x^2)^3 \underline{\quad} + 6(x^2)^2 \underline{\quad} + 4(x^2) \underline{\quad} + 1 \underline{\quad}.$

Third, write the ascending powers of $-5y$ using parentheses:

$1(x^2)^4 + 4(x^2)^3(-5y) + 6(x^2)^2(-5y)^2 + 4(x^2)(-5y)^3 + 1(-5y)^4.$

Last, simplify each term:

$x^8 - 40x^6y + 150x^4y^2 - 500x^2y^3 + 625y^4.$

Errors Students Make
A typical student error in the above is to omit the parentheses in the second and/or third steps.

Enrichment
You might have a student look into the life and accomplishments of Blaise Pascal.

Before the presentation of the lesson, you could have the students expand for themselves the binomials $(a + b)^0$, $(a + b)^1$, $(a + b)^2$, $(a + b)^3$, $(a + b)^4$, and $(a + b)^5$ to show how tedious the process becomes as you increase the power of the binomial. This might help them appreciate both Pascal's triangle and the binomial theorem.

Cumulative Review
Solve for x.

1. $\sqrt{x + 2} = 2\sqrt{x - 1}$ **2.** $x - \sqrt{4x - 7} = 1$

3. $10^{2x - 1} = 1000$ **4.** $10^x = \frac{1}{100}$

1. 2   2. 2, 4   3. 2   4. -2

Computer Activities
This program applies arrays and makes an interesting use of place references in line 60. Be sure the students understand where the results of the computations are being stored.

15
Chapter and Lesson Commentaries

Chapter 15 Logarithmic and Exponential Functions

Chapter Objectives

To find the base-10 (or the base-n) logarithm of a positive number

To find the base-10 (or the base-n) antilogarithm of a real number

To find products, quotients, powers, and roots using logarithms and linear interpolation

To solve a logarithmic equation containing a sum or difference of logarithms

To write a logarithmic expression in expanded form

To write a formula as a logarithmic equation in expanded form

To write an indicated sum of logarithmic terms as the log of one expression

To solve a base-n logarithmic equation for n

To solve an exponential equation, using base-10 logarithms

To read, draw, and interpret the graphs of exponential and logarithmic functions

Chapter Overview

The rules for finding $\log a \cdot b$, $\log \frac{a}{b}$, $\log a^r$, and $\log a^{\frac{1}{n}}$ are developed and applied to numerical computation, solving logarithmic equations, expanding logarithmic expressions, and simplifying an indicated sum of logarithmic terms. The work with base-10, or common, logarithms is extended to base-n logarithms, where $n > 0$ and $n \neq 1$. Exponential equations are solved, using base-10 logarithms, and base-n exponential and logarithmic functions and their graphs are studied.

15.1 Common Logarithms and Antilogarithms (page 390)

Vocabulary
base-10 antilogarithm of x (antilog$_{10}x$ or antilog x), base-10 logarithm of y ($\log_{10}y$ or log y), common logarithms

Background
The base-10 log y is not defined for $y \leq 0$. For example, $\log(-100)$ is not a real number because -100 cannot be written as 10^x for some real number x. However, the base-10 antilog x is defined for each real number x because 10^x does exist for each real number x.

In this lesson, base-10 log y and base-10 antilog x are restricted as shown below.

Function	Restriction	Example
log y	1. y is a positive integral power of 10,	log 100, or log 10^2
	2. $y = 0$, or	log 1, or log 10^0
	3. $1 < y < 10$,	log 8.34
antilog x	4. x is a positive integer, or	antilog 3
	5. $0 < x < 1$	antilog 0.8142

In the next lesson, the domains of these functions are extended and the characteristic and the mantissa of a log are introduced.

Suggestions
Encourage students to think of log 100 as an exponent, the exponent 2, for which $10^2 = 100$. Likewise, encourage them to think of antilog 2 as a power, the value of 10^2, or 100.

For level-B and level-C students, you might consider covering Lessons 15.1 and 15.2 in the same class period.

Cumulative Review
Find the slope of $\overleftrightarrow{AB}$ for the given coordinates. Also, describe the slant of $\overleftrightarrow{AB}$.

1. $A(2, -4)$, $B(-3, -11)$ 2. $A(15, 4)$, $B(12, 4)$
3. $A(2, -4)$, $B(4, -10)$ 4. $A(4, 15)$, $B(4, 12)$

1. $\frac{7}{5}$; up to the right   2. 0; horizontal
3. -3; down to the right   4. undefined; vertical

15.2 Characteristic and Mantissa (page 392)

Vocabulary
characteristic, mantissa, scientific notation

Suggestions
Introduce this lesson with a review of scientific notation. Use examples such as the following:

1. Write each number in scientific notation.

Number	Scientific Notation
0.00643	6.43×10^{-3}
0.643	6.43×10^{-1}
6.43	6.43×10^{0}
64,300	6.43×10^{4}

2. Write each number in ordinary notation.

Scientific Notation	Ordinary Notation
8.72×10^{-2}	0.0872
8.72×10^{0}	8.72
8.72×10^{3}	8,720

Students will wonder why log 0.0546 should be written 8.7372-10, rather than $-2 + 0.7372$. You can explain this by discussing the table of logs of the trigonometric functions on page 592, where 10 must be subtracted from each entry. See the footnote on page 592.

Errors Students Make
Students may write a log such as $-2 + 0.7372$ as -2.7372. Point out that $-2.7372 = -2 + (-0.7372)$, which is not the same as $-2 + (0.7372)$. Also, note that $-2 + 0.7372 = -1.2628$, which is the same as $-1 + (-0.2628)$, and means that the mantissa is -0.2628. The mantissas in the table are positive, *not* negative.

Cumulative Review
1. Give the x-intercepts and the y-intercepts of the ellipse with equation $\dfrac{x^2}{25} + \dfrac{y^2}{16} = 1$.
2. Solve $a - 2x = bx - cx$ for x.
3. Simplify $(2a^{-3}b^4)^3$ and write the answer with positive exponents.

1. $\pm 5; \pm 4$ 2. $x = \dfrac{a}{b - c + 2}$ 3. $\dfrac{8b^{12}}{a^9}$

15.3 Logs of Products and Quotients (page 394)

Background
The use of logarithms as an aid in numerical computation has decreased greatly since the widespread use of the pocket calculator. Such computation with logs is minimized in this book and the emphasis is shifted to solving logarithmic equations and simplifying expressions that require the use of the logarithmic properties of products, quotients, powers, and roots.

You may wish to allow the students to use pocket calculators in this chapter.

Suggestions
Students should arrange their work in a vertical format for exercises such as those in Examples 1–4. They should begin with an outline, then fill in the details, as shown below for Examples 3 and 4.

Outline		Completed Work
log 8.12	0.	0.9096
log 0.00321 (+)	7. ____ $- 10$ (+)	$7.5065 - 10$
		$18.4161 - 20$
log 0.0476 (−)	8. ____ $- 10$ (−)	$8.6776 - 10$
		$9.7385 - 10$
		$(8.4161 - 10)$

Cumulative Review
1. Write $\sqrt{x}$ in exponential form.
2. Write $x^{\frac{1}{3}}$ in radical form.
3. Write $\sqrt[3]{x^2}$ in exponential form.
4. Write $x^{\frac{3}{4}}$ in radical form.

1. $x^{\frac{1}{2}}$ 2. $\sqrt[3]{x}$ 3. $x^{\frac{2}{3}}$ 4. $\sqrt[4]{x^3}$

log 0.076	8.	$- 10$	$8.8808 - 10$
log 3.24 (−)	0. ____	(−)	0.5105
			$8.3703 - 10$
log 27 (−)	1. ____	(−)	1.4314
			$6.9389 - 10$

With some students, it may be necessary to review the definition of extraneous solutions. Emphasize that all apparent solutions of a logarithmic equation should be checked in the original equation.

15.4 Logs of Powers and Radicals (page 397)

Background

The logarithm of a root is developed as the logarithm of a power rather than by stating a *fourth rule*, $\log \sqrt[n]{x} = \frac{1}{n} \cdot \log x$.

Suggestions

In the second part of Example 2, for $\log 0.0532$ you can show the need for rewriting the characteristic $8 - 10$ as $28 - 30$ as follows:

$$\frac{8.7259 - 10}{3} = 2.9086 - 3\tfrac{1}{3}$$

But, $2 - 3\tfrac{1}{3}$ cannot be used as a characteristic because $2 - 3\tfrac{1}{3}$, or $-1\tfrac{1}{3}$ is not an integer.

As in Lesson 15.3, encouraging students to use a vertical format will help to overcome computational errors. A possible format is shown below for Examples 3 and 4.

Outline   Completed Work

$\log 0.0047$	7.	-10	$7.6721 - 10$
$\log 62.9$ (+)	1.	(+)	1.7987
			$9.4708 - 10$
(×)		5 (×)	5
			$47.3540 - 50$

$\log 0.094$	8.	-10	$38.9731 - 40$
$\log 22.7$ (−)	1.	(−)	1.3560
			$37.6171 - 40$
(×)	$\tfrac{1}{4}$	(×)	$\tfrac{1}{4}$
			$9.404275 - 10$
			$(7.4161 - 10)$

Cumulative Review

Factor completely.

1. $3x^3 - 18x^2 + 27x$ **2.** $3x^3 - 4x^2 + 6x - 8$
3. $2x^3 - 16$ **4.** $x^2 + 6x + 9 - 4y^2$
1. $3x(x - 3)^2$ 2. $(x^2 + 2)(3x - 4)$
3. $2(x - 2)(x^2 + 2x + 4)$
4. $(x + 3 + 2y)(x + 3 - 2y)$

15.5 Logarithmic Expressions (page 402)

Suggestions

In Example 3, point out that $\log \sqrt[3]{\dfrac{xy^4}{z}}$ is an acceptable answer, even though $\sqrt[3]{\dfrac{xy^4}{z}}$ is not in simplest radical form, because it is the log of one expression.

With some students, you may wish to use simpler examples than those provided in the Pupil's Edition. A parallel example and its solution is provided below for each of the examples in the Pupil's Edition.

For Additional Chalkboard Work

1. Write $\log \dfrac{a^2}{c}$ in expanded form.

2. Given the formula $c = 2\pi r$, write $\log r$ in expanded form.

3. Write $\frac{1}{2}(\log c + \log m - \log t)$ as the log of one expression.

1. $\log \dfrac{a^2}{c} = \log a^2 - \log c$
    $= 2 \log a - \log c$

2. $c = 2\pi r$
  $\log c = \log (2\pi r)$
  $\log c = \log 2 + \log \pi + \log r$
  $\log r = \log c - \log 2 - \log \pi$

3. $\dfrac{1}{2}(\log c + \log m - \log t) = \dfrac{1}{2} \log \dfrac{cm}{t}$

      $= \log \left(\dfrac{cm}{t}\right)^{\frac{1}{2}}$

      $= \log \sqrt{\dfrac{cm}{t}}$

Cumulative Review

1. Find three consecutive odd integers so that the sum of the squares of the second and third integers is 130.
2. A triangle's height is 2 cm less than twice the length of its base. Find the height if the area of the triangle is 20 cm^2.
1. 5, 7, 9, or $-11, -9, -7$ 2. 8 cm

15.6 Base-*n* Logarithms and Antilogarithms (page 404)

Vocabulary
base-*n* antilogarithm, base-*n* logarithm

Background
The transition to other bases should be fairly easy because of the emphasis that has been placed on a logarithm as an exponent and an antilogarithm as a power. The key is to be able to write logarithmic equations in exponential form.

Suggestions
Encourage students to think of an expression such as $\log_2 8$ as one in which they are to find the exponent, or power of 2, that is equal to 8. That is, they are to solve the equation $2^x = 8$ for x. Also encourage students to think of an expression such as antilog$_5$ 2 as finding the value of the power 5^2, which is the second power of 5, or 25.

Exercises 35–42 require students to solve base-*n* logarithmic equations of the form $\log_4 3 + \log_4 (y - 2) = \log_4 2 + \log_4 y$ for y. If necessary, refer students to Examples 5 and 6 on pages 398 and 399 or use the exercises below.

For Additional Chalkboard Work
Solve each equation for y.

1. $\log_6 5 + \log_6 (2y - 3) = \log_6 25$
2. $\log_8 (y - 2) + \log_8 (y - 10) = 2 \log_8 (y - 4)$

1. $\log_6 5 + \log_6 (2y - 3) = \log_6 25$
$$\log_6 5(2y - 3) = \log_6 25$$
$$5(2y - 3) = 25$$
$$10y - 15 = 25$$
$$y = 4$$

2. $\log_8 (y + 2) + \log_8 (y - 10) = 2 \log_8 (y - 4)$
$$\log_8 (y - 2)(y - 10) = \log_8 (y - 4)^2$$
$$y^2 - 12y + 20 = y^2 - 8y + 16$$
$$-4y = -4$$
$$y = 1$$
No solution—log of negative is undefined

Cumulative Review
Solve for x.

1. $5^{3x-2} = 125$ **2.** $8^{x+4} = 32$ **3.** $6^{2x-1} = \frac{1}{36}$

1. $\frac{5}{3}$ 2. $-\frac{7}{3}$ 3. $-\frac{1}{2}$

15.7 Exponential Equations (page 406)

Suggestions
In this lesson, base-10 logarithms are used to solve exponential equations such as $3^x = 17$ and $4^{2x-1} = 7.65$. It would be very advantageous to permit the use of a pocket calculator because the division can become tedious.

For Additional Chalkboard Work
1. Solve $12^x = 5$ for x to three significant digits.
2. Solve $6^{3x-2} = 59.7$ for x to three significant digits.
3. Find $\log_6 9.56$ to three significant digits.

1.
$$12^x = 5$$
$$\log 12^x = \log 5$$
$$x \cdot \log 12 = \log 5$$
$$x = \frac{\log 5}{\log 12}$$
$$x = \frac{0.6990}{1.0792}$$
$$x = 0.6477 = 0.648$$

2.
$$6^{3x-2} = 59.7$$
$$\log 6^{3x-2} = \log 59.7$$
$$(3x - 2) \log 6 = \log 59.7$$
$$3x - 2 = \frac{\log 59.7}{\log 6}$$
$$3x - 2 = \frac{1.7760}{0.7782}$$
$$3x - 2 = 2.282$$
$$3x = 4.282$$
$$x = 1.427 = 1.43$$

3. Let $\log_6 9.56 = x$
$$6^x = 9.56$$
$$\log 6^x = \log 9.56$$
$$x \log 6 = \log 9.56$$
$$x = \frac{\log 9.56}{\log 6}$$
$$x = \frac{0.9805}{0.7782}$$
$$x = 1.260 = 1.26.$$

Cumulative Review
Specify the domain and the range of each relation. Is the relation a function?

1. $A = \{(3,4), (4,6), (5,8), (6,10)\}$
2. $B = \{(5,1), (6,-4), (3,2), (6,-2)\}$

1. $\{3, 4, 5, 6\}$; $\{4, 6, 8, 10\}$; yes
2. $\{5, 6, 3\}$; $\{1, -4, 2, -2\}$; no

15.8 Graphs of Exponential and Logarithmic Functions (page 410)

Vocabulary
base-n exponential function, base-n logarithmic function, constantly decreasing function, constantly increasing function

Suggestions
Emphasize that to graph either an exponential or a logarithmic function, students should begin by constructing a table of ordered pairs of real numbers (x, y). Point out that although any real number can be assigned to x in $y = n^x$, or to y in $y = \log_n x$, the computations are less tedious when integral values are used. Thus:

1. to graph $y = n^x$, for some real number n, assign integral values, such as -3, -2, -1, 0, 1, 2, 3, to x and
2. to graph $y = \log_n x$, for $n > 0$ and $n \neq 1$, assign integral values to y.

Discuss the summary on page 413. Emphasize that students should refer to the graphs found in this summary repeatedly when they are working on the exercises on page 414.

For Additional Chalkboard Work
$A = P\left(1 + \frac{r}{n}\right)^{nt}$, where P represents the principal invested at r percent annual interest compounded n times per year for t years, and A represents the amount accumulated. Use this formula to draw a graph that shows the amount accumulated in an account at the end of each year for ten years, if $10,000 was deposited at 12% compounded quarterly. Round all amounts to the nearest dollar.
Amount at end of each year: $11,255; $12,668; $14,258; $16,047; $18,061; $20,328; $22,879; $25,751; $28,983; $32,620

Cumulative Review
Solve each proportion.

1. $\dfrac{y}{10} = \dfrac{5}{12}$ **2.** $\dfrac{7}{10} = \dfrac{x}{14}$

1. $4\frac{1}{6}$ 2. 9.8

15.9 Linear Interpolation (page 415)

Background
Linear interpolation will be used again in the study of trigonometry.

Suggestions
You can use the table of common logarithms found on page 595 to help students see that the graph of $y = \log x$ is very "close to" a line. Have students read across a row in the table and point out the increases in the mantissas. For example, note that over the interval $8.90 \leq x \leq 8.95$, $\log x$ increases by 0.0005, 0.0005, 0.0005, 0.0004, and 0.0005.

x	8.90	8.91	8.92	8.93	8.94	8.95
$\log x$	0.9494	0.9499	0.9504	0.9509	0.9513	0.9518

This suggests that the graph of the logarithmic function, over this interval, is very "close to" a line with a slope of approximately $\dfrac{5}{10,000}$.

Notice that decimal points are omitted from the significant digits in the number and in the mantissa while interpolating.

Cumulative Review
1. Find the arithmetic mean of -7 and 11.
2. Find the positive geometric mean of 4 and 12.
3. Find the sum of the first 40 terms of $3 + 5 + 7 + 9 + \ldots$.
4. Find the 10th term of the G.P. whose first term is $\frac{1}{4}$ and whose common ratio is 2.

1. 2   2. $4\sqrt{3}$ 3. 1,680   4. 128

Computer Activities (p. 419)
This program is an excellent example of how a repeated procedure can be written in a program and used for any values. Exercise 5 requires the printing out of a table. Let the students work on table layout and titles.

16
Chapter and Lesson Commentaries

Chapter 16 Permutations, Combinations, and Probability

Chapter Objectives

To find the number of possible arrangements of objects by using the Fundamental Counting Principle

To find the number of permutations of objects when conditions are attached to the arrangement

To find the quotient of numbers given in factorial notation

To find the number of distinguishable permutations when some of the objects in an arrangement are alike

To find the number of possible permutations of objects in a circle

To find the number of possible selections of n objects taken r at a time without regard to order

To find the value of $\binom{n}{r}$ for nonnegative integers n and r where $n \geq r$

To determine the probability of a simple event

To determine the probability of an event using a sample space

To determine the probability of an event using the Fundamental Counting Principle, permutations, and combinations

Chapter Overview

The Fundamental Counting Principle is used to find the number of possible arrangements, or permutations, of
1. n distinct objects, taken r at a time, on a straight line
2. n objects when some of the objects are alike
3. n distinct objects on a circle.

The formula $\binom{n}{r} = \dfrac{n}{r!(n-r)!}$ is used to find the number of combinations of n distinct objects taken r at a time.

Special Features

16.1 Fundamental Counting Principle (page 424)

Vocabulary
choice, decision, number of choices, number of decisions, permutation, $n!$

Background
The Fundamental Counting Principle, rather than the formula

$$nPr = n(n - 1)(n - 2) \cdots (n - r + 1),$$

is used to find the number of permutations of n objects taken r at a time. The principle is also used to solve other types of problems.

Suggestions
Make careful distinctions among the following four phrases:

1. decision   3. number of decisions
2. choice   4. number of choices.

For the truck driver's problem at the top of page 424, the number of decisions is 2. "Choose a letter" is one decision. "Choose a number" is the other decision. For the first decision, the number of choices is 4. Each of A, C, G, and T is a choice. For the second decision, the number of choices is 3. Each of 1, 7, and 9 is a choice.

The strategy for problem solving in this lesson is as follows:
1. Determine the number of decisions
2. Draw a blank (_____) for each decision
3. Determine the number of choices for each decision
4. Write the number of choices in the blank for that decision
5. Use the Fundamental Counting Principle

Cumulative Review
1. Expand $(x^2 - y)^4$. Simplify each term.
2. Find the sum of the infinite geometric series:

   $8 + 2 + \frac{1}{2} + \frac{1}{8} + \cdots$.

1. $x^8 - 4x^6y + 6x^4y^2 - 4x^2y^3 + y^4$
2. $\frac{32}{3}$, or $10\frac{2}{3}$

16.2 Conditional Permutations (page 428)

Suggestions
Emphasize that an "or" decision involves addition, as shown in Example 2, and that an "and" decision involves multiplication, as shown in Example 3.

Exercise 15 involves both "and" and "or" decisions:
(novels left *and* short stories right) *or* (short stories left *and* novels right), which leads to $(5! \times 6!) + (6! \times 5!)$.

Cumulative Review
1. Add. $\frac{3}{4x^2} + \frac{5}{6x}$
2. Find the positive geometric mean of 3 and 12.
3. Find the solution set of $|2x| > 10$.

1. $\frac{10x + 9}{12x^2}$ 2. 6
3. $\{x \mid x < -5 \text{ or } x > 5\}$

16.3 Distinguishable Permutations (page 431)

Background
Finding the value of an expression like
$\dfrac{8!}{4! \times 3!}$ in this lesson will occur again in Lesson
16.5 where $\dbinom{10}{4} = \dfrac{10!}{4! \times 6!}$.

Suggestions
The Short Method shown in Example 1 requires the skill of rewriting factorial notation like $8!$ as $8 \times 7 \times 6 \times 5 \times (4!)$.
Additional practice similar to Example 1 is given below.

1. $\dfrac{6!}{4! \times 2!} = \dfrac{6 \times 5 \times (4!)}{(4!) \times 2 \times 1} = \dfrac{6 \times 5}{2 \times 1} = 15$

2. $\dfrac{12!}{3! \times 9!} = \dfrac{12 \times 11 \times 10 \times (9!)}{3 \times 2 \times 1 \times (9!)}$
$= \dfrac{12 \times 11 \times 10}{3 \times 2 \times 1}$
$= 220$

Cumulative Review
1. Identify the conic section whose equation is
$\dfrac{x^2}{16} + \dfrac{y^2}{36} = 1$.
2. Solve. $x^2 + 2x = 8$
3. Rationalize the denominator of $\dfrac{3}{2 + i}$.

1. ellipse 2. $-4, 2$ 3. $\dfrac{6 - 3i}{5}$

16.4 Circular Permutations (page 433)

Suggestions
If Exercises 7 and 8 are to be assigned, then extend the Example on page 433 to create the following second example.
In how many different ways can the 6 guests be seated around the circular table if men and women must be seated alternately?
Solution: Draw and interpret the following diagrams.

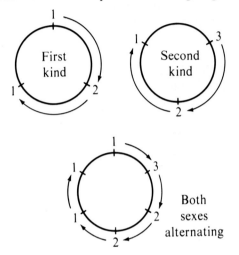

Cumulative Review
Given $f(x) = 5x + 4$ and $g(x) = x^2 - 3$, find the following.
1. $f(g(2))$ **2.** $g(f(1))$
3. $g(f(a))$ **4.** $f(g(c))$
1. 9 2. 78 3. $25a^2 + 40a + 13$ 4. $5c^2 - 11$

16.5 Combinations (page 435)

Vocabulary
combination, zero factorial (0!)

Suggestions
Emphasize the difference between a combination and a permutation:
Combination: a *selection* of objects *without* regard to order
Permutation: an arrangement of objects in a *definite order*
Use the Reading in Algebra exercises to discuss this difference.

Enrichment
Simplify the triangular display below. Have you seen the result before?

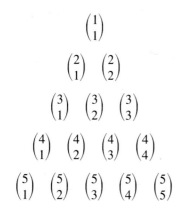

Cumulative Review
1. Find the coordinates of M, the midpoint of $\overline{PQ}$ for $P(-3,4)$, $Q(7,6)$.
2. Write an equation of the circle with radius 4 and center at the origin.

1. $M(2,5)$ 2. $x^2 + y^2 = 16$

16.6 Probability: Simple Events (page 438)

Vocabulary
favorable outcomes, possible outcomes, simple event, probability

Background
If an event can occur successfully in s different ways and the total number of equally likely events is t, then the probability of success of an event happening is $P(s) = \frac{s}{t}$.

If an event can occur unsuccessfully in f different ways and the total number of equally likely events is t, then the probability of an event being unsuccessful is $P(f) = \frac{f}{t}$.

However, $P(s) + P(f)$, of the same event is $\frac{s}{t} + \frac{f}{t}$ or $\frac{s}{t} + \frac{t-s}{t} = \frac{t}{t} = 1$. Note: $s + f = t$ or $f = t - s$.

This discussion suggests that in order to find the probability of an event *not* happening, the probability of the event happening must be found and subtracted from 1.

Suggestions
Only ideal situations are considered in this study of elementary probability. It is assumed that a die is not heavier at one corner and that each face has an equally likely chance to come up as any other face. It is assumed that a coin is fair, that it is equally balanced, and a head is just as likely to occur on a flip as a tail. It is assumed that, in a roll of a die or a flip of a coin, the person rolling the die or flipping the coin will not introduce any bias.

Errors Students Make
Students might make errors in determining the number of favorable outcomes. This type of error might be caused by the students' lack of knowledge of the event itself. Some students may not know that there are four Jacks in a deck of cards, for example. You may wish to review such details.

Cumulative Review
Simplify each expression.
1. $-3a^4 b^3 c^{-2} \cdot 5a^{-6} b^2 c$
2. $-8xy^{-3} z^5 \cdot -2x^{-2} y^{-3} z$

16.7 Probability: Compound Events (page 441)

Vocabulary
sample space, inclusive events, mutually exclusive events, independent events, dependent events

Background
Compound sentences in mathematics are formed with the connectives *or* and *and*. The connective *or* is the inclusive *or*. Two simple sentences connected with *or* form a compound sentence that is true if one or both parts are true. For a compound sentence formed with the connective *and* to be true, both parts must be true.

The $P(A \text{ or } B) = P(A) + P(B) - P(A \text{ and } B)$ if the two events are inclusive, since the sets A and B overlap and are counted twice. To remove that space counted twice, subtract $P(A \text{ and } B)$. If the events are mutually exclusive events, then there are no points in common. Thus, $P(A \text{ and } B) = 0$.

Suggestions
Encourage students to use both the sample-space approach and the formulas and to use one as a check of the other.

Errors Students Make
This lesson has much new vocabulary and care must be taken not to confuse terms. Sometimes independent events are confused with mutually exclusive events. Events that are mutually exclusive occur if not more than one of them can happen in a single trial. That is, mutually exclusive events have nonoverlapping sets. Independent events A and B mean that the probability of event A does not depend on event B. Independent events must have equally likely outcomes.

Cumulative Review
A line has the given slope, y-intercept, or contains the indicated point (s). Write an equation, in standard form, of each line.

1. $P(-3, -4)$, $m = -\frac{2}{3}$ **2.** $m = \frac{3}{5}$, $b = -2$
3. $P(-6,1)$, $Q(-3,-1)$ **4.** $P(1, -4)$,
   $Q(-2,-6)$
1. $2x + 3y = -18$ 2. $3x - 5y = 10$
3. $2x + 3y = -9$ 4. $2x - 3y = 14$

16.8 Probability and Arrangements (page 445)

Suggestions
Review the Fundamental Counting Principle: If one choice can be made in a ways and a second choice can be made in b ways, then the choices in order can be made in $a \times b$ different ways.

Also review that a combination is a selection of objects without regard to order and that the number of combinations $\binom{n}{r} = \dfrac{n!}{r!(n-r)!}$.

This lesson combines probability and the notions of the Fundamental Counting Principle and Combinations. In this lesson objects are selected without regard to order.

Errors Students Make
Unless students know how to reduce factorial division, computational errors may occur.

$$\binom{52}{5} = \frac{52!}{5!47!} = \frac{52 \cdot 51 \cdot 50 \cdot 49 \cdot 48 \cdot 47!}{5! \, 47!}$$
$$= \frac{52 \cdot 51 \cdot 50 \cdot 49 \cdot 48}{5 \cdot 4 \cdot 3 \cdot 2}$$

In general,

$$\binom{n}{r} = \frac{n!}{r!(n-r)!} = \frac{n(n-1)(n-2) \cdots (n-r)!}{r!(n-r)!}.$$

Cumulative Review
Factor each polynomial completely.
1. $x^2 + 3x - 10$ **2.** $4x^2 - 25$
3. $x^3 - 2x^2 - 3x$ **4.** $x^3 - 16x$
5. $x^3 - 8$ **6.** $x^3 + 27$
1. $(x + 5)(x - 2)$ 2. $(2x + 5)(2x - 5)$
3. $x(x + 1)(x - 3)$ 4. $x(x + 4)(x - 4)$
5. $(x - 2)(x^2 + 2x + 4)$ 6. $(x + 3)(x^2 + 3x + 9)$

Computer Activities
This program uses the randomize function. Be sure students are aware of what random numbers are and what numbers can be found with line 30. This program lends itself to the creation of all sorts of games. Let students create their own game after completing exercise 3.

17

Chapter and Lesson Commentaries

Chapter 17   Trigonometric Functions

Chapter Objectives

To sketch an angle of rotation associated with a directed degree measure and to determine its corresponding reference angle and reference triangle

To find lengths of sides in a 30°–60° or 45°–45° right triangle and to find the coordinates of the points that their terminal sides make with a circle

To define the six trigonometric functions

To find the trigonometric functions of special degree measure like 30°, 45° and 90°

To determine the quadrants where the trig functions are positive and the quadrants where they are negative

To solve linear trigonometric equations

To find the trig functions of angles of negative measure

To find trigonometric identities

To find the other five trigonometric functions of an angle of rotation given one function

To use trigonometric tables

To interpolate with trigonometry

To define and use trigonometry of a right triangle

Chapter Overview

Trigonometry is initially approached through the study of the six trigonometric functions of angles of rotation. Special angle measure like 0°, 30°, 45°, and 60° are first considered and then the trigonometric functions of any positive or negative angle degree measure are presented. After explaining how to use trig tables, interpolation, an art that is fast becoming extinct in this age of pocket calculators, is also discussed.

Chapter Overview (cont.)

Once the student has an understanding of the six trigonometric functions, he or she utilizes them in the lesson on solving linear trigonometric equations. Finally, the trigonometry of a right triangle, which is considered as a special case of the trigonometry of an angle of rotation, is presented along with applications.

For students who have taken geometry, the names of the trigonometric functions should sound familiar. Mention that secant and tangent are defined differently in trigonometry than in geometry. It might interest students to find out where the strange names of *sine, secant* and *tangent* originated. Have some students look up the roots of the words and their formal definitions in a dictionary.

You might have some students give a short presentation on the life of Leonhard Euler. He led a very interesting life and some of his many mathematics discoveries dealt with the sine and cosine functions. As mentioned before, this type of independent project helps to "humanize" the subject matter. Another project might be a report on how the conventional angle of rotation is different when used in navigation, where the initial side of an angle starts on the positive *y*-axis and is rotated in a clockwise direction. The measure associated with this type of rotation is called *positive measure*.

Some mnemonics are presented in the lesson commentaries. There are quite a few details that the students must remember in this chapter. After they understand the theory, memory aids will be helpful.

Special Features

Reading in Algebra   pp. 457, 465
Calculator Activities   p. 482
Cumulative Review   pp. 465, 472, 474, 476, 480, 485
Computer Activities   p. 494
Chapter Review   p. 492
Chapter Test   p. 493
College Prep Test   p. 495
A Challenge to You   p. 472

17.1　Angles of Rotation
(page 455)

Vocabulary
angle of rotation, initial ray, terminal ray, clockwise rotation, counterclockwise rotation, quadrantal angles, coterminal angles, reference triangle, reference angle

Background
An angle of rotation with a measure of 90° has a corresponding revolution measure of $\frac{1}{4}$ revolution, which is $\frac{1}{4}$ the circumference or $\frac{1}{4}(2\pi m) = \frac{\pi m}{2}$.
Similarly, an angle of rotation with a measure of 180° has a corresponding measure of πm.

Suggestions
The idea of rotation is usually thought of as it occurs in the physical world, as in the rotation of a wheel or a fan blade.

A distinction should be made between an angle of rotation and an angle. An angle of rotation is the angle associated with a rotating ray while an angle is defined as a set of points.

A distinction should also be made between an angle of rotation and angle measure. An angle of rotation can be measured by degrees, number of revolutions, or radians.

An angle of rotation with a measure of 90° has a corresponding revolution measure of $\frac{1}{4}$ revolution, which is $\frac{1}{4}$ the circumference or $\frac{1}{4}(2\pi r) = \frac{\pi r}{2}$.
Similarly, an angle of rotation with a measure of 180° has a corresponding measure of πr.

Errors Students Make
Errors may be made by the students in the formation of the reference triangles. Stress that triangles are always formed by drawing a perpendicular to the x-axis and that the reference angle has the x-axis as one of its rays and is acute.

Cumulative Review
Determine whether P and Q are symmetric with respect to the x-axis, the origin, or none of these.
1. $P(3, -6), Q(-3, -6)$　**2.** $P(-5, 3), Q(5, -3)$
1. y-axis　2. origin

17.2　Special Right Triangles
(page 458)

Vocabulary
30°–60° right triangle, 45°–45° right triangle

Background
It might be a good idea to review rationalizing a denominator:

Suggestions
It is important that students memorize the properties of the 30°–60° right triangle and those of the isosceles right triangle since they will be used throughout the study of trigonometry.

For Additional Chalkboard Work
Determine the point (x, y) and the radius r for each of the following.

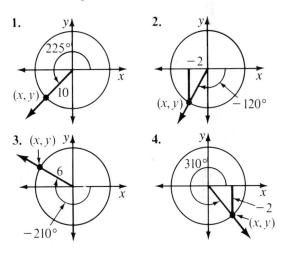

Errors Students Make
In Examples 5 and 6 students must know in what quadrant x and y lie: If $|x| = 3$, and x is in quadrant II, then $|x| = -x = 3$ or $x = -3$.

Cumulative Review
For each point, find the coordinates of the corresponding point symmetric with respect to the x-axis, the y-axis, and the origin.
1. $A(-4, -9)$　**2.** $B(6, -3)$　**3.** $C(-5, 9)$
1. $(-4, 9)(4, -9)(4, 9)$　2. $(6, 3)(-6, -3)$
$(-6, 3)$　3. $(-5, -9)(5, 9)(5, -9)$

17.3   Sine and Cosine Functions
(page 462)

Vocabulary
sine, cosine

Background
The sine and cosine functions are defined in terms of an angle of rotation. The sine is defined as the ratio of the ordinate to the radius and the cosine is defined as the ratio of the abscissa to the radius.

Suggestions
Let the radius of a circle have length 1 as shown. The circle intersects the axes at $(1,0)$, $(0,1)$, $(-1,0)$ and $(0,-1)$. Thus, since the radius is 1, sin function is y and the cos is x.

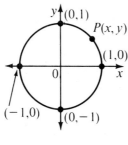

$\sin 0° = 0$, $\sin 90° = 1$,
$\sin 180° = 0$, $\sin 22° = 1$
$\cos 0° = 1$, $\cos 90° = 0$,
$\cos 180° = -1$, $\cos 22° = 0$

Errors Students Make
A systematic approach to finding the sine or cosine of the measure of an angle will help to reduce errors.
1. Draw the angle of rotation.
2. Draw the reference angle and triangle.
3. Determine x, y and r.
4. Find sin and cos.

Enrichment
From the unit circle above find each of these.
1. $\sin 360°$ 2. $\cos 360°$ 3. $\sin (-90°)$
4. $\cos (-90°)$ 5. $\sin (-180°)$ 6. $\cos (-180°)$
7. $\sin (-270°)$ 8. $\cos (-270°)$ 9. $\sin (-360°)$
10. $\cos (-360°)$ 11. $\cos 720°$

Cumulative Review
Solve each system of equations.
1. $-3x - 5y = -7$
   $-4x + 2y = 8$
2. $-3(x - 2) + (y - 1) = 5$
   $-(x - 3y) - (2 - x) = 7$
1. $(-1,2)$ 2. $(1,3)$

17.4   Tangent And Cotangent Functions
(page 466)

Vocabulary
tangent, cotangent

Suggestions
The tangent function is defined as the ratio of the ordinate to the abscissa. Thus, the tangent is the ratio of the sine to the cosine. Similarly, the cotangent function is defined as the ratio of the abscissa to the ordinate. Thus, it is the ratio of the cosine to the sine. Students should make use of both definitions of tan and cot.

In Example 1, $\tan 45° = \dfrac{y}{x} = \dfrac{1}{1} = 1$ or

$$\tan 45° = \frac{\sin 45°}{\cos 45°} = \frac{\frac{\sqrt{2}}{2}}{\frac{\sqrt{2}}{2}} = 1$$

Errors Students Make
Follow the same systematic approach suggested in the previous TE lesson.
1. Draw the angle of rotation.
2. Draw the reference angle and triangle.
3. Determine x, y and r. Be careful to get correct sign.
4. Find tan and cot.

Enrichment
From the unit circle, find each of the following.
1. $\tan 360°$ 2. $\cot 360°$
3. $\tan (-90°)$ 4. $\cot (-90°)$
5. $\tan (-180°)$ 6. $\cot (-180°)$
7. $\tan (-270°)$ 8. $\cot (-270°)$
9. $\tan (-360°)$ 10. $\cot (-360°)$
11. $\tan (720°)$ 12. $\cot (720°)$

Cumulative Review
Solve each system of equations.
1. $-2x + 3y - z = 2$
   $-x - 2y + 2z = -5$
   $3x + 2y + z = 3$
2. $3x - 2y + 2z = 10$
   $2x + 3y - 2z = -1$
   $-3x - 3y - z = -4$
1. $(1, 1, -1)$ 2. $(2, -1, 1)$

17.5 Secant and Cosecant Functions (page 470)

Vocabulary
secant, cosecant

Suggestions
The secant function is defined as the ratio of the radius to the abscissa. Thus, the secant is $\dfrac{1}{\cos}$. The cosecant function is defined as the ratio of the radius to the ordinate, or $\dfrac{1}{\sin}$.

Show students that if $\sec u = \dfrac{1}{\cos u}$, then $\cos u = \dfrac{1}{\sec u}$. Also, if $\csc u = \dfrac{1}{\sin u}$, then $\sin u = \dfrac{1}{\csc u}$. Thus secant is positive in the same quadrants that the cosine is positive and the cosecant is positive in the same quadrants that the sine is positive.

Errors Students Make
Sketching the angle of rotation can help determine the reference angle and the signs of x and y.

Enrichment
From the unit circle find the following.

1. $\sec 360°$ **2.** $\csc 360°$
3. $\sec (-90°)$ **4.** $\csc (-90°)$
5. $\sec (-270°)$ **6.** $\csc (-270°)$
7. $\sec (-180°)$ **8.** $\csc (-180°)$

Cumulative Review
Graph the following equations.

1. $y = |x - 1|$ **2.** $y = |x| - 2$
3. $y = |x + 1| + 3$

1. **2.** **3.**

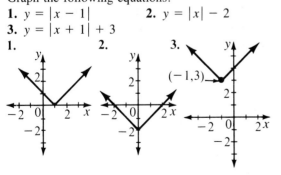

17.6 Functions of Negative Angles (page 473)

Vocabulary
negative measure

Background
Refer to the unit circle: then $(-u)$ determines point $Q(a, -b)$ and u determines $P(a, b)$, so, $\sin u = b$, $\sin (-u) = -b$, and $\sin (-u) = -\sin u$, $\cos u = a$, $\cos (-u) = a$, and $\cos (-u) = \cos u$, $\tan u = \dfrac{b}{a}$, $\tan (-u) = -\dfrac{b}{a}$, and $\tan (-a) = -\tan u$.

Suggestions
There are basically two ways to solve problems involving functions of negative angles. Students can use the formulas for negative angles or they can sketch the angle of rotation, determine the reference angle and triangle, find the sign of the trig function, and then determine the function. Have students make up a saying for ASTC: A Smart Trig Class is an old reliable. Remind students that function has the same sign as its reciprocal function.

Errors Students Make
Sometimes, students make errors with a double negative.

For example, $\sin (-300°) = -\sin 300° = -[-\sin 60°] = +\dfrac{\sqrt{3}}{2}$.

This can be avoided by sketching the angle of rotation.

Cumulative Review
Graph each equation.

1. $y = (x + 1)^2$ **2.** $y = x^2 - 1$
3. $y = (x - 1)^2 + 2$

1. **2.** **3.**

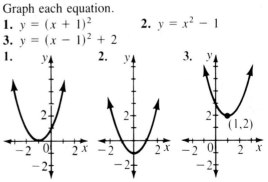

17.7 Values of Trigonometric Functions (page 475)

Suggestions
Students should memorize lengths of sides of special right triangles, such as 3-4-5, 5-12-13, and 8-15-17. It will save them much time. Students should also understand that multiples of these sides also yield right triangles. For example, if a triangle has sides with lengths $6(2 \cdot 3)$, $8(2 \cdot 4)$ and $10(2 \cdot 5)$, the triangle is a right triangle. Also, if a right triangle has two sides with lengths $15(3 \cdot 5)$ and $36(3 \cdot 12)$, then the third side has length $39 (3 \cdot 13)$.

Review the quadrants in which each trig function is positive and in which each trig function is negative.

After the students understand why the functions have different signs in different quadrants, the coordinate systems below may be useful.

Errors Students Make
In Example 1, $|x| = 3$. Since the terminal side is in quadrant 2, x is negative. Hence, $x = -3$. Students sometimes have difficulty with this idea.

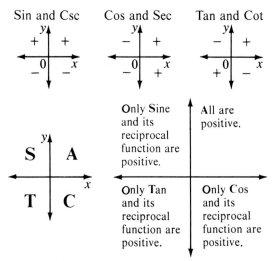

Cumulative Review
Graph each equation.
1. $(x - 1)^2 + (y + 2)^2 = 4$
2. $(x + 2)^2 + (y - 1)^2 = 16$
1. a circle whose center is at the point $(1, -2)$ and whose radius is 2
2. a circle whose center is at the point $(-2, 1)$ and whose radius is 4

17.8 Using Trigonometric Tables (page 477)

Vocabulary
trigonometric table, complementary or cofunction

Suggestions
Students are expected to read a trig table for any degree measure even though the trig tables only go from 0° to 45° in the left-hand column and from 45° to 90° in the right-hand column. Show students that corresponding measure in the left-hand/right-hand columns add to 90°. Also show that corresponding functions at the top of the table and at the bottom of the table are cofunctions.

Students are also expected to find the corresponding angular measure if its trig function value is given. Finally, the use of trigonometric tables to solve trigonometric equations is illustrated.

Errors Students Make
Difficulty occurs when students must read tables from bottom to top using the right-hand column. Some oral exercises may avoid such difficulty.

For Additional Chalkboard Work
Use the table to find each of the following.
1. sin 38°   2. cos 73°   3. tan 18°
4. cot 43°20′   5. sec 50°40′   6. csc 74°30′
7. sin 52°50′   8. cos 10°20′   9. cot 80°10′
Use the table to find u, $u < 90°$.
10. $\sin u = 0.1965$ 11. $\cos u = 0.3719$
12. $\tan u = 0.6577$ 13. $\cot u = 0.5280$
14. $\sec u = 1.2779$ 15. $\csc u = 1.1471$

Cumulative Review
Graph the following equations.
1. $\dfrac{(x + 1)^2}{9} + \dfrac{(y - 2)^2}{4} = 1$

2. $\dfrac{(x - 1)^2}{4} + \dfrac{(y + 2)^2}{16} = 1$

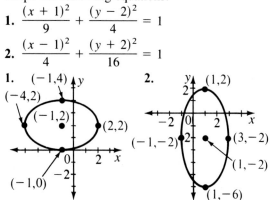

17.9   Linear Trigonometric Equations (page 481)

Vocabulary
linear trigonometric equations

Suggestions
Solving linear trigonometric equations is like solving algebraic equations with the additional steps of determining the reference measure and then the angle. Students should again be encouraged to make diagrams showing the reference angle in the indicated quadrant. Also remind students that they have not necessarily solved the equation after finding the reference angle but must still find the measure of the angle of rotation. Students should understand that, unlike finding one solution for linear algebraic equations, it is frequently necessary to find at least two solutions for linear trigonometric equations.

Errors Students Make
Remind students that both sin and cos must have values between or including ± 1. Also, students should be cautioned to observe the restrictions placed on θ.

Cumulative Review
Graph the following equations.

1. $\dfrac{(x + 1)^2}{16} - \dfrac{(y - 2)^2}{4} = 1$

2. $\dfrac{(x - 2)^2}{25} - \dfrac{(y + 1)^2}{9} = 1$

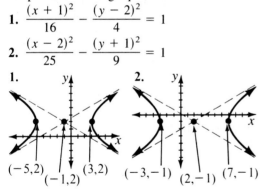

1. $(-5,2)$ $(-1,2)$ $(3,2)$

2. $(-3,-1)$ $(2,-1)$ $(7,-1)$

17.10   Interpolation with Trigonometry (page 483)

Vocabulary
trigonometric interpolation

Background
An alternate approach to interpolation that can be used with some more advanced students is to explain the theory of linear interpolation so that it applies to interpolation that is not linear. Trigonometric interpolation is not linear. Consider the idea of a slope in the study of linear interpolation. To find the sin 33°37′, for example, assume that the graph of the sin function is linear between the points $P(33°30')$, sin 33°30′ and $Q(33°40')$, sin 33°40′. Find the value of sin 33°37′ or (33°37′, y).

Since the slope of a line is the same between any points on the line, you get

$$\frac{y - \sin 33°30'}{33°37' - 33°30'} = \frac{\sin 33°40' - \sin 33°30'}{33°40' - 33°30'}.$$

Solve for y and get $y = \sin 33°37'$.

Suggestions
As hand-held calculators become more common, the need to interpolate becomes less. However, it is the feeling of the authors that students should understand the process and have some practice with interpolation.

Errors Students Make
To avoid errors in interpolation, have students set each problem up in the same manner. Students must then be careful with the signs. When they subtract the sin, tan, or sec of a measure, the sign is positive. When they subtract cos, cot or csc of a measure, the sign is negative. Examples 1 and 2 illustrate this.

Cumulative Review
Let $g(x) = -x^2 - 3x + 2$. Find each of the following function values.

1. $g(-3)$ 2. $g(0)$ 3. $g(a + b)$

1. 2   2. 2

3. $-a^2 - 2ab - b^2 - 3a - 3b + 2$

17.11 Trigonometry of a Right Angle (page 486)

Vocabulary
opposite side, adjacent side

Suggestions
Although some courses in trigonometry begin with the study of right triangles, right-triangle trigonometry is just a special case of trigonometry of an angle of rotation. Some of the work encountered here may be a review for some students.

Show students the relationship between the trigonometry of angles of rotation and the trigonometry of the right triangle. The reference triangles formed by an angle of rotation are right triangles.

Only acute angles are used in the trig of right triangles; one of the angles is a right angle and the other two are acute.

You may wish to include the secant and cosecant in this lesson.

$$\sec A = \frac{\text{hypotenuse}}{\text{adjacent}} = \frac{c}{b} \quad \csc A = \frac{\text{hypotenuse}}{\text{opposite}} = \frac{c}{a}$$

Example: For a $30° - 60°$ right triangle find sec 30°, csc 30°, sec 60°, and csc 60° (see Example 1).

$$\text{Sec } 30° = \frac{2}{\sqrt{3}} = \frac{2\sqrt{3}}{3}; \ \csc 30° = \frac{2}{1} = 2;$$

$$\sec 60° = \frac{2}{1}; \ \csc 60° = \frac{2}{\sqrt{3}} = \frac{2\sqrt{3}}{3}$$

For Additional Chalkboard Work
Evaluate and simplify. Rationalize all denominators.

1. $\dfrac{\sec 60° - \csc 60°}{\sec 45°}$ 2. $\dfrac{\csc 30° - \sec 45°}{\csc 60°}$

3. $\dfrac{\sec 45° - \sec 30°}{\csc 30°}$ 4. $\dfrac{\csc 45° - \csc 30°}{\sec 60°}$

Cumulative Review
If $f(x) = x^2 - 2$ and $g(x) = 2x - 1$, then find the following function values.

1. $f(g(2))$ 2. $g(f(-1))$ 3. $g(f(-a))$
1. 7   2. -3 3. $2a^2 - 5$

17.12 Using Trigonometry of a Right Angle (page 489)

Vocabulary
angle of depression, angle of elevation

Suggestions
For those students who have had some geometry, remind them that the measure of the angle of depression is equal to the measure of the angle of elevation because if two parallel lines are cut by a transversal, the measures of the alternate interior angles are equal. Help students set up problems to avoid dividing by a 4-place decimal. If students have calculators, then it makes no difference whether a student multiplies or divides by decimals.

Exercises 18 and 35 are useful exercises but not realistic. It is inconceivable that anyone would want to find the distance from a point directly below a plane to a ship to the nearest meter. Such exercises are used only to provide for right-triangular trigonometric calculation.

Errors Students Make
The most difficult task for students seems to be deciding which function to use. Have students draw a diagram and then list the measures that are given and those to be found.

You might also introduce the old mnemonic SOHCAHTOA to help students remember the functions:

$$\text{Sine} = \frac{\text{opposite}}{\text{hypotenuse}} \text{ is represented by SOH,}$$

and so on.

Cumulative Review
Draw the graph of each equation.
1. $3x - 2y = 8$ 2. $\frac{1}{2}x - \frac{3}{2}y = 6$
1. a straight line with a y-intercept of -4 and a slope of $\frac{3}{2}$
2. a straight line with a y-intercept of -4 and a slope of $\frac{1}{3}$

Computer Activities (page 494)
This program applies the angle conversions from degrees to radians so that the BASIC SIN function can be used. Exercise 5 also deals with angle measures.

18

Chapter and Lesson Commentaries

Chapter 18 Trigonometric Graphs and Identities

Chapter Objectives

To graph $y = \sin x$ and $y = \cos x$
To determine the amplitude and the period of the sine, cosine, tangent, and cotangent functions
To sketch graphs of $y = a \sin bx$, $y = a \cos bx$, $y = \tan x$, and $y = \cot x$, and to solve a system of trigonometric equations graphically
To prove trigonometric identities
To graph the inverses of the sin, cos, tan, and cot functions and to apply inverse function notation

Chapter Overview

This chapter presents the graphs of the sine, cosine, tangent, and cotangent as functions of degree measure and shows how the coefficients a and b in the function $y = a \sin bx$ control the amplitude and period of its graph. Trigonometric equations are solved both graphically and algebraically. The basic identities are presented and examples show how these can be used to prove more complex identities.

Special Features

18.1   Graphing $y = \sin x$ and $y = \cos x$ (page 497)

Vocabulary

amplitude, periodic function

Suggestions

Understanding the graphs of $y = \sin x$ and $y = \cos x$ is important because many of the properties of these functions can be observed. These properties can also be observed by using a unit circle.

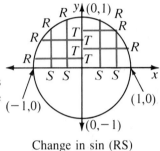

By observing the changes in the length of the vertical line segment, notice that the maximum value is 1, the minimum value is -1, and the period is $360°$. Also, notice:

Change in Angle	Change in sin (RS)
0° to 90°	increase from 0 to 1
90° to 180°	decrease from 1 to 0
180° to 270°	decrease from 0 to -1
270° to 360°	increase from -1 to 0

Similarly, by observing the changes in the length of RT, properties of the cosine can be observed.

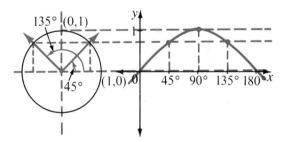

Errors Students Make

Labeling the x-axis sometimes causes difficulty. Have students label 90°, 180°, 270°, 360°, and the corresponding negative angles, then bisect the spaces to get the multiples of 45°.

Cumulative Review

Solve.

1. $35 + \dfrac{5x}{6} = \dfrac{1x}{6} + 29$;

2. $\dfrac{1}{2}(14n - 8) - (2 - 3n) = 4$ 1. -9;   2. 1

18.2 Determining Amplitude
(page 500)

Background

The amplitude of a periodic function is often defined as *one half* of the *absolute* value of the *difference* of the maximum and minimum function values, if such values exist. This definition is essential if the graph of the function is translated so that the absolute value of the maximum is *not* the same as the absolute value of the minimum.

Suggestions

In this lesson, students will learn how a change in amplitude affects the graph of $y = \sin x$, or $y = \cos x$. When $\sin x$ or $\cos x$ is multiplied by a nonzero constant, that is, when $y = a \sin x$, or $y = a \cos x$, there will be either a *vertical* "stretching" or "shrinking" of the function $y = \sin x$, or $y = \cos x$, for each $a \neq 1$. Specifically:

1. When $a > 1$, there is a vertical "stretching" of the function $y = \sin x$, or $y = \cos x$.
2. When $0 < a < 1$, there is a vertical "shrinking" of the function $y = \sin x$, or $y = \cos x$.
3. When $a < 0$, there is a reflection of the function $y = \sin x$, or $y = \cos x$, across the x-axis.

Having students verbalize these properties will save much time and effort when they sketch the graphs, as assigned in the exercise set.

Errors Students Make

Students who always begin by constructing a table of values to graph a sine, or cosine function in which the amplitude has been altered will have difficulty. Students should have a general understanding of how the change in amplitude will affect the appearance of the graph prior to graphing the function. To avoid problems, provide drill, using the above discussion.

Cumulative Review

Solve each equation.
1. $3.2(2x - 0.3) = 1.3x + 9.24$;
2. $|3x + 7| = 10$
1. 2;   2. 1, $-\frac{17}{3}$

18.3 Determining Period
(page 503)

Suggestions

In this lesson, students will learn how a change in period affects the graph of $y = \sin x$, or $y = \cos x$. When the abscissa, x, is multiplied by a nonzero constant, that is, when $y = \sin bx$, or $y - \cos bx$, there is a *horizontal* "stretching" or "shrinking" of the function $y = \sin x$, or $y = \cos x$. Specifically:

1. When $b > 1$, there is a horizontal "shrinking" of the function $y = \sin x$, or $y = \cos x$.
2. When $0 < b < 1$, there is a horizontal "stretching" of the function $y = \sin x$, or $y = \cos x$.
3. When $b < 0$, there is a reflection across the x-axis for the function $y = \sin x$ and there is a reflection across the y-axis for the function $y = \cos x$.

Errors Students Make

Students sometimes do not have a general understanding of how the change in period will affect the appearance of the graph prior to graphing the function. To avoid problems, provide drill, using the above discussion.

Enrichment

Suppose $h(x) = f(ax)$. Describe the graph as: shrinking, stretching, a reflection, a combination of these, for the given values of a.
1. $\frac{1}{3}$ 2. -2 3. 3   4. $\frac{-1}{2}$ 5. -3
1. stretching;   2. a reflection and shrinking;
3. shrinking;   4. a reflection and stretching;
5. a reflection and shrinking

Cumulative Review

Solve each equation.
1. $2^{2x - 4} = 64$ 2. $6x^2 + 7x = 3$
1. 5;   2. $\frac{1}{3}, \frac{-3}{2}$

18.4 Change of Period and Amplitude (page 506)

Background
The concepts of Lessons 18.2 and 18.3 are combined in this lesson. As a result of multiplying both the amplitude and the period by nonzero constants, a vertical and a horizontal "stretching," or "shrinking," can occur simultaneously.

Suggestions
Students should be able to discuss how the graphs of $y = a \sin bx$ and $y = a \cos bx$ change for different values of a and b. As preparation for this, you may wish to compare the graphs of the trigonometric functions with the graphs of algebraic equations. A good topic of discussion is, "How does a change in a for a family of parabolas of the form $y = ax^2$ affect the shape of the graph of the basic function $y = x^2$?"

Graphing $y = a \sin bx$ and $y = a \cos bx$ by first constructing a table of values is very tedious. Encourage more advanced students to sketch the graphs by determining key values mentally from the graph of the basic function, as shown below.

Key Values	$y = \cos x$	$y = \frac{1}{2}\cos 2x$
x-intercepts at	90°, 270°	45°, 135°
maximum at	0°, 360°	0°, 180°
minimum at	180°	90°
maximum	1	$\frac{1}{2}$
minimum	-1	$\frac{-1}{2}$

Errors Students Make
Labeling the axes and determining where the graph will cross the axes causes difficulty for some students. If students do not set up a table of values to lessen this difficulty, they should determine maximum points, minimum points, x-intercepts, and y-intercepts before sketching the graph.

Cumulative Review
Solve. Graph the solutions on a number line.
1. $3(2x - 1) \leq 3x + 6$ 2. $|n - 5| \leq 7$
1. $x \leq 3$ 2. $-2 \leq n \leq 12$

18.5 Graphing $y = \tan x$ and $y = \cot x$ (page 509)

Suggestions
Students should realize that the functions *tangent* and *cotangent* are reciprocals of each other, that is, $\tan x = \dfrac{1}{\cot x}$ and $\cot x = \dfrac{1}{\tan x}$. Therefore,
1. whenever the cotangent is positive, the tangent is positive; and
2. whenever the cotangent increases, the tangent decreases.

Use the graphs of $y = \tan x$ and $y = \cot x$ on pages 509 and 510, respectively, to emphasize that:
1. the graph of $y = \tan x$ is asymptotic to the vertical lines through $-90°$ and $90°$; the graph of $y = \cot x$ is asymptotic to the vertical lines through 0° and 180°;
2. the graph of $y = \tan x$ passes through $(0, 0)$ and the graph of $y = \cot x$ passes through $(90, 0)$;
3. the period for both graphs is 180° and the graphs of $y = \tan x$ and $y = \cot x$ repeat this cycle every 180°;
4. neither function has a maximum point and therefore neither has an amplitude; and
5. the tangent function always increases while the cotangent function always decreases.

Encourage students to sketch graphs of the tangent and cotangent by plotting key points. These points can be found by substituting 0°, 45°, 90°, $-45°$, and $-90°$ for x in the definitions $\tan x = \dfrac{\sin x}{\cos x}$ and $\cot x = \dfrac{\cos x}{\sin x}$. For example, if $x = 45°$, then $\tan 45° = \dfrac{\sin 45°}{\cos 45°} = 1$

and $\cot 45° = 1$.

Errors Students Make
Errors will be avoided if students lightly draw the vertical lines that will serve as asymptotes and find the x-intercepts before they sketch the graphs of the tangent and cotangent functions.

Cumulative Review
Find p in dollars if $A = \$5,350$, $r = 12.5\%$, and $t = 7$ yr. Use the formula $A = p + prt$. $\$2,853$.

18.6 Finding Logarithms of Trigonometric Functions (page 512)

Background
If $0° < x < 90°$, then $0 < \sin x < 1$ and $0 < \cos x < 1$

Therefore, for $0° < x < 90°$, log sin x and log cos x will have negative characteristics. Similarly, for $0° < x < 45°$, log tan x will have a negative characteristic and for $45° < x < 90°$, log cot x will have a negative characteristic.

Suggestions
Review the basic notions of logarithms, as stated on page 512. Point out that the tables of logarithms of trigonometric functions were formed by combining the tables of trigonometric functions and the tables of common logarithms.

Errors Students Make
Students sometimes have difficulty when interpolating is involved. Encouraging them to stay with a single format will help to avoid confusion. Students also have difficulty with signs. To avoid confusion, encourage students to set up the entire problem before they use the tables.

For Additional Chalkboard Work
Use logarithms to find each value.

1. $\dfrac{(32.6)^3 \csc 48°30'}{\sec 18°40'}$ 2. $\dfrac{\sqrt{48.3 \sec 50°42'}}{(\csc 37°58')^3}$

1. $\dfrac{(32.6)^3 \dfrac{1}{\sin 48°30'}}{\dfrac{1}{\cos 18°40'}}$; 43,800

2. $\dfrac{\sqrt{\dfrac{48.3}{\cos 50°42'}}}{\dfrac{1}{(\sin 37°58')^3}}$; 2.03

Cumulative Review
Simplify.

1. $-6a^3b^5c^2 \cdot 5a^2b^2c^5$ 2. $-10(3x^5y^7)^4$

3. $\dfrac{5n - 15}{2n^2 - 12n + 18}$

1. $-30a^5b^7c^7$ 2. $-810x^{20}y^{28}$ 3. $\dfrac{5}{2(n-3)}$

18.7 Quadratic Trigonometric Equations (page 515)

Vocabulary
quadratic trigonometric equations

Background
The method of completing the square can be used with quadratic trigonometric equations.

$2 \sin^2 \theta - 6 \sin \theta - 1 = 0$

$2\left(\sin^2 \theta - 3 \sin \theta + \dfrac{(3)^2}{(2)}\right) = 1 + \dfrac{9}{2}$

$\left(\sin \theta - \dfrac{3}{2}\right)^2 = \dfrac{11}{4}$

$\sin \theta - \dfrac{3}{2} = \pm \dfrac{1}{2}\sqrt{11}$

$\sin \theta = \dfrac{3}{2} \pm \dfrac{1}{2}\sqrt{11}$, or $\dfrac{3 \pm \sqrt{11}}{2}$

Since $-1 \le \sin \theta \le 1$, reject $\dfrac{3 + \sqrt{11}}{2}$.

Suggestions
You may wish to review the methods for solving quadratic algebraic equations, such as those below, which are similar to the trigonometric equations in this lesson.

1. $x^2 = 16$ 2. $x^2 - 4 = 0$ 3. $x^2 - 3x = 0$
4. $x^2 - 2x + 1 = 0$ 5. $x^2 + 5x - 3 = 0$
1. $\pm\sqrt{16}$; ± 4 2. $(x - 2)(x + 2)$; 2, -2
3. $x(x - 3)$; 0, 3   4. $(x - 1)^2$; 1
5. $\dfrac{-5 \pm \sqrt{25 + 12}}{2}$; $\dfrac{-5 \pm \sqrt{37}}{2}$

Emphasize that while a quadratic algebraic equation usually yields two solutions, a quadratic trigonometric equation may yield four solutions if θ is between $0°$ and $360°$.

Errors Students Make
Students sometimes find the reference angle and then stop. Remind them that they must determine all possible quadrants in which the reference angle may be and include all measures as solutions.

Cumulative Review
Multiply.

1. $(3a^2 - 2)(4a^2 + 1)$ 2. $2(2x - 3)(3x + 2)$
3. $(8x^2 - 1)(8x^2 + 1)$
1. $12a^4 - 5a^2 - 2$
2. $12x^2 - 10x - 12$ 3. $64x^4 - 1$

18.8 Basic Trigonometric Identities (page 518)

Background
Reciprocal identities, quotient identities, and Pythagorean identities are verified for the general case, then for particular degree measures.

Suggestions
You can use a unit circle to show how the identities got their names. For example,

1. $\sin x = \dfrac{1}{\csc x}$ is called a *reciprocal identity*

   because $\sin x$, $\dfrac{y}{r}$, and $\csc x$, $\dfrac{r}{y}$ are reciprocals;

2. $\tan x = \dfrac{\sin x}{\cos x}$ is called a *quotient identity*

   because $\dfrac{\sin x}{\cos x} = \dfrac{y}{r} \div \dfrac{x}{r} = \dfrac{y}{x} = \tan x$; and

3. $\cos^2 x + \sin^2 x = 1$ is called a *Pythagorean identity* because $x^2 + y^2 = 1$.

   Students should memorize the identities. A line representation of the six trigonometric functions is useful for this purpose.

$$\sin^2 \theta + \cos^2 \theta = 1$$
$$\tan^2 \theta + 1 = \sec^2 \theta$$
$$\cot^2 \theta + 1 = \csc^2 \theta$$
$$\tan \theta = \frac{\sin \theta}{\cos \theta}$$
$$\cot \theta = \frac{\cos \theta}{\sin \theta}$$
$$\sec \theta = \frac{1}{\cos \theta}$$
$$\csc \theta = \frac{1}{\sin \theta}$$

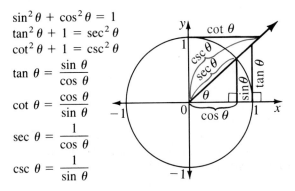

Errors Students Make
One source of error occurs when students do not understand that $\sin^2 \theta = (\sin \theta)^2$. Simplifying $(\sin \theta)^2 + (\cos \theta)^2$ for $\theta = 150°$ will help. Note that $\left(\dfrac{1}{2}\right)^2 + \left(-\dfrac{\sqrt{3}}{2}\right)^2 = \dfrac{1}{4} + \dfrac{3}{4} = 1$, or $\sin^2 \theta + \cos^2 \theta = 1$.

Cumulative Review
Simplify.

1. $(3a + 4b)^2$ **2.** $\dfrac{2a + 10}{4a - 12} \cdot \dfrac{a^2 - 9}{a^2 + 7a + 10}$

1. $9a^2 + 24ab + 16b^2$ 2. $\dfrac{a + 3}{2(a + 2)}$

18.9 Proving Trigonometric Identities (page 521)

Background
A common misconception in proving trigonometric identities, or identities in general, is to write a series of identities until both members are the same. In doing so, restrictions may be introduced, but not recorded. For example, when $\dfrac{\sin x}{\cos x}$ replaces $\tan x$, the restriction $\cos x \neq 0$ is introduced. When one member simplifies into the other, all restrictions must be considered.

Manipulating one member to arrive at the second does not prove an identity. To prove that the given expressions are really identical, one should start with the conclusion and reverse the process until arriving at the given expressions. Thus, one would proceed as follows in Example 1:

$$\tan x = \tan x = \frac{\sin x}{\cos x} = \frac{\dfrac{1}{\csc x}}{\dfrac{1}{\sec x}} = \frac{\sec x}{\csc x}.$$

Suggestions
In mathematics it is often important to know when two expressions are identical. Therefore, in this lesson students will be given opportunities to determine if certain trigonometric expressions are identical.

Point out that it is often helpful to use known identities for one member to arrive at the other member in verifying two trigonometric expressions. Caution students that they must work on each side separately because they have not yet proved that the equality holds.

Errors Students Make
There is no well-defined method that will eliminate all errors. Whenever students have a problem with proving a trigonometric identity, they should try to express each side of the identity in terms of sine and cosine.

Cumulative Review
Factor.
1. $8a^2 + 22a + 5$ **2.** $6x^4 + 7x^2 - 3$
3. $25a^2 - 9b^2$
1. $(4a + 1)(2a + 5)$ 2. $(2x^2 + 3)(3x^2 - 1)$
3. $(5a + 3b)(5a - 3b)$

18.10   Radian Measure
(page 523)

Vocabulary
radian

Background
The radian measure of an angle of rotation, θ, is the ratio of the distance, s, on the circumference of a circle to the length of a radius, r, of the circle. Thus, $\theta = \frac{s}{r}$ and when $s = r$, $\theta = 1$ radian. Note that $\frac{s}{r}$ is dimensionless because s and r are both measured in the same unit. It is not necessary, then, to use the word *radian* to express angular rotations in radians.

This simple conversion proportion can be used to change from one system of angular measure to the other:

$$\text{other: } \frac{\text{radian measure}}{\pi} = \frac{\text{degree measure}}{180°}$$

Suggestions
Explain that radian measure is a real number and that this type of angular measure will be used almost exclusively in advanced mathematics. Point out that students will use the new system to review many concepts which they already learned for degree measures. To save time and to avoid errors, students should memorize some basic conversions, such as the following.

0°	30°	45°	60°	90°	180°	270°	360°
$\updownarrow$	$\updownarrow$	$\updownarrow$	$\updownarrow$	$\updownarrow$	$\updownarrow$	$\updownarrow$	$\updownarrow$
0	$\frac{\pi}{6}$	$\frac{\pi}{4}$	$\frac{\pi}{3}$	$\frac{\pi}{2}$	π	$\frac{3\pi}{2}$	2π

Additional Exercises
Evaluate each of the following.

1. $\dfrac{\cos \frac{\pi}{6} - \sin \frac{\pi}{6}}{\tan \frac{\pi}{4}}$

2. $\dfrac{\sin \frac{\pi}{4} + \cos \frac{\pi}{4}}{\cot \frac{\pi}{3}}$

1. 0.366   2. 2.451

Cumulative Review
Factor completely.
1. $6y^2 + 21y - 45$ 2. $6a^3 - 7a^2 - 5a$
1. $3(y + 5)(2y - 3)$
2. $a(2a + 1)(3a - 5)$

18.11   Applying Radian Measure
(page 526)

Background
This lesson serves as a good review of many of the concepts developed earlier. Using radian measure, students will get additional practice in sketching graphs of trigonometric functions whose periods and amplitudes have been altered and in solving trigonometric equations.

Suggestions
Although this lesson may serve as a review, you should emphasize how important the lesson really is. Most advanced mathematics courses do not introduce degree measure until late because those courses are defined for real numbers, and radian measure, not degree measure.

As with degree measure, you may wish to have some students graph a circular function by referring to a unit circle. This method is shown below for $\sin \theta$. Note that $\sin \theta = y$ and $\cos \theta = x$; therefore, vertical segments represent the values of $\sin \theta$.

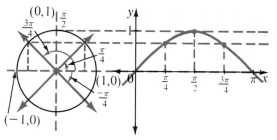

Errors Students Make
Problems may occur when students label the x-axis, because most students must translate from radian measure to degree measure. To avoid this, you may wish to label the x-axis in degrees, then have students write the corresponding radian measure beneath each degree measure.

Cumulative Review
Solve.
The greater of two numbers is 11 less than 3 times the smaller number. Twenty one less than 3 times the greater number is equal to 6 times the smaller number. Find both numbers.
18 and 43

18.12 Inverses of Trigonometric Functions (page 529)

Vocabulary

inverse of a trigonometric function, inverse trigonometric function, principal values

Background

Recall that if a function is strictly increasing or strictly decreasing in an interval, then the inverse of the function is an inverse function in that interval. The sine function is strictly increasing in the interval $\left[-\frac{\pi}{2}, \frac{\pi}{2} \right]$; therefore, its inverse is an inverse function in that interval. Similarly, the inverses of the cosine and tangent functions are inverse functions in the intervals $[0, \pi]$ and $\left[-\frac{\pi}{2}, \frac{\pi}{2} \right]$, respectively. Note that each of the three functions has more than one interval where it is strictly increasing, or strictly decreasing, but the interval closest to the orgin is used.

Suggestions

Emphasize that the inverses of the trigonometric functions are *not* functions. However, it is possible to make the inverses functions by restricting their range to values of the range called *principal values*. Using only part of the graph of an inverse of a trigonometric function is sufficient because to define a function, it is necessary to restrict only one choice for y for each x in the domain. Use the graph to help students visualize this discussion.

Cumulative Review

Side a of a triangle is $1\frac{1}{2}$ times as long as side b. Side c is 5 cm longer than side a. The perimeter of the triangle is 53 cm. Find a, b, and c.
18 cm, 12 cm, 23 cm

Computer Activities

This program combines the graphing and computation for trigonometric function. The Student can use the values found to graph the function. Advanced students can write a program that both calculates the values and prints a graph. Exercise 6 is an interesting application of the Sin function.

19
Chapter and Lesson Commentaries

Chapter 19 Trigonometric Laws and Formulas

Chapter Objectives

To use the Law of Cosines to find the length of a side or the degree measure of an angle of a triangle

To use the formula $K = \frac{1}{2} ab \sin C$ to find the area of a triangle or, given the area, find an unknown in the formula

To apply the Law of Sines to find the length of a side or the degree measure of an angle of a triangle

To investigate the "Ambiguous Case" in determining a triangle

To derive and apply the formulas for
sin $(A + B)$ and sin $2A$;
cos $(A + B)$ and cos $2A$; and
tan $(A + B)$ and tan $2A$

To derive and apply the formulas for sine, cosine and tangent of half-angles

Chapter Overview

The first half of this chapter deals with the applications of the trigonometric relations in triangles. It attempts to give students practice in manipulating identities and formulas to gain information about a triangle.

It may be a good idea to present a particular problem to the students, have them consider it, and then show how it can be solved. This may be more motivating than deriving the formula and plugging in given values. Ask the students if it is possible to find the area of a triangle given only the measures of two sides and the included angle.

Chapter Overview (cont).

Give them a specific example and some time to think about it. Some may come to the conclusion that it is impossible while others may be on their way to deriving the formula themselves. Ask the students, before doing Lesson 19.1, to find the third side of a triangle given two sides and the included angle, or to find the measure of an angle given three sides of a triangle. Again, give a specific example and ample time for consideration. Then, derive the formula for the Law of Cosines and show how it can be used to solve the problems.

If two angles and a side of a triangle are known, can the third angle be found? That is easy, but can the lengths of the other two sides also be found? This problem will lead into the formula for the Law of Sines.

Students may also find the Ambiguous Case more interesting if the problem is presented first. Have students try to construct an "unconstructable triangle" as a lead-in to the lesson on the Ambiguous Case.

The second half of the chapter derives and applies the formulas for the sine, cosine and tangent of the sum of two angles, double-angles and half-angles. The last section gives the student an opportunity to draw on his knowledge of trigonometric relations and formulas to solve identities. Proving identities is an excellent way for students to exercise independent thinking based on logic and knowledge of algebra.

Special Features

19.1   Law of Cosines   (page 539)

Vocabulary
Law of Cosines

Suggestions
The Law of Cosines is used to find the measure of a side when the measures of two sides and the included angle are known. The Law of Cosines is a generalization of the Pythagorean theorem or the Pythagorean theorem is a special case of the Law of Cosines.

Let $m\angle A = 90°$, then for $a^2 = b^2 + c^2 - 2bc \cos A$, $a^2 = b^2 + c^2 - 2bc \cos 90°$ or $a^2 = b^2 + c^2$ since $\cos 90° = 0$.

Background
The following is a coordinate proof of the Law of Cosines and serves as a good alternative to the one found on Page 538.

$$C = PQ =$$
$$\sqrt{(a \cos \theta - b \cos \alpha)^2 + (a \sin \theta - b \sin \alpha)^2}$$
$$C^2 = a^2 \cos^2 \theta - 2ab \cos \theta \cos \alpha + b^2 \cos^2 \alpha + a^2 \sin^2 \theta - 2ab \sin \theta \sin \alpha + b^2 \sin^2 \alpha$$
$$= a^2(\cos^2 \theta + \sin^2 \theta) + b^2(\cos^2 \alpha + \sin^2 \alpha) - 2ab(\cos \theta \cos \alpha + \sin \theta \sin \alpha) \, c^2 = a^2 + b^2 - 2ab \cos (\alpha - \theta), \text{ but } \alpha - \theta \text{ is angle } C$$
$$c^2 = a^2 + b^2 - 2ab \cos C.$$

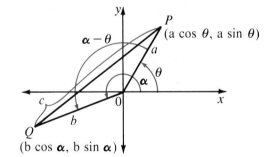

Errors Students Make
Students might make errors in computing the square root. Let them use a table of values, a calculator, or review how to find square roots.

Cumulative Review
Solve each equation for x.

1. $a(2x + b) = c(x + b)$ **2.** $\dfrac{4}{a} = \dfrac{3}{b} + \dfrac{2}{x}$

1. $\dfrac{bc - ab}{2a - c}$ 2. $\dfrac{2ab}{4b - 3a}$

19.2 Using the Law of Cosines to Find Angle Measures (page 542)

Suggestions
This short lesson deals with finding the measure of an angle using the Law of Cosines. To do so, first solve for the cosine of the angle, then use trigonometric tables to find the measure of the angle. Remind students that the longest side of a triangle is opposite the greatest angle, and the smallest side is opposite the smallest angle.

For Additional Chalkboard Work
Have students *set up* the formula for finding the measure of $\angle A$, $\angle B$ and $\angle C$. Do not have them solve.

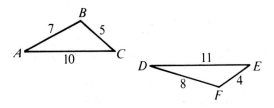

Do the same for $\angle D$, $\angle E$ and $\angle F$.

Errors Students Make
Determining which formula to use from the given data may cause some problems. To lessen the chance of error, provide some chalkboard drill.

Cumulative Review
Simplify each expression.

1. $(-2a^{-3}b^2)^{-4}$ **2.** $\dfrac{-28x^{-5}y^2}{7x^2y^{-5}}$ **3.** $-2(a^4b^{-6})^{-4}$

1. $\dfrac{a^{12}}{16b^8}$ 2. $\dfrac{-4y^7}{x^7}$ 3. $\dfrac{-2b^{24}}{a^{16}}$

19.3 Area of a Triangle (page 544)

Suggestions
A formula for finding the area of a triangle given the measures of two sides and the included angle is developed. The formulas presented in this lesson will be used to derive the Law of Sines as well as to derive the formulas for $\sin (A + B)$.

An acute triangle was used to derive the formulas for the area of a triangle. Consider now an obtuse triangle.

$\sin (180° - C) = \dfrac{h}{a}$
$h = a \sin (180° - C)$
but $\sin (180° - C) = \sin C$
So, $h = a \sin C$
but area of $\triangle ABC = \frac{1}{2} bh$
So, area of $\triangle ABC = \frac{1}{2} ba \sin C$ or $\frac{1}{2} ab \sin C$.

Background
A formula for finding the area of a triangle given the measures of three sides of a triangle is given by $A = \sqrt{s(s - a)(s - b)(s - c)}$ where $s = \frac{1}{2}(a + b + c)$. This formula is known as *Hero's Formula*. Find the area of triangle ABC if $a = 40$, $b = 60$, and $c = 50$.

$A = \sqrt{75(75 - 40)(75 - 60)(75 - 50)}$
$\quad = \sqrt{75(35)(15)(25)}$ $S = \frac{1}{2}(40 + 60 + 50)$
$\quad = 992.2$ $= 75$

For Additional Chalkboard Work
Find the area of each of the given triangles.
1. $a = 46$, $b = 53$, $c = 58$
2. $a = 9.6$, $b = 10.3$, $c = 15.3$
3. $a = 70$, $b = 80$, $c = 90$
4. $a = 123.5$, $b = 79.6$, $c = 100.5$

Errors Students Make
Not knowing which formula to use may cause some difficulty. Some oral drill could reduce error.

Cumulative Review
Evaluate the following if $a = -1$, $b = 2$.

1. $\dfrac{3a^2(2a)^2}{(a^3 + 4)^2}$ **2.** $((ab)^2 - ab^2 + a^2b)^{-2}$

1. $\dfrac{4}{3}$ 2. $\dfrac{1}{100}$

19.4 Law of Sines (page 546)

Vocabulary
Law of Sines

Background
Place $\triangle ABC$ so that vertex A is at the origin and $\overline{BC} \parallel$ to the x-axis as shown.

Since $\overline{BC} \parallel x$-axis, $\angle 1 \cong \angle 2$, and $b \sin (A + B) = c \sin B$

$A + B + C = 180°$

$A + B = 180° - C$

$b \sin (180° - C) = c \sin B$

$\dfrac{c}{\sin C} = \dfrac{b}{\sin B}$ or $\dfrac{\sin C}{c} = \dfrac{\sin B}{b}$.

[b cos (A+B), b sin (A+B)]

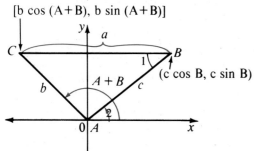

Suggestions
The Law of Sines is a useful proportion for solving triangles when the measures of two angles and a side opposite one of them are given, or when two sides and an angle opposite one of them are given.

While it is possible to solve oblique triangles by drawing altitudes and forming right triangles, it is easier to solve such triangles using the Law of Sines.

It is possible to solve triangles for either sides or angles using the Law of Sines.

Logarithms can be used to solve the derived proportion.

Errors Students Make
At times the computation becomes tedious. Logarithms and calculators will help reduce error.

Cumulative Review
Evaluate each of the following.
1. $2n^2 - 12n + 7$ if $n = 2$
2. $3n^3 - 6n^2 + 5n - 8$ if $n = -2$

1. -9 2. -66

T–104

19.5 The Ambiguous Case (page 549)

Vocabulary
Ambiguous Case

Suggestions
Students may wish to create a physical model that demonstrates the Ambiguous Case. Although students can memorize all the rules of the Ambiguous Case, it seems more appropriate to have them understand the concepts and determine the number of constructable triangles directly from the given conditions.

Solving triangles given two sides and the angle opposite one of them is known as the Ambiguous Case. In studying the Ambiguous Case, students should realize that all cases can be tested by inspection except the case in which the angle is acute and the opposite side is less than the other given side. This is the only time the opposite side must be compared with the length of the altitude, h, that is drawn to the third side.

Errors Students Make
When students can't determine the number of triangles that can be constructed, they should sketch figures and label the parts.

Cumulative Review
Simplify each expression.
1. $-3a^2 b \sqrt{32a^5 b^7 c^4}$
2. $\sqrt{4a^3 b^3} + a \sqrt{9ab^3} - ab \sqrt{ab}$

1. $-12a^4 b^4 c^2 \sqrt{2ab}$
2. $4ab \sqrt{ab}$

19.6 Sin $(A \pm B)$ and Sin $2A$
(page 552)

Vocabulary
sum of two angles, double-angle, difference of two angles

Background
You may wish to derive the formula for $\cos (A - B) = \cos A \cos B + \sin A \sin B$ first, and then use it to derive the formula for $\sin (A + B)$.

$$\sin (A + B) = \cos \left[\frac{\pi}{2} - (A + B) \right]$$
$$= \cos \left[\left(\frac{\pi}{2} - A \right) - B \right]$$
$$= \cos (\pi - A) \cos B +$$
$$\sin \left(\frac{\pi}{2} - A \right) \sin B$$
$$\sin (A + B) = \sin A \cos B + \cos A \sin B$$

Suggestions
The $\sin (A + B)$ is derived from using the three formulas for finding the area of a triangle. However, the derivation shown for $\sin (A + B)$ is valid only if $x + y < 180°$. Nevertheless, a rigorous proof of the more general case can be developed using the appropriate reduction formulas. The formula for $\sin (A + B)$ is basic to the development of the other sum and difference formulas. The formula for $\sin 2A$ is derived for $\sin (A + B)$, where $A = B$.
To derive $\sin (A - B)$, rewrite $A - B = A + (-B)$ and use $\sin [A + (-B)]$.
To derive $\sin 2A$, rewrite $2A = A + A$ and use $\sin (A + A)$.

For Additional Chalkboard Work
Show $\sin (x + 2\pi)$ is periodic with a period of 2π. That is, show $\sin (x + 2\pi) = \sin x$.
$\sin (x + 2\pi) = \sin x \cos 2\pi + \cos x \sin 2\pi$
$$= \sin x (1) + \cos x (0).$$
So, $\sin (x + 2\pi) = \sin x$.

Cumulative Review
Write an equation of each circle whose center is at the origin with the given radius.
1. 12   **2.** 15   **3.** 20
1. $x^2 + y^2 = 144$ 2. $x^2 + y^2 = 225$
3. $x^2 + y^2 = 400$

19.7 cos $(A \pm B)$ and cos $2A$
(page 556)

Vocabulary
sum of two angles, double-angle

Background
Start with identity $\cos 2A = 1 - 2 \sin^2 A$ and solve for $\sin^2 A$.

$$2 \sin^2 A = 1 - \cos 2A \text{ or}$$
$$\sin^2 A = \frac{1 - \cos 2A}{2}$$

Similarly, $\cos 2A = 2 \cos^2 A - 1$
$$2 \cos^2 A = 1 + \cos 2A$$
$$\cos^2 A = \frac{1 + \cos 2A}{2}.$$

The identities for $\sin^2 A$ and $\cos^2 A$ are defined in terms of $\cos 2A$. These forms are very useful and important in calculus since they allow us to integrate easily the $\sin^2 A$ and $\cos^2 A$ functions.

Suggestions
The cos $(A + B)$ and cos $2A$ formulas are easily derived from the results of the previous lesson. Students should be encouraged to derive them.
To derive $\cos (A + B)$, use $\sin [90° - (A + B)]$ and expand. Remind students that $\cos \theta = \sin (90° - \theta)$.
To derive $\cos (A - B)$, rewrite $A - B = A + (-B)$ and use $\cos (A + B)$.
To derive cos $2A$, rewrite $2A$ as $A + A$ and use $\cos (A + A)$.
Students are expected to be familiar with all three cases for cos $2A$.
Show cos $(1 + 2\pi)$ is periodic with a period of 2π. That is, show $\sin (x + 2\pi) = \sin x$.
$\cos (x + 2\pi) = \cos x \cos 2\pi - \sin x \sin 2\pi$
$$= \cos x (1) \quad - \sin x (0)$$
$$= \cos x$$
So, $\cos (x + 2\pi) = \cos x$.

Cumulative Review
Identify each conic section whose equation is given.
1. $\frac{x^2}{25} - \frac{y^2}{9} = 1$ **2.** $\frac{x^2}{15} + \frac{y^2}{15} = 1$
3. $5x^2 + 3y^2 = 36$ **4.** $xy = -3$
1. hyperbola   2. circle   3. ellipse
4. hyperbola

19.8 Tan $(A \pm B)$ and Tan $2A$ (page 560)

Suggestions

If time permits, develop $\cot (A + B)$ and $\cot 2A$.

$$\cot (A + B) = \frac{\cos (A + B)}{\sin (A + B)}$$

$$= \frac{\cos A \cos B - \sin A \sin B}{\sin A \cos B + \cos A \sin B}$$

$$= \frac{\dfrac{\cos A \cos B}{\sin A \sin B} - \dfrac{\cos A \sin B}{\sin A \sin B}}{\dfrac{\sin A \cos B}{\sin A \sin B} + \dfrac{\cos A \sin B}{\sin A \sin B}}$$

$$= \frac{\cot A \cot B - 1}{\cot B + \cot A}$$

Thus, $\cot (2A) = \dfrac{\cot A \cot A - 1}{\cot A + \cot A} = \dfrac{\cot^2 A - 1}{2 \cot A}$.

Replace B by $(-B)$ in derivation of $\cot (A + B)$ above to find

$$\cot (A - B) = \frac{\cot A \cot B + 1}{\cot B - \cot A}.$$

For Additional Chalkboard Work

1. Show $\tan (x + \pi)$ is periodic with a period of π.

$$\tan (x + \pi) = \frac{\tan x + \tan \pi}{1 - \tan x \tan \pi} = \frac{\tan x + 0}{1 - \tan x(0)}$$
$$= \tan x$$

Find the value of each. Use special angles and the formula for $\cot (A + B)$ or $\cot (A - B)$.

2. $\cot 105°$ **3.** $\cot 15°$ **4.** $\cot 135°$
5. $\cot 120°$ **6.** $\cot 375°$

Find $\tan (A + B)$ for each of the following.

7. $\cot A = \frac{4}{3}$ and $\cot B = \frac{5}{6}$
8. $\cot A = -\sqrt{3}$ and $\cot B = \frac{\sqrt{2}}{2}$

Errors Students Make

Students may need to review methods of rationalizing the denominator.

Cumulative Review

Find the coordinates of the center of each circle and the radius.

1. $x^2 + 6x + y^2 + 4y = -12$
2. $x^2 + y^2 - 4x + 8y = -11$
1. $(-3, -2)$, $r = 1$ 2. $(2, -4)$, $r = 3$

19.9 Half-Angle Formulas (page 563)

Vocabulary

sin of half an angle, cos of half an angle, tan of half an angle

Suggestions

Half-angle formulas are used to find trigonometric values of certain angular measures such as tan 15° or sin 75°.

To derive $\sin \frac{A}{2}$, start with the identity $\cos 2A = 1 - 2 \sin^2 A$, replace A by $\frac{x}{2}$ and solve for $\sin \frac{x}{2}$.

To derive $\cos \frac{A}{2}$, start with the identity $\cos 2A = 2 \cos^2 A - 1$, replace A by $\frac{x}{2}$ and solve for $\cos \frac{x}{2}$.

To derive $\tan \frac{x}{2}$, start with the identity

$$\tan \frac{x}{2} = \frac{\sin \frac{x}{2}}{\cos \frac{x}{2}}$$ and substitute for $\sin \frac{x}{2}$ and $\cos \frac{x}{2}$.

If time permits derive the formula for $\cot \frac{x}{2}$. Start with

$$\cot \frac{x}{2} = \frac{\cos \frac{x}{2}}{\sin \frac{x}{2}}$$

$$= \frac{\pm \sqrt{\dfrac{1 + \cos x}{2}}}{\pm \sqrt{\dfrac{1 - \cos x}{2}}} = \pm \sqrt{\frac{1 + \cos x}{2} \cdot \frac{2}{1 - \cos x}}$$

This is asked in Exercise 33.

Errors Students Make

Determining the quadrant for $\frac{x}{2}$, given the quadrant of x, may cause some difficulty, since the sign of the trig function of an angle may not be the same sign of the trig function of a half-angle.

For example, $\tan x > 0$ if $180° \leq x \leq 220°$ but $\tan \frac{x}{2} < 0$ since $90° \leq \frac{x}{2} \leq 135°$.

Cumulative Review

Solve algebraically.

1. $y = x^2 + 3x - 13$ **2.** $x^2 + y^2 = 10$
    $2x - 3y = 13$ $5x + 2y = -13$
1. $(2, -3)$ 2. $(-3, 1)$

19.10 Double- and Half-Angle Identities (page 566)

Vocabulary
double-angle identities, half-angle identities

Suggestions
Double-angle and half-angle formulas are used to prove identities. While it is not always necessary, it is often useful to express functions of double-angle and half-angle formulas as functions of single angles. Remind students that

$\csc 2x = \dfrac{1}{\sin 2x}$ and $\sec 2x = \dfrac{1}{\cos 2x}$. Similarly,

$\csc \dfrac{x}{2} = \dfrac{1}{\sin \frac{x}{2}}$ and $\sec \dfrac{x}{2} = \dfrac{1}{\cos \frac{x}{2}}$.

Have students put one side of the identity in one column and the other side in another column. Then, have them try to write each side in terms of sin and cos. Watch from one column to another to see if a formula from the chapter occurs. The last step is to have the final line in each column identical.

In Example 1 in the text, one might have replaced $\cos 2\theta$ on the left with $1 - 2\sin^2 \theta$. If so, then the final line on the right would also be $1 - 2\sin^2 \theta$.

Students may go about proving an identity in a variety of ways.

Errors Students Make
When students have difficulty, they should express functions of half-angle and double-angle formulas as functions of a single angle. They should also express functions in terms of sine and cosine.

Cumulative Review
1. Find the length $\overline{AB}$, $A(-3, -5)$, $B(7, -2)$.
2. Find the slope of $\overleftrightarrow{PQ}$, $P(6, -8)$, $Q(-3, -9)$.

1. $\sqrt{109}$ 2. $m = \dfrac{-1}{-9}$ or $\dfrac{1}{9}$

Computer Activities (page 570)
This program computes distance using the COS function. Students could compare these results to results from a similar program using the distance formula or the formula $A^2 + B^2 = C^2$. Careful attention should be given to format of line 100—watch all signs, variables and parenthesis.

Computer Section (page 574)

Chapter Objectives
To run and debug a BASIC program
To use problem solving steps to write a computer program
To write numerical expressions with BASIC arithmetic symbols
To write algebraic expressions using BASIC variables in equations and inequalities
To write BASIC statements using the statements LET, PRINT, AND END
To write BASIC programs using the INPUT statement or the READ/DATA statement
To write BASIC Programs that use the statements IF . . . THEN and GO/TO
To use the FOR . . . NEXT loop in BASIC programs to repeat a group of instructions
To write BASIC program statements using the REM statements, BASIC functions, character strings, arrays and dimension statements

Chapter Overview
This section is devoted to the BASIC computer programming language. All programs and exercises are written is a common BASIC language compatible with most microcomputers. However, minor adjustments may be necessary when running these programs on some computers. The fundamental statements of BASIC are introduced. The format of the statement should be checked against the commands given in the BASIC user's guide associated with the computer you are using in your classroom.

Background
The statements covered are the simplest BASIC commands; however, many interpreters are able to understand matrix commands, format print commands, and graphic display commands. If these facilities are available to you, they will be explained in the manufacturer's user's guide. You may also need to check the user's guide for symbols, spacing techniques, and reserved words that may be different for your computer.

Teacher's Notes

Teacher's Notes

Teacher's Notes

Teacher's Notes

Daily Lesson Guide

Holt Algebra 2 contains an abundance of exercises for each lesson. The *Assignment Chart* suggests the number of exercises and the range that are needed to cover the objectives for each level. It includes exercises under Reading in Algebra, Oral Exercises, Written Exercises, A Challenge to You, Applications, Chapter Review, and Chapter Test.

ASSIGNMENT CHART	EXTRA MATERIAL (optional)		
	Practice	**Testing**	**Enrichment**
A (Basic) B (Average) C (Enriched)	Cumulative Reviews	College Prep Test	Calculator Activities
	Chalkboard Exercises in TE	Extra Test in TE	Computer Activity Enrichment in TE

Extra Material that is not listed in the Assignment Chart can be used in a number of ways:

1. Additional examples for teaching the lesson;
2. Practice Exercises for seat work or chalkboard work;
3. Items for quizzes;
4. Practice Exercises for extra help outside of class time;
5. Extra testing.

The chart is meant to be used as a guide and may be adapted by you to meet the needs of your students more effectively. Note that the answers to the odd-numbered exercises are given in the back of the Pupil's Edition. If you prefer to assign exercises without answers provided, you can choose to assign the even-numbered exercises instead.

Assignment Chart

Day	Level A		Level B		Level C	
1	3–4	Orals All	3–4	Orals All	3–4	Ex. Odd 21–41;
		Ex. 1–26		Ex. Even 12–46		43–46
			7	Reading Ex. 1–6	7	Reading Ex. 1–6
				Orals All		Orals Ex. 5–8
				Ex. 3, 6, 9, 12,		Ex. Odd 17–27;
				15, 18–30		28–33

Day	Level A		Level B		Level C	
2	7	Reading Ex. 1 – 6 Orals All Ex. 1, 2, 4, 5, 7, 8, 10, 11, 13, 14, 16, 17, 19, 20	10	Reading Ex. 1 – 9 Orals All Ex. 5 – 8, 13 – 16, 21 – 36	10	Reading Ex. 1 – 9 Orals All Ex. Odd 17 – 37; 38 – 44
3	10	Reading Ex. 1, 2 Orals All Ex. 1 – 20	13 – 15	Reading Ex. 1 – 8 Orals All Ex. 5 – 8, Even 16 – 28	14 – 15 17	Ex. Odd 15 – 27; 29 – 34 Ex. 11 – 16
4	13 – 15	Reading Ex. 1 – 8 Ex. 1 – 20	17	Ex. Even 2 – 8, Odd 9 – 13	18 – 19 22	Reading Ex. 1, 2 Orals Ex. 5 – 8 Ex. 9 – 14 Ex. 13 – 24
5	17	Ex. 1 – 8	18 – 19 21 – 22	Reading Ex. 1, 2 Orals All Ex. 5, 7 – 13 Ex. Even 2 – 10; 14 – 22	24 25	Applications Ex. 7 – 15 Problem Solving Ex. 1 – 8
6	18 – 19	Reading Ex. 1, 2 Orals Ex. 1 – 6 Ex. 1 – 7	24 25	Applications All Problem Solving Ex. 1 – 8	26	Chapter Review
7	21 – 22	Ex. 1 – 14	26	Chapter Review	27	Chapter Test
8	24	Applications Ex. 1 – 8	27	Chapter Test	33 36	Reading All Ex. 5, 7, Odd 17 – 27; 29 – 44 Reading Ex. 1 – 6 Orals All Ex. 7 – 18, 49 – 52, 57 – 71
9	25	Problem Solving Ex. 1 – 4, 6, 7	33 36	Reading All Ex. 4, 8, 12, 16, 20, 24, 25 – 36 Reading Ex. 1 – 6 Orals All Ex. 1 – 24, 28 – 36, 40 – 44, 48 – 51, 53 – 59, 61 – 63, 65 – 67	39 – 40 43	Reading Ex. 1 – 12 Orals All Ex. Odd 25 – 43; 45, 46 Ex. Odd 29 – 47; 49 – 55
10	26	Chapter Review	39 – 40 43	Reading Ex. 1 – 12 Orals All Ex. 25 – 44 Orals All Ex. 21 – 48	46 – 48	Reading Ex. 1 – 12 Ex. 10 – 14, Odd 15 – 23; 24, 25 Challenge

Day	Level A		Level B		Level C	
11	27	Chapter Test	46–48	Reading Ex. 1–12 Ex. Odd 1–15; 16–23 Challenge	51	Ex. 7–9, 11–14
12	33	Ex. 1–3, 5–7, 9–11, 13–15, 17–19, 21–23, 25–27	51	Ex. 5–12	52	Chapter Review
13	36	Reading Ex. 1–6 Orals All Ex. Even 2–50	52	Chapter Review	53	Chapter Test
14	39–40	Reading Ex. 7–12 Orals Ex. 1–17 Ex. 1–24	53	Chapter Test	59	Ex. 34, 37, 40, 43, 46, 49, 52, 55, 58, 61–64
15	43	Orals All Ex. 1–28	59	Orals All Ex. 18, 21, 24, 27, 30, 33–60	61 64	Ex. 23–32 Reading Ex. 1–12 Orals All Ex. Odd 13–33; 35–44
16	46–48	Reading Ex. 1–12 Ex. 1–14, 16–18, 20	61 64	Ex. 13–32 Reading Ex. 1–12 Orals All Ex. 1–6, 13–20, Even 22–34; 35–40	67 70	Reading Ex. 1–8 Orals All Ex. Odd 27–37; 39–53 Reading Ex. 1–8 Orals All Ex. 37, 40, 43, 46, 49, 52, 55–63
17	51	Ex. 1–6	67 70	Reading Ex. 1–8 Orals All Ex. 15, 16, 19–42 Reading Ex. 1–8 Orals All Ex. 38, 39, 41, 42, 44, 45, 47, 48, 50, 51, 53, 54, 56, 57	73	Reading Ex. 1–6 Orals All Ex. Even 20–40; 41–49

Day	Level A	Level B	Level C
18	52 — Chapter Review	73 — Reading Ex. 1 – 6 / Orals All / Ex. 3, 5, 9, 11, 13; / Odd 19 – 39	76 – 77 — Orals All / Ex. Odd 13 – 21; 23 – 26 / 80 – 82 — Ex. 7, 9, Odd 15 – 19; 20 – 26 / Challenge
19	53 — Chapter Test	76 – 77 — Orals All / Ex. Odd 1 – 11; 13 – 21	83 — Applications All / 84 — Chapter Review
20	59 — Orals All / Ex. 1 – 33	80 – 82 — Ex. 3, 5, 9, 15 – 21 / 83 — Challenge Applications All	85 — Chapter Test
21	61 — Ex. 1 – 16	84 — Chapter Review	90 — Ex. 1 – 4, Odd 13 – 23; 25 – 28 / 93 — Reading Ex. 1 – 10 / Ex. 4 – 12, Odd 25 – 33; 34 – 39
22	64 — Ex. 15 – 20, 35, 37	85 — Chapter Test	95 — Ex. Odd 19 – 25; 27 – 30
23	67 — Reading Ex. 1 – 8 / Orals All / Ex. 1 – 18	90 — Ex. 11 – 26 / 93 — Reading Ex. 1 – 10 / Ex. 1 – 12	97 — Ex. Odd 21 – 27; 29, 30 / 101 — Orals All / Ex. Odd 19 – 33; 35 – 40
24	70 — Reading Ex. 1 – 8 / Orals All / Ex. 1 – 18	95 — Ex. 1 – 3, 6 – 8, 19 – 26	104 — Ex. Odd 15 – 23; 25 – 29
25	73 — Reading Ex. 1 – 6 / Orals All 1 – 4 / Ex. 1 – 22	97 — Ex. 1, 4, 7, 10, 13, 16, 19, 21 – 28 / 101 — Orals All / Ex. 18, 21, 24 – 34	105 – 106 — Applications All
26	76 – 77 — Orals All / Ex. Even 2 – 12; 13 – 16	104 — Ex. 4 – 6, 16 – 24, 28, 29	108 — Chapter Review
27	80 – 81 — Ex. 1 – 14 / 83 — Applications All	105 – 106 — Applications All / 107 — Problem Solving Ex. 1 – 11	109 — Chapter Test

Day	Level A		Level B		Level C	
28	84	Chapter Review	108	Chapter Review	118	Reading All Ex. 10 – 12, Odd 29 – 37; 38, 39 Challenge
					121	Orals All Ex. 5 – 12
29	85	Chapter Test	109	Chapter Test	123 – 124	Reading Ex. 1 – 6 Ex. 5, 7 – 12
					126 – 127	Orals All Ex. Odd 23 – 41; 42 – 47
30	90 93	Ex. 1 – 16 Reading Ex. 6 – 10 Ex. 1, 2, 4, 5, 7, 8, 10, 11, 13, 14, 16, 17, 19, 20, 22. 23	118	Reading All Ex. 1, 3, 6, 10 – 13, 18, Even 26 – 36 Challenge	129	Orals All Ex. Even 12 – 22; 23 – 25
31	95	Ex. 1 – 18	121	Orals All Ex. Odd 1 – 7; 9 – 12	132 – 133	Reading All Orals All Ex. Odd 21 – 35; 37, 38
32	97 101	Ex. 1 – 22 Orals All Ex. 1 – 24	123 – 124	Reading Ex. 1 – 6 Ex. 2, 3, 7 – 12	134	Chapter Review
33	104 107	Ex. 1 – 14 Problem Solving Ex. 1 – 11	126 – 127	Orals All Ex. 4 – 9, 13 – 15, Even 16 – 40	135	Chapter Test
34	108	Chapter Review	129	Orals All Ex. Even 2 – 14; 15 – 22	141	Reading Ex. 1 – 6 Ex. 17 – 20, 27 – 46
					143 – 144	Reading Ex. 1 – 8 Ex. 5, 7, Odd 21 – 31; 33 – 40 Challenge
35	109	Chapter Test	132 – 133	Reading All Orals All Ex. Even 22 – 36	147	Ex. 3, Odd 23 – 43; 45 – 48

Day	Level A			Level B			Level C	
36	118	Reading All Ex. 16 – 24		134	Chapter Review		150 – 151	Reading Ex. 1 – 4 Orals All Ex. Odd 21 – 39; 41 – 48 Challenge
37	121	Orals All Ex. 1 – 8		135	Chapter Test		154	Ex. Odd 33 – 57; 59 – 66 Challenge
38	123 – 124	Reading Ex. 1 – 6 Ex. 1 – 8		141	Reading Ex. 1 – 12 Ex. 4, 8, 12, 16 – 42		156	Ex. Odd 25 – 47
				143 – 144	Reading Ex. 1 – 8 Ex. 1 – 8, 21 – 32 Challenge		158 – 159	Ex. Odd 25 – 43; 45 – 61 Challenge
39	126 – 127	Orals All Ex. 1 – 25		147	Orals All Ex. 17 – 44		160	Chapter Review
				150 – 151	Reading Ex. 1 – 4 Orals All Ex. 7, 8, 11, 12, 15, 16, 19, 20, 23, Even 24 – 40 Challenge			
40	129	Orals All Ex. 1 – 11, 12 – 14		154	Ex. 4, 8, 12, 16, 20, 24, 28, 32, 36, 40 – 58 Challenge		161	Chapter Test
41	134	Chapter Review		156	Ex. 25 – 48		166	Orals All Ex. 5, 7, Odd 17 – 23; 25 – 30
							168	Applications All
42	135	Chapter Test		158 – 159	Ex. 21 – 44 Challenge		171	Ex. Odd 29 – 35; 37 – 47
43	141	Reading Ex. 1 – 12 Ex. 1 – 3, 5 – 7, 9 – 11, 13 – 15, 17 – 19, 21 – 23, 25 – 27		160	Chapter Review		173 – 174	Ex. 3, 4, 7 – 16
44	143 – 144	Reading Ex. 1 – 8 Ex. 1 – 3, 5 – 6, 9 – 23 Challenge		161	Chapter Test		176 – 177	Ex. 2 – 5, 7, 9, 11, 12 Challenge

Day	Level A		Level B		Level C	
45	147	Orals All Ex. 1 – 8	166 168	Orals All Ex. 10 – 24 Applications Ex. 1 – 10	180	Orals All Ex. 1, 4, 7, 10, 13, 16, 19, 22, 25, 27, 28, 30, 31, 33, 34, 36, 37, 39, 40, 42, 43, 45, 46, 48 – 56
46	150 – 151	Reading Ex. 1 – 4 Orals All Ex. 21 – 28 Challenge	171	Reading All Orals All Ex. 1 – 6, 7, 10, 13, 16, 19, 22, 25, 28 – 36	181 182	Applications All Chapter Review
47	154	Ex. 1 – 3, 5 – 7, 9 – 11, 13 – 15, 17 – 19, 21 – 23, 25 – 27, 29 – 31, 33 – 35, 37 – 39	173 – 174	Ex. Odd 1 – 7; 8 – 11	183	Chapter Test
48	156	Ex. 1 – 24	176 – 177	Ex. 2, 3, 7 – 11 Challenge	188 – 189	Reading Ex. 1 – 6 Orals All Ex. 3, 6, 9, 12, 15, 18, 21, 24, 27, 30, Odd 31 – 47; 49 – 52
49	158 – 159	Ex. 1 – 24	180 181	Orals All Ex. 1, 4, 7, 10, 13, 16, 19, 22, 25 – 48 Applications All	192	Reading Ex. 1 – 4 Ex. 3, 6, 9, 12, 15, 18, 21, 24, 28, 32, 36, 40, 44, 48, 52 – 56
50	160	Chapter Review	182	Chapter Review	194	Ex. 4, 7, 10, 13, 16, 21 – 24, Odd 25 – 33, 34 – 42
51	161	Chapter Test	183	Chapter Test	197 200	Reading Ex. 1 – 6 Ex. 5 – 8, 15 – 18, Odd 19 – 27; 28 – 32 Challenge Ex. Odd 5 – 35; 37 – 40

Day	Level A		Level B		Level C	
52	166	Orals All Ex. 1–15	188–189	Reading Ex. 1–6 Orals All Ex. 3, 6, 9, 12, 15, 18, 21, 24, 27, 30–48	202	Chapter Review
	168	Applications Ex. 1–8				
53	171	Ex. 8, 9, 11, 12, 14, 15, 17, 18, 20, 21, 23, 24, 26, 27	192	Reading Ex. 1–4 Ex. 3, 6, 9, 12, 15, 18, 21, 24, 28, 32, 36–52	203	Chapter Test
54	173	Ex. 1–7	194	Ex. 4, 7, 10, 13, 16, 22–33	211	Reading Ex. 1–7 Ex. 6–13, 15, 18, 21, 22, 24, 30–33, 38, 39, 42, 43
55	176–177	Ex. 1–6	197	Reading Ex. 1–6 Ex. 1–4, 16–27 Challenge	215	Reading Ex. 1–8 Ex. Odd 1–23; 27, 28, 32–44
56	180	Orals All Ex. 2, 3, 5, 6, 8, 9, 11, 12, 14, 15, 17, 18, 20, 21, 23, 24	200	Ex. 4, 8, 12, 16, 20–36	219	Reading Ex. 1–5 Ex. 14–27, 30, 33, 36, 41, 43–52
			201	Problem Solving Ex. Odd 1–11		
	181	Applications All				
57	182	Chapter Review	202	Chapter Review	221–222	Orals All Ex. 11, 13, 15, 17, 19, 21, 22, 29, 32, 33, 36, 39–42
58	183	Chapter Test	203	Chapter Test	225	Ex. 5, 6, 9, 12, 15, 18, 21, 25, 28, 31, 34, 37, 43–55
59	188–189	Reading Ex. 1–6 Orals All Ex. 1–30	211	Reading Ex. 1–7 Ex. 6–13, 15, 18, 21, 22, 24, 30–33, 38, 39, 42, 43	227	Orals All Ex. 2, 5, 8, 11, 14, 18, 21, 22, 25, 28, 30, 34, 36–42
60	192	Reading Ex. 1–4 Ex. 1, 2, 4, 5, 7, 8, 10, 11, 13, 14, 16, 17, 19, 20, 22, 23, 25–36	215	Reading Ex. 1–8 Ex. Even 2–22; 25–38	230	Ex. 4–6, 10–12, 16–18, 22–24, 28–34
61	194	Ex. 1–24	219	Reading Ex. 1–5 Ex. 1–13, 28, 31, 34, 37–43	233	Ex. 4–14
					234	Applications All

Day	Level A		Level B		Level C	
62	197	Reading Ex. 1 – 6 Ex. 1 – 15	221 – 222	Orals All Ex. 1, 3, 5, 7, 9, 25 – 32, 34, 35, 37, 38	236	Chapter Review
63	200	Ex. 1 – 3, 5 – 7, 9 – 11, 13 – 15, 17 – 19, 21 – 23	225	Ex. 5, 6, 7, 10, 13, 16, 19, 23 – 37, 43 – 47	237	Chapter Test
	201	Problem Solving Ex. 1 – 8				
64	202	Chapter Review Ex. Even 2 – 28	227	Orals All Ex. 3, 6, 9, 12, 15, 17 – 37	241 – 242	Reading Ex. 1 – 4 Ex. Even 2 – 14; 16 – 22
65	203	Chapter Test	230	Ex. Even 2 – 18; 19 – 30	246	Ex. 1 – 20
66	211	Reading Ex. 1 – 7 Ex. 1 – 13, 14, 16, 17, 20, 23, 24, 26, 28, 29	233 234	Ex. 2, 4, 5 – 11 Applications All	249	Reading Ex. 1 – 4 Ex. Even 2 – 16
67	215	Reading Ex. 1 – 8 Ex. 1 – 26	236	Chapter Review	252	Ex. Even 2 – 28; 30 – 33
68	219	Reading Ex. 1 – 5 Ex. Even 2 – 26; 28 – 36	237	Chapter Test	255	Ex. 5 – 12, 14, 16 – 20 Challenge
69	221 – 222	Orals All Ex. Even 2 – 20; 21 – 26	241 – 242	Reading Ex. 1 – 4 Ex. 1 – 9, Odd 11 – 15	258	Ex. 1 – 4, 6 – 8, 10 – 16
70	225	Ex. 5 – 7, 10, 13, 16, 19, 23 – 37, 43 – 47	246	Ex. 1 – 20	262	Ex. Even 2 – 14, Odd 17 – 21; 22 – 27
71	227	Orals All Ex. 1 – 19, 26 – 31	249	Reading Ex. 1 – 4 Ex. Odd 1 – 15	266	Ex. Even 2 – 14
72	230	Ex. 1 – 21	252	Ex. Odd 1 – 31	270	Ex. Odd 1 – 13
73	236	Chapter Review Ex. Even 2 – 40	255	Ex. Odd 1 – 17	272	Chapter Review
74	237	Chapter Test	258	Ex. 1 – 9, Even 10 – 16	273	Chapter Test

Day	Level A		Level B		Level C	
75	241 – 242	Reading Ex. 1 – 4 Ex. 1 – 9	262	Ex. Odd 1 – 11; 12 – 21	278	Orals All Ex. Even 2 – 18; 19 – 26
76	246	Ex. 1 – 16	266	Ex. Odd 1 – 9; 10 – 15	281	Ex. Even 2 – 52; 53 – 56 Challenge
77	249	Reading Ex. 1 – 4 Ex. 1 – 6	270	Ex. Even 2 – 12	284	Reading Ex. 1 – 4 Ex. Even 2 – 24; 25 – 33
78	252	Orals All Ex. 1 – 23	272	Chapter Review	287	Reading Ex. 1 – 5 Ex. Even 2 – 26; 28 – 38 Challenge
79	255	Ex. 1 – 11	273	Chapter Review	290	Orals All Ex. Even 2 – 22; 26 – 33
80	270	Ex. 1 – 6	278	Orals All Ex. 1 – 19	293	Orals All Ex. Even 2 – 18; 20 – 26
81	272	Chapter Review Ex. Even 2 – 28	281	Ex. Odd 1 – 51 Challenge	296	Ex. Even 2 – 20; 22 – 25
82	273	Chapter Test	284	Reading Ex. 1 – 4 Ex. Odd 1 – 27	297	Applications All
83	278	Orals All Ex. 1 – 16	287	Reading Ex. 1 – 5 Ex. Odd 1 – 17; 19 – 27 Challenge	298	Chapter Review
84	281	Ex. 1 – 18, Odd 19 – 33	290	Orals All Ex. Odd 1 – 33	299	Chapter Test
85	284	Reading Ex. 1 – 4 Ex. Odd 1 – 27	293	Orals All Ex. Even 2 – 26	305	Orals All Ex. Even 2 – 32; 34 – 47
86	287	Reading Ex. 1 – 5 Ex. 1 – 18	296 297	Ex. Odd 1 – 21 Applications All	309	Ex. Odd 1 – 11, Even 14 – 24; 26 – 32

Day	Level A			Level B			Level C		
87	290	Orals All Ex. Even 2 – 30		298	Chapter Review		312 – 313	Orals All Reading Ex. 1 – 3 Ex. Even 2 – 52; 54 – 57	
88	293	Orals All Ex. Odd 1 – 25		299	Chapter Test		316	Ex. Even 2 – 30; 31 – 40	
89	296	Ex. 1 – 17		305	Orals All Ex. 1 – 37		320	Ex. Even 2 – 32; 33 – 40	
90	298	Chapter Review Ex. Even 2 – 40		309	Ex. Even 2 – 12; 13 – 25		322	Ex. Even 2 – 46	
91	299	Chapter Test		312 – 313	Orals All Reading Ex. 1 – 3 Ex. Odd 1 – 53		326	Orals All Ex. 4, 8, 12, 16, 20, 24, 28, 31, 35 – 44 Challenge	
92	305	Orals All Ex. 1 – 33		316	Ex. Odd 1 – 29		330	Ex. Even 2 – 30; 31, 32	
93	309	Ex. 1 – 15		320	Ex. Odd 1 – 31		332	Chapter Review	
94	312 – 313	Orals All Reading Ex. 1 – 3 Ex. Odd 1 – 43		322	Ex. Odd 1 – 47		333	Chapter Test	
95	316	Ex. 1 – 18		326	Orals All Ex. Odd 1 – 37 Challenge		339 – 340	Orals All Ex. 5 – 8, 13 – 16, 21 – 28 Challenge	
96	320	Ex. 1 – 20		330	Ex. Odd 1 – 29		343	Orals All Ex. Even 2 – 16; 17 – 19	
97	322	Ex. 1 – 24		332	Chapter Review		345	Applications All	
98	326	Orals All Ex. Even 2 – 36		333	Chapter Test		348	Reading Ex. 1 – 8 Ex. 9 – 16, 21 – 24, 29 – 36	
99	330	Ex. 1 – 8, Even 10 – 16; 17 – 20, 23, 24		339 – 340	Orals All Ex. 3, 4, 7, 8, 11, 12, 15, 16, 19, 20, 23, 24		351	Orals All Ex. 3, 4, 7, 8, 11, 12, 15, 16, 19, 20, 23, 24, 27, 28, 31, 32, 36 – 40	

Day	Level A		Level B		Level C	
100	332	Chapter Review Ex. Even 2 – 50	343	Orals All Ex. 3, 4, 7, 8, 11, 12, 15 – 17	352	Chapter Review
			345	Applications All		
101	333	Chapter Test	348	Reading Ex. 1 – 8 Ex. 3, 4, 7, 8, 11, 12, 15, 16, 19, 20, 23, 24, 27, 28, 31 – 34	353	Chapter Test
102	339 – 340	Orals All Ex. 1, 2, 5, 6, 9, 10, 13, 14, 17, 18, 21, 22	351	Orals All Ex. 3, 4, 7, 8, 11, 12, 15, 16, 19, 20, 23, 24, 27, 28, 31 – 35	359 – 360	Reading Ex. 1 – 5 Orals All Ex. 1 – 3, 7 – 9, Odd 11 – 31; 32 – 35, 37, 39, 41 – 49
103	343	Orals All Ex. 1, 2, 5, 6, 9, 10, 13, 14	352	Chapter Review	362 – 363	Orals All Ex. Odd 1 – 27; 29 – 33
104	348	Reading Ex. 1 – 8 Ex. 1, 2, 5, 6, 9, 10, 13, 14, 17, 18, 21, 22, 25, 26	353	Chapter Test	366 – 367	Orals All Ex. Odd 5 – 31; 33 – 38
105	351	Orals All Ex. 1, 2, 5, 6, 9, 10, 13, 14, 17, 18, 21, 22, 25, 26, 29, 30	359 – 360	Reading Ex. 1 – 5 Orals All Ex. Even 2 – 40	370 – 371	Reading Ex. 1 – 5 Orals All Ex. 1, 4, 7, 10, 13, 19, 22, 25, 28, 31, 34, 37, 40, 43 – 53
106	352	Chapter Review Ex. Even 2 – 32	362 – 363	Orals All Ex. Even 2 – 14; 15 – 18, Even 20 – 28	374	Ex. Odd 11 – 35; 37 – 46
107	353	Chapter Test	366 – 367	Orals All Ex. Odd 1 – 19; 21 – 32	377 – 378	Reading Ex. 1 – 6 Orals All Ex. Odd 1 – 7, 23 – 39; 41 – 46
108	359 – 360	Reading Ex. 1 – 5 Orals All Ex. 1 – 15, 32 – 35	370 – 371	Reading Ex. 1 – 5 Orals All Ex. 1, 4, 7, 10, 13, 16, 19, 22, 25, 28 – 49	381	Ex. Odd 1 – 9; 15, 17, 18 – 21, Odd 23 – 33; 34 – 36

Day	Level A		Level B		Level C	
109	362–363	Orals All Ex. 1–14	374	Ex. Even 2–36	384	Reading All Ex. Odd 11–27; 28–30
110	366–367	Orals All Ex. 1–20	377–378	Reading Ex. 1–6 Orals All Ex. Odd 1–9, Even 28–40; 41–44	386	Chapter Review
111	370–371	Reading Ex. 1–5 Orals All Ex. 1–27	381	Ex. Odd 1–17; 18–21, Even 22–32	387	Chapter Test
112	374	Ex. Odd 1–25	384	Reading All Ex. Even 2–8; 13–15, Even 16–26	391 393	Ex. 1–8, 17–26 Reading Ex. 1–7 Ex. 1–11, 18–21 Challenge
113	377–378	Reading Ex. 1–6 Orals All Ex. Even 2–26	386	Chapter Review	396	Orals All Ex. Odd 17–31; 32–35
114	381	Ex. 1–9, Even 10–16	387	Chapter Test	399 401	Ex. 6–9, 16–20, Odd 21–25; 27–30 Applications All
115	384	Reading All Ex. Odd 1–9; 10–12	391 393	Ex. Even 2–22 Reading Ex. 1–7 Ex. 1, 2, 4, 5, 7, 8, 10, 11, 13, 14, 16, 17, 19, 20 Challenge	403	Orals All Ex. 7–12, 18–21, 26–37
116	386	Chapter Review Ex. Even 2–38	396	Orals All Ex. Even 2–30	405	Ex. Odd 1–33; 35–42
117	387	Chapter Test	399 401	Ex. 1, 3, 5, 11, 13, 15, Even 18–28 Applications All	407 409	Reading Ex. 1–4 Ex. 1–3, 9–12, Odd 13–17; 19–24 Applications All
118	391 393	Ex. 1–12 Reading Ex. 1–7 Ex. 1–15	403	Orals All Ex. Odd 7–11; 17–35	414	Reading All Ex. 1–4, Odd 11–21; 23–26
119	396	Orals All Ex. Odd 1–21	405	Ex. Odd 1–23; 24–38	416–417 418	Reading All Ex. Odd 1–7; 18–23 Applications All

Day	Level A		Level B		Level C	
120	399	Ex. Even 2 – 16	407	Reading Ex. 1 – 4 Ex. 1 – 3, 9 – 18	420	Chapter Review
	401	Applications All	409	Applications All		
121	403	Orals All Ex. 1 – 7, 9, 11 – 25	414	Reading Ex. 1 – 4 Ex. 4 – 8, Even 10 – 22	421	Chapter Test
122	405	Ex. 1 – 23	416 – 417	Reading All Ex. Odd 1 – 7; 13 – 17	427	Orals All Ex. 1 – 3, 5, 7, 9 – 20
			418	Applications All		
123	407	Reading Ex. 1 – 4 Ex. 1 – 9	420	Chapter Review	429 – 430	Ex. 1 – 7, 10 – 22 Challenge
	409	Applications All				
124	416 – 417	Ex. Even 2 – 8; 9 – 12	421	Chapter Test	432	Ex. 3 – 9, 13 – 19 Challenge
					433 – 434	Orals All Reading Ex. 1 – 4 Ex. 1 – 8
125	420	Chapter Review Ex. Even 2 – 40	427	Orals All Ex. 1, 2, Odd 3 – 19	437	Reading Ex. 1 – 8 Ex. 1 – 8, Odd 9 – 15; 16 – 21 Challenge
126	421	Chapter Test	429 – 430	Ex. 1 – 7, 9 – 19, 21 Challenge	440	Ex. Even 2 – 12; 13, 14
127	427	Orals All Ex. 1, 2, Even 4 – 16	432	Ex. 3 – 9, 13 – 19 Challenge	444	Ex. Odd 1 – 31; 32 – 36
	432	Ex. 1 – 13 Challenge	433 – 434	Orals All Reading Ex. 1 – 4 Ex. 1 – 8		
128	437	Reading Ex. 1 – 8 Ex. 1 – 12 Challenge	437	Reading Ex. 1 – 8 Ex. Even 2 – 12; 13 – 18	446 – 447	Ex. 7 – 16
129	440	Ex. 1 – 8	440	Ex. Even 2 – 8; 9 – 12	448	Chapter Review
130	446 – 447	Ex. 1 – 4	444	Ex. Even 2 – 30; 33, 35	449	Chapter Test
131	448	Chapter Review Ex. Even 2 – 22	446 – 447	Ex. 2, 4 – 12	457	Reading Ex. 1 – 5 Orals All Ex. Even 2 – 42; 43 – 46

Day	Level A		Level B		Level C	
132	449	Chapter Test	448	Chapter Review	460–461	Orals All Ex. 1–16, 22–33
133	457	Reading Ex. 1–5 Ex. 1–4 Orals All	449	Chapter Test	465	Reading Ex. 1–5 Ex. Even 2–48; 49–54
134	457	Ex. Odd 5–41	457	Reading Ex. 1–5 Orals All Ex. Odd 1–45	469	Ex. 1–6, 19–24, 31–36, Even 38– 50; 52–55
135	460–461	Orals All Ex. 1–6	460–461	Orals All Ex. 1–21	472	Orals All Ex. Even 2–44; 45–48 Challenge
136	461	Ex. 7–16	465	Reading Ex. 1–5 Ex. Odd 1–43; 45–50	474	Ex. Even 2–42; 44–47
137	465	Reading Ex. 1–5 Ex. 1–6	469	Ex. Odd 1–43; 44–51	476	Orals All Ex. Even 2–20; 21–30
138	465	Ex. 7–40	472	Orals All Ex. Odd 1–35; 37–44 Challenge	480	Ex. 5, 10, 15, 20, 25, 28, 31, 34, 37, 45–47, 49, 52, 55, Even 58–66; 67–89
139	469	Ex. 1–30	474	Ex. Odd 1–29	482	Ex. Even 2–26; 28–42
140	469	Ex. Odd 31–41; 44–46	476	Orals All Ex. Even 2–12; 13–24	485	Ex. 4, 8, 12, 15, 18, 21, 25–27, 34–39, 43–52
141	472	Orals All Ex. 1–19	480	Ex. Odd 1–47; 48–66	488	Orals All Ex. Even 2–26; 27–32
142	472	Ex. 20–36; 38	482	Ex. Odd 1–9; 10– 30	490–491	Orals All Ex. Even 2–14; 16–19, 26–35
143	474	Ex. Odd 1–25; 29	485	Ex. 8–12, 18–21, 25–45	492	Chapter Review
144	474	Ex. Even 2–30; 40	488	Orals All Ex. 1–19, 21–28	493	Chapter Test
			490–491	Orals All Ex. Odd 1–15; 16–28		

Day	Level A		Level B		Level C	
145	476	Orals All Ex. Even 1 – 14	492	Chapter Review	499	Ex. 1 – 6, Even 8 – 18; 21 – 30 Challenge
146	476	Ex. Even 2 – 14; 16, 17	493	Chapter Test	502	Orals All Ex. 3, 6, 8, 10, 16, 18 – 30
147	480	Ex. Even 2 – 46; 49, 57	499	Ex. 1 – 20	505	Orals All Ex. 9 – 12, 17 – 27 Challenge
148	480	Ex. Odd 1 – 45; 48, 60, 61	502 505	Orals All Ex. 2, 4, 6, 8 – 20, 25, 26 Orals All Ex. Even 2 – 12, 13 – 22	508	Reading Ex. 1 – 3 Ex. 6 – 8, 14 – 16, 21 – 34
149	482	Ex. Odd 1 – 19; 20	508	Reading Ex. 1 – 3 Ex. Even 2 – 16; 17 – 26	511	Ex. 1 – 7, 15 – 18, 20, 24 – 26, 28, 31, 33, 35 – 38 Challenge
150	482	Ex. Even 2 – 18; 21	511	Ex. 1 – 7, Even 8 – 26; 27 – 34 Challenge	514	Ex. 4, 8, 11, 12, 19 – 31
151	485	Ex. Odd 1 – 17; 22, 26	514	Ex. 1 – 4, 8 – 10, 16 – 20, 22 – 27	517	Orals All Ex. 10 – 15, 22 – 33
152	485	Ex. Even 2 – 18; 23, 27	517	Orals All Ex. Odd 1 – 15; 16 – 24	520	Ex. Even 2 – 28; 29 – 32
153	488	Orals All Ex. Odd 1 – 17; 22, 23	520	Ex. 1 – 4, Even 6 – 20; 21 – 28, 30	522	Ex. 4 – 6, Even 8 – 14; 15 – 18
154	488	Ex. Even 2 – 18; 21, 24	522	Ex. 1 – 14	525	Reading Ex. 1 – 5 Ex. 1 – 28, 34 – 40
155	490 – 491	Orals All Ex. Odd 1 – 21	525	Reading Ex. 1 – 5 Ex. 1 – 36	528	Ex. 1 – 10, 23 – 26, Odd 29 – 39; 41 – 56
156	491	Ex. Even 2 – 20; 23	528	Ex. 1 – 6, Even 8 – 26; 27, 28, Even 30 – 40	532 533	Reading Ex. 1 – 6 Ex. 1 – 17, 19, 21 – 23, 30 – 35 Applications All

Day	Level A		Level B		Level C	
157	493	Chapter Review Ex. Even 2 – 66	532	Reading Ex. 1 – 6 Ex. 1 – 29	534	Chapter Review
			533	Applications All		
158	494	Chapter Test	534	Chapter Review	535	Chapter Test
159	520	Ex. 1 – 20	535	Chapter Test	540 – 541	Reading Ex. 1 – 3 Orals All Ex. Even 2 – 18; 19 – 26
160	525	Reading Ex. 1 – 5 Ex. 1 – 28; 29, 31	540 – 541	Reading Ex. 1 – 3 Orals All Ex. Odd 1 – 9; 11 – 22	543	Ex. Even 2 – 14; 15, 16, 18, 20, 21
161	202	Chapter Review Ex. Odd 1 – 29	543	Ex. Odd 1 – 13, 15 – 19	545	Orals All Ex. Even 2 – 14; 15 – 18
162	236	Chapter Review Ex. Odd 1 – 39	545	Orals All Ex. 2, 3, 5, 6 – 16	548	Orals All Ex. Even 2 – 12; 13 – 16
163	272	Chapter Review Ex. Odd 1 – 27	548	Orals All Ex. Even 2 – 8; 9 – 14	551	Ex. 1 – 10
			551	Ex. Even 2 – 10		
164	298	Chapter Review Ex. Odd 1 – 39	554 – 555	Orals All Ex. 1 – 10, Odd 11 – 25; 26 – 36	554 – 555	Orals All Ex. Even 2 – 34; 35 – 46
165	332	Chapter Review Ex. Odd 1 – 51	559	Ex. 1 – 10, Odd 11 – 23; 24 – 28, 32, 33	559	Ex. 2, 7, 9, 10, 14 – 16, 18, 20, 22, 26 – 40
166	352	Chapter Review Ex. Odd 1 – 31	562	Ex. Odd 1 – 31; 34, 35	562	Ex. Even 2 – 32; 33 – 38
167	386	Chapter Review Ex. Odd 1 – 39	565	Ex. Odd 1 – 21; 23 – 29, 33, 34	565	Ex. Even 2 – 28; 29 – 36 Challenge
168	420	Chapter Review Ex. Odd 1 – 41	567	Ex. 1 – 12	567	Ex. 1 – 18
169	448	Chapter Review Ex. Odd 1 – 23	568	Chapter Review	568	Chapter Review
170	493	Chapter Review Ex. Odd 1 – 67	569	Chapter Test	569	Chapter Test

Holt Algebra 2
with Trigonometry

About the Authors

Eugene D. Nichols
Distinguished Professor of Mathematics Education
and Lecturer, Mathematics Department
Florida State University
Tallahassee, Florida

Mervine L. Edwards
Chairman of Mathematics Department
Shore Regional High School
West Long Branch, New Jersey

E. Henry Garland
Head of the Mathematics Department
Developmental Research School
DRS Professor
Florida State University
Tallahassee, Florida

Sylvia A. Hoffman
Resource Consultant in Mathematics
Illinois State Board of Education
State of Illinois

Albert Mamary
Assistant Superintendent of Schools for Instruction
Johnson City Central School District
Johnson City, New York

William F. Palmer
Professor and Chairman
Department of Education
Catawba College, and
Mathematics Consultant
Salisbury City Schools
Salisbury, North Carolina

Consulting Author for Computer Strand

Barbara L. Kurshan
Assistant Professor, and
Director of Academic Computing
Hollins College
Hollins College, Virginia

Holt Algebra 2
with Trigonometry

Eugene D. Nichols
Mervine L Edwards
E. Henry Garland
Sylvia A. Hoffman
Albert Mamary
William F. Palmer

HOLT, RINEHART AND WINSTON, PUBLISHERS
New York • Toronto • London • Sydney

Staff Credits

Editorial Development   Eleanor R. Spencer, Everett T. Draper, Dennis Rogan, Earl D. Paisley, Arlene Grodkiewicz

Editorial Processing   Margaret M. Byrne, Regina Chilcoat, Holly L. Massey, Elizabeth Santiago

Art and Production   Vivian Fenster, Fred C. Pusterla, Robin M. Swenson, Russell Dian, Annette Sessa-Galbo, Susan Woolhiser, Anita Dickhuth, Ellen Lokiec, Donna Bogdanowich, Richard Haynes

Product Manager   John W. M. Cooke

Advisory Board   Robert Wolff, Patricia M. Cominsky, Jose Contreras, Roy V. Eliason, C. Paul Moore, Randolph Ragsdale, Kenneth C. Scupp

Consultants   Patricia M. Cominsky

Researchers   James R. George, Erica S. Felman

Acknowledgements for Photographs

Cover Photo: Computer-generated block graph "Birds Refueling in Air," MCA-A15. The x-axis is parallel to the spine and the origin is in the center. Both x-values and y-values are from -38 to 38. Colors are 31245670. The equation is $(Y - 10 * SIN (X \wedge 2/25 + Y/4))/(X + ABS(Y))$. By E. P. Miles, Jr. on an Intecolor 8051 at Florida State University, program by William Jasiniecki, Photo by John Owen. © 1980 EPM. All rights reserved. Used by permission.

Pages: *105–106; 114,* HRW Photos by Russell Dian; *pages 23–24* NASA; *page 83* HRW Photo by William Hubbell; *page 138 (l.)* Bill Anderson/Monkmeyer Press Photo, (r.) Dan River, Inc.; *pages 167–168* Monkmeyer Press Photo; *page 186* The Granger Collection; *page 208* NASA; *page 234* Richard Haynes; *page 275* Michal Heron/Monkmeyer Press Photo; *page 297* Rona Weissler Tuccillo; *page 337* David Smith Collection, Columbia University; *pages 334–335* HRW Photo by Ken Lax; *page 356* The Granger Collection; *page 389* Oficina de Control de Espesies, Postales y Filatella, Managua, Nicaragua; *page 454* The Granger Collection; *page 538* Hugh Rogers/ Monkmeyer Press Photo.

Line art prepared by Graphic Concern, Inc

ISBN 0-03-053916-1
  2345   032   98765432

Contents

1 Linear Equations and Inequalities   x

2 Polynomials and Problem Solving   30

3 Factoring and Special Products   56

4 Rational Expressions   88

10 Linear Systems, Matrices, and Determinants 239

11 Functions 275

12 Conic Sections 302

13 Linear-Quadratic Systems 337

18 Trigonometric Graphs and Identities 496

19 Trigonometric Laws and Formulas 538

Four Steps in Problem Solving

Problem: The combined population of Watertown, River City, and Coldstream is 89,400. How many people live in Watertown if the population of River City is 7,400 more than that of Coldstream, and the number of people in Watertown is twice the number in River City?

READ
−−*Identify* what is to be found.
−−*Identify* what is given.

You are asked to find the population of Watertown. The combined population of Watertown and two other cities is given. The population of Watertown is expressed *in terms of* the population of Coldstream.

PLAN
−−*Analyze* the information.
−−*Decide* on the operations.
−−*Represent* the data.
−−*Write* a mathematical sentence.

Let x = pop. of Coldstream.
$x + 7400$ = pop. of River City
$2(x + 7400)$ = pop. of Watertown

"Combined" indicates *addition*.

$$x + (x + 7400) + 2(x + 7400) = 89,400$$

SOLVE
−−*Perform* the necessary operations.
−−*Solve* the sentence.

$$x + x + 7400 + 2x + 14,800 = 89,400$$
$$4x + 22,200 = 89,400$$
$$4x = 67,200$$
$$x = 16,800$$

INTERPRET
−−*Check* the solution.
−−*Decide* if the answer is reasonable.

Coldstream: x ▶ 16,800
River City: $x + 7400$ ▶ 24,200
Watertown: $2(x + 7400)$ ▶ 48,400
Combined: 89,400

Thus, pop. of Watertown is 48,400.

1.1 Linear Equations

OBJECTIVE ▶ **To solve a linear equation in one variable**

Each of the equations below is a **linear equation** in one variable.

$$6x + 32 - 10x = 7 + 8x - 39 \qquad \frac{3}{5}y - 3 = 8 - \frac{1}{5}y \qquad 3.8n + 2.3 = 7.58 - 0.6n$$

You can solve a linear equation in one variable by
(1) combining the like terms, if any, on each side of the equation, and
(2) using one or more of the following equation properties.

Equation Properties

> For all numbers a, b, and c,
> Addition: if $a = b$, then $a + c = b + c$.
> Subtraction: if $a = b$, then $a - c = b - c$.
> Multiplication: if $a = b$, then $a \cdot c = b \cdot c$.
> Division: if $a = b$, then $\dfrac{a}{c} = \dfrac{b}{c}$; $c \neq 0$.

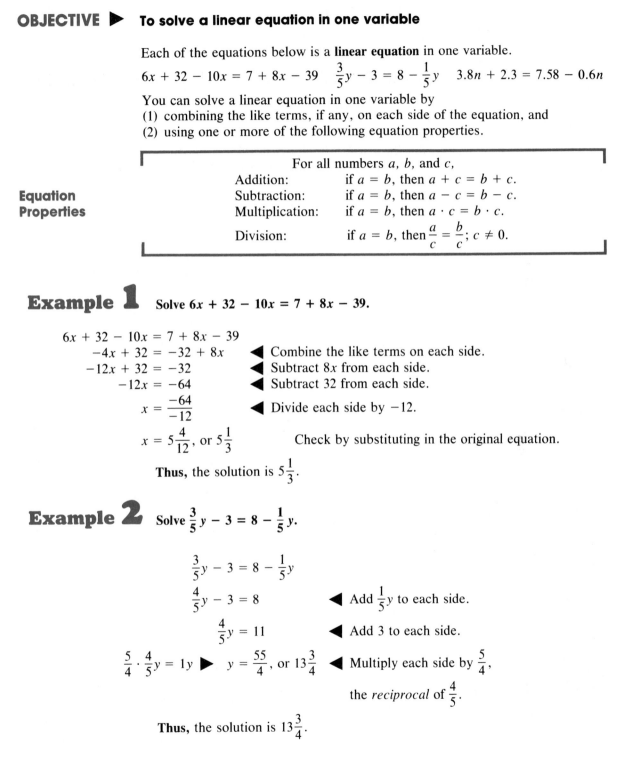

Example 1 Solve $6x + 32 - 10x = 7 + 8x - 39$.

$$6x + 32 - 10x = 7 + 8x - 39$$
$$-4x + 32 = -32 + 8x \qquad \blacktriangleleft \text{ Combine the like terms on each side.}$$
$$-12x + 32 = -32 \qquad \blacktriangleleft \text{ Subtract } 8x \text{ from each side.}$$
$$-12x = -64 \qquad \blacktriangleleft \text{ Subtract 32 from each side.}$$
$$x = \frac{-64}{-12} \qquad \blacktriangleleft \text{ Divide each side by } -12.$$
$$x = 5\frac{4}{12}, \text{ or } 5\frac{1}{3} \qquad \text{Check by substituting in the original equation.}$$

Thus, the solution is $5\frac{1}{3}$.

Example 2 Solve $\frac{3}{5}y - 3 = 8 - \frac{1}{5}y$.

$$\frac{3}{5}y - 3 = 8 - \frac{1}{5}y$$
$$\frac{4}{5}y - 3 = 8 \qquad \blacktriangleleft \text{ Add } \frac{1}{5}y \text{ to each side.}$$
$$\frac{4}{5}y = 11 \qquad \blacktriangleleft \text{ Add 3 to each side.}$$
$$\frac{5}{4} \cdot \frac{4}{5}y = 1y \blacktriangleright \quad y = \frac{55}{4}, \text{ or } 13\frac{3}{4} \blacktriangleleft \text{ Multiply each side by } \frac{5}{4},$$
$$\text{the } \textit{reciprocal} \text{ of } \frac{4}{5}.$$

Thus, the solution is $13\frac{3}{4}$.

Example 3 Solve $3.8n + 2.3 = 7.58 - 0.6n$.

$$3.8n + 2.3 = 7.58 - 0.6n$$
$$4.4n + 2.3 = 7.58 \qquad \blacktriangleleft \text{ Add } 0.6n \text{ to each side.}$$
$$4.4n = 5.28 \qquad \blacktriangleleft \text{ Subtract 2.3 from each side.}$$
$$n = 1.2 \qquad \blacktriangleleft \text{ Divide each side by 4.4.}$$
Thus, the solution is 1.2.

Sometimes the variable appears on the right side of the equation but not on the left side. In that case, it may be more convenient to get the variable alone on the right side of the equation as shown below.

Example 4 Solve $78 = 22 - 8t$. Check the solution by substitution.

$$78 = 22 - 8t$$
$$56 = -8t$$
$$-7 = t$$

Check:

78	$22 - 8t$
78	$22 - 8(-7)$
	$22 + 56$
	78

True: $78 = 78$

Thus, the solution is -7.

A linear equation may contain parentheses. You can remove parentheses by using the **Distributive Property.**

Distributive Property

> For all numbers a, b, and c,
> $a(b + c) = ab + ac$ and $(b + c)a = ba + ca$.

Even though the Distributive Property is stated for multiplication over addition, the property remains true for multiplication over subtraction as well.

Example 5 Solve $9x - (4x - 6) = 17 + 2(3x + 8)$.

$$9x - 1(4x - 6) = 17 + 2(3x + 8) \qquad \blacktriangleleft -(4x - 6) = -1(4x - 6)$$
$$9x - 4x + 6 = 17 + 6x + 16 \qquad \blacktriangleleft \text{ Use Distributive Property on each side.}$$
$$5x + 6 = 33 + 6x$$
$$-1x + 6 = 33$$
$$-1x = 27$$
$$x = -27 \qquad \blacktriangleleft \text{ Divide each side by } -1.$$

Thus, the solution is -27.

In Example 5 on page 2, the following multiplication property is used: For each number a, $(-1)(a) = -a$.

Example 6 Solve $\frac{1}{3}(6y - 15) - \frac{3}{4}(12y + 16) = 11$.

$$\frac{1}{3}(6y) + \frac{1}{3}(-15) - \frac{3}{4}(12y) - \frac{3}{4}(16) = 11$$
$$2y - 5 - 9y - 12 = 11$$
$$-7y - 17 = 11$$
$$-7y = 28$$
$$y = -4$$

Thus, the solution is -4.

Example 7 Solve $0.1 + 1.2(4n - 0.3) = 5(0.3n + 0.74)$.

$$0.1 + 1.2(4n) + 1.2(-0.3) = 5(0.3n) + 5(0.74)$$
$$0.1 + 4.8n - 0.36 = 1.5n + 3.70$$
$$3.3n = 3.96$$
$$n = 1.2$$

Thus, the solution is 1.2.

Oral Exercises

Solve each equation.
1. $x - 7 = 12$ **19**
2. $9a = 27$ **3**
3. $10 = y - 8$ **18**
4. $28 = -7x$ **−4**
5. $-c = 0.3$ **−0.3**
6. $3y = 10$ $\frac{10}{3}$
7. $8a = 4$ $\frac{1}{2}$
8. $\frac{1}{4}n = 12$ **48**

Simplify each expression.
9. $3(5x - 8)$ **15x − 24**
10. $-4(3y + 11)$ **−12y − 44**
11. $-(5n - 7)$ **−5n + 7**
12. $-(8 + 6t)$ **−8 − 6t**
13. $\frac{1}{2}(6a + 20)$ **3a + 10**
14. $\frac{1}{3}(12x - 27)$ **4x − 9**
15. $0.4(0.3t - 11)$ **0.12t − 4.4**
16. $1.32(10y + 0.1)$ **13.2y + 0.132**

Written Exercises

Solve each equation.
Ⓐ 1. $18x + 20 + x = 5 + 10x - 3$ **−2**
2. $5y - 3 - 2y = 4y - 18 - 6y$ **−3**
3. $10 + \frac{2}{3}t = 6$ **−6**
4. $7 = \frac{3}{4}n - 24$ $41\frac{1}{3}$
5. $4.9y + 17 = 1.4y - 60$ **−22**
6. $0.3x - 12 = 18 + 0.8x$ **−60**
7. $54n + 9.8 = 0.2 + 22n$ **−0.3**
8. $6a - 15.3 = 26.5 + 25a$ **−2.2**
9. $-27 = 12w + 27$ **−4.5**
10. $126 - a = -9a$ **−15.75**

LINEAR EQUATIONS

11. $3(2n + 4) + 5(3 - 2n) = 7 - 2n$ **10**

13. $5y - (2 - 3y) = 54$ **7**

15. $\frac{1}{4}(12x - 24) - 4x = \frac{1}{3}(18 + 15x) + 24$ **−6**

17. $0.4t + 3(1.2t + 0.9) = 21.1$ **4.6**

19. $6(3.2y - 2.3) = 7.2y - 13.32$ **0.04**

B **21.** $3n - 8 - 5n = 2 - 6n - 7$ **0.75**

23. $3t - 7 - 8t + 4 = 4t + 8 - 3t$ **−1$\frac{5}{6}$**

25. $\frac{2}{7}x + 18 = 8 - \frac{3}{7}x$ **−14**

27. $\frac{2}{9}n - 31 = 16 + \frac{7}{9}n$ **−84$\frac{3}{5}$**

29. $18.2x + 2.02 = 15.9x + 2.71$ **0.3**

31. $3.2n - 0.05 = n + 0.06$ **0.05**

33. $2 - 5(2a - 3) = 4(3 - 4a)$ **−$\frac{5}{6}$**

35. $x - (9x - 5) = -(3x + 7)$ **2$\frac{2}{5}$**

37. $\frac{2}{3}(6c - 12) + \frac{1}{2}(8c - 12) = 22 - c$ **4**

39. $\frac{3}{5}(15n + 20) + 3n = \frac{2}{7}(14n - 28) - 12$ **−4**

41. $2.5(1.2x + 6) = 1.92 + 8(4.3x + 2.42)$ **−0.2**

C **43.** $5(2n + 4) - 3(4n - 6) = 2(20 - n)$ **no solution**

45. $5[3(5y - 4) - 2(7y + 6)] + 3y - 8 = 0$ **16**

12. $2(7x - 4) - 4(2x - 6) = 3x + 31$ **5**

14. $6(3 + 2c) - (7c - 2) = 3c - 4$ **−12**

16. $\frac{1}{5}(30n + 25) - \frac{1}{8}(32n + 16) = 14n - 33$ **3**

18. $0.7(5a - 1.2) = 2a - 0.39$ **0.3**

20. $2.6(4x + 2.3) = 8.2x + 49.98$ **20**

22. $2m + 7 - 4m = -3m - 5 + 6m$ **2$\frac{2}{5}$**

24. $14 - 5c - 2 = 8 - 6c + 2 + 4c$ **$\frac{2}{3}$**

26. $\frac{4}{5}y - 22 = \frac{1}{5}y + 14$ **60**

28. $18 - \frac{2}{11}a = \frac{5}{11}a - 19$ **58$\frac{1}{7}$**

30. $1.6y + 0.86 = 8 - 1.8y$ **2.1**

32. $x - 0.01 = 12.2 - 2.3x$ **3.7**

34. $3n - 7(2n + 3) = -2(8n + 5)$ **2$\frac{1}{5}$**

36. $-4(2y - 5) - (7 - 3y) = 4(y + 3)$ **$\frac{1}{9}$**

38. $\frac{3}{4}(16n - 8) - \frac{2}{3}(9n + 12) = 4 - 3n$ **2**

40. $21 + \frac{5}{6}(30x + 18) = 19x - \frac{2}{5}(35x - 15)$ **−1$\frac{1}{2}$**

42. $7(3.2n + 9.4) = 4.4(3.5n + 4.5) - 0.2$ **−6.6**

44. $4(x - 3) - (x + 6) = 3(x - 6)$ **all numbers**

46. $10 - 4[6(2a + 5) - (20 + 10a)] - 2a = 0$ **−3**

CALCULATOR ACTIVITIES

A calculator can help you solve linear equations containing decimals.

$$-5.76 + 37.2x = 8.46$$

$$\frac{38.5}{7.16}y + 6.93 = 94.2$$

Rewrite: $\quad x = \dfrac{8.46 + 5.76}{37.2}$

Rewrite: $\quad y = \dfrac{7.16}{38.5}(94.2 - 6.93)$

Press $\quad \blacktriangleright$ 8.46 $\oplus$ 5.76 $\ominus$ 37.2 $\ominus$

Display $\quad \blacktriangleright$ 0.382258

Press $\quad \blacktriangleright$ 94.2 $\ominus$ 6.93 $\otimes$ 7.16 $\oplus$ 38.5 $\ominus$

Display $\quad \blacktriangleright$ 16.229953

Round to nearest hundredth: $x = 0.38$

Round to nearest hundredth: $y = 16.23$

Solve each equation and round the solution to the nearest hundredth.

1. $5.43x - 72.8 = 6.92$ **14.68**

3. $\frac{3.6}{4.5}t = \frac{48}{7.5}$ **8**

2. $\frac{2}{3.75}y + 4.03 = 10.54$ **12.21**

4. $\frac{2.4}{3.2}n - \frac{6.2}{4.5} = \frac{58}{4.5}$ **19.02**

4

1.2 Linear Inequalities

OBJECTIVES ► **To find the solution set of a linear inequality in one variable**
To graph the solutions of a linear inequality in one variable

A mathematical sentence such as $5 + 8x > 16$ or $7 - 5x < 27$ is called a **linear inequality** in one variable. The procedures used to solve a linear inequality are similar to those you have been using to solve a linear equation, with one major exception. This exception occurs when you need to multiply or divide by a negative number.

$$
\begin{array}{cc}
-8 \ \ < \ \ 6 & -8 < 6 \\
-8(-2) \Big\downarrow 6(-2) & \dfrac{-8}{-2} \Big\downarrow \dfrac{6}{-2} \\
16 \ \ > \ \ -12 & 4 \ \ > -3
\end{array}
\qquad
\begin{array}{cc}
-8 \ \ < \ \ 6 & -8 < 6 \\
-8(2) \Big\downarrow 6(2) & \dfrac{-8}{2} \Big\downarrow \dfrac{6}{2} \\
-16 \ \ < \ \ 12 & -4 < 3
\end{array}
$$

Notice that the *order* changes from $<$ to $>$ when each side of $-8 < 6$ is multiplied or divided by -2. Multiplying or dividing each side by 2 does not reverse the order. Also, adding the same number to each side of an inequality or subtracting the same number from each side does not reverse the order.

Inequality Properties

For all numbers a, b, and c,

Addition: if $a < b$, then $a + c < b + c$.

Subtraction: if $a < b$, then $a - c < b - c$.

Multiplication: if $a < b$, $c > 0$, then $a \cdot c < b \cdot c$.
    if $a < b$, $c < 0$, then $a \cdot c > b \cdot c$.

Division: if $a < b$, $c > 0$, then $\dfrac{a}{c} < \dfrac{b}{c}$.
    if $a < b$, $c < 0$, then $\dfrac{a}{c} > \dfrac{b}{c}$.

Example 1   **Find the solution set of $8 - 3x < 2x + 28$.**
Graph the solutions on a number line.

$$8 - 3x < 2x + 28$$
$$8 - 5x < 28$$
$$-5x < 20$$
$$\dfrac{-5x}{-5} \Big\downarrow \dfrac{20}{-5}$$ ◄ Divide each side by -5.
$$x > -4$$ ◄ Reverse the order from $<$ to $>$.

Thus, $\{x \mid x > -4\}$ is the solution set.   ◄ Read: "The set of all x such that x is greater than -4."
To graph the solutions, plot all numbers greater than -4.

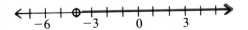

You will find it easier to read and graph an inequality like $5 > x$ if you write the variable first. Thus, $5 > x$ can be replaced by $x < 5$, and read as *x is less than 5*.

Even though the inequality properties on page 5 are stated for $<$, they are true for $>$ as well. In Example 2, the properties are applied to the $>$ relation.

Example 2 Find the solution set of $3x - 2 > 5x + 7$.

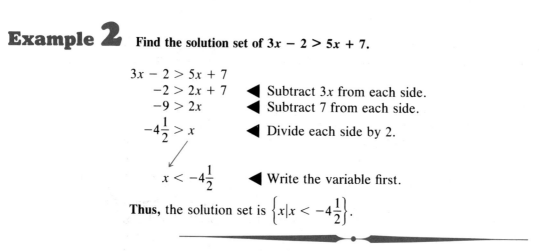

$$3x - 2 > 5x + 7$$
$$-2 > 2x + 7 \quad \blacktriangleleft \text{ Subtract } 3x \text{ from each side.}$$
$$-9 > 2x \quad \blacktriangleleft \text{ Subtract } 7 \text{ from each side.}$$
$$-4\tfrac{1}{2} > x \quad \blacktriangleleft \text{ Divide each side by 2.}$$

$$x < -4\tfrac{1}{2} \quad \blacktriangleleft \text{ Write the variable first.}$$

Thus, the solution set is $\left\{ x \mid x < -4\tfrac{1}{2} \right\}$.

Some linear inequalities contain the relation $\geq$, *is greater than or equal to*. You can solve such an inequality by using both equation and inequality properties. This is shown in Example 3.

Example 3 Find the solution set of $3(4 - 2x) \geq 4x - 23$.
Graph the solutions on a number line.

$$3(4 - 2x) \geq 4x - 23$$
$$12 - 6x \geq 4x - 23 \qquad \text{Combined division properties:}$$
$$-10x \geq -35 \qquad \qquad \text{If } a = b, \text{ then } \frac{a}{c} = \frac{b}{c}, c \neq 0.$$
$$x \leq 3\tfrac{1}{2} \qquad \blacktriangleleft \qquad \text{If } a > b, c < 0, \text{ then } \frac{a}{c} < \frac{b}{c}.$$

Thus, the solution set is $\left\{ x \mid x \leq 3\tfrac{1}{2} \right\}$.

Horizontal number line

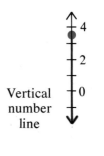

Vertical number line

CHAPTER ONE

Reading in Algebra

Match each inequality to exactly one graph.

1. $5 < x$ **C**
2. $5 \le x$ **A**
3. $x < 5$ **D**
4. $x \le 5$ **B**
5. $x < 2$ **E**
6. $x > 2$ **F**

A $\underset{5\quad 6}{\bullet\!\!-\!\!\!\rightarrow}$ B $\underset{4\quad 5}{\leftarrow\!\!-\!\!\bullet}$ E $\underset{}{\overset{2}{\underset{1}{\bullet}}}$ F $\overset{3}{\underset{2}{\bigcirc}}$

C $\underset{5\quad 6}{\bigcirc\!\!-\!\!\!\rightarrow}$ D $\underset{4\quad 5}{\leftarrow\!\!-\!\!\bigcirc}$

Oral Exercises

True or false?
1. $-7 < 3$ **T**
2. $-4 \le -6$ **F**
3. $5 > -9$ **T**
4. $8 \ge 8$ **T**
5. If $5a + 2 < 12$, then $5a > 10$. **F**
6. If $8 \le y$, then $y \ge 8$. **T**
7. If $-a < -8$, then $a < 8$. **F**
8. If $-\frac{1}{2}x < 6$, then $x > -12$. **T**

Written Exercises

Find the solution set of each inequality. Graph the solutions on a number line.

(A)
1. $-5y \le 15$ $\{y|y \ge -3\}$
2. $-7a > -28$ $\{a|a < 4\}$
3. $32 < 8x$ $\{x|x > 4\}$
4. $3 > x - 2$ $\{x|x < 5\}$
5. $4 \le n + 6$ $\{n|n \ge -2\}$
6. $-4 \ge y - 6$ $\{y|y \le 2\}$

Find the solution set of each inequality.
10. $\{n|n > 7\}$ 11. $\{x|x \le -3\}$ 12. $\{y|y > -3\}$

7. $6 - 4x < 30$ $\{x|x > -6\}$
8. $3y - 6 > 9y$ $\{y|y < -1\}$
9. $5n + 27 \le -4n$ $\{n|n \le -3\}$
10. $8n - 2 > 6n + 12$
11. $4 - 2x \ge 3x + 19$
12. $7y - 6 > 3(y - 6)$
13. $3(2y + 6) < 8y + 11$
14. $4(2n - 3) > 5(n + 4)$
15. $-2(3x - 2) \ge 7(2 - x)$

$\{y|y > 3\frac{1}{2}\}$ $\{n|n > 10\frac{2}{3}\}$ $\{x|x \ge 10\}$

Find the solution set of each inequality. Graph the solutions on a number line.

(B)
16. $-x < 0$ $\{x|x > 0\}$
17. $22 - 3a > 29$ $\{a|a < -2\frac{1}{3}\}$
18. $\frac{1}{2}y \le 4$ $\{y|y \le 8\}$

19. $18 - 5y \ge 7 - 3y$
20. $\frac{2}{3}n < 12$ $\{n|n < 18\}$
21. $8x - 7 - 10x \le 7 + 2x$

$\{y|y \le 5\frac{1}{2}\}$ $\{x|x \ge -3\frac{1}{2}\}$

Find the solution set of each inequality. 22. $\{x|x > 1\frac{1}{2}\}$ 23. $\{n|n \ge 1\frac{1}{3}\}$ 24. $x|x < 2.75$

22. $8 - 2(2x + 1) < 2x - 3$
23. $2n + 3(n - 2) \ge 2(3 - 2n)$
24. $5(x - 4) - (2 - 3x) < 0$
25. $\frac{1}{4}(8y - 12) > \frac{1}{3}(9 - 12y)$ $\{y|y > 1\}$
26. $\frac{3}{5}(10a + 25) < \frac{2}{3}(6a - 9)$ $\{a|a < -10.5\}$
27. $8n - \frac{3}{4}(12n + 28) \le 0$ $\{n|n \ge -21\}$

(C)
28. $\frac{2x - 1}{-3} < 5$ $\{x|x > -7\}$
29. $\frac{2(2y + 3)}{-5} > 6 - 2y$
30. $\frac{3(5a + 6)}{-4} < \frac{8 - 5a}{-4}$

$\{y|y > 6\}$ $\{a|a > -0.5\}$

31. Use algebraic properties to prove: If $x < y$, then $-y < -x$.
   $x < y$; $-1 \cdot x > -1 \cdot y$; $-x > -y$; $-y < -x$

Show that each statement is false by giving a numerical counterexample.

32. If $b \ne 0$ and $a < b$, then $a^2 < b^2$.

Let $a = -3$, $b = -2$. (Answers may vary.)

33. If $a \ne 0$, $b \ne 0$, and $a < b$, then $\frac{1}{a} > \frac{1}{b}$.

Let $a = -2$, $b = 4$. (Answers may vary.)

1.3 Absolute Value

OBJECTIVES ▶ To solve an equation involving absolute value
To find the solution set of an inequality involving absolute value
To graph the solutions of an inequality involving absolute value

The **absolute value** of any number x is the distance between x and the origin, 0, on a number line. Therefore, the absolute value of -5 is 5 and the absolute value of 5 is 5.

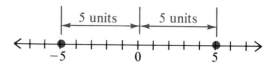

The symbol $|x|$ means the absolute value of x, so $|-5| = |5| = 5$.

Definition: Absolute Value

$|x| = -x$, if x is a negative number.

$|x| = x$, if x is a positive number or 0.

From the definition of absolute value, the solutions of the equation $|x| = 12$ are -12 and 12 since $|-12| = 12$ and $|12| = 12$. This leads to the following equation property.

Equation Property for Absolute Value

For each number x and each number $k \geq 0$,
if $|x| = k$, then $x = -k$ or $x = k$.

Example 1 Solve $|3n - 5| = 7$.

$$|3n - 5| = 7$$

$3n - 5 = -7$	or	$3n - 5 = 7$	◀ If $|x| = k$, then $x = -k$ or $x = k$.
$3n = -2$		$3n = 12$	
$n = -\dfrac{2}{3}$		$n = 4$	

Check: $n = -\dfrac{2}{3}$

$|3n - 5|$	7
$\left\lvert 3 \cdot \dfrac{-2}{3} - 5 \right\rvert$	7
$|-2 - 5|$	
$|-7|$	
7	

True: $7 = 7$

Check: $n = 4$

$|3n - 5|$	7
$|3 \cdot 4 - 5|$	7
$|12 - 5|$	
$|7|$	
7	

True: $7 = 7$

Thus, the solutions are $-\dfrac{2}{3}$ and 4.

CHAPTER ONE

The graph for $|x| < 4$ is shown below on the left. The graph for $|x| > 4$ is shown below on the right.

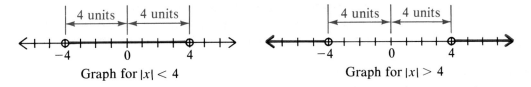

Graph for $|x| < 4$ Graph for $|x| > 4$

All numbers between -4 and 4 are solutions of the inequality. In symbols, $-4 < x < 4$. The compound inequality $-4 < x < 4$ means $-4 < x$ *and* $x < 4$.

All numbers less than -4 and all numbers greater than 4 are solutions of the inequality. In symbols, $x < -4$ *or* $x > 4$.

The graphs suggest the following inequality properties:

Inequality Properties for Absolute Value	For all numbers x and k, if $k > 0$ and $|x| < k$, then $-k < x < k$. if $k \geq 0$ and $|x| > k$, then $x < -k$ or $x > k$.

The inequality properties for absolute value are applied in the following examples. Notice that Example 3 involves the $\geq$ relation, so combined equation and inequality properties are used.

Example 2 Find the solution set of $|4y + 2| < 10$. Graph the solutions on a number line.

$$|4y + 2| < 10$$
$$-10 < 4y + 2 < 10 \quad \blacktriangleleft \text{ If } |x| < k, \text{ then } -k < x < k.$$
$$-12 < 4y < 8 \quad \blacktriangleleft \text{ Subtract 2 from each side.}$$
$$-3 < y < 2 \quad \blacktriangleleft \text{ Divide each side by 4.}$$

The solution set is $\{y | -3 < y < 2\}$.

Example 3 Find the solution set of $|2n - 1| \geq 5$. Graph the solutions on a number line.

$$|2n - 1| \geq 5$$

$2n - 1 \leq -5$	or	$2n - 1 \geq 5$	$\blacktriangleleft$ Combined properties:
$2n \leq -4$		$2n \geq 6$	If $|x| = k$, then $x = -k$, or $x = k$.
$n \leq -2$		$n \geq 3$	If $|x| > k$, then $x < -k$, or $x > k$.

The solution set is $\{n | n \leq -2 \text{ or } n \geq 3\}$.

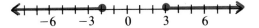

ABSOLUTE VALUE   **9**

Reading in Algebra

True or false? If a statement is false, give a numerical counterexample which shows that it is false.

1. $|-x| = x$, if $x > 0$. **T**
2. $|-x| = -x$, if $x < 0$. **T**
3. $|x - 2| = x - 2$, if $x > 0$.
4. $|x - 2| = 2 - x$, if $x \leq 0$. **T**
5. $|4 - x| = 4 - x$, if $x \geq 0$.
6. $|-x - 6| = x + 6$, if $x < 0$.
7. $|5 - x| = |x - 5|$, for each x. **T**
8. $|-x - 8| = |x + 8|$, for each x. **T**
9. $|x| = |-x|$, for each x. **T**

3. **F: Let x = 1.**   5. **F: Let x = 5.**   6. **F: Let x = −8.**

Oral Exercises

Find the value of each expression.

1. $|-9 + 4|$ **5**
2. $|-5 - 8|$ **13**
3. $|-6 + 9|$ **3**
4. $|7 - 7|$ **0**
5. $|-3 \cdot 5|$ **15**
6. $|-2(-4)|$ **8**
7. $|2(-5) - 10|$ **20**
8. $|-5(-4) - 2|$ **18**

Written Exercises

Solve each equation.

(A)
1. $|x - 3| = 7$ **−4, 10**
2. $|a + 6| = 2$ **−8, −4**
3. $|4 - y| = 6$ **−2, 10**
4. $|2 - x| = 3$ **5, −1**
5. $|2x + 15| = 5$ **−10, −5**
6. $|3y - 9| = 18$ **−3, 9**
7. $|4n + 6| = 2$ **−2, −1**
8. $|5 - 2a| = 9$ **−2, 7**

9. $\{x \mid -3 < x < 3\}$ 10. $\{n \mid n \leq -6 \text{ or } n \geq 6\}$ 11. $\{y \mid y < -8 \text{ or } y > 8\}$ 12. $\{a \mid -4 \leq a \leq 4\}$

Find the solution set of each inequality. Graph the solutions on a number line.
9. $|x| < 3$
10. $|2n| \geq 12$
11. $|y| > 8$
12. $|5a| \leq 20$
13. $|x - 3| \geq 1$
14. $|y + 4| < 7$
15. $|a - 2| \leq 6$
16. $|n + 5| > 3$
$\{x \mid x \leq 2 \text{ or } x \geq 4\}$ $\{y \mid -11 < y < 3\}$ $\{a \mid -4 \leq a \leq 8\}$ $\{n \mid n < -8 \text{ or } n > -2\}$

Solve each equation. 17. **−2, ½**   18. **−1⅔, 5**   19. **−2.8, −2**   20. **4, ⅔**
(B)
17. $|4y + 3| = 5$
18. $|3x - 5| = 10$
19. $|5n + 12| - 2 = 0$
20. $|14 - 6z| = 10$
21. $|2x - 3.5| = 10.5$
22. $|4y + 6.8| = 9.2$
23. $2.7 - |3z + 9.3| = 0$
24. $|14.2 - 5n| = 0.8$
   −3.5, 7   **−4, 0.6**   **−4, −2.2**   **3, 2.68**

Find the solution set of each inequality. Graph the solutions on a number line.
25. $|2x - 5| < 17$
26. $|3y + 6| > 21$
27. $|3z - 15| \geq 6$
28. $|2n + 17| \leq 1$
29. $|4y + 6| \geq 2$
30. $10 \geq |5a - 15|$
31. $|5x + 10| - 35 < 0$
32. $20 < |4z - 4|$
25. $\{x \mid -6 < x < 11\}$ 26. $\{y \mid y < -9 \text{ or } y > 5\}$ 27. $\{z \mid z \leq 3 \text{ or } z \geq 7\}$

(C)
33. $|18 - 3x| < 6$ $\{x \mid 4 < x < 8\}$
34. $|75 - 2y| > 5$ $\{y \mid y < 35 \text{ or } y > 40\}$
35. $|x - 2| < 6 \text{ or } |x - 2| > 10$
36. $|y + 5| \leq 2 \text{ or } |y - 5| \leq 2$
   $\{x \mid -4 < x < 8 \text{ or } x < -8 \text{ or } x > 12\}$ $\{y \mid -7 \leq y \leq -3 \text{ or } 3 \leq y \leq 7\}$

Solve each equation.
37. $|x - 2| + |2 - x| = 10$ **7, −3**
38. $|2y + 4| + |6 - 2y| = 22$ **6, −5**
39. $|n + 2| + |-n - 6| = 18$ **−13, 5**
40. $|1 - 2x| + |-x - 7| = 21$ **−9, 5**

Find the solution set of each inequality.
41. $|x - 4| < 0.1$ $\{x \mid 3.9 < x < 4.1\}$
42. $|y + 6| < 0.001$ $\{y \mid -6.001 < y < -5.999\}$
43. $|x - 2.5| < 0.01$ $\{x \mid 2.49 < x < 2.51\}$
44. $|x + 3.4| < 0.0001$ $\{x \mid -3.4001 < x < -3.3999\}$
28. $\{n \mid -9 \leq n \leq -8\}$
29. $\{y \mid y \leq -2 \text{ or } y \geq -1\}$
30. $\{a \mid 1 \leq a \leq 5\}$
31. $\{x \mid -9 < x < 5\}$
32. $\{z \mid z < -4 \text{ or } z > 6\}$

Cumulative Review

1. Solve $\frac{2}{3}(12y - 15) - \frac{3}{5}(15y + 20) = 3y - 2$ **−5**
2. Solve $0.9n + 2.2(0.5n - 3) = 0.4(10n - 1.5)$. **−3**

1.4 Problem Solving: Number Problems

OBJECTIVES ▶ **To write a word phrase in algebraic terms**
To solve a word problem about one or more numbers

Many mathematical problems are presented using a word phrase or several word phrases. To solve such problems, you begin by writing the word phrases in algebraic terms. Some typical word phrases and their algebraic translations are listed below.

Word Phrase	Written in Algebraic Terms
Ten decreased by a number	$10 - n$
Twice a number, increased by 12	$2x + 12$
Six less than a number	$y - 6$
Seven more than a number	$n + 7$ or $7 + n$
Eight decreased by 5 times the sum of a number and 14	$8 - 5(x + 14)$
Is, or is the same as	$=$

Notice that two translations are given for the word phrase "Seven more than a number." The two translations are equivalent since addition is commutative. However, there is only one correct translation for the word phrase "Six less than a number." Subtraction is not commutative. Remember, for *4 less than x* write $x - 4$, not $4 - x$.

You can solve a word problem about one number if you are given enough information about the number. Example 1 illustrates this situation.

Example 1 **Seven less than twice a number is 20 more than 5 times the number. What is the number?**

Represent the data.
Let x be the number.
7 less than twice x is   20 more than $5x$.

Write an equation.
$$2x - 7 = 5x + 20$$
$$-27 = 3x$$

Solve the equation.
$$-9 = x$$

Check in the problem.

Seven less than twice x	20 more than $5x$
$2(-9) - 7$	$5(-9) + 20$
$-18 - 7$	$-45 + 20$
-25	-25

Answer the question.   **Thus, the number is -9.**

In some word problems you will be asked to find more than one number. To do this, you begin by representing each of the numbers in terms of one variable, as shown in Example 2.

Example 2

The greater of two numbers is 8 less than twice the sum of the smaller number and 5. Represent each number in terms of one variable.

The *greater* number is *described in terms of* the *smaller* number. Represent the *smaller* number by a variable.

Let s = smaller number.

Twice the sum of s and 5   8 less than

$$2(s + 5) \quad - \quad 8$$

Thus, s = smaller number and $2(s + 5) - 8$ = greater number.

The four steps you should use in solving any word problem are given at the beginning of this chapter. They are illustrated again in Example 3 below.

Example 3

The second of three numbers is 3 times the first. The third number is 2 more than the second number. Seven less than twice the second is the same as 12 more than the third. What are the three numbers?

READ

You are asked to find three numbers. The third number is described *in terms of* the second number. The second number is described *in terms of* the first number.

PLAN

Let $\quad f$ = 1st number
$\quad\quad 3f$ = 2nd number
$\quad 3f + 2$ = 3rd number

7 less than twice the 2nd   is   12 more than the 3rd.

SOLVE

$$
\begin{aligned}
2(3f) - 7 &= (3f + 2) + 12 \\
6f - 7 &= 3f + 14 \\
3f &= 21 \\
f &= 7
\end{aligned}
$$

$f = 7 \quad\quad 3f = 21 \quad\quad 3f + 2 = 23$

INTERPRET

7 less than twice the 2nd	12 more than the 3rd
$2(21) - 7$	$23 + 12$
$42 - 7$	35
35	

Thus, the three numbers are 7, 21, and 23.

In Example 3, you saw the four major steps in solving a word problem.

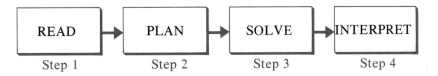

| READ | → | PLAN | → | SOLVE | → | INTERPRET |
| Step 1 | | Step 2 | | Step 3 | | Step 4 |

Step 2 may require some information that is not stated directly in the problem. For example, some problems require a knowledge of *consecutive integers*. Four such typical word phrases and their algebraic translations are shown in the table below, along with a numerical example of each.

Word Phrase	Example	Written in Algebraic Terms	
Consecutive integers	$-1, 0, 1, 2, 3$	$x, x + 1, x + 2, \ldots$	(x is an integer.)
Consecutive odd integers	$5, 7, 9, 11, 13$	$y, y + 2, y + 4, \ldots$	(y is an odd integer.)
Consecutive even integers	$-2, 0, 2, 4, 6$	$n, n + 2, n + 4, \ldots$	(n is an even integer.)
Consecutive multiples of 4	$12, 16, 20, 24$	$a, a + 4, a + 8, \ldots$	(a is a multiple of 4.)

A word problem about consecutive odd integers is solved in Example 4.

Example 4 The sum of three consecutive odd integers is 69 more than twice the third odd integer. What are the three odd integers?

Let y = 1st odd integer, $y + 2$ = 2nd odd integer, and $y + 4$ = 3rd odd integer.

Their sum is 69 more than twice the third.

$$y + (y + 2) + (y + 4) = 2(y + 4) + 69$$
$$3y + 6 = 2y + 77$$
$$y = 71$$

$$y = 71 \qquad y + 2 = 73 \qquad y + 4 = 75$$

Check:

The sum of the 3 integers	69 more than twice the 3rd
$71 + 73 + 75$	$2 \cdot 75 + 69$
219	$150 + 69$
	219

Thus, the three consecutive odd integers are 71, 73, and 75.

Reading in Algebra

State each word phrase in algebraic terms.
1. Twelve less than a number $n - 12$
2. The sum of a number and 14 $x + 14$
3. Twenty increased by a number $20 + y$
4. A number decreased by 15 $n - 15$
5. Eight more than twice a number $2x + 8$
6. Five less than 3 times a number $3y - 5$
7. Four times the sum of 8 and n $4(8 + n)$
8. Ten times the difference of n and 2
$$10(n - 2)$$

Oral Exercises

1. State 4 consecutive even integers, beginning with 6. **6, 8, 10, 12**
2. State 4 consecutive multiples of 10, beginning with 30. **30, 40, 50, 60**
3. State 4 consecutive integers, beginning with −10. **−10, −9, −8, −7**
4. State 4 consecutive odd integers, beginning with −3. **−3, −1, 1, 3**

Written Exercises

Solve each problem.

(A) 1. Nine less than 5 times a number is 1 less than the number. What is the number? **2**
2. Sixteen more than a number is 20 more than twice the number. Find the number. **−4**
3. Five times the sum of 6 and a number is 2 more than the number. Find the number. **−7**
4. Fourteen more than twice a number is 6 times the difference of the number and 7. What is the number? **14**

5. smaller: x, greater: 5x+7

Represent each number in terms of one variable.

5. The greater of two numbers is 7 more than 5 times the smaller number.

6. first: n, second: 9n − 6

6. The second of two numbers is 6 less than 9 times the first number.

7. The second of three numbers is 7 times the first number. The third number is 6 less than the second number.
1st: x, 2nd: 7x, 3rd: 7x − 6

8. A second number is 5 times a first number. A third number is 8 more than twice the second number.
1st: n, 2nd: 5n, 3rd: 10n + 8

Solve each problem.

9. The greater of two numbers is 3 less than twice the smaller number. The sum of the two numbers is 18. What are the two numbers? **7, 11**

10. The smaller of two numbers is 10 less than 4 times the greater number. The greater number is 19 more than the smaller. Find the two numbers. **−3, −22**

11. The second of three numbers is 5 times the first number. The third number is 12 less than the first. Find the three numbers if their sum is 51. **9, 45, −3**

12. The second of three numbers is 6 more than the first and the third is 7 times the second. If the third number is 12 more than 10 times the first number, what are the three numbers? **10, 16, 112**

13. The sum of three consecutive integers is 12 less than 4 times the first integer. What are the three integers? **15, 16, 17**

14. There are three consecutive even integers such that the sum of the first two is 22 more than the third. Find the three even integers. **24, 26, 28**

15. The population of city A is 4 times the population of city B. City C has 670 fewer people than city A. What is the population of each city if their combined population is 8,330? **A: 4,000, B: 1,000, C: 3,330**

16. A company's total sales were $150,000 for a 3-year period. Sales for the second year were $20,000 more than the first year's sales. The third year's sales were 3 times those of the second year. Find the sales amount for each year.
1st yr: $14,000, 2nd yr: $34,000, 3rd yr: $102,000

17. There are four consecutive multiples of 3 such that the sum of the first three multiples is twice the fourth. Find the four multiples of 3. **9, 12, 15, 18**

18. The sum of three consecutive multiples of 6 is 30 more than the fifth consecutive multiple of 6. Find the fourth of these five consecutive multiples of 6. **36**

19. Twice the sum of three consecutive multiples of 15 is 270. What are the three multiples of 15? **30, 45, 60**

20. One-half of the sum of three consecutive multiples of 10 is 75. Find the three multiples of 10. **40, 50, 60**

21. The third of three numbers is 7 times the first and the second is 8 more than the first. Six more than the third, decreased by 3 times the second, is 9 less than the first. Find the three numbers. **3, 11, 21**

22. The second of three numbers is twice the first and the third is 4 less than the second. If 9 less than the first is decreased by the third, the result is −12. What are the three numbers? **7, 14, 10**

23. A size A box holds twice as many jars as a size B box and a size C box holds one dozen fewer jars than a size A box. Ten size A boxes, 5 size B boxes, and 3 size C boxes will hold a total of 522 jars. Find the number of jars that each type of box will hold. **A: 36, B: 18, C: 24**

24. A company's sales for February increased $400 over its January sales figure. The March sales were twice the February figure and the sales for April doubled the figure for March. If the sales total was $18,000 for the four months, find the sales figure for each month.
Jan.: $1,900, Feb.: $2,300, Mar.:$4,600 Apr.: $9,200

25. Find three consecutive integers so that 8 times the first, decreased by the third, is 488. **70, 71, 72**

26. Find three consecutive odd integers so that 6 times the second, decreased by the third, is 363. **71, 73, 75**

27. Find three consecutive even integers so that 7 times the third is equal to 20 less than the first. **−8, −6, −4**

28. Find three consecutive integers so that 25 more than the second is equal to 5 times the third. **4, 5, 6**

29. Find three consecutive integers so that 3 less than twice the third integer is the sum of the first and second integers.
any three consecutive integers

30. Find three consecutive multiples of 5 for which the sum of the first and third multiples is twice the second multiple of 5.
any three consecutive multiples of 5

31. Six decreased by 3 times a number is less than 12. Find the set of all such numbers.
{x|x > −2}

32. Seven more than 4 times a number is greater than 3. Find the set of all these numbers. **{x|x > −1}**

33. Eight less than 5 times a number is greater than or equal to 8 more than the number. Find the set of all these numbers.
{x|x ≥ 4}

34. Twenty increased by twice a number is less than or equal to 6 times the number. Find the set of all such numbers.
{x|x ≥ 5}

1.5 Problem Solving: Perimeter Problems

OBJECTIVE ▶ **To solve a word problem involving the perimeter of a geometric figure**

The **perimeter** of a geometric figure is the sum of the lengths of its sides. To solve a problem that involves perimeter, you may find it helpful to draw the geometric figure and label the lengths of the sides. If the measures of any of the sides are unknown, represent these lengths in terms of one variable.

Example 1

READ

The length of a rectangle is 4 meters (m) more than twice the width. The perimeter is 26 m. Find the length and the width. Find the area of the rectangle in square meters (m^2).

PLAN

Let w = width of rectangle and $2w + 4$ = length of rectangle. Draw the figure and label each side.

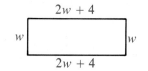

SOLVE

$$w + (2w + 4) + w + (2w + 4) = 26 \qquad \text{or} \qquad 2(w) + 2(2w + 4) = 26$$
$$6w + 8 = 26$$
$$6w = 18$$
$$w = 3 \qquad\qquad 2w + 4 = 10$$

INTERPRET

Check:

$2(w) + 2(2w + 4)$	26
$2(3) + 2(10)$	26
26	

The area, length × width, is $10 \cdot 3$, or 30.

Thus, the length is 10 m, the width is 3 m, and the area is 30 m^2.

Example 2

Side a of a triangle is 3 times as long as side b. Side c is 2 cm longer than side a. Find the length of each side of the triangle if its perimeter is 72 cm.

Let x = length of side b, $3x$ = length of side a, and $3x + 2$ = length of side c.

$$x + 3x + (3x + 2) = 72$$
$$7x = 70$$
$$x = 10 \qquad 3x = 30 \qquad 3x + 2 = 32$$

Check:

$x + 3x + (3x + 2)$	72
$10 + 30 + 32$	72
72	

Thus, the lengths of the three sides are 10 cm, 30 cm, and 32 cm.

Written Exercises _____

Solve each problem.

(A) 1. The length of a rectangle is 12 cm more than the width. The perimeter is 44 cm. Find the length and the width. Find the area of the rectangle in cm².
width: 5 cm, length: 17 cm, area: 85 cm²

2. The width of a rectangle is 4 m less than the length and the perimeter is 40 m. Find the width, the length, and the area of the rectangle.
width: 8 m, length: 12 m, area: 96 m²

3. Side a of a triangle is 4 cm longer than side b. Side c is twice as long as side b. What is the length of each side of the triangle if its perimeter is 28 cm?
a: 10 cm, b: 6 cm, c: 12 cm

4. Side c of a triangle is 6 m longer than side a. Side b is 8 m shorter than side a. The perimeter is 52 m. Find the length of each of the three sides.
a: 18 m, b: 10 m, c: 24 m

5. The length of a rectangle is 5 dm more than 3 times the width. Find the length, the width, and the area of the rectangle if its perimeter is 42 dm.
width: 4 dm, length: 17 dm, area: 68 dm²

6. The length of side b of a triangle is 6 m less than twice the length of side a. Sides b and c have the same length. If the perimeter is 28 m, find the lengths of the three sides. **a: 8 m, b: 10 m, c: 10 m**

7. The two longest sides of a *pentagon* (5-sided figure) are each 3 times as long as the shortest side. The other sides are each 8 m longer than the shortest side. Find the length of each side if the perimeter is 79 m.
7 m, 21 m, 21 m, 15 m, 15 m

8. Each of the three longest sides of a *hexagon* (6-sided figure) is 3 cm less than 4 times the length of each of the three shortest sides. If the perimeter is 111 cm, find the length of each side.
8 cm, 8 cm, 8 cm, 29 cm, 29 cm, 29 cm

(B) 9. A rectangle and a square have the same width. The rectangle is 6 cm longer than the square. One perimeter is twice the other. Find the dimensions of the rectangle.
width: 3 cm, length: 9 cm

10. One side of an equilateral triangle is 7 dm shorter than one side of a square. The sum of the perimeters of the two figures is 49 dm. Find the perimeter of each figure.
square: 40 dm, triangle: 9 dm

11. The hypotenuse of a right triangle is 10 m long and one leg is 2 m longer than the other leg. If the perimeter is 24 m, find the area of the right triangle in square meters. **24 m²**

12. One leg of a right triangle is 2 cm longer than twice the length of the other leg. The hypotenuse is 1 cm longer than the longer leg. Find the area if the perimeter is 30 cm. **30 cm²**

13. A longer side of a parallelogram is 4 dm shorter than 5 times the length of a shorter side. One side of a *rhombus* (equilateral quadrilateral) and a longer side of the parallelogram are equal in length. If the difference in the two perimeters is 48 dm, find the perimeter of the rhombus. **124 dm**

14. The lengths of the sides of a quadrilateral are in the ratio of 2 to 3 to 5 to 6. What is the length of each side if the perimeter is 104 m?
13 m, $19\frac{1}{2}$ m, $32\frac{1}{2}$ m, 39 m

(C) 15. The length of a rectangle is 4 cm more than 5 times the width. The perimeter is less than 44 cm. Find the set of all such possible widths.
{$w|0$ cm $< w <$ 3 cm}

16. The length of a rectangle is 7 dm less than 3 times the width. Find the set of all possible lengths if the perimeter must be greater than 18 dm.
{$l|l >$ 5 dm}

PROBLEM SOLVING: PERIMETER PROBLEMS **17**

1.6 Problem Solving: Age Problems

OBJECTIVE ▶ **To solve a word problem about ages**

Word problems about people's ages may include information about their present ages, past ages, and future ages. If you are x years old now, then 3 years ago you were $x - 3$ years old. Ten years from now, you will be $x + 10$ years old.

To solve a word problem about ages, it may be helpful to use a table to organize the information.

Example

Carol is 6 times as old as her nephew Howard. Betty is 22 years younger than her aunt Carol. In 4 years, Carol's age will be twice the sum of Howard's and Betty's ages. How old is each person now?

In a table, represent their ages *now* and their ages *in 4 years*. Let $h =$ Howard's age now.

	Howard	Carol	Betty
Ages now	h	$6h$	$6h - 22$
Ages in 4 yr	$h + 4$	$6h + 4$	$(6h - 22) + 4$, or $6h - 18$

In 4 years, Carol's age will be 2 times the sum of Howard's and Betty's ages.

$$6h + 4 = 2[(h + 4) + (6h - 18)]$$
$$6h + 4 = 2(7h - 14)$$
$$6h + 4 = 14h - 28$$
$$32 = 8h$$
$$4 = h$$
$$h = 4 \qquad 6h = 24 \qquad 6h - 22 = 2$$

Check:

Carol's age in 4 years	twice the sum of Howard's and Betty's ages in 4 years
$24 + 4$	$2[(4 + 4) + (2 + 4)]$
28	$2(14)$
	28

Thus, Harold is now 4 years old, Carol is 24, and Betty is 2.

Reading in **Algebra** _____

Select the correct equation for each situation.

1. He is x years old and she is y years old. She is 4 times as old as he is. **(a)**
   (a) $y = 4x$ **(b)** $4y = x$ **(c)** $y = x + 4$ **(d)** $x + 4 = y + 4$

2. She is $x - 10$ years old and he is $x - 2$ years old. He is 3 times as old as she is. **(c)**
   (a) $3(x - 2) = x - 10$ **(b)** $x - 2 = (x - 10) + 3$ **(c)** $x - 2 = 3(x - 10)$ **(d)** $x = 3(x - 10)$

Oral Exercises

Represent each age now in terms of one variable.

1. Karen is 7 years older than Jane.

2. Ed is 5 years younger than Frank.

3. Eloise is 5 times as old as Robert.

4. Sarah is half as old as Richard.

5. A horse is 10 years older than twice the age of a colt. **colt: x, horse: 2x + 10**

6. A redwood tree is 80 years older than 4 **oak: x,** times the age of an oak tree. **redwood: 4x + 80**

7. A second city was chartered 20 years before a first city. A third city is 4 times as old as the first city. **1st city: x, 2nd city: x +20, 3rd city: 4x**

8. An eagle is 3 times as old as a hawk. A robin was hatched 15 years after the eagle was hatched.
hawk: x, eagle: 3x, robin: 3x − 15

Written Exercises

Solve each problem.

(A)

1. Fred is 4 times as old as his niece, Selma. Ten years from now, he will be twice as old as she will be. How old is each now?
Selma: 5, Fred: 20

2. Raymond is 12 years younger than Susan. Four years ago, she was 4 times as old as he was. Find their present ages.
Sue: 20, Ray: 8

3. Byron is 2 years younger than Cindy. Eight years ago, the sum of their ages was 14. Find their present ages.
Cindy: 16, Byron: 14

4. A fir tree is 5 times as old as a pine tree. Seven years from now, the sum of their ages will be 32. How old is the fir tree now? **15**

5. Brenda is 4 years older than Walter and Carol is twice as old as Brenda. Three years ago, the sum of their ages was 35. How old is each now?
Walt: 8, Brenda: 12, Carol: 24

6. Denise is 3 times as old as Conrad and Billy is 8 years younger than Denise. Five years from now, the sum of their ages will be 49. How old is Billy? **10**

(B)

7. An eagle is 4 times as old as a falcon. Three years ago, the eagle was 7 times as old as the falcon. Find the present age of each bird. **falcon: 6, eagle, 24**

8. An oak tree is 20 years older than a pine tree. In eight years, the oak will be 3 times as old as the pine will be. How old is each tree now? **pine: 2, oak: 22**

9. Adam is 3 times as old as Cynthia and Fred is 16 years younger than Adam. One year ago, Adam's age was twice the sum of Cynthia's and Fred's ages. Find their present ages. **Cynthia: 7, Adam: 21, Fred: 5**

10. Building A was built 20 years before building B and 30 years after building C. In 10 years, building C will be 20 years younger than the combined ages of buildings A and B. What is the present age of each building? **A: 60, B: 40, C: 90**

11. Phyllis is 6 years older than Keith and Manuel is 10 years older than twice Keith's age. If Manuel's age is added to 5 years less than twice Phyllis' age, the result is the same as 7 years more than 5 times Keith's age. How old is each now? **Keith: 10, Phyllis: 16, Manuel: 30**

12. The present ages of three portraits are in the ratio of 1 to 3 to 4. In 3 years, the sum of their ages will be 49 years. Find the present ages of the portraits. **5, 15, 20**

(C)

13. A person is x years old now and 10 years ago was t years old. Represent the person's age f years from now in terms of t and f.
t + 10 + f

14. In x years, a person will be y years old. Represent the person's age z years ago in terms of x, y, and z. **y − x − z**

PROBLEM SOLVING: AGE PROBLEMS

1.7 Problem Solving: Using Formulas

OBJECTIVE ▶ **To solve a word problem by using a given formula**

Many applications of mathematics involve the use of **formulas.** One such application is the formula for finding *simple interest* on money borrowed or loaned.

If you borrow $2,500 at $8\frac{1}{2}\%$ per year for 3 years (yr) 6 months (mo), you will pay $743.75 in simple interest, since $2,500 \times 0.085 \times 3.5 = $743.75. At the end of 3 yr 6 mo, you will pay $3,243.75, since $2,500 + $743.75 = $3,243.75.

In general, a principal p borrowed at a rate of $r\%$ per year for t years is charged a simple interest i, where $i = prt$.
The simple interest i, or prt, added to the principal p gives the total amount A that is owed, or $A = p + prt$.

To find the value of one variable in a formula, you substitute given values for the other variables and then solve the resulting equation. This procedure is shown in the following examples, using the formulas $i = prt$ and $A = p + prt$.

Example 1 **Jack borrowed $4,000 and paid $585 in simple interest after 1 yr 6 mo. What was the annual rate of interest?**

Use the formula $i = prt$. Find r.

$$p = \$4,000 \qquad i = \$585 \qquad t = 1 \text{ yr } 6 \text{ mo, or } 1.5 \text{ yr}$$

$$i = p \cdot r \cdot t$$

Substitute for p, i, and t. ▶ $\quad 585 = 4,000 \cdot r \cdot 1.5$
Solve the equation for r. ▶ $\quad 585 = 6,000r$
$$0.0975 = r \qquad 0.0975 = 9.75\%, \text{ or } 9\frac{3}{4}\%$$

Thus, the rate of interest was $9\frac{3}{4}\%$ per year.

Example 2 **At the end of 2 yr, Maria paid $3,780 to cover a loan for her junior college tuition. If she was charged 4% in simple interest per year, how much money did Maria borrow?**

Use the formula $A = p + prt$. Find p.
$$A = \$3,780 \qquad r = 4\%, \text{ or } 0.04 \qquad t = 2 \text{ yr}$$

$$A = p + prt$$
$$3,780 = p + p(0.04)(2)$$
$$3,780 = 1.08\,p$$
$$3,500 = p$$

Thus, Maria borrowed $3,500.

A parallel electric circuit with two resistances is shown at the right. The bulbs have resistances of r_1 and r_2 (r-sub-one and r-sub-two) ohms. The circuit has a total resistance of R ohms, where
$$R(r_1 + r_2) = r_1 \cdot r_2.$$

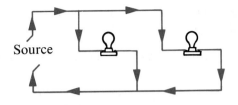

Source

Example 3 Find r_2 in ohms if R = 4 ohms and r_1 = 6 ohms. Use the formula $R(r_1 + r_2) = r_1 \cdot r_2$.

$$R = 4 \text{ ohms} \qquad r_1 = 6 \text{ ohms}$$

$$R(r_1 + r_2) = r_1 \cdot r_2$$
$$4(6 + r_2) = 6 \cdot r_2 \qquad \blacktriangleleft \text{ Substitute for } R \text{ and } r_1.$$
$$24 + 4r_2 = 6r_2 \qquad \blacktriangleleft \text{ Solve the equation for } r_2.$$
$$24 = 2r_2$$
$$12 = r_2$$

Thus, r_2 is 12 ohms.

Written Exercises

Solve each problem. Use the formula $i = prt$.

(A) 1. For a loan of $6,500 for 8 yr, Jose was charged $3,640 in simple interest. What was the annual interest rate? **7%**

2. For a loan of $2,500 for 5 yr 9 mo, Muna was charged $1,150 in simple interest. What was the annual interest rate? **8%**

3. When would a borrower owe $6,528 in simple interest on a loan of $6,400 at $8\frac{1}{2}\%$ per year? **12 yr**

4. When would a borrower owe $1,152 in simple interest on a loan of $3,200 at 8% per year? **4 yr 6 mo**

5. Ms. Brown borrowed some money on February 1, 1972, at 6% per year. How much did she borrow if Ms. Brown paid off the debt, including $3,000 in simple interest, on February 1, 1982? **$5,000**

6. Mr. Adamshick borrowed some money on July 1, 1974, at $7\frac{1}{2}\%$ per year. How much did he borrow if Mr. Adamshick paid off the debt, including $1,485 in simple interest, on October 1, 1982? **$2,400**

Solve each problem. Use the formula $A = p + prt$.

7. Find p in dollars if A = $9,780, r = 9%, and t = 7 yr. **$6,000**

8. Find p in dollars if $r = 8\frac{1}{2}\%$, t = 6 yr, and A = $5,285. **$3,500**

Solve each problem. Use the formula $R(r_1 + r_2) = r_1 \cdot r_2$.

9. Find R in ohms if r_1 = 50 ohms and r_2 = 30 ohms. **18.75 ohms**

10. Find r_2 in ohms if R = 19.2 ohms and r_1 = 32 ohms. **48 ohms**

11. Find r_2 in ohms if R = 24 ohms and r_1 = 60 ohms. **40 ohms**

12. Find r_1 in ohms if R = 21 ohms and r_2 = 70 ohms. **30 ohms**

PROBLEM SOLVING: USING FORMULAS

13. Find r_2 in ohms if $R = 3.2$ ohms and $r_1 = 4.8$ ohms. **9.6 ohms**

14. Find r_1 in ohms if $R = 4.2$ ohms and $r_2 = 8.7$ ohms. **8.12 ohms**

Solve each problem.

15. Find p in dollars if $A = \$8,295$, $r = 8\frac{1}{2}\%$, and $t = 4$ yr 6 mo. **\$6,000**

16. Find p in dollars if $A = \$4,650$, $r = 7\frac{1}{4}\%$, and $t = 6$ yr 3 mo. **\$3,200**

17. Find t in years and months if $A = \$12,160$, $p = \$8,000$, and $r = 8\%$. **6 yr 6 mo**

18. Find the annual interest rate r if $A = \$697$, $p = \$400$, and $t = 9$ yr. **$8\frac{1}{4}\%$**

19. When will an investment of \$1,000 at 8% per year in simple interest be doubled in total value? **12 yr 6 mo**

20. When will an investment of p dollars at 12.5% per year in simple interest be doubled in total value? **8 yr**

21. You buy a truck and pay \$1,000 down. The finance charge is 8% per year on the original unpaid balance. If you must pay the finance company \$9,900 in 48 equal monthly payments, what is the original price of the truck? **\$8,500**

22. Susan earned some money last summer, spent \$700 of it, and put the remainder in an account that paid 6% per year. At the end of 6 mo, she had \$2,575 in her account. Find the total amount she earned last summer. **\$3,200**

23. When will an investment of p dollars at $r\%$ per year in simple interest be doubled in total value? **$\frac{1}{r}$ yr**

24. Prove: If $R(r_1 + r_2) = r_1 \cdot r_2$, then
$$\frac{1}{R} = \frac{1}{r_1} + \frac{1}{r_2}.$$

For Ex. 24, see TE Answer Section.

CALCULATOR ACTIVITIES

In using the formula $A = p + prt$, the result of each operation gives some information about a given loan. This is shown in the example that follows.

Find the simple interest and the total amount owed if \$3,600 is borrowed at $8\frac{1}{4}\%$ per year for 2 yr 9 mo.

$$A = p + prt \qquad \text{or} \qquad A = prt + p \qquad A = (3600 \times .0825 \times 2.75) + 3600$$

Press	Display	Information Given
3600 ⊗ .0825 ⊗	297	Interest for 1 yr
2.75 ⊕	816.75	Interest for 2 yr 9 mo
3600 ⊜	4416.75	Total amount owed

Find the simple interest for the given number of years and the total amount owed for each loan.

1. $p = \$814$, $r = 9\%$, $t = 15$ yr
\$1,098.90 and \$1,912.90

2. $p = \$6,400$, $r = 8\frac{1}{2}\%$, $t = 4$ yr 6 mo
\$2,448 and \$8,848

3. $p = \$3,200$, $r = 11\frac{1}{4}\%$, $t = 2$ yr 3 mo
\$810 and \$4,010

4. $p = \$16,000$, $r = 10\frac{3}{4}\%$, $t = 8$ yr 9 mo
\$15,050 and \$31,050

Applications

Read → Plan → Solve → Interpret

An object is launched straight up into the air with an initial velocity of 50 meters per second (m/s). The figure below shows the height, in meters, of the object at the end of t seconds. The height h is determined by the formula

$$h = 50t - 5t^2.$$

Use this formula to verify the heights for the times given in the figure.

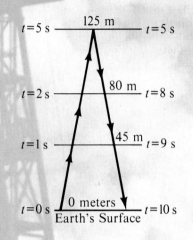

If an object is shot upward from the surface of the earth with an initial velocity of v meters per second, then at the end of t seconds its height h in meters is given by the formula below.

$$h = vt - 5t^2.$$

Use the formula to find v if $h = 120$ m and $t = 3$ s.

$$h = vt - 5t^2$$
$$120 = v \cdot 3 - 5 \cdot 3^2$$
$$165 = 3v$$
$$55 = v$$

Thus, v is 55 m/s.

Use the formula $h = vt - 5t^2$ for Exercises 1–8.

1. Find v in meters per second if $h = 150$ m and $t = 5$ s. **55 m/s**

2. Find h in meters if $v = 60$ m/s and $t = 4$ s. **160 m**

3. At the end of 3 seconds, what will be the height of an arrow if an archer shoots it upward with an initial velocity of 120 meters per second? **315 m**

4. A certain baseball pitcher can throw a ball with an initial velocity of 35 m/s. If the pitcher throws the ball straight up, what will its height be at the end of 2 seconds and at the end of 5 seconds? **50 m, 50 m**

5. Explain how the two answers in Exercise 4 can be equal. **5. The first is on the way up and the second is on the way down.**

6. If an object is sent upward, what initial velocity is required to reach a height of 132 m at the end of 4.4 s? **52 m/s**

7. Find the initial velocity needed for a missile, launched upward, to achieve an altitude of 3,000 m at the end of 12 s. **310 m/s**

8. Find v in meters per second if $h = 26.25$ m and $t = 3.5$ s. **25 m/s**

9. If $h = vt - 5t^2$, the maximum value of h is $\dfrac{v^2}{20}$. What initial velocity is required to launch an object to a maximum height of 8,000 meters? **400 m/s**

10. Find the maximum height achieved by a missile launched with an initial velocity of 250 m/s. Use the maximum value of h as $\dfrac{v^2}{20}$ from Ex. 9. **3,125 m**

The diagram shows an object launched from a platform 80 m above the earth's surface. If an object is sent upward from d meters above the surface of the earth with an initial velocity of v meters per second, then its height h in meters at the end of t seconds is determined by the formula $h = d + vt - 5t$.

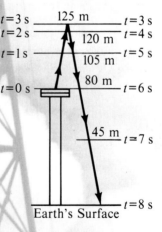

Use the formula $h = d + vt - 5t^2$ for Exercises 11.–15.

11. Find h if $d = 120$ m, $v = 90$ m/s, and $t = 5$ s. **445 m**

12. Find v if $h = 195$ m, $d = 75$ m, and $t = 3$ s. **55 m/s**

13. Find d if $h = 765$ m, $v = 150$ m/s, and $t = 6$ s. **45 m**

14. Write a formula to find h in terms of t if $v = 30$ m/s. Check your formula in the diagram.

15. At the end of 3 s, what is the height of an object shot upward from the top of a 60 m tower with an initial velocity of 75 m/s? **240 m**

14. $h = 80 + 30t - 5t^2$

APPLICATIONS

1.8 Problem Solving: Mixed Types

OBJECTIVE ▶ **To solve word problems of various types**

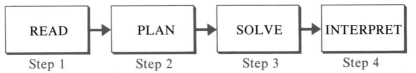

READ	→	PLAN	→	SOLVE	→	INTERPRET
Step 1		Step 2		Step 3		Step 4

Your ability to solve word problems will improve as you encounter and solve problems of many different types. The exercises below include a random selection of the types of problem-solving situations that are presented in this chapter. The four steps used in solving word problems are repeated at the top of this page. Following these steps, use your algebraic skills to solve the problems.

Recall that you can represent the data for a given problem in several ways:
(1) List the data in terms of one variable.
(2) Draw and label a geometric figure.
(3) Use a table to organize the data.

Written Exercises

Solve each problem.

(A) 1. Twenty increased by 5 times the sum of a number and 2 is the same as 6 decreased by 3 times the number. What is the number? **−3**

2. Wanda is 20 years older than Ted and 8 years from now she will be 3 times as old as he will be. How old is each now? **Ted: 2, Wanda: 22**

3. The hypotenuse of a right triangle is 6 m longer than one leg and 3 m longer than the other leg. Find the area of the right triangle if its perimeter is 36 m. **54 m²**

4. Find three consecutive even integers such that twice the sum of the first two integers is 72 more than 3 times the third integer. **80, 82, 84**

(B) 5. Building M is 3 times as old as building P and building H was constructed 20 years after M was built. In 12 years, the age of the oldest building will be the same as the combined ages of the other two buildings. How old is each building now? **P: 8 yr, M: 24 yr, H: 4 yr**

6. A hat store has 50 more women's hats than twice its number of men's hats. The number of children's hats is 90 less than twice the number of women's hats. If the total stock is 270 hats, find the number of each kind of hat. **men's: 30, women's: 110, children's: 130**

7. Find four consecutive multiples of 6 so that the first number, increased by 3 times the third number, is 84 more than twice the fourth number. **42, 48, 54, 60**

8. The length of a rectangle is 6 cm less than 4 times its width, and one side of an equilateral triangle is as long as the rectangle. If the sum of the two perimeters is 80 cm, find the dimensions of the rectangle. **width: 5 cm, length: 14 cm**

Chapter One Review

Vocabulary

absolute value [1.3]
consecutive integers [1.4]
linear equation [1.1]
linear inequality [1.2]
perimeter [1.5]

Solve each equation.

1. $5a + 8 - 3a = 4a - 5 - 6a$ **−3.25** [1.1]
2. $12 + \frac{3}{5}x = \frac{2}{5}x - 3$ **−75**
3. $7.2c + 2.3 = 1.4c - 0.6$ **−0.5**
4. $0.05 + 2.7(3n - 0.3) = 4.3n$ **0.2**
5. $-2x - (4 - 5x) = x - 3$ $\frac{1}{2}$
6. $4c - 2(4c - 3) = 3(2c - 5)$ $2\frac{1}{10}$
7. $\frac{2}{3}(6x - 9) + \frac{3}{4}(8x + 4) = 28 - 4x$ $2\frac{3}{14}$
★ 8. $12 - 7[6(2x + 5) - 3(7x + 8)] = 0$ $\frac{10}{21}$

9. $|3x - 15| = 6$ **3, 7** [1.3]
10. $|4y + 3| = 9$ **−3, $1\frac{1}{2}$**
★ 11. $|n + 4| + |3 - 2n| = 16$ **$-5\frac{2}{3}$, 5**

Find the solution set of each inequality. Graph the solutions on a number line.

12. $-5n - 3 \le 17$ **$\{n | n \ge -4\}$** [1.2]
13. $2x - 15 > 6x$ **$\{x | x < -3\frac{3}{4}\}$**
14. $|y + 4| < 6$ **$\{y | -10 < y < 2\}$** [1.3]
15. $|5z - 15| \ge 30$ **$\{z | z \le -3 \text{ or } z \ge 9\}$**
★ 16. $|x - 4| < 6$ or $|x - 4| > 12$
$\{x | -2 < x < 10 \text{ or } x < -8 \text{ or } x > 16\}$

Find the solution set of each inequality.

17. $8 - 3y \ge 2y - 2$ **$\{y | y \le 2\}$** [1.2]
18. $2(3a + 1) > 3(4a - 5) - 2a$ **$\{a | a < 4\frac{1}{4}\}$**
★ 19. $\frac{4(y - 6)}{-3} > 12 - 2y$ **$\{y | y > 6\}$**

Represent each of the three numbers in terms of one variable. [1.4]

20. A second number is 8 times a first number. A third number is 5 more than 3 times the second number. **1st: x, 2nd: $8x$, 3rd: $24x + 5$**

Solve each problem.

21. Twice the sum of a number and 3 is the same as 24 less than 7 times the number. What is the number? [1.4] **6**

22. The sum of three consecutive even integers is 20 more than twice the second integer. Find the three integers. [1.4] **18, 20, 22**

23. Side a of a triangle is 3 times as long as side b and side c is 2 cm shorter than side a. Find the length of each side if the perimeter is 26 cm. [1.5]
a: 12 cm, b: 4 cm, c: 10 cm

24. Paul is 7 years younger than Carol. Three years from now, she will be twice as old as he will be. How old is each now? [1.6]
Carol: 11, Paul: 4

25. An oak tree is 6 times as old as a pine tree and a spruce tree is 20 years younger than the oak tree. Three years ago, the age of the oak was 3 times the sum of the ages of the pine and the spruce. Find the present ages of the trees. [1.6]
pine: 5, oak: 30, spruce: 10

26. Find p in dollars if $A = \$7,623$, $r = 8\frac{1}{2}\%$, and $t = 4$ yr 3 mo. Use the formula $A = p + prt$. [1.7] **\$5,600**

27. Find r_2 in ohms if $R = 8.4$ ohms and $r_1 = 12$ ohms. Use the formula $R(r_1 + r_2) = r_1 \cdot r_2$. [1.7] **28 ohms**

28. Find the initial velocity needed for a missile, launched upward, to reach a height of 4,875 m at the end of 15 s. Use the formula $h = vt - 5t^2$. [Applications]
400 m/s

★ 29. The length of a rectangle is 6 cm more than the width. Find the set of all possible lengths if the perimeter must be less than 54 cm. [1.5] **$\{l | 6 \text{ cm} < l < 16.5 \text{ cm}\}$**

★ 30. In $x + 4$ years, a tree will be y years old. Represent the age of the tree z years ago in terms of x, y, and z. [1.6] **$y - x - 4 - z$**

Chapter One Test

Solve each equation.

1. $8 + 5c - 6 = 9c - 22 - 12c$ **−3**
2. $6 + \frac{3}{5}n = 14 - \frac{1}{5}n$ **10**
3. $3 + 5(2y - 1) = 2y - 4(y + 1)$ **$-\frac{1}{6}$**
4. $2.5(6y - 1.2) = 22.8 - 2.2y$ **1.5**
5. $\frac{1}{2}(16x + 24) + \frac{2}{3}(6x - 9) = 42$ **3**
6. $|2a - 7| = 15$ **−4, 11**

Find the solution set of each inequality. Graph the solutions on a number line.

7. $3 - 4n \geq 19$ **$\{n|n \leq -4\}$**
8. $|y + 2| < 5$ **$\{y|-7 < y < 3\}$**

Find the solution set of each inequality.

9. $4(y - 2) + 1 \leq 3(2y + 1)$ **$\{y|y \geq -5\}$**
10. $|2a + 3| > 11$ **$\{a|a < -7 \text{ or } a > 4\}$**
11. $\frac{2}{5}(15n + 25) < \frac{2}{3}(12n - 6)$ **$\{n|n > 7\}$**

Represent each number in terms of one variable.

12. A third number is 7 less than a first number. A second number is 5 times the first number. **1st: x, 2nd: 5x, 3rd: x − 7**

Solve each problem.

13. The sum of three consecutive integers is 40 less than 4 times the third integer. Find the three integers. **35, 36, 37**

14. Room A has twice as many chairs as room B. Room C has 20 more chairs than room A. If the number of chairs in C is 10 less than the total number of chairs in A and B, find the number of chairs in each room. **A: 60, B: 30, C: 80**

15. Gloria is 4 times as old as Theotis. Three years ago, she was 7 times as old as he was. How old is each now? **Theotis: 6, Gloria: 24**

16. Sides a and b of a triangle have the same length. Side c is 12 cm less than 3 times the length of b. Find the length of each side if the perimeter is 23 cm. **a: 7 cm, b: 7 cm, c: 9 cm**

17. Find p in dollars if $A = \$5,620$, $r = 9\%$, and $t = 4$ yr 6 mo. Use the formula $A = p + prt$. **$4,000**

18. Find r_2 in ohms if $R = 4.8$ ohms and $r_1 = 8$ ohms. Use the formula $R(r_1 + r_2) = r_1 \cdot r_2$. **12 ohms**

19. Building A was built 10 years before building B and 5 years after building C. In 20 years, the combined ages of buildings A and C will be 3 times that of building B. What is the present age of each building? **A: 15, B: 5, C: 20**

20. If an object is sent upward, what initial velocity is required to reach a height of 200 m at the end of 3.2 s? Use the formula $h = vt - 5t^2$ [Applications] **78.5 m/s**

★ 21. Solve. $5[4(6x - 3) - 7(5x - 2)] = 12(1 - 5x)$ **$\frac{2}{5}$**

★ 22. Find and graph the solution set of $|x + 7| \leq 3$ or $|x - 7| \leq 3$. **$\{x|-10 \leq x \leq -4 \text{ or } 4 \leq x \leq 10\}$**

★ 23. The length of a rectangle is 10 m less than 3 times the width. Find the set of all possible widths if the perimeter must be less than 36 m. **$\{w|0 \text{ m} < w < 7 \text{ m}\}$**

★ 24. Solve $|n - 5| + |-n - 3| = 12$. **−5, 7**

Computer Activities

Finding a Good Buy

A real estate agency keeps data on available lots for sale. The data is stored in a computer by lot length, width, and cost. A client comes to the agency and requests a lot with a given perimeter for a given maximum cost.

In the program below, the perimeter is represented by the formula $T = 2L + 2W$ where L is the length of the lot and W is the width. Statements 160 and 170 evaluate linear inequalities to find lots that satisfy the perimeter and maximum cost that is specified by a client.

PROGRAM

```
10 PRINT "PROGRAM FINDS REAL ESTATE LOTS OF"
20 PRINT "A GIVEN PERIMETER AND MAXIMUM COST"
30 PRINT "TYPE IN PERIMETER, COST DESIRED"
40 INPUT P, D
50 REM THE DIM STATEMENT STORES THE REALTORS DATA
60 DIM L(10), W(10), C(10)
70 REM THE Y LOOP READS IN THE DATA FROM LINES 200, 210, 220
80 FOR Y = 1 TO 10
90 READ L(Y), W(Y), C(Y)
100 NEXT Y
110 REM THE X LOOP FINDS ALL LOTS THAT MATCH COST AND
       PERIMETER
120 PRINT "ALL LOTS THAT ARE AVAILABLE ARE LISTED"
130 PRINT "IF NONE AVAILABLE NOTHING WILL BE PRINTED"
140 FOR X = 1 TO L
150 LET T = 2 * L(X) + 2 * W(X)
160 IF P > T THEN 190
170 IF C(X) > D THEN 190
180 PRINT "LOT"; X; "PERIMETER IN METERS"; T; "COST IN
       DOLLARS"; C(X)
190 NEXT X
200 DATA 13, 11, 2300, 10, 5, 2500, 7, 8, 1800
210 DATA 9, 3, 2000, 6, 11, 4800, 4, 8, 1500
220 DATA 8, 11, 1200, 15, 9, 4800, 9, 10, 1700, 8, 9, 2100
230 END
```

Exercise

Enter and run the above program for the data in lines 200, 210, 220. Use 48 meters for the perimeter and $3000 for the cost as input to the program.
LOT 1 PERIMETER IN METERS 48 COST IN DOLLARS 2300

College Prep Test

DIRECTIONS: Choose the *one* best answer to each question or problem.

1. Which investment earns the most simple interest? **E**

   (A) \$4,444 at $8\frac{1}{2}\%$ per year for 2yr 3mo
   (B) \$4,444 at $4\frac{1}{4}\%$ per year for 4 yr 6 mo
   (C) \$2,222 at $8\frac{1}{2}\%$ per year for 4 yr 6 mo
   (D) \$1,111 at $8\frac{1}{2}\%$ per year for 9 yr
   (E) They all earn the same amount of interest.

2. If 2 more than $\frac{2}{3}$ of a certain number is 8, then the number is **C**

   (A) 6   (B) 8   (C) 9
   (D) 15   (E) 18

3. In the equation $4x + 6x = 3(8 + tx)$, for what value of t is x equal to 6? **A**

   (A) 2   (B) 4   (C) 6
   (D) 8   (E) 10

4. If $ax < b$, where a, x, and b are integers, then **E**

   (A) $x < \dfrac{b}{a}$ (B) $x < b - a$

   (C) $x > \dfrac{b}{a}$ (D) $x > b - a$
   (E) None of these

5. Which fraction is greater than $\frac{1}{5}$ but less than $\frac{1}{4}$? **B**

   (A) $\dfrac{9}{20}$ (B) $\dfrac{2}{9}$ (C) $\dfrac{1}{9}$ (D) $\dfrac{2}{7}$ (E) $\dfrac{1}{6}$

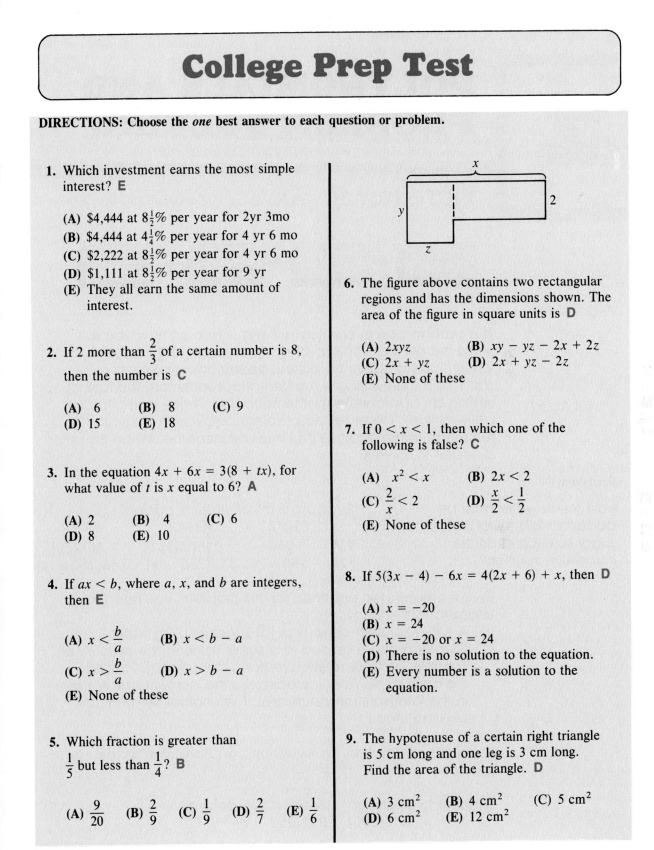

6. The figure above contains two rectangular regions and has the dimensions shown. The area of the figure in square units is **D**

   (A) $2xyz$ (B) $xy - yz - 2x + 2z$
   (C) $2x + yz$ (D) $2x + yz - 2z$
   (E) None of these

7. If $0 < x < 1$, then which one of the following is false? **C**

   (A) $x^2 < x$ (B) $2x < 2$
   (C) $\dfrac{2}{x} < 2$ (D) $\dfrac{x}{2} < \dfrac{1}{2}$
   (E) None of these

8. If $5(3x - 4) - 6x = 4(2x + 6) + x$, then **D**

   (A) $x = -20$
   (B) $x = 24$
   (C) $x = -20$ or $x = 24$
   (D) There is no solution to the equation.
   (E) Every number is a solution to the equation.

9. The hypotenuse of a certain right triangle is 5 cm long and one leg is 3 cm long. Find the area of the triangle. **D**

   (A) 3 cm^2 (B) 4 cm^2 (C) 5 cm^2
   (D) 6 cm^2 (E) 12 cm^2

2

POLYNOMIALS AND PROBLEM SOLVING

Plan How to Solve A Problem

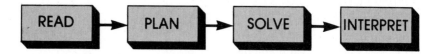

The second step in problem solving is to *plan* how you will solve the problem. This involves analyzing the information that is known, deciding on the correct operations, representing the data, and then writing a mathematical sentence. The task of writing an appropriate mathematical sentence can often be quite difficult. Consider the problem below with particular reference to the analysis that must be done before an equation is written to solve it.

Problem:

How much water must be added to 250 mL of a 15% sugar solution to dilute it to a 12% solution?

Suppose x mL of water is added.

	TOTAL	SUGAR	WATER
15%	250	0.15(250)	0.85(250)
12%	250 + x	0.12(250 + x)	0.88(250 + x)

In order to write an equation for this problem, you need to understand the following:
(1) A sugar solution consists of (a) sugar and (b) water.
(2) If water alone is added to a sugar solution, the *amount of sugar* in the total solution *remains the same.* (Of course, the amount of water increases, so the *percentage of sugar* in the total solution *decreases.* The original solution has been diluted.)

Using this information, an equation can be written for the problem.

Sugar in 15% solution = Sugar in 12% solution
$$0.15(250) = 0.12(250 + x)$$

2.1 Properties of Exponents

The *third power* of x, or the *cube* of x, is written as x^3. In the expression x^3, x is the **base** and 3 is the **exponent.** Exponents that are positive integers indicate the number of times the base is used as a factor. Thus, x^3 means $x \cdot x \cdot x$. When no exponent is written for a base, the exponent is understood to be 1. For example, the first power of y may be written as either y^1 or y.

You can use the meaning of exponents to discover how to multiply powers of the same base.

$$x^3 \cdot x \cdot x^4 = (xxx)(x)(xxxx) = x^8$$

Notice that the sum of the exponents in $x^3 \cdot x^1 \cdot x^4$ is $3 + 1 + 4$, or 8. This suggests the following property of exponents.

Product of Powers

> For each number x and all positive integers m and n,
> $$x^m \cdot x^n = x^{m+n}.$$

Example 1 Simplify $-5a^4b \cdot 6a^3b^2$.

$-5 \cdot a^4 \cdot b^1 \cdot 6 \cdot a^3 \cdot b^2$
$(-5 \cdot 6)(a^4 \cdot a^3)(b^1 \cdot b^2)$ ◀ Group powers with the same base.
$-30a^7b^3$

You can use the meaning of exponents to discover how to divide powers of the same base.

$$\frac{x^5}{x^2} = \frac{xx \cdot xxx}{xx} = x^3 \qquad \frac{y^3}{y^6} = \frac{yyy}{yyy \cdot yyy} = \frac{1}{y^3} \qquad \frac{z^3}{z^3} = \frac{zzz}{zzz} = 1$$

Notice that $\frac{x^5}{x^2} = x^{5-2}$ and that $\frac{y^3}{y^6} = \frac{1}{y^{6-3}}$. This leads to the following *Quotient of Powers* properties.

Quotient of Powers

> For each number $x \neq 0$ and all positive integers m and n,
> $$\frac{x^m}{x^n} = x^{m-n} \text{ if } m > n, \quad \frac{x^m}{x^n} = \frac{1}{x^{n-m}} \text{ if } m < n, \text{ and}$$
> $$\frac{x^m}{x^n} = 1 \text{ if } m = n.$$

Example 2 Simplify $\frac{-9a^7b^5c}{12a^4b^5c^6}$.

$$\frac{-9}{12} \cdot \frac{a^7}{a^4} \cdot \frac{b^5}{b^5} \cdot \frac{c^1}{c^6} = \frac{-3}{4} \cdot a^{7-4} \cdot 1 \cdot \frac{1}{c^{6-1}} = \frac{-3a^3}{4c^5}$$

The Product of Powers and the Quotient of Powers properties on page 31 apply only when the bases are the same. Neither property can be used with $a^7 \cdot b^3$ in Example 1 or with $\dfrac{a^3}{c^5}$ in Example 2.

An expression such as $(x^4)^3$ is called a *power of a power*. For the exponent 3, the base is x^4. From the meaning of exponents and the Product of Powers property, it follows that

$$(x^4)^3 = x^4 \cdot x^4 \cdot x^4 = x^{4+4+4} = x^{12}.$$

Notice that the product of the two exponents in $(x^4)^3$ is $4 \cdot 3$, or 12. This leads to the following property.

Power of a Power

For each number x and all positive integers m and n,
$$(x^m)^n = x^{m \cdot n}.$$

Example 3 Simplify $6(c^4)^5$.

$$6(c^4)^5 = 6 \cdot c^{4 \cdot 5} = 6c^{20}$$

An expression such as $(2a)^3$ or $\left(\dfrac{a}{b}\right)^4$ can be simplified using the following Power of a Product or Power of a Quotient property, respectively.

Power of a Product
Power of a Quotient

For all numbers x and y and each positive integer n,
(1) $(xy)^n = x^n \cdot y^n$; and
(2) $\left(\dfrac{x}{y}\right)^n = \dfrac{x^n}{y^n}$, $(y \neq 0)$.

Using these properties, $(2a)^3 = 2^3 \cdot a^3$, or $8a^3$ and $\left(\dfrac{a}{b}\right)^4 = \dfrac{a^4}{b^4}$.

Sometimes you must use more than one property of exponents to simplify an expression. This is shown in Examples 4 and 5.

Example 4 Simplify $4a^2(5a^4b^2c)^3$.

$$
\begin{aligned}
4a^2(5a^4b^2c)^3 &= 4a^2 \cdot 5^3(a^4)^3(b^2)^3(c^1)^3 & \blacktriangleleft \text{ Power of a Product} \\
&= 4a^2 \cdot 125a^{12}b^6c^3 & \blacktriangleleft \text{ Power of a Power} \\
&= 500a^{14}b^6c^3 & \blacktriangleleft \text{ Product of Powers}
\end{aligned}
$$

Example 5 Simplify $\left(\dfrac{-5a^3b}{2c^2}\right)^4$.

$$\left(\frac{-5a^3b}{2c^2}\right)^4 = \frac{(-5a^3b)^4}{(2c^2)^4} = \frac{(-5)^4(a^3)^4b^4}{2^4(c^2)^4} = \frac{625a^{12}b^4}{16c^8}$$

Equations such as $2^x = 16$, $4^{5x} = 64$, and $5^{4x+1} = 125$ are called **exponential equations** since the variable appears in the exponent. To solve an exponential equation, you must be familiar with powers of numbers like 2^4, 3^4, 4^3, and 5^3.

Example 6 Solve $5^{4x+1} = 125$.

$$5^{4x+1} = 125$$
$$5^{4x+1} = 5^3 \quad \blacktriangleleft \quad 125 = 5^3$$
$$4x + 1 = 3 \quad \blacktriangleleft \quad \text{If } 5^a = 5^b, \text{ then } a = b.$$
$$4x = 2$$
$$x = \frac{1}{2}$$

Check:
$$5^{4 \cdot \frac{1}{2} + 1} = 5^3 = 125$$

Thus, the value of x is $\frac{1}{2}$.

Reading in **Algebra** _____

Supply the missing words and expressions in the following paragraph.

In the expression $9y^4$, the exponent is _____ and its base is _____, but in the expression $(9y)^4$, the _____ is 4 and its _____ is _____. Notice that in the expression _____, the base is $7c^3$, the _____ is 2, and the second power of $7c^3$ is multiplied by $5c$.

    4   **y**   **exponent**   **base**   **9y**   **5c(7c³)²**   **exponent**

Written **Exercises** _____

1. $20a^3b^8$ 2. $-72m^4n^9$ 3. $36x^9y^5$ 4. $280c^9d^9$ 7. $\dfrac{-2}{3m^9p^5q^2}$

Simplify each expression.

(A)
1. $5a^2b^3 \cdot 4ab^5$
2. $-12mn^7 \cdot 6m^3n^2$
3. $-4x^5y^4(-9x^4y)$
4. $7c^3d^2 \cdot 4c^2d \cdot 10c^4d^6$
5. $\dfrac{10a^4b^7}{-5a^9b^2} - \dfrac{2b^5}{a^5}$
6. $\dfrac{8x^9y^3z^2}{12x^3y^3z^8}$ $\dfrac{2x^6}{3z^6}$
7. $\dfrac{-4m^3np^5}{6m^{12}np^{10}q^2}$
8. $\dfrac{-9a^9bc^2d^7}{-6ac^{12}d^7}$ $\dfrac{3a^8b}{2c^{10}}$
9. $(y^6)^5$ y^{30}
10. $(n^4)^7$ n^{28}
11. $(5x)^3$ $125x^3$
12. $(-3c)^4$ $81c^4$
13. $7(10n^5)^3$ $7{,}000n^{15}$
14. $3(-3x^2)^4$ $243x^8$
15. $4y(11y)^2$ $484y^3$
16. $2a(5a^3)^4$ $1{,}250a^{13}$
17. $\left(\dfrac{-5a}{4}\right)^3$ $\dfrac{-125a^3}{64}$
18. $\left(\dfrac{x^2}{y^6}\right)^4$ $\dfrac{x^8}{y^{24}}$
19. $\left(\dfrac{-7c^5}{10d^3}\right)^2$ $\dfrac{49c^{10}}{100d^6}$
20. $\left(\dfrac{2ab^2}{3c^3d}\right)^5$ $\dfrac{32a^5b^{10}}{243c^{15}d^5}$
29. $-36a^9b^{11}c^4$
30. $70m^8n^6p^9$
31. $-1{,}250x^6y^9$
32. $1{,}875m^{12}n^8p^{16}$

Solve each equation.

(B)
21. $3^{x-2} = 81$ 6
22. $10^{n+1} = 1{,}000$ 2
23. $2^{3y} = 64$ 2
24. $6^{-x} = 36$ -2
25. $5^{3x+1} = 625$ 1
26. $4^{6-y} = 256$ 2
27. $3^{1-2n} = 243$ -2
28. $2^{8x+6} = 1{,}024$ $\frac{1}{2}$
33. $384a^7b^9$
34. $-405x^{17}y^{12}$
35. $-4{,}000c^6d^{18}$
36. $162a^6b^{21}$

Simplify each expression. 41. $x^{4a}y^{2b}$ 42. $x^{3a+2b}y^{a-b}$ 43. $x^{2c+3}y^{3d-4}$ 44. $x^{4n+6}y^{4n-2}$
29. $-4a^6b^4c^3 \cdot 9a^3b^7c$
30. $5m^7n^2p^6 \cdot 14mn^4p^3$
31. $10(-5x^2y^3)^3$
32. $3(5m^3n^2p^4)^4$
33. $6a(4a^2b^3)^3$
34. $-5x(3x^4y^3)^4$
35. $4d^3(-10c^2d^5)^3$
36. $2a^2b(-3ab^5)^4$

(C)
37. $x^ay^{3b} \cdot x^{2c}y^{4d}$
38. $x^{2a+3}y^{2b} \cdot x^{5a}y^{3b-1}$
39. $x^a(x^by^c)^d$
40. $x^{2m}y^n(x^{m+3}y^n)^3$
41. $\dfrac{x^{6a}y^{3b}}{x^{2a}y^b}$
42. $\dfrac{x^{4a+3b}y^{2a-4b}}{x^{a+b}y^{a-3b}}$
43. $\dfrac{x^{3c+2}y^{5d-1}}{x^{c-1}y^{2d+3}}$
44. $\dfrac{x^{6n-2}y^{3n+2}}{x^{2n-8}y^{4-n}}$
37. $x^{a+2c}y^{3b+4d}$
38. $x^{7a+3}y^{5b-1}$
39. $x^{a+bd}y^{cd}$
40. $x^{5m+9}y^{4n}$

PROPERTIES OF EXPONENTS   **33**

2.2 Zero and Negative Integral Exponents

OBJECTIVES ▶ To evaluate expressions containing zero and negative integral exponents
To simplify expressions containing zero and negative integral exponents

In general, the Quotient of Powers properties indicate that to divide powers of the same base, you should subtract the exponents of the powers. Observe below what happens when this is applied to the quotient $\frac{5^3}{5^3}$.

$$\frac{5^3}{5^3} = 5^{3-3} = 5^0$$

But you know that $\frac{5^3}{5^3}$ is 1: $\frac{5^3}{5^3} = \frac{125}{125} = 1$

This implies that $5^0 = 1$, which leads to the following definition.

**Definition:
Zero Exponent**

> For each number $x \neq 0$, $x^0 = 1$.

You can define 5^{-3} to mean $\frac{1}{5^3}$ and define x^{-n} to mean $\frac{1}{x^n}$, for each $x \neq 0$, by using the definition of zero exponent and extending the Quotient of Powers properties to include negative exponents.

$$\frac{5^0}{5^3} = 5^{0-3} = 5^{-3} \text{ and } \frac{5^0}{5^3} = \frac{1}{5^3}. \text{ Thus, } 5^{-3} = \frac{1}{5^3}.$$

This view of zero and negative exponents may be seen in the following pattern where any term is divided by 5 to obtain the next term. Notice that $5^0 = 1$ and $5^{-3} = \frac{1}{5^3}$.

... 5^3	5^2	5^1	5^0	5^{-1}	5^{-2}	5^{-3} ...
... 125	25	5	1	$\frac{1}{5}$	$\frac{1}{25}$, or $\frac{1}{5^2}$	$\frac{1}{125}$, or $\frac{1}{5^3}$ ...

Sometimes a negative exponent appears in a denominator, as in $\frac{1}{2^{-4}}$. Study the steps below which show that $\frac{1}{2^{-4}} = 2^4$.

$$\frac{1}{2^{-4}} = 1 \div (2^{-4}) = 1 \div \frac{1}{2^4} = 1 \div \frac{1}{16} = 1 \times 16 = 16 = 2^4$$

**Definition:
Negative
Exponent**

> For each number $x \neq 0$ and each positive integer n,
> $$x^{-n} = \frac{1}{x^n} \text{ and } \frac{1}{x^{-n}} = x^n.$$

Example 1 Find the value of each expression.

$$7 \cdot 9^0 \qquad\qquad \frac{4}{7 \cdot 5^{-3}}$$

$$7 \cdot 9^0 = 7 \cdot 1 = 7 \qquad \frac{4}{7 \cdot 5^{-3}} = \frac{4}{7} \cdot \frac{1}{5^{-3}} = \frac{4}{7} \cdot \frac{5^3}{1} = \frac{4 \cdot 125}{7} = \frac{500}{7}$$

Example 2 Find the value of 8.64×10^{-3} and $\dfrac{2.35}{10^{-4}}$.

$$8.64 \times 10^{-3} = \frac{8.64}{1} \times \frac{1}{10^3} = \frac{8.64}{1,000} = 0.00864$$

$$\frac{2.35}{10^{-4}} = \frac{2.35}{1} \times \frac{1}{10^{-4}} = 2.35 \times 10^4 = 2.35 \times 10,000 = 23,500$$

Each of the five properties of exponents can now be extended to, and used with, expressions containing zero and negative integral exponents.

Example 3 Simplify and write each expression with positive exponents.

$$-5x^4 \cdot 3y^{-2} \cdot x^{-7} \cdot y^5 \qquad\qquad \frac{-8a^8 b^{-3} c^{-4}}{12a^{-2} b^{-5} c^5}$$

$$-5 \cdot x^4 \cdot 3 \cdot y^{-2} \cdot x^{-7} \cdot y^5 \qquad \frac{-8}{12} \cdot \frac{a^8}{a^{-2}} \cdot \frac{b^{-3}}{b^{-5}} \cdot \frac{c^{-4}}{c^5}$$

$$(-5 \cdot 3)(x^4 \cdot x^{-7})(y^{-2} \cdot y^5) \qquad \frac{-2}{3} \cdot \frac{a^8 \cdot a^2}{1} \cdot \frac{b^5}{b^3} \cdot \frac{1}{c^5 \cdot c^4} \quad \blacktriangleleft \quad \frac{b^{-m}}{b^{-n}} = \frac{b^n}{b^m}$$

$$-15x^{4+(-7)} y^{-2+5}$$

$$-15x^{-3} y^3 \qquad\qquad \frac{-2a^{10} b^2}{3c^9}$$

$$\frac{-15y^3}{x^3} \quad \blacktriangleleft \quad x^{-3} = \frac{1}{x^3}$$

In expressions like $6c^{-2}$ and $(6c)^{-2}$, you should be careful in determining the base for the exponent -2. The base for the exponent -2 in $6c^{-2}$ is c and the base in $(6c)^{-2}$ is $(6c)$.

Example 4 Simplify $(5a^{-3}b^4)^{-2}$ and $\left(\dfrac{-4x^{-2}}{y^4 z^{-3}}\right)^3$.

$$(5a^{-3}b^4)^{-2} = 5^{-2}(a^{-3})^{-2}(b^4)^{-2} \qquad \left(\frac{-4x^{-2}}{y^4 z^{-3}}\right)^3 = \frac{(-4x^{-2})^3}{(y^4 z^{-3})^3} = \frac{(-4)^3 (x^{-2})^3}{(y^4)^3 (z^{-3})^3} = \frac{-64x^{-6}}{y^{12} z^{-9}}$$

$$= 5^{-2} a^6 b^{-8} \qquad\qquad\qquad\qquad\qquad\qquad\qquad\qquad = \frac{-64z^9}{y^{12} x^6}$$

$$= \frac{a^6}{25b^8}$$

ZERO AND NEGATIVE INTEGRAL EXPONENTS

Reading in Algebra

For each phrase at the left, find its one correct match at the right.

1. The base of -3 in $5 \cdot 2^{-3}$ **D**
2. The base of -3 in $(5 \cdot 2)^{-3}$ **E**
3. An exponent in $5 \cdot 2^{-3}$ **B**
4. An exponent in $(5 \cdot 2)^{-3}$ **B**
5. The value of $5 \cdot 2^{-3}$ **H**
6. The value of $(5 \cdot 2)^{-3}$ **G**

A 3   **B** -3 **C** 5
D 2   **E** $5 \cdot 2$ **F** 1,000
G $\dfrac{1}{1,000}$ **H** $\dfrac{5}{8}$

Oral Exercises

Evaluate each expression if $x = 2$.

1. x^0 1   2. $4x^0$ 4   3. $(4x)^0$ 1   4. x^{-1} $\frac{1}{2}$ 5. $5x^{-1}$ $\frac{5}{2}$ 6. $(5x)^{-1}$ $\frac{1}{10}$

Written Exercises

Find the value of each expression.

(A)

1. 8^0 1
2. $6 \cdot 4^0$ 6
3. $(6 \cdot 4)^0$ 1
4. 4^{-3} $\frac{1}{64}$
5. 2^{-4} $\frac{1}{16}$
6. $6^2 \cdot 6^0$ 36

7. $4 \cdot 3^{-2}$ $\frac{4}{9}$
8. $(4 \cdot 3)^{-2}$ $\frac{1}{144}$
9. $\dfrac{2}{5^{-3}}$ 250
10. $\dfrac{10}{3^{-4}}$ 810
11. $\dfrac{2}{3 \cdot 4^{-2}}$ $10\frac{2}{3}$
12. $\dfrac{2}{(3 \cdot 4)^{-2}}$ 288

13. $\dfrac{3^2}{2^{-3}}$ 72
14. $\dfrac{3^{-2}}{2^3}$ $\frac{1}{72}$
15. $\dfrac{3^{-2}}{2^{-3}}$ $\frac{8}{9}$
16. $\dfrac{5^{-4}}{2^{-4}}$ $\frac{16}{625}$
17. $7^4 \cdot 7^{-6}$ $\frac{1}{49}$
18. $7^{-4} \cdot 7^6$ 49

19. 2.7×10^{-2} 0.027
20. $\dfrac{6.5}{10^{-3}}$ 6,500
21. 1.23×10^{-4} 0.000123
22. $\dfrac{3.57}{10^{-2}}$ 357
23. 46.8×10^{-3} 0.0468
24. $\dfrac{0.097}{10^0}$ 0.097

Simplify and write each expression with positive exponents.

25. $9x^{-3}$ $\frac{9}{x^3}$
26. $(3y)^{-4}$ $\frac{1}{81y^4}$
27. $-10a^{-3}$ $\frac{-10}{a^3}$
28. $(-2c)^{-5}$ $\frac{1}{-32c^5}$
29. $x^{-4} \cdot x^7$ x^3
30. $4y^3 \cdot y^{-7}$ $\frac{4}{y^4}$
31. $n^{-5} \cdot 7n^{-3}$ $\frac{7}{n^8}$
32. $6a^{-4} \cdot 2a^0$ $\frac{12}{a^4}$

33. $\dfrac{1}{10x^{-3}}$ $\frac{x^3}{10}$
34. $\dfrac{1}{(10x)^{-3}}$ $1,000x^3$
35. $\dfrac{5}{6a^{-2}}$ $\frac{5a^2}{6}$
36. $\dfrac{5}{(6a)^{-2}}$ $180a^2$

37. $\dfrac{x^6}{x^{-3}}$ x^9
38. $\dfrac{a^{-4}}{a^2}$ $\frac{1}{a^6}$
39. $\dfrac{10n^{-5}}{15n^{-8}}$ $\frac{2n^3}{3}$
40. $\dfrac{-7c^{-6}}{14c^{-4}}$ $\frac{-1}{2c^2}$

41. $(x^{-2})^5$ $\frac{1}{x^{10}}$
42. $(4a^3)^{-2}$ $\frac{1}{16a^6}$
43. $(2n^{-4})^{-5}$ $\frac{n^{20}}{32}$
44. $5(-5y^{-2})^4$ $\frac{3,125}{y^8}$

45. $\left(\dfrac{y^{-4}}{-5}\right)^3$ $\frac{1}{-125y^{12}}$
46. $\left(\dfrac{x^3}{y^{-2}}\right)^5$ $x^{15}y^{10}$
47. $\left(\dfrac{c^{-3}}{d^5}\right)^4$ $\frac{1}{c^{12}d^{20}}$
48. $\left(\dfrac{a^{-3}}{b^{-2}}\right)^6$ $\frac{b^{12}}{a^{18}}$

Find the value of each expression.

(B)

49. $\dfrac{8.4 \times 10^2}{4.2 \times 10^{-2}}$ 20,000
50. $\dfrac{6.3 \times 10^{-7}}{0.9 \times 10^{-9}}$ 700
51. $\dfrac{9.63 \times 10^{-1}}{3 \times 10^0}$ 0.321
52. $\dfrac{6.6 \times 10^{-20}}{8.8 \times 10^{-18}}$ 0.0075

61. $\frac{10}{x^5y^2}$
62. $\frac{30a^4}{b^6}$
63. $-\frac{c^9}{27d^{12}}$
64. $\frac{16c^8}{d^{24}}$

Simplify and write each expression with positive exponents.

53. $\dfrac{a^5b^{-4}}{c^3d^{-6}}$ $\frac{a^5d^6}{b^4c^3}$
54. $\dfrac{x^3y^{-4}}{z^{-5}}$ $\frac{x^3z^5}{y^4}$
55. $\dfrac{4a^{-2}b^5}{9c^3d^{-4}}$ $\frac{4b^5d^4}{9a^2c^3}$
56. $\dfrac{6x^{-5}}{8y^{-2}z^{-1}}$ $\frac{3y^2z}{4x^5}$

57. $\dfrac{x^8y^{-14}}{x^{-2}y^{12}}$ $\frac{x^{10}}{y^{26}}$
58. $\dfrac{a^6b^{-6}}{a^{10}b^{-8}}$ $\frac{b^2}{a^4}$
59. $\dfrac{6c^{-6}d^8}{9c^{-3}d^{-2}}$ $\frac{2d^{10}}{3c^3}$
60. $\dfrac{25m^{-12}n^{-10}}{45m^{-15}n^5}$ $\frac{5m^3}{9n^{15}}$

61. $2x^{-8} \cdot 5y^{-2} \cdot x^3$
62. $10a^7 \cdot b^{-6} \cdot 3a^{-3}$
63. $(-3c^{-3}d^4)^{-3}$
64. $(-2c^2d^{-6})^4$

65. $\left(\dfrac{12x^{-3}}{y^3z^{-5}}\right)^2$ $\frac{144z^{10}}{x^6y^6}$
66. $\left(\dfrac{5a^{-2}b^3}{3c^{-1}}\right)^4$ $\frac{625b^{12}c^4}{81a^8}$
67. $\left(\dfrac{-2x^{-4}y}{3z^3w^{-2}}\right)^3$ $\frac{-8y^3w^6}{27x^{12}z^9}$
68. $\left(\dfrac{ab^{-2}c^3}{d^{-3}ef^2}\right)^4$ $\frac{a^4c^{12}d^{12}}{b^8e^4f^8}$

(C)

69. x^{a-b} if $0 < a < b$ $\frac{1}{x^{b-a}}$
70. y^{c-d} if $c < d < 0$ $\frac{1}{y^{d-c}}$
71. z^{3m-3n} if $m < 0 < n$ $\frac{1}{z^{3n-3m}}$

2.3 Polynomials

OBJECTIVES ▶ **To evaluate a polynomial for given values of its variables**
To add polynomials
To subtract polynomials

Three examples of **monomials** are -8, x, and $\frac{3}{4}m^2n$. They are a numeral, a variable, and a product of a numeral and variables, respectively. An expression such as $\frac{3}{n}$ in which a variable appears in the denominator of a fraction is not classified as a monomial.

Two examples of **polynomials** are $\frac{3}{4}m^2n$ and $2x^2y - 6x + 4y + 5$. The first is a monomial and the second is a sum of monomials, or terms. Some polynomials are classified by the number of terms they contain. For example, $2x^2 + xy - 4$ is a **trinomial** (three terms), $9n^4 - 1$ is a **binomial** (two terms), and $5ab^3$ is a **monomial** (one term).

Definition:
Monomial
Polynomial
Binomial
Trinomial

> A *monomial* is either a numeral, a variable, or a product of a numeral and one or more variables.
> A *polynomial* is a monomial or a sum of monomials (terms).
> A *binomial* is a polynomial with two terms.
> A *trinomial* is a polynomial with three terms.

A polynomial may also be classified by its *degree*. The **degree of a monomial** is the sum of the exponents of its variables. For example, $5x^2y^4z$ is of degree 7. The sum of the exponents is $2 + 4 + 1$, or 7.

The **degree of a polynomial** is the same as the degree of its term that has the greatest degree. For example, $4xy^2 + 7x^2y^3 - 3x$ is of degree 5. Its terms are of degrees 3, 5, and 1, respectively, and 5 is the greatest of these degrees.

Example 1 Give the degree of each polynomial.

Polynomial	Degree		Polynomial	Degree
$5x + 7$	1		$3x + 2y - 6$	1
$3x^2 - 2x - 1$	2		$x^2 - 4xy + 4y^2$	2
$x^3 + 9x^2 - 6x + 4$	3		$a^2 + 3ab^3 + a^3bc$	5

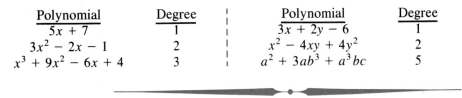

First degree polynomials, such as $5x + 7$ and $3x + 2y - 6$, are called **linear polynomials.** Second degree polynomials, such as $3x^2 - 2x - 1$ and $x^2 - 4xy + 4y^2$, are called **quadratic polynomials.**

You can evaluate a polynomial for the given values of its variables by substitution, as shown in the example below.

Example 2 Evaluate $5x^3y - 2x^2y^2 - xy + 14$ if $x = -2$ and $y = 3$.

$$5 \cdot x^3 \cdot y \quad - \quad 2 \cdot x^2 \cdot y^2 \quad - \quad x \cdot y \quad + 14$$
$$5 \cdot (-2)^3 \cdot 3 - 2 \cdot (-2)^2 \cdot 3^2 - (-2) \cdot 3 + 14 \qquad \blacktriangleleft \text{ Substitute for } x \text{ and } y.$$
$$5(-8) \cdot 3 \quad - \quad 2 \cdot 4 \cdot 9 \quad - \quad (-6) \quad + 14$$
$$-120 \quad - \quad 72 \quad + \quad 6 \quad + 14$$
$$-172$$

Terms of a polynomial are *like* (or *similar*) if they have the same variables with the same exponents. For example, $3a^2b$ and a^2b are like terms, but $-5x^2y^3$ and $14x^3y^2$ are not. You can add polynomials by combining any like terms as shown in Example 3.

Example 3 Add $7xy - 3xy^2 + x^2$ and $4xy^2 - 6x^2 - 5xy$.

$$(7xy - 5xy) + (-3xy^2 + 4xy^2) + (x^2 - 6x^2) \qquad \blacktriangleleft \text{ Group like terms.}$$
$$= 2xy + xy^2 - 5x^2 \qquad\qquad\qquad\qquad\qquad\quad \blacktriangleleft \text{ Combine like terms.}$$

Since $a - b = a + (-b)$, you can subtract a second polynomial from a first polynomial by adding the opposite of the second polynomial to the first polynomial. The format may be either horizontal or vertical, as shown in Examples 4 and 5, respectively.

Example 4 Subtract: $(7a^2b - 3ab + b^2) - (-3ab - 9a^2b + c^2)$.

$$(7a^2b - 3ab + b^2) - 1(-3ab - 9a^2b + c^2) \qquad \blacktriangleleft \ -(x) = -1(x)$$
$$= 7a^2b - 3ab + b^2 + 3ab + 9a^2b - c^2 \qquad \blacktriangleleft \text{ Use the Distributive Property.}$$
$$= (7a^2b + 9a^2b) + (-3ab + 3ab) + b^2 - c^2$$
$$= 16a^2b + b^2 - c^2$$

Example 5 Subtract: $-8x^3 - 2x^2 - 4x$
$$\underline{\quad -8x^3 + 7x^2 \qquad - 10}$$

Multiply the second $-8x^3 - 2x^2 - 4x$
polynomial by -1. $\blacktriangleright$ $\underline{\quad 8x^3 - 7x^2 \qquad\quad + 10}$
Then add. $\blacktriangleright$ $\quad\quad\quad -9x^2 - 4x + 10$

In the polynomial $8x^2 - 5x - 7x^4 + 6 + 2x^5$, the order of the exponents of the variables from left to right is 2, 1, 4, 0, 5. It is often useful to arrange the terms of a polynomial in *descending order* of the exponents of one of its variables, if possible. The polynomial above can be written as $2x^5 - 7x^4 + 8x^2 - 5x + 6$, with its terms in descending (or decreasing) order of the exponents.

Reading in Algebra

Determine whether each expression is a polynomial. If it is not a polynomial, state why it is not.

1. $5a - 3b + 6$ **yes**

2. $7m + n^4 + \dfrac{4}{p^2}$

3. $\dfrac{1}{3}x^2 y$ **yes**

4. $5xy + \dfrac{3}{y}$

no; variable in denom.

5. $\dfrac{1}{4}a + b^2 + \dfrac{2}{3}$ **yes**

no; variable in denom.

6. 9 **yes**

Determine whether each polynomial is linear (L), quadratic (Q), or neither (N).

7. $8y^2 - 6y - 2$ **Q**

8. $-6x + 12$ **L**

9. $3n^3 + 2n^2 - 1$ **N**

10. $10x + 5y + 15$ **L**

11. $3x^2 y + 4xy + 5y$ **N**

12. $xy - x^2 + y^2$ **Q**

Oral Exercises

Classify each polynomial by the number of terms.

1. $y^2 - 16$ **binomial**

2. $4n^2 - 4n + 1$

trinomial

3. $\dfrac{5}{8}a$ **monomial**

4. $x^3 + y^2 - xy - x + y$

polynomial with five terms

Give the degree of each polynomial.

5. $9x - 8y + 7$ **1**

6. $5xy$ **2**

7. $a^2 - 25a^2 b^2$ **4**

8. $2a^2 b + bc - a^3 b^2$ **5**

Arrange the terms of each polynomial in descending order of the exponents.

9. $x^2 - x + x^4 - 5$

$x^4 + x^2 - x - 5$

10. $8 + 3y + 4y^2 + 2y^3$

$2y^3 + 4y^2 + 3y + 8$

11. $-8 - x^3$

$-x^3 - 8$

12. $-n^2 + n^6 - n^4$

$n^6 - n^4 - n^2$

Evaluate each polynomial if $x = 2$ and $y = -1$.

13. $y - x$ **−3**

14. $7x - 5y$ **19**

15. $x^4 y^3$ **−16**

16. $5x^2 y^3$ **−20**

17. $-xy$ **2**

18. $x^3 - x^2 + y$ **3**

19. $xy - y$ **−1**

20. $-10x - 2y$ **−18**

Written Exercises

5. $17x^2 + 2x + 11$ **6.** $-9a^2 - 5a - 6$ **7.** $-5y + 41$

8. $16n^2 + n - 3$ **9.** $-15a^4 + 6a^2 - 8a$ **10.** $x^5 + 12x^3 - x^2$

Evaluate each polynomial for the given values of its variables.

Ⓐ **1.** $3x^2 y - 5y$ if $x = 3$ and $y = -2$ **−44**

2. $7x^3 - 4y^2$ if $x = 10$ and $y = 5$ **6,900**

3. $2x^4 + 3y^3$ if $x = -2$ and $y = 3$ **113**

4. $8xy^2 + 5xy$ if $x = -4$ and $y = 5$ **−900**

Add. Arrange the terms of each sum in descending order of the exponents.

5. $2x^2 - 5x + 19$ and $7x + 15x^2 - 8$

6. $2 - a - 6a^2$ and $-3a^2 - 4a - 8$

7. $3y - 12y^2 + 24$ and $17 - 8y + 12y^2$

8. $16 + n^2 - 12n$ and $13n + 15n^2 - 19$

9. $-15a^4 + a - 25a^3$ and $-9a + 25a^3 + 6a^2$

10. $12x^3 - 6x^2 - 6x$ and $5x^2 + 6x + x^5$

11. $7x^3 - 5x^2 + 3x$
$\underline{8x^2 - 3x - 4}$ $\mathbf{7x^3 + 3x^2 - 4}$

12. $4y^2 - 9y + 6$
$\underline{-4y^2 - y - 8}$ $\mathbf{-10y - 2}$

13. $6 + 2a + a^2$
$\underline{3 - 2a + a^2}$ $\mathbf{2a^2 + 9}$

14. $8 - 2n - 4n^2$
$\underline{ - 6n + n^2 - 8n^3}$ $\mathbf{-8n^3 - 3n^2 - 8n + 8}$

15. $\mathbf{3x^2 + 7x + 1}$ **16.** $\mathbf{-23a^2 + a - 1}$ **17.** $\mathbf{-4n^2 + 10n + 4}$ **18.** $\mathbf{-4y^2 - 2y - 3}$

Subtract. Arrange the terms of each difference in descending order of the exponents.

15. $(5x^2 + 3x - 4) - (2x^2 - 4x - 5)$

16. $(-9a^2 - 15a + 26) - (14a^2 - 16a + 27)$

17. $(2n - 3n^2 + 9) - (5 + n^2 - 8n)$

18. $(12y - 12y^2 + 12) - (-8y^2 + 14y + 15)$

19. $(7c^3 - 2c^5 + c) - (6c^4 + c - 12c^5 - 7c^3)$
$\mathbf{10c^5 - 6c^4 + 14c^3}$

20. $(-x^4 + x^6 - x^2 + 10) - (5x^2 + 6x^6 - x^4)$
$\mathbf{-5x^6 - 6x^2 + 10}$

21. $5a^2 + 9a - 2$
$\underline{5a^2 - 3a + 7}$ $\mathbf{12a - 9}$

22. $-4n^3 + 8n - 2$
$\underline{-4n^3 - 5n^2 - n}$ $\mathbf{5n^2 + 9n - 2}$

23. $8x^2 - 4x + 3$
$\underline{-2x^2 - 7x - 6}$ $\mathbf{10x^2 + 3x + 9}$

24. $-3y^4 - 2y$
$\underline{y^4 + 6y^2}$ $\mathbf{-4y^4 - 6y^2 - 2y}$

Evaluate each polynomial for the given values of its variables.

Ⓑ **25.** $10xy - 5x^2$ if $x = 0.4$ and $y = 0.5$ **1.2**

26. $a^3 + 100ab$ if $a = 0.2$ and $b = 1.25$ **25.008**

27. $m^2n^2 - m^2 - n^2$ if $m = -8$ and $n = 10$ **6,236**

28. $20c^2 - 10d^2$ if $c = 1.5$ and $d = 3.5$ **−77.5**

29. $1.4xy + 2.2y^2$ if $x = 2.5$ and $y = 4$ **49.2**

30. $3.6x^2 - 0.4xy$ if $x = 0.5$ and $y = 10$ **−1.1**

Add. $\mathbf{10xy + 11xy^2 + 3x^2}$

31. $6xy + 3xy^2 + x^2$ and $8xy^2 + 2x^2 + 4xy$

32. $4ab - 8a^3b + b^2$ and $7a^3b - 4b^2 - 5ab$ $\mathbf{-ab - a^3b - 3b^2}$

33. $8x^2y^2 - 6xy^2$ and $2x^2y + x^2y^2$
$\mathbf{9x^2y^2 + 2x^2y - 6xy^2}$

34. $2a^2 - 3b^2 + ab$ and $6ab - a^2$
$\mathbf{a^2 - 3b^2 + 7ab}$

Subtract. $\mathbf{14x^2y^2 - 7xy + 12}$

35. $(6x^2y^2 - 2xy + 4) - (-8x^2y^2 + 5xy - 8)$

36. $(a^2b^2 - 2ab + 6) - (9a^2b^2 - 8)$ $\mathbf{-8a^2b^2 - 2ab + 14}$

37. $(18rs + 20r^2 - 30s^2) - (19 + rs - r^2s^2)$
$\mathbf{17rs + 20r^2 - 30s^2 + r^2s^2 - 19}$

38. $(28xy + 29x^2 - y^2) - (xy - y^2 - x^2)$
$\mathbf{27xy + 30x^2}$

39. $12n^3 - n^2 + 6n$
$\underline{8n - 5n^2 - 3n^3}$ $\mathbf{15n^3 + 4n^2 - 2n}$

40. $6n^4 + 5n^2 - 4n - 30$
$\underline{6n^4 + 2n^3 - 9n + 20}$ $\mathbf{-2n^3 + 5n^2 + 5n - 50}$

Evaluate each polynomial if $x = 10$.

41. $9x^4 + 8x^3 + 7x^2 + 6x + 5$ **98,765**

42. $4x^5 + 4x^3 + 4x$ **404,040**

43. $-x^5 - 2x^4 - 3x^3 - 4x^2 - 5x - 6$
$\mathbf{-123,456}$

44. $-7x^6 - 7x^4 - 7x^2 - 7$ **−7,070,707**

Evaluate each polynomial for the given values of its variables.

Ⓒ **45.** $5xy^3 + 5x^2y^2 + 10x^3y$
if $x = 2a$ and $y = -3a$ **−330a⁴**

46. $10x^4y^2 - 2x^3y^3 - x^2y^4 + 5xy^5$
if $x = c^2$ and $y = -2c^2$ **−120c¹²**

Cumulative Review

$\mathbf{15n^4 - 3n^3 - 12n^2}$

1. Multiply: $3n^2(5n^2 - n - 4)$.

2. Simplify $3a \cdot 5a^4b(-4a^3b^3)$. $\mathbf{-60a^8b^4}$

3. Simplify $10c(5c^4d)^2$. $\mathbf{250c^9d^2}$

4. Solve $|x - 9| = 3$. **6, 12**

5. Find the solution set of $|x - 9| > 3$.
$\mathbf{\{x|x < 6 \text{ or } x > 12\}}$

6. Solve $5 + 0.75x = 23$. **24**

2.4 Multiplying Polynomials

OBJECTIVE ▶ **To multiply two or more polynomials**

To multiply a monomial and a trinomial, you use the Distributive Property.

$$3x(2x^2 - 4x + 6) = 3x \cdot 2x^2 + 3x(-4x) + 3x \cdot 6 = 6x^3 - 12x^2 + 18x.$$

Let $(a + b)(c + d)$ represent the indicated product of any two binomials. The four terms in $(a + b)(c + d)$ are a, b, c, and d. These four terms are named as follows.

a and c are the First terms (F).
a and d are the Outer terms (O).
b and c are the Inner terms (I).
b and d are the Last terms (L).

Applying the Distributive Property, $(a + b)(c + d)$ can be simplified as follows.

$$(a + b)(c + d) = a(c + d) + b(c + d) = ac + ad + bc + bd$$

Notice that the product, $ac + ad + bc + bd$, is the sum of the products of the First terms (ac), Outer terms (ad), Inner terms (bc), and Last terms (bd). This suggests an efficient method for multiplying any pair of binomials. It is referred to as the **FOIL** method. You begin by identifying the F, O, I, L terms as shown in Example 1.

Example 1 Multiply: $(3x + 4)(2x - 5)$.

$$(3x + 4)(2x - 5)$$

F	O	I	L
$3x \cdot 2x$	$+ 3x(-5)$	$+ 4 \cdot 2x$	$+ 4(-5)$
$6x^2$	$-15x$	$+8x$	-20

$$6x^2 - 7x - 20$$

Thus, $(3x + 4)(2x - 5) = 6x^2 - 7x - 20$.

From the discussion above, you can see that the product of two polynomials is the polynomial obtained by multiplying each term of one polynomial by each term of the other and then adding these monomial products.

Example 2 Multiply: $(3n^2 + 5)(2n^2 + 6)$.

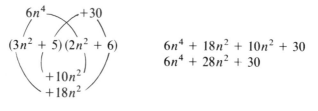

$$6n^4 + 18n^2 + 10n^2 + 30$$
$$6n^4 + 28n^2 + 30$$

Sometimes the binomials you are multiplying contain more than one variable. An example with two variables follows.

Example 3 Multiply: $(2.4x - 0.6y)(0.2x + 2.5y)$.

$$0.48x^2 + 6.00xy - 0.12xy - 1.5y^2$$
$$0.48x^2 + 5.88xy - 1.5y^2$$

In Example 4, you will notice that there are two ways to arrange your work when you multiply a binomial and a trinomial. The FOIL method cannot be used for this type of multiplication.

Example 4 Multiply: $(3x + 2)(5x^2 - x - 4)$.

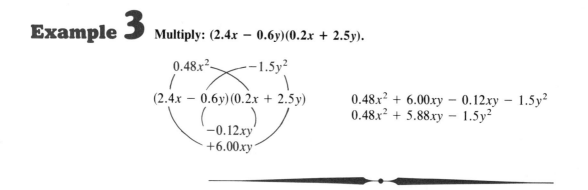

First Way:

$$
\begin{array}{r}
5x^2 - 1x - 4 \\
3x + 2 \\
\hline
15x^3 - 3x^2 - 12x \\
+ 10x^2 - 2x - 8 \\
\hline
15x^3 + 7x^2 - 14x - 8
\end{array}
$$

Second Way:

$(3x + 2)(5x^2 - x - 4)$

$3x(5x^2 - x - 4) + 2(5x^2 - x - 4)$

$3x \cdot 5x^2 + 3x(-x) + 3x(-4) + 2 \cdot 5x^2 + 2(-x) + 2(-4)$

$15x^3 - 3x^2 - 12x + 10x^2 - 2x - 8$

$15x^3 + 7x^2 - 14x - 8$

Some indicated products contain more than two polynomials. For example, $3n(2n + 1)(5n - 4)$ consists of one monomial and two binomials.

To multiply $3n(2n + 1)(5n - 4)$, it is easier to find the product of the binomials first and then multiply the result by the monomial.

Example 5 Multiply: $3n(2n + 1)(5n - 4)$.

$$3n[(2n + 1)(5n - 4)] = 3n[10n^2 - 3n - 4] = 30n^3 - 9n^2 - 12n$$

Oral Exercises

Multiply.

1. $-2(8a^2 + 4a - 5)$
$-16a^2 - 8a + 10$

2. $5x^2(2x^2 - x + 3)$
$10x^4 - 5x^3 + 15x^2$

3. $-3x(4x - 5y - 1)$
$-12x^2 + 15xy + 3x$

Written Exercises

35. $12a^2 + 7ab + 9a - 10b^2 - 6b$
36. $2x^2 + 3xy + 6x - 5y^2 + 15y$

Multiply.
37. $3n^4 + 4n^3 - 17n^2 - 16n + 20$
38. $8a^4 - 2a^3 + 24a^2 - 3a + 18$

Ⓐ
1. $(3y - 5)(4y + 3)$ $12y^2 - 11y - 15$
2. $(3a + 2)(5a - 2)$ $15a^2 + 4a - 4$
3. $(4t + 5)(2t - 4)$ $8t^2 - 6t - 20$
4. $(6n - 3)(2n - 1)$ $12n^2 - 12n + 3$
5. $(2a - 7)(a + 5)$ $2a^2 + 3a - 35$
6. $(6x + 1)(x + 3)$ $6x^2 + 19x + 3$
7. $(2n + 8)(2n - 8)$ $4n^2 - 64$
8. $(3y - 4)(3y + 4)$ $9y^2 - 16$
9. $(3x - 2y)(2x + 4y)$ $6x^2 + 8xy - 8y^2$
10. $(5m + 4n)(3m + 2n)$ $15m^2 + 22mn + 8n^2$
11. $(4a + b)(3a - b)$ $12a^2 - ab - b^2$
12. $(x - y)(5x - 2y)$ $5x^2 - 7xy + 2y^2$
13. $(x^2 + 10)(x^2 + 15)$ $x^4 + 25x^2 + 150$
14. $(n^3 - 8)(n^3 - 9)$ $n^6 - 17n^3 + 72$
15. $(2y^3 - 3)(5y^3 - 7)$ $10y^6 - 29y^3 + 21$
16. $(8x^2 + 5)(3x^2 + 4)$ $24x^4 + 47x^2 + 20$
17. $(7x + 0.4)(3x + 0.8)$ $21x^2 + 6.8x + 0.32$
18. $(5n - 0.6)(4n - 0.7)$ $20n^2 - 5.9n + 0.42$
19. $(0.8a + 6)(0.4a - 9)$ $0.32a^2 - 4.8a - 54$
20. $(0.7x - 3)(0.6x + 5)$ $0.42x^2 + 1.7x - 15$
21. $(5x + 4)(x^2 - 3x + 2)$ $5x^3 - 11x^2 - 2x + 8$
22. $(4y - 3)(2y^2 + 6y - 1)$ $8y^3 + 18y^2 - 22y + 3$
23. $(3y - 2)(3y^2 - y + 4)$ $9y^3 - 9y^2 + 14y - 8$
24. $(2x + 4)(4x^2 + 2x - 3)$ $8x^3 + 20x^2 + 2x - 12$
25. $4(2x - 5)(x + 3)$ $8x^2 + 4x - 60$
26. $3(4a + 5)(2a - 3)$ $24a^2 - 6a - 45$
27. $-2(3y - 4)(3y - 4)$ $-18y^2 + 48y - 32$
28. $-4(2x + 10)(2x - 10)$ $-16x^2 + 400$

Ⓑ
29. $(2x^2 + 3y)(4x^2 - 8y)$ $8x^4 - 4x^2y - 24y^2$
30. $(8a - 5b^2)(3a + 5b^2)$ $24a^2 + 25ab^2 - 25b^4$
31. $(4m^3 + n)(4m^3 + n)$ $16m^6 + 8m^3n + n^2$
32. $(5x - 2y^3)(5x - 2y^3)$ $25x^2 - 20xy^3 + 4y^6$
33. $(3x^2 + 4y^2)(3x^2 - 5y^2)$ $9x^4 - 3x^2y^2 - 20y^4$
34. $(2c^3 - 3d^2)(2c^3 + 6d^2)$ $4c^6 + 6c^3d^2 - 18d^4$
35. $(3a - 2b)(4a + 5b + 3)$
36. $(2x + 5y)(x - y + 3)$
37. $(n^2 - 4)(3n^2 + 4n - 5)$
38. $(2a^2 + 3)(4a^2 - a + 6)$
39. $(3.2x + 0.4)(0.7x + 0.3)$ $2.24x^2 + 1.24x + 0.12$
40. $(5.3n - 0.5)(0.5n - 0.7)$ $2.65n^2 - 3.96n + 0.35$
41. $(0.8y - 0.7)(4.1y + 0.6)$ $3.28y^2 - 2.39y - 0.42$
42. $(0.9x + 0.6)(3.4x - 0.3)$ $3.06x^2 - 1.77x - 0.18$
43. $(3.5x + 0.9)(3.5x - 0.9)$ $12.25x^2 - 0.81$
44. $(5.4n - 0.7)(5.4n + 0.7)$ $29.16n^2 - 0.49$
45. $4x(3x + 2)(2x + 5)$ $24x^3 + 76x^2 + 40x$
46. $-2y(4y - 3)(5y + 2)$ $-40y^3 + 14y^2 + 12y$
47. $2y(5y^2 - 2)(5y^2 - 2)$ $50y^5 - 40y^3 + 8y$
48. $-3x(10x^3 - 5)(10x^3 + 5)$ $-300x^7 + 75x$

$4x^2 + y^2 + 25 + 4xy + 20x + 10y$
$64x^2 + y^2 + 16z^2 - 16xy - 64xz + 8yz$

Ⓒ
49. $(2x + y + 5)(2x + y + 5)$
50. $(8x - y - 4z)(8x - y - 4z)$
51. $(x^n + 3)(x^n - 5)$ $x^{2n} - 2x^n - 15$
52. $(3x^{2a} + 4)(x^{2a} + 1)$ $3x^{4a} + 7x^{2a} + 4$
53. $(x^c + y^{2c})(x^c + 4y^{2c})$
54. $(4x^{2a} - 3y^b)(5x^{2a} + 2y^b)$
55. Show that $(a + b + c)^2 = a^2 + b^2 + c^2 + 2ab + 2ac + 2bc$.

For Ex. 55, see TE Answer Section.
53. $x^{2c} + 5x^c y^{2c} + 4y^{4c}$
54. $20x^{4a} - 7x^{2a}y^b - 6y^{2b}$

MULTIPLYING POLYNOMIALS

43

2.5 Problem Solving: Mixture Problems

OBJECTIVE ▶ **To solve a word problem involving a collection or mixture of items**

To solve certain problems that involve a *collection* or *mixture* of items, it is helpful to convert the values of the items to a common unit. For example, a collection of x nickels, $4x$ dimes, and $x + 6$ quarters is worth

$$5 \cdot x + 10 \cdot 4x + 25(x + 6) \text{ cents.}$$

You will use this technique in solving the problem below.

Example 1

READ

The number of dimes in Martha's coin collection is 4 less than the number of nickels and the number of quarters is 3 times the number of dimes. If the value of her collection is $7.40, how many nickels, dimes, and quarters does she have?

PLAN
Represent the data.

Let $\quad n$ = number of nickels.
$\quad n - 4$ = number of dimes
$\quad 3(n - 4)$ = number of quarters

Write an equation.

$$\left(\begin{array}{c} \text{Value of} \\ \text{nickels in } \cent \end{array} \right) + \left(\begin{array}{c} \text{Value of} \\ \text{dimes in } \cent \end{array} \right) + \left(\begin{array}{c} \text{Value of} \\ \text{quarters in } \cent \end{array} \right) = \left(\begin{array}{c} \text{Value of} \\ \text{collection in } \cent \end{array} \right)$$

SOLVE
Solve the equation.

$$\begin{array}{rcl} 5n \quad + \quad 10(n - 4) \ + \ 25 \cdot 3(n - 4) &=& 100(7.40) \\ 5n + 10n - 40 + 75n - 300 &=& 740 \\ 90n - 340 &=& 740 \\ 90n &=& 1{,}080 \\ n &=& 12 \end{array}$$

$n = 12,\ n - 4 = 8,\ 3(n - 4) = 24$

INTERPRET
Check the solution.

12 nickels + 8 dimes + 24 quarters	$7.40
$12 \cdot 5\cent \ + \ 8 \cdot 10\cent \ + \ 24 \cdot 25\cent$	$7.40 \cdot 100\cent$
$60\cent \quad + \quad 80\cent \quad + \quad 600\cent$	$740\cent$
$740\cent$	

Answer the question.

Thus, there are 12 nickels, 8 dimes, and 24 quarters.

———————————————●———————————————

Example 2 on page 45 is an example of a *dry mixture* problem. In such situations, a mixture is obtained by combining two types of items. The intent is to gain the same amount of money for the mixture as would be realized if the items to be mixed were sold individually. In other words, (Value of 1st Item) + (Value of 2nd Item) = (Value of Mixture).

Example 2 Peanuts worth $2.10/kg are mixed with almonds worth $3.60/kg to make 20 kg of a mixture worth $2.40/kg. How many kilograms of peanuts and how many kilograms of almonds are there in the mixture?

Let x = number of kilograms (kg) of peanuts.

	No. of kg	Value/kg	Value in ¢
Peanuts	x	210¢	$210x$
Almonds	$20 - x$	360¢	$360(20 - x)$
Mixture	20	240¢	$240 \cdot 20$

(Value of peanuts) + (Value of almonds) = (Value of mixture)

$$210x \quad + \quad 360(20 - x) \quad = \quad 240 \cdot 20$$
$$210x + 7{,}200 - 360x = 4{,}800$$
$$-150x = -2{,}400$$
$$x = 16 \qquad 20 - x = 4$$

Check:

$(16 \text{ kg at } \$2.10/\text{kg}) + (4 \text{ kg at } \$3.60/\text{kg})$	$20 \text{ kg at } \$2.40/\text{kg}$
$(16 \cdot \$2.10) \quad + \quad (4 \cdot \$3.60)$	$20 \cdot \$2.40$
$\$33.60 \quad + \quad \$14.40$	$\$48.00$
$\$48.00$	

Thus, there are 16 kg of peanuts and 4 kg of almonds in the mixture.

If a given liquid is classified as a 25% iodine solution, this means that 25% of the solution is iodine and 75% is water. Thus, 6 liters (L) of a 25% iodine solution is made up of 1.5 L of iodine and 4.5 L of water: $0.25 \cdot 6 \text{ L} = 1.5 \text{ L}$ and $0.75 \cdot 6 \text{ L} = 4.5 \text{ L}$. Example 3 presents a situation in which a solution is obtained that contains a given percentage of a particular ingredient.

Example 3 How many liters of water must be evaporated from 60 L of a 12% vinegar solution to make it a 36% vinegar solution?

Let x = number of liters (L) of water to be evaporated.

	Total L	L of vinegar	L of water
12% solution	60	$0.12(60)$	$0.88(60)$
36% solution	$60 - x$	$0.36(60 - x)$	$0.64(60 - x)$

Vinegar in 12% solution = Vinegar in 36% solution
$$0.12(60) = 0.36(60 - x)$$
$$7.20 = 21.60 - 0.36x$$
$$0.36x = 14.40$$
$$x = 40 \qquad \text{(Check in the problem.)}$$

Thus, 40 L of water must be evaporated.

A pharmacist can mix a 90% iodine solution with a 20% iodine solution to obtain a 45% iodine solution. Notice that the

$$\left(\begin{array}{c}\text{Iodine in the} \\ \text{20\% solution}\end{array}\right) + \left(\begin{array}{c}\text{Iodine in the} \\ \text{90\% solution}\end{array}\right) = \left(\begin{array}{c}\text{Iodine in the} \\ \text{45\% solution}\end{array}\right).$$

This concept is used in Example 4.

Example 4 How many milliliters (mL) of an 80% iodine solution should be added to 20 mL of a 16% iodine solution to obtain a 30% iodine solution?

Let x = number of milliliters of 80% solution added.

	Total milliliters	Milliliters of iodine
16% solution	20	0.16(20)
80% solution	x	0.80(x)
30% solution	20 + x	0.30(20 + x)

Mixture ▶

$$\left(\begin{array}{c}\text{Iodine in} \\ \text{16\% sol.}\end{array}\right) + \left(\begin{array}{c}\text{Iodine in} \\ \text{80\% sol.}\end{array}\right) = \left(\begin{array}{c}\text{Iodine in} \\ \text{30\% sol.}\end{array}\right)$$

$$0.16(20) + 0.80x = 0.30(20 + x)$$
$$3.20 + 0.80x = 6.00 + 0.30x$$
$$0.50x = 2.80$$
$$x = 5.6$$

Check:

(16% of 20 mL) + (80% of 5.6 mL)	30% of (20 + 5.6) mL
0.16(20 mL) + 0.80(5.6 mL)	0.30(25.6 mL)
3.20 mL + 4.48 mL	7.68 mL
7.68 mL	

Thus, 5.6 mL of the 80% solution should be added.

Reading in Algebra

If x items are mixed with y items to make a collection containing z items, which of these statements are true?
1. $z = x + y$ **True**   **2.** $y = x - z$ **False**   **3.** $y = z - x$ **True**

If an x% salt solution and a y% salt solution are mixed to form a z% salt solution, which of these statements are true?
4. x is between y and z. **False**   **5.** y is between x and z. **False**   **6.** z is between x and y. **True**

State each word phrase in algebraic terms.

10x + 25 · 3x + 5(x + 6)

5x + 10(x − 4) + 50 · 6x

7. The total value in cents of x dimes, $3x$ quarters, and $(x + 6)$ nickels ←
8. The total value in cents of x nickels, $(x − 4)$ dimes, and $6x$ half-dollars ←
9. The number of liters of acid in $(x + 20)$ L of a 40% acid solution   **0.40(x + 20)**
10. The number of liters of water in $(15 − x)$ L of a 30% saline solution   **0.70(15 − x)**

11. The total value in cents of x kg of peanuts worth 95¢/kg and $(18 - x)$ kg of cashews worth $1.15/kg **95x + 115(18 − x)**

12. The total value in cents of x kg of chocolate worth $2.60/kg and $(x + 6)$ kg of chocolate worth 90¢/kg **260x + 90(x +6)**

Written Exercises

(A)

1. A parking meter takes only dimes and quarters. At the end of one day, the meter held $7.55 and the number of dimes was 8 more than 20 times the number of quarters. What was the number of dimes and quarters? **68 dimes, 3 quarters**

2. A collection of nickels and quarters is worth $2.40. Find the number of nickels and quarters if the number of nickels is 6 less than 4 times the number of quarters.
18 nickels, 6 quarters

3. Some brand A dog food worth 70¢/kg is to be added to 9 kg of brand B dog food worth 50¢/kg. The mixture will be worth 58¢/kg. How many kilograms of brand A should be added? **6 kg**

4. Some salt tablets worth $3.50/kg were mixed with some cheaper tablets worth $2.00/kg to make 12 kg of a mixture worth $2.50/kg. How many kilograms of each kind were mixed?
4 kg at $3.50, 8 kg at $2.00

5. How many milliliters of water must be evaporated from 160 mL of a 20% iodine solution to make it a 40% iodine solution?
80 mL

6. A chemist has 120 mL of a 15% vinegar solution. How much water must be evaporated in order to obtain a 20% vinegar solution? **30 mL**

7. How many liters of an 80% sulfuric acid solution must be added to 60 L of a 30% sulfuric acid solution to obtain a 50% acid solution? **40 L**

8. How many liters of a 52% citrus solution must be added to 30 L of a 24% citrus solution to make a 40% citrus solution?
40 L

9. Gerry paid $11.92 to buy some 10¢, 13¢, and 50¢ stamps. If the number of 13¢ stamps was twice the number of 50¢ stamps, and there were 4 more 10¢ stamps than 13¢ stamps, how many of each kind did she buy? **12 at 50¢, 24 at 13¢, 28 at 10¢**

10. A vending machine contains 12 more dimes than quarters and twice as many nickels as dimes. Find the number of each kind of coin if their total value is $6.00.
— A: 10 kg, B: 6 kg   **8 quarters, 20 dimes, 40 nickels**

11. Some brand A bulk tea worth $1.40/kg and some brand B tea worth $3.00/kg are mixed to make 16 kg of a brand C worth $2.00/kg. How many kilograms of each brand are used?

12. Fifty kilograms of oats worth 90¢/kg is added to some corn worth 60¢/kg to make some animal feed worth 75¢/kg. How many kilograms of corn should be used? **50 kg**

13. How many liters of water must be added to 15 L of a 28% salt solution to dilute it to a 12% solution? **20 L**

14. Skimmed milk contains no butterfat. How many liters of skimmed milk must be added to 600 L of milk that is 3.5% butterfat to obtain milk with 2% butterfat?
450 L

(B)

15. A store sells the Red Dot golf ball for 60¢, the Black Dot ball for 96¢, and the Gold Dot ball for $1.08. A golf pro bought two dozen more Red Dot than Gold Dot balls and three times as many Black Dot as Red Dot balls. If the golf balls and one dollar's worth of tees cost $130.12, how many golf balls of each kind were bought? **10 Gold, 34 Red, 102 Black**

8 at 80¢, 16 at 60¢

16. A package of paper tablets sells for $16.00 and contains twice as many 60¢ tablets as 80¢ tablets. How many paper tablets of each kind are in the package?

cheese: 15, meat: 25

17. Some 8¢ slices of cheese and some 16¢ slices of meat make up a package of 40 slices worth $5.20. How many slices of each kind are in the package?

18. How many liters of a 72% alcohol solution must be added to 15 L of an 18% alcohol solution to obtain a 45% alcohol solution? **15 L**

19. A chemist added 9 mL of a 40% citrus solution and some milliliters of a 60% citrus solution to 210 mL of a 20% citrus solution to make a 30% solution. How many milliliters of the 60% solution were added? **67 mL**

20. How many liters of water must be evaporated from 48 L of a $12\frac{1}{2}$% saline solution to make it a $37\frac{1}{2}$% saline solution? **32 L**

21. How many milliliters of water must be added to 120 mL of a $62\frac{1}{2}$% glucose solution to dilute it to a $37\frac{1}{2}$% glucose solution? **80 mL**

22. Some powdered milk worth $2.00/kg and some cocoa worth $2.60/kg make up a mixture worth $50.40. If there are 16 kg more milk than cocoa, find the number of kilograms of milk used. **20 kg**

23. A box of birthday cards is worth $6.30 and contains 14 more 20¢ cards than 30¢ cards. How many cards of each kind are in the box? **7 at 30¢, 21 at 20¢**

24. A chemist added some 40% and 24% iodine solutions to 50 mL of a 32% solution to make a 28% iodine solution. The amount of the 24% solution was 4 times the amount of the 40% solution. Find the amount of each solution added to the 50 mL of the 32% solution. **40%: 50 mL, 24%: 200 mL**

25. Chemicals A, B, and C are worth 60¢, 40¢, and 80¢/g, respectively. They are mixed so that the mass of B is twice that of A and is 3 g less than the mass of C. How many grams of each chemical should be used if the mixture is worth $11.40? **A: 3 g, B: 6 g, C: 9 g**

A Challenge To You

In an apartment complex, the monthly rental for an apartment is $200 if it is on the 1st floor, $160 on the 2nd floor, and $120 on the 3rd floor. The number of 2nd floor apartments is 4 less than the number of 3rd floor apartments and 4 more than the number of 1st floor apartments. Find the number of 1st floor apartments if the monthly rental for the entire complex is $9,280. **16**

CALCULATOR ACTIVITIES

2. $51.25   **3. 30.91 mL**

Compute the value or amount for each expression. Round the answer to the nearest 0.01.
1. 18.32 kg at $7.58/kg **$138.87**   2. $34.93 + (7.45 kg × $2.19/kg)   3. 42% of (23.7 + 49.9) mL
4. $5.12 + (4.96 g × 6.25¢/g)   5. 7.38 L + (57.4% of 12 L)   6. 72% of (28% of 346 mL)
           $5.43   **14.27 L**   **69.75 mL**

2.6 Problem Solving: Motion Problems

OBJECTIVE ▶ **To solve a word problem involving two objects in motion**

An automobile that is driven at an average rate of 90 kilometers per hour (km/h) for 3 hours travels 90 · 3, or 270 km. An Olympic sprinter who runs at an average rate of 8 meters per second (m/s) for 50 seconds travels 8 · 50, or 400 m. The relationship between distance, rate, and time of an object in motion is stated below.

Distance of Object in Motion

> The distance (d) traveled by a moving object is equal to its rate of speed (r) times the time in motion (t): $d = rt$.

The formula $d = rt$ is a mathematical *model* for solving problems involving motion.

Example 1

READ

Two trains started toward each other at the same time from stations 732 km apart. One train traveled at 148 km/h and the other train traveled at 96 km/h. In how many hours did they meet?

PLAN

Represent the data in a diagram and in a table.
Let t = number of hours for each train.

Faster train→   Meet   ←Slower train
| 148 km/h for t hours | 96 km/h for t hours |

732 km

	rate (r)	time (t)	distance (d)
Faster train	148	t	$148t$
Slower train	96	t	$96t$

◀ Use $d = rt$.

(Distance of faster train) + (Distance of slower train) = Total distance
$$148t \quad + \quad 96t \quad = \quad 732$$

SOLVE
$$244t = 732$$
$$t = 3$$

INTERPRET

Check:

(Distance of faster train) + (Distance of slower train)	Total distance
148 km/h · 3 h + 96 km/h · 3 h	732 km
444 km + 288 km	
732 km	

Thus, the trains met in 3 hours.

Suppose a car leaves a certain city at 2:00 P.M., traveling at 60 km/h. Then, at 4:00 P.M. a second car leaves the same city, traveling the same route at 90 km/h. The second car will overtake the first car as indicated below.

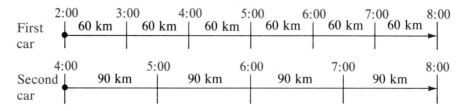

The second car will overtake the first car at 8:00 P.M. Notice that the two cars travel the same distance: 60 km/h · 6 h = 90 km/h · 4 h = 360 km.

Motion problems of this type can also be solved using the formula $d = rt$ along with appropriate equation properties. The procedure is shown in the next example.

Example 2

An aircraft carrier, traveling at 30 km/h, left a port at 7:00 A.M. At 9:00 A.M., a destroyer left the same port, traveling the same route at 40 km/h. At what time did the destroyer overtake the carrier?

Let t = number of hours the carrier traveled.

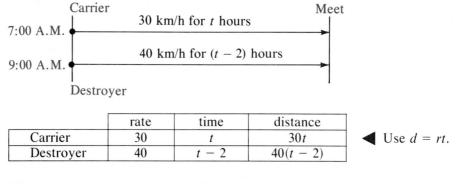

	rate	time	distance
Carrier	30	t	$30t$
Destroyer	40	$t - 2$	$40(t - 2)$

◀ Use $d = rt$.

(Distance traveled by carrier) = (Distance traveled by destroyer)

$$30t = 40(t - 2)$$
$$30t = 40t - 80$$
$$-10t = -80$$
$$t = 8$$

Check:

(Distance traveled by carrier)	(Distance traveled by destroyer)
30 km/h · 8 h	40 km/h · 6 h
240 km	240 km

The time, 8 hours after 7:00 A.M., is 3:00 P.M.

Thus, the destroyer overtook the carrier at 3:00 P.M.

Written Exercises _____

(A)

1. A passenger train and a freight train start toward each other at the same time from towns 870 km apart. The passenger train travels 80 km/h and the freight train travels 65 km/h. In how many hours will they meet? **6 h**

2. Two hockey players start toward each other at the same time from opposite ends of an ice rink that is 60 m long. In how many seconds will they meet if one player skates at a rate of 9.5 m/s and the other skates at a rate of 10.5 m/s? **3 s**

3. A ship left port at 2:00 P.M. and traveled at 30 km/h. At 6:00 P.M., a helicopter left the same port and flew at 120 km/h in the same direction as the ship. At what time did the helicopter reach the ship? **7:20 P.M.**

4. John began the marathon run at 8:30 A.M. and averaged 12 km/h. Mary began at 9:00 A.M. and averaged 14 km/h. At what time did Mary pass John on the marathon course? **12:00 P.M.**

5. Two cars start from the same point at the same time but travel in opposite directions. One car averages 80 km/h and the other averages 70 km/h. In how many hours will they be 600 km apart? **4 h**

6. From a dock in a river, Cindy swam downstream at 4.4 m/s while George swam upstream at 2.8 m/s. In how many seconds were they 108 m apart? **15 s**

(B)

7. At 7:00 A.M., an armored van left city A and traveled at 70 km/h toward city B. At 11:00 A.M. a helicopter, headed toward the van, left city B and traveled at 110 km/h. At approximately what time did the copter reach the van if the cities are 550 km apart? **12:30 P.M.**

8. One bus left the city at 2:00 P.M. and averaged 75 km/h. Another bus, traveling in the opposite direction, left the city at 5:00 P.M. and averaged 85 km/h. At what time were the buses 705 km apart? **8:00 P.M.**

9. A plane left an airfield and averaged 600 km/h. Two hours later, a pursuit plane left the same field and traveled at 900 km/h in the same direction. How long did it take the pursuit plane to catch the slower plane?
4 h

10. A thief left a bank by car at 8:45 A.M. and averaged 110 km/h. The police left the scene at 8:48 A.M. and pursued the thief at 140 km/h. At what time was the thief caught? **8:59 A.M.**

11. A carrier and a destroyer left the same port at 8:00 A.M. and sailed in the same direction. The carrier averaged 30 km/h and the destroyer traveled at 75 km/h. At what time will they be 375 km apart?
4:20 P.M.

12. A jet plane and a cargo plane left the same terminal at the same time and flew in the same direction. The jet flew at 1,000 km/h. After 6 hours, the planes were 2,100 km apart. Find the rate of the cargo plane.
650 km/h

(C)

13. An Olympic cyclist rode the first 6 hours of a race with a planned strategy. The cyclist pedaled at a constant rate for the first 3 hours and then reduced his speed by one-half for 1 hour. The last 2 hours, the rate was 3 times that of the fourth hour. Find the three different speeds if 78 km were traveled in the first 6 hours. **12 km/h, 6 km/h, 18 km/h**

14. An object moved in one direction for 6.25 seconds at a constant speed. It then reversed direction for 2.50 seconds with its rate doubled, and then reversed direction again for 0.75 seconds at 40% of its initial speed. Find the three speeds if the object was 5.89 m from its start at the end of 9.50 seconds. **3.80 m/s, 7.60 m/s, 1.52 m/s**

Chapter Two Review

Vocabulary
base, exponent [2.1]
exponential equation [2.1]
negative exponent, zero exponent [2.2]
polynomial [2.3]

binomial	linear	quadratic
degree of	monomial	trinomial

Simplify and write each expression with positive exponents. 1. $-40a^6b^7c^6$ 2. $128m^4n^{15}$

1. $-5a^4bc^5 \cdot 8a^2b^6c$ 2. $2m(4mn^5)^3$ [2.1]
3. $\dfrac{10x^3y^7z^8}{15x^7y^7z^7}$ $\dfrac{2z}{3x^4}$ 4. $\left(\dfrac{-5c^4}{2d^3}\right)^3$ $\dfrac{-125c^{12}}{8d^9}$

★ 5. $x^my^n(x^{2m}y^{n+3})^2$ $x^{5m}y^{3n+6}$
6. $7x^{-3} \cdot 2y^0 \cdot x^{-4} \cdot 4y^2$ $\dfrac{56y^2}{x^7}$

7. $(2a^{-2}b^3)^{-4}$ $\dfrac{a^8}{16b^{12}}$ [2.2]
8. $\dfrac{6c^{-5}d^{-3}}{8c^4d^{-7}}$ $\dfrac{3d^4}{4c^9}$ 9. $\left(\dfrac{-3xy^{-2}}{2z^3w^{-3}}\right)^4$ $\dfrac{81x^4w^{12}}{16y^8z^{12}}$

★ 10. x^{2c-2d} if $c < d < 0$ $\dfrac{1}{x^{2d-2c}}$

Find the value of each expression. [2.2]

11. $\dfrac{3.45}{10^{-3}}$ 3,450   12. $\dfrac{6.9 \times 10^{-5}}{0.3 \times 10^{-2}}$ 0.023

Solve each equation. [2.1]
13. $5^{x-3} = 625$ 7   14. $3^{4x-3} = 81$ $\frac{7}{4}$

Evaluate each polynomial for the given values of its variables. (Ex. 15–17) [2.3]

15. $3xy - 2x^2y^3 - 4$ if $x = 3$ and $y = -2$ **122**
16. $3.2c^2 + 5.4d^2$ if $c = -0.5$ and $d = -5$ **135.8**
★ 17. $10x^3 + 5x^2y - 5xy^2$ if $x = a^2$ and $y = 2a^2$
   0

18. Add $6mn - 3m^2n + 4mn^2$ and $-mn^2 + 8m^2n$. [2.3] $6mn + 5m^2n + 3mn^2$
19. Subtract: $(9xy^2 - 5x^3y) - (3xy - 5x^3y)$. [2.3]
   $9xy^2 - 3xy$

Multiply. [2.4]
20. $(5x - 2)(3x - 1)$ $15x^2 - 11x + 2$
21. $(4x^2 + 3y^2)(4x^2 + 3y^2)$ $16x^4 + 24x^2y^2 + 9y^4$
22. $(3a - 1)(2a^2 - a - 1)$ $6a^3 - 5a^2 - 2a + 1$
23. $7c(5c^3 - 2)(4c^3 + 3)$ $140c^7 + 49c^4 - 42c$

Solve each problem.
24. The number of nickels in a coin box is 8 more than the number of quarters and the number of dimes is 3 times the number of nickels. Find the number of each kind of coin if their total value is $7.00. [2.5]
   7 quarters, 15 nickels, 45 dimes
25. Some caramels worth $2.60/kg are mixed with some peppermints worth $3.00/kg to make 8 kg of a mixture worth $2.85/kg. How many kilograms of each kind are there in the mixture? [2.5]
   caramels: 3 kg, mints: 5 kg
26. How many liters of water must be evaporated from 90 L of a 15% saline solution to make it a 45% saline solution? [2.5] **60 L**

27. How many milliliters of a 25% iodine solution should be added to 90 mL of a 65% iodine solution to obtain a 55% iodine solution? [2.5] **30 mL**

28. At 6:00 A.M., a car left city A and headed for city B at 80 km/h. At 9:00 A.M., another car left city B and headed for city A at 90 km/h. At what time did the cars meet if the two cities are 580 km apart? [2.6]
   11:00 A.M.
29. A ship left a port at 25 km/h, and 4 hours later, a helicopter left the same port in the same direction at 100 km/h. How long did it take the helicopter to overtake the ship? [2.6] **1 h 20 min**

30. In problem 29 above, how long did it take the helicopter to reach a distance of 10 km behind the ship? [2.6] **1 h 12 min**

31. Steve left the gymnasium at 7:45 A.M. and jogged in one direction at 10 km/h. At 8:15 A.M., Karla left the gym and jogged in the opposite direction at 12 km/h. At what time were they 10.5 km apart? [2.6] **8:30 A.M.**

Chapter Two Test

Simplify and write each expression with positive exponents.

1. $-6x^2yz^4 \cdot 3xy^5z^3$ $-18x^3y^6z^7$

2. $8a^{-5} \cdot 5b^0 \cdot a^8 \cdot b^{-3}$ $\frac{40a^3}{b^3}$

3. $\frac{5m^8n^3p^2}{15m^4n^3p^{10}}$ $\frac{m^4}{3p^8}$

4. $\frac{4x^{-6}y^{-2}}{6x^{-4}y^{-4}}$ $\frac{2y^2}{3x^2}$

5. $(-4c^2)^3$ $-64c^6$

6. $10m(2m^3n)^4$

7. $\left(\frac{3x^2}{-2y}\right)^4$ $\frac{81x^8}{16y^4}$

8. $(3c^{-4}d^5)^{-2}$ $\frac{c^8}{9d^{10}}$

9. $4a^2(-5a^3b)^3$ $-500a^{11}b^3$ $160m^{13}n^4$

10. $\left(\frac{6x^{-4}}{x^4y^{-3}}\right)^2$ $\frac{36y^6}{x^{16}}$

Find the value of each expression.

11. $\frac{7^{-2}}{2^{-4}}$ $\frac{16}{49}$

12. $\frac{4.8 \times 10^{-1}}{1.2 \times 10^{-3}}$ 400

Solve each equation.

13. $2^{x-3} = 64$ 9

14. $6^{3x+1} = 36$ $\frac{1}{3}$

Evaluate each polynomial for the given values of its variables. (Ex. 15–16)

15. $8x^2y - 2xy^2$ if $x = 2$ and $y = -2$ -80

16. $3cd^3 - cd$ if $c = -2.4$ and $d = -5$ 888

17. Add $-8ab + 6a^3b - ab^2$ and $7ab^2 - 6a^3b$. $-8ab + 6ab^2$

18. Subtract: $(5x^5 - x^3 + 2x) - (x^3 - 6x - 8x^5)$. $13x^5 - 2x^3 + 8x$

Multiply.

19. $(5x - 3)(2x + 1)$ $10x^2 - x - 3$

20. $(7m^3 + 5n)(7m^3 + 5n)$

21. $(3.5a - 0.5)(4a + 6)$ $14a^2 + 19a - 3$

22. $4n(3n + 7)(3n - 7)$ $36n^3 - 196n$

23. $(2x + 3)(x^2 - 4x - 5)$ $2x^3 - 5x^2 - 22x - 15$

20. $49m^6 + 70m^3n + 25n^2$

Solve each problem.

24. A collection of dimes and quarters is worth $2.85. If the number of dimes is 3 less than twice the number of quarters, find the number of dimes and quarters.   **11 dimes, 7 quarters**

25. How many liters of water must be added to 30 L of a 20% chlorine solution to dilute it to a 15% chlorine solution? **10 L**

26. One train left a depot at 3:00 P.M. and traveled at 80 km/h. Another train left the depot at 6:00 P.M. and traveled in the opposite direction at 150 km/h. At what time were the trains 1,620 km apart?   **12:00 A.M.**

27. Some Brand A cleanser worth 80¢/kg is to be mixed with some Brand B cleanser worth 60¢/kg to make 15 kg of a mixture worth 68¢/kg. How many kilograms of each brand should be used? **A: 6 kg, B: 9 kg**

28. John and Everett ran in the local marathon. If John averaged 17 km/h and Everett averaged 14 km/h, how long did it take John to be 4.5 km ahead of Everett? **$1\frac{1}{2}$ h**

29. Wheat flour worth 40¢/kg was mixed with some bran flour worth 60¢/kg. The amount of bran flour used in the mixture was 10 kg less than the amount of wheat flour used. If the mixture was worth $14.00, how many kilograms of each kind of flour were in the mixture? **wheat: 20 kg, bran: 10 kg**

★30. An automobile dealer purchased some model A, B, and C automobiles worth $3,000, $6,000, and $4,000 each, respectively. The ratio of model A to model B to model C automobiles purchased was 8 to 3 to 4. If their total value was $116,000, how many automobiles of each model were purchased?   **A: 16, B: 6, C: 8**

★31. **Simplify and write with positive exponents.**
$\frac{x^{6a+4}y^{3b-2}}{x^{2a-2}y^{b+3}}$ $x^{4a+6}y^{2b-5}$

★32. **Evaluate the polynomial for the given values of its variables.**
$4x^3y + 10x^2y^2 - 10xy^3$ if $x = a$ and $y = 2a$ $-32a^4$

★33. Multiply: $(3c + 2d - 5)(2c - d + 4)$. $6c^2 + cd + 2c - 2d^2 + 13d - 20$

Computer Activities

Diluting Drug Solutions

Drugs are often sent to drug stores in the form of rather concentrated solutions. In filling a prescription, the pharmacist may need to dilute a certain solution by adding water to it. You can use a computer to calculate the amount of water to add in order to obtain the proper percentage of the drug that is required in the prescription.

In the program below, the amount of drug in the original solution and the amount of drug in the diluted solution are each expressed as a polynomial. The program may be used to find the number of liters of water to be added in order to dilute a given solution so that it contains a specified percentage of a particular drug.

PROGRAM

```
10 PRINT "THIS PROGRAM PRINTS OUT"
20 PRINT "THE AMOUNT OF WATER NEEDED"
30 PRINT "TO DILUTE A SOLUTION"
40 PRINT "TYPE IN TOTAL AMOUNT OF ORIGINAL SOLUTION IN
   LITERS"
50 INPUT X
60 PRINT "TYPE IN PERCENT OF DRUG IN ORIGINAL LIQUID"
70 PRINT "SOLUTION AS A DECIMAL—30% AS .30"
80 INPUT P1
90 PRINT "ENTER PERCENT SOLUTION YOU NEED AS A DECIMAL"
100 INPUT P2
110 REM D-DRUG IN ORIGINAL SOLUTION
120 D = X * P1
130 REM W-WATER TO ADD
140 W = (D-P2 * X)/P2
150 PRINT W; "LITERS OF WATER MUST BE ADDED"
160 END
```

Exercises

Enter and run the above program for:
1. $x = 4$ $P1 = 30\%$ $P2 = 20\%$ **1.999999 L**
2. $x = 10$ $P1 = 35\%$ $P2 = 15\%$ **13.33334 L**

3. Alter the computer program above to get a program that can be used to find the number of liters of water that must be evaporated from a solution in order to increase the percentage of a drug in the resulting solution.
Alter statements 30, 130, 140, and 150.   **140: Let W = (P2 * X − D)/P2**

54   **ACTIVITY: DILUTING DRUG SOLUTIONS**

College Prep Test

SAMPLE ITEMS AND ANSWERS

Column 1	Column 2
	$x = 7$
S1. $x + x$	x^2

The answer is B, since $7^2 > 7 + 7$.

S2. $2x$	$3x$

The answer is D, since $2x > 3x$ if $x = -1$; $3x > 2x$ if $x = 1$; and $2x = 3x$ if $x = 0$.

	Column 1	Column 2	
1.	$21 \cdot 1{,}234 \cdot 20$	$20 \cdot 1{,}234 \cdot 22$	**B**
		$x = -3$	
2.	$x^3 - 2x$	$x^2 + 10x$	**C**
3.	$5 + 2^4 + 7$	$6 + 4^2 + 5$	**A**
4.	$(y + 2)(y + 3)$	$(y + 4)(y + 5)$	**D**
		$x = 10$	
5.	$2x^4 + 3x^2 + 4$	$9x^3 + 8x^2 + 7x + 6$	**A**

	Column 1	Column 2	
6.	The greater solution of $|x + 5| = 2$	The smaller solution of $|x - 5| = 7$	**B**
		$y = \frac{4}{3}x + 15$	
7.	x, if $y = -45$	y, if $x = -45$	**C**
		$x^y = 16$	
8.	x	y	**D**
9.	Number of liters of iodine in 60 L of a 25% iodine solution	Number of liters of water in 40 L of a 20% salt solution	**B**
10.	Area of a rectangle, 1.5 m by 0.3 m	Area of a rectangle, 9 cm by 5 cm	**A**
11.	$(x + 2)^2$	$(x + 2)(x - 2)$	**D**

30 mi/h for 5 h
A   B
50 mi/h for 3 h

12.	Average speed for round trip from A to B to A	40 mph	**B**

3 FACTORING AND SPECIAL PRODUCTS

Formulating A Problem-Solving Situation

FORMULATE → PLAN → SOLVE → INTERPRET

Sometimes a mathematical problem-solving situation involves a question of concern, but the problem is not precisely stated for you. Your first step in solving a problem of this type is to **formulate** the problem-solving situation. That is, *analyze* the situation with particular *focus* on the question to be answered. You should *identify* what information is needed to answer the question. Finally, it may be helpful to *propose* the problem in your own words. Notice how this is done with the problem-solving situation below.

Question: How many cans of liquid floor wax must you buy to cover the floor of your recreation room?

To answer the question, you must obtain the following information:
   (a) Dimensions of floor
   (b) Sizes of cans of floor wax available
   (c) Surface area covered by one unit of wax of your choice.

Suppose your analysis of the situation reveals these facts:
   (a) The dimensions of the floor are 700 cm × 600 cm.
   (b) The floor wax brand of your choice comes only in 1-L cans.
   (c) One liter of floor wax covers an area of 20 m^2.

You can now state the problem formally.

Problem: How many 1-L cans of liquid floor wax must you buy to cover the floor of your recreation room that measures 700 cm by 600 cm, if one liter of wax covers an area of 20 m^2?

PROJECT

Question: What is the total cost of the transportation for a trip from your town to a distant city?

Identify some of the information you would need in order to state the problem that is to be solved.

3.1 Factoring Trinomials

OBJECTIVE ▶ **To factor a trinomial of degree 2 or greater into two binomials**

You have multiplied two binomials, such as $(3x - 5)(2x + 1)$, by the FOIL method as shown below.

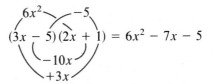

$$(3x - 5)(2x + 1) = 6x^2 - 7x - 5$$

Notice that the middle term of the trinomial is $3x - 10x$, or $-7x$.

A trinomial of the form $ax^2 + bx + c\,(a \neq 0)$ is called a **quadratic trinomial.** You can *factor* a quadratic trinomial into two binomials by reversing the multiplication process above. Begin by listing the possible pairs of binomial factors. Then check each pair until you find the factorization that gives the correct middle term.

Example 1 Factor $3x^2 - 8x + 5$ into two binomials.

$$3x^2 - 8x + 5 = (3x \ \underline{\ ?\ })(x \ \underline{\ ?\ })$$

The first terms of the binomial factors are $3x$ and x. The last terms are either $+1$ and $+5$ or -1 and -5. Since the middle term of the trinomial is negative, $(-8x)$, try -1 and -5.

Possible Factors	Middle Term
$(3x - 1)(x - 5)$	$-15x - x = -16x$
$(3x - 5)(x - 1)$	$-3x - 5x = -8x$ ◀ *Correct middle term:* $-8x$

Thus, $3x^2 - 8x + 5 = (3x - 5)(x - 1)$.

Example 2 Factor $2n^2 + 11n + 12$ into two binomials.

$$2n^2 + 11n + 12 = (2n + \underline{\ ?\ })(n + \underline{\ ?\ })$$

Try 6 and 2,
1 and 12,
3 and 4 ▶
for last terms
of the factors.

Possible Factors	Middle Term
$(2n + 6)(n + 2)$	$4n + 6n = 10n$
$(2n + 2)(n + 6)$	$12n + 2n = 14n$
$(2n + 1)(n + 12)$	$24n + n = 25n$
$(2n + 12)(n + 1)$	$2n + 12n = 14n$
$(2n + 3)(n + 4)$	$8n + 3n = 11n$ ◀ *Correct middle term.* $11n$
$(2n + 4)(n + 3)$	$6n + 4n = 10n$

Thus, $2n^2 + 11n + 12 = (2n + 3)(n + 4)$.

To factor a polynomial of any type, express it as a product of other polynomials of a lower degree. Using integers only, some polynomials cannot be factored in this manner.

Example 3 Factor $y^2 + y + 9$ into two binomials.

$$y^2 + y + 9 = (y + \underline{\ ?\ })(y + \underline{\ ?\ })$$

Possible Factors	Middle Term
$(y + 3)(y + 3)$	$3y + 3y = 6y$
$(y + 9)(y + 1)$	$y + 9y = 10y$

Neither pair of factors gives the correct middle term, y.
Thus, $y^2 + y + 9$ cannot be factored using integers.

Similar procedures should be followed when factoring quadratic trinomials that contain more than one variable or trinomials of a degree greater than 2. This is shown in Examples 4 and 5, respectively.

Example 4 Factor $2x^2 - 11xy + 5y^2$ into two binomials.

$$2x^2 - 11xy + 5y^2 = (2x - \underline{\ ?\ })(x - \underline{\ ?\ })$$

Possible Factors	Middle Term	
$(2x - 5y)(x - y)$	$-2xy - 5xy = -7xy$	
$(2x - y)(x - 5y)$	$-10xy - xy = -11xy$	◀ *Correct middle term: $-11xy$*

Thus, $2x^2 - 11xy + 5y^2 = (2x - y)(x - 5y)$.

Example 5 Factor $2x^4 - 9x^2 - 5$ into two binomials.

The first terms of the binomial factors are $2x^2$ and x^2.
The last terms are either -5 and $+1$ or $+5$ and -1.

$$2x^4 - 9x^2 - 5 = (2x^2 \ \underline{\ ?\ })(x^2 \ \underline{\ ?\ })$$

Possible Factors	Middle Term	
$(2x^2 - 5)(x^2 + 1)$	$2x^2 - 5x^2 = -3x^2$	
$(2x^2 + 1)(x^2 - 5)$	$-10x^2 + x^2 = -9x^2$	◀ *Correct middle term: $-9x^2$*
$(2x^2 - 1)(x^2 + 5)$	$10x^2 - x^2 = 9x^2$	
$(2x^2 + 5)(x^2 - 1)$	$-2x^2 + 5x^2 = 3x^2$	

Thus, $2x^4 - 9x^2 - 5 = (2x^2 + 1)(x^2 - 5)$.

Oral Exercises

1. $(x - 3)(x - 4)$ 2. $(x - 12)(x - 1)$ 3. $(x + 4)(x - 3)$ 4. $(x - 4)(x + 3)$ 5. $(x + 2)(x + 6)$
Factor each trinomial into two binomials. 6. $(x - 6)(x + 2)$

1. $x^2 - 7x + 12$ 2. $x^2 - 13x + 12$ 3. $x^2 + x - 12$
4. $x^2 - x - 12$ 5. $x^2 + 8x + 12$ 6. $x^2 - 4x - 12$
7. $x^2 + x + 3$ ← cannot be factored 8. $x^2 - 5x + 6$ $(x - 3)(x - 2)$ 9. $x^2 - 5x - 6$ $(x - 6)(x + 1)$

Written Exercises

16. $(5n + 4)(3n - 1)$ 17. $(x + 6y)(x - 2y)$ 19. $(x + 3y)(x - 4y)$

For complete solutions to Ex. 1–60, see TE Answer Section.
Factor each trinomial into two binomials. 20. $(4a + b)(2a - b)$ 26. $(5c^2 - 1)(2c^2 + 1)$

(A)
1. $7x^2 - 12x + 5$ $(7x - 5)(x - 1)$ 2. $5y^2 - 36y + 7$ $(5y - 1)(y - 7)$ 3. $5y^2 + 14y - 3$ $(5y - 1)(y + 3)$
4. $7n^2 + 4n - 11$ $(7n + 11)(n - 1)$ 5. $5a^2 - 54a - 11$ $(5a + 1)(a - 11)$ 6. $3x^2 - 10x - 13$ $(3x - 13)(x + 1)$
7. $6x^2 - 7x - 2$ **below** 8. $8n^2 + 14n + 3$ $(4n + 1)(2n + 3)$ 9. $2a^2 + a - 10$ $(2a + 5)(a - 2)$
10. $2x^2 - 11x + 14$ $(2x - 7)(x - 2)$ 11. $5x^2 - 28x + 15$ $(5x - 3)(x - 5)$ 12. $3y^2 + 11y + 6$ $(3y + 2)(y + 3)$
13. $9a^2 + 18a + 8$ $(3a + 4)(3a + 2)$ 14. $6t^2 - 11t - 10$ $(3t + 2)(2t - 5)$ 15. $4c^2 - 15c + 9$ $(4c - 3)(c - 3)$
16. $15n^2 + 7n - 4$ 17. $x^2 + 4xy - 12y^2$ 18. $x^2 + 13xy + 36y^2$ $(x + 9y)(x + 4y)$
19. $x^2 - xy - 12y^2$ 20. $8a^2 - 2ab - b^2$ 21. $15c^2 - 8cd + d^2$ $(5c - d)(3c - d)$
22. $21m^2 + 10mn + n^2$ **below** 23. $x^4 - 9x^2 + 14$ $(x^2 - 2)(x^2 - 7)$ 24. $n^4 + 8n^2 + 15$ $(n^2 + 3)(n^2 + 5)$
25. $a^4 - 3a^2 - 18$ $(a^2 + 3)(a^2 - 6)$ 26. $10c^4 + 3c^2 - 1$ 27. $15a^4 + 16a^2 - 7$ $(5a^2 + 7)(3a^2 - 1)$
28. $21d^4 - 8d^2 - 5$ 29. $x^2 - 14x - 72$ $(x + 4)(x - 18)$ 30. $72x^2 + 21x - 1$ $(3x + 1)(24x - 1)$
31. $64y^2 - 12y - 1$ 32. $8a^2 - 5a - 10$ 33. $y^2 + 30y - 64$ $(y - 2)(y + 32)$
7. cannot be factored cannot be factored 22. $(7m + n)(3m + n)$

(B)
34. $10x^2 + 23x + 12$ 35. $12n^2 - 17n + 6$ 36. $12y^2 - 8y - 15$ $(2y - 3)(6y + 5)$
37. $18a^2 - 35a + 12$ 38. $24x^2 - 46x - 35$ 39. $16n^2 + 10n - 21$ $(8n - 7)(2n + 3)$
40. $20c^2 - 48c + 27$ 41. $24a^2 - 5a - 36$ 42. $6y^2 + yz - 12z^2$
43. $5x^2 + 4xy - 12y^2$ 44. $36m^2 - 7mn - 15n^2$ 45. $24c^2 + 17cd - 20d^2$
46. $15x^4 - 8x^2 - 12$ 47. $12x^4 - 23x^2 + 10$ 48. $18y^4 + 9y^2 - 20$ $(3y^2 + 4)(6y^2 - 5)$
49. $6y^4 - 23y^2 - 18$ 50. $10n^4 - 31n^2 + 24$ 51. $9a^4 + 24a^2 - 20$
52. $2x^4y^4 - 7x^2y^2 + 6$ 53. $3a^4b^4 - a^2b^2 - 10$ 54. $5m^4n^4 + 4m^2n^2 - 12$
55. $6c^4d^4 + 23c^2d^2 + 20$ 56. $5x^4 + 23x^2y^2 + 24y^4$ 57. $14c^4 - 9c^2d^2 - 18d^4$
58. $2x^8 + 2x^4 - 1$ 59. $x^6 - 7x^3y^2 + 6y^4$ 60. $5m^4 - 4m^2n^3 - n^6$
28. $(7d^2 - 5)(3d^2 + 1)$ 31. $(16y + 1)(4y - 1)$

(C)
61. $x^{6m} - 7x^{3m} + 12$ $(x^{3m} - 3)(x^{3m} - 4)$ 62. $6x^{2m} + 19x^m + 15$ $(3x^m + 5)(2x^m + 3)$
63. $9x^{4m} + 24x^{2m} - 20$ $(3x^{2m} + 10)(3x^{2m} - 2)$ 64. $8x^{6m} - 2x^{3m} - 21$ $(4x^{3m} - 7)(2x^{3m} + 3)$
65. $5x^{2a} + 23x^a y^b + 12y^{2b}$ 66. $8x^{4a} - 26x^{2a}y^{2b} + 15y^{4b}$
67. $12x^{6a} - 8x^{3a}y^{2b} - 15y^{4b}$ 68. $x^{2n+4} + 7x^{n+2} + 12$
69. $x^{2n-2} + 3x^{n-1} - 10$ 70. $x^{8n+6} - 2x^{4n+3} - 3$
71. $x^{2a+6} + 2x^{a+3}y^{a-2} + y^{2a-4}$ 72. $2x^{2a+2} + 5x^{a+1}y^a + 3y^{2a}$
73. $x^2 + (m + n)x + mn$ $(x + m)(x + n)$ 74. $acx^2 + (ad + bc)x + bd$ $(ax + b)(cx + d)$
65. $(5x^a + 3y^b)(x^a + 4y^b)$ 66. $(4x^{2a} - 3y^{2b})(2x^{2a} - 5y^{2b})$ 67. $(2x^{3a} - 3y^{2b})(6x^{3a} + 5y^{2b})$

Cumulative Review

68. $(x^{n+2} + 3)(x^{n+2} + 4)$ 69. $(x^{n-1} - 2)(x^{n-1} + 5)$ 70. $(x^{4n+3} - 3)(x^{4n+3} + 1)$
Multiply. 71. $(x^{a+3} + y^{a-2})(x^{a+3} + y^{a-2})$ 72. $(2x^{a+1} + 3y^a)(x^{a+1} + y^a)$

1. $(x + 6)(x + 6)$ 2. $(x + 10)(2x^2 - 3x - 4)$ 3. $(3x^2 - 2y)(3x^2 + 2y)$
   $x^2 + 12x + 36$ $2x^3 + 17x^2 - 34x - 40$ $9x^4 - 4y^2$

3.2 Special Products

OBJECTIVE ▶ **To multiply a pair of related polynomials**

When working with polynomials, one special product that often occurs is the *product of the sum and the difference of two terms*. The general form is $(a + b)(a - b)$. As shown below, the FOIL method can be used to complete the multiplication.

$$(4x + 5)(4x - 5) = 16x^2 - 20x + 20x - 25 = 16x^2 - 25$$

Notice that there is no middle term in the product. Since $16x^2$ and 25 are both squares, you can rewrite $16x^2 - 25$ as $(4x)^2 - (5)^2$.

Product of Sum and Difference of Two Terms

> The product of the sum and difference of two terms is the difference of the squares of the two terms.
> $$(a + b)(a - b) = a^2 - b^2, \text{ for all numbers } a \text{ and } b.$$

Example 1 Multiply: $(5x + 3y)(5x - 3y)$.

$$(5x + 3y)(5x - 3y) = (5x)^2 - (3y)^2$$
$$= 25x^2 - 9y^2$$

Multiply: $(6n^2 - 10)(6n^2 + 10)$.

$$(6n^2 - 10)(6n^2 + 10) = (6n^2)^2 - 10^2$$
$$= 36n^4 - 100$$

The *square of a binomial* is another special product. The general form is $(a + b)^2$ or $(a - b)^2$. [Recall that $a - b$ means $a + (-b)$.] You can simplify $(3n + 5)^2$ by using the FOIL method.

$$(3n + 5)^2 = (3n + 5)(3n + 5) = 9n^2 + 15n + 15n + 25 = 9n^2 + 30n + 25$$

Notice that the product $9n^2 + 30n + 25$ can be written as $(3n)^2 + 2 \cdot 3n \cdot 5 + 5^2$. This leads to the following statement and corresponding formulas.

Square of a Binomial

> The square of a binomial is the sum of the square of the first term, twice the product of the terms, and the square of the last term. $(a + b)^2 = a^2 + 2ab + b^2$ and $(a - b)^2 = a^2 - 2ab + b^2$, for all numbers a and b.

Example 2 Multiply: $(6c + 5d)^2$.

$$(a + b)^2 = a^2 + 2ab + b^2$$
$$(6c + 5d)^2 = (6c)^2 + 2(6c \cdot 5d) + (5d)^2$$
$$= 36c^2 + 60cd + 25d^2$$

Multiply: $(4x^2 - 3)^2$.

$$(a - b)^2 = a^2 - 2ab + b^2$$
$$(4x^2 - 3)^2 = (4x^2)^2 - 2(4x^2 \cdot 3) + 3^2$$
$$= 16x^4 - 24x^2 + 9$$

The trinomials, $36c^2 + 60cd + 25d^2$ and $16x^4 - 24x^2 + 9$, are *perfect square trinomials*. A perfect square trinomial is the square of a binomial.

Expressions such as $(x + 3)(x^2 - 3x + 9)$ and $(x - 5)(x^2 + 5x + 25)$ represent two other special products. You can use the distributive property to expand such products, as shown below.

$$(x + 3)(x^2 - 3x + 9)$$
$$= x(x^2 - 3x + 9) + 3(x^2 - 3x + 9)$$
$$= x^3 - 3x^2 + 9x + 3x^2 - 9x + 27$$
$$= x^3 + 27, \text{ or } x^3 + 3^3$$

$$(x - 5)(x^2 + 5x + 25)$$
$$= x(x^2 + 5x + 25) - 5(x^2 + 5x + 25)$$
$$= x^3 + 5x^2 + 25x - 5x^2 - 25x - 125$$
$$= x^3 - 125, \text{ or } x^3 - 5^3$$

Notice that each product is either a *sum* or a *difference of two cubes*. This suggests the special product formulas stated below.

Two Special Products

$$(a + b)(a^2 - ab + b^2) = a^3 + b^3 \text{ and } (a - b)(a^2 + ab + b^2) = a^3 - b^3,$$
for all numbers a and b.

Example 3 Multiply: $(4x + 5)(16x^2 - 20x + 25)$.

Use $(a + b) [\ a^2\ -\ ab\ +\ b^2] =\ a^3\ +\ b^3$.

$$(4x + 5)(16x^2 - 20x + 25) = (4x + 5)[(4x)^2 - 4x \cdot 5 + 5^2] = (4x)^3 + 5^3$$
$$= 64x^3 + 125$$

Example 4 Multiply: $(2x - 3y)(4x^2 + 6xy + 9y^2)$.

Use $(a - b) [\ a^2\ +\ ab\ +\ b^2] =\ a^3\ -\ b^3$.

$$(2x - 3y)(4x^2 + 6xy + 9y^2) = (2x - 3y)[(2x)^2 + 2x \cdot 3y + (3y)^2] = (2x)^3 - (3y)^3$$
$$= 8x^3 - 27y^3$$

Written Exercises
2. $100y^2 - 49$ 6. $64y^2 + 160y + 100$ 7. $100 - 36a^2$
8. $144x^2 - 121$ 9. $625 - 9y^2$ 11. $49c^2 + 140c + 100$ 12. $225 - 60x + 4x^2$

Multiply each pair of polynomials

(A)
1. $(n + 12)(n - 12)$ $n^2 - 144$ 2. $(10y - 7)(10y + 7)$ **above**   3. $(9x + 6)(9x - 6)$ $81x^2 - 36$
4. $(2x + 5)^2$ $4x^2 + 20x + 25$ 5. $(1 - 6n)^2$ $1 - 12n + 36n^2$ 6. $(8y + 10)^2$ **above**
7. $(10 - 6a)(10 + 6a)$ **above**   8. $(12x + 11)(12x - 11)$ **above**   9. $(25 - 3y)(25 + 3y)$ **above**
10. $(1 - 9n)^2$ $1 - 18n + 81n^2$ 11. $(7c + 10)^2$ **above**   12. $(15 - 2x)^2$ **above**
13. $(x + 2)(x^2 - 2x + 4)$ $x^3 + 8$ 14. $(3y - 1)(9y^2 + 3y + 1)$ $27y^3 - 1$
15. $(4 - 5a)(16 + 20a + 25a^2)$ $64 - 125a^3$ 16. $(4c + 10)(16c^2 - 40c + 100)$ $64c^3 + 1,000$
17. $25x^2 - 64y^2$ 18. $a^2 - 36b^2$ 19. $16n^4 - 1$ 21. $9x^2 - 60xy + 100y^2$

(B)
17. $(5x + 8y)(5x - 8y)$ **above**   18. $(a - 6b)(a + 6b)$ **above**   19. $(4n^2 + 1)(4n^2 - 1)$ **above**
20. $(a + 7b)^2$ $a^2 + 14ab + 49b^2$ 21. $(3x - 10y)^2$ **above**   22. $(c^2 + 5d)^2$
23. $(7y^2 - 4)(7y^2 + 4)$ $49y^4 - 16$ 24. $(12c + 3d^2)(12c - 3d^2)$ 25. $(10y^2 - 5z^2)(10y^2 + 5z^2)$
26. $(5x - 4y^2)^2$ 27. $(4m^2 + 3n^2)^2$ 28. $(10x^3 - 2y^3)^2$
29. $(8x + y)(64x^2 - 8xy + y^2)$ $512x^3 + y^3$ 30. $(5c - 6d)(25c^2 + 30cd + 36d^2)$ $125c^3 - 216d^3$
31. $(m^2 - 3n)(m^4 + 3m^2n + 9n^2)$ $m^6 - 27n^3$ 32. $(3x + 4y^2)(9x^2 - 12xy^2 + 16y^4)$ $27x^3 + 64y^6$
22. $c^4 + 10c^2d + 25d^2$ 24. $144c^2 - 9d^4$ 25. $100y^4 - 25z^4$ 26. $25x^2 - 40xy^2 + 16y^4$
27. $16m^4 + 24m^2n^2 + 9n^4$ 28. $100x^6 - 40x^3y^3 + 4y^6$

SPECIAL PRODUCTS

3.3 Special Factors

OBJECTIVES ▶ **To factor a difference of two squares**
To factor a perfect square trinomial
To factor a sum or a difference of two cubes

Many polynomials have the form of one of the following special products that were discussed in the previous lesson.

$$a^2 + 2ab + b^2 \qquad\qquad a^2 - b^2 \qquad\qquad a^3 + b^3 \qquad\qquad a^3 - b^3$$

You can factor polynomials of these types by reversing the appropriate special product formulas. For example, since $(y + 6)(y - 6) = y^2 - 6^2 = y^2 - 36$, you can factor $y^2 - 36$ as follows:

$$y^2 - 36 = y^2 - 6^2 = (y + 6)(y - 6).$$

The expression $y^2 - 36$ is called a **difference of two squares.**

Factoring a Difference of Two Squares

$$a^2 - b^2 = (a + b)(a - b), \text{ for all numbers } a \text{ and } b.$$

Example 1

Factor $49c^2 - 16$.

$$\begin{aligned} 49c^2 - 16 &= (7c)^2 - 4^2 \\ &= (7c + 4)(7c - 4) \end{aligned}$$

Factor $9x^4 - 25y^2$.

$$\begin{aligned} 9x^4 - 25y^2 &= (3x^2)^2 - (5y)^2 \\ &= (3x^2 + 5y)(3x^2 - 5y) \end{aligned}$$

Trinomials of the form $a^2 + 2ab + b^2$ and $a^2 - 2ab + b^2$ are **perfect square trinomials.** When a given trinomial is to be factored, you should first check to see if it is a perfect square trinomial. For example, $x^2 + 10x + 25$ is a perfect square trinomial since it can be written in the form $a^2 + 2ab + b^2$ as $x^2 + 2 \cdot x \cdot 5 + 5^2$.

You can factor $x^2 + 10x + 25$ by reversing one of the special product formulas.

$$(x + 5)^2 = x^2 + 2 \cdot x \cdot 5 + 5^2 = x^2 + 10x + 25$$
$$x^2 + 10x + 25 = x^2 + 2 \cdot x \cdot 5 + 5^2 = (x + 5)^2$$

Factoring a Perfect Square Trinomial

$$a^2 + 2ab + b^2 = (a + b)^2 \text{ and}$$
$$a^2 - 2ab + b^2 = (a - b)^2, \text{ for all numbers } a \text{ and } b.$$

Example 2

Factor $16n^2 + 40n + 25$.

$$\begin{aligned} &16n^2 + 40n + 25 \\ &= (4n)^2 + 2 \cdot 4n \cdot 5 + 5^2 \\ &= (4n + 5)^2 \end{aligned}$$

Factor $36c^4 - 12c^2d + d^2$.

$$\begin{aligned} &36c^4 - 12c^2d + d^2 \\ &= (6c^2)^2 - 2 \cdot 6c^2 \cdot d + d^2 \\ &= (6c^2 - d)^2 \end{aligned}$$

The factorization of $16n^2 + 40n + 25$ in Example 2 can be checked by squaring $4n + 5$: $(4n + 5)^2 = (4n)^2 + 2 \cdot 4n \cdot 5 + 5^2 = 16n^2 + 40n + 25$.

You can factor a **sum** or a **difference of two cubes** by using the reverse of the two special product formulas below.

$$(a + b)(a^2 - ab + b^2) = a^3 + b^3$$
$$(a - b)(a^2 + ab + b^2) = a^3 - b^3$$

Factoring a Sum or Difference of Two Cubes

Sum: $a^3 + b^3 = (a + b)(a^2 - ab + b^2)$ and
Difference: $a^3 - b^3 = (a - b)(a^2 + ab + b^2)$, for all numbers a and b.

Example 3 Factor $8x^3 + 27$.

$8x^3 + 27$, or $(2x)^3 + 3^3$, is a sum of two cubes.

$$a^3 + b^3 = (a + b)(a^2 - ab + b^2)$$

$$8x^3 + 27 = (2x)^3 + 3^3 = (2x + 3)[(2x)^2 - 2x \cdot 3 + 3^2]$$
$$= (2x + 3)(4x^2 - 6x + 9)$$

Example 4 Factor $125x^3 - 64y^3$.

$125x^3 - 64y^3$, or $(5x)^3 - (4y)^3$, is a difference of two cubes.

$$a^3 - b^3 = (a - b)(a^2 + ab + b^2)$$

$$125x^3 - 64y^3 = (5x)^3 - (4y)^3 = (5x - 4y)[(5x)^2 + 5x \cdot 4y + (4y)^2]$$
$$= (5x - 4y)(25x^2 + 20xy + 16y^2)$$

Sometimes a polynomial can be factored after its terms are grouped appropriately.

$$m^2 - 2mn + n^2 - c^2 - 2cd - d^2 = (m^2 - 2mn + n^2) - (c^2 + 2cd + d^2)$$
$$= (m - n)^2 - (c + d)^2$$
$$= [(m - n) + (c + d)][(m - n) - (c + d)]$$
$$= (m - n + c + d)(m - n - c - d)$$

Example 5 Factor each polynomial.

$9x^2 - 12xy + 4y^2 - 30x + 20y + 25$

$$(9x^2 - 12xy + 4y^2) - (30x - 20y) + 25$$
$$(3x - 2y)^2 - 10(3x - 2y) + 5^2$$
$$(3x - 2y)^2 - 2(3x - 2y) \cdot 5 + 5^2$$

$$a^2 - 2 \cdot a \cdot b + b^2$$

$$(a - b)^2$$

$$(3x - 2y - 5)^2$$

$x^2 + 2xy + y^2 - c^2 + 6c - 9$

$$(x^2 + 2xy + y^2) - (c^2 - 6c + 9)$$
$$(x + y)^2 - (c - 3)^2$$

$$a^2 - b^2$$

$$(a + b)(a - b)$$

$$[(x + y) + (c - 3)][(x + y) - (c - 3)]$$
$$(x + y + c - 3)(x + y - c + 3)$$

SPECIAL FACTORS

Reading In Algebra

Determine whether each polynomial is a difference of two squares (DS), a perfect square trinomial (PS), a sum of two cubes (SC), a difference of two cubes (DC), or none of these (N).

1. $x^3 - 8$ **DC**
2. $y^2 + 16$ **N**
3. $x^2 + 6x + 9$ **PS**
4. $9c^2 - 4$ **DS**
5. $n^2 - 10n - 25$ **N**
6. $27x^3 + 1$ **SC**
7. $(a + b)^2 - 4$ **DS**
8. $x^6 - 1$ **DS, DC**
9. $z^2 + 2z - 1$ **N**
10. $b^3 - 15c^3$ **N**
11. $x^2y^2 - 1$ **DS**
12. $49 - 14y + y^2$ **PS**

Oral Exercises

1. $(10n)^2 - 3^2$
2. $(5n)^3 + 1^3$
3. $5^2 - (2y)^2$
4. $10^3 - (3n)^3$

State each binomial as a difference of two squares, a sum of two cubes, or a difference of two cubes.

1. $100n^2 - 9$
2. $125n^3 + 1$
3. $25 - 4y^2$
4. $1,000 - 27n^3$
5. $x^6 + 8z^3$ $(x^2)^3 + (2z)^3$
6. $64x^2 - 81y^2$ $(8x)^2 - (9y)^2$
7. $x^9 - 125y^3$ $(x^3)^3 - (5y)^3$
8. $x^4 - 36y^2$ $(x^2)^2 - (6y)^2$

Determine whether each trinomial is a perfect square trinomial.

9. $25x^2 + 50x + 16$ **no**
10. $4y^2 - 20y + 25$ **yes**
11. $9n^2 - 13n + 4$ **no**
12. $9m^4 + 24m^2 + 16$ **yes**

Written Exercises

28. $(10x + 3y)(100x^2 - 30xy + 9y^2)$

32. $(3xy - 5z^2)(9x^2y^2 + 15xyz^2 + 25z^4)$ 37. $(x + c + d)^2$ 38. $(2x - 3y - 5)^2$

Factor each polynomial.

(A)
1. $4b^2 - 49$ $(2b + 7)(2b - 7)$
2. $121 - 36n^2$ $(11 + 6n)(11 - 6n)$
3. $y^2 + 8y + 16$ $(y + 4)^2$
4. $1 - 20a + 100a^2$ $(1 - 10a)^2$
5. $x^3 + 27$ $(x + 3)(x^2 - 3x + 9)$
6. $y^3 - 8$ $(y - 2)(y^2 + 2y + 4)$
7. $c^4 - 25$ $(c^2 + 5)(c^2 - 5)$
8. $49 - d^4$ $(7 + d^2)(7 - d^2)$
9. $9n^2 - 24n + 16$ $(3n - 4)^2$
10. $25a^2 + 20a + 4$ $(5a + 2)^2$
11. $y^4 + 18y^2 + 81$ $(y^2 + 9)^2$
12. $16d^4 - 40d^2 + 25$ $(4d^2 - 5)^2$
13. $125c^3 - 1$ $(5c - 1)(25c^2 + 5c + 1)$
14. $1,000x^3 + 1$ $(10x + 1)(100x^2 - 10x + 1)$
15. $x^2 + 6x + 9 - y^2$ $(x + 3 + y)(x + 3 - y)$
16. $m^2 - 2mn + n^2 - 25$ $(m - n + 5)(m - n - 5)$
17. $x^2 + 2xy + y^2 + 4x + 4y + 4$ $(x + y + 2)^2$
18. $c^2 - 2cd + d^2 + 10c - 10d + 25$ $(c - d + 5)^2$
19. $x^2 - y^2 - 10y - 25$ $(x + y + 5)(x - y - 5)$
35. $(m - n + x + y)(m - n - x - y)$ 36. $(2x + y + c - 2)(2x + y - c + 2)$

(B)
21. $49c^4d^4 - 100$ $(7c^2d^2 + 10)(7c^2d^2 - 10)$
22. $36x^6 - y^2$ $(6x^3 + y)(6x^3 - y)$
23. $25c^2 + 20cd + 4d^2$ $(5c + 2d)^2$
24. $36x^4 - 60x^2y + 25y^2$ $(6x^2 - 5y)^2$
25. $64m^3 + n^3$ $(4m + n)(16m^2 - 4mn + n^2)$
26. $c^3 - 125d^3$ $(c - 5d)(c^2 + 5cd + 25d^2)$
27. $125t^3 - 8v^3$ $(5t - 2v)(25t^2 + 10tv + 4v^2)$
28. $1,000x^3 + 27y^3$ **above**
29. $16c^6 - 40c^3d + 25d^2$ $(4c^3 - 5d)^2$
30. $4a^6b^4 + 28a^3b^2 + 49$ $(2a^3b^2 + 7)^2$
31. $25x^6 - 36d^4$ $(5x^3 + 6d^2)(5x^3 - 6d^2)$
32. $27x^3y^3 - 125z^6$ **above**
33. $0.25x^2 - 1.21y^2$ $(0.5x + 1.1y)(0.5x - 1.1y)$
34. $1.44a^2 - 6ab + 6.25b^2$ $(1.2a - 2.5b)^2$
35. $m^2 - 2mn + n^2 - x^2 - 2xy - y^2$ **above**
36. $4x^2 + 4xy + y^2 - c^2 + 4c - 4$ **above**
37. $x^2 + 2cx + 2dx + c^2 + 2cd + d^2$ **above**
38. $4x^2 - 12xy + 9y^2 - 20x + 30y + 25$ **above**
39. $25x^2 - 30x + 9 - 4a^2 + 4ab - b^2$
39. $(5x - 3 + 2a - b)(5x - 3 - 2a + b)$
40. $25x^2 + 40xy - 30x + 16y^2 - 24y + 9$
40. $(5x + 4y - 3)^2$

(C)
41. $9x^{4m+6} + 12x^{2m+3}y^n + 4y^{2n}$
42. $x^{4n} - y^{6n+2}$ $(x^{2n} + y^{3n+1})(x^{2n} - y^{3n+1})$
43. $x^{3c} + y^{12d}$ $(x^c + y^{4d})(x^{2c} - x^cy^{4d} + y^{8d})$
44. $8x^{6a} - y^{3b+9}$
41. $(3x^{2m+3} + 2y^n)^2$
44. $(2x^{2a} - y^{b+3})(4x^{4a} + 2x^{2a}y^{b+3} + y^{2b+6})$

3.4 Combined Types of Factoring

OBJECTIVE ▶ **To factor a polynomial completely**

Some numbers can be factored into more than two factors. For example,

$$30 = 3 \cdot 10 = 3 \cdot 2 \cdot 5 \qquad \text{and} \qquad 36 = 4 \cdot 9 = 2 \cdot 2 \cdot 3 \cdot 3.$$

Likewise, some polynomials can be factored into more than two factors. To factor a polynomial *completely,* you may have to use several types of factoring. The following steps show you the order in which the factoring should be accomplished.

Factoring a Polynomial Completely

Step 1	Factor out the *greatest common factor* (GCF), if any.
Step 2	Factor the resulting polynomial, if possible.
Step 3	Factor each polynomial factor where possible.

Example 1 Factor $12x^4y^3 + 18x^2y^2 - 24x^2y$ completely.

Step 1 The GCF of 12, 18, and 24 is 6. The GCF of x^4 and x^2 is x^2. The GCF of y^3, y^2, and y is y. Factor out $6x^2y$

$$12x^4y^3 + 18x^2y^2 - 24x^2y = 6x^2y(2x^2y^2 + 3y - 4)$$

Step 2 The resulting polynomial, $2x^2y^2 + 3y - 4$, cannot be factored.

Thus, $12x^4y^3 + 18x^2y^2 - 24x^2y = 6x^2y(2x^2y^2 + 3y - 4)$.

In Example 1, the monomial $6x^2y$ is called a **common monomial factor.** It is a factor of each term of the original polynomial.

Example 2 Factor $15x^2 + 10x - 40$ completely.

$$15x^2 + 10x - 40$$

Step 1 Factor out 5, the GCF. $\qquad = 5(3x^2 + 2x - 8)$

Step 2 Factor $3x^2 + 2x - 8$. $\qquad = 5(3x - 4)(x + 2)$

Step 3 $3x - 4$ and $x + 2$ cannot be factored.

Thus, $15x^2 + 10x - 40 = 5(3x - 4)(x + 2)$.

Example 3 Factor $27y^4 - 75y^2$ completely.

$$27y^4 - 75y^2$$

Step 1 Factor out $3y^2$, the GCF. $\qquad = 3y^2(9y^2 - 25)$ ◀ *Difference of*

Step 2 Factor $9y^2 - 25$. $\qquad = 3y^2(3y + 5)(3y - 5)$ *two squares*

Step 3 $3y + 5$ and $3y - 5$ cannot be factored.

Thus, $27y^4 - 75y^2 = 3y^2(3y + 5)(3y - 5)$.

A complete factorization may contain more than two binomials, as shown in the next example.

Example 4 **Factor $8x^4 + 10x^2 - 3$ completely.**

Step 1 There is no common monomial factor other than 1.

$$8x^4 + 10x^2 - 3$$

Step 2 Factor $8x^4 + 10x^2 - 3$. $= (2x^2 + 3)(4x^2 - 1)$
Step 3 Factor $4x^2 - 1$. $= (2x^2 + 3)(2x + 1)(2x - 1)$

Thus, $8x^4 + 10x^2 - 3 = (2x^2 + 3)(2x + 1)(2x - 1)$.

To factor a polynomial in which the coefficient of the first term is negative, begin by factoring out -1 as a common monomial factor.

Example 5 **Factor $-9x^2 + 12x - 4$ completely.**

$$-9x^2 + 12x - 4$$

Step 1 Factor out -1. $= -1(9x^2 - 12x + 4)$ ◀ *Perfect square trinomial*
Step 2 Factor $9x^2 - 12x + 4$. $= -1(3x - 2)^2$

Thus, $-9x^2 + 12x - 4 = -1(3x - 2)^2$.

Factoring completely may involve factoring a sum or a difference of two cubes. This is shown in Example 6.

Example 6 **Factor $24x^3 - 81$ completely.**

$$24x^3 - 81$$

Step 1 Factor out 3, the GCF. $= 3(8x^3 - 27)$
Step 2 Factor $8x^3 - 27$. $= 3(2x - 3)(4x^2 + 6x + 9)$

Thus, $24x^3 - 81 = 3(2x - 3)(4x^2 + 6x + 9)$.

Some polynomials with an even number of terms may be factored by "grouping pairs of terms" and factoring out a **common binomial factor.**

Example 7 **Factor $5xy - 15x - 2yz + 6z$ completely.**

$$5xy - 15x - 2yz + 6z = (5xy - 15x) + (-2yz + 6z) = 5x(y - 3) - 2z(y - 3)$$
$$= (5x - 2z)(y - 3)$$

Thus, $5xy - 15x - 2yz + 6z = (5x - 2z)(y - 3)$.

Reading in Algebra

Determine whether each expression is factored completely. If not, state why not.

1. $17 \cdot 21 \cdot 59$ **No**
2. $19 \cdot 23 \cdot 37$ **Yes**
3. $8(2x + 6y)$ **No**
4. $4a(5a + 4b)$ **Yes**
5. $-7(x^2 + xy)$ **No**
6. $5(x^2 - 2x + 3)$ **Yes**
7. $2y(y^2 - 7y + 12)$ **No**
8. $-3(9n^2 - 1)$ **No**

Oral Exercises

Find the GCF of each group of expressions.

1. $18x^2$; $36x$; 12 **6**
2. $5x^4$; $-2x^2$; $7x$ **x**
3. x^4; x^2; x^3 **x^2**
4. $12y^2$; $6y$; $24y^3$ **6y**
5. $-10x^2$; $15x^3$ **$5x^2$**
6. $x(5a - 3b)$; $-4(5a - 3b)$
   $5a - 3b$

Factor -1 out of each polynomial.

7. $-5a + 3b$ **$-1(5a - 3b)$**
8. $-2x^2 - 7y$ **$-1(2x^2 + 7y)$**
9. $-y^2 + y - 12$
   $-1(y^2 - y + 12)$
48. $x^{3c}(x^c + 3)(x^c - 3)$

Written Exercises

49. $x^2(x^{2n} + 3)^2$ 50. $y^n(y^n - 1)(y^{2n} + y^n + 1)$

42. $4(c + d)(c - d)(c + 2d)$ 39. $(3a - 7d)(4b - 3c)$

Factor each polynomial completely.

(A)
1. $12n^2 - 15n - 3$ **$3(4n^2 - 5n - 1)$**
2. $3a^4 - 8a^3 + a^2$ **$a^2(3a^2 - 8a + 1)$**
3. $3x^2 - 21x + 36$ **$3(x - 3)(x - 4)$**
4. $2n^2 + 4n - 30$ **$2(n + 5)(n - 3)$**
5. $16y^2 - 4$ **$4(2y + 1)(2y - 1)$**
6. $18c^2 - 50$ **$2(3c + 5)(3c - 5)$**
7. $4n^2 + 40n + 100$ **$4(n + 5)^2$**
8. $5x^2 - 40x + 80$ **$5(x - 4)^2$**
9. $y^4 - 7y^2 - 18$ **$(y^2 + 2)(y + 3)(y - 3)$**
10. $2a^4 - 9a^2 + 4$ **$(2a^2 - 1)(a + 2)(a - 2)$**
11. $-x^2 + 8x - 16$ **$-1(x - 4)^2$**
12. $-y^2 + 36$ **$-1(y + 6)(y - 6)$**
13. $3y^3 + 81$ **$3(y + 3)(y^2 - 3y + 9)$**
14. $5n^3 - 625$ **$5(n - 5)(n^2 + 5n + 25)$**
15. $8xy + 20x + 6y + 15$ **$(4x + 3)(2y + 5)$**
16. $6cd - 21c - 10d + 35$ **$(3c - 5)(2d - 7)$**
17. $-4n^2 + 4n + 3$ **$-1(2n - 3)(2n + 1)$**
18. $-9t^2 - 30t - 25$ **$-1(3t + 5)^2$**

21. $15x^2y^3(5y^2 - 2xy + 3x^2)$ 22. $4x^2y^2z^3(11xz - 25yz^2 - 16xy)$

(B)
19. $x^3 + 4x^2 + 6x + 24$ **$(x^2 + 6)(x + 4)$**
20. $6a^3 + 20a^2 - 21a - 70$ **$(2a^2 - 7)(3a + 10)$**
21. $75x^2y^5 - 30x^3y^4 + 45x^4y^3$
22. $44x^3y^2z^4 - 100x^2y^3z^5 - 64x^3y^3z^3$
23. $8a^3 - 4a^2 - 40a$ **$4a(2a - 5)(a + 2)$**
24. $3a^3 - 75ab^2$ **$3a(a + 5b)(a - 5b)$**
25. $2x^3y - 4x^2y + 2xy$ **$2xy(x - 1)^2$**
26. $36a^3b + 120a^2b^2 + 100ab^3$ **$4ab(3a + 5b)^2$**
27. $9x^4 - 7x^2 - 16$ **$(x^2 + 1)(3x + 4)(3x - 4)$**
28. $4n^4 - 17n^2 + 18$ **$(n^2 - 2)(2n + 3)(2n - 3)$**
29. $n^4 - 13n^2 + 36$ **$(n + 2)(n - 2)(n + 3)(n - 3)$**
30. $25y^4 - 101y^2 + 4$ **$(5y + 1)(5y - 1)(y + 2)(y - 2)$**
31. $-3y^2 + 27$ **$-3(y + 3)(y - 3)$**
32. $-18x^2 + 32$ **$-2(3x + 4)(3x - 4)$**
33. $-4ac^2 - 4ac - a$ **$-a(2c + 1)^2$**
34. $-x^3 + 6x^2y - 9xy^2$ **$-x(x - 3y)^2$**
35. $24x^3 - 375$ **$3(2x - 5)(4x^2 + 10x + 25)$**
36. $-54y^3 - 128$ **$-2(3y + 4)(9y^2 - 12y + 16)$**
37. $y^4 + 64y$ **$y(y + 4)(y^2 - 4y + 16)$**
38. $3x^4 - 3,000x$ **$3x(x - 10)(x^2 + 10x + 100)$**
39. $12ab - 9ac - 28bd + 21cd$ **above**
40. $8x^3 - 15y - 20xy + 6x^2$ **$(2x^2 - 5y)(4x + 3)$**
41. $a^3 - a^2b - a^2b^2 + ab^3$ **$a(a - b^2)(a - b)$**
42. $4c^3 + 8c^2d - 4cd^2 - 8d^3$ **above**
43. $4y^8 - 13y^4 + 9$
44. $36x^8 - 13x^4 + 1$
43. $(2y^2 + 3)(2y^2 - 3)(y^2 + 1)(y + 1)(y - 1)$
44. $(3x^2 + 1)(3x^2 - 1)(2x^2 + 1)(2x^2 - 1)$

(C)
45. $x^{a+6} + x^4$ **$x^4(x^{a+2} + 1)$**
46. $x^{5c} - x^{4c}$ **$x^{4c}(x^c - 1)$**
47. $y^{n+5} + y^{n+4}$ **$y^{n+4}(y + 1)$**
48. $x^{5c} - 9x^{3c}$ **above**
49. $x^{4n+2} + 6x^{2n+2} + 9x^2$ **above**
50. $y^{4n} - y^n$ **above**
51. Factor $x^6 - y^6$ completely as a difference of two squares. **below**
52. Factor $x^6 - y^6$ completely as a difference of two cubes. **below**
53. Use factoring to show that the answers in Exercises 51 and 52 are equivalent.

51. $(x + y)(x^2 - xy + y^2)(x - y)(x^2 + xy + y^2)$ 52. $(x + y)(x - y)(x^4 + x^2y^2 + y^4)$

COMBINED TYPES OF FACTORING

3.5 Quadratic Equations

OBJECTIVE ▶ To solve a quadratic equation by factoring

Equations such as $5x^2 + 17x - 12 = 0$, $9x^2 - 25 = 0$, and $7x^2 + 14x = 0$ are called **quadratic equations.** Each equation contains a polynomial of the second degree.

Standard Form of a Quadratic Equation

> The *standard form of a quadratic equation* is $ax^2 + bx + c = 0$ where a, b, and c are numbers, and $a \neq 0$.

You can solve some quadratic equations by writing the equation in standard form, factoring, and then setting each factor equal to 0. The method is based upon the following property.

Zero-Product Property

> For all numbers m and n, if $mn = 0$, then $m = 0$ or $n = 0$.

Example 1 Solve $3c^2 - 10c - 8 = 0$.

The equation is in standard form. $3c^2 - 10c - 8 = 0$
Factor $3c^2 - 10c - 8$. $(3c + 2)(c - 4) = 0$
Use the Zero-Product Property. $3c + 2 = 0$ or $c - 4 = 0$
Solve both linear equations. $3c = -2$ $c = 4$

$$c = -\frac{2}{3}$$

Check both solutions:

$3c^2 - 10c - 8$	0
$3\left(-\dfrac{2}{3}\right)^2 - 10\left(-\dfrac{2}{3}\right) - 8$	0
$\dfrac{4}{3} + \dfrac{20}{3} - 8$, or 0	

$3c^2 - 10c - 8$	0
$3 \cdot 4^2 - 10 \cdot 4 - 8$	0
$48 - 40 - 8$	
0	

Thus, the solutions are $-\frac{2}{3}$ and 4.

Example 2 Solve $5x = 6 - 4x^2$.

Step 1 Write in standard form. $4x^2 + 5x - 6 = 0$
Step 2 Factor. $(4x - 3)(x + 2) = 0$
Step 3 Set each factor equal to 0. $4x - 3 = 0$ or $x + 2 = 0$
Step 4 Solve the linear equations. $4x = 3$ $x = -2$

$$x = \frac{3}{4}$$

Thus, $\frac{3}{4}$ and -2 are the solutions.

Sometimes it is more convenient to use the standard form, $0 = ax^2 + bx + c$, so that the coefficient of x^2 is a positive number.

Example 3   Solve $-7x^2 = 21x$.   Solve $25 = 9n^2$.

$$0 = 7x^2 + 21x$$
$$0 = 7x(x + 3) \qquad \blacktriangleleft \text{ } \textit{The GCF is 7x.}$$

$$7x = 0 \qquad \text{or} \qquad x + 3 = 0$$
$$x = 0 \qquad\qquad\qquad x = -3$$

Thus, the solutions are 0 and -3.

$$0 = 9n^2 - 25$$
$$0 = (3n + 5)(3n - 5)$$

$$3n + 5 = 0 \qquad \text{or} \qquad 3n - 5 = 0$$
$$3n = -5 \qquad\qquad\qquad 3n = 5$$
$$n = -\frac{5}{3} \qquad\qquad\qquad n = \frac{5}{3}$$

Thus, the solutions are $-\frac{5}{3}$ and $\frac{5}{3}$.

The Zero-Product Property can be extended to any number of factors. In the next example, the property is used to solve the *fourth degree equation* $x^4 - 13x^2 + 36 = 0$. The fourth degree polynomial is factored completely, and then each of the four factors is set equal to 0.

Example 4   Solve $x^4 - 13x^2 + 36 = 0$.

$$x^4 - 13x^2 + 36 = 0$$
$$(x^2 - 4)(x^2 - 9) = 0$$
$$(x + 2)(x - 2)(x + 3)(x - 3) = 0 \qquad \blacktriangleleft \textit{ Factor completely.}$$

$$x + 2 = 0 \quad \text{or} \quad x - 2 = 0 \quad \text{or} \quad x + 3 = 0 \quad \text{or} \quad x - 3 = 0$$
$$x = -2 \qquad\qquad x = 2 \qquad\qquad x = -3 \qquad\qquad x = 3$$

Thus, the solutions are $-2, 2, -3,$ and 3.

In some quadratic equations, the terms contain a common numerical factor.

Example 5   Solve $3n^2 - 15n + 18 = 0$.

Divide each side by 3, the GCF.

$$n^2 - 5n + 6 = 0$$
$$(n - 2)(n - 3) = 0$$

$$n - 2 = 0 \qquad \text{or} \qquad n - 3 = 0$$
$$n = 2 \qquad\qquad\qquad n = 3$$

Thus, the solutions are 2 and 3.

Reading In Algebra

Determine whether each statement is true or false.

1. $4x^2 - 8x = 0$ is a quadratic equation. **T**
2. $5x - 15 = 0$ is a quadratic equation. **F**
3. A quadratic equation may have two solutions. **T**
4. A fourth degree equation may have four solutions. **T**
5. If $x(x - 5) = 0$, then $x = 0$ or $x - 5 = 0$. **T**
6. If $(x - 1)(x - 3) = 8$, then $x - 1 = 8$ or $x - 3 = 8$. **F**
7. If $(n - 6)(n - 2) = 0$, then $n + 6 = 0$. **F**
8. If $(y - 5)(y - 5) = 0$, then $y = 5$. **T**

Written Exercises

13. $-5, 5, 1, -1$ 14. $-5, 5, -2, 2$ 15. $-10, 10, -3, 3$

Solve each equation.

(A)
1. $x^2 - 13x + 40 = 0$ **5, 8**
2. $a^2 - a - 42 = 0$ **-6, 7**
3. $0 = x^2 + 15x + 50$ **-10, -5**
4. $y^2 = 12 - y$ **-4, 3**
5. $6 = b^2 - b$ **-2, 3**
6. $6y = 16 - y^2$ **-8, 2**
7. $2a^2 - 10a = 0$ **0, 5**
8. $3x^2 = -12x$ **0, -4**
9. $15a = a^2$ **0, 15**
10. $z^2 - 64 = 0$ **-8, 8**
11. $0 = c^2 - 36$ **-6, 6**
12. $16 = z^2$ **-4, 4**
13. $x^4 - 26x^2 + 25 = 0$ **above**
14. $a^4 - 29a^2 + 100 = 0$ **above**
15. $900 + x^4 = 109x^2$ **above**
16. $3y^2 - 21y + 30 = 0$ **2, 5**
17. $5c^2 + 20c - 60 = 0$ **-6, 2**
18. $0 = 40z + 100 + 4z^2$ **-5**
19. $2c^2 - 9c + 4 = 0$ **$\frac{1}{2}$, 4**
20. $3z^2 = 8z + 3$ **$-\frac{1}{3}$, 3**
21. $-3c^2 = c - 2$ **$\frac{2}{3}$, -1**
22. $8n^2 + 2n - 1 = 0$ **$\frac{1}{4}, -\frac{1}{2}$**
23. $1 = 7w - 10w^2$ **$\frac{1}{5}, \frac{1}{2}$**
24. $0 = 12t^2 + 7t + 1$ **$-\frac{1}{4}, -\frac{1}{3}$**
25. $9c^2 - 16 = 0$ **$-1\frac{1}{3}, 1\frac{1}{3}$**
26. $16z^2 = 1$ **$-\frac{1}{4}, \frac{1}{4}$**
27. $36 = 25c^2$ **$-1\frac{1}{5}, 1\frac{1}{5}$**
28. $y^4 - y^2 - 12 = 0$ **-2, 2**
29. $b^4 = 24b^2 + 25$ **-5, 5**
30. $4y^2 = y^4 - 45$ **-3, 3**
31. $2b^2 + 12b + 18 = 0$ **-3**
32. $36y^2 = 12 - 6y$ **$-\frac{2}{3}, \frac{1}{2}$**
33. $60x - 180 = 5x^2$ **6**
34. $(x - 7)^2 = 29 - x^2$ **2, 5**
35. $(8 - n)^2 = 2(24 - n^2)$ **$1\frac{1}{3}$, 4**
36. $(3y + 2)^2 = (2y - 5)^2$ **$\frac{3}{5}$, -7**

(B)
37. $2b^2 - 7b + 6 = 0$ **$1\frac{1}{2}$, 2**
38. $3y^2 = 15 - 4y$ **$1\frac{2}{3}$, -3**
39. $0 = 7 + 9n + 2n^2$ **$-3\frac{1}{2}$, -1**
40. $25n^2 - 4n = 0$ **$0, \frac{4}{25}$**
41. $12p^2 = 30p$ **$0, 2\frac{1}{2}$**
42. $-22y = 6y^2$ **$0, -3\frac{2}{3}$**
43. $30t^2 - 125t + 120 = 0$ **$2\frac{2}{3}, 1\frac{1}{2}$**
44. $30y + 24y^2 = 75$ **$1\frac{1}{4}, -2\frac{1}{2}$**
45. $70 + 2m = 24m^2$ **$1\frac{3}{4}, -1\frac{2}{3}$**
46. $4y^4 - 37y^2 + 9 = 0$ **below**
47. $25b^4 = 34b^2 - 9$ **below**
48. $52y^2 = 9y^4 + 64$ **below**
49. $4x^4 + 31x^2 - 90 = 0$ **$-1\frac{1}{2}, 1\frac{1}{2}$**
50. $16c^4 + 23c^2 = 18$ **$-\frac{3}{4}, \frac{3}{4}$**
51. $10 - 36t^2 = 16t^4$ **$-\frac{1}{2}, \frac{1}{2}$**
52. $a^3 - 7a^2 + 10a = 0$ **0, 2, 5**
53. $5x^3 = 30x - 25x^2$ **0, -6, 1**
54. $4y^3 + 48y^2 = 4y^4$ **0, -3, 4**
55. $x(x + 5)(x - 4) = x^3$ **0, 20**
56. $3y(y - 2)(y + 4) = 3y^3$ **0, 4**
57. $(2x^2 + 3)^2 = 4x(x^3 + 6)$ **$\frac{1}{2}, 1\frac{1}{2}$**

Solve each equation for x in terms of a.   46. $-\frac{1}{2}, \frac{1}{2}, -3, 3$ 47. $-\frac{3}{5}, \frac{3}{5}, -1, 1$ 48. $-1\frac{1}{3}, 1\frac{1}{3}, -2, 2$

(C)
58. $3x^2 + 9a^2 = 12ax$
59. $0 = 6x^2 + 8ax - 8a^2$
60. $x^4 - 10a^2x^2 + 9a^4 = 0$
61. $42a^2 = 24x^2 - 38ax$
62. $36a^4 = 25a^2x^2 - 4x^4$
63. $a^8 + 100x^4 = 29a^4x^2$

58. $a, 3a$ 59. $\frac{2a}{3}, -2a$ 60. $-3a, 3a, -a, a$ 61. $\frac{-3a}{4}, \frac{7a}{3}$

62. $\frac{-3a}{2}, \frac{3a}{2}, -2a, 2a$ 63. $\frac{-a^2}{5}, \frac{a^2}{5}, \frac{-a^2}{2}, \frac{a^2}{2}$

Cumulative Review

Find the solution set of each inequality. Graph the solutions on a number line.

1. $-3x < 2x + 35$
   $\{x | x > -7\}$
2. $|x - 2| < 5$
   $\{x | -3 < x < 7\}$
3. $|x + 3| > 7$
   $\{x | x < -10 \text{ or } x > 4\}$

3.6 Quadratic Inequalities

OBJECTIVES ▶ **To find the solution set of a quadratic inequality by factoring**
To graph the solutions of a quadratic inequality

An inequality such as $x^2 - x - 6 > 0$ is called a **quadratic inequality.** The standard form of a quadratic inequality is $ax^2 + bx + c > 0$ (or $ax^2 + bx + c < 0$), where $a \neq 0$. Each quadratic inequality contains a polynomial of the second degree.

You can determine whether the value of the polynomial $x^2 - x - 6$ is positive, negative, or 0 for given values of x by substituting in the factored form $(x + 2)(x - 3)$.

x	$(x + 2)(x - 3)$	
-4	$(-4 + 2)(-4 - 3) = 14$	positive
-2	$(-2 + 2)(-2 - 3) = 0$	0
1	$(1 + 2) \ (1 - 3) = -6$	negative

In Example 1, to find the solution set of $x^2 - x - 6 > 0$, *all values* of x that make $(x + 2)(x - 3)$ positive are found.

Example 1 **Find the solution set of $x^2 - x - 6 > 0$. Graph the solutions.**

Solve the related equation, $x^2 - x - 6 = 0$.

$$x^2 - x - 6 = 0$$
$$(x + 2)(x - 3) = 0$$
$$x = -2 \quad \text{or} \quad x = 3$$

Locate -2 and 3 on a number line.

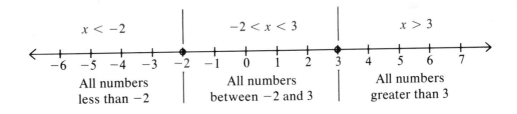

The points corresponding to -2 and 3 separate the number line into three parts. Select the coordinate of a point in each part.

Part	$(x + 2)(x - 3)$	
$x < -2$: Let $x = -5$	$(-5 + 2)(-5 - 3) = 24$	positive
$-2 < x < 3$: Let $x = 2$	$(2 + 2)(2 - 3) = -4$	negative
$x > 3$: Let $x = 6$	$(6 + 2)(6 - 3) = 24$	positive

Thus, the solution set is $\{x | x < -2 \text{ or } x > 3\}$.

To solve a quadratic inequality in which the coefficient of the square term is negative, it may be helpful to multiply the inequality by -1.

Example 2 Find the solution set of $-x^2 + 16 \geq 0$. Graph the solutions.

$$-x^2 + 16 \geq 0$$
$$-1(-x^2 + 16) \leq -1 \cdot 0 \quad \blacktriangleleft \quad \textit{Multiply each side by } -1 \textit{ and}$$
$$x^2 - 16 \leq 0 \qquad\qquad \textit{reverse the order to } \leq.$$

Solve the related equation, $x^2 - 16 = 0$.

$$x^2 - 16 = 0$$
$$(x + 4)(x - 4) = 0$$
$$x = -4 \quad \text{or} \quad x = 4$$

The points on a number line corresponding to -4 and 4 separate the number line into three parts with coordinates as follows:
$$x \leq -4 \qquad -4 \leq x \leq 4 \qquad x \geq 4$$
Select the coordinate of a point in each part and test to determine where $(x + 4)(x - 4)$ is negative.

<u>Part</u>	<u>$(x + 4)(x - 4)$</u>	
$x \leq -4$: Let $x = -6$	$(-6 + 4)(-6 - 4) = 20$	positive
$-4 \leq x \leq 4$: Let $x = 1$	$(1 + 4)(1 - 4) = -15$	negative
$x \geq 4$: Let $x = 7$	$(7 + 4)(7 - 4) = 33$	positive

Thus, the solution set is $\{x \mid -4 \leq x \leq 4\}$.

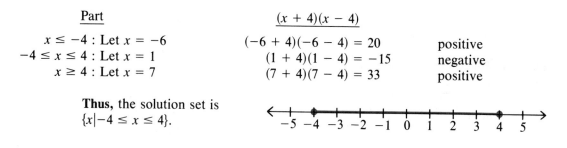

You can use similar procedures to solve an inequality of degree greater than 2.

Example 3 Find the solution set of $x^3 - 2x^2 - 15x \geq 0$. Graph the solutions.

$$x^3 - 2x^2 - 15x \geq 0$$
$$x(x^2 - 2x - 15) \geq 0$$
$$x(x + 3)(x - 5) \geq 0$$

The solutions of $x(x + 3)(x - 5) = 0$ are 0, -3, and 5. The number line is divided into four parts:
$$-3 \leq x \leq 0 \qquad x \leq -3$$
$$0 \leq x \leq 5 \qquad x \geq 5.$$

<u>Part</u>	<u>$x(x + 3)(x - 5)$</u>	
$x \leq -3$: Let $x = -4$	$-4(-4 + 3)(-4 - 5) = -36$	negative
$-3 \leq x \leq 0$: Let $x = -2$	$-2(-2 + 3)(-2 - 5) = 14$	positive
$0 \leq x \leq 5$: Let $x = 3$	$3(3 + 3)(3 - 5) = -36$	negative
$x \geq 5$: Let $x = 6$	$6(6 + 3)(6 - 5) = 54$	positive

Thus, the solution set is $\{x \mid -3 \leq x \leq 0 \text{ or } x \geq 5\}$.

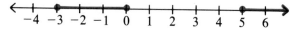

CHAPTER THREE

Reading In Algebra

Match each inequality to exactly one graph.
1. $3 < x < 7$ **D**
2. $x < 3$ or $x > 7$ **C**
3. $x < 3$ or $7 < x < 9$ **A**
4. $3 < x < 7$ or $x > 9$ **B**
5. $x^2 \geq 0$ **F**
6. $x^2 < 0$ **E**

A
B
C
D
E
F

Oral Exercises

Tell whether each sentence is true or false.
1. If $x = 4$, then $(x - 2)(x - 6) < 0$. **T**
2. If $x = -2$, then $(x + 4)(x - 3) > 0$. **F**
3. If $x = 8$, then $(x - 2)(x - 6) < 0$. **F**
4. If $x = -6$, then $(x + 4)(x - 3) > 0$. **T**
5. If $x < -5$, then $(x + 5)(x - 5) > 0$. **T**
6. If $x > 7$, then $(x + 1)(x - 7) < 0$. **F**
7. If $-3 < x < 2$, then $(x + 3)(x - 2) > 0$. **F**
8. If $1 < x < 5$, then $(x - 1)(x - 5) < 0$. **T**

Written Exercises

Find the solution set of each inequality. Graph the solutions.

(A)
1. $(x - 3)(x - 6) < 0$ {x|$3 < x < 6$}
2. $(y + 5)(y + 2) > 0$ {y|$y < -5$ or $y > -2$}
3. $n^2 - 8n + 15 > 0$ {n|$n < 3$ or $n > 5$}
4. $x^2 - 2x - 8 < 0$ {x|$-2 < x < 4$}
5. $c^2 + 8c + 12 \leq 0$ {c|$-6 \leq c \leq -2$}
6. $n^2 - 7n + 10 \geq 0$ {n|$n \leq 2$ or $n \geq 5$}
7. $y^2 - 3y - 18 < 0$ {y|$-3 < y < 6$}
8. $x^2 + 9x + 18 > 0$ {x|$x < -6$ or $x > -3$}
9. $x^2 - 9 \geq 0$ {x|$x \leq -3$ or $x \geq 3$}
10. $y^2 - 25 \leq 0$ {y|$-5 \leq y \leq 5$}
11. $-y^2 + 4 < 0$ {y|$y < -2$ or $y > 2$}
12. $-c^2 + 36 \geq 0$ {c|$-6 \leq c \leq 6$}
13. $n^2 - 5n > 0$ {n|$n < 0$ or $n > 5$}
14. $a^2 + 8a < 0$ {a|$-8 < a < 0$}
15. $-n^2 + 2n > 0$ {n|$0 < n < 2$}
16. $-a^2 - 7a \leq 0$ {a|$a \leq -7$ or $a \geq 0$}
17. $4c^2 + 12c \leq 0$ {c|$-3 \leq c \leq 0$}
18. $2x^2 - 10x \geq 0$ {x|$x \leq 0$ or $x \geq 5$}
19. $y^3 - y^2 - 6y < 0$ {y|$y < -2$ or $0 < y < 3$}
20. $x^3 + 6x^2 - 16x > 0$ {x|$-8 < x < 0$ or $x > 2$}
21. $x^3 - 25x \geq 0$ {x|$-5 \leq x \leq 0$ or $x \geq 5$}
22. $y^3 - 100y \leq 0$ {y|$y \leq -10$ or $0 \leq y \leq 10$}
35. {y|$-3 < y < -2$ or $2 < y < 3$}
36. {x|$x < -5$ or $-1 < x < 1$ or $x > 5$}

(B)
23. $2x^2 - x - 10 < 0$ {x|$-2 < x < 2.5$}
24. $4a^2 + 5a \geq 9$ {a|$a \leq -2.25$ or $a \geq 1$}
25. $4z^2 - 20z + 21 > 0$ {z|$z < 1.5$ or $z > 3.5$}
26. $8c^2 \leq 35 - 6c$ {c|$-2.5 \leq c \leq 1.75$}
27. $4x^2 - 25 \leq 0$ {x|$-2.5 \leq x \leq 2.5$}
28. $9z^2 > 100$ {z|$z < -3\frac{1}{3}$ or $z > 3\frac{1}{3}$}
29. $2y^2 + 7y \geq 0$ {y|$y \leq -3.5$ or $y \geq 0$}
30. $3a^2 < 10a$ {a|$0 < a < 3\frac{1}{3}$}
31. $-c^2 - c + 12 < 0$ {c|$c < -4$ or $c > 3$}
32. $-x^2 \geq 8 - 6x$ {x|$2 \leq x \leq 4$}
33. $0 < -n^2 + 4n - 3$ {n|$1 < n < 3$}
34. $0 \geq 35 - 2y - y^2$ {y|$y \leq -7$ or $y \geq 5$}
35. $y^4 - 13y^2 + 36 < 0$
36. $x^4 - 26x^2 + 25 > 0$
37. $a^4 - 16 \geq 0$ {a|$a \leq -2$ or $a \geq 2$}
38. $n^4 < 81$ {n|$-3 < n < 3$}
39. $n^4 - 14n^2 - 32 > 0$ {n|$n < -4$ or $n > 4$}
40. $-y^4 + 4y^2 + 45 < 0$ {y|$y < -3$ or $y > 3$}
44. {y|$-5 \leq y \leq 3$ or $y \geq 5$}
45. {y|$y < -4$ or $2 < y < 4$}

(C)
41. $x^2 - 4x + 4 > 0$ {x|$x \neq 2$}
42. $x^2 - 6x + 9 \leq 0$ {3}
43. $3x^2 + 1 \geq 2x^2$ {all numbers}
44. $y^3 - 3y^2 - 25y + 75 \geq 0$
45. $y^3 - 2y^2 - 16y + 32 < 0$
46. $y^2 - 5 > 2y^2 + 5$
47. $a^2 < 4$ or $a^2 > 25$
48. $a^2 \geq 4$ and $a^2 \leq 25$
49. $a^2 < 16$ and $a^3 < 4a$
46. ϕ
48. {a|$-5 \leq a \leq -2$ or $2 \leq a \leq 5$}
47. {a|$a < -5$ or $-2 < a < 2$ or $a > 5$}
49. {a|$-4 < a < -2$ or $0 < a < 2$}

QUADRATIC INEQUALITIES

3.7 Problem Solving: Number Problems

OBJECTIVE ▶ **To solve a word problem that leads to a quadratic equation**

Many word problems can be solved by using quadratic equations. Since a quadratic equation often has two solutions, a given word problem may have two sets of answers.

In Example 1, a problem about *consecutive integers* is solved. Recall that consecutive multiples of 5 can be represented by $x, x + 5, x + 10, \ldots$, where x is a multiple of 5.

Example 1

Find three consecutive multiples of 5 so that the square of the third number, decreased by 5 times the second number, is the same as 25 more than twice the product of the first two numbers.

Represent the data.

Let x, $x + 5$, and $x + 10$ be the three consecutive multiples of 5, where x is a multiple of 5.

Write an equation.

$$(\text{third})^2 - (5 \cdot \text{second}) = (2 \cdot \text{first} \cdot \text{second}) + 25$$
$$(x + 10)^2 - 5(x + 5) = 2x(x + 5) + 25$$
$$x^2 + 20x + 100 - 5x - 25 = 2x^2 + 10x + 25$$

Solve the equation.

$$0 = x^2 - 5x - 50$$
$$0 = (x + 5)(x - 10)$$
$$x + 5 = 0 \qquad \text{or} \qquad x - 10 = 0$$
$$x = -5 \qquad\qquad\qquad x = 10$$

There are two sets of answers. The first multiple, x, may be either -5 or 10. If $x = -5$, then $x + 5 = 0$ and $x + 10 = 5$. If $x = 10$, then $x + 5 = 15$ and $x + 10 = 20$.

Check in the problem.

$(-5, 0, 5)$

$(\text{third})^2 - (5 \cdot \text{second})$	$(2 \cdot \text{first} \cdot \text{second}) + 25$
$5^2 \quad - \quad 5 \cdot 0$	$2(-5 \cdot 0) \qquad + 25$
$25 \quad - \quad 0$	$0 \qquad\qquad + 25$
25	25

$(10, 15, 20)$

$(\text{third})^2 - (5 \cdot \text{second})$	$(2 \cdot \text{first} \cdot \text{second}) + 25$
$20^2 \quad - \quad 5 \cdot 15$	$2 \cdot 10 \cdot 15 \qquad + 25$
$400 \quad - \quad 75$	$300 \qquad\qquad + 25$
325	325

Answer the questions.

Thus, the three consecutive multiples are -5, 0, 5, or 10, 15, 20.

When using a quadratic equation to solve a word problem, you should determine if both solutions of the equation provide answers that are "reasonable" in the problem. In Example 1, both solutions check in the equation, and both provide logical answers to the word problem.

Example  Some light bulbs are placed in boxes, and the boxes are then packed in cartons. The number of bulbs in each box is 4 less than the number of boxes in each carton. Find the number of bulbs in each box if a full carton contains 60 light bulbs.

Let $\quad x$ = number of boxes in each carton.

$\quad x - 4$ = number of bulbs in each box

$$\begin{pmatrix} \text{Number of boxes} \\ \text{in each carton} \end{pmatrix} \cdot \begin{pmatrix} \text{Number of bulbs} \\ \text{in each box} \end{pmatrix} = \begin{pmatrix} \text{Total number of bulbs} \\ \text{in each carton} \end{pmatrix}$$

$$x(x - 4) = 60$$
$$x^2 - 4x = 60$$
$$x^2 - 4x - 60 = 0$$
$$(x + 6)(x - 10) = 0$$
$$x = -6 \quad \text{or} \quad x = 10$$

The number of boxes in each carton cannot be -6. If $x = 10$, then there are 10 boxes in each carton and $10 - 4$, or 6 bulbs in each box.

Check: $\dfrac{\text{(No. of boxes in each carton)(No. of bulbs in each box)}}{\begin{matrix} 10 \cdot 6 \\ 60 \end{matrix}} \quad \begin{matrix} 60 \\ \hline 60 \end{matrix}$

Thus, there are 6 bulbs in each box.

To solve a word problem involving two numbers, read carefully to see if the second number is described *in terms of* the first number. If so, you should use a variable to represent the first number. This is shown in Example 3.

Example 3 A second number is 5 less than twice a first number. If the second number is multiplied by 3 more than the first number, the result is 21. Find all such pairs of numbers.

Let $\quad x$ = first number.

$\quad 2x - 5$ = second number

Second number times 3 more than first number is 21.

$$(2x - 5)(x + 3) = 21$$
$$2x^2 + x - 15 = 21$$
$$2x^2 + x - 36 = 0$$
$$(2x + 9)(x - 4) = 0$$

$$2x + 9 = 0 \qquad \text{or} \qquad x - 4 = 0$$
$$2x = -9 \qquad \qquad \qquad x = 4$$
$$x = -4.5$$

There are two sets of answers. The first number may be either -4.5, or 4. If $x = -4.5$, then $2x - 5 = -14$. If $x = 4$, then $2x - 5 = 3$. Check both pairs of numbers in the problem.

Thus, the pairs of first and second numbers are $(-4.5, -14)$ or $(4, 3)$.

Oral Exercises

Beginning with 12, give four integers for each description.

1. consecutive integers **12, 13, 14, 15**
2. consecutive even integers **12, 14, 16, 18**
3. consecutive multiples of 12 **12, 24, 36, 48**
4. consecutive multiples of 3 **12, 15, 18, 21**

Beginning with −9, give four integers for each description.

5. consecutive integers **−9, −8, −7, −6**
6. consecutive odd integers **−9, −7, −5, −3**
7. consecutive multiples of 3 **−9, −6, −3, 0**
8. consecutive multiples of 9 **−9, 0, 9, 18**

Written Exercises

Solve each problem. 1. **−6, −4, −2 or 4, 6, 8**

Ⓐ 1. Find three consecutive even integers so that the first integer times the second integer is 24. [Hint: Use x, $x + 2$, and $x + 4$ to represent the integers.]

2. Find three consecutive integers so that the product of the second and the third integers is 42. **−8, −7, −6 or 5, 6, 7**

3. Find three consecutive integers so that the square of the first, increased by the square of the third, is 100. **−8, −7, −6 or 6, 7, 8**

4. Find three consecutive odd integers so that the sum of the squares of the first two integers is 130. **−9, −7, −5 or 7, 9, 11**

5. Forty chairs are placed in rows so that the number of chairs in each row is 3 less than the number of rows. Find the number of chairs in each row. **5 chairs**

6. Forty-four students are seated in rows in a lecture hall. The number of students in each row is 7 more than the number of rows. Find the number of students seated in each row. **11 students**

7. One-hundred forty peaches were packed in some boxes so that the number of boxes was 6 less than twice the number of peaches in each box. Find the number of boxes used. **14 boxes**

8. An album contains 1,020 stamps. How many pages are in the album if the number of pages is 8 more than 4 times the number of stamps on each page?

68 pages

9. One number is 4 less than another number. Their product is 21. Find all such pairs of numbers. **−3, −7, or 7, 3**

10. The product of two numbers is 33. One number is 2 more than 3 times the other number. Find both numbers.

$-3\frac{2}{3}$, −9 or 3, 11

11. The product of two numbers is 9, and one number is 4 times the other number. Find the two numbers. **$-\frac{3}{2}$, −6 or $\frac{3}{2}$, 6**

12. Find two numbers whose product is 25 if one number is 9 times the other number. **$-1\frac{2}{3}$, −15 or $1\frac{2}{3}$, 15**

Ⓑ 13. Find three consecutive multiples of 5 so that the product of the first and the third numbers is 200. **−20, −15, −10 or 10, 15, 20**

14. Find three consecutive multiples of 10 so that 15 times the third number is the same as the product of the first two numbers. **20, 30, 40**

15. For which three consecutive multiples of 4 is 400 equal to the square of the first number, increased by the square of the second number? **−16, −12, −8 or 12, 16, 20**

16. For which three consecutive multiples of 6 will the sum of their squares be 504? **−18, −12, −6 or 6, 12, 18**

CHAPTER THREE

17. An 8-story hotel has the same number of rooms on each of the 8 floors. The number of square meters of carpet in each room is 10 more than twice the number of rooms on each floor. Find the area of the carpet in one room if there are 8,000 m² of carpet in the hotel. **50 m²**

18. Twelve kilograms of flour are placed in some bags and the bags are packed in boxes. The number of kilograms of flour in each bag is 3 less than the number of bags in each box, and the number of boxes is 1 less than the number of bags in each box. Find the number of boxes used. **3 boxes**

19. A second number is 5 more than a first number. If the second number is multiplied by 2 less than the first number, the product is 8. Find the numbers. **−6, −1 or 3, 8**

20. A first number is 3 less than twice a second number. If the first number is multiplied by 3 less than the second number, the result is 5. Find the numbers. $\frac{1}{2}$, −2 4, 5

21. Find four consecutive multiples of 5 such that the product of the second and the third numbers is 50 more than 10 times the fourth number.
−15, −10, −5, 0 or 10, 15, 20, 25

22. For which five consecutive multiples of 3 is the product of the second and the fourth numbers equal to 90 less than the sum of the squares of the first and the fifth numbers?

Ⓒ **23.** Find four consecutive multiples of 0.5 in which the product of the first and the third numbers is 0.25 less than 3 times the second number. **−0.5, 0, 0.5, 1 or 2.5, 3, 3.5, 4**

24. Find four consecutive multiples of π in which the product of the second and the third multiples is $2\pi^2$ more than 3π times the fourth multiple.

25. For which three consecutive integers is the sum of the first and the second integers the same as 3 less than twice the third integer?
every 3 consecutive integers

22. **−9, −6, −3, 0, 3 or −3, 0, 3, 6, 9**

26. Find three consecutive odd integers so that the square of the second integer is equal to the product of the first and the third integers. **no such integers**

24. **−3π, −2π, −π, 0 or 3π, 4π, 5π, 6π**

CALCULATOR ACTIVITIES

Compute each of the following for four consecutive multiples of 1.2 beginning with 2.4.
1. Their product **248.832**
2. The product of the first three numbers divided by the fourth number **6.912**
3. The product of the first two numbers divided by the product of the last two numbers
4. The product of the last two numbers divided by the product of the first two numbers
5. The square of the second number divided by the square of the third number
6. The cube of the second number divided by the product of the first number and the third number. **3. 0.3 4. $3\frac{1}{3}$ 5. 0.5625 6. 4.05**

Cumulative Review

1. The length of a rectangle is 5 units more than its width. Represent the perimeter and the area of the rectangle in algebraic terms.

2. The base of a triangle is 8 units shorter than 4 times its height. Represent the area of the triangle in algebraic terms. $A = \frac{1}{2}h(4h - 8)$

$P = 2w + 2(w + 5)$
$A = w(w + 5)$

PROBLEM SOLVING: NUMBER PROBLEMS

3.8 Problem Solving: Geometric Problems

OBJECTIVES ▶ **To find the length of each side of a right triangle by using the Pythagorean relation**
To solve an area problem that leads to a quadratic equation

For each right triangle ABC with right angle C as shown below, the lengths a, b, and c of the three sides are related by the **Pythagorean relation:** $a^2 + b^2 = c^2$.

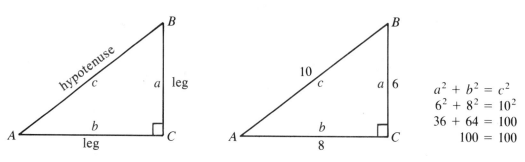

$$a^2 + b^2 = c^2$$
$$6^2 + 8^2 = 10^2$$
$$36 + 64 = 100$$
$$100 = 100$$

Example 1 One leg of a right triangle is 7 m longer than the other leg. The length of the hypotenuse is 13 m. Find the length of each leg.

Represent the data.

Let $\quad x = $ length of one leg.
$x + 7 = $ length of other leg

Write an equation.

$$a^2 + b^2 = c^2$$
$$x^2 + (x + 7)^2 = 13^2$$
$$x^2 + (x^2 + 14x + 49) = 169$$
$$2x^2 + 14x - 120 = 0$$

Solve the equation.

$$x^2 + 7x - 60 = 0 \quad \blacktriangleleft \textit{ Divide each side by 2, the GCF.}$$
$$(x + 12)(x - 5) = 0$$
$$x = -12 \quad \text{or} \quad x = 5$$

Check in the problem.

The length of a side of a triangle cannot be -12 m.
If $x = 5$, then $x + 7 = 12$. Check to determine if $a^2 + b^2 = c^2$.

$$a = 5, b = 12, c = 13$$

$a^2 + b^2$	c^2
$5^2 + 12^2$	13^2
$25 + 144$	169
169	

Answer the questions.

Thus, the length of one leg is 5 m and the length of the other leg is 12 m.

The surface enclosed by a rectangle is measured in *square units*. This measure is the **area** of the rectangle. The word problem in Example 2 on page 79 involves the area of a rectangle.

Example 2 The length of a rectangle is 3 cm more than twice its width. Find the width and the length if the area is 44 cm^2.

Let w = width.
     $2w + 3$ = length

$$\text{width} \times \text{length} = \text{area of rectangle}$$
$$w(2w + 3) = 44$$
$$2w^2 + 3w = 44$$
$$2w^2 + 3w - 44 = 0$$
$$(2w + 11)(w - 4) = 0$$
$$2w + 11 = 0 \qquad \text{or} \qquad w - 4 = 0$$
$$2w = -11 \qquad\qquad\qquad w = 4$$
$$w = -5.5$$

The width of a rectangle cannot be -5.5 cm.
If $w = 4$, then $2w + 3 = 11$.

width $\times$ length	area
4 cm $\times$ 11 cm	44 cm^2
44 cm^2	

Thus, the width is 4 cm and the length is 11 cm.

The word problem in Example 3 involves the area of a triangle. The area of a triangle equals $\frac{1}{2}$ times the length of the base times the height of the triangle.

Example 3 The height of a triangle is 6 m less than three times the length of its base. Find the length of the base and the height of the triangle if its area is 36 m^2.

Let b = length of base.
     $3b - 6$ = height

height: $3b - 6$

base: b

$$\frac{1}{2} \times \text{base} \times \text{height} = \text{area of triangle}$$

$$\frac{1}{2} b(3b - 6) = 36$$

$$2 \cdot \frac{1}{2} \cdot b(3b - 6) = 36 \cdot 2 \qquad \blacktriangleleft \; \textit{Multiply each side by 2,}$$
$$b(3b - 6) = 72 \qquad\qquad \textit{the reciprocal of } \frac{1}{2}.$$
$$3b^2 - 6b - 72 = 0$$
$$b^2 - 2b - 24 = 0 \qquad \blacktriangleleft \; \textit{Divide each side by 3, the GCF.}$$
$$(b - 6)(b + 4) = 0$$
$$b = 6 \qquad \text{or} \qquad b = -4 \qquad \blacktriangleleft \; \textit{The length of the base cannot be } -4 \; m.$$

If $b = 6$, then $3b - 6 = 12$. Check to see that 6 m and 12 m work in the problem.

Thus, the length of the base is 6 m and the height is 12 m.

Some geometric problems involve addition or subtraction of measures. In the next example, one area is subtracted from another area.

Example 4
The length of a rectangular floor is 4 m shorter than 3 times its width. The width of a rectangular carpet on the floor is 2 m shorter than the floor's width. The carpet is 2 m longer than twice its own width. Find the area of the floor if 44 m² of the floor are not covered by the carpet.

Let $\quad x$ = width of floor.
$3x - 4$ = length of floor

Sketch the two rectangles.

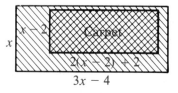

(Area of floor) − (Area of carpet) = (Area not covered)
$$x(3x - 4) - (x - 2)(2x - 2) = 44$$
$$3x^2 - 4x - (2x^2 - 6x + 4) = 44$$
$$x^2 + 2x - 48 = 0$$
$$(x - 6)(x + 8) = 0$$
$$x = 6 \quad \text{or} \quad x = -8 \quad ◄ \text{ } \textit{The width cannot be } -8 \text{ m.}$$

If $x = 6$, then $3x - 4 = 14$, $x - 2 = 4$, and $2(x - 2) + 2 = 10$.

(Area of floor) − (Area of carpet)	(Area not covered)
6 m × 14 m − 4 m × 10 m	44 m²
84 m² − 40 m²	
44 m²	

Thus, the area of the floor is 6 m × 14 m, or 84 m².

Written Exercises _____

Solve each problem.

(A)

1. One leg of a right triangle is 2 m longer than the other leg. The length of the hypotenuse is 10 m. Find the length of each leg. **6 m, 8 m**

2. One leg of a right triangle is 4 m long. The hypotenuse is 1 m shorter than twice the length of the other leg. Find the length of the other leg and the length of the hypotenuse. **3 m, 5 m**

3. One leg of a right triangle is 7 cm longer than the other leg. The hypotenuse is 1 cm longer than the longer leg. Find the lengths of the three sides. **5 cm, 12 cm, 13 cm**

4. In a right triangle, the hypotenuse is 8 dm longer than one leg and 4 dm longer than the other leg. Find the lengths of the three sides. **12 dm, 16 dm, 20 dm**

5. The length of a rectangle is 3 cm less than twice its width. Find the length and the width if the area is 20 cm². **4 cm, 5 cm**

6. The length of a rectangle is 5 m more than three times its width. Find the length and the width if the area is 42 m². **3 m, 14 m**

7. The height of a triangle is six times the length of its base. Find the length of the base and the height of the triangle if its area is 12 m^2. **2 m, 12 m**

8. The base of a triangle is 2 m shorter than its height and the area is 24 m^2. Find the height and the length of the base. **8 m, 6 m**

9. The base of a triangle is 4 dm longer than twice the height. If the area is 63 dm^2, find the length of the base. **18 dm**

10. The area of a triangle is 54 cm^2. Find the height of the triangle if the height is 6 cm less than 4 times the length of the base. **18 cm**

11. The width of one square is twice the width of another square. The sum of their areas is 125 m^2. Find the area of each square. **25 m^2, 100 m^2**

12. One square is 3 times as wide as another square. Find the area of each square if the difference of the two areas is 32 cm^2. **4 cm^2, 36 cm^2**

13. A square and a rectangle have the same width. The length of the rectangle is 4 times its width. If the sum of the two areas is 45 cm^2, find the area of each figure. **sq: 9 cm^2, rect: 36 cm^2**

14. The length of a rectangle is 5 m more than twice its width. The width of a square is the same as the length of the rectangle. Find the area of each figure if one area, decreased by the other area, is 88 m^2. **sq: 121 m^2, rect: 33 m^2**

Ⓑ 15. A rectangle is 1 m narrower than it is long, and one of its diagonals is 2 m longer than the width of the rectangle. What is the length of the diagonal? **5 m**

16. A diagonal of a rectangle is 5 cm longer than 4 times the width of the rectangle. Find the length of the rectangle if it is 1 cm less than the length of the diagonal. **40 cm**

17. The length of a rectangle is 4 cm more than its width and 4 cm less than the length of a diagonal of the rectangle. What is the area of the rectangle? **192 cm^2**

18. The length of a rectangle is 2 m more than twice its width and 1 m less than the length of a diagonal of the rectangle. Find the area of the rectangle. **60 m^2**

19. A rectangle is twice as long as it is wide. The height of a triangle is twice the length of its base and the same as the length of the rectangle. Find the area of each figure if the sum of their areas is 108 m^2. **rect: 72 m^2, triangle: 36 m^2**

20. The base of a triangle is 2 cm shorter than the width of a rectangle. The rectangle's length is 4 times its width and the triangle's height is the same as the rectangle's length. Find the area of each figure if the difference of the two areas is 30 cm^2. **triangle: 6 cm^2, rect. 36 cm^2**

21. The length of a rectangular wall is 3 m more than twice its height. The width of a picture on the wall is 1 m less than the height of the wall. The picture is 2 m longer than it is wide. Find the area of the wall if 19 m^2 of the wall are not covered by the picture. **27 m^2**

22. The length of a patio floor is 1 m less than twice its width. The floor is extended by building a second patio floor that is 3 m longer and 2 m narrower than the first floor. Find the area of the original floor if the total area of the patio is 48 m^2 after the extension is built. **28 m^2**

PROBLEM SOLVING: GEOMETRIC PROBLEMS

Ⓒ **23.** A rectangular lawn measures 26 m by 36 m and is surrounded by a uniform sidewalk. The outer edge of the sidewalk is a rectangle with an area of 1,200 m². Find the width of the sidewalk. **2 m**

24. A rectangular picture measures 32 cm by 50 cm. It is surrounded by a uniform frame whose outer edge is a rectangle with an area of 2,320 cm². Find the width of the the frame. **4 cm**

25. A rectangular piece of cardboard is 5 cm longer than it is wide. A 3-centimeter square (3 cm by 3 cm) is cut out of each corner. Then the four flaps are turned up to form an open box with a volume of 450 cm³. Find the length and the width of the original piece of cardboard. **16 cm, 21 cm**

26. A 4-decimeter square is cut from each corner of a rectangular piece of plastic whose length is 2 dm less than twice its width. Then the four flaps are folded to form an open carton with a volume of 1,040 dm³. Find the length and the width of the original piece of plastic. **18 dm, 34 dm**

CALCULATOR ACTIVITIES

Find the area of each rectangle described below, in terms of the given unit of measure.

1. 296 in. by 225 in., in square feet
462.5 ft²

2. 17.5 ft by 38.75 ft, in square inches
97,650 in.²

3. 1.24 m by 0.35 m, in square centimeters
4,340 cm²

4. 4,225 cm by 2,416 cm, in square meters
1,020.76 m²

5. 222 ft by 363 ft, in square yards
8,954 yd²

6. 497 yd by 268 yd, in square feet
1,198,764 ft²

The lengths of the three sides of a triangle are given. Determine whether each triangle is a right triangle by using the Pythagorean relation.

7. 98 cm, 336 cm, 350 cm **yes**

8. 0.75 yd, 0.4 yd, 0.85 yd **yes**

9. 110 in., 226 in., 286 in. **no**

10. 0.65 m, 4.2 m, 4.25 m **yes**

➤ A Challenge To You

Each edge of a cube is 3 in. long. The cube is painted on each of its six faces, and then it is cut up to form 27 one-inch cubes.

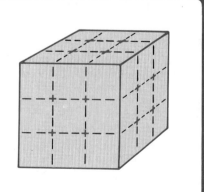

1. What is the least number of straight cuts needed to form the 27 one-inch cubes?
6

Find the number of one-inch cubes that are painted on the given number of faces.

2. three faces **8**   **3.** exactly two faces **12**

4. exactly one face **6** **5.** zero faces **1**

Applications

A certain investment plan requires regular payments of $30 a month with an expected earnings rate of 2% per month.

The expected value in the plan at the end of the 1st month is the payment plus the interest the payment earned for the month.

$$= \quad 30 \quad + \quad 30(0.02) \quad 30(1 + 0.02)$$

or 30(1.02)

The expected value in the plan at the end of the 2nd month is the payment and the 1st month's value, plus the 2nd month's interest on both.

$$[30 \quad + \quad 30(1.02)] \quad + \quad [30 + 30(1.02)](0.02)$$
$$= [30 + 30(1.02)](1 + 0.02)$$
or 30(1.02) + 30(1.02)²

Now find the expected value in the plan at the end of the 3rd month.

Payment + Value already in the plan + 3rd month's earnings on both

$$[30 \quad + \quad 30(1.02) + 30(1.02)^2 \quad + \quad [30 + 30(1.02) + 30(1.02)^2](0.02)$$
$$= [30 + 30(1.02) + 30(1.02)^2](1 + 0.02)$$
or, 30(1.02) + 30(1.02)² + 30(1.02)³

Generalize the formula for $r\%$ per month. Let $x = 1 + 0.01r$.
$$30x + 30x^2 + 30x^3$$

If p dollars, rather than 30 dollars, is added monthly to the investment plan above, show the expected value at the end of n months.

$$px + px^2 + px^3 + \cdots + px^{n-1} + px^n$$

Solve each problem.

Tina's pension plan requires regular payments of $40 a month. The plan has an expected earnings rate of 3% per month.

1. What is the expected value after 6 months if she doubles the payments beginning with the fourth month? **$405.66**
2. What would the earnings be on Tina's plan after 6 months if she makes double payments from the first month but only receives half the monthly earnings rate? **$25.84**

Chapter Three Review

Vocabulary

area [3.8]

common binomial factor [3.4]

common monomial factor [3.4]

difference of two cubes [3.3]

difference of two squares [3.3]

perfect square trinomial [3.3]

Pythagorean relation [3.8]

quadratic trinomial [3.1]

standard form

  quadratic equation [3.5]

  quadratic inequality [3.6]

sum of two cubes [3.3]

For complete solutions, see TE Answer Section.

Factor each polynomial.

1. $5c^2 - 37c + 14$ **$(5c - 2)(c - 7)$** [3.1]
2. $9y^4 + 18y^2 + 8$ **$(3y^2 + 2)(3y^2 + 4)$**
3. $25a^4b^4 + 5a^2b^2 - 12$
★ 4. $2x^{2n+2} - 11x^{n+1} + 5$
5. $9a^2 - 16$ 6. $n^3 + 64$ [3.3]
7. $a^4 - 16a^2 + 64$ 8. $100x^4 - 49y^2$
9. $8c^3 - 125d^3$ **$(2c - 5d)(4c^2 + 10cd + 25d^2)$**
10. $25x^2 + 40xy + 16y^2$ **$(5x + 4y)^2$**
11. $4x^2 + 4xy + y^2 + 16x + 8y + 16$
★ 12. $x^{6m} + 10x^{3m}y^n + 25y^{2n}$
  7. $(a^2 - 8)^2$ 8. $(10x^2 + 7y)(10x^2 - 7y)$

Multiply each pair of polynomials. [3.2]

13. $(4n + 6)(4n - 6)$ 14. $(3a - 5)^2$
15. $(x + 3)(x^2 - 3x + 9)$ **$x^3 + 27$**
16. $(5x^2 + 4y)^2$ **$25x^4 + 40x^2y + 16y^2$**
17. $(8y^2 - 6z)(8y^2 + 6z)$ **$64y^4 - 36z^2$**
18. $(2m - n)(4m^2 + 2mn + n^2)$ **$8m^3 - n^3$**

Factor each polynomial completely. [3.4]

19. $18x^3 - 15x^2 + 3x$ 20. $-2a^2 + 3a + 14$
21. $12y^2 - 27$ 22. $-y^2 + 10y - 25$
23. $2n^4 - 15n^2 - 27$ 24. $4c^4 - 25c^2 + 36$
25. $2a^3b - 4a^2b - 30ab$
26. $3x^3 - 24y^3$
27. $x^3 + 4x^2 + 5x + 20$
28. $15ac - 6bc - 20ad + 8bd$
★29. $2x^{7n} - 18x^{3n}$

Solve each equation. [3.5]

30. $x^2 = x + 12$ **4, −3**   31. $-6y^2 = 14y$ **0, $-2\frac{1}{3}$**
32. $25a^2 = 4$ **$-\frac{2}{5}, \frac{2}{5}$**
33. $n^4 - 29n^2 + 100 = 0$ **−5, 5, −2, 2**

Find the solution set of each inequality.
Graph the solutions. [3.6]   **34. $\{y|-4 < y < 2\}$**

34. $y^2 + 2y - 8 < 0$ 35. $-x^2 + 25 \leq 0$
36. $x^3 - 2x^2 - 24x > 0$ **below**
37. $2n^2 + n \geq 15$ **$\{n|n \leq -3 \text{ or } n \geq 2.5\}$**
38. $y^4 - 23y^2 - 50 > 0$ **below**
★ 39. $x^2 - 8x + 16 > 0$ **$\{x|x \neq 4\}$**
35. **$\{x|x \leq -5 \text{ or } x \geq 5\}$**

Solve each problem.

40. Find three consecutive odd integers so that the product of the second integer and the third integer is 63. [3.7]
                −11, −9, −7 or 5, 7, 9

41. Fifty-four cans are packed in some boxes so that the number of boxes is 3 more than the number of cans in each box. Find the number of boxes used. [3.7]
                           9 boxes

42. Find three consecutive multiples of 6 so that 36 less than the product of the second and third numbers is equal to the sum of the squares of the first and the second numbers. [3.7] **0, 6, 12 or 6, 12, 18**

43. A second number is 1 less than 3 times a first number. If the second number is multiplied by 2 more than the first number, the product is 10. Find both numbers. [3.7]
                    $\frac{4}{3}$, 3 or −3, −10

44. One leg of a right triangle is 3 m longer than the other leg. The hypotenuse is 6 m longer than the shorter leg. Find the lengths of the three sides. [3.8]
                9 m, 12 m, 15 m

45. The height of a triangle is 8 cm less than twice the length of its base. Find the length of the base and the height of the triangle if its area is 12 cm². [3.8] **6 cm, 4 cm**

46. The length of one rectangle is 6 m more than 2 times its width. The length and width of a second rectangle are twice the length and width, respectively, of the first rectangle. Find the area of each rectangle if the difference of the two areas is 324 m². [3.8] **108 m², 432 m²**

CHAPTER THREE REVIEW
36. **$\{x|-4 < x < 0 \text{ or } x > 6\}$**   38. **$\{y|y < -5 \text{ or } y > 5\}$**

Chapter Three Test

Factor each polynomial.

1. $3x^2 - 13x - 10$ $(3x + 2)(x - 5)$
2. $9a^2 + 30ab + 25b^2$ $(3a + 5b)^2$
3. $4c^2 - 81$ $(2c + 9)(2c - 9)$
4. $27n^3 - 125$ $(3n - 5)(9n^2 + 15n + 25)$
5. $9x^2 + 6xy + y^2 - 16$
$$(3x + y + 4)(3x + y - 4)$$

Multiply each pair of polynomials.

6. $(7y + 8)(7y - 8)$ $49y^2 - 64$
7. $(4a + 5b)^2$ $16a^2 + 40ab + 25b^2$
8. $(2y - 3)(4y^2 + 6y + 9)$ $8y^3 - 27$

Factor each polynomial completely.

9. $98 - 32x^2$ $2(7 - 4x)(7 + 4x)$
10. $2xy^2 - 2xy - 12x$ $2x(y - 3)(y + 2)$
11. $-24x^2 - 6x + 45$ $-3(4x - 5)(2x + 3)$
12. $4a^4 - a^2 - 18$ $(2a + 3)(2a - 3)(a^2 + 2)$

Solve each equation.

13. $a^2 = 11a$ $0, 11$
14. $2x^2 = 12 - 5x$ $1\frac{1}{2}, -4$
15. $0 = a^4 - 37a^2 + 36$ $-6, 6, -1, 1$

Find the solution set of each inequality. Graph the solutions.

16. $x^2 + 3x - 18 \le 0$ $\{x | -6 \le x \le 3\}$
17. $x^3 - 64x \ge 0$ $\{x | -8 \le x \le 0 \text{ or } x \ge 8\}$
18. $a^4 - 29a^2 + 100 < 0$
$$\{a | -5 < a < -2 \text{ or } 2 < a < 5\}$$

Solve each problem.

19. One number is 6 less than another number. The product of the smaller number and 3 more than the larger number is 10. Find both numbers. **7, 1 or −4, −10**

20. The length of the base of a triangle is 10 cm less than 4 times the height. Find the length of the base and the height of the triangle if its area is 25 cm². **5 cm, 10 cm**

21. Find three consecutive even integers such that the square of the second integer, increased by twice the product of the first two integers, is the same as 24 more than twice the square of the first integer. **−10, −8, −6 or 2, 4, 6**

22. The length of a rectangle is 2 m more than its width and 2 m shorter than the length of a diagonal. Find the length of the diagonal and the area of the rectangle. **10 m, 48 m²**

23. A rectangular garden is 10 m longer than 4 times its width. The garden is to be enlarged by adding a second rectangular garden, 3 times as wide but half as long as the first garden. Find the area of the original garden if the total area of the enlarged garden will be 665 m². **266 m²**

★ 24. Factor $2x^{2n+2} - x^{n+1}y^{2n} - y^{4n}$.
$$(x^{n+1} - y^{2n})(2x^{n+1} + y^{2n})$$

★ 25. Solve $25x^2 = 40ax - 16a^2$ for x in terms of a. $\frac{4a}{5}$

★ 26. Find and then graph the solution set of $x^2 < 25$ and $x^2 > 9$.
$$\{x | -5 < x < -3 \text{ or } 3 < x < 5\}$$

Computer Activities

Triangular and Square Numbers

Numbers such as 1, 3, 6, and 10 are called **triangular numbers.**

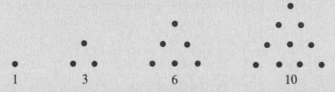

Similarly, numbers such as 1, 4, 9, and 16 are called **square numbers.**

Triangular numbers can be found by using the following formula:
$$T = \frac{A(A + 1)}{2}, \text{ where } A = 1, 2, 3, \ldots.$$

Square numbers can be found by using the following formula:
$$S = B^2, \text{ where } B = 1, 2, 3, \ldots.$$

A computer can be programmed to find triangular or square numbers for specified values of A or B, respectively. Also, an interesting task for the computer is to find numbers that are *both* triangular and square. For a number to be both triangular and square, the positive square root of the triangular number must be an integer.

PROGRAM

```
10 PRINT "THIS PROGRAM FINDS THE TRIANGULAR"
20 PRINT "NUMBERS FOR VALUES OF A FROM 1 TO 50"
30 PRINT "TRIANGULAR NUMBERS"
40 FOR A = 1 TO 50
50 LET T = (A * (A + 1))/2
60 PRINT T
70 NEXT A
80 END
```

Exercises

1. Enter in and run the program above. Find the *range* of triangular numbers for values of A from 1 to 50. **1 to 1275**

2. Alter the computer program above to get a program for finding numbers that are both triangular and square. **For Ex. 2, see TE Answer Section.**

College Prep Test

DIRECTIONS: Choose the *one* best answer to each question or problem.

1. Which value of x is not a solution of the inequality $(x + 40)(x - 20)(x + 60) \geq 0$? **B**

   (A) -53 (B) -7 (C) 20
   (D) 36   (E) None of these

2. For which equation is the product of its solutions not a negative number? **D**

   (A) $x^2 - 10x - 24 = 0$ (B) $x^2 - 25 = 0$
   (C) $x^2 + 7x - 18 = 0$ (D) $x^2 + 6x = 0$
   (E) None of these

3. Which figure has an area different from the other four figures? **C**
   [1 meter (m) = 100 centimeters (cm)]

   (A) A rectangle, 1.2 m by 0.3 m
   (B) A rectangle, 2 m by 0.18 m
   (C) A rectangle, 9 cm by 4 cm
   (D) A triangle, height of 120 cm and base 60 cm long
   (E) A parallelogram, height of 60 cm and base 60 cm long

4. If x is an integer, for what value(s) of x will $x^2 + 12x + 36$ be a positive perfect square? **D**

   (A) -6 (B) 0   (C) 6
   (D) Every integer except -6
   (E) Every integer except 0

5. If $y = \frac{5}{4}x + 20$, then $y = x$ only if **D**

   (A) $x = 0$ (B) $y = 20$ (C) $x = 100$
   (D) $y = -80$ (E) None of these

6. Howard is n years old now. Ten years ago, he was t years old. Find his age y years from now. **A**

   (A) $t + y + 10$ (B) $t + 10$
   (C) $t + y$ (D) $y + 10$
   (E) $n + t + y$

7. Represent the total value of x nickels, y dimes, and z quarters. **C**

   (A) $x + y + z$ cents   (B) 40 cents
   (C) $0.05x + 0.10y + 0.25z$ dollars
   (D) $5x + 10y + 25z$ dollars
   (E) None of these

8. What is the GCF of $2(6x^2y - 9xy^3) + (15a^3x + 10ay^2)$? **E**

   (A) 2   (B) $6xy$ (C) $10a$
   (D) $30axy$ (E) None of these

9. For which equation is the product of its solutions the greatest number? **E**

   (A) $x^2 - 36 = 0$
   (B) $x^2 + 8x = 0$
   (C) $x^2 + 5x + 6 = 0$
   (D) $x^2 - 2x - 15 = 0$
   (E) $x^2 - 7x + 12 = 0$

10. A car traveled x miles in a hours, then y miles in b hours, and finally z miles in c hours. Find the average speed in miles per hour for the trip of $x + y + z$ miles. **B**

    (A) $\frac{x}{a} + \frac{y}{b} + \frac{z}{c}$ (B) $\frac{x + y + z}{a + b + c}$
    (C) $\left(\frac{x}{a} + \frac{y}{b} + \frac{z}{c}\right) \div 3$
    (D) $(x + y + z)(a + b + c)$
    (E) None of these

4 RATIONAL EXPRESSIONS

Is 2 Equal to 1?

READ → PLAN → SOLVE → INTERPRET

Study each step in the following "proof."

1. Let $a = b$.

2. $a \cdot a = a \cdot b$ Multiply each side by a.

3. $a^2 = ab$ Simplify.

4. $a^2 - b^2 = ab - b^2$ Add $-b^2$ to each side.

5. $(a + b)(a - b) = b(a - b)$ Factor each side.

6. $\dfrac{(a + b)(a - b)}{(a - b)} = \dfrac{b(a - b)}{(a - b)}$ Divide each side by $(a - b)$.

7. $a + b = b$ Divide out the common factor, $a - b$.

8. $b + b = b$ From Step 1, $a = b$. Substitute.

9. $2b = 1b$ Simplify.

10. $\dfrac{2b}{b} = \dfrac{1b}{b}$ Divide each side by b.

11. **Thus,** $2 = 1$.   Divide out the common factor, b.

Since $2 \neq 1$, there must be an error in the "proof" above.
Can you find the error?
Step 6. Since $a = b$, then $a - b = 0$. Dividing by $a - b$ is
dividing by zero (0), which is undefined.

4.1 Rational Numbers and Decimals

OBJECTIVE ▶ **To show that a given number is a rational number**

Every integer, mixed number, and terminating decimal can be expressed in the form $\frac{a}{b}$ where a and b are integers. These numbers are examples of **rational numbers.**

**Definition:
Rational
Number**

> A *rational number* is one that can be written in the form $\frac{a}{b}$, where a and b are integers, $b \neq 0$.

Example 1 **Show that each of 18, $-7\frac{3}{4}$ and 27.89 is a rational number.**

Rewrite each number in the form $\frac{a}{b}$, where a and b are integers.

$$18 = \frac{18}{1} \qquad \qquad -7\frac{3}{4} = \frac{-31}{4} \qquad \qquad 27.89 = \frac{2,789}{100}$$

You can use division to express a rational number as a decimal.

$$\frac{5}{4} = 4\overline{)5.00}^{\,1.25} \qquad \qquad \frac{2}{3} = 3\overline{)2.000\ldots}^{\,0.666\ldots}$$

The decimal for $\frac{5}{4}$ is a **terminating decimal.** The decimal for $\frac{2}{3}$ is a **repeating decimal** and can be written either as 0.666 . . . or as $0.6\overline{6}$ with a bar above the repeating digit.
A repeating decimal may have more than one digit in its repeating block of digits. For example,

$$\frac{26}{11} = 11\overline{)26.00\ 00\ 00\ \ldots}^{\,2.36\ 36\ 36\ \ldots} .$$

Notice that $2.3\overline{636}$ is a repeating decimal with a repeating block of two digits.

As shown on page 90, the procedure above can be reversed. That is, every repeating decimal can be written in the form $\frac{a}{b}$, where a and b are integers.

Summary

> Every rational number has an equivalent decimal that either terminates or repeats.
> Every terminating decimal is a rational number.
> Every repeating decimal is a rational number.

Example 2 Show that $2.36\overline{36}$ and $1.62\overline{2}$ are rational numbers.

Each must be rewritten in the form $\frac{a}{b}$, where a and b are integers.

Let $n = 2.363636\ldots$
$$100n = 236.363636\ldots$$
Subtract. $\quad\underline{n = 2.363636\ldots}$
$$99n = 234.0$$
$$n = \frac{234}{99}, \text{ or } \frac{26}{11}$$

Let $n = 1.6222\ldots$
$$10n = 16.2222\ldots$$
Subtract. $\quad\underline{n = 1.6222\ldots}$
$$9n = 14.60$$
$$n = \frac{14.6}{9} \quad\blacktriangleleft \text{ 14.6 is not an integer.}$$
$$n = \frac{146}{90}, \text{ or } \frac{73}{45}$$

Notice in Example 2 that when a two-digit block like $\overline{36}$ repeats, you multiply each side of the equation by 100. When a one-digit block like $\overline{2}$ repeats, you multiply by 10.

Written Exercises

Show that each of the following is a rational number.

(Answers may vary.)

(A)
1. $-9 \quad \frac{-9}{1}$
2. $-2\frac{3}{10} \quad \frac{-23}{10}$
3. $-34.719 \quad \frac{-34,719}{1000}$
4. $0 \quad \frac{0}{1}$

5. $0.8\overline{8} \quad \frac{8}{9}$
6. $0.25\overline{25} \quad \frac{25}{99}$
7. $0.78\overline{8} \quad \frac{71}{90}$
8. $0.70\overline{70} \quad \frac{70}{99}$

9. $0.43\overline{43} \quad \frac{43}{99}$
10. $0.624\overline{4} \quad \frac{281}{450}$
11. $0.463\overline{63} \quad \frac{51}{110}$
12. $0.517\overline{7} \quad \frac{233}{450}$

(B)
13. $4\,4\overline{4} \quad \frac{40}{9}$
14. $68.68\overline{68} \quad \frac{6800}{99}$
15. $5.05\overline{05} \quad \frac{500}{99}$
16. $22.2\overline{2} \quad \frac{200}{9}$

17. $5.38\overline{8} \quad \frac{97}{18}$
18. $8.741\overline{41} \quad \frac{4327}{495}$
19. $3.81\overline{6} \quad \frac{229}{60}$
20. $47.239\overline{39} \quad \frac{15,589}{330}$

21. $0.571\overline{571} \quad \frac{571}{999}$
22. $0.743\overline{8438} \quad \frac{2477}{3330}$
23. $8.31\overline{831} \quad \frac{2770}{333}$
24. $1.234\overline{72347} \quad \frac{12,346}{9,999}$

(C)
25. $0.999\ldots \quad \frac{9}{9}$
26. $0.4999\ldots \quad \frac{1}{2}$
27. $3.74999\ldots \quad \frac{15}{4}$
28. $-4.124999\ldots \quad \frac{-33}{8}$

CALCULATOR ACTIVITIES

Three different ways of expressing the repeating block of digits in the decimal for $\frac{1810}{333}$ are given below.

$1810 \oplus 333 \ominus 5.4354354$
$\quad 5.43\overline{543} \quad\quad 5.435\overline{435} \quad\quad 5.4354\overline{354}$

$9.90\overline{9909};$
$9.909\overline{9099};$
$9.9099\overline{0990}$

Find all of the different ways to express the repeating block of digits in the decimal for each rational number.

1. $\frac{80}{33}$ $2.4\overline{24};$ $2.42\overline{42}$
2. $\frac{532}{99}$ $5.37\overline{37};$ $5.373\overline{73}$
3. $\frac{235}{111}$ $2.117\overline{117};$ $2.1171\overline{171};$ $2.11711\overline{711}$
4. $\frac{7700}{777}$

Express each rational number as a decimal and tell whether it terminates or repeats.

$23.452\overline{3452}3;$ repeats

5. $\frac{19}{40}$
6. $\frac{37}{30}$
7. $\frac{5}{8}$
8. $\frac{4}{9}$
9. $\frac{119}{125}$
10. $\frac{22}{7}$
11. $\frac{234,500}{9,999}$

$0.475;$ terminates
$1.23\overline{3};$ repeats
$0.625;$ terminates
$0.4\overline{4};$ repeats
$0.952;$ terminates
$3.142857\overline{142857};$ repeats

CHAPTER FOUR

4.2 Simplifying Rational Expressions

OBJECTIVES ▶ To evaluate a rational expression for given values of its variables, if possible

To determine the values of the variables for which a rational expression is undefined.

To simplify a rational expression

Each expression below is a quotient of polynomials.

$$\frac{2x - y}{5x^2 + 3xy - y^2} \qquad \frac{a^2 - 7a + 12}{3a - 9} \qquad \frac{0}{4n} \qquad \frac{x + 3}{1}$$

Such expressions are called **rational expressions.**

Definition:
Rational
Expression

> A *rational expression* is either a polynomial or a quotient of polynomials.

Notice that an expression like $\dfrac{\sqrt{x + 3}}{2y}$ is not a rational expression since $\sqrt{x + 3}$ is not a polynomial.

You can evaluate a rational expression by substituting given values for its variables and computing.

Example 1 Evaluate $\dfrac{2x + y}{3x - 2y}$ for $x = 5$ and $y = 6$, if possible.

$$\frac{2x + y}{3x - 2y} = \frac{2 \cdot 5 + 6}{3 \cdot 5 - 2 \cdot 6} = \frac{16}{3}, \text{ or } 5\frac{1}{3}$$

Example 2 Evaluate $\dfrac{2n}{n - 4}$ for $n = 4$, if possible.

$$\frac{2n}{n - 4} = \frac{2 \cdot 4}{4 - 4} = \frac{8}{0} \qquad \text{Not possible; division by 0 is undefined.}$$

As shown in Example 3, a rational expression is undefined for values of the variables which make the value of the denominator equal to zero (0).

Example 3 For what values of x is the rational expression $\dfrac{5}{x^2 - 7x + 12}$ undefined?

The rational expression is undefined when $x^2 - 7x + 12 = 0$.

If $x^2 - 7x + 12 = 0$, then $(x - 3)(x - 4) = 0$, and $x = 3$ or $x = 4$.

Thus, $\dfrac{5}{x^2 - 7x + 12}$ is undefined if $x = 3$ or $x = 4$.

SIMPLIFYING RATIONAL EXPRESSIONS

To simplify a fraction, you can factor the numerator and the denominator completely and then divide out common factors. For example,

$$\frac{30}{42} = \frac{2 \cdot 5 \cdot 3}{2 \cdot 3 \cdot 7} = \frac{\overset{1}{\cancel{2}} \cdot 5 \cdot \overset{1}{\cancel{3}}}{\underset{1}{\cancel{2}} \cdot \underset{1}{\cancel{3}} \cdot 7} = \frac{5}{7}.$$

Rational expressions are simplified in a similar way.

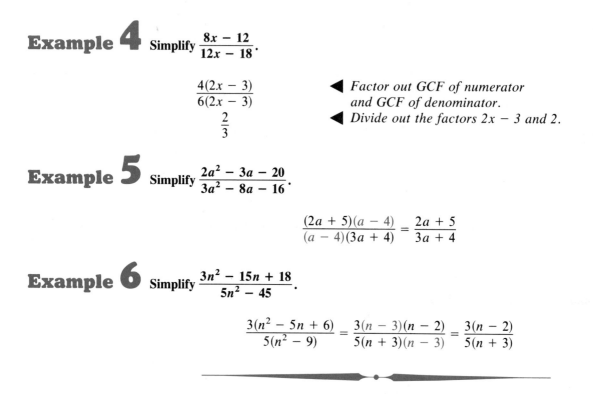

Example 4 Simplify $\dfrac{8x - 12}{12x - 18}$.

$\dfrac{4(2x - 3)}{6(2x - 3)}$ ◀ *Factor out GCF of numerator and GCF of denominator.*

$\dfrac{2}{3}$ ◀ *Divide out the factors $2x - 3$ and 2.*

Example 5 Simplify $\dfrac{2a^2 - 3a - 20}{3a^2 - 8a - 16}$.

$$\frac{(2a + 5)(a - 4)}{(a - 4)(3a + 4)} = \frac{2a + 5}{3a + 4}$$

Example 6 Simplify $\dfrac{3n^2 - 15n + 18}{5n^2 - 45}$.

$$\frac{3(n^2 - 5n + 6)}{5(n^2 - 9)} = \frac{3(n - 3)(n - 2)}{5(n + 3)(n - 3)} = \frac{3(n - 2)}{5(n + 3)}$$

As shown in Examples 7 and 8, sometimes a rational expression can be simplified after a negative number is factored out of the numerator or the denominator.

Example 7 Simplify $\dfrac{a^2 + 2a - 8}{6 - 3a}$.

$$\frac{a^2 + 2a - 8}{6 - 3a} = \frac{(a + 4)(a - 2)}{-3a + 6} = \frac{(a + 4)(a - 2)}{-3(a - 2)} = \frac{a + 4}{-3}$$

Example 8 Simplify $\dfrac{25 - c^2}{c^2 - 8c + 15}$.

$$\frac{-1(c^2 - 25)}{(c - 5)(c - 3)} = \frac{-1(c - 5)(c + 5)}{(c - 5)(c - 3)} = \frac{-1(c + 5)}{c - 3} \text{ or } \frac{-c - 5}{c - 3}$$

Reading In Algebra

Determine whether each expression is a rational expression. If it is not, then tell why not.

1. $\dfrac{3x^2 - 15x + 18}{4x - 8}$ **yes**   2. $\dfrac{\sqrt{y - 3}}{2y - 6}$ **no**   3. $4a^2 - 25b^2$ **yes**   4. $\dfrac{5n + 10}{10}$ **yes**   5. $\dfrac{0}{x + 6}$ **yes**

Evaluate each expression, if possible.

6. $\dfrac{-8}{4}$ **−2**   7. $\dfrac{0}{6}$ **0**   8. $\dfrac{7 + 7}{5 - 5}$ **not possible**   9. $\dfrac{5 - 5}{6 + 6}$ **0**   10. $\dfrac{18}{6^2 - 9 \cdot 4}$ **not possible**

Written Exercises

Evaluate each rational expression for $x = 4$ and $y = -3$, if possible.

Ⓐ 1. $\dfrac{x + y}{3x + 4y}$ **not possible**   2. $\dfrac{5x - y}{x - 2y}$ **$\frac{23}{10}$**   3. $\dfrac{x^2 + 2xy + y^2}{x + y}$ **1**

4. $\dfrac{y^2 + y}{x^2 - 16}$ **not possible**   5. $\dfrac{x^2 - y^2}{x^2 + y^2}$ **$\frac{7}{25}$**   6. $\dfrac{x^3}{y^3 - 9y}$ **not possible**

For what value(s) of the variable is each rational expression undefined?

7. $\dfrac{5}{3x}$ **0**   8. $\dfrac{n - 3}{n + 4}$ **−4**   9. $\dfrac{7}{3 - y}$ **3**

10. $\dfrac{x + 4}{x^2 - 25}$ **−5, 5**   11. $\dfrac{2c}{c^2 - 8c + 15}$ **3, 5**   12. $\dfrac{a^2 - 2a - 24}{a^2 + 2a - 15}$ **−5, 3**

Simplify each rational expression.

13. $\dfrac{6a + 8}{4}$ **$\frac{3a + 4}{2}$**   14. $\dfrac{12n}{12n - 8}$ **$\frac{3n}{3n - 2}$**   15. $\dfrac{15 - 10x}{25x}$ **$\frac{3 - 2x}{5x}$**

16. $\dfrac{4c + 20}{6c + 30}$ **$\frac{2}{3}$**   17. $\dfrac{10y - 20}{25y - 75}$ **$\frac{2(y - 2)}{5(y - 3)}$**   18. $\dfrac{3a - 15}{10 - 2a}$ **$-\frac{3}{2}$**

19. $\dfrac{x^2 - 2x - 15}{x^2 + 2x - 3}$ **$\frac{x - 5}{x - 1}$**   20. $\dfrac{3n^2 + 21n + 36}{2n^2 - 4n - 48}$ **$\frac{3(n + 3)}{2(n - 6)}$**   21. $\dfrac{6x^2 - 30x + 24}{10x^2 - 100x + 240}$ **$\frac{3(x - 1)}{5(x - 6)}$**

22. $\dfrac{6 - 2a}{a^2 + a - 12}$ **$\frac{-2}{a + 4}$**   23. $\dfrac{4 - c^2}{5c - 10}$ **$\frac{2 + c}{-5}$**   24. $\dfrac{n^2 - 7n + 10}{8 - 4n}$ **$\frac{n - 5}{-4}$**

Ⓑ 25. $\dfrac{3c^2 - 12c + 12}{12 - 4c - c^2}$ **$\frac{-3(c - 2)}{c + 6}$**   26. $\dfrac{5y^2 + 15y - 50}{50 - 2y^2}$ **$\frac{5(y - 2)}{2(5 - y)}$**   27. $\dfrac{16 - 14x - 2x^2}{4 - 8x + 4x^2}$ **$\frac{x + 8}{2(1 - x)}$**

28. $\dfrac{x^3 - 8}{3x - 6}$ **$\frac{x^2 + 2x + 4}{3}$**   29. $\dfrac{y^3 + 64}{y^2 - 4y + 16}$ **$y + 4$**   30. $\dfrac{5x^2 + 15x + 45}{x^3 - 27}$ **$\frac{5}{x - 3}$**

31. $\dfrac{8x^7 y^3 (3x^2 - 12x + 9)}{6x^3 y (3 - 2x - x^2)}$ 32. $\dfrac{15a^{12} b^4 (2a^2 - 8a - 24)}{14a^{15} b (5a^2 + 40a + 60)}$ 33. $\dfrac{15c^2 d^{-6} (-5c^2 - 30c - 45)}{-10c^{-7} d^{-2} (3c^2 - 12c - 63)}$

Ⓒ 34. $\dfrac{x^{4n+1} + x^{5n}}{x^{6n} - x^{5n+2}}$ **$\frac{x + x^n}{x^{2n} - x^{n+2}}$**   35. $\dfrac{x^{4n} + 7x^{2n} + 12}{x^{3n} + 5x^{2n} + 4x^n + 20}$ 36. $\dfrac{x^{6n} - y^{3n}}{x^{4n} - y^{2n}}$ **$\frac{x^{4n} + x^{2n} y^n + y^{2n}}{x^{2n} + y^n}$**

For what values of the variables is each rational expression undefined?

37. $\dfrac{5x}{x^2 - 2xy + y^2}$ **$x = y$**   38. $\dfrac{x + 1}{x^2 - y^2}$ **$x = y, x = -y$**   39. $\dfrac{3x + 4}{x^3 + 4x^2 y - 5xy^2}$ **$x = 0,$ $x = y,$ $x = -5y$**

31. $\dfrac{-4x^4 y^2 (x - 3)}{x + 3}$ 32. $\dfrac{3b^3 (a - 6)}{7a^3 (a + 6)}$ 33. $\dfrac{5c^9 (c + 3)}{2d^4 (c - 7)}$ 35. $\dfrac{x^{2n} + 3}{x^n + 5}$

SIMPLIFYING RATIONAL EXPRESSIONS   **93**

4.3 Products and Quotients

OBJECTIVES ▶ **To multiply rational expressions**
To divide rational expressions

To multiply rational numbers, it is convenient to divide out common factors.

$$\frac{5}{6} \cdot \frac{14}{15} = \frac{\overset{1}{\cancel{5}} \cdot \overset{1}{\cancel{2}} \cdot 7}{\underset{1}{\cancel{2}} \cdot 3 \cdot \underset{1}{\cancel{5}} \cdot 3} = \frac{1 \cdot 1 \cdot 7}{1 \cdot 3 \cdot 1 \cdot 3} = \frac{7}{9}.$$

Rational expressions are multiplied in a similar way, using the following rule.

Multiplying Rational Expressions

If $\dfrac{a}{b}$ and $\dfrac{c}{d}$ are rational expressions, $b \neq 0$, $d \neq 0$, then

$$\frac{a}{b} \cdot \frac{c}{d} = \frac{a \cdot c}{b \cdot d}.$$

Example 1 Multiply: $\dfrac{3x^8}{ay^7} \cdot \dfrac{ay^2}{6x^3}$.

$$\frac{3x^8}{ay^7} \cdot \frac{ay^2}{6x^3} = \frac{3x^8 \cdot ay^2}{ay^7 \cdot 6x^3} = \frac{3ax^8y^2}{6ax^3y^7}$$
$$= \frac{x^5}{2y^5}$$

Common factors divided out were 3, a, x^3, and y^2.

Multiply: $\dfrac{10c + 15}{10x - 50} \cdot \dfrac{x^2 - 25}{6c + 9}$.

$$\frac{10c + 15}{10x - 50} \cdot \frac{x^2 - 25}{6c + 9} = \frac{5(2c + 3) \cdot (x + 5)(x - 5)}{10(x - 5) \cdot 3(2c + 3)}$$
$$= \frac{x + 5}{6}$$

Common factors divided out were 5, $2c + 3$, and $x - 5$.

After the multiplication is completed, the rational expression in the answer should be simplified by dividing out any common factors that occur in the numerator and the denominator. Before identifying the common factors, be sure that each polynomial is factored completely.

Example 2 Multiply: $\dfrac{2x^2 - 18}{6x - 24} \cdot \dfrac{2x^2 - 9x + 4}{3x^2 + 24x + 45}$.

$$\frac{2(x^2 - 9)}{6(x - 4)} \cdot \frac{(2x - 1)(x - 4)}{3(x^2 + 8x + 15)} = \frac{2(x + 3)(x - 3) \cdot (2x - 1)(x - 4)}{6(x - 4) \cdot 3(x + 5)(x + 3)} = \frac{(x - 3)(2x - 1)}{9(x + 5)}$$

──────────────── ● ────────────────

To divide a rational number by a nonzero second rational number, you multiply the first number by the **reciprocal** (*multiplicative inverse*) of the second number.

$$\frac{8}{9} \div \frac{2}{3} = \frac{8}{9} \cdot \frac{3}{2} = \frac{4}{3}.$$

The reciprocal of $\frac{2}{3}$ is $\frac{3}{2}$, since $\frac{2}{3} \cdot \frac{3}{2} = 1$. Rational expressions are divided in a similar way, using the following rule.

If $\dfrac{a}{b}$ and $\dfrac{c}{d}$ are rational expressions, $b \neq 0$, $c \neq 0$, $d \neq 0$, then

$$\dfrac{a}{b} \div \dfrac{c}{d} = \dfrac{a}{b} \cdot \dfrac{d}{c} = \dfrac{a \cdot d}{b \cdot c}.$$

Example 3 Divide: $\dfrac{4a + 8}{5a - 20} \div \dfrac{a^2 - 3a - 10}{a^2 - 4a}$.

The reciprocal of $\dfrac{a^2 - 3a - 10}{a^2 - 4a}$ is $\dfrac{a^2 - 4a}{a^2 - 3a - 10}$.

$$\dfrac{4a + 8}{5a - 20} \cdot \dfrac{a^2 - 4a}{a^2 - 3a - 10} = \dfrac{4(a + 2) \cdot a(a - 4)}{5(a - 4) \cdot (a - 5)(a + 2)} = \dfrac{4a}{5(a - 5)}$$

Written **Exercises**

Multiply. Write each answer in simplest form.

(A) 1. $\dfrac{x^6 y}{8} \cdot \dfrac{6}{x^4 y^5} \; \dfrac{3x^2}{4y^4}$

2. $\dfrac{-xy}{6a^6} \cdot \dfrac{4a^2}{-5xy^3 z} \; \dfrac{2}{15a^4 y^2 z}$

3. $\dfrac{5bc^4}{3} \cdot \dfrac{3}{10ab^4 c} \; \dfrac{c^3}{2ab^3}$

4. $\dfrac{9c^3}{8x + 32} \cdot \dfrac{2x + 8}{-3c^4} \; \dfrac{3}{-4c}$

5. $\dfrac{5x - 10}{14x + 14} \cdot \dfrac{7x + 28}{3x - 6} \; \dfrac{5(x + 4)}{6(x + 1)}$

6. $\dfrac{5n + 15}{2d - 8} \cdot \dfrac{12 - 3d}{4n + 12} \; -\dfrac{15}{8}$

7. $\dfrac{3x - 15}{2x + 6} \cdot \dfrac{x^2 - 9}{x^2 - 25} \; \dfrac{3(x - 3)}{2(x + 5)}$

8. $\dfrac{c^2 - 16}{2 - d} \cdot \dfrac{d^2 - 4}{4 - c}$

9. $\dfrac{(7x + 28)}{n} \cdot \dfrac{3n}{x^2 + 8x + 16}$

10. $\dfrac{n^2 - 5n + 6}{3n + 12} \cdot \dfrac{4n + 16}{n^2 + 3n - 10}$

11. $\dfrac{9a + 27}{2a^2 + 8a + 8} \cdot \dfrac{4a^2 - 16}{6a + 18}$

12. $\dfrac{y^2 + 6y}{3y^2 + 6y - 24} \cdot \dfrac{10 - 5y}{-10y}$

8. $(c + 4)(d + 2)$ 9. $\dfrac{21}{x + 4}$ 10. $\dfrac{4(n - 3)}{3(n + 5)}$ 11. $\dfrac{3(a - 2)}{a + 2}$ 12. $\dfrac{y + 6}{6(y + 4)}$

Divide. Write each answer in simplest form.

13. $\dfrac{x^2 y^3}{10} \div \dfrac{x^7 y}{12} \; \dfrac{6y^2}{5x^5}$

14. $\dfrac{-10a^5}{b^6} \div \dfrac{15a^3 b}{2c^2} \; \dfrac{-4a^2 c^2}{3b^7}$

15. $\dfrac{7x + 35}{15n} \div \dfrac{9x + 45}{10n^2} \; \dfrac{14n}{27}$

16. $\dfrac{-4a + 8}{-2x - 10} \div \dfrac{6 - 3a}{x^2 - 25}$

17. $\dfrac{3x + 12}{5x} \div \dfrac{(x^2 - 16)}{5} \; \dfrac{3}{x(x - 4)}$

18. $\dfrac{5a + 25}{4a - 12} \div \dfrac{2a^2 - 2a - 60}{a^2 - 3a}$

(B) 19. $\dfrac{6a}{2n^2 + 3n - 9} \div \dfrac{8a^4}{4n^2 - 9} \; \dfrac{3(2n + 3)}{4a^3(n + 3)}$

20. $\dfrac{3x^2 - 7x + 2}{4a^5 b^2} \div \dfrac{2x^2 - 3x - 2}{8a^4 b^2} \; \dfrac{2(3x - 1)}{a(2x + 1)}$

21. $\dfrac{x^2 - 5xy + 6y^2}{x + y} \div 4x - 12y \; \dfrac{x - 2y}{4(x + y)}$

22. $\dfrac{c^2 + 2cd + d^2}{7a^2 - 7b^2} \div \dfrac{8c + 8d}{4b - 4a} \; \dfrac{c + d}{-14(a + b)}$

16. $\dfrac{-2(x - 5)}{3}$ 18. $\dfrac{5a}{8(a - 6)}$

Multiply or divide as indicated. Write each answer in simplest form.

23. $\dfrac{3c^2 - 5c - 2}{6c^2} \cdot \dfrac{4c^2 - 8c}{c^2 - 4c + 4} \; \dfrac{2(3c + 1)}{3c}$

24. $\dfrac{2x^2 + 7x + 6}{2x^2 - 6x - 20} \cdot \dfrac{15 - 3x}{6x + 6} \; \dfrac{2x + 3}{-4(x + 1)}$

25. $\dfrac{10x^3 - 4x^2 + 15x - 6}{10x^2 - 24x + 8} \cdot \dfrac{2x^3 - 4x^2 - 3x + 6}{4x^4 - 9} \; \dfrac{1}{2}$

26. $\dfrac{y^3 - 8}{y^2 - 4y + 16} \cdot \dfrac{y^3 + 64}{3y - 6} \; \dfrac{(y + 4)(y^2 + 2y + 4)}{3}$

(C) 27. $\dfrac{x^{7a}}{y^{6a}} \cdot \dfrac{y^a}{z^a} \cdot \dfrac{z^{3a}}{x^{5a}} \; \dfrac{x^{2a} z^{2a}}{y^{5a}}$

28. $\dfrac{x^{2a} - 7x^a + 12}{2x^{2a} + 6} \div \dfrac{3x^a - 12}{x^{4a} - 9} \; \dfrac{(x^a - 3)(x^{2a} - 3)}{6}$

29. $\dfrac{x^{2a} - y^{2b}}{4x^{2c} - 20x^c + 25} \cdot \dfrac{8x^c - 20}{3x^a + 3y^b} \; \dfrac{4(x^a - y^b)}{3(2x^c - 5)}$

30. $\dfrac{x^{3a} + x^{2a+1}}{x^{b+c}} \div \dfrac{x^{3a} - x^{a+2}}{x^{a+2b} - x^{2b+1}} \; \dfrac{x^a x^b}{x^c}$

PRODUCTS AND QUOTIENTS   **95**

4.4 Sums and Differences: Common Denominator

OBJECTIVES ▶ **To add rational expressions with a common denominator**
To subtract rational expressions with a common denominator

To add rational numbers with a common denominator, you add the numerators and use the common denominator. The result should be simplified whenever possible. For example,

$$\frac{3}{10} + \frac{4}{10} + \frac{1}{10} = \frac{3 + 4 + 1}{10} = \frac{8}{10} = \frac{4}{5}.$$

Rational expressions with a common denominator are added in a similar way.

Adding Rational Expressions with Common Denominator

If $\frac{a}{c}$ and $\frac{b}{c}$ are rational expressions, $c \neq 0$, then

$$\frac{a}{c} + \frac{b}{c} = \frac{a + b}{c}.$$

Example 1 Add: $\frac{4n}{3x^4 y} + \frac{n}{3x^4 y} + \frac{10n}{3x^4 y}$.

$$\frac{4n + n + 10n}{3x^4 y} = \frac{15n}{3x^4 y} = \frac{5n}{x^4 y}$$

Example 2 Add: $\frac{12t - 19}{6t - 9} + \frac{4 - 2t}{6t - 9}$.

$$\frac{12t - 19 + 4 - 2t}{6t - 9} = \frac{10t - 15}{6t - 9} = \frac{5(2t - 3)}{3(2t - 3)} = \frac{5}{3}$$

Example 3 Add: $\frac{n^2 - 6n}{n^2 + 8n + 16} + \frac{4n - 24}{n^2 + 8n + 16}$.

$$\frac{n^2 - 6n + 4n - 24}{n^2 + 8n + 16} = \frac{n^2 - 2n - 24}{n^2 + 8n + 16} = \frac{(n - 6)(n + 4)}{(n + 4)(n + 4)} = \frac{n - 6}{n + 4}$$

As shown in Example 1, the property of addition can be extended to any number of rational expressions with a common denominator.
You can subtract rational expressions by using the definition of subtraction, $x - y = x + (-y)$. To subtract a rational expression, you add its **opposite** (*additive inverse*).

Subtracting Rational Expressions with Common Denominator

If $\frac{a}{c}$ and $\frac{b}{c}$ are rational expressions, $c \neq 0$, then

$$\frac{a}{c} - \frac{b}{c} = \frac{a}{c} + \frac{-b}{c} = \frac{a + (-b)}{c}.$$

The opposite of a rational number may be written in a convenient form. For example, $-\frac{8}{2} = \frac{-8}{2}$, since $-\frac{8}{2} = -4$ and $\frac{-8}{2} = -4$. Similarly, $-\frac{b}{c} = \frac{-b}{c}$.

The expression $-\frac{3x-2}{x^2-4}$ may be written as $\frac{-(3x-2)}{x^2-4}$, or $\frac{-3x+2}{x^2-4}$.

Example 4 Subtract: $\dfrac{7x+15}{6x+12} - \dfrac{2x+5}{6x+12}$.

$$\frac{7x+15}{6x+12} + \frac{-(2x+5)}{6x+12} = \frac{7x+15-2x-5}{6x+12} = \frac{5x+10}{6x+12} = \frac{5(x+2)}{6(x+2)} = \frac{5}{6}$$

In Example 4, notice that $\dfrac{2x+5}{6x+12}$ was subtracted by adding its opposite. The opposite of $\dfrac{2x+5}{6x+12}$ may be written as $\dfrac{-(2x+5)}{6x+12}$.

Written Exercises

Add or subtract as indicated. Write each answer in simplest form.

Ⓐ 1. $\dfrac{3a}{10} + \dfrac{a}{10} + \dfrac{11a}{10}$ **$\dfrac{3a}{2}$**

2. $\dfrac{7x}{12} + \dfrac{13x}{12} - \dfrac{5x}{12}$ **$\dfrac{5x}{4}$**

3. $\dfrac{5a}{4} - \dfrac{3b}{4} + \dfrac{7c}{4}$ **$\dfrac{5a-3b+7c}{4}$**

4. $\dfrac{x+1}{6xy} + \dfrac{3x-4}{6xy} + \dfrac{3-x}{6xy}$ **$\dfrac{1}{2y}$**

5. $\dfrac{9d+5}{2cd} - \dfrac{d+5}{2cd}$ **$\dfrac{4}{c}$**

6. $\dfrac{11c}{2x^2y} - \dfrac{5c}{2x^2y}$ **$\dfrac{3c}{x^2y}$**

7. $\dfrac{7}{3n-12} + \dfrac{14}{3n-12}$ **$\dfrac{7}{n-4}$**

8. $\dfrac{17x}{4x+16} - \dfrac{37x}{4x+16}$ **$\dfrac{-5x}{x+4}$**

9. $\dfrac{5c}{2c-6} + \dfrac{3c}{2c-6}$ **$\dfrac{4c}{c-3}$**

10. $\dfrac{2x+5}{5x+10} + \dfrac{x+1}{5x+10}$ **$\dfrac{3}{5}$**

11. $\dfrac{7a-10}{3a-12} - \dfrac{a+8}{3a-12}$ **$\dfrac{2(a-3)}{a-4}$**

12. $\dfrac{6n+5}{2n+6} - \dfrac{2n-7}{2n+6}$ **2**

13. $\dfrac{3c}{c^2-25} + \dfrac{15}{c^2-25}$ **$\dfrac{3}{c-5}$**

14. $\dfrac{4n+30}{n^2-16} + \dfrac{3n-2}{n^2-16}$ **$\dfrac{7}{n-4}$**

15. $\dfrac{7x-4}{x^2+5x} + \dfrac{4-15x}{x^2+5x}$ **$\dfrac{-8}{x+5}$**

16. $\dfrac{2x^2-55}{x^2+7x} + \dfrac{6-x^2}{x^2+7x}$ **$\dfrac{x-7}{x}$**

17. $\dfrac{7a-15}{a^2-36} - \dfrac{2a+15}{a^2-36}$ **$\dfrac{5}{a+6}$**

18. $\dfrac{5c^2-8c}{c^2-9} - \dfrac{4c+9c^2}{c^2-9}$ **$\dfrac{-4c}{c-3}$**

19. $\dfrac{2a-5}{a^2+2a-15} + \dfrac{2a-7}{a^2+2a-15}$ **$\dfrac{4}{a+5}$**

20. $\dfrac{4x-19}{x^2-6x+8} + \dfrac{3x+5}{x^2-6x+8}$ **$\dfrac{7}{x-4}$**

Ⓑ 21. $\dfrac{4x-5}{x^2-7x+12} - \dfrac{x+7}{x^2-7x+12}$ **$\dfrac{3}{x-3}$**

22. $\dfrac{7n+5}{n^2-3n-10} - \dfrac{2n-5}{n^2-3n-10}$ **$\dfrac{5}{n-5}$**

23. $\dfrac{y^2-8y}{y^2+10y+16} + \dfrac{3y-14}{y^2+10y+16}$ **$\dfrac{y-7}{y+8}$**

24. $\dfrac{x^2-20}{x^2-4x-21} + \dfrac{2-3x}{x^2-4x-21}$ **$\dfrac{x-6}{x-7}$**

25. $\dfrac{3n^2+11n}{n^2+16n+64} - \dfrac{n^2+40}{n^2+16n+64}$ **$\dfrac{2n-5}{n+8}$**

26. $\dfrac{4a^2-16}{a^2-8a+16} - \dfrac{a^2+8a}{a^2-8a+16}$ **$\dfrac{3a+4}{a-4}$**

27. $\dfrac{3x+7}{2x^2+10x+12} + \dfrac{x+5}{2x^2+10x+12}$ **$\dfrac{2}{x+2}$**

28. $\dfrac{9y+40}{3y^2+12y-36} + \dfrac{3y+32}{3y^2+12y-36}$ **$\dfrac{4}{y-2}$**

Ⓒ 29. $\dfrac{3n}{n^3-16n} - \dfrac{12}{n(n^2-16)}$ **$\dfrac{3}{n(n+4)}$**

30. $\dfrac{2c^2-7}{c(c-5)^2} - \dfrac{10c-7}{c^3-10c^2+25c}$ **$\dfrac{2}{c-5}$**

4.5 Sums and Differences: Different Denominators

OBJECTIVES ▶ **To add rational expressions with different denominators**
To subtract rational expressions with different denominators

To add or subtract rational numbers with different denominators, you can proceed through the following steps:

Step 1 Factor each denominator completely.
Step 2 Find the *least common denominator* (LCD) of the fractions. [The LCD of the fractions is the least common multiple (LCM) of their denominators.]
Step 3 Express each fraction in terms of the LCD.
Step 4 Add or subtract the equivalent fractions with a common denominator.

$$\frac{7}{15} + \frac{3}{10} - \frac{2}{9} = \frac{7}{3 \cdot 5} + \frac{3}{2 \cdot 5} + \frac{-2}{3 \cdot 3} = \frac{7}{3 \cdot 5} \cdot \frac{2 \cdot 3}{2 \cdot 3} + \frac{3}{2 \cdot 5} \cdot \frac{3 \cdot 3}{3 \cdot 3} + \frac{-2}{3 \cdot 3} \cdot \frac{2 \cdot 5}{2 \cdot 5}$$

$$= \frac{7 \cdot 2 \cdot 3}{2 \cdot 3 \cdot 3 \cdot 5} + \frac{3 \cdot 3 \cdot 3}{2 \cdot 3 \cdot 3 \cdot 5} + \frac{-2 \cdot 2 \cdot 5}{2 \cdot 3 \cdot 3 \cdot 5} = \frac{42}{90} + \frac{27}{90} + \frac{-20}{90} = \frac{49}{90}$$

Notice that 90 is both the LCD of the fractions and the LCM of 15, 10, and 9. Rational expressions with different denominators are added or subtracted in a similar way.

Example 1 Simplify: $\dfrac{7x + 16}{15} + \dfrac{4x - 2}{25} - \dfrac{x + 3}{5}$.

$$\frac{7x + 16}{15} + \frac{4x - 2}{25} - \frac{x + 3}{5} = \frac{7x + 16}{3 \cdot 5} + \frac{4x - 2}{5 \cdot 5} + \frac{-(x + 3)}{5}$$ ◀ *The LCD is $3 \cdot 5 \cdot 5$.*

$$= \frac{7x + 16}{3 \cdot 5} \cdot \frac{5}{5} + \frac{4x - 2}{5 \cdot 5} \cdot \frac{3}{3} + \frac{-(x + 3)}{5} \cdot \frac{3 \cdot 5}{3 \cdot 5}$$

$$= \frac{5(7x + 16)}{3 \cdot 5 \cdot 5} + \frac{3(4x - 2)}{3 \cdot 5 \cdot 5} + \frac{-15(x + 3)}{3 \cdot 5 \cdot 5}$$ ◀ *Express each fraction in terms of the LCD.*

$$= \frac{5(7x + 16) + 3(4x - 2) - 15(x + 3)}{3 \cdot 5 \cdot 5}$$ ◀ $\dfrac{a}{c} + \dfrac{b}{c} = \dfrac{a + b}{c}$

$$= \frac{35x + 80 + 12x - 6 - 15x - 45}{3 \cdot 5 \cdot 5}$$

$$= \frac{32x + 29}{3 \cdot 5 \cdot 5}, \text{ or } \frac{32x + 29}{75}$$

Example 2 Add: $\dfrac{3}{ab^2} + \dfrac{2b}{ac} + \dfrac{5a}{c^3}$.

$$\frac{3}{ab^2} + \frac{2b}{ac} + \frac{5a}{c^3} = \frac{3}{a \cdot b^2} \cdot \frac{c^3}{c^3} + \frac{2b}{a \cdot c} \cdot \frac{b^2 c^2}{b^2 c^2} + \frac{5a}{c^3} \cdot \frac{ab^2}{ab^2}$$ ◀ *The LCD is $a \cdot b^2 \cdot c^3$.*

$$= \frac{3 \cdot c^3}{a \cdot b^2 \cdot c^3} + \frac{2b \cdot b^2 c^2}{a \cdot b^2 \cdot c^3} + \frac{5a \cdot ab^2}{a \cdot b^2 \cdot c^3} = \frac{3c^3 + 2b^3 c^2 + 5a^2 b^2}{ab^2 c^3}$$

Example 3 Subtract: $\dfrac{4x + 3}{5x + 10} - \dfrac{x - 1}{3x + 6}$.

$$\dfrac{4x + 3}{5(x + 2)} + \dfrac{-(x - 1)}{3(x + 2)} = \dfrac{3}{3} \cdot \dfrac{4x + 3}{5(x + 2)} + \dfrac{5}{5} \cdot \dfrac{-x + 1}{3(x + 2)}$$

$$= \dfrac{3 \cdot (4x + 3)}{3 \cdot 5 \cdot (x + 2)} + \dfrac{5 \cdot (-x + 1)}{3 \cdot 5 \cdot (x + 2)}$$

$$= \dfrac{12x + 9 - 5x + 5}{3 \cdot 5(x + 2)}$$

$$= \dfrac{7x + 14}{3 \cdot 5(x + 2)} \qquad \blacktriangleleft \textit{Factor } 7x + 14.$$

$$\dfrac{7(x + 2)}{3 \cdot 5(x + 2)}, \text{ or } \dfrac{7}{15} \qquad \blacktriangleleft \textit{Simplify by dividing out the common factor, } x + 2.$$

If one of the rational expressions to be added or subtracted is a polynomial with no denominator, rewrite the expression with 1 as the denominator.

Example 4 Add: $3c + 2 + \dfrac{5c - 3}{c - 1}$.

$$3c + 2 + \dfrac{5c - 3}{c - 1} = \dfrac{3c + 2}{1} + \dfrac{5c - 3}{c - 1} \qquad \blacktriangleleft \textit{Rewrite } 3c + 2 \textit{ as } \dfrac{3c + 2}{1}.$$

$$= \dfrac{c - 1}{c - 1} \cdot \dfrac{3c + 2}{1} + \dfrac{5c - 3}{c - 1} \qquad \blacktriangleleft \textit{The LCD is } (c - 1).$$

$$= \dfrac{(3c^2 - c - 2) + 5c - 3}{c - 1}$$

$$= \dfrac{3c^2 + 4c - 5}{c - 1}$$

The LCD for some rational expressions may contain a pair of binomials. This situation is shown in Example 5.

Example 5 Subtract: $\dfrac{3}{4n - 12} - \dfrac{5 - 2n}{n^2 + 2n - 15}$.

$$\dfrac{3}{4(n - 3)} + \dfrac{-(5 - 2n)}{(n - 3)(n + 5)} = \dfrac{n + 5}{n + 5} \cdot \dfrac{3}{4(n - 3)} + \dfrac{4}{4} \cdot \dfrac{-5 + 2n}{(n - 3)(n + 5)} \qquad \blacktriangleleft \begin{array}{l} \textit{The LCD is} \\ 4 \cdot (n - 3) \cdot (n + 5). \end{array}$$

$$= \dfrac{3n + 15 - 20 + 8n}{4(n - 3)(n + 5)}$$

$$= \dfrac{11n - 5}{4(n - 3)(n + 5)}$$

SUMS AND DIFFERENCES: DIFFERENT DENOMINATORS

Previously, you rewrote expressions of the form $-\dfrac{c}{d}$ as $\dfrac{-c}{d}$. You can also

rewrite $-\dfrac{c}{d}$ as $\dfrac{c}{-d}$. For example, $-\dfrac{8}{2} = \dfrac{8}{-2}$ since $-\dfrac{8}{2} = -4$ and $\dfrac{8}{-2} = -4$.

Definition:
Opposite of a Rational Expression

If $\dfrac{x}{y}$ is a rational expression, $y \neq 0$, then

$$-\dfrac{x}{y} = \dfrac{x}{-y} = \dfrac{-x}{y}.$$

In the expression, $\dfrac{3n - 29}{n - 7} - \dfrac{8}{7 - n}$, the denominators $n - 7$ and $7 - n$ are a *pair of opposites*. That is, $-(7 - n) = n - 7$. As shown in Example 6, to perform the subtraction, $n - 7$ can be used for the LCD.

Example 6 Subtract: $\dfrac{3n - 29}{n - 7} - \dfrac{8}{7 - n}$.

$$\dfrac{3n - 29}{n - 7} - \dfrac{8}{7 - n} = \dfrac{3n - 29}{n - 7} + \dfrac{8}{-(7 - n)} \quad \blacktriangleleft \quad -\dfrac{x}{y} = \dfrac{x}{-y}$$

$$= \dfrac{3n - 29}{n - 7} + \dfrac{8}{n - 7}$$

$$= \dfrac{3n - 21}{n - 7}$$

$$= \dfrac{3(n - 7)}{n - 7}, \text{ or } 3$$

You can use the property, $\dfrac{x}{y} = \dfrac{-x}{-y}$, to simplify $\dfrac{6}{a - 5} + \dfrac{2}{5 - a}$ where the denominators are a pair of opposites. The steps are shown below.

$$\dfrac{6}{a - 5} + \dfrac{2}{5 - a} = \dfrac{6}{a - 5} + \dfrac{-2}{-(5 - a)} = \dfrac{6}{a - 5} + \dfrac{-2}{a - 5} = \dfrac{4}{a - 5}$$

The next example applies the two properties: $-\dfrac{x}{y} = \dfrac{-x}{y}$ and $\dfrac{x}{y} = \dfrac{-x}{-y}$.

Example 7 Simplify: $\dfrac{5a}{a^2 - 9} - \dfrac{4}{a + 3} + \dfrac{2}{3 - a}$.

$$\dfrac{5a}{(a + 3)(a - 3)} - \dfrac{4}{a + 3} + \dfrac{-2}{-(3 - a)} = \dfrac{5a}{(a + 3)(a - 3)} + \dfrac{-4}{a + 3} + \dfrac{-2}{a - 3}$$

$$= \dfrac{5a}{(a + 3)(a - 3)} + \dfrac{-4}{a + 3} \cdot \dfrac{a - 3}{a - 3} + \dfrac{-2}{a - 3} \cdot \dfrac{a + 3}{a + 3}$$

$$= \dfrac{5a - 4a + 12 - 2a - 6}{(a + 3)(a - 3)}, \text{ or } \dfrac{-a + 6}{(a + 3)(a - 3)}$$

Oral Exercises

Determine whether each statement is true or false.

1. $\dfrac{48}{-3} = -\dfrac{48}{3}$ T

2. $-\dfrac{6}{9} = \dfrac{-6}{-9}$ F

3. $\dfrac{12}{-4} = \dfrac{-12}{4}$ T

4. $\dfrac{x-7}{-(x+3)} = \dfrac{-(x-7)}{x+3}$ T

5. $8 - x = x - 8$ F

6. $-(9 - x^2) = x^2 - 9$ T

7. $-\dfrac{2y}{-(3-y)} = \dfrac{2y}{y-3}$ F

8. $\dfrac{2n+3}{4-n^2} = \dfrac{-2n-3}{n^2-4}$ T

Written Exercises For complete solutions, see TE Answer Section.

2. $\dfrac{21n - 33}{50}$

3. $\dfrac{23a - 27}{15a}$

4. $\dfrac{4ab^2c^3 + 2b^4c + 3a}{a^2 b^3 c^2}$

5. $\dfrac{9c + 10cd - 42d}{12c^2 d^2}$

Add or subtract as indicated. Write each answer in simplest form.

(A)

1. $\dfrac{7x}{12} + \dfrac{3x}{8} - \dfrac{5x}{6}$ $\dfrac{x}{8}$

2. $\dfrac{3n+9}{10} - \dfrac{2n-1}{25} + \dfrac{n-8}{5}$

3. $\dfrac{a+2}{a} + \dfrac{a-6}{3a} + \dfrac{a-9}{5a}$

4. $\dfrac{4c}{ab} + \dfrac{2b}{a^2c} + \dfrac{3}{ab^3c^2}$

5. $\dfrac{3}{4cd^2} + \dfrac{5}{6cd} - \dfrac{7}{2c^2d}$

6. $\dfrac{3d}{8a^3b^2c} - \dfrac{5d}{12a^2b^4c^6}$

7. $\dfrac{2x}{3x+12} + \dfrac{5x}{6x+24}$ $\dfrac{3x}{2(x+4)}$

8. $\dfrac{3y-5}{2y-6} - \dfrac{4y-2}{5y-15}$ $\dfrac{7}{10}$

9. $\dfrac{5}{2n-4} + \dfrac{4}{3n+12}$ $\dfrac{23n+44}{6(n-2)(n+4)}$

10. $2a + 1 + \dfrac{5a}{a-3}$ $\dfrac{2a^2-3}{a-3}$

11. $3x - 4 - \dfrac{10}{x+4}$ $\dfrac{3x^2+8x-26}{x+4}$

12. $\dfrac{3y+7}{2y+5} - (5y-1)$ below

13. $\dfrac{2x}{x^2-4} + \dfrac{4}{x+2}$ $\dfrac{6x-8}{(x+2)(x-2)}$

14. $\dfrac{8}{n+5} - \dfrac{2n-15}{n^2-25}$

15. $\dfrac{3y-20}{y^2-y-20} + \dfrac{6}{y-5}$ below

16. $\dfrac{c-10}{c-4} - \dfrac{c+2}{4-c}$ 2

17. $\dfrac{2a+11}{a+2} - \dfrac{2a-3}{-a-2}$ 4

18. $\dfrac{3x}{x-5} + \dfrac{x}{5-x} - \dfrac{2x-3}{5-x}$ $\dfrac{4x-3}{x-5}$

19. $\dfrac{3n}{n^2-16} - \dfrac{12}{16-n^2}$ $\dfrac{3}{n-4}$

20. $\dfrac{2y}{y^2-36} + \dfrac{12}{36-y^2}$ $\dfrac{2}{y+6}$

21. $\dfrac{10a-3}{2a-4} + \dfrac{2a-5}{4-2a} - \dfrac{2a+5}{a-2}$ 2

22. $\dfrac{4}{x+3} + \dfrac{x+2}{x^2-9} + \dfrac{3}{x-3}$

23. $\dfrac{3c-4}{c^2-25} - \dfrac{2}{c+5} + \dfrac{6}{5-c}$

24. $\dfrac{6}{x+2} - \dfrac{8x+5}{x^2-4} - \dfrac{5}{2-x}$

(B)

25. $\dfrac{x-2}{x^2+4x} - \dfrac{x+10}{5x+20} + \dfrac{2}{3x}$ $\dfrac{-3x^2-5x+10}{15x(x+4)}$

26. $\dfrac{5a}{4a-20} - \dfrac{3a+8}{2a^2-10a} - \dfrac{7}{8a}$ $\dfrac{10a^2-19a+3}{8a(a-5)}$

27. $\dfrac{2y+3}{3y^2+6y-9} + \dfrac{3}{2y+6} - \dfrac{1}{3y-3}$

28. $\dfrac{7}{6x-30} - \dfrac{9x-6}{2x^2-18x+40} + \dfrac{11}{3x-12}$

29. $\dfrac{8m+2n}{m^2-2mn+n^2} + \dfrac{4m}{5am-5an}$

30. $\dfrac{2a-5b}{18a^2-8b^2} - \dfrac{3b}{6ac+4bc}$

31. $\dfrac{3x-5}{x^2-9} + \dfrac{7-x}{9-x^2} - \dfrac{1}{x+3}$ $\dfrac{3}{x+3}$

32. $\dfrac{5y+2}{2y^2-72} - \dfrac{3y-50}{72-2y^2}$ $\dfrac{4}{y+6}$

33. $\dfrac{3}{4y+12} + \dfrac{7}{6-2y} - \dfrac{5y}{9-y^2}$ $\dfrac{9y-51}{4(y+3)(y-3)}$

34. $\dfrac{3x}{4-x^2} - \dfrac{4}{5x+10} + \dfrac{5}{6-3x}$ $\dfrac{-82x-26}{15(x+2)(x-2)}$

(C)

35. $\dfrac{y^2+y+1}{y+3} + \dfrac{y^2-3y+9}{y-1}$ $\dfrac{2y^3+26}{(y+3)(y-1)}$

36. $\dfrac{x^2-2x+4}{x-4} - \dfrac{x^2+4x+16}{x+2}$ $\dfrac{72}{(x-4)(x+2)}$

37. $\dfrac{20-x^c}{x^{2c}+4x^c} + \dfrac{x^c+10}{x^c+4}$ $\dfrac{x^c+5}{x^c}$

38. $\dfrac{y^n}{y^n+6} - \dfrac{6-5y^n}{y^{2n}+6y^n}$ $\dfrac{y^n-1}{y^n}$

39. $\dfrac{1}{x^{3a}y^{5n}} + \dfrac{1}{x^{2a+4}y^{n+3}}$ $\dfrac{x^4y^3 + x^ay^{4n}}{x^{3a+4}y^{5n+3}}$

40. $\dfrac{5y^b}{6x^c} - \dfrac{2}{9x^cy^b} + \dfrac{4x^c}{3y^{2b}}$ $\dfrac{24x^{2c}+15y^{3b}-4y^b}{18x^cy^{2b}}$

12. $\dfrac{-10y^2-20y+12}{2y+5}$

15. $\dfrac{9y+4}{(y-5)(y+4)}$

4.6 Complex Rational Expressions

OBJECTIVE ▶ **To simplify a complex rational expression**

Each of the two expressions at the right contains at least one fraction or one rational expression in the numerator and the denominator. The first expression is a **complex fraction,** and the second is a **complex rational expression.**

$$\dfrac{\dfrac{3}{8} + \dfrac{7}{12}}{\dfrac{5}{6} - \dfrac{1}{4}} \qquad \dfrac{\dfrac{2}{x} + \dfrac{3}{xy}}{\dfrac{3}{x^2} + \dfrac{1}{5}}$$

You can simplify a complex fraction or a complex rational expression by multiplication. For example, the LCD of the four fractions in $\dfrac{\dfrac{3}{8} + \dfrac{7}{12}}{\dfrac{5}{6} - \dfrac{1}{4}}$ is 24.

To simplify, multiply the numerator and denominator by 24.

$$\dfrac{24\left(\dfrac{3}{8} + \dfrac{7}{12}\right)}{24\left(\dfrac{5}{6} - \dfrac{1}{4}\right)} = \dfrac{\overset{3}{24} \cdot \dfrac{3}{\underset{1}{8}} + \overset{2}{24} \cdot \dfrac{7}{\underset{1}{12}}}{\overset{4}{24} \cdot \dfrac{5}{\underset{1}{6}} + \overset{6}{24} \cdot \dfrac{-1}{\underset{1}{4}}} = \dfrac{9 + 14}{20 - 6} = \dfrac{23}{14}$$

Example 1 Simplify $\dfrac{\dfrac{2}{x} + \dfrac{3}{xy}}{\dfrac{3}{x^2} + \dfrac{1}{5}}$.

Simplify $\dfrac{5a - \dfrac{1}{2a}}{\dfrac{1}{3b} + 4b}$.

Multiply the numerator and denominator by $5x^2y$, the LCD of the fractions.

Multiply the numerator and denominator by $6ab$, the LCD of the fractions.

$$\dfrac{5x^2y\left(\dfrac{2}{x} + \dfrac{3}{xy}\right)}{5x^2y\left(\dfrac{3}{x^2} + \dfrac{1}{5}\right)}$$

$$\dfrac{6ab\left(5a + \dfrac{-1}{2a}\right)}{6ab\left(\dfrac{1}{3b} + 4b\right)}$$

$$\dfrac{5x^2y \cdot \dfrac{2}{x} + 5 \cdot x^2y \cdot \dfrac{3}{xy}}{5x^2y \cdot \dfrac{3}{x^2} + 5 \cdot x^2y \cdot \dfrac{1}{5}}$$

$$\dfrac{6ab \cdot 5a + 6ab \cdot \dfrac{-1}{2a}}{6ab \cdot \dfrac{1}{3b} + 6ab \cdot 4b}$$

$$\dfrac{10xy + 15x}{15y + x^2y}$$

$$\dfrac{30a^2b - 3b}{2a + 24ab^2}$$

You should examine every answer to see if it can be simplified further by factoring the numerator or denominator (or both) and then dividing out any common factors.

Example 2 Simplify $\dfrac{1 - \dfrac{6}{x} + \dfrac{5}{x^2}}{1 - \dfrac{3}{x} - \dfrac{10}{x^2}}$.

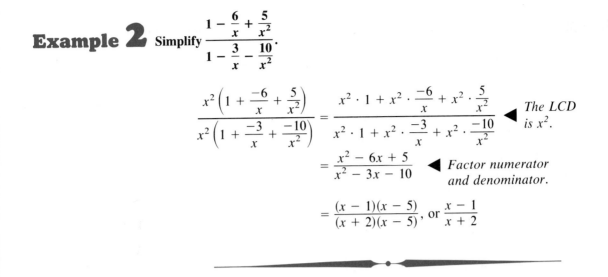

$$\dfrac{x^2\left(1 + \dfrac{-6}{x} + \dfrac{5}{x^2}\right)}{x^2\left(1 + \dfrac{-3}{x} + \dfrac{-10}{x^2}\right)} = \dfrac{x^2 \cdot 1 + x^2 \cdot \dfrac{-6}{x} + x^2 \cdot \dfrac{5}{x^2}}{x^2 \cdot 1 + x^2 \cdot \dfrac{-3}{x} + x^2 \cdot \dfrac{-10}{x^2}}$$ ◄ *The LCD is x^2.*

$$= \dfrac{x^2 - 6x + 5}{x^2 - 3x - 10}$$ ◄ *Factor numerator and denominator.*

$$= \dfrac{(x - 1)(x - 5)}{(x + 2)(x - 5)}, \text{ or } \dfrac{x - 1}{x + 2}$$

For some complex rational expressions, you will need to factor the denominators of the individual fractions to find their LCD. This is shown in Example 3.

Example 3 Simplify $\dfrac{\dfrac{2x}{x^2 - 25} + \dfrac{5}{x - 5}}{\dfrac{4}{x + 5} + \dfrac{3x}{x^2 - 25}}$.

$$\dfrac{\dfrac{2x}{(x + 5)(x - 5)} + \dfrac{5}{x - 5}}{\dfrac{4}{x + 5} + \dfrac{3x}{(x + 5)(x - 5)}}$$

$$\dfrac{(x + 5)(x - 5) \cdot \dfrac{2x}{(x + 5)(x - 5)} + (x + 5)(x - 5) \cdot \dfrac{5}{x - 5}}{(x + 5)(x - 5) \cdot \dfrac{4}{x + 5} + (x + 5)(x - 5) \cdot \dfrac{3x}{(x + 5)(x - 5)}}$$ ◄ *The LCD is $(x + 5)(x - 5)$.*

$$\dfrac{2x + 5(x + 5)}{4(x - 5) + 3x}$$

$$\dfrac{2x + 5x + 25}{4x - 20 + 3x}$$

$$\dfrac{7x + 25}{7x - 20}$$

Written Exercises _____

Simplify each complex expression.

9. $\dfrac{42m^2n - 18mn^2 + 12}{27n + 8m - 30mn}$

(A) 1. $\dfrac{\dfrac{3}{5} - \dfrac{1}{4}}{\dfrac{5}{2} - \dfrac{7}{10}}$ $\dfrac{7}{36}$

2. $\dfrac{5 + \dfrac{1}{4}}{2 + \dfrac{2}{3}}$ $\dfrac{63}{32}$

3. $\dfrac{3\dfrac{1}{2} + 4\dfrac{2}{3}}{5\dfrac{1}{6} + 2\dfrac{3}{4}}$ $\dfrac{98}{95}$

4. $\dfrac{\dfrac{4}{xy} - \dfrac{6}{y^2}}{\dfrac{8}{x^2} + \dfrac{3}{xy}}$ $\dfrac{4xy - 6x^2}{8y^2 + 3xy}$

5. $\dfrac{\dfrac{4}{3a} + \dfrac{3}{2b}}{\dfrac{1}{6a} - \dfrac{3}{4b}}$ $\dfrac{16b + 18a}{2b - 9a}$

6. $\dfrac{\dfrac{5}{3x^2} + \dfrac{7}{2x}}{\dfrac{1}{6x} + \dfrac{10}{x^2}}$ $\dfrac{10 + 21x}{x + 60}$

7. $\dfrac{\dfrac{3}{5x} + 4}{2 - \dfrac{3}{10y}}$ $\dfrac{6y + 40xy}{20xy - 3x}$

8. $\dfrac{2a - \dfrac{1}{4c^2}}{\dfrac{5}{6c} - 3a}$ $\dfrac{24ac^2 - 3}{10c - 36ac^2}$

9. $\dfrac{7m - 3n + \dfrac{2}{mn}}{\dfrac{9}{2m} + \dfrac{4}{3n} - 5}$

10. $\dfrac{1 + \dfrac{8}{x} + \dfrac{12}{x^2}}{1 + \dfrac{6}{x} + \dfrac{8}{x^2}}$ $\dfrac{x + 6}{x + 4}$

11. $\dfrac{1 - \dfrac{2}{a} - \dfrac{8}{a^2}}{1 - \dfrac{7}{a} + \dfrac{12}{a^2}}$ $\dfrac{a + 2}{a - 3}$

12. $\dfrac{2 + \dfrac{5}{c} + \dfrac{3}{c^2}}{\dfrac{2}{c^2} + \dfrac{5}{c} + 3}$ $\dfrac{2c + 3}{3c + 2}$

13. $\dfrac{\dfrac{2y}{y^2 - 4} + \dfrac{3}{y - 2}}{\dfrac{5}{y + 2} + \dfrac{4}{y - 2}}$ $\dfrac{5y + 6}{9y - 2}$

14. $\dfrac{\dfrac{3a}{a^2 - 3a - 10} + \dfrac{2}{a + 2}}{\dfrac{2a}{a^2 - 3a - 10} + \dfrac{3}{a - 5}}$

14. $\dfrac{5a - 10}{5a + 6}$

15. $\dfrac{\dfrac{5n}{2n^2 - n - 1} - \dfrac{4}{n - 1}}{\dfrac{6}{2n + 1} + \dfrac{7n}{2n^2 - n - 1}}$ $\dfrac{-3n - 4}{13n - 6}$

(B) 16. $\dfrac{\dfrac{4}{x - 2} + \dfrac{3}{x}}{\dfrac{5}{x} + \dfrac{3}{x - 2}}$ $\dfrac{7x - 6}{8x - 10}$

17. $\dfrac{\dfrac{6}{a + 3} - \dfrac{4}{a - 4}}{\dfrac{2}{a - 4} + \dfrac{5}{a + 3}}$ $\dfrac{2a - 36}{7a - 14}$

18. $\dfrac{1 - \dfrac{9}{x^2}}{\dfrac{1}{x} - \dfrac{3}{x^2}}$ $x + 3$

19. $\dfrac{\dfrac{10a}{a^2 + 6a + 8}}{\dfrac{7}{a + 4} + \dfrac{3}{a + 2}}$ $\dfrac{5a}{5a + 13}$

20. $\dfrac{\dfrac{6}{c + 5} - \dfrac{4}{c - 5}}{\dfrac{8c}{c^2 - 25}}$ $\dfrac{c - 10}{c}$

21. $\dfrac{\dfrac{x - 7}{x^2 - 5x + 6}}{\dfrac{5}{x - 2} - \dfrac{4}{x - 3}}$ 1

22. $\dfrac{\dfrac{x}{y} + 3 - \dfrac{4y}{x}}{\dfrac{x}{y} - \dfrac{y}{x}}$ $\dfrac{x + 4y}{x + y}$

23. $\dfrac{\dfrac{a}{b} - 1 - \dfrac{6b}{a}}{\dfrac{a}{b} + 4 + \dfrac{4b}{a}}$ $\dfrac{a - 3b}{a + 2b}$

24. $\dfrac{\dfrac{3}{y} + \dfrac{3}{x} - \dfrac{6}{xy}}{\dfrac{4}{x} + \dfrac{4}{y} - \dfrac{8}{xy}}$ $\dfrac{3}{4}$

(C) 25. $\dfrac{1 + \dfrac{8}{x^c} + \dfrac{15}{x^{2c}}}{1 + \dfrac{9}{x^c} + \dfrac{18}{x^{2c}}}$ $\dfrac{x^c + 5}{x^c + 6}$

26. $\dfrac{\dfrac{5}{x^{a+1}} + \dfrac{2}{y^{3b}}}{\dfrac{7}{x^{4a}} - \dfrac{3}{y^{b+2}}}$

27. $\dfrac{\dfrac{2x^n}{x^{2n} - 25} + \dfrac{4}{x^n + 5}}{\dfrac{8}{x^n + 5} - \dfrac{6x^n}{x^{2n} - 25}}$ $\dfrac{3x^n - 10}{x^n - 20}$

28. $5 + \dfrac{1}{4 + \dfrac{1}{3 + \dfrac{1}{2 + \dfrac{1}{1 + x}}}}$ $\dfrac{157x + 225}{30x + 43}$

29. $2 - \dfrac{1}{2 - \dfrac{1}{2 - \dfrac{1}{2 - x}}}$ $\dfrac{6 - 5x}{5 - 4x}$

26. $\dfrac{5x^{3a}y^{3b+2} + 2x^{4a+1}y^2}{7xy^{3b+2} - 3x^{4a+1}y^{2b}}$

Applications

In designing a new type of tire, an engineer needed to convert a speed of 90 *miles per hour* to *yards per second*. To do this, he used the following four identities:

$$1 \text{ h} = 60 \text{ min} \qquad 1 \text{ min} = 60 \text{ s} \qquad 1 \text{ mi} = 5280 \text{ ft} \qquad 1 \text{ yd} = 3 \text{ ft}$$

Four **conversion factors** were set up:

$$\frac{1 \text{ h}}{60 \text{ min}} \qquad \frac{1 \text{ min}}{60 \text{ s}} \qquad \frac{5280 \text{ ft}}{1 \text{ mi}} \qquad \frac{1 \text{ yd}}{3 \text{ ft}}$$

These conversion factors were used to convert 90 mi/h to yards per second as shown below.

$$\frac{90 \text{ mi}}{1 \text{ h}} \times \frac{1 \text{ h}}{60 \text{ min}} \times \frac{1 \text{ min}}{60 \text{ s}} \times \frac{5280 \text{ ft}}{1 \text{ mi}} \times \frac{1 \text{ yd}}{3 \text{ ft}}$$

$$\frac{90 \times 5280 \times 1 \text{ yd}}{60 \times 60 \text{ s} \times 3} = \frac{44 \text{ yd}}{1 \text{ s}}, \text{ or } 44 \text{ yd/s}$$

This procedure for converting from one measurement unit to another measurement unit is called **dimensional analysis**. The process is similar to the one you have used for multiplying rational expressions.

You are cautioned to inspect each conversion factor to determine whether it or its reciprocal is needed. For example,

to convert 180 ft to inches, use $\dfrac{12 \text{ in.}}{1 \text{ ft}}$

to convert 180 in. to feet, use $\dfrac{1 \text{ ft}}{12 \text{ in.}}$

$$\frac{180 \text{ ft}}{1} \times \frac{12 \text{ in.}}{1 \text{ ft}} = 2{,}160 \text{ in.} \qquad \frac{180 \text{ in.}}{1} \times \frac{1 \text{ ft}}{12 \text{ in.}} = 15 \text{ ft.}$$

Convert each measure as indicated. Use only one conversion factor in each exercise.

1. 24 pt to quarts 12 qt
2. 12 gal to quarts 48 qt
3. 15 yd to feet 45 ft
4. 144 in. to yards 4 yd
5. 42 oz to pounds $2\frac{5}{8}$ lb
6. 6 T to pounds 12,000 lb

7. 20 g to milligrams **20,000 mg**
8. 400 g to kilograms **0.4 kg**
9. 750 mL to liters **0.75 L**
10. 5 m to centimeters **500 cm**
11. 24 ft² to square inches **3,456 in.²**
12. 36 ft² to square yards **4 yd²**
13. 135 ft³ to cubic yards **5 yd³**
14. 2.5 m² to square centimeters **25,000 cm²**

Use dimensional analysis to convert each measure to the indicated unit.
15. 30 m/h to feet per second **44 ft/s**
16. 15 T/h to pounds per minute **500 lb/min**
17. 10 ounces per pint to pounds per gallon
5 lb/gal
18. 8 ounces per square inch to pounds per square foot **72 lb/ft²**

Example

For 11 h a test car was driven at an average speed of 45 mi/h. The car averaged 22 mi/gal of gasohol. Determine the dollar cost of the fuel used if gasohol costs 129¢/gal.

$$\frac{11 \text{ h}}{1} \times \frac{45 \text{ mi}}{1 \text{ h}} \times \frac{1 \text{ gal}}{22 \text{ mi}} \times \frac{129 \text{ ¢}}{1 \text{ gal}} \times \frac{\$1}{100 \text{ ¢}}$$

$$= \frac{11 \times 45 \times 129 \times \$1}{22 \times 100}, \text{ or } \$29.03$$

Use dimensional analysis to solve each problem.

19. How many platforms can be built with 14 kegs of rivets if each keg contains 660 rivets, each platform contains 21 braces, and each brace requires 44 rivets?
10 platforms

20. A construction crew uses 135 ft³ of sand per day during a 5-day work week. If sand weighs 1.215 tons per cubic yard (T/yd³), how many pounds of sand does the crew use in one work week? **60,750 lb**

21. Each football player must have both ankles taped before each practice session and before each game. One roll of tape is needed for every 3 ankles that are taped. One carton of tape costs $12.75 and contains 6 rolls of tape. What is the cost for all of the tape used by a 45-player football team during a season that consists of 60 practice sessions and 10 games? **$4,462.50**

22. A city recreation department enrolled 450 youths in its summer softball program and assigned 15 players to each team. Each team was furnished with 20 bats for the season. They were purchased at $37.80 per carton with a dozen bats in each carton. What was the cost of the bats if the department received a 5% discount for buying in quantity? **$1,795.50**

APPLICATIONS

4.7 Problem Solving: Mixed Types (Optional)

OBJECTIVE ▶ To solve word problems of various types

Written Exercises

Solve each problem.

1. Box-type A holds 18 fewer vitamin capsules than box-type B, and box-type C contains three times as many capsules as box-type A. If 10 type A boxes, 8 type B boxes, and 4 type C boxes hold 27 dozen of the capsules, find the number of capsules that each box-type contains.
   box-type A: 6; box-type B: 24; box-type C: 18

2. One leg of a right triangle is 5 m shorter than the other leg and 10 m shorter than the hypotenuse. Find the area of the triangle if the perimeter is 60 m.
   150 m²

3. Maria is 2 years older than Nedra and Todd is 3 times as old as Maria. In 7 years, Todd's age will be 5 years more than the sum of the girls' ages. Find each age.
   Maria: 10; Nedra: 8; Todd: 30

4. Donald borrowed some money three summers ago at $10\frac{1}{4}\%$ in simple interest. At the end of 3 years, Donald owed $5,230. How much money did he borrow? Use the formula $A = p + prt$. **$4,000**

5. Tonya mixed some Brand A dog food worth 45¢/lb and some Brand B dog food worth 63¢/lb to make a 20-lb package that was worth $10.44. Find the amount of each brand that was used.
   Brand A: 12 lb; Brand B: 8 lb

6. One bus left a terminal at 7:00 A.M. and headed north at 80 km/h. A second bus left the same terminal at 8:30 A.M. and traveled south at 90 km/h. At what time were the buses 460 km apart?
   10:30 A.M.

7. Find three consecutive multiples of 4 such that the product of the second and the third numbers is 80 more than 20 times the first number. **12, 16, 20 or −4, 0, 4**

8. How many milliliters of water must be added to 240 mL of an $87\frac{1}{2}\%$ iodine solution to dilute it to a $62\frac{1}{2}\%$ solution?
   96 mL

9. A rectangular garden is 9 m longer than it is wide. A second rectangular garden is planned so that it will be 6 m wider and twice as long as the first garden. Find the area of the first garden if the sum of the areas of both gardens will be 528 m². **112 m²**

10. How many liters of a 24% alcohol solution must be added to 16 L of a 72% alcohol solution to obtain a 40% alcohol solution?
    32 L

11. Martin started a long-distance run at 9:00 A.M. and averaged 12 km/h. Carl started on the same course at 9:20 A.M. and averaged 15 km/h. At what time did Carl pass Martin on the course? **10:40 A.M.**

Chapter Four Review

Vocabulary

complex rational expression [4.6]
least common denominator (LCD) [4.5]
opposite of rational expression [4.5]
rational expression [4.2]
rational number [4.1]
reciprocal [4.3]
repeating decimal [4.1]
terminating decimal [4.1]

Evaluate each rational expression for $x = 3$ and $y = -2$, if possible. [4.2]

1. $\dfrac{x - y}{4x + 6y}$
not possible

2. $\dfrac{y^2 + 5y + 6}{x^2 + 5x + 6}$ $\;0$

For what values of the variable is each rational expression undefined? [4.1]

3. $\dfrac{a - 4}{5a + 10}$ $\;-2$

4. $\dfrac{4c}{c^2 - 5c + 6}$ $\;2, 3$

Simplify each rational expression. [4.2]

5. $\dfrac{9y + 18}{12y + 48}$ $\;\dfrac{3(y + 2)}{4(y + 4)}$

6. $\dfrac{x^3 + 27}{2x^2 - 4x - 30}$

7. $\dfrac{3n - 6}{8 - 4n}$ $\;-\dfrac{3}{4}$

8. $\dfrac{2a^2 - 50}{30 + 9a - 3a^2}$

6. $\dfrac{x^2 - 3x + 9}{2(x - 5)}$

8. $\dfrac{2(a + 5)}{-3(a + 2)}$

9. $\dfrac{4a - \dfrac{2}{3a^2}}{\dfrac{5}{6b} + 3b^2}$ $\;\dfrac{24a^3b - 4b}{5a^2 + 18a^2b^3}$ [4.6]

10. $\dfrac{\dfrac{4n}{n^2 - 5n + 6} - \dfrac{2}{n - 3}}{\dfrac{6}{n - 2} + \dfrac{2n}{n^2 - 5n + 6}}$ $\;\dfrac{n + 2}{4n - 9}$

★ 11. $\dfrac{1 + \dfrac{9}{x^a} + \dfrac{20}{x^{2a}}}{1 + \dfrac{7}{x^a} + \dfrac{10}{x^{2a}}}$ $\;\dfrac{x^a + 4}{x^a + 2}$

Multiply. Write each answer in simplest form. [4.3]

12. $\dfrac{10a^2}{3b} \cdot \dfrac{b^4c^2}{-15a^3}$ $\;-\dfrac{2b^3c^2}{9a}$

13. $\dfrac{x^2 - 1}{3x + 12} \cdot \dfrac{x^2 - 16}{x^2 - 5x + 4}$ $\;\dfrac{x + 1}{3}$

14. $\dfrac{3c^2 + c - 2}{6 - 9c} \cdot \dfrac{9}{8 + 8c}$ $\;-\dfrac{3}{8}$

★ 15. $\dfrac{x^{2a}}{y^{2a}} \cdot \dfrac{y^{5a}}{z^{8a}} \cdot \dfrac{z^{3a}}{x^a}$ $\;\dfrac{x^a y^{3a}}{z^{5a}}$

Divide. Write each answer in simplest form. [4.3]

16. $\dfrac{-9x^7}{2y^5} \div \dfrac{12x^3}{y^3z}$ $\;\dfrac{-3x^4z}{8y^2}$

17. $\dfrac{5c - 10}{3x + 3y} \div \dfrac{2c^2 - 8}{x^2 + 2xy + y^2}$ $\;\dfrac{5(x + y)}{6(c + 2)}$

18. $\dfrac{n^2 - 2n - 8}{8n^3} \div \dfrac{n^2 + 6n + 8}{6n^2}$ $\;\dfrac{3(n - 4)}{4n(n + 4)}$

Add or subtract as indicated. Write each answer in simplest form.

19. $\dfrac{11c}{5xy^2} - \dfrac{3c}{5xy^2} + \dfrac{2c}{5xy^2}$ [4.4] $\;\dfrac{2c}{xy^2}$

20. $\dfrac{7a + 5}{3a + 6} - \dfrac{2a - 5}{3a + 6}$

21. $\dfrac{2x + 5}{x^2 - 9} + \dfrac{3x + 10}{x^2 - 9}$ $\;\dfrac{5}{x - 3}$ $\;20.\ 1\dfrac{2}{3}$

22. $\dfrac{2x + 7}{x^2 - x - 12} + \dfrac{2x + 5}{x^2 - x - 12}$ $\;\dfrac{4}{x - 4}$

23. $\dfrac{3n + 2}{2n^2 + 3n - 5} - \dfrac{9 - 4n}{2n^2 + 3n - 5}$ $\;\dfrac{7}{2n + 5}$

24. $\dfrac{5a}{6bc} + \dfrac{2b}{9a^2c} - \dfrac{4c}{3ab^3}$ [4.5] $\;\dfrac{15a^3b^2 + 4b^4 - 24ac^2}{18a^2b^3c}$

25. $\dfrac{2y + 1}{5y - 10} - \dfrac{5 - y}{3y - 6}$ $\;\dfrac{11}{15}$

26. $3x + 2 + \dfrac{4x}{x + 3}$ $\;\dfrac{3x^2 + 15x + 6}{x + 3}$

27. $\dfrac{2y + 17}{3y - 12} - \dfrac{11 - 9y}{12 - 3y}$ $\;-2\dfrac{1}{3}$

28. $\dfrac{7}{x + 5} - \dfrac{x + 3}{25 - x^2} + \dfrac{1}{5 - x}$ $\;\dfrac{7x - 37}{(x + 5)(x - 5)}$

29. $\dfrac{3n - 1}{2n^2 + 4n - 30} + \dfrac{2}{3n - 9} - \dfrac{5}{6n + 30}$ $\;\dfrac{4(n + 4}{3(n + 5)(n -}$

★ 30. $\dfrac{a^2 - a + 1}{a - 3} - \dfrac{a^2 + 3a + 9}{a + 1}$ $\;\dfrac{28}{(a - 3)(a + 1)}$

Show that each of the following is a rational number. [4.1]

31. $-3\dfrac{4}{5}$ $\;\dfrac{-19}{5}$

32. $0.58\overline{8}$ $\;\dfrac{53}{90}$

33. 18.63 $\;\dfrac{1863}{100}$

34. $2.73\overline{434}$ $\;\dfrac{2707}{990}$

Chapter Four Test

1. Evaluate $\dfrac{4x + 3y}{x - 3y}$ for $x = 5$ and $y = -1$.
   $2\dfrac{1}{8}$

2. For what values of the variable is the rational expression $\dfrac{n + 3}{n^2 - 6n + 8}$ undefined? **2, 4**

Simplify each rational expression.

3. $\dfrac{4y - 12}{21 - 7y}$ $-\dfrac{4}{7}$

4. $\dfrac{3x^2 - 75}{2x^2 - 9x - 5}$
   $\dfrac{3(x + 5)}{2x + 1}$

Multiply. Write each answer in simplest form.

5. $\dfrac{4ac}{b^2} \cdot \dfrac{3b^5}{16a^3c}$ $\dfrac{3b^3}{4a^2}$

6. $\dfrac{6n^2 - 24}{3n^2 - 5n - 2} \cdot \dfrac{9n + 3}{8n + 16}$ $2\dfrac{1}{4}$

Divide. Write each answer in simplest form.

7. $\dfrac{n^2 - 4}{2x - 3y} \div \dfrac{5n + 10}{6x - 9y}$ $\dfrac{3(n - 2)}{5}$

8. $\dfrac{3a^2 - 5a - 12}{x^2 - 9y^2} \div \dfrac{4a^2 - 36}{5x + 15y}$ $\dfrac{5(3a + 4)}{4(a + 3)(x - 3y)}$

Add or subtract as indicated. Write each answer in simplest form.

9. $\dfrac{5c}{12} + \dfrac{14c}{12} - \dfrac{c}{12}$ $\dfrac{3c}{2}$

10. $\dfrac{4a + 21}{3a + 15} + \dfrac{2a - 4}{3a + 15} - \dfrac{a - 8}{3a + 15}$ $1\dfrac{2}{3}$

11. $\dfrac{4y + 3}{y^2 - 3y - 10} - \dfrac{y - 3}{y^2 - 3y - 10}$ $\dfrac{3}{y - 5}$

12. $\dfrac{3a}{4b^2c} - \dfrac{5b}{6ac^3} + \dfrac{c}{2ab}$ $\dfrac{9a^2c^2 - 10b^3 + 6bc^4}{12ab^2c^3}$

13. $2x - 3 + \dfrac{6x}{x + 2}$ $\dfrac{2x^2 + 7x - 6}{x + 2}$

Add or subtract as indicated. Write each answer in simplest form.

14. $\dfrac{3}{4y - 12} - \dfrac{3}{15 - 5y}$ $\dfrac{27}{20(y - 3)}$

15. $\dfrac{2c + 1}{c^2 - 5c + 6} + \dfrac{3}{2c - 6} - \dfrac{1}{c - 2}$ $\dfrac{5c + 2}{2(c - 2)(c - 3)}$

16. $\dfrac{6}{x + 4} - \dfrac{3x}{x^2 - 16} + \dfrac{5}{4 - x}$ $\dfrac{-2x - 44}{(x + 4)(x - 4)}$

Simplify each complex rational expression.

17. $\dfrac{\dfrac{1}{5a^2} - \dfrac{2}{b}}{\dfrac{7}{10a} + \dfrac{3}{2b^2}}$ $\dfrac{2b^2 - 20a^2b}{7ab^2 + 15a^2}$

18. $\dfrac{\dfrac{2x}{x^2 - 9} + \dfrac{4}{x + 3}}{\dfrac{2}{x - 3} + \dfrac{4x}{x^2 - 9}}$ $\dfrac{x - 2}{x + 1}$

Show that each of the following is a rational number.

19. $-8\dfrac{2}{3}$ $\dfrac{-26}{3}$

20. $2.47\overline{7}$ $\dfrac{223}{90}$

21. $2.6\overline{969}$ $\dfrac{89}{33}$

Simplify.

★22. $\dfrac{6x^{a+n}}{x^{2n} + 6x^n} \cdot \dfrac{x^{3n} - 36x^n}{x^{a+n} - 6x^a}$ $6x^n$

★23. $\dfrac{c^2 - 2c + 4}{c - 5} + \dfrac{c^2 + 5c + 25}{c + 2}$ $\dfrac{2c^3 - 117}{(c - 5)(c + 2)}$

★24. $\dfrac{\dfrac{8y^n}{y^{2n} - 16} - \dfrac{6}{y^n - 4}}{\dfrac{10}{y^n + 4} - \dfrac{4y^n}{y^{2n} - 16}}$ $\dfrac{y^n - 12}{3y^n - 20}$

Computer Activities

Banking Your Interest

The banking industry uses computers continuously to compute interest on loans and savings accounts. It is important to the bank and to the customers that financial records are up to date and accurate to the smallest fraction.

You may express total amount of money saved by using the formula $A = P + PR$ or $A = P + I$, where P is the principal and I is the interest. To compute compound interest, you evaluate this formula $Y \cdot Q$ times. Y represents the number of years and Q represents the compounding frequency.

PROGRAM

```
10 PRINT "PRINCIPAL $5000, COMPOUNDED QUARTERLY AT 5 1/2%
   AND"
20 PRINT "INVESTED FOR 6 YEARS"
30 LET P = 5000
40 FOR Y = 1 TO 6
50 FOR Q = 1 TO 4
60 LET I = (.055 * P)/4
70 REM ADD INTEREST TO PRINCIPAL
80 LET P = P + I
90 NEXT Q
100 NEXT Y
110 PRINT "AFTER 6 YEARS THE SAVED AMOUNT IS"; P
120 END
```

Exercises

1. Enter in and run the above program. What is the total amount of money saved after 6 yr? How many times does the program go through the Q FOR loop?
   $6939.152; 4 × 6, or 24

2. Alter the program to get a program that computes the total amount saved for *any* principal, interest rate, and number of years, but still with quarterly compounding.
   For Ex. 2, see TE Answer Section.

3. Write a program to compare the total amount saved if a principal of $3,000 is invested at 8%, 8¼%, 8½%, 8¾%, and 9%, respectively. Use quarterly compounding for a period of 3 years. **For Ex. 3, see TE Answer Section.**

College Prep Test

DIRECTIONS: Choose the *one* best answer to each question or problem.

1. Let $\frac{a}{b}$ represent a rational number where a and b are positive integers. Which statement is always true? **E**

   (A) $3a > 2b$ (B) $b - a < a$

   (C) $\frac{a + b}{a - b} > \frac{a - b}{a + b}$ (D) $\frac{6a}{6b} = 1$

   (E) None of these

2. Let $\frac{a}{b}$ and $\frac{c}{d}$ represent any two *unequal* rational numbers, $b \neq 0$, $d \neq 0$. Which statement is always true? **C**

   (A) $\frac{a}{b} < \frac{c}{d}$ (B) $a \cdot d = b \cdot c$

   (C) If $\frac{a}{b} < \frac{c}{d}$, then $\frac{a}{b} < \frac{a + c}{b + d} < \frac{c}{d}$.

   (D) If $\frac{a}{b} < \frac{c}{d}$, then $a \cdot b < c \cdot d$.

   (E) None of these

3. Let $\frac{a}{b}$ and $\frac{c}{d}$ represent any two nonzero rational expressions. Which statement is true? **A**

   (A) $\frac{a}{b} \div \frac{c}{d} = \frac{d}{c} \div \frac{b}{a}$ (B) $\frac{a}{b} + \frac{c}{d} = \frac{a + c}{b + d}$

   (C) $\frac{a}{b} \cdot \frac{c}{d} = \frac{a \cdot d}{b \cdot c}$ (D) $\frac{a}{b} \div \frac{c}{d} = \frac{b}{a} \cdot \frac{c}{d}$

   (E) None of these

4. There are $x + 6$ males and $y - 3$ females in a choir. Find the ratio of the number of females to the total number of people in the choir. **B**

   (A) $\frac{y - x - 9}{x + y + 3}$ (B) $\frac{y - 3}{x + y + 3}$

   (C) $\frac{y - 3}{x + 6}$ (D) $\frac{x + 6}{y - 3}$

   (E) $\frac{x + y + 3}{y - 3}$

5. If $\frac{x + y}{a - b} = \frac{2}{3}$, find the value of $\frac{9x + 9y}{10a - 10b}$. **B**

   (A) $\frac{2}{3}$ (B) $\frac{3}{5}$ (C) $\frac{9}{10}$ (D) $\frac{20}{27}$

   (E) None of these

6. If $\frac{ax^2 + 2ax + a}{x^2 + 2x + 1} = 6$, find the value of a. **D**

   (A) $x^2 + 2x + 1$ (B) $x + 1$ (C) 0

   (D) 6 (E) $\frac{1}{6}$

7. If $a = \frac{1}{3}$ and $b = \frac{1}{5}$, find the value of $\frac{a + b}{a - b}$. **E**

   (A) $\frac{1}{4}$ (B) $\frac{2}{15}$ (C) $\frac{8}{15}$ (D) $\frac{16}{15}$ (E) 4

8. Find the arithmetic mean (average) of $\frac{x}{2}, \frac{x}{3}$, and $\frac{x}{6}$. **C**

   (A) x (B) $\frac{x}{2}$ (C) $\frac{x}{3}$ (D) $\frac{x}{6}$ (E) $\frac{x}{18}$

Cumulative Review (Chapters 1–4)

DIRECTIONS: Choose the *one* best answer to each question or problem. (Exercises 1–11)

1. Solve $\frac{5}{9}x - 17 = 25 - \frac{2}{9}x$. **C**

(A) $10\frac{2}{7}$ (B) 24

(C) 54 (D) 126

2. Solve $|7 - 4x| = 21$. **D**

(A) 7 (B) −7

(C) $-7, 3\frac{1}{2}$ (D) $7, -3\frac{1}{2}$

3. Find two numbers such that the first number is 9 more than 4 times the second number, and 4 more than the second number is twice the first number. **B**

(A) $7, -\frac{1}{2}$ (B) $1, -2$

(C) $-1, 2$ (D) $-7, \frac{1}{2}$

4. Solve $5^{3x-2} = 625$. **A**

(A) 2 (B) 4 (C) 125 (D) 209

5. Simplify $-3xy^3(-2x^2yz^3)^4$. **D**

(A) $6x^9y^7z^{12}$ (B) $16x^8y^4z^{12}$
(C) $-48x^7y^7z^7$ (D) $-48x^9y^7z^{12}$

6. Some powdered milk worth \$3.50/kg and some cocoa worth \$4.25/kg form a 10-kg mixture that is worth \$39.20. How much cocoa is in the mixture? **C**

(A) 2.5 kg (B) 4.4 kg
(C) 5.6 kg (D) 5.8 kg

7. Factor $-4c^3 + 20c^2 + 24c$ completely. **B**

(A) $-4c(c - 3)(c - 2)$
(B) $-4c(c - 6)(c + 1)$
(C) $-c(c - 6)(4c + 4)$
(D) $4(6 - c)(c + 1)$

8. Solve $7x^2 - 8 = 8 - 2x^2$. **D**

(A) 0 (B) $\frac{4}{3}$

(C) $-\frac{3}{4}, \frac{3}{4}$ (D) $-\frac{4}{3}, \frac{4}{3}$

9. Choose the graph of the solutions of $x^3 - 9x \le 0$. **B**

(A)
(B)
(C)
(D)

10. If $x = 7$ and $y = -2$, find the value of $\frac{5x + 4y}{x^2 - y^2}$. **C**

(A) Does not exist

(B) $\frac{43}{53}$ (C) $\frac{3}{5}$ (D) 0

11. Simplify: $\frac{5a - 10}{6a + 12} \cdot \frac{2a^2 - 8}{a^2 - 2a - 8}$. **C**

(A) $\frac{5a - 20}{12a + 24}$ (B) $\frac{12a + 24}{5a - 20}$

(C) $\frac{5(a - 2)^2}{3(a + 2)(a - 4)}$ (D) $\frac{5}{12}$

Solve each equation.

12. $23 + \frac{6}{7}x = \frac{1}{7}x + 33$ **14**

13. $\frac{2}{3}(18a + 6) - (5a - 12) = 14$ $-\frac{2}{7}$

14. $4.2(3n - 0.8) = 4.9n - 12.6$ **−1.2**

15. $|3y - 8| = 7$ $\frac{1}{3}$, **5**

16. $2^{4x+3} = 32$ $\frac{1}{2}$

17. $2x^2 = 20 - 3x$ $2\frac{1}{2}$, **−4**

Find the solution set of each inequality. Graph the solutions.

18. $4(7 - x) < 2x - 14$ $\{x|x > 7\}$

19. $|y + 2| \leq 5$ $\{y|-7 \leq y \leq 3\}$

20. $x^2 - 4x - 12 > 0$ $\{x|x < -2 \text{ or } x > 6\}$

Simplify each expression.

21. $-8a^3b^4c^{-2} \cdot 4a^{-5}bc^6$ $\dfrac{-32b^5c^4}{a^2}$

22. $-10x^2y(5x^4y)^3$ $-1{,}250x^{14}y^4$

23. $\dfrac{9m^{-8}n^7(5n + 25)}{10m^{-2}n^{-2}(3n^2 - 75)}$ $\dfrac{3n^9}{2m^6(n - 5)}$

Multiply. $21m^4 - 20m^2n - 25n^2$

24. $(7m^2 + 5n)(3m^2 - 5n)$

25. $6x(5x - 3)(4x + 5)$ $120x^3 + 78x^2 - 90x$

26. $(9y^2 - 8)(9y^2 + 8)$ $81y^4 - 64$

27. $(5c - 3d)^2$ $25c^2 - 30cd + 9d^2$

28. $\dfrac{4a - 28}{a^2 - 36} \cdot \dfrac{a^2 + 2a - 24}{6a - 42}$ $\dfrac{2(a - 4)}{3(a - 6)}$

Factor each polynomial.

29. $12x^2 + 8xy - 15y^2$ $(6x - 5y)(2x + 3y)$

30. $3x^4 - 14x^2 - 5$ $(3x^2 + 1)(x^2 - 5)$

31. $36a^2 - 49b^2$ $(6a - 7b)(6a + 7b)$

32. $8x^3 + 125$ $(2x + 5)(4x^2 - 10x + 25)$

33. $x^2 + 8xy + 16y^2 - 9$ $(x + 4y + 3)(x + 4y - 3)$

Factor each polynomial completely.

34. $6y^2 - 45y - 24$ $3(2y + 1)(y - 8)$

35. $50c^3 + 40c^2 + 8c$ $2c(5c + 2)^2$

36. $10x^4 - 160y^4$ $10(x^2 + 4y^2)(x + 2y)(x - 2y)$

37. $4a^4 - 29a^2 + 25$ **below**

38. $y^4 - 8y$ $y(y - 2)(y^2 + 2y + 4)$

39. $x^3 + 2x^2 - 6x - 12$ $(x + 2)(x^2 - 6)$

37. $(2a - 5)(2a + 5)(a + 1)(a - 1)$

Solve each problem.

40. The larger of two numbers is 4 less than 7 times the smaller number. Thirty more than the larger number is the same as 6 more than 9 times the smaller number. Find the numbers. **10, 66**

41. Side b of a triangle is 4 times as long as side a, and side c is 6 cm shorter than side b. Find the length of each side if the perimeter is 66 cm.

   a: **8 cm;** b: **32 cm;** c: **26 cm**

42. Find p in dollars if $A = \$4{,}832$, $r = 8\frac{1}{2}\%$, and $t = 6$ years. Use the formula $A = p + prt$. **$3,200**

43. How many liters of water must be added to 20 L of a 40% sugar solution to obtain a 25% solution? **12 L**

44. At 8:00 A.M., a car left city A and headed for city B at 75 km/h. At 10:00 A.M., a car left city B at 90 km/h and headed for city A. At what time did the cars meet if the two cities are 645 km apart? **1:00 P.M.**

45. Find three consecutive even integers such that the product of the second and the third integers is 80. **6, 8, 10 or −12, −10, −8**

46. The height of a triangle is 10 cm less than twice the length of its base. Find the length of the base and the height if the area of the triangle is 14 cm².

   base: 7 cm; height: 4 cm

5 USING RATIONAL EXPRESSIONS

Zero

For many centuries civilized people did not use numerals such as 230 or 403. The concept of place value was unheard of, and there was no symbol for **zero.** In China, line marks like = and ≡ were used for the numbers 2 and 3, but = ≡ was not used to show the number 23.

People have used a counting board, or abacus, like the one shown below for thousands of years. If one person had invented a symbol, such as a dot (·), to stand for an empty column on the abacus, then 230 could have been written as = ≡ ·, and ≡ · ≡ would have represented the number 403.

The world is indebted to the unknown Hindu who, in an early century A.D., first conceived of the idea of place value and invented a symbol to represent *zero* ("the empty place"). The Hindu word for the symbol for zero is **sunya,** which means **empty.**

5.1 Fractional Equations

OBJECTIVE ▶ **To solve a fractional equation**

The equation $\frac{3}{4} + \frac{1}{6} = \frac{11}{12}$ is a true equation. If you multiply each side by 12, the LCD of all fractions in the equation, the resulting equation is also true, but it contains no fractions.

As shown in Examples 1 and 2 below, this multiplication procedure can be used to simplify the work of solving equations that contain rational number coefficients.

$$\frac{3}{4} + \frac{1}{6} = \frac{11}{12} : \textit{True}$$

$$12\left(\frac{3}{4} + \frac{1}{6}\right) = 12 \cdot \frac{11}{12}$$

$$12 \cdot \frac{3}{4} + 12 \cdot \frac{1}{6} = 12 \cdot \frac{11}{12}$$

$$9 + 2 = 11 : \textit{True}$$

Example 1 Solve $\dfrac{x - 2}{6} + \dfrac{3x}{8} - \dfrac{3x + 8}{24} = 1$.

Multiply each side by 24, the LCD. ▶
$$24\left(\frac{x-2}{6} + \frac{3x}{8} + \frac{-(3x + 8)}{24}\right) = 24 \cdot 1$$

$$24 \cdot \frac{x-2}{6} + 24 \cdot \frac{3x}{8} + 24 \cdot \frac{-3x - 8}{24} = 24 \cdot 1$$

$$4(x - 2) + 3 \cdot 3x + 1(-3x - 8) = 24$$

$$4x - 8 + 9x - 3x - 8 = 24$$

$$10x = 40$$

$$x = 4$$

Thus, the solution is 4.

Example 2 Solve $\dfrac{1}{3}y^2 + \dfrac{5}{12}y = \dfrac{1}{2}$.

Multiply each side by 12, the LCD. ▶
$$12 \cdot \frac{1}{3}y^2 + 12 \cdot \frac{5}{12}y = 12 \cdot \frac{1}{2}$$

$$4y^2 + 5y = 6 \quad \blacktriangleleft \textit{Quadratic equation}$$

$$4y^2 + 5y - 6 = 0 \quad \blacktriangleleft \textit{Standard form}$$

$$(4y - 3)(y + 2) = 0$$

$$4y - 3 = 0 \quad \text{or} \quad y + 2 = 0$$

$$y = \frac{3}{4} \qquad\qquad y = -2$$

Thus, $\dfrac{3}{4}$ and -2 are the solutions.

An equation such as $\dfrac{2n - 9}{n - 7} + \dfrac{n}{2} = \dfrac{5}{n - 7}$, in which a variable appears in a denominator, is called a **fractional equation.** You can use multiplication to help solve a fractional equation. However, multiplying by the LCD may produce an equation that is *not* equivalent to the original equation, as is shown in Example 3.

Example 3 Solve $\dfrac{2n - 9}{n - 7} + \dfrac{n}{2} = \dfrac{5}{n - 7}$.

Multiply each side by $2(n - 7)$, the LCD. ▶

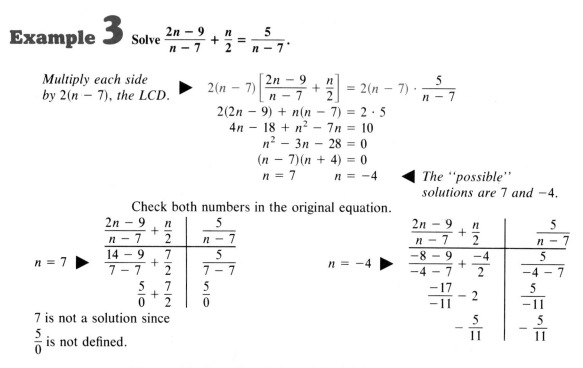

$$2(n - 7)\left[\frac{2n - 9}{n - 7} + \frac{n}{2}\right] = 2(n - 7) \cdot \frac{5}{n - 7}$$
$$2(2n - 9) + n(n - 7) = 2 \cdot 5$$
$$4n - 18 + n^2 - 7n = 10$$
$$n^2 - 3n - 28 = 0$$
$$(n - 7)(n + 4) = 0$$
$$n = 7 \qquad n = -4 \qquad \blacktriangleleft \text{ } \textit{The ''possible''}$$
$$\textit{solutions are 7 and } -4.$$

Check both numbers in the original equation.

$n = 7$ ▶

$\dfrac{2n - 9}{n - 7} + \dfrac{n}{2}$	$\dfrac{5}{n - 7}$
$\dfrac{14 - 9}{7 - 7} + \dfrac{7}{2}$	$\dfrac{5}{7 - 7}$
$\dfrac{5}{0} + \dfrac{7}{2}$	$\dfrac{5}{0}$

7 is not a solution since $\dfrac{5}{0}$ is not defined.

$n = -4$ ▶

$\dfrac{2n - 9}{n - 7} + \dfrac{n}{2}$	$\dfrac{5}{n - 7}$
$\dfrac{-8 - 9}{-4 - 7} + \dfrac{-4}{2}$	$\dfrac{5}{-4 - 7}$
$\dfrac{-17}{-11} - 2$	$\dfrac{5}{-11}$
$-\dfrac{5}{11}$	$-\dfrac{5}{11}$

Thus, -4 is the only solution of the original equation.

In Example 3, 7 is a solution of the *derived equation,* $n^2 - 3n - 28 = 0$, but it is not a solution of the original equation. In this case, 7 is called an **extraneous solution.**

Definition:
Extraneous
Solution

An *extraneous solution* of an equation is a solution of a derived equation that is not a solution of the original equation.

Even though multiplying both sides of a fractional equation by a polynomial may produce extraneous solutions, all of the solutions of the original equation are retained. For this reason, all possible solutions must be checked in the original equation. You should notice that the extraneous solutions of a fractional equation are the numbers that make the value of at least one denominator equal to 0. In Example 3, 7 is an extraneous solution and 7 is also the number for which $n - 7$ has the value of 0.

Example 4 Solve $\dfrac{5}{2y + 6} - \dfrac{2y - 4}{y^2 - y - 12} = \dfrac{3}{y - 4}$.

$$\dfrac{5}{2(y + 3)} + \dfrac{-(2y - 4)}{(y + 3)(y - 4)} = \dfrac{3}{y - 4} \quad \blacktriangleleft \begin{array}{l}\textit{The LCD is}\\ 2(y + 3)(y - 4).\end{array}$$

$$2(y + 3)(y - 4) \cdot \dfrac{5}{2(y + 3)} + 2(y + 3)(y - 4) \cdot \dfrac{-2y + 4}{(y + 3)(y - 4)} = 2(y + 3)(y - 4) \cdot \dfrac{3}{y - 4}$$

$$5(y - 4) + 2(-2y + 4) = 3 \cdot 2(y + 3)$$
$$5y - 20 - 4y + 8 = 6(y + 3)$$
$$y - 12 = 6y + 18$$
$$-5y = 30$$
$$y = -6$$

Check in the original equation. If $y = -6$, none of the denominators has the value of 0.

Thus, -6 is the solution.

A fractional equation like $\dfrac{3}{x + 1} = \dfrac{2}{x - 4}$ is called a **proportion.** A precise definition of *proportion* follows.

Definition:
Proportion

> A *proportion* is an equation of the form $\dfrac{a}{b} = \dfrac{c}{d}$, where a, b, c, and d are numbers, $b \neq 0$, $d \neq 0$.

For the proportion $\dfrac{a}{b} = \dfrac{c}{d}$, a and d are called the **extremes** and b and c are called the **means.** In the true proportion $\dfrac{2}{3} = \dfrac{10}{15}$, notice that *the product of the extremes equals the product of the means*: $2 \cdot 15 = 3 \cdot 10$. This suggests the Proportion Property below.

Proportion
Property

> For all numbers a, b, c, and d, $b \neq 0$, $d \neq 0$, if $\dfrac{a}{b} = \dfrac{c}{d}$, then $a \cdot d = b \cdot c$.

Example 5 Solve $\dfrac{3}{x + 1} = \dfrac{2}{x - 4}$.

$$\dfrac{3}{x + 1} = \dfrac{2}{x - 4} \quad \blacktriangleleft \dfrac{a}{b} = \dfrac{c}{d}$$
$$3(x - 4) = (x + 1)2 \quad \blacktriangleleft a \cdot d = b \cdot c$$
$$3x - 12 = 2x + 2$$
$$x = 14$$

Thus, the solution is 14.

Check:

$\dfrac{3}{x + 1}$	$\dfrac{2}{x - 4}$
$\dfrac{3}{14 + 1}$	$\dfrac{2}{14 - 4}$
$\dfrac{1}{5}$	$\dfrac{1}{5}$

Reading in Algebra

Supply the missing words and expressions in the paragraph below.

$\dfrac{2x}{15} = \dfrac{6}{5x}$ is a special type of fractional equation. It is called a __proportion__.

The extremes are $2x$ and __5x__, and the __means__ are 15 and __6__. A

derived equation is $10x^2 = $ __90__, or $x^2 = $ __9__. So, the solutions are

__3__ and __−3__. Neither solution is an __extraneous__ solution, since the

value of $5x$ is not equal to __0__ if $x = 3$ or if $x = -3$.

Written Exercises

Solve each equation.

(A)

1. $\dfrac{x}{10} + \dfrac{x}{6} + \dfrac{x}{15} = 1$ 3

2. $\dfrac{2n-3}{2} = \dfrac{3}{4} + \dfrac{n-4}{8}$ 2

3. $\dfrac{a-1}{3} + \dfrac{a+2}{6} = 2$ 4

4. $\dfrac{2}{5} + \dfrac{2}{y} = 1$ $\dfrac{10}{3}$

5. $\dfrac{6}{x} + \dfrac{9}{2x} = 3$ $\dfrac{7}{2}$

6. $\dfrac{2}{3n^2} = \dfrac{1}{4n^2} + \dfrac{5}{6n}$ $\dfrac{1}{2}$

7. $\dfrac{1}{2}x^2 + x = 12$ −6, 4

8. $\dfrac{1}{9}y^2 + \dfrac{4}{3}y + 3 = 0$ −9, −3

9. $\dfrac{1}{10}x^2 - \dfrac{1}{2}x = 5$ −5, 10

10. $\dfrac{3n-7}{n-5} + \dfrac{n}{2} = \dfrac{8}{n-5}$ −6

11. $\dfrac{a-4}{a+3} = \dfrac{3a+2}{a+3} + \dfrac{a}{4}$ −8

12. $\dfrac{4c-3}{c-4} - \dfrac{2c}{3} = \dfrac{2c+5}{c-4}$ 3

13. $\dfrac{2}{y-3} + \dfrac{2}{y} = 1$ 1, 6

14. $\dfrac{3}{x} + \dfrac{2}{x+2} = 2$ $-\dfrac{3}{2}$, 2

15. $\dfrac{10}{n+4} - \dfrac{1}{n} = 1$ 1, 4

16. $\dfrac{5}{x+4} = \dfrac{3}{x-2}$ 11

17. $\dfrac{4a+3}{3} = \dfrac{2a+5}{4}$ $\dfrac{3}{10}$

18. $\dfrac{3}{2y+1} = \dfrac{2}{3y-2}$ $\dfrac{8}{5}$

19. $\dfrac{a+1}{8} = \dfrac{2}{a+1}$ −5, 3

20. $\dfrac{x-3}{2} = \dfrac{1}{x-4}$ 2, 5

21. $\dfrac{2z-3}{2z+3} = \dfrac{z-2}{2z-3}$ $\dfrac{5}{2}$, 3

22. $\dfrac{5}{x-3} - \dfrac{6}{x^2-9} = \dfrac{4}{x+3}$ $\dfrac{-21}{?}$

23. $\dfrac{5}{n+2} = \dfrac{3}{n-2} - \dfrac{2n}{n^2-4}$ 4

24. $\dfrac{7y-9}{y^2-25} - \dfrac{3}{y-5} = \dfrac{2}{y+5}$ 7

(B)

25. $\dfrac{3}{4}y^2 + y = 1$ −2, $\dfrac{2}{3}$

26. $\dfrac{1}{7}x^2 = 1 - \dfrac{9}{28}x$ −4, $\dfrac{7}{4}$

27. $\dfrac{7}{4} = \dfrac{13}{6}y - \dfrac{2}{3}y^2$ $\dfrac{3}{2}$, $\dfrac{7}{4}$

28. $\dfrac{3}{x+1} + \dfrac{x-2}{3} = \dfrac{13}{3x+3}$ −2, 3

29. $\dfrac{3}{10}a^2 = \dfrac{11}{20}a + \dfrac{1}{2}$ $-\dfrac{2}{3}$, $\dfrac{5}{2}$

30. $\dfrac{n}{n-3} + \dfrac{n-2}{6} = \dfrac{5n-1}{4n-12}$

31. $\dfrac{4y+9}{y+1} = \dfrac{2y+7}{y-1}$ −2, 4

32. $\dfrac{2x+2}{3x+1} = \dfrac{x-2}{x-1}$ 0, 5

33. $\dfrac{a^2+5a-2}{a+3} = \dfrac{4a-1}{3}$ 1, 3

34. $\dfrac{3}{n-2} + \dfrac{6}{n^2-5n+6} = \dfrac{4}{n-3}$ 5

35. $\dfrac{1}{x-2} = \dfrac{2x+1}{x^2+2x-8} + \dfrac{2}{x+4}$ $\dfrac{7}{3}$

$\dfrac{3}{2}$, 5

36. $\dfrac{x}{2x-6} - \dfrac{3}{x^2-6x+9} = \dfrac{x-2}{3x-9}$ −6, 5

37. $\dfrac{1}{2a} - \dfrac{9}{a^2+6a} = \dfrac{2-a}{2a+12}$ −3, 4

(C)

38. $\dfrac{4}{x^2+2x-15} + \dfrac{5}{x^2-x-6} = \dfrac{3}{x^2+7x+10}$ −7

39. $\dfrac{6}{y^2-9} + \dfrac{4}{6+y-y^2} + \dfrac{2}{y^2+5y+6} = 0$ $\dfrac{3}{2}$

A Challenge To You

Solve $\dfrac{10}{2x^3-x^2-8x+4} + \dfrac{24}{2x^3-x^2-2x+1} = \dfrac{40}{x^4-5x^2+4}$. $-\dfrac{11}{17}$, 3

5.2 Problem Solving: Work Problems

OBJECTIVE ▶ **To solve a work problem that leads to a fractional equation**

A certain house can be painted in 6 days. The chart below indicates the part of the house that can be painted in a given number of days.

Number of days	1	2	5	x	6
Part of job done	$\frac{1}{6}$	$\frac{2}{6}$, or $\frac{1}{3}$	$\frac{5}{6}$	$\frac{x}{6}$	$\frac{6}{6}$, or 1

In general, if a job can be done in 6 days, then $\frac{x}{6}$ represents the part of the job completed in x days and $\frac{6}{6}$, or 1, represents the *total job*.

Example 1 Palmer's crew can do the cement work for a new building in 6 days. Hoffman's crew would need 8 days to complete the same job. How many days will the job take if the two crews work together?

Let x = the number of days it will take if the crews work together.
Represent the data in a table.

Represent the data.

Job takes x days. ▶

	Palmer	Hoffman
Part done in 1 day	$\frac{1}{6}$	$\frac{1}{8}$
Part done in x days	$\frac{x}{6}$	$\frac{x}{8}$

After x days ▶ (Palmer's part) + (Hoffman's part) = Total job

Write an equation.

$$\frac{x}{6} + \frac{x}{8} = 1$$

The LCD is 24. ▶ $24 \cdot \frac{x}{6} + 24 \cdot \frac{x}{8} = 24 \cdot 1$

Solve the equation.

$$4x + 3x = 24$$
$$7x = 24$$
$$x = \frac{24}{7}, \text{ or } 3\frac{3}{7}$$

Check in the problem.

To check, add the parts done in $\frac{24}{7}$ days.

$$\frac{x}{6} + \frac{x}{8} = \frac{1}{6} \cdot \frac{24}{7} + \frac{1}{8} \cdot \frac{24}{7} = \frac{4}{7} + \frac{3}{7} = \frac{7}{7}, \text{ or } 1$$

Answer the question.

Thus, the job will take $3\frac{3}{7}$ days if the two crews work together.

If a job requires x hours to complete, then $\frac{1}{x}$ represents the part of the job that is done in 1 hour and $\frac{n}{x}$ represents the part of the job done in n hours.

Example 2

Al, Betty, and Carl can harvest a strawberry crop in 12 hours (h) if they work together. If each person worked alone, Al could complete the job in 30 h, and Carl would take twice as long as Betty. How long would it take Carl to do the job alone?

Let x = Betty's time to do the job alone.
$2x$ = Carl's time to do the job alone

	Al	Betty	Carl
Part done in 1 h	$\dfrac{1}{30}$	$\dfrac{1}{x}$	$\dfrac{1}{2x}$
Part done in 12 h	$\dfrac{12}{30}$	$\dfrac{12}{x}$	$\dfrac{12}{2x}$

Job takes 12 h if they work together. ▶

After 12 h ▶

$$\begin{array}{ccccccc} \text{Al's} & + & \text{Betty's} & + & \text{Carl's} & = & \text{Total} \\ \text{part} & & \text{part} & & \text{part} & & \text{job} \end{array}$$

$$\frac{12}{30} + \frac{12}{x} + \frac{12}{2x} = 1$$

The LCD is 30x. ▶

$$30x \cdot \frac{12}{30} + 30x \cdot \frac{12}{x} + 30x \cdot \frac{12}{2x} = 30x \cdot 1$$
$$12x + 360 + 180 = 30x$$
$$540 = 18x$$
$$30 = x \qquad 2x = 60$$

To check, add the parts done in 12 h.
$$\frac{12}{30} + \frac{12}{x} + \frac{12}{2x} = \frac{12}{30} + \frac{12}{30} + \frac{12}{60} = \frac{2}{5} + \frac{2}{5} + \frac{1}{5} = \frac{5}{5}, \text{ or } 1$$

Thus, it would take Carl 60 h to do the job alone.

Example 3

Machine A can do a job in 12 h and machine B can do the job in 8 h. If B starts 2 h after A has started, find the total time needed for the two machines to do the complete job.

Let x = the time that A and B work together.
(Part done by A in 2 hours) + (Part done by A and B together in x hours) = Total job
$$\frac{2}{12} + \left(\frac{x}{12} + \frac{x}{8} \right) = 1$$
$$4 + 2x + 3x = 24$$
$$x = 4 \qquad 2\text{ h} + 4\text{ h} = 6\text{ h}$$

Thus, the two machines need 6 h to do the complete job.

Oral Exercises

A farmer takes 15 days to harvest a crop. Represent the part harvested in the given period of time.

1. 1 day $\frac{1}{15}$ 2. 4 days $\frac{4}{15}$ 3. x days $\frac{x}{15}$ 4. 15 days 1

A carpenter can build a cabinet in x hours. Represent the part built in the given period of time.

5. 1 hour $\frac{1}{x}$ 6. 3 hours $\frac{3}{x}$ 7. y hours $\frac{y}{x}$ 8. x hours 1

Written Exercises

Solve each problem.

(A) 1. Mr. Adams can plant a wheat crop in 10 days and his daughter can do it in 15 days. How many days will it take if they work together? **6 days**

2. Mrs. Brown can paint 3 average-sized rooms in 8 hr. Her son would need 12 h to do it. If they work together, how long will it take to paint 6 average-sized rooms? $9\frac{3}{5}$ h

3. Paul can put carpet on a floor in 10 h. If Irene helps him, the job is done in 6 h. How long would it take Irene if she worked alone? **15 h**

4. Diane can clean the attic in 6 h. If Sam helps her, the attic can be cleaned in 4 h. How long would it take Sam working alone? **12 h**

5. Machine A can do a job in 15 h. Machines B and C can do the same job in 12 h and 20 h, respectively. How many hours will the job take if the three machines operate at the same time? **5 h**

6. Work crews 1, 2, 3, and 4 can load a freight train in 16 h, 10 h, 12 h, and 15 h, respectively. When will the freight train be loaded if the four crews start at 8:00 A.M. and work together? **11:12 A.M.**

7. Kim can complete a job in 6 weeks (wk) and the same job would take Kevin 10 wk. How long would it take Derek working alone if, working together, all three can complete the job in 2 wk? $4\frac{2}{7}$ **wk**

8. Linda can keypunch 1,000 cards in 150 minutes (min). The same job would take John 3 h. How long would it take Martha to keypunch 1,000 cards if, working together, all three can keypunch 2,000 cards in 2 h? $3\frac{3}{4}$ h

(B) 9. Work crew A takes 15 h to do a job and crew B can do it in 10 h. If B starts 3 h after A has begun, what is the total time needed for the two crews to do the job?
$7\frac{4}{5}$ h

10. Ned can mow a lawn in 75 min and Pedro can do it in 50 min. If Pedro watches Ned mow for 20 min and then helps to finish the job, find the total time for the job. **42 min**

11. Gene, Marie, and Merv can complete a job in 20 h if they work together. Gene can do the job alone in twice the time it would take Marie and half the time that Merv would need. Find the time each person would take to do the job if each worked alone. **Gene: 70 h, Marie: 35 h, Merv: 140 h**

12. Work crews A, B, and C can pave a road in 10 days if they work together. If they work alone, crew A would take 60 days to do the job and crew B would take 3 times as long as crew C to do the job. How long would it take crews B and C if each worked alone? **crew B: 48 days, crew C: 16 days**

5·3 Problem Solving: Round Trips

OBJECTIVE ▶ **To solve a motion problem that leads to a fractional equation**

An automobile that is driven a distance of 240 km at an average rate of 80 km/h will take $\dfrac{240 \text{ km}}{80 \text{ km/h}}$, or 3 h, for the trip. You can use the formula below to solve motion problems involving *time*.

$$\text{time}(t) = \frac{\text{distance}(d)}{\text{rate}(r)}$$

Example 1

The Pai family drove from their home into the country at a speed of 80 km/h. They returned over the same road at 70 km/h. If the round trip took 6 hours, how far did the Pais drive into the country?

Let x = the distance of the trip to the country.
Represent the data with a diagram.

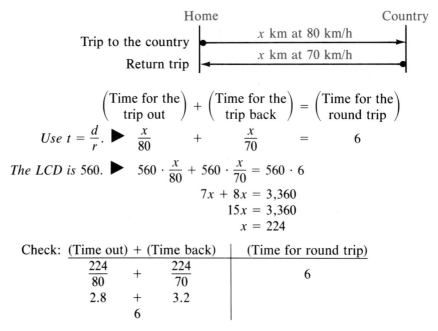

$$\left(\begin{matrix}\text{Time for the} \\ \text{trip out}\end{matrix}\right) + \left(\begin{matrix}\text{Time for the} \\ \text{trip back}\end{matrix}\right) = \left(\begin{matrix}\text{Time for the} \\ \text{round trip}\end{matrix}\right)$$

Use $t = \dfrac{d}{r}$. ▶ $\quad \dfrac{x}{80} \quad + \quad \dfrac{x}{70} \quad = \quad 6$

The LCD is 560. ▶ $\quad 560 \cdot \dfrac{x}{80} + 560 \cdot \dfrac{x}{70} = 560 \cdot 6$

$$7x + 8x = 3{,}360$$
$$15x = 3{,}360$$
$$x = 224$$

Check:

(Time out) + (Time back)	(Time for round trip)
$\dfrac{224}{80} \quad + \quad \dfrac{224}{70}$	6
$2.8 \quad + \quad 3.2$	
6	

Thus, the Pais drove 224 km into the country.

⬤

A certain falcon can fly at a speed of 40 km/h in still air. If a wind is blowing at 12 km/h, the falcon can fly at 40 + 12, or 52 km/h, with the wind and at 40 − 12, or 28 km/h, against the wind. A wind in the direction of an object's motion is called a *tailwind* and a wind in the direction against the object's motion is called a *headwind*.

If a boat can travel at 20 km/h in still water and if a river has a current of 4 km/h, then the boat can travel *downstream,* or with the current, at 24 km/h. The boat can travel *upstream,* or against the current, at 20 − 4, or 16 km/h.

Example 2

A boat can travel 20 km/h in still water. It can travel 47 km downstream in the same time that it can travel 33 km upstream. What is the rate of the current?

Let c = the rate of the current. Represent the data in a table.

	distance (d)	rate (r)	time (t)	
Downstream	47	$20 + c$	$\dfrac{47}{20 + c}$	◀ $t = \dfrac{d}{r}$
Upstream	33	$20 - c$	$\dfrac{33}{20 - c}$	◀ $t = \dfrac{d}{r}$

Time downstream = Time upstream

$$\frac{47}{20 + c} = \frac{33}{20 - c}$$
$$47(20 - c) = 33(20 + c)$$
$$940 - 47c = 660 + 33c$$
$$280 = 80c$$
$$3.5 = c$$

Check:

Time downstream	Time upstream
$\dfrac{47}{20 + c}$	$\dfrac{33}{20 - c}$
$\dfrac{47}{20 + 3.5}$	$\dfrac{33}{20 - 3.5}$
$\dfrac{47}{23.5}$	$\dfrac{33}{16.5}$
2	2

Thus, the rate of the current is 3.5 km/h.

Reading in Algebra

A car traveled from P to Q at 50 mi/h for 3 h and then returned from Q to P at 30 mi/h for 5 h. Choose the one correct ending for each statement.

1. The distance of the round
   trip was
   A   80 mi.
   B 150 mi. **C**
   C 300 mi.

2. The time for the round
   trip was
   A 8 h.
   B 5 h. **A**
   C 3 h.

3. The average speed for the
   round trip was
   A   40 mi/h.
   B 37.5 mi/h. **B**
   C   80 mi/h.

4. For the trip from P to Q and for the trip from Q to P, the two
   A times were equal.   B distances were equal.   C rates were equal. **B**
5. At the end of the first 2 h, the car was
   A 50 mi from Q.   B 50 mi from P.   C 60 mi from P. **A**
6. The car was halfway between P and Q at the end of the first
   A $\frac{1}{2}$ h.   B $3\frac{1}{2}$ h.   C $5\frac{1}{2}$ h. **C**

Written Exercises _____

Solve each problem.

(A)
1. Alice drove to the ocean at 90 km/h. She returned home on the same road at 60 km/h. If the round trip took 2 h, how far does Alice live from the ocean? **72 km**

2. You left home at 9:00 A.M. and drove to the seaquarium at 75 km/h. After 2 h of sightseeing, you returned home at 50 km/h. If you arrived home at 2:00 P.M., how far do you live from the seaquarium? **90 km**

3. A scout in a canoe can travel 12 km/h in still water. If the scout traveled 30 km downstream in the same time that it took to travel 15 km upstream, what was the rate of the current? **4 km/h**

4. A plane flew 780 km with a tailwind in the same time it would have flown 720 km in the opposite direction. Find the rate of the tailwind if the plane flies at 500 km/h in still air. **20 km/h**

5. You jog along a straight trail at 15 km/h. Then you rest for 1 hour and jog back home on that trail at 18 km/h. If you were gone from home for 3 h, how far away from home did you go? **$16\frac{4}{11}$ km**

6. A certain salmon can swim 3 km/h in still water. In a river, the salmon traveled 8 km upstream in the same time it took to swim 24 km downstream. What was the rate of the current? **1.5 km/h**

(B)
7. A camper rowed 24 km downstream and then returned the same distance upstream in twice the time of the downstream trip. If the camper can row 6 km/h in still water, find the rate of the current. **2 km/h**

8. Harvey hiked along a road at 5 km/h. Sara met him with a truck and they returned on the same road at 40 km/h. If the round trip took Harvey 4 h and 30 min, find the distance that he hiked. **20 km**

9. One plane flew 390 km with the help of a tailwind in twice the time that another plane flew 180 km against the headwind. If each plane can fly 500 km/h in still air, find the rate of the tailwind. **20 km/h**

10. With the help of a tailwind, a plane flew 378 km in $\frac{3}{4}$ of the time that a second plane flew 456 km in the opposite direction. Find the rate of the tailwind if each plane can fly 600 km/h in still air. **30 km/h**

11. A marathon race course is in the shape of a square and each side of the square is called a leg of the race. Find the length of the course if a runner ran each leg at 12 km/h, 15 km/h, 10 km/h, and 16 km/h, respectively, in a total time of 3.75 h. **48 km**

12. A gymnast climbed a vertical rope at 3.2 m/s and then descended at 4.8 m/s. Find the height of the rope if the gymnast was timed at 6.25 s for the round trip. **12 m**

Cumulative Review _____

Solve each equation.

1. $8(3 - 5x) - (6x + 15) - 4(-7x - 8) = 95$
    -3

2. $10^{3x-1} = 1,000$
    $\frac{4}{3}$

3. $|5x + 3| = 18$
    $-4\frac{1}{5}, 3$

5.4 Literal Equations and Formulas

OBJECTIVE ▶ **To solve a formula or a literal equation for one of its variables**

A formula for the perimeter of a rectangle is
$p = 2(l + w)$. Since a formula is an equation,
$p = 2(l + w)$ can be solved for the length l in
terms of the perimeter p and the width w using
equation properties, as shown at the right.

$$p = 2(l + w)$$
$$p = 2l + 2w$$
$$p - 2w = 2l$$
$$\frac{p - 2w}{2} = l$$

A formula like $p = 2(l + w)$ and an equation like $ax + b = cx + d$ are called
literal equations, since they contain more than one letter, or variable. To solve
a literal equation for one specific variable, you should rewrite the equation so
that all of the terms containing that variable are alone on one side of the
equation.

Example 1 Solve $ax + b = cx - d$ for x.

$$ax + b = cx - d$$
$$ax - cx = -d - b \qquad \blacktriangleleft \text{ All } x\text{-terms are alone on the left side.}$$
$$(a - c)x = -d - b \qquad \blacktriangleleft \text{ Factor out } x.$$
$$x = \frac{-d - b}{a - c} \qquad \blacktriangleleft \text{ Divide by } a - c.$$

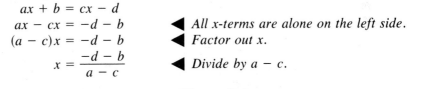

There are several expressions that are equivalent to $\dfrac{-d - b}{a - c}$ in Example 1.

If $x = \dfrac{-d - b}{a - c}$, then $x = -\dfrac{d + b}{a - c} = -\dfrac{-d - b}{c - a} = \dfrac{d + b}{c - a}$.

To solve the equation $3(5 - 2y) = 7$, you would simplify the equation by
applying the Distributive Property. As shown in Example 2, a similar
procedure is followed in solving the literal equation $a(b - cy) = d$ for y.

Example 2 Solve $a(b - cy) = d$ for y.

$$a(b - cy) = d$$
$$ab - acy = d \qquad \blacktriangleleft \text{ Use the Distributive Property.}$$
$$-acy = d - ab \qquad \blacktriangleleft \text{ The } y\text{-term is alone on the left side.}$$
$$y = \frac{d - ab}{-ac}, \text{ or } \frac{ab - d}{ac}$$

The formula $\dfrac{1}{R} = \dfrac{1}{x} + \dfrac{1}{y}$ is a *literal fractional equation*. Recall that a fractional
equation can be simplified by multiplying each side by the LCD.

Example 3

Solve $\frac{1}{R} = \frac{1}{x} + \frac{1}{y}$ for x. Then find the value of x if $R = 3.2$ and $y = 4.8$.

Multiply each side by Rxy, the LCD.

$$Rxy \cdot \frac{1}{R} = Rxy \cdot \frac{1}{x} + Rxy \cdot \frac{1}{y}$$
$$xy = Ry + Rx$$
$$xy - Rx = Ry$$
$$x(y - R) = Ry$$
$$x = \frac{Ry}{y - R}$$

$R = 3.2 \qquad y = 4.8$

$$x = \frac{Ry}{y - R}$$
$$= \frac{3.2(4.8)}{4.8 - 3.2}$$
$$= \frac{15.36}{1.6}$$
$$x = 9.6$$

To solve a literal equation like $\frac{y - 3}{x + 4} = -5$ for either x or y, you can first rewrite it as a proportion. This technique is used in Example 4.

Example 4

Solve $\frac{y - 3}{x + 4} = -5$ for y.

$$\frac{y - 3}{x + 4} = \frac{-5}{1} \qquad \blacktriangleleft \text{ Rewrite as a proportion.}$$
$$(y - 3)1 = (x + 4)(-5) \qquad \blacktriangleleft \text{ If } \frac{a}{b} = \frac{c}{d}, \text{ then } ad = bc.$$
$$y - 3 = -5x - 20$$
$$y = -5x - 17$$

Oral Exercises

Solve each equation for x.

1. $a + x + b = c$ **1.** $x = c - a - b$
2. $-x = a - b$ **2.** $x = -a + b$
3. $ax = bc$ **3.** $x = \frac{bc}{a}$
6. $x = \frac{b + c}{a}$
4. $ax = ab$ $x = b$
5. $\frac{x}{a} = b$ $x = ab$
6. $ax = b + c$
7. $\frac{x}{a} = \frac{b}{c}$ $x = \frac{ab}{c}$
8. $1 = \frac{a}{x}$ $x = a$

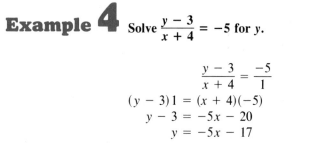

1. $x = \frac{b + c}{a}$ **2.** $x = \frac{a - c}{b}$ **3.** $x = \frac{b}{a - c}$ **4.** $x = \frac{b + 4}{a - 5}$

Written Exercises

5. $x = \frac{b}{4a}$ **6.** $x = \frac{4b + 5d}{3a - 2c}$ **8.** $x = \frac{-2ab - cd}{a - c}$ **9.** $x = \frac{ab - c}{2a - cd}$

Solve each equation for x.

(A)
1. $ax - b = c$
4. $5x + 4 = ax - b$
7. $a(x - b) = c$ $x = \frac{ab + c}{a}$
10. $\frac{a}{x} = b$ $x = \frac{a}{b}$
13. $\frac{a}{b} = \frac{x}{c} + d$ $x = \frac{ac - bcd}{b}$

2. $a = bx + c$
5. $7ax + b = 3b - ax$
8. $a(x + 2b) = c(x - d)$
11. $\frac{a}{b} \cdot x = c + d$ $x = \frac{bc + bd}{a}$
14. $\frac{2}{x} = \frac{3}{a} + \frac{4}{b}$ $x = \frac{2ab}{3b + 4a}$

3. $ax = b + cx$
6. $3ax - 4b = 2cx + 5d$
9. $a(2x - b) = c(dx - 1)$
12. $\frac{ax}{b} = \frac{c}{d}$ $x = \frac{bc}{ad}$
15. $\frac{8}{a} = \frac{6}{x} - \frac{4}{b}$ $x = \frac{3ab}{4b + 2a}$

Solve each equation for _y_.

16. $\dfrac{y-10}{x-8}=\dfrac{1}{2}$ $y=\dfrac{x+12}{2}$ **17.** $\dfrac{y-2}{x+5}=\dfrac{4}{5}$ $y=\dfrac{4x+30}{5}$ **18.** $\dfrac{y+3}{x+6}=\dfrac{-2}{3}$ $y=\dfrac{-2x-21}{3}$

19. $\dfrac{y-6}{x+1}=4$ $y=4x+10$ **20.** $\dfrac{y+8}{x-4}=-3$ $y=-3x+4$ **21.** $\dfrac{y-a}{x-b}=m$ $y=mx-bm+a$

Solve each formula for the specified variable. Then find the value of that variable for the given data.

22. Solve $p=2(l+w)$ for _w_. $w=\dfrac{p-2l}{2}$; 6.9
$p=23.4;\ l=4.8$

23. Solve $A=B+BCD$ for _B_. $B=\dfrac{A}{1+CD}$; 0.5
$A=48.35;\ C=5.8;\ D=16.5$

24. Solve $A=\dfrac{1}{2}bh$ for _b_. $b=\dfrac{2A}{h}$; 17
$A=30.6;\ h=3.6$

25. Solve $\dfrac{1}{x}=\dfrac{1}{a}+\dfrac{1}{b}$ for _x_. $x=\dfrac{ab}{a+b}$; 4.2
$a=8.12;\ b=8.7$

Solve each equation for _x_.

Ⓑ **26.** $\dfrac{2x}{g}=t^2$ $x=\dfrac{gt^2}{2}$ **27.** $gt^2=2(200t-x)$ $x=\dfrac{400t-gt^2}{2}$

28. $ax+b(x-c)=d(x+e)$ $x=\dfrac{bc+de}{a+b-d}$ **29.** $3a(2x-b)-a(b-x)=3ab+7c(a+b)$

30. $\dfrac{5a}{x+b}=\dfrac{a}{x-b}$ $x=\dfrac{3b}{2}$ **31.** $\dfrac{x-a}{x-b}=\dfrac{c}{d}$ $x=\dfrac{ad-bc}{d-c}$ $x=\dfrac{ab+ac+bc}{a}$

32. $\dfrac{x-a}{4}+\dfrac{x+b}{12}=\dfrac{c}{3}$ $x=\dfrac{3a-b+4c}{4}$ **33.** $\dfrac{x-4}{a}+\dfrac{3}{b}=\dfrac{2x-3}{c}$ $x=\dfrac{4bc-3ac-3ab}{bc-2ab}$

34. $\dfrac{ax-b}{cx+d}=5$ $x=\dfrac{b+5d}{a-5c}$ **35.** $\dfrac{ax+b}{c}=dx+e$ $x=\dfrac{ce-b}{a-cd}$

Solve each formula for the specified variable. Then find the value of that variable for the given data.

36. Solve $T=mg-mf$ for _m_. $m=\dfrac{T}{g-f}$; 10
$T=912.7;\ g=93.7;\ f=2.43$

37. Solve $A=ah+bh+ch$ for _h_. $h=\dfrac{A}{a+b+c}$; 24
$A=252;\ a=2.8;\ b=3.5;\ c=4.2$

38. Solve $\dfrac{1}{R}=\dfrac{1}{a}+\dfrac{1}{b}$ for _b_. $b=\dfrac{Ra}{a-R}$; 6.4
$R=4.8;\ a=19.2$

39. Solve $V=\dfrac{1}{3}Bh$ for _h_. $h=\dfrac{3V}{B}$; 1.5×10^3, or 1,500
$V=2.4\times10^5;\ B=4.8\times10^2$

40. Solve $gt^2-h=3(400t-h)$ for _h_. $h=\dfrac{1200t-gt^2}{2}$; 4,104
$g=32;\ t=9$

41. Solve $\dfrac{h-80}{16t}=30-t$ for _h_. $h=-16t^2+480t+80$; 1,744
$t=4$

Solve each equation for _x_.

Ⓒ **42.** $x^4-5a^2x^2+4a^4=0$ $a,\ -a,\ 2a,\ -2a$ **43.** $16x^4-40a^2x^2+9a^4=0$ $\dfrac{3a}{2},\ -\dfrac{3a}{2},\ \dfrac{a}{2},\ -\dfrac{a}{2}$

44. $x^3-ax^2-b^2x+ab^2=0$ $a,\ b,\ -b$ **45.** $4x^4-36a^2x^2-b^2x^2+9a^2b^2=0$ $3a,\ -3a,\ \dfrac{b}{2},\ -\dfrac{b}{2}$

46. $|ax-b|=c$, if $c\ge0$ $\dfrac{b+c}{a},\ \dfrac{b-c}{a}$ **47.** $\dfrac{x-a}{x-b}=\dfrac{x-a}{x-c}$ a

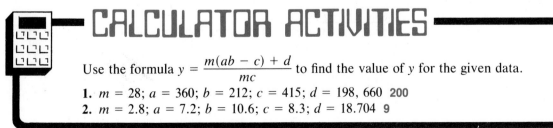

CALCULATOR ACTIVITIES

Use the formula $y=\dfrac{m(ab-c)+d}{mc}$ to find the value of _y_ for the given data.

1. $m=28;\ a=360;\ b=212;\ c=415;\ d=198,\,660$ 200
2. $m=2.8;\ a=7.2;\ b=10.6;\ c=8.3;\ d=18.704$ 9

5.5 Dividing Polynomials

OBJECTIVE ▶ To divide a polynomial of two or more terms by a binomial

Two forms for dividing 679 by 32 are shown below.

ORDINARY FORM

$$\begin{array}{r} 21 = 21\frac{7}{32} \\ 32\,\overline{)\,679} \\ \underline{64} \\ 39 \\ \underline{32} \\ 7 \end{array}$$

Divide: $600 \div 30$.
Multiply: $20(30 + 2)$.
Subtract: $(600 + 70) - (600 + 40)$.
Divide: $30 \div 30$.
Multiply: $1(30 + 2)$.
Subtract: $(30 + 9) - (30 + 2)$.

EXPANDED FORM

$$\begin{array}{r} 20 + 1 = 21\frac{7}{32} \\ 30 + 2\,\overline{)\,600 + 70 + 9} \\ \underline{600 + 40} \\ 30 + 9 \\ \underline{30 + 2} \\ 7 \end{array}$$

Dividing a polynomial of two or more terms by a binomial is similar to dividing a whole number of two or more digits by a two-digit number in expanded form. The divide-multiply-subtract cycle shown above is used in the following example.

Example 1 Divide: $(4x^2 - 5x - 30) \div (x - 3)$.

Step 1

Divide: $4x^2 \div x$. ▶
Multiply: $4x(x - 3)$. ▶
Subtract: ▶
$(4x^2 - 5x) - (4x^2 - 12x)$.

$$\begin{array}{r} 4x \\ x - 3\,\overline{)\,4x^2 - 5x - 30} \\ \underline{4x^2 - 12x} \\ 7x \end{array}$$

Step 2

$$\begin{array}{r} 4x + 7 \\ x - 3\,\overline{)\,4x^2 - 5x - 30} \\ \underline{4x^2 - 12x} \\ 7x - 30 \\ \underline{7x - 21} \\ -9 \end{array}$$

Divide: $7x \div x$. ▶
Multiply: $7(x - 3)$. ▶
Subtract: ▶
$(7x - 30) - (7x - 21)$.

Thus, the quotient is $4x + 7 + \dfrac{-9}{x - 3}$.

In Example 1, notice how the *remainder* is written as a fractional part of the *divisor*. In division problems of this type, the divide-multiply-subtract cycle is repeated as many times as is necessary, but the process ends when the degree of the remainder is less than that of the divisor, or when the remainder is 0.

Example 2 Divide: $(30 - 2x^2 - 2x + 6x^3) \div (3x + 5)$.

$$\begin{array}{r} 2x^2 - 4x + 6 \\ 3x + 5\,\overline{)\,6x^3 - 2x^2 - 2x + 30} \\ \underline{6x^3 + 10x^2} \\ -12x^2 - 2x \\ \underline{-12x^2 - 20x} \\ 18x + 30 \\ \underline{18x + 30} \\ 0 \end{array}$$

◀ *Arrange the terms of the dividend in descending order of the exponents.*

Thus, the quotient is $2x^2 - 4x + 6$.

Before dividing, you should arrange the terms of both the dividend and the divisor in descending order of the exponents in one variable. If either the dividend or divisor has missing powers of the variable, you can use 0 as the coefficient to replace the missing terms.

Example 3 Divide: $(10x^3 - 34x + 4) \div (2x + 4)$.

$$
\begin{array}{r}
5x^2 - 10x + 3 \\
2x + 4 \overline{\smash{)}\ 10x^3 + 0x^2 - 34x + 4} \\
\underline{10x^3 + 20x^2} \\
-20x^2 - 34x \\
\underline{-20x^2 - 40x} \\
6x + 4 \\
\underline{6x + 12} \\
-8
\end{array}
$$

◀ *Replace the missing x^2 term with $0x^2$.*

Thus, the quotient is $5x^2 - 10x + 3 + \dfrac{-8}{2x + 4}$.

Oral Exercises

1. $2x^4 - 3x^2$ 2. $5n + 6m$ 3. $6b - 4$ 4. $3m^2 - 5m - 4$
5. $-3d^3 + 5c^4d - 8c^2d^2$ 6. $6x^2y + 4x - 7y$

Simplify each quotient. Assume that no divisor is equal to 0.

1. $(14x^5 - 21x^3) \div (7x)$ 2. $(5mn^2 + 6m^2n) \div (mn)$ 3. $(18a^2b^2 - 12a^2b) \div (3a^2b)$

4. $\dfrac{15m^4 - 25m^3 - 20m^2}{5m^2}$ 5. $\dfrac{-6cd^4 + 10c^5d^2 - 16c^3d^3}{2cd}$ 6. $\dfrac{24x^3y^3 + 16x^2y^2 - 28xy^3}{4xy^2}$

20. $4x^2 + 3x + 33 + \frac{200}{x^2 - 5}$ 23. $x^{2m} + 3 + \frac{2}{x^m - 4}$

Written Exercises

Divide. Assume that no divisor is equal to 0.

(A) 1. $(x^2 - 5x + 6) \div (x - 3)$ $x - 2$
3. $(2c^2 + c - 2) \div (c + 1)$ $2c - 1 + \frac{-1}{c + 1}$
5. $(10x^2 - 8x - 24) \div (x - 2)$ $10x + 12$
7. $(4y^2 + 7y - 4) \div (y + 3)$ $4y - 5 + \frac{11}{y + 3}$
9. $(3x^3 - x^2 - 17x + 9) \div (x - 3)$
11. $(15 - 14n + 8n^2) \div (4n - 5)$ $2n - 1 + \frac{10}{4n - 5}$
13. $(a^3 - 13a - 12) \div (a + 3)$ $a^2 - 3a - 4$
9. $3x^2 + 8x + 7 + \frac{30}{x - 3}$

2. $(b^2 - 10b + 9) \div (b - 1)$ $b - 9$
4. $(y^2 + 3y + 1) \div (y + 2)$ $y + 1 + \frac{-1}{y + 2}$
6. $(2n^2 + 19n + 35) \div (2n + 5)$ $n + 7$
8. $(6a^2 - 13a + 2) \div (3a - 2)$ $2a - 3 + \frac{-4}{3a - 2}$
10. $(3n^4 + 13n^3 + 4n^2 - 2n - 8) \div (n + 4)$
12. $(14x^2 - 3x + 3x^3 + 7) \div (x + 5)$
14. $(9y^4 + 5y^2 - 12) \div (3y - 2)$

$3x + 2 + \frac{-6}{2x^2 - 1}$ 16. $3c^2 + 2c + 12$ $3y^3 + 2y^2 + 3y + 2 + \frac{-8}{3y - 2}$

(B) 15. $(6x^3 + 4x^2 - 3x - 8) \div (2x^2 - 1)$
17. $(a^3 + 1) \div (a + 1)$ $a^2 - a + 1$
19. $(2n^4 - 4n^3 + 7n^2 - 12n + 3) \div (n^2 + 3)$
21. $(y^6 - y^5 - y^4 + y^2 - y - 1) \div (y^4 + 1)$
$y^2 - y - 1$

16. $(3c^4 + 2c^3 - 8c - 48) \div (c^2 - 4)$
18. $(8y^3 - 125) \div (2y - 5)$ $4y^2 + 10y + 25$
20. $(4x^4 + 3x^3 + 13x^2 - 15x + 35) \div (x^2 - 5)$
22. $(9a^6 - 3a^5 + a^2 - 4) \div (3a^3 - 1)$
$3a^3 - a^2 + 1 + \frac{-3}{3a^3 - 1}$

(C) 23. $(x^{3m} - 4x^{2m} + 3x^m - 10) \div (x^m - 4)$
25. $(24x^3y + 7x^2y^2 - 6x^2y - 6xy^3 - 4xy^2) \div (3x + 2y)$ $8x^2y - 3xy^2 - 2xy$
10. $3n^3 + n^2 - 2$ 12. $3x^2 - x + 2 + \frac{-3}{x + 5}$

24. $(x^{3c} + 3x^{2c} - x^{2c+1} - 3x^{c+1} + 2) \div (x^c + 3)$
$x^{2c} - x^{c+1} + \frac{2}{x^c + 3}$
19. $2n^2 - 4n + 1$

Cumulative Review

1. Simplify $5x(10x^3y^4)^3$. $5{,}000x^{10}y^{12}$

2. Factor $3ax^4 - 30ax^2 + 27a$ completely.
$3a(x - 3)(x + 3)(x - 1)(x + 1)$

DIVIDING POLYNOMIALS

129

5.6 Synthetic Division

OBJECTIVES ▶ **To divide a polynomial by a binomial, using synthetic division**
To determine if a given binomial is a factor of a given polynomial, using synthetic division
To evaluate a polynomial for a given value of its variable, using synthetic division

The division at the right can be done in a shorter way. The shorter method eliminates repetitious rewriting of the variable and some of the coefficients.
The method is called **synthetic division** and is illustrated below.

$$
\begin{array}{r}
3x^3 - 4x^2 + 5x - 6 \\
x - 2 \overline{\smash{\big)}\ 3x^4 - 10x^3 + 13x^2 - 16x + 8} \\
\underline{3x^4 - 6x^3} \\
-4x^3 + 13x^2 \\
\underline{-4x^3 + 8x^2} \\
5x^2 - 16x \\
\underline{5x^2 - 10x} \\
-6x + 8 \\
\underline{-6x + 12} \\
-4
\end{array}
$$

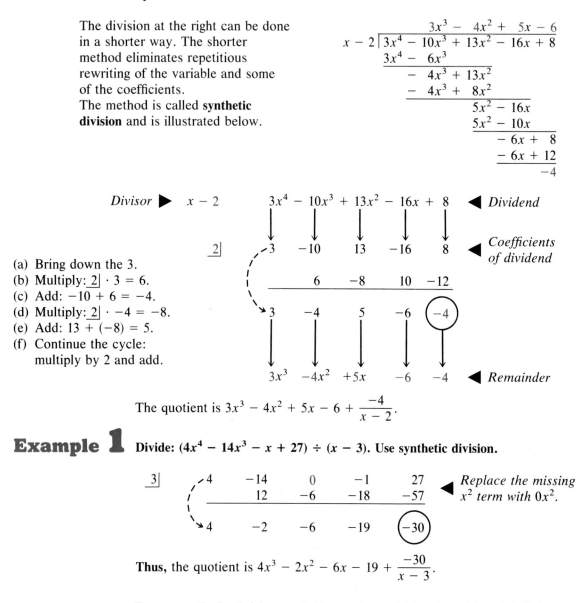

(a) Bring down the 3.
(b) Multiply: $\underline{2}| \cdot 3 = 6$.
(c) Add: $-10 + 6 = -4$.
(d) Multiply: $\underline{2}| \cdot -4 = -8$.
(e) Add: $13 + (-8) = 5$.
(f) Continue the cycle: multiply by 2 and add.

The quotient is $3x^3 - 4x^2 + 5x - 6 + \dfrac{-4}{x - 2}$.

Example 1

Divide: $(4x^4 - 14x^3 - x + 27) \div (x - 3)$. **Use synthetic division.**

$$
\begin{array}{r|rrrrr}
3| & 4 & -14 & 0 & -1 & 27 \\
& & 12 & -6 & -18 & -57 \\
\hline
& 4 & -2 & -6 & -19 & \boxed{-30}
\end{array}
$$
◀ *Replace the missing x^2 term with $0x^2$.*

Thus, the quotient is $4x^3 - 2x^2 - 6x - 19 + \dfrac{-30}{x - 3}$.

To use synthetic division to divide a polynomial in x by a binomial divisor, the divisor must be of the form $x - a$. A divisor like $x + 5$ can be rewritten as $x - (-5)$ where a is -5.

Example 2 Divide $(2x^5 + 11x^4 - x^3 - 30x^2 + 6x + 30) \div (x + 5)$. Use synthetic division.

Rewrite $x + 5$ as $x - (-5)$. ▶

$$
\begin{array}{r|rrrrrr}
-5 & 2 & 11 & -1 & -30 & 6 & 30 \\
 & & -10 & -5 & 30 & 0 & -30 \\
\hline
 & 2 & 1 & -6 & 0 & 6 & \boxed{0}
\end{array}
$$

Thus, the quotient is $2x^4 + 1x^3 - 6x^2 + 0x + 6$, or $2x^4 + x^3 - 6x^2 + 6$.

Using whole numbers,
(1) 9 is a factor of 27   since $27 \div 9$ is 3   with remainder 0, but
(2) 8 is not a factor of 37   since $37 \div 8$ is 4   with remainder 5.

Using the polynomials in Example 2, $x + 5$ is a factor of $2x^5 + 11x^4 - x^3 - 30x^2 + 6x + 30$ since the remainder upon division is 0.
This leads to the following statement.

Definition:
Binomial Factor
of a Polynomial

> A *binomial* $(x - a)$ is a *factor of a polynomial P* if
> $$P \div (x - a) = Q,$$
> where Q is a polynomial and the remainder is 0.

To determine whether a given binomial is a factor of a given polynomial, synthetic division can be used. This is shown in Example 3.

Example 3 Determine whether $x + 3$ is a factor of $2x^5 + 7x^4 + 2x^3 - 3x^2 - 5x - 15$.

Rewrite $x + 3$ as $x - (-3)$. ▶

$$
\begin{array}{r|rrrrrr}
-3 & 2 & 7 & 2 & -3 & -5 & -15 \\
 & & -6 & -3 & 3 & 0 & 15 \\
\hline
 & 2 & 1 & -1 & 0 & -5 & \boxed{0}
\end{array}
$$ ◀ *Remainder*

The polynomial quotient is $2x^4 + x^3 - x^2 - 5$, and the remainder is 0.
Thus, $x + 3$ is a factor of $2x^5 + 7x^4 + 2x^3 - 3x^2 - 5x - 15$.

You can evaluate $4x^2 - 3x - 5$ for $x = 3$ by substituting 3 for x.
$$4x^2 - 3x - 5 = 4 \cdot 3^2 - 3 \cdot 3 - 5 = 36 - 9 - 5 = 22$$
The same value can be found by synthetic division of $4x^2 - 3x - 5$ by $x - 3$.

$$
\begin{array}{r|rrr}
3 & 4 & -3 & -5 \\
 & & 12 & 27 \\
\hline
 & 4 & 9 & \boxed{22}
\end{array}
$$

Notice that the remainder, 22, is the value of $4x^2 - 3x - 5$ when $x = 3$.

This can be explained as follows:

If $(4x^2 - 3x - 5) \div (x - 3)$ is $4x + 9$ with remainder 22,

then $4x^2 - 3x - 5 = (4x + 9)(x - 3) + 22$, or

dividend = polynomial quotient × divisor + remainder.

If $x = 3$, then $(4x + 9)(x - 3) + 22 = (4 \cdot 3 + 9)(3 - 3) + 22$
$$= 21 \cdot 0 + 22$$
$$= 22$$

This result may be generalized into the following statement.

Remainder Theorem

> For the polynomials P, Q, and $x - a$, if $P = (x - a) \cdot Q + R$ for some number R, then R is the value of P when $x = a$.

Example 4

Evaluate $10x^4 + 25x^3 - x - 64$ if $x = -4$.

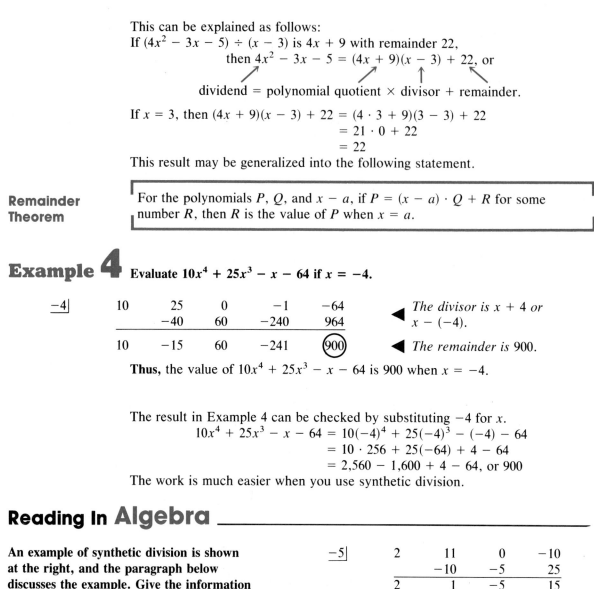

$$\begin{array}{r|rrrrr} -4 & 10 & 25 & 0 & -1 & -64 \\ & & -40 & 60 & -240 & 964 \\ \hline & 10 & -15 & 60 & -241 & \boxed{900} \end{array}$$

◀ *The divisor is $x + 4$ or $x - (-4)$.*

◀ *The remainder is 900.*

Thus, the value of $10x^4 + 25x^3 - x - 64$ is 900 when $x = -4$.

The result in Example 4 can be checked by substituting -4 for x.
$$10x^4 + 25x^3 - x - 64 = 10(-4)^4 + 25(-4)^3 - (-4) - 64$$
$$= 10 \cdot 256 + 25(-64) + 4 - 64$$
$$= 2,560 - 1,600 + 4 - 64, \text{ or } 900$$
The work is much easier when you use synthetic division.

Reading In Algebra

An example of synthetic division is shown at the right, and the paragraph below discusses the example. Give the information needed for each blank to complete the paragraph.

$$\begin{array}{r|rrrr} -5 & 2 & 11 & 0 & -10 \\ & & -10 & -5 & 25 \\ \hline & 2 & 1 & -5 & 15 \end{array}$$

The dividend is $2x^3 + 11x^2 - 10$, the divisor is __x + 5__, $2x^2 + x - 5 + \dfrac{15}{x + 5}$ is the __quotient__, and 15 is the __remainder__. Since the remainder is __15__, the value of $2x^3 + 11x^2 - 10$ is __15__ when __x = -5__, and $x + 5$ is not a __factor__ of $2x^3 + 11x^2 - 10$.

Oral Exercises

Determine whether each statement is true or false.

1. 5 is a factor of 12,345. **T**

2. One factor of 27 is 7. **F**

3. If $P = (x + 2)(x^2 - 3x - 12) + 4$, then **F** $x + 2$ is a factor of P.

4. If $P = (x - 4)(2x^2 + 7x - 4)$, then **T** $x - 4$ is a factor of P.

5. If $P = (x - 3)(x^2 - 7x + 12)$, then **T** $P = 0$ when $x = 3$.

6. If $P = (x + 6)(x^2 + 8x + 16) + 4$, then **T** $P = 4$ when $x = -6$.

3. $3y^3 - 8y^2 + 10y - 20 + \frac{51}{y + 3}$

Written Exercises

1. $x^2 + 3x - 5 + \frac{-8}{x - 1}$

4. $-4y^2 + 6y - 9 + \frac{10}{y + 1}$

$x^2 - 8x - 20 + \frac{-60}{x - 5}$

Divide. Use synthetic division.

Ⓐ **1.** $(x^3 + 2x^2 - 8x - 3) \div (x - 1)$ **above**
2. $(x^3 - 13x^2 + 20x + 40) \div (x - 5)$ ✓
3. $(3y^4 + y^3 - 14y^2 + 10y - 9) \div (y + 3)$ **above**
4. $(-4y^3 + 2y^2 - 3y + 1) \div (y + 1)$ **above**
5. $(n^5 - 2n^3 + n - 2) \div (n + 2)$ ⬊
$n^4 - 2n^3 + 2n^2 - 4n + 9 + \frac{-20}{n + 2}$
6. $(2n^5 - 6n^4 - 12n^2 - 15) \div (n - 4)$ ⬊
$2n^4 + 2n^3 + 8n^2 + 20n + 80 + \frac{305}{n - 4}$

Determine whether the binomial is a factor of the polynomial in each case.

7. $x - 3;\ 2x^3 - 11x^2 + 18x - 12$ **no**
8. $x + 6;\ 3x^3 + 17x^2 - 8x - 12$ **yes**
9. $y + 2;\ y^4 + 2y^3 - 3y^2 + 2y + 16$ **yes**
10. $y - 5;\ 3y^4 - 12y^3 - 20y^2 + 30y + 5$ **no**
11. $n - 1;\ 4n^5 - 2n^3 + 6n^2 - 9n + 1$ **yes**
12. $n + 3;\ 5n^5 + 10n^4 - 10n^3 - 34n + 33$ **yes**

Evaluate each polynomial for the given data. Use synthetic division.

13. $6x^5 - 5x^4 - 4x^3 - 3x^2 - 2x + 1$ if $x = 2$ **65**
14. $2x^5 + 9x^4 + 8x^3 - 7x^2 - 6x + 8$ if $x = -3$ **−10** ↵
15. $3y^3 + 22y^2 + 10y + 20$ if $y = -10$ **−880**
16. $5y^3 - 80y^2 + 80y - 5$ if $y = 15$ **70**
17. $n^4 - n^3 + n^2 - n + 1$ if $n = 8$ **3,641**
18. $n^4 - n^3 - n^2 - n - 1$ if $n = -6$ **1,481**
19. $6x^4 + 4x^2 - 2$ if $x = -4$ **1,598**
20. $4x^5 - 6x^3 + 7x$ if $x = 2$ **94**

23. 379,642

Ⓑ **21.** $n^6 - 2n^4 - 3n^2 - 4$ if $n = -5$ **14, 296**
22. $4n^7 + 3n^5 + 2n^3 + n$ if $n = 2$ **626**
23. $3x^5 + 7x^4 + 9x^3 + 6x^2 + 4x + 2$ if $x = 10$
24. $7x^6 + 8x^4 + 9x^2$ if $x = 2$ **612**
25. $y^3 - 5y^2 + 2y - 3$ if $y = 0.2$ **−2.792**
26. $2y^3 - 3y + 4$ if $y = 1.2$ **3.856**
27. $n^4 + n^3 + n^2 + 1$ if $n = -1.5$ **4.9375**
28. $8n^3 + 9n^2 - 2n - 3$ if $n = -1.25$ **−2.0625**

Determine whether the binomial is a factor of the polynomial in each case.

29. $y + 8;\ 3y^4 + 21y^3 - 31y^2 - 51y + 40$ **yes**
30. $y - 9;\ 12y^3 - 8y^2 - 30y - 630$ **no**
31. $n - 10;\ n^3 + 900$ **no**
32. $n + 20;\ n^3 + 8,000$ **yes**
33. $x + 2;\ x^6 + x^4 + x^2 - 84$ **yes**
34. $x - 3;\ x^5 - x^3 - 9$ **no**
35. $y - 5;\ y^8 - 30y^6 + 130y^4 - 130y^2 + 130$ **no**
36. $y + 1;\ y^7 + 1$ **yes**

Ⓒ **37.** $P = 2x^4 + 7x^3 - 38x^2 - 103x + 60$ and two factors of P are $x + 3$ and $x - 4$. Factor the polynomial P completely.
$(x + 3)(x - 4)(2x - 1)(x + 5)$

38. $P = 3x^4 - 18x^3 - 60x^2 + 72x + 192$ and two factors of P are $x - 8$ and $x + 2$. Factor the polynomial P completely.
$3(x - 8)(x - 2)(x + 2)^2$

CALCULATOR ACTIVITIES

You can evaluate $5x^4 - 17x^3 + 23x^2 - 49x + 90$ for $x = 7$ by using the *multiply-by-7-and-add* cycle of synthetic division.

$5 \otimes 7 \ominus 17 \otimes 7 \oplus 23 \otimes 7 \ominus 49 \otimes 7 \oplus 90 \ominus 7048$, the value of the polynomial when $x = 7$.

Evaluate each polynomial for $x = 12$.
1. $18x^3 - 47x^2 + 62x - 75$ **25,005**
2. $24x^4 + 25x^3 - 26x^2 - 27x - 28$ **536,768**
3. $8x^5 - 7x^4 - 6x^3 + 5x^2 + 4x - 3$ **1,835,901**

Chapter Five Review

Vocabulary

extraneous solution [5.1]
fractional equation [5.1]
literal equation [5.4]
proportion [5.1]
    extremes of [5.1]
    means of [5.1]
synthetic division [5.6]

Solve each equation. [5.1]

1. $\dfrac{n-4}{3} - \dfrac{n-2}{4} = \dfrac{n}{2}$ **−2**

2. $\dfrac{1}{6}y^2 = \dfrac{3}{2}y - 3$ **3, 6**

3. $\dfrac{8}{5n-2} = \dfrac{4}{2n+7}$ **16**

4. $\dfrac{a-1}{3a-7} = \dfrac{a-2}{a+1}$ $\dfrac{3}{2}$**, 5**

5. $\dfrac{3}{x+2} + \dfrac{2}{x} = 3$ $-\dfrac{4}{3}$**, 1**

6. $\dfrac{2y-1}{y-3} = \dfrac{y+2}{y-3} - \dfrac{y}{4}$ **−4**

7. $\dfrac{7}{n-2} = \dfrac{n-3}{n^2-7n+10} + \dfrac{1}{n-5}$ **6**

8. $\dfrac{a}{a+5} - \dfrac{5}{a^2-25} = \dfrac{a-6}{2a-10}$ **4**

★9. $\dfrac{3}{x^2+2x-24} + \dfrac{4}{x^2+8x+12} = \dfrac{5}{x^2-2x-8}$ **20**

Solve each problem.

10. Mr. Brown can plant his crops in 30 days. His son would take 40 days and his daughter 60 days. How many days will it take if they work together? [5.2] **$13\frac{1}{3}$ days**

11. Lori can put carpet on a floor in 9 hours. If Brent helps her, the job is done in 6 hours. How many hours would it take Brent if he works alone? [5.2] **18 h**   **12. 192 km**

12. A train traveled from city A to city B at 40 km/h and then returned at 60 km/h. If the round trip took 8 h, what is the rail distance between cities A and B? [5.3]

13. A family can row their boat 5 km/h in still water. They traveled 30 km downstream in the same time that they traveled 20 km upstream. What was the rate of the current? [5.3] **1 km/h**

14. One plane flew 498 km with a tailwind in $\dfrac{3}{4}$ of the time that another plane flew 616 km against the headwind. If each plane can fly 400 km/h in still air, find the rate of the tailwind. [5.3] **15 km/h**

Solve each equation for x. [5.4]

15. $a(x-b) = c(2x+3)$ $x = \dfrac{3c+ab}{a-2c}$

★16. $\dfrac{7a}{x+b} = \dfrac{3c}{x-b}$ $x = \dfrac{3bc+7ab}{7a-3c}$

17. $x^4 - a^2x^2 - 9b^2x^2 + 9a^2b^2 = 0$
                                  a, $-a$, $3b$, $-3b$

Solve each formula for the specified variable. Then find the value of that variable for the given data. [5.4]

18. Solve $\dfrac{1}{a} = \dfrac{2}{b} + \dfrac{3}{c}$ for b. $b = \dfrac{2ac}{c-3a}$**; 22.08**
    $a = 2.4$; $c = 9.2$

19. Solve $A = \dfrac{1}{2}h(a+b)$ for h. $h = \dfrac{2A}{a+b}$**; 15**
    $A = 300$; $a = 17$; $b = 23$

                  20. $3x^2 + 5x + 2 + \dfrac{3}{3x-5}$

Divide. Assume that no divisor is equal to 0. [5.5]

20. $(9x^3 - 19x - 7) \div (3x - 5)$

21. $(4y - 3y^2 + 2y^3 - 6) \div (y^2 + 2)$ **$2y - 3$**

★22. $(x^{2n+2} + 2x^{2n+1} - 5x^{n+2} - 10x^{n+1})$
    $\div (x^n - 5)$**$x^{n+2} + 2x^{n+1}$**

23. Divide: $(n^3 + 5n^2 - 4n - 6) \div (n - 2)$. Use synthetic division. [5.6] **below**

Determine whether the binomial is a factor of the polynomial in each case. [5.6]

24. $x + 5$; $3x^3 + 17x^2 + 8x - 10$ **yes**
25. $y - 3$; $4y^3 - 10y^2 - 12$ **no**
26. $c + 5$; $4c^4 - 80c^2 + 500$ **no**

              23. $n^2 + 7n + 10 + \dfrac{14}{n-2}$

Evaluate each polynomial for the given data. Use synthetic division. [5.6]

27. $5n^3 - 7n^2 - 10n - 22$ if $n = 3$ **20**
28. $x^6 - 24x^4 - 75x^2 + 250$ if $x = -5$ **−1,000**

★29. $P = 2x^4 - 7x^3 - 23x^2 + 28x + 60$ and two factors of P are $x + 2$ and $x - 5$. Factor the polynomial P completely.
            $(x + 2)(x - 5)(2x + 3)(x - 2)$

Chapter Five Test

Solve each equation.

1. $\dfrac{y+8}{4} - \dfrac{2y-3}{6} = \dfrac{y}{3}$ **6**

2. $\dfrac{1}{4}n^2 = \dfrac{5}{2}n - 6$ **4, 6**

3. $\dfrac{9}{2x-12} = \dfrac{3}{x-2}$ **−6**

4. $\dfrac{2y+1}{y-1} + \dfrac{y}{5} = \dfrac{y+2}{y-1}$ **−5**

5. $\dfrac{n-6}{n^2-2n-8} + \dfrac{3}{n-4} = \dfrac{2}{n+2}$ **−4**

Solve each problem.

6. Sandra can decorate a room for a party in 8 h and Edward can do it in 12 h. If Lois helps, all three can do the job in 3 h, working together. How long would it take Lois if she works alone? **8 h**

7. Samuel jogged along a straight trail at 18 km/h and returned on the same trail at 9 km/h. If the round trip took 2 h, how far did he jog in one direction? **12 km**

8. With the help of a tailwind, a plane flew 1,230 km in twice the time that a second plane flew 585 km against the headwind. Find the rate of the wind if both planes can fly 800 km/h in still air. **20 km/h**

Solve each equation for x.

9. $5ax + c = 4c - ax$ $x = \dfrac{c}{2a}$

10. $\dfrac{x+a}{d} = \dfrac{bx+c}{4}$ $x = \dfrac{cd-4a}{4-bd}$

11. Solve $A = \dfrac{h}{2}(b+c)$ for c. Then find c if $A = 26$, $h = 4$, and $b = 5$. $c = \dfrac{2A-bh}{h}$; **8**

Divide. Assume that no divisor is equal to 0.

12. $(6x^3 + 4 - 2x - 17x^2) \div (3x + 2)$
$2x^2 - 7x + 4 + \dfrac{-4}{3x+2}$

13. $(27n^3 - 8) \div (3n - 2)$ $9n^2 + 6n + 4$

14. Divide: $(y^5 - 16y^3 + 5y - 20) \div (y - 4)$. Use synthetic division. $y^4 + 4y^3 + 5$

Determine whether the binomial is a factor of the polynomial in each case.

15. $n + 3$; $4n^3 + 8n^2 - 10n + 6$ **yes**

16. $x - 5$; $x^4 - 20x^2 - 25$ **no**

Evaluate each polynomial for the given data. Use synthetic division.

17. $7y^3 - 18y^2 + 25y - 39$ if $y = 2$ **−5**

18. $8n^4 + 50n^3 - 60n + 80$ if $n = -6$ **8**

★19. Solve $\dfrac{5}{x^2-25} + \dfrac{4}{x^2-9x+20} = \dfrac{3}{x^2+x-20}$. $-\dfrac{5}{2}$

★20. Divide: $(3x^{4n} + 4x^{3n} + x^{2n}) \div (x^{2n} + x^n)$. $3x^{2n} + x^n$

★21. $P = x^4 - x^3 - 22x^2 - 44x - 24$ and two factors of P are $x - 6$ and $x + 1$. Factor the polynomial P completely. $(x-6)(x+1)(x+2)^2$

Computer Activities

Synthetic Division

The program below determines whether a binomial is a factor of a given polynomial by using synthetic division. If you analyze the steps used in synthetic division, you will notice that it is a repetitive process that you can perform quite easily on a computer. Statements 120 to 140 set up the loop that performs the calculations.

PROGRAM

```
10 PRINT "PROGRAM DIVIDES A 4TH DEGREE"
20 PRINT "POLYNOMIAL BY A BINOMIAL"
30 DIM C(5), A(5)
40 PRINT "ENTER 5 COEFFICIENTS OF POLYNOMIAL"
50 FOR I = 1 TO 5
60 INPUT C(I)
70 NEXT I
80 PRINT "ENTER 2ND TERM OF BINOMIAL"
90 INPUT D
100 LET D = -D
110 LET A(1) = C(1)
120 FOR I = 2 TO 5
130 LET A(I) = A(I - 1) * D + C(I)
140 NEXT I
150 PRINT "COEFFICIENTS OF QUOTIENT ARE"
160 FOR I = 1 TO 4
170 PRINT A(I)
180 NEXT I
190 PRINT "REMAINDER IS"; A(5)
200 IF A(5) < > 0 THEN 230
210 PRINT "THE BINOMIAL IS A FACTOR"
220 GO TO 240
230 PRINT "THE BINOMIAL IS NOT A FACTOR"
240 END
```

Exercises

1. Run the program above with the following values:
   Coefficients are 2, −3, −5, −14, 10; 2nd term of binomial is −3.
REMAINDER IS 4 THE BINOMIAL IS NOT A FACTOR
2. Change the program above to divide a 5th degree polynomial by a binomial.
For Ex. 2, see TE Answer Section.

136   **ACTIVITY: SYNTHETIC DIVISION**

College Prep Test

DIRECTIONS: Choose the *one* best answer to each question or problem.

1. The expression $\frac{5}{0}$ is undefined. Which expression could be undefined if x and y are two *different positive* numbers? **D**

   (A) $\frac{x + y}{x - y}$ (B) $\frac{x}{y}$ (C) $\frac{2x - y}{x + y}$

   (D) $\frac{x + y}{3x - 4y}$ (E) None of these

2. If 15, 22, and 30 are each factors of a certain number, then another factor of the number must be   **D**

   (A) 4   (B) 9   (C) 25
   (D) 55   (E) None of these

3. Which numeral does not represent $\frac{11}{4}$?   **E**

   (A) $2\frac{3}{4}$ (B) 2.75   (C) 2.75000 . . .

   (D) 2.74999 . . .   (E) None of these

4. $\dfrac{\frac{1}{2} + \frac{1}{4} + \frac{1}{8}}{\frac{1}{16} + \frac{1}{32} + \frac{1}{64}} =$ **C**

   (A) $\frac{1}{24}$ (B) $\frac{1}{8}$ (C) 8   (D) 24

   (E) None of these

5. If $\frac{1}{6} + \frac{1}{1.5} = \frac{1}{x}$, then $x =$ **B**

   (A) $\frac{5}{6}$ (B) 1.2   (C) 7.5   (D) 12
   (E) None of these

6. Juan drove 6 mi to the airport in 12 min and returned in 18 min. Find the average speed for the round trip in miles per hour.   **A**

   (A) 24 mi/h   (B) 30 mi/h   (C) 35 mi/h
   (D) 40 mi/h   (E) None of these

7. If $\frac{1}{x + y} = \frac{1}{x - y}$, then   **B**

   (A) $x = 0$ and $y \neq 0$ (B) $y = 0$ and $x \neq 0$
   (C) $x = y$ and $x \neq 0$ (D) $x = -y$ and $x \neq 0$
   (E) None of these

8. Albert can do a certain job in 6 days, and Brenda can do it in x days. Carol works 3 times as fast as Albert. What part of the job will be done at the end of y days if all three work together?   **A**

   (A) $\frac{y}{6} + \frac{y}{x} + \frac{y}{2}$ (B) $\frac{1}{6} + \frac{1}{x} + \frac{1}{2}$

   (C) $\frac{y}{6} + \frac{y}{x} + \frac{y}{18}$ (D) $\frac{1}{6} + \frac{1}{x} + \frac{1}{18}$

   (E) $\frac{6}{y} + \frac{x}{y} + \frac{2}{y}$

9. A certain plane can fly 400 mi/h in still air. The plane can go round trip between points M and N in 4 h when the wind is blowing at a rate of 20 mi/h from M toward N. Find the distance between M and N.   **B**

   (A) 780 mi   (B) 798 mi
   (C) 800 mi   (D) 802 mi
   (E) 805 mi

6 RADICALS AND RATIONAL NUMBER EXPONENTS

Careers: Chemical Science

If you complete courses in chemistry and mathematics at the secondary or college level, you may qualify for an interesting and well-paid career in chemical science. The chemical industry is among the five leading manufacturing industries in the United States.

Chemical laboratory research has led to the production of textiles of high quality. More than 25 percent of textiles produced are made from synthetic fibers such as rayon or nylon. Chemical treatments are used to provide us with fabrics that are water-repellent, shrink proof, and wrinkle resistant.

6.1 Square Roots

OBJECTIVES ▶ **To solve a quadratic equation by using the definition of square root**
To approximate a square root to the nearest hundredth by using a square root table
To determine whether a given number is rational or irrational

You can solve the quadratic equation $x^2 = 16$ by factoring:

$$x^2 = 16$$
$$x^2 - 16 = 0$$
$$(x + 4)(x - 4) = 0$$

The solutions are -4 and 4.

The solutions to this equation can also be found by using the concept of **square root** as shown below.

$$x^2 = 16$$

$$x = \sqrt{16} = 4 \quad \text{or} \quad x = -\sqrt{16} = -4$$

$\sqrt{16}$ represents the *positive* square root of 16, which is 4.
$-\sqrt{16}$ represents the *negative* square root of 16, which is -4.
Notice that $(\sqrt{16})^2 = 16$ since $4^2 = 16$ and $(-\sqrt{16})^2 = 16$ since $(-4)^2 = 16$.

Definition:
Square Root

> If $x^2 = k$, then $x = \sqrt{k}$ or $x = -\sqrt{k}$, for each number $k \geq 0$.
> $\sqrt{k}$ is the *principal,* or *positive,* *square root* of k and $-\sqrt{k}$ is the *negative square root* of k.

The symbol $\sqrt{k}$ (read "the square root of k") is called a **radical,** where k is the **radicand,** and $\sqrt{}$ is the **radical sign,** or **square root sign.**

The number $\sqrt{25}$ can easily be rewritten without a radical sign since the radicand, 25, is a *perfect square.* That is, 25 is the square of an integer. The number $\sqrt{10}$ cannot be simplified in this way since the radicand, 10, is not a perfect square.

Example 1

Solve each equation.

$$x^2 + 5 = 15 \qquad\qquad\qquad 3y^2 = 75$$

Subtract 5 from each side of the equation to obtain the form $x^2 = k$.

$$x^2 = 10$$
$$x = \sqrt{10} \quad \text{or} \quad x = -\sqrt{10}$$

Thus, the solutions are $\sqrt{10}$ and $-\sqrt{10}$.

Divide each side of the equation by 3 to obtain the form $y^2 = k$.

$$y^2 = 25$$
$$y = \sqrt{25} \quad \text{or} \quad y = -\sqrt{25}$$
$$y = \sqrt{5^2} = 5 \quad \text{or} \quad y = -\sqrt{5^2} = -5$$

Thus, the solutions are 5 and -5.

In Example 1, $\sqrt{10}$ and $-\sqrt{10}$ cannot be rewritten as integers, but each number can be approximated to the nearest hundredth by using the table of square roots in the back of the book. To the nearest hundredth, $\sqrt{10} \doteq 3.16$ and $-\sqrt{10} \doteq -3.16$. The symbol $\doteq$ means *is approximately equal to*.

Example 2 Solve each equation. Give the solutions to the nearest hundredth.

$$5y^2 - 9 = 206 \qquad\qquad\qquad 20n^2 = 4n^2 + 81$$

$$5y^2 = 215 \qquad\qquad\qquad\qquad 16n^2 = 81$$
$$y^2 = 43 \qquad\qquad\qquad\qquad\qquad n^2 = \frac{81}{16}$$
$$y = \sqrt{43} \quad \text{or} \quad y = -\sqrt{43} \qquad\qquad n = \sqrt{\frac{81}{16}} = \frac{9}{4} \quad \text{or} \quad n = -\sqrt{\frac{81}{16}} = -\frac{9}{4}$$

Use the table of square roots.

The solutions are 6.56 and −6.56. | The solutions are 2.25 and −2.25.

The numbers $\sqrt{\dfrac{81}{16}}$ and $\sqrt{1.44}$ can be rewritten as rational numbers:

$$\sqrt{\frac{81}{16}} = \sqrt{\left(\frac{9}{4}\right)^2} = \frac{9}{4} \qquad \sqrt{1.44} = \sqrt{(1.2)^2} = 1.2$$

Notice that $\dfrac{81}{16}$ and 1.44 are *perfect squares* since they are the squares of the rational numbers $\dfrac{9}{4}$ and 1.2, respectively.

The number $\sqrt{35}$ is not a rational number. It cannot be written in the form $\dfrac{a}{b}$ where a and b are integers since 35 is not a perfect square. To 13 decimal places, $\sqrt{35} \doteq 5.9160797830996$. The decimal for $\sqrt{35}$ is *nonterminating and nonrepeating*. Numbers of this type are called **irrational numbers.** In general, for $k \geq 0$,

(1) $\sqrt{k}$ is a rational number if k is a perfect square, and
(2) $\sqrt{k}$ is an irrational number if k is not a perfect square.

Example 3 Determine whether each number is rational or irrational.

Number	Answer	(Reason)
3.888 . . .	Rational	A repeating decimal
5.37	Rational	A terminating decimal
4.3131131113 . . .	Irrational	A nonterminating, nonrepeating decimal
$\sqrt{\dfrac{2}{9}}$	Irrational	$\dfrac{2}{9}$ is not a perfect square.
$\sqrt{\dfrac{169}{9}}$	Rational	$\dfrac{169}{9} = \left(\dfrac{13}{3}\right)^2$
$\sqrt{99}$	Irrational	99 is not a perfect square.
$-\sqrt{6.25}$	Rational	$6.25 = 2.5^2$

Your work in mathematics often involves both rational and irrational numbers. All the rational numbers together with all the irrational numbers are called the **real numbers**.

Reading In Algebra

Determine whether each statement is true or false.

1. $\sqrt{17}$ is a radical sign. **F**
2. The radical sign in $\sqrt{6}$ is $\sqrt{}$. **T**
3. $\sqrt{15}$ is a radical. **T**
4. The radicand in $\sqrt{52}$ is 52. **T**
5. $\dfrac{4}{9}$ is a perfect square. **T**
6. $\dfrac{25}{11}$ is not a perfect square. **T**
7. 0.9 is a perfect square. **F**
8. 0.49 is not a perfect square. **F**
9. $\sqrt{2}$ is a real number. **T**
10. $\sqrt{4}$ is a real number. **T**
11. $\sqrt{17} \doteq 4.12$ to the nearest hundredth. **T**
12. $\sqrt{19} \doteq 4.35$ to the nearest hundredth. **F**

Written Exercises

Solve each equation.

Ⓐ
1. $x^2 = 64$ $-8, 8$
2. $y^2 = 3$ $-\sqrt{3}, \sqrt{3}$
3. $4n^2 = 64$ $-4, 4$
4. $c^2 + 6 = 21$ $-\sqrt{15}, \sqrt{15}$
5. $a^2 - 7 = 22$ $-\sqrt{29}, \sqrt{29}$
6. $900 = x^2$ $-30, 30$
7. $6y^2 + 14 = 434$ $-\sqrt{70}, \sqrt{70}$
8. $16n^2 = 7n^2 + 4$ $-\frac{2}{3}, \frac{2}{3}$

Solve each equation. Approximate the solutions to the nearest hundredth.

9. $x^2 = 87$ $-9.33, 9.33$
10. $3y^2 = 195$ below
11. $4n^2 = 25$ below
12. $25c^2 - 7 = 9$ below
13. $9a^2 = 2a^2 + 294$ $-6.48, 6.48$
14. $4n^2 = 20n^2 - 9$ $-0.75, 0.75$
15. $3x^2 - 86 = x^2 + 86$ $-9.27, 9.27$
16. $6n^2 + 75 = n^2 + 455$ $-8.72, 8.72$

Determine whether each number is rational or irrational.

17. $5.282282228\ldots$ **I**
18. $0.123123123\ldots$ **R**
19. $4.343343334\ldots$ **I**
20. $7.65765765\ldots$ **R**
21. $\sqrt{169}$ **R**
22. $\sqrt{47}$ **I**
23. $-\sqrt{400}$ **R**
24. $-\sqrt{75}$ **I**
25. 87.6543 **R**
26. $19.47\overline{47}$ **R**
27. $-\sqrt{3{,}000}$ **I**
28. $\sqrt{2{,}025}$ **R**

Ⓑ
29. $\sqrt{\dfrac{49}{81}}$ **R**
30. $\sqrt{\dfrac{18}{100}}$ **I**
31. $\sqrt{\dfrac{18}{8}}$ **R**
32. $\sqrt{\dfrac{20}{40}}$ **I**
33. $\sqrt{2.5}$ **I**
34. $\sqrt{2.25}$ **R**
35. $\sqrt{0.36}$ **R**
36. π **I**

10. $-8.06, 8.06$ 11. $-2.50, 2.50$ 12. $-0.80, 0.80$

Solve each equation. Approximate the solutions to the nearest hundredth.

37. $144n^2 = 64$ $-0.67, 0.67$
38. $60x^2 = 9 - 4x^2$ $-0.38, 0.38$
39. $7y^2 - 9 = 16y^2 - 58$ $-2.33, 2.33$
40. $y^2 = 0.25$ $-0.50, 0.50$
41. $n^2 - 0.0009 = 0.004$ $-0.07, 0.07$
42. $5x^2 - 1 = 4x^2 + 0.21$ $-1.10, 1.10$

Ⓒ
43. $x^4 - 30x^2 + 125 = 0$ $-5.00, 5.00, -2.24, 2.24$
44. $6x^4 = 30x^2 - 36$ $-1.73, 1.73, -1.41, 1.41$
45. $\dfrac{x^2 + 3}{4} + \dfrac{2x^2 - 5}{3} = \dfrac{3x^2 + 2}{6}$ $-1.73, 1.73$
46. $\dfrac{2}{3}(9x^2 + 21) - \dfrac{3}{4}(12x^2 - 20) + 148 = 0$ $-7.68, 7.68$

Cumulative Review

Simplify each expression.

1. $(-7x^2y^5z^9)^2$ $49x^4y^{10}z^{18}$
2. $(-4ab^2c^7)^3$ $-64a^3b^6c^{21}$
3. $10m^2n(3m^3np^6)^4$ $810m^{14}n^5p^{24}$

6.2 Simplifying Radicals

OBJECTIVE ▶ **To simplify a radical in which the radicand contains a perfect square factor**

At the right, you see that $\sqrt{100 \cdot 36} = \sqrt{100} \cdot \sqrt{36}$. In general, the square root of the product of two or more real numbers is the product of the square roots of the numbers.

$\sqrt{100 \cdot 36}$	$\sqrt{100} \cdot \sqrt{36}$
$\sqrt{3,600}$	$10 \cdot 6$
60	60

Square Root of a Product

$$\sqrt{x \cdot y} = \sqrt{x} \cdot \sqrt{y} \text{ for all real numbers } x \geq 0, y \geq 0.$$

Example 1 **Simplify $\sqrt{189}$. Approximate the result to the nearest hundredth.**

$\sqrt{189} = \sqrt{9 \cdot 21}$ ◀ 9 is a perfect square factor of 189.
$\quad\quad\;\; = \sqrt{9} \cdot \sqrt{21}$ ◀ $\sqrt{x \cdot y} = \sqrt{x} \cdot \sqrt{y}$
$\quad\quad\;\; = 3 \cdot \sqrt{21}, \text{ or } 3\sqrt{21}$
$\quad\quad\;\; \doteq 3 \cdot 4.583$ ◀ $\sqrt{21} \doteq 4.583$
$\quad\quad\;\; \doteq 13.749$
$\quad\quad\;\; \doteq 13.75$ ◀ Round to the nearest hundredth.
Thus, $\sqrt{189} \doteq 13.75$.

In Example 1, the expression $3\sqrt{21}$ is the **simplest radical form** of $\sqrt{189}$. A radical or square root expression is in simplest radical form whenever the radicand is the smallest possible integer. In other words, the radicand must be an integer that does not contain a perfect square factor, other than 1. Unless otherwise indicated, all answers involving radicals should be given in simplest radical form.

Example 2 **Simplify $-5\sqrt{72}$.**

$$-5\sqrt{72} = -5\sqrt{36 \cdot 2}$$
$$= -5\sqrt{36} \cdot \sqrt{2}$$
$$= -5 \cdot 6 \cdot \sqrt{2}$$
$$= -30\sqrt{2}$$

Thus, $-5\sqrt{72} = -30\sqrt{2}$.

When simplifying a radical, the work is easier if you identify the *greatest perfect square* factor of the radicand. In Example 2, 9 and 4 are also perfect square factors of 72. Notice what happens when these numbers are used to simplify $-5\sqrt{72}$.

$$-5\sqrt{72} = -5\sqrt{9 \cdot 4 \cdot 2} = -5\sqrt{9} \cdot \sqrt{4} \cdot \sqrt{2} = -5 \cdot 3 \cdot 2\sqrt{2} = -30\sqrt{2}$$

In this case, the Square Root of a Product property is extended to three numbers.

A radicand may contain a power of a variable as in $\sqrt{x^6}$ and $\sqrt{x^{11}}$. In Example 3, you will simplify these two radicals by using the greatest perfect square factors of x^6 and x^{11}. In the remainder of this chapter, all variables represent positive real numbers or 0, unless stated otherwise.

Example 3 Simplify $\sqrt{x^6}$ and $\sqrt{x^{11}}$.

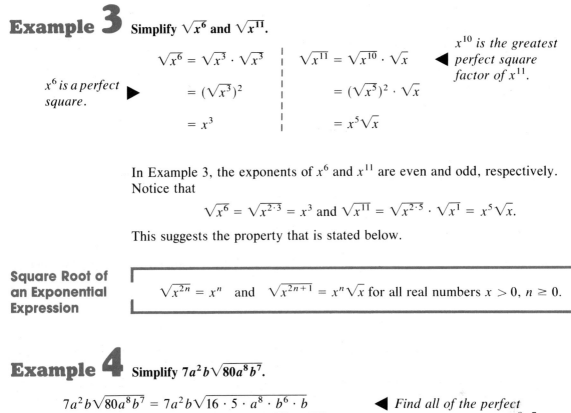

x^{10} *is the greatest perfect square factor of* x^{11}.

$\sqrt{x^6} = \sqrt{x^3} \cdot \sqrt{x^3}$ $\sqrt{x^{11}} = \sqrt{x^{10}} \cdot \sqrt{x}$

x^6 *is a perfect square.*

$= (\sqrt{x^3})^2$ $= (\sqrt{x^5})^2 \cdot \sqrt{x}$

$= x^3$ $= x^5 \sqrt{x}$

In Example 3, the exponents of x^6 and x^{11} are even and odd, respectively. Notice that

$$\sqrt{x^6} = \sqrt{x^{2 \cdot 3}} = x^3 \text{ and } \sqrt{x^{11}} = \sqrt{x^{2 \cdot 5}} \cdot \sqrt{x^1} = x^5 \sqrt{x}.$$

This suggests the property that is stated below.

Square Root of an Exponential Expression

$$\sqrt{x^{2n}} = x^n \quad \text{and} \quad \sqrt{x^{2n+1}} = x^n \sqrt{x} \text{ for all real numbers } x > 0, \, n \geq 0.$$

Example 4 Simplify $7a^2 b \sqrt{80a^8 b^7}$.

$7a^2 b \sqrt{80a^8 b^7} = 7a^2 b \sqrt{16 \cdot 5 \cdot a^8 \cdot b^6 \cdot b}$ *Find all of the perfect square factors of* $80a^8 b^7$.

$= 7a^2 b \sqrt{16} \cdot \sqrt{5} \cdot \sqrt{a^8} \cdot \sqrt{b^6} \cdot \sqrt{b}$

$= 7a^2 b \cdot 4 \cdot \sqrt{5} \cdot a^4 \cdot b^3 \cdot \sqrt{b}$

$= 28a^6 b^4 \sqrt{5b}$

Reading In Algebra

Determine whether each statement is true or false.

1. The square root of the product of three positive real numbers is the product of their square roots. **T**
2. The greatest perfect square factor of 200 is 25. **F**
3. The greatest perfect square factor of 88 is 4. **T**
4. The simplest radical form of $\sqrt{12}$ is $4\sqrt{3}$. **F**
5. The simplest radical form of $\sqrt{32}$ is $2\sqrt{8}$. **F**
6. There are exactly nine integers between 0 and 101 that are perfect squares. **F**
7. $4x^{14}$ is a perfect square. **T**
8. $9y^9$ is a perfect square. **F**

Written Exercises

Simplify each expression. Approximate the result to the nearest hundredth.

2. $-3\sqrt{15}$; -11.62

$-9\sqrt{3}$;

(A)
1. $\sqrt{250}$ $5\sqrt{10}$; 15.81   2. $-\sqrt{135}$ 3. $\sqrt{180}$ $6\sqrt{5}$; 13.42   4. $-\sqrt{243}$ -15.59

5. $3\sqrt{120}$ $6\sqrt{30}$; 32.86   6. $-10\sqrt{490}$ $-70\sqrt{10}$;   7. $2.5\sqrt{162}$ $22.5\sqrt{2}$;   8. $0.75\sqrt{512}$ $12\sqrt{2}$;

-221.34 31.82   16.97

Simplify each expression. Assume that no denominator has the value of 0.

9. $2\sqrt{27}$ $6\sqrt{3}$ 10. $5\sqrt{32}$ $20\sqrt{2}$ 11. $-6\sqrt{45}$ $-18\sqrt{5}$ 12. $-10\sqrt{96}$ $-40\sqrt{6}$

13. $5\sqrt{4x^6}$ $10x^3$ 14. $\sqrt{12b^2}$ $2b\sqrt{3}$ 15. $9a\sqrt{16a^{12}}$ $36a^7$ 16. $6y^3\sqrt{24y^{10}}$ $12y^8\sqrt{6}$

17. $\sqrt{n^9}$ $n^4\sqrt{n}$ 18. $8\sqrt{y^{15}}$ $8y^7\sqrt{y}$ 19. $-2y^4\sqrt{25y^5}$ 20. $-12c^2\sqrt{8c^{17}}$

$-10y^6\sqrt{y}$ $-24c^{10}\sqrt{2c}$

(B)
21. $\sqrt{24c^{10}d^3}$ $2c^5d\sqrt{6d}$ 22. $ab^2\sqrt{a^{11}b^{16}}$ $a^6b^{10}\sqrt{a}$ 23. $8x^2\sqrt{9x^5y^5}$ $24x^4y^2\sqrt{xy}$

24. $5mn\sqrt{8m^{20}n^7}$ $10m^{11}n^4\sqrt{2n}$ 25. $\sqrt{90a^4b^{15}c^{18}}$ $3a^2b^7c^9\sqrt{10b}$ 26. $c^2d\sqrt{180c^8d^9}$ $6c^6d^5\sqrt{5d}$

27. $7c^2\sqrt{128c^{12}d}$ $56c^8\sqrt{2d}$ 28. $m^2n^4\sqrt{m^{11}n^6p^3}$ $m^7n^7p\sqrt{mp}$ 29. $x^{10}\sqrt{243x^{30}y^{25}}$ $9x^{25}y^{12}\sqrt{3y}$

30. $\dfrac{\sqrt{x^7y^8z^9}}{x^2y^3z^4}$ $xy\sqrt{xz}$ 31. $\dfrac{\sqrt{27a^8b^{11}c^{12}}}{6ab^5c^{10}}$ $\dfrac{a^3\sqrt{3b}}{2c^4}$ 32. $\dfrac{3z\sqrt{108x^5y^7z^9}}{14x^2y^2}$ $\dfrac{9yz^5\sqrt{3xyz}}{7}$

(C)
33. $\sqrt{x^{4m}}$ x^{2m} 34. $\sqrt{x^{4m+1}}$ $x^{2m}\sqrt{x}$ 35. $\sqrt{x^{2m+3}}$ $x^{m+1}\sqrt{x}$ 36. $x^m\sqrt{x^{6m+5}}$ $x^{4m+2}\sqrt{x}$

37. $x^my^n\sqrt{x^{6m}y^{8n}}$ 38. $x^{2m-3}\sqrt{x^{4m+9}}$ 39. $xy\sqrt{x^{6m}y^{8n+3}}$ 40. $x^{2m}y^{3n}\sqrt{x^{2m}y^{3n}}$

$x^{4m}y^{5n}$ $x^{4m+1}\sqrt{x}$ $x^{3m+1}y^{4n+2}\sqrt{y}$ $x^{3m}y^{4n}\sqrt{y^n}$

CALCULATOR ACTIVITIES

You can evaluate $\dfrac{-\sqrt{21}+3\sqrt{55}}{2\sqrt{37}}$, correct to the nearest hundredth, by using the square root table to find decimal values for $\sqrt{21}$, $\sqrt{55}$, and $\sqrt{37}$.

$3 \otimes 7.416 \ominus 4.583 \oslash 2 \oslash 6.083 \ominus 1.4519973 \doteq 1.45$

Find the value of each expression, correct to the nearest hundredth.

-19.39

1. $\dfrac{-37+16\sqrt{83}}{28}$ 3.88   2. $\dfrac{68.4+1.21\sqrt{31}}{\sqrt{19}}$ 3. $\dfrac{-\sqrt{6}+\sqrt{500}}{\sqrt{58}}$ 2.61   4. $\dfrac{-\sqrt{77}-34\sqrt{17}}{\sqrt{59}}$

17.24

A Challenge To You

At a party, Mantia placed 8 saucers around a rectangular table. She put 24 peanuts in the 8 saucers so that there were 9 peanuts along each side of the table.
Ira said, "I can pick up the 24 peanuts, add 8 more, and place the 32 peanuts in the 8 saucers so there will still be 9 peanuts along each side of the table." How can Ira do this?
Place 1–7–1 peanuts along each side.

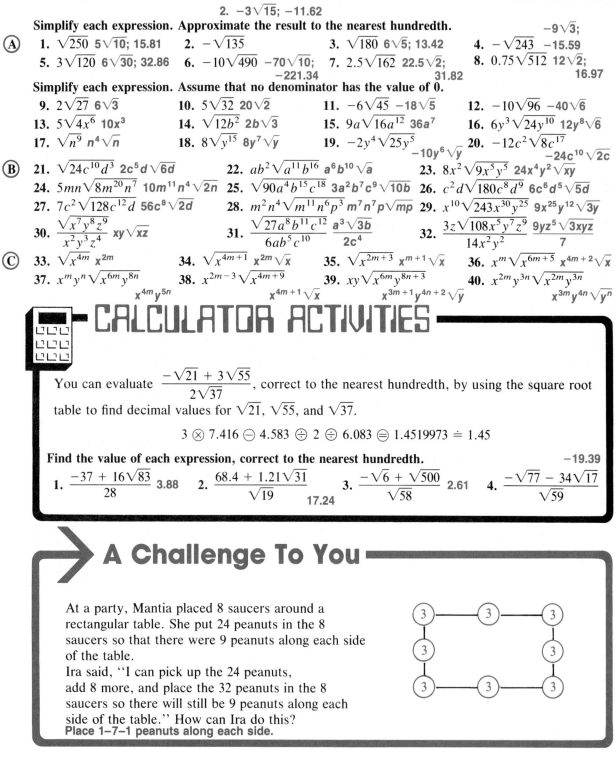

6.3 Sums, Differences, and Products of Radicals

OBJECTIVES ▶ To simplify an expression containing sums or differences of radicals
To simplify an expression containing products of radicals

You have simplified algebraic expressions by combining (adding or subtracting) like terms, using the Distributive property. For example, $5x^2y + 3x^2y + 2xy^2 = (5 + 3)x^2y + 2xy^2 = 8x^2y + 2xy^2$. Expressions containing like radicals can be simplified in a similar way.

$$6\sqrt{10} + 8\sqrt{10} + 2\sqrt{7} = (6 + 8)\sqrt{10} + 2\sqrt{7} = 14\sqrt{10} + 2\sqrt{7}$$

The expression $14\sqrt{10} + 2\sqrt{7}$ is in its simplest radical form since $14\sqrt{10}$ and $2\sqrt{7}$ are *not* like radicals and, therefore, cannot be combined. The like radicals in this case are $6\sqrt{10}$ and $8\sqrt{10}$.

Example 1 Simplify: $8\sqrt{3} + 4\sqrt{6} - 2\sqrt{3} - 7\sqrt{6} + 9\sqrt{5}$.

$$8\sqrt{3} + 4\sqrt{6} - 2\sqrt{3} - 7\sqrt{6} + 9\sqrt{5}$$
$$= (8\sqrt{3} - 2\sqrt{3}) + (4\sqrt{6} - 7\sqrt{6}) + 9\sqrt{5} \quad ◀ \text{ } Group\ the\ like\ radicals\ together.$$
$$= 6\sqrt{3} - 3\sqrt{6} + 9\sqrt{5} \quad ◀ \text{ } Combine\ the\ like\ radicals.$$

Example 2 Simplify each expression.

$$4\sqrt{18} - \sqrt{8} + \sqrt{2} \qquad\qquad \sqrt{36ab^3} - \sqrt{ab^3} + 5b\sqrt{ab}$$

$$4\sqrt{9 \cdot 2} - \sqrt{4 \cdot 2} + \sqrt{2} \qquad\qquad \sqrt{36 \cdot a \cdot b^2 \cdot b} - \sqrt{a \cdot b^2 \cdot b} + 5b\sqrt{ab}$$
$$= 4 \cdot 3\sqrt{2} - 2\sqrt{2} + \sqrt{2} \qquad\qquad = 6b\sqrt{ab} - b\sqrt{ab} + 5b\sqrt{ab}$$
$$= 12\sqrt{2} - 2\sqrt{2} + \sqrt{2} \qquad\qquad = 10b\sqrt{ab}$$
$$= 11\sqrt{2}$$

You can simplify $\sqrt{50} \cdot \sqrt{12}$ as shown at the right. In general, the product of the square roots of two or more real numbers is the square root of the product of the numbers.

$$\sqrt{50} \cdot \sqrt{12} = \sqrt{50 \cdot 12}$$
$$= \sqrt{600}$$
$$= \sqrt{100 \cdot 6}$$
$$= 10\sqrt{6}$$

Product of Square Roots

> For all real numbers $x \geq 0$, $y \geq 0$, $\sqrt{x} \cdot \sqrt{y} = \sqrt{x \cdot y}$
> and $\sqrt{x} \cdot \sqrt{x} = x$.

Using the first product property above,
$$\sqrt{12} \cdot \sqrt{2} = \sqrt{12 \cdot 2} = \sqrt{24} = \sqrt{4 \cdot 6} = 2\sqrt{6}.$$

The second product property on page 145 involves a special case in the multiplication of radicals. Notice that $\sqrt{x} \cdot \sqrt{x} = (\sqrt{x})^2 = x$. Using this property, $\sqrt{17} \cdot \sqrt{17} = 17$ and $\sqrt{m+n} \cdot \sqrt{m+n} = m + n$.

Example 3 Simplify each expression.

$$-7\sqrt{30} \cdot 6\sqrt{30} \qquad\qquad \sqrt{6a^3b^8} \cdot \sqrt{8a^5b^3}$$

$$-7 \cdot 6 \cdot \sqrt{30} \cdot \sqrt{30}$$
$$= -42 \cdot 30 \quad\blacktriangleleft\ \sqrt{x} \cdot \sqrt{x} = x$$
$$= -1{,}260$$

$$\sqrt{6a^3b^8 \cdot 8a^5b^3} \quad\blacktriangleleft\ \sqrt{x} \cdot \sqrt{y} = \sqrt{x \cdot y}$$
$$= \sqrt{6 \cdot 8 \cdot a^3 \cdot a^5 \cdot b^8 \cdot b^3}$$
$$= \sqrt{48a^8b^{11}}$$
$$= \sqrt{16 \cdot 3 \cdot a^8 \cdot b^{10} \cdot b}$$
$$= 4a^4b^5\sqrt{3b}$$

You can also simplify expressions containing products of radicals in which binomials or trinomials are involved. Two such cases are shown in Example 4.

Example 4 Simplify each expression.

$$5\sqrt{3}(2\sqrt{6} + 4\sqrt{3} - \sqrt{7}) \qquad\qquad (3\sqrt{5} + \sqrt{2})(4\sqrt{5} - 6\sqrt{2})$$

Use the Distributive property to multiply.
$$5\sqrt{3} \cdot 2\sqrt{6} + 5\sqrt{3} \cdot 4\sqrt{3} - 5\sqrt{3} \cdot \sqrt{7}$$
$$= 10\sqrt{18} + 20 \cdot 3 - 5\sqrt{21}$$
$$= 10 \cdot \sqrt{9 \cdot 2} + 60 - 5\sqrt{21}$$
$$= 30\sqrt{2} + 60 - 5\sqrt{21}$$

Use the FOIL method to multiply.
$$3\sqrt{5} \cdot 4\sqrt{5} - 3\sqrt{5} \cdot 6\sqrt{2} + \sqrt{2} \cdot 4\sqrt{5} - \sqrt{2} \cdot 6\sqrt{2}$$
$$= 12 \cdot 5 - 18\sqrt{10} + 4\sqrt{10} - 6 \cdot 2$$
$$= 60 - 18\sqrt{10} + 4\sqrt{10} - 12$$
$$= 48 - 14\sqrt{10}$$

The special product formulas, $(a + b)(a - b) = a^2 - b^2$ and $(a - b)^2 = a^2 - 2ab + b^2$, can sometimes be used to simplify expressions containing products of radicals.

Example 5 Simplify each expression.

$$(2\sqrt{7} + 4\sqrt{3})(2\sqrt{7} - 4\sqrt{3}) \qquad (3\sqrt{c} - 5\sqrt{d})^2$$

$$(a + b)(a - b) = a^2 - b^2 \blacktriangleright \begin{aligned}&(2\sqrt{7} + 4\sqrt{3})(2\sqrt{7} - 4\sqrt{3}) \\ &= (2\sqrt{7})^2 - (4\sqrt{3})^2 \\ &= 28 - 48,\ \text{or} -20 \end{aligned}$$

$$\begin{aligned}&(3\sqrt{c} - 5\sqrt{d})^2 \\ &= (3\sqrt{c})^2 - 2 \cdot 3\sqrt{c} \cdot 5\sqrt{d} + (5\sqrt{d})^2 \\ &= 9c - 30\sqrt{cd} + 25d \end{aligned}$$

In Example 5, notice how the Power of a Product property, $(xy)^n = x^n \cdot y^n$, is used with radical expressions:
$$(2\sqrt{7})^2 = (2)^2 \cdot (\sqrt{7})^2 = 4 \cdot 7 = 28 \text{ and}$$
$$(5\sqrt{d})^2 = (5)^2 \cdot (\sqrt{d})^2 = 25 \cdot d = 25d.$$

Simplify each expression. $-3\sqrt{30}$ $10\sqrt{cd}$ $\sqrt{6ab}$
1. $\sqrt{11} \cdot \sqrt{7}$ $\sqrt{77}$ 2. $-3\sqrt{6} \cdot \sqrt{5}$ 3. $5\sqrt{c} \cdot 2\sqrt{d}$ 4. $\sqrt{2a} \cdot \sqrt{3b}$ 5. $(\sqrt{c})^2$ c
6. $\sqrt{2} \cdot \sqrt{32}$ 8 7. $\sqrt{3} \cdot \sqrt{12}$ 6 8. $\sqrt{5} \cdot \sqrt{2} \cdot \sqrt{10}$ 9. $\sqrt{3} + \sqrt{3}$ $2\sqrt{3}$ 10. $5\sqrt{2} - \sqrt{2}$
10 $4\sqrt{2}$

Simplify each expression.   11. $60 - 15\sqrt{2} + 6\sqrt{35}$ 2. $3\sqrt{5} - 6\sqrt{6} + 10\sqrt{3}$

Ⓐ 1. $3\sqrt{10} + 9\sqrt{7} - 8\sqrt{10} - 3\sqrt{7}$ $-5\sqrt{10} + 6\sqrt{7}$ 2. $4\sqrt{5} - 7\sqrt{6} - \sqrt{5} + 10\sqrt{3} + \sqrt{6}$
3. $7\sqrt{45} - \sqrt{20} + \sqrt{5} - \sqrt{80}$ $16\sqrt{5}$ 4. $3\sqrt{50} + 4\sqrt{18} - 2\sqrt{32} - \sqrt{8}$ $17\sqrt{2}$
5. $\sqrt{25n} - 7\sqrt{n} + \sqrt{16n}$ $2\sqrt{n}$ 6. $\sqrt{x} - 6\sqrt{4x} - \sqrt{9x} + 5\sqrt{36x}$ $16\sqrt{x}$
7. $8\sqrt{6} \cdot 5\sqrt{10}$ $80\sqrt{15}$ 8. $-2\sqrt{15} \cdot 4\sqrt{5} \cdot \sqrt{6}$ $-120\sqrt{2}$
9. $\sqrt{6y} \cdot \sqrt{3y^9}$ $3y^5\sqrt{2}$ 10. $4\sqrt{3x^3} \cdot 5\sqrt{15x^8}$ $60x^5\sqrt{5x}$
11. $3\sqrt{5}(4\sqrt{5} - \sqrt{10} + 2\sqrt{7})$ **above**   12. $-4\sqrt{6}(\sqrt{15} + 8\sqrt{7} - 2\sqrt{6})$ **below**
13. $(4\sqrt{11} + 6)(2\sqrt{11} - 8)$ $40 - 20\sqrt{11}$ 14. $(\sqrt{10} - 2\sqrt{3})(6\sqrt{10} - \sqrt{3})$ $66 - 13\sqrt{30}$
15. $(2\sqrt{7} - 4\sqrt{2})(5\sqrt{7} + 6\sqrt{2})$ $22 - 8\sqrt{14}$ 16. $(8\sqrt{30} + 4\sqrt{7})(\sqrt{30} + \sqrt{7})$ $268 + 12\sqrt{210}$
17. $(-3\sqrt{11})^2$ 99 18. $(7\sqrt{x})^2$ $49x$
19. $(20\sqrt{17})^2$ $6{,}800$ 20. $(-8\sqrt{y} + 2)^2$ $64y + 128$
21. $(5\sqrt{3} + 7)(5\sqrt{3} - 7)$ 26 22. $(6\sqrt{5} + 4\sqrt{6})(6\sqrt{5} - 4\sqrt{6})$ 84
23. $(\sqrt{7} + \sqrt{6})^2$ $13 + 2\sqrt{42}$ 24. $(5\sqrt{2} - 4\sqrt{3})^2$ $98 - 40\sqrt{6}$
25. $(4\sqrt{x} + 2\sqrt{5})(4\sqrt{x} - 2\sqrt{5})$ $16x - 20$ 26. $(3\sqrt{7} - 8\sqrt{y})(3\sqrt{7} + 8\sqrt{y})$ $63 - 64y$
27. $(6\sqrt{n} - 6)^2$ $36n - 72\sqrt{n} + 36$ 28. $(5\sqrt{c} + 4\sqrt{10})^2$ $25c + 40\sqrt{10c} + 160$

12. $-12\sqrt{10} - 32\sqrt{42} + 48$ 30. $15\sqrt{2} - 17\sqrt{5}$ 36. $-160x^5y^6\sqrt{3xy}$

Ⓑ 29. $\sqrt{8} + \sqrt{12} + \sqrt{18} + \sqrt{27}$ $5\sqrt{2} + 5\sqrt{3}$ 30. $5\sqrt{2} - 4\sqrt{20} - 3\sqrt{45} + 2\sqrt{50}$
31. $2\sqrt{c^2d} + \sqrt{36c^2d} - 3c\sqrt{d}$ $5c\sqrt{d}$ 32. $12b^2\sqrt{ab} - \sqrt{25ab^5} + 10\sqrt{ab^5}$ $17b^2\sqrt{ab}$
33. $5\sqrt{3m^2n^3} + 2mn\sqrt{27n}$ $11mn\sqrt{3n}$ 34. $2x^2\sqrt{20x^3y} - x^2\sqrt{45x^3y} - x^3\sqrt{5xy}$ 0
35. $\sqrt{3c^3d^5} \cdot 8\sqrt{8cd^7}$ $16c^2d^6\sqrt{6}$ 36. $-8x\sqrt{6xy^5} \cdot 5y\sqrt{8x^5y^3} \cdot xy\sqrt{xy}$ **above**
37. $(4\sqrt{c} + \sqrt{7})(8\sqrt{c} - 3\sqrt{7})$ $32c - 4\sqrt{7c} - 21$ 38. $(5\sqrt{a} - \sqrt{b})(4\sqrt{a} - \sqrt{b})$ $20a - 9\sqrt{ab} + b$
39. $(\sqrt{x} - 3\sqrt{y})(3\sqrt{x} + \sqrt{y})$ $3x - 8\sqrt{xy} - 3y$ 40. $(x\sqrt{y} + y\sqrt{x})(2x\sqrt{y} + 3y\sqrt{x})$ **below**
41. $(5\sqrt{c} - 4\sqrt{d})(5\sqrt{c} + 4\sqrt{d})$ $25c - 16d$ 42. $(7\sqrt{a} + 2b)(7\sqrt{a} - 2b)$ $49a - 4b^2$
43. $(\sqrt{a} + \sqrt{b})^2$ $a + 2\sqrt{ab} + b$ 44. $(6\sqrt{c} - 5\sqrt{d})^2$ $36c - 60\sqrt{cd} + 25d$

$x + 39 + 12\sqrt{x + 4}$ 40. $2x^2y + 5xy\sqrt{xy} + 3xy^2$

Ⓒ 45. $(\sqrt{x + 4} + 5)(\sqrt{x + 4} + 7)$ 46. $(\sqrt{3x - 7} - 4)(\sqrt{3x - 7} + 4)$ $3x - 23$
47. $(\sqrt{x + y} + \sqrt{y})(\sqrt{x + y} - \sqrt{y})$ x 48. $(6 - \sqrt{y - 3})^2$ $y + 33 - 12\sqrt{y - 3}$
49. $(\sqrt{n + 5} - \sqrt{n})^2$ $2n + 5 - 2\sqrt{n^2 + 5n}$ 50. $(3\sqrt{c - 8} + 4\sqrt{c})^2$ $25c - 72 + 24\sqrt{c^2 - 8c}$
51. $(\sqrt{m} - \sqrt{n})(\sqrt{m} + \sqrt{n})$ 52. $(2\sqrt{x} - \sqrt{y})(2\sqrt{x} + \sqrt{y})$ 53. $(\sqrt{c} - 6\sqrt{d})(\sqrt{c} + 6\sqrt{d})$
Factor each binomial as a difference of two squares.   54. $(\sqrt{5a} - \sqrt{3b})(\sqrt{5a} + \sqrt{3b})$
[Hint: Rewrite $x - y$ as $(\sqrt{x})^2 - (\sqrt{y})^2$.]   56. $(3\sqrt{c} - d\sqrt{7})(3\sqrt{c} + d\sqrt{7})$
51. $m - n$ 52. $4x - y$ 53. $c - 36d$ 54. $5a - 3b$
55. $x^2 - 2y$ 56. $9c - 7d^2$ 57. $6m^2 - 25n$ 58. $49a^2b - 10cd^2$
$(x - \sqrt{2y})(x + \sqrt{2y})$ 57. $(m\sqrt{6} - 5\sqrt{n})(m\sqrt{6} + 5\sqrt{n})$ $(7a\sqrt{b} - d\sqrt{10c})(7a\sqrt{b} + d\sqrt{10c})$

SUMS, DIFFERENCES, AND PRODUCTS OF RADICALS

6.4 Quotients of Radicals

OBJECTIVE ▶ To simplify an expression containing a quotient of radicals

The quotient of the square roots of two real numbers is the square root of the quotient of the numbers.

Quotient of Square Roots

$$\text{For all real numbers } x \geq 0,\, y > 0,\, \frac{\sqrt{x}}{\sqrt{y}} = \sqrt{\frac{x}{y}}.$$

The expression $\dfrac{\sqrt{24}}{\sqrt{3}}$ contains a quotient of two square roots in which the radicand in the numerator is exactly divisible by the radicand in the denominator. Expressions of this type can be simplified by applying the Quotient of Square Roots property, as shown in Example 1.

Example 1

Simplify each expression.

$$\frac{\sqrt{24}}{\sqrt{3}} \qquad\qquad \frac{\sqrt{28n^6}}{\sqrt{7n^2}} \qquad\qquad \frac{\sqrt{18c^7}}{\sqrt{6c^2}}$$

$$= \sqrt{\frac{24}{3}} \quad \blacktriangleleft\; \frac{\sqrt{x}}{\sqrt{y}} = \sqrt{\frac{x}{y}} \qquad = \sqrt{\frac{28n^6}{7n^2}} \qquad = \sqrt{\frac{18c^7}{6c^2}}$$

$$= \sqrt{8} \qquad\qquad\qquad\qquad\quad = \sqrt{4n^4} \qquad\qquad = \sqrt{3c^5}$$

$$= 2\sqrt{2} \qquad\qquad\qquad\qquad\; = 2n^2 \qquad\qquad\quad = c^2\sqrt{3c}$$

To simplify an expression like $\dfrac{\sqrt{5}}{3\sqrt{2}}$, in which the radicand in the numerator is *not* exactly divisible by the radicand in the denominator, a procedure called **rationalizing the denominator** is used. The denominator, $3\sqrt{2}$, is an irrational number. Notice what happens when $\dfrac{\sqrt{5}}{3\sqrt{2}}$ is multiplied by $\dfrac{\sqrt{2}}{\sqrt{2}}$, or 1.

$$\frac{\sqrt{5}}{3\sqrt{2}} = \frac{\sqrt{5}}{3\sqrt{2}} \cdot \frac{\sqrt{2}}{\sqrt{2}} = \frac{\sqrt{5}\cdot\sqrt{2}}{3\sqrt{2}\cdot\sqrt{2}} = \frac{\sqrt{10}}{3\cdot 2} = \frac{\sqrt{10}}{6}$$

The new denominator, 6, is a rational number.

Example 2

Simplify $\dfrac{6\sqrt{8}}{\sqrt{6}}$.

$$\frac{6\sqrt{8}}{\sqrt{6}} = \frac{6\sqrt{8}}{\sqrt{6}} \cdot \frac{\sqrt{6}}{\sqrt{6}} = \frac{6\sqrt{8}\cdot\sqrt{6}}{\sqrt{6}\cdot\sqrt{6}} = \frac{6\sqrt{48}}{6} = \sqrt{48} = \sqrt{16\cdot 3} = 4\sqrt{3}$$

Contrast the following two methods of rationalizing the denominator of $\dfrac{1}{\sqrt{12}}$:

Method 1: $\qquad \dfrac{1}{\sqrt{12}} = \dfrac{1}{2\sqrt{3}} \cdot \dfrac{\sqrt{3}}{\sqrt{3}} = \dfrac{\sqrt{3}}{6}$

Method 2: $\qquad \dfrac{1}{\sqrt{12}} = \dfrac{1}{\sqrt{12}} \cdot \dfrac{\sqrt{12}}{\sqrt{12}} = \dfrac{\sqrt{12}}{12} = \dfrac{2\sqrt{3}}{12} = \dfrac{\sqrt{3}}{6}$

In Method 1, simplifying the radical in the denominator before rationalizing made the work easier. The numerator and denominator of the original fraction were multiplied by a smaller number, $\sqrt{3}$, as opposed to $\sqrt{12}$, which was used in Method 2.

Example 3

Simplify $\dfrac{5\sqrt{7}}{\sqrt{12}}$ and $\dfrac{9\sqrt{5x}}{\sqrt{24x^4 y^3}}$.

$$\begin{aligned} \dfrac{5\sqrt{7}}{\sqrt{12}} &= \dfrac{5\sqrt{7}}{2\sqrt{3}} = \dfrac{5\sqrt{7}}{2\sqrt{3}} \cdot \dfrac{\sqrt{3}}{\sqrt{3}} \\ &= \dfrac{5\sqrt{7} \cdot \sqrt{3}}{2\sqrt{3} \cdot \sqrt{3}} \\ &= \dfrac{5\sqrt{21}}{6} \end{aligned}$$

$$\begin{aligned} \dfrac{9\sqrt{5x}}{\sqrt{24x^4 y^3}} &= \dfrac{9\sqrt{5x}}{2x^2 y \sqrt{6y}} \\ &= \dfrac{9\sqrt{5x}}{2x^2 y \sqrt{6y}} \cdot \dfrac{\sqrt{6y}}{\sqrt{6y}} \\ &= \dfrac{9\sqrt{30xy}}{12x^2 y^2}, \text{ or } \dfrac{3\sqrt{30xy}}{4x^2 y^2} \end{aligned}$$

The denominator of $\dfrac{7}{\sqrt{15} - \sqrt{10}}$ contains two terms. To rationalize this denominator, you use the **conjugate** of $\sqrt{15} - \sqrt{10}$, which is $\sqrt{15} + \sqrt{10}$. The product of these two irrational expressions is $(\sqrt{15} - \sqrt{10})(\sqrt{15} + \sqrt{10})$, which is equal to $15 - 10$, or the rational number 5.

Property of Conjugates

> The two binomials, $a + b$ and $a - b$, are a pair of *conjugates.* Their product is a difference of two squares: $(a + b)(a - b) = a^2 - b^2$.

The Property of Conjugates is used in Example 4 to simplify two radical expressions whose denominators are binomials.

Example 4

Simplify $\dfrac{7}{\sqrt{15} - \sqrt{10}}$ and $\dfrac{6\sqrt{y}}{5x + 2\sqrt{y}}$.

$$\begin{aligned} \dfrac{7}{\sqrt{15} - \sqrt{10}} &= \dfrac{7}{\sqrt{15} - \sqrt{10}} \cdot \dfrac{\sqrt{15} + \sqrt{10}}{\sqrt{15} + \sqrt{10}} \\ &= \dfrac{7(\sqrt{15} + \sqrt{10})}{(\sqrt{15} - \sqrt{10})(\sqrt{15} + \sqrt{10})} \\ &= \dfrac{7\sqrt{15} + 7\sqrt{10}}{(\sqrt{15})^2 - (\sqrt{10})^2} \\ &= \dfrac{7\sqrt{15} + 7\sqrt{10}}{5} \end{aligned}$$

$(a - b)(a + b) = a^2 - b^2$

$$\begin{aligned} \dfrac{6\sqrt{y}}{5x + 2\sqrt{y}} &= \dfrac{6\sqrt{y}}{5x + 2\sqrt{y}} \cdot \dfrac{5x - 2\sqrt{y}}{5x - 2\sqrt{y}} \\ &= \dfrac{6\sqrt{y}(5x - 2\sqrt{y})}{(5x + 2\sqrt{y})(5x - 2\sqrt{y})} \\ &= \dfrac{30x\sqrt{y} - 12y}{(5x)^2 - (2\sqrt{y})^2} \\ &= \dfrac{30x\sqrt{y} - 12y}{25x^2 - 4y} \end{aligned}$$

QUOTIENTS OF RADICALS

To simplify $\sqrt{\dfrac{7}{10}}$, you use the Quotient of Square Roots property to rewrite it as $\dfrac{\sqrt{7}}{\sqrt{10}}$ and then proceed to rationalize the denominator.

Example 5 Simplify $\sqrt{\dfrac{7}{10}}$.

$$\sqrt{\frac{7}{10}} = \frac{\sqrt{7}}{\sqrt{10}} = \frac{\sqrt{7}}{\sqrt{10}} \cdot \frac{\sqrt{10}}{\sqrt{10}} = \frac{\sqrt{70}}{10}$$

Example 6 Simplify $\sqrt{\dfrac{5c}{12d^3}}$.

$$\sqrt{\frac{5c}{12d^3}} = \frac{\sqrt{5c}}{\sqrt{12d^3}} = \frac{\sqrt{5c}}{2d\sqrt{3d}} = \frac{\sqrt{5c}}{2d\sqrt{3d}} \cdot \frac{\sqrt{3d}}{\sqrt{3d}} = \frac{\sqrt{15cd}}{6d^2}$$

Summary	An expression is in simplest radical form when (1) each radicand contains no factor, other than 1, that is a perfect square, (2) the denominator contains no radicals, and (3) each radicand contains no fractions.

Reading In Algebra

Indicate why each expression is not in simplest radical form.

1. $\dfrac{5x^2}{\sqrt{3x}}$ The denominator contains a radical.

2. $\dfrac{\sqrt{8y}}{5y}$ The radicand contains a perfect square factor.

3. $\sqrt{\dfrac{7m}{3n}}$ The radicand contains a fraction.

4. $\dfrac{4\sqrt{3}}{6 - 5\sqrt{2}}$ The denominator contains a radical.

Oral Exercises

Determine the conjugate of each expression.

1. $3x + 2y$ $3x - 2y$ 2. $2\sqrt{3} - 5\sqrt{2}$ $2\sqrt{3} + 5\sqrt{2}$ 3. $-2 + \sqrt{6}$ $-2 - \sqrt{6}$ 4. $-\sqrt{30} - \sqrt{10}$ $-\sqrt{30} + \sqrt{10}$

Written Exercises

Simplify each expression. Assume that no denominator has the value of 0.

(A) 1. $\dfrac{\sqrt{21}}{\sqrt{7}}$ $\sqrt{3}$ 2. $\dfrac{\sqrt{90}}{\sqrt{10}}$ 3 3. $\dfrac{\sqrt{88}}{\sqrt{11}}$ $2\sqrt{2}$ 4. $\dfrac{\sqrt{150}}{\sqrt{2}}$ $5\sqrt{3}$

5. $\dfrac{\sqrt{a^{10}}}{\sqrt{a^6}}$ a^2 6. $\dfrac{\sqrt{x^6}}{\sqrt{x}}$ $x^2\sqrt{x}$ 7. $\dfrac{\sqrt{45n^9}}{\sqrt{5n^3}}$ $3n^3$ 8. $\dfrac{\sqrt{24x^{12}}}{\sqrt{3x^5}}$ $2x^3\sqrt{2x}$

9. $\dfrac{1}{\sqrt{7}}$ $\dfrac{\sqrt{7}}{7}$ 10. $\dfrac{8}{5\sqrt{3}}$ $\dfrac{8\sqrt{3}}{15}$ 11. $\dfrac{\sqrt{11}}{2\sqrt{6}}$ $\dfrac{\sqrt{66}}{12}$ 12. $\dfrac{-7\sqrt{6}}{6\sqrt{5}}$ $\dfrac{-7\sqrt{30}}{30}$

13. $\dfrac{7}{\sqrt{12}}$ $\dfrac{7\sqrt{3}}{6}$ 14. $\dfrac{6}{\sqrt{8}}$ $\dfrac{3\sqrt{2}}{2}$ 15. $\dfrac{-5}{\sqrt{32}}$ $\dfrac{-5\sqrt{2}}{8}$ 16. $\dfrac{5\sqrt{44}}{\sqrt{18}}$ $\dfrac{5\sqrt{22}}{3}$

17. $\dfrac{5}{\sqrt{x^3}}$ $\dfrac{5\sqrt{x}}{x^2}$ 18. $\dfrac{6}{\sqrt{9c^5}}$ $\dfrac{2\sqrt{c}}{c^3}$ 19. $\dfrac{-10d}{\sqrt{32d^3}}$ $\dfrac{-5\sqrt{2d}}{4d}$ 20. $\dfrac{15x^2}{\sqrt{5x^7}}$ $\dfrac{3\sqrt{5x}}{x^2}$

21. $\dfrac{7}{6-\sqrt{30}}$ $\dfrac{42+7\sqrt{30}}{6}$ 22. $\dfrac{-5}{3+\sqrt{2}}$ $\dfrac{-15+5\sqrt{2}}{7}$ 23. $\dfrac{\sqrt{2}}{\sqrt{15}-3}$ $\dfrac{\sqrt{30}+3\sqrt{2}}{6}$ 24. $\dfrac{-\sqrt{7}}{\sqrt{26}+4}$ $\dfrac{-\sqrt{182}+4\sqrt{7}}{10}$

25. $\sqrt{\dfrac{5}{11}}$ $\dfrac{\sqrt{55}}{11}$ 26. $\sqrt{\dfrac{3c}{5d}}$ $\dfrac{\sqrt{15cd}}{5d}$ 27. $\sqrt{\dfrac{23x}{8y}}$ $\dfrac{\sqrt{46xy}}{4y}$ 28. $\sqrt{\dfrac{27m}{32n}}$ $\dfrac{3\sqrt{6mn}}{8n}$

Ⓑ 29. $\sqrt{\dfrac{4x^7}{7y^3}}$ $\dfrac{2x^3\sqrt{7xy}}{7y^2}$ 30. $\sqrt{\dfrac{7a^3}{8m^3n^5}}$ $\dfrac{a\sqrt{14amn}}{4m^2n^3}$ 31. $\sqrt{\dfrac{3c-5}{6}}$ $\dfrac{\sqrt{18c-30}}{6}$ 32. $\sqrt{\dfrac{5}{4x+9}}$ $\dfrac{\sqrt{20x+45}}{4x+9}$

33. $\dfrac{10}{\sqrt{22}+\sqrt{11}}$ 34. $\dfrac{2}{5\sqrt{3}-\sqrt{15}}$ $\dfrac{5\sqrt{3}+\sqrt{15}}{30}$ 35. $\dfrac{\sqrt{5}}{2\sqrt{5}+3\sqrt{2}}$ $\dfrac{10-3\sqrt{10}}{2}$ 36. $\dfrac{2\sqrt{3}}{4\sqrt{2}-3\sqrt{3}}$ $\dfrac{8\sqrt{6}+18}{5}$

37. $\dfrac{5+\sqrt{10}}{8-\sqrt{10}}$ $\dfrac{50+13\sqrt{10}}{54}$ 38. $\dfrac{\sqrt{7}+2}{3\sqrt{7}+9}$ $\dfrac{1-\sqrt{7}}{-6}$ 39. $\dfrac{3\sqrt{x}}{5\sqrt{x}-2\sqrt{y}}$ 40. $\dfrac{\sqrt{cd}}{6\sqrt{c}-3\sqrt{d}}$ below

Ⓒ 41. $\dfrac{3\sqrt{x+y}}{\sqrt{x+y}+2}$ 42. $\dfrac{\sqrt{c+d}}{5-\sqrt{c+d}}$ below   43. $\dfrac{4\sqrt{5}}{(\sqrt{5}+\sqrt{3})-2}$ 44. $\dfrac{\sqrt{2}}{(\sqrt{30}-\sqrt{2})+3}$

45. $\dfrac{2\sqrt{c-d}}{6-\sqrt{c-d}}$ 46. $\dfrac{2\sqrt{7}}{1+(\sqrt{7}-\sqrt{5})}$ 47. $\dfrac{3\sqrt{11}}{(\sqrt{11}+\sqrt{7})+5}$ below   48. $\dfrac{-2\sqrt{c}+\sqrt{c+d}}{\sqrt{c}-\sqrt{c+d}}$

$\dfrac{12\sqrt{c-d}+2c-2d}{36-c+d}$ $\dfrac{-22\sqrt{7}+14+6\sqrt{35}-28\sqrt{5}}{-19}$ $\dfrac{-c+d-\sqrt{c^2+cd}}{-d}$

➤ A Challenge To You

33. $\dfrac{10\sqrt{22}-10\sqrt{11}}{11}$ 39. $\dfrac{15x+6\sqrt{xy}}{25x-4y}$

Simplify each expression.   47. $\dfrac{693+87\sqrt{77}-105\sqrt{11}-330\sqrt{7}}{259}$ 40. $\dfrac{2c\sqrt{d}+d\sqrt{c}}{12c-3d}$

1. $\dfrac{\sqrt{\sqrt{\sqrt{16x^{12}}}}}{\sqrt{\sqrt{25y^{10}}}}$ $\dfrac{x\sqrt{10xy}}{5y^3}$ 2. $\dfrac{\sqrt{\sqrt{\sqrt{\sqrt{256x^{64}}}}}}{\sqrt{\sqrt{\sqrt{81y^{32}}}}}$ $\dfrac{x^4\sqrt{6}}{3y^4}$

CALCULATOR ACTIVITIES

41. $\dfrac{3x+3y-6\sqrt{x+y}}{x+y-4}$ 42. $\dfrac{5\sqrt{c+d}+c+d}{25-c-d}$ 43. $\dfrac{-10-6\sqrt{15}+8\sqrt{5}-20\sqrt{3}}{-11}$

To find the value of $\dfrac{2\sqrt{3}}{3\sqrt{7}+\sqrt{19}}$ to the nearest hundredth, you can proceed as follows:

$$\dfrac{2\sqrt{3}}{3\sqrt{7}+\sqrt{19}} \cdot \dfrac{3\sqrt{7}-\sqrt{19}}{3\sqrt{7}-\sqrt{19}} = \dfrac{2\sqrt{3}(3\sqrt{7}-\sqrt{19})}{44} \doteq \dfrac{2\times1.732\times(3\times2.646-4.359)}{44}$$

$$\doteq 0.2817649$$
$$\doteq 0.28 \text{ to the nearest } 0.01$$

Find the value of each expression to the nearest hundredth.

1. $\dfrac{5\sqrt{6}}{4\sqrt{11}+\sqrt{33}}$ 0.64   2. $\dfrac{14\sqrt{2}}{15\sqrt{3}-\sqrt{97}}$ 1.23   3. $\dfrac{8\sqrt{89}}{\sqrt{74}-3\sqrt{6}}$ 60.19

QUOTIENTS OF RADICALS   44. $\dfrac{74-69\sqrt{2}+38\sqrt{15}-12\sqrt{30}}{289}$

6.5 Other Radicals

OBJECTIVE ▶ **To simplify expressions containing cube roots, fourth roots, or fifth roots**

You have solved equations like $x^2 = 49$ by using the definition of square root. In a similar way, you can solve equations such as $x^3 = -8$, $x^4 = 16$, and $x^5 = -32$.

If $x^3 = -8$,	If $x^4 = 16$,	If $x^5 = -32$,
then $x = \sqrt[3]{-8} = -2$	then $x = \sqrt[4]{16} = 2$ or $x = -\sqrt[4]{16} = -2$	then $x = \sqrt[5]{-32} = -2$
since $(-2)^3 = -8$.	since $2^4 = 16$ and $(-2)^4 = 16$.	since $(-2)^5 = -32$.

The three illustrations above suggest that:
(1) if $x^3 = k$, then $x = \sqrt[3]{k}$,
(2) if $x^4 = k$, and $k \geq 0$, then $x = \sqrt[4]{k}$ or $x = -\sqrt[4]{k}$, and
(3) if $x^5 = k$, then $x = \sqrt[5]{k}$.
This leads to the following definition of the **nth root** of a real number k.

Definition: nth Root

> For all odd integers $n > 1$ and all real numbers k, if $x^n = k$, then $x = \sqrt[n]{k}$.
> For all even integers $n > 1$ and all real numbers $k \geq 0$, if $x^n = k$, then $x = \sqrt[n]{k}$ or $x = -\sqrt[n]{k}$.

The symbol $\sqrt[n]{k}$ (read "the nth root of k") is called a **radical** where k is the **radicand**, $\sqrt[n]{}$ is the **radical sign,** and n is the **index.** [Note: The index 2 is usually omitted so that $\sqrt{k}$ and $\sqrt[2]{k}$ both mean "the square root of k."]
You may find the following table of powers helpful when you are required to simplify cube roots, fourth roots, or fifth roots.

Base	n	2	3	4	5	10	x^2	x^3	x^4
3rd power	n^3	8	27	64	125	1,000	x^6	x^9	x^{12}
4th power	n^4	16	81	256	625	10,000	x^8	x^{12}	x^{16}
5th power	n^5	32	243	1,024	3,125	100,000	x^{10}	x^{15}	x^{20}

All the properties involving operations with square roots can be extended to other radicals. For example, the Square Root of a Product property can be extended to cube roots as shown below.

$$\sqrt[3]{8x^{12}} = \sqrt[3]{8} \cdot \sqrt[3]{x^{12}} = 2x^4$$

Use the table above to verify that $\sqrt[3]{8} = 2$ and $\sqrt[3]{x^{12}} = x^4$.

nth Root of a Product

> For all odd integers $n > 1$ and all real numbers x and y, $\sqrt[n]{x \cdot y} = \sqrt[n]{x} \cdot \sqrt[n]{y}$.
> For all even integers $n > 1$ and all real numbers $x \geq 0$, $y \geq 0$, $\sqrt[n]{x \cdot y} = \sqrt[n]{x} \cdot \sqrt[n]{y}$.

You can use the *n*th Root of a Product property to simplify radicals such as $\sqrt[5]{-64}$. First find the greatest 5th power that is also a factor of -64, as shown in Example 1.

Example 1 Simplify $\sqrt[5]{-64}$.

$$\sqrt[5]{-64} = \sqrt[5]{-32 \cdot 2} = \sqrt[5]{-32} \cdot \sqrt[5]{2} = -2\sqrt[5]{2}$$

Example 2 Simplify $\sqrt[3]{c^8}$.

$$\sqrt[3]{c^8} = \sqrt[3]{c^6} \cdot \sqrt[3]{c^2} = c^2\sqrt[3]{c^2}$$

Example 3 Simplify $\sqrt[4]{64a^{21}}$.

$$\sqrt[4]{64a^{21}} = \sqrt[4]{16 \cdot 4 \cdot a^{20} \cdot a} = \sqrt[4]{16} \cdot \sqrt[4]{4} \cdot \sqrt[4]{a^{20}} \cdot \sqrt[4]{a} = 2a^5\sqrt[4]{4a}$$

You can combine (add or subtract) like radicals and simplify products of radicals for *n*th roots as you have done previously with square roots.

Example 4 Simplify $5\sqrt[3]{3} + \sqrt[3]{24} + \sqrt[3]{81}$.

$$5\sqrt[3]{3} + \sqrt[3]{24} + \sqrt[3]{81} = 5\sqrt[3]{3} + \sqrt[3]{8 \cdot 3} + \sqrt[3]{27 \cdot 3} = 5\sqrt[3]{3} + 2\sqrt[3]{3} + 3\sqrt[3]{3} = 10\sqrt[3]{3}$$

Example 5 Simplify $\sqrt[4]{8d^3} \cdot \sqrt[4]{10d} \cdot \sqrt[4]{d^2}$.

$$\sqrt[4]{8d^3} \cdot \sqrt[4]{10d} \cdot \sqrt[4]{d^2} = \sqrt[4]{8d^3 \cdot 10d \cdot d^2} = \sqrt[4]{80d^6} = \sqrt[4]{16 \cdot 5 \cdot d^4 \cdot d^2} = 2d\sqrt[4]{5d^2}$$

Recall that $\sqrt{5} \cdot \sqrt{5} = (\sqrt{5})^2 = 5$. Similarly, notice that

$$\sqrt[3]{27} \cdot \sqrt[3]{27} \cdot \sqrt[3]{27} = (\sqrt[3]{27})^3 = (3)^3 = 27 \text{ and}$$
$$\sqrt[4]{16} \cdot \sqrt[4]{16} \cdot \sqrt[4]{16} \cdot \sqrt[4]{16} = (\sqrt[4]{16})^4 = (2)^4 = 16.$$

In general, $(\sqrt[n]{k})^n = k$. This property may be used to *rationalize the denominator* of a radical expression, as shown in Example 6.

Example 6 Simplify $\dfrac{5}{\sqrt[3]{36}}$.

$$\frac{5}{\sqrt[3]{36}} = \frac{5}{\sqrt[3]{6 \cdot 6}} = \frac{5}{\sqrt[3]{6} \cdot \sqrt[3]{6}} = \frac{5}{\sqrt[3]{6} \cdot \sqrt[3]{6}} \cdot \frac{\sqrt[3]{6}}{\sqrt[3]{6}} = \frac{5 \cdot \sqrt[3]{6}}{(\sqrt[3]{6})^3} = \frac{5\sqrt[3]{6}}{6}$$

nth Root of a Quotient

For all odd integers $n > 1$ and all real numbers x and y, $y \neq 0$, and for all even integers $n > 1$ and all real numbers $x \geq 0$, $y > 0$,

$$\sqrt[n]{\frac{x}{y}} = \frac{\sqrt[n]{x}}{\sqrt[n]{y}}.$$

Example 7 Simplify $\sqrt[4]{\dfrac{7}{25a^3}}$.

$$\sqrt[4]{\frac{7}{25a^3}} = \frac{\sqrt[4]{7}}{\sqrt[4]{25a^3}} = \frac{\sqrt[4]{7}}{\sqrt[4]{5 \cdot 5 \cdot a \cdot a \cdot a}} = \frac{\sqrt[4]{7}}{\sqrt[4]{5 \cdot 5 \cdot a \cdot a \cdot a}} \cdot \frac{\sqrt[4]{5 \cdot 5 \cdot a}}{\sqrt[4]{5 \cdot 5 \cdot a}} = \frac{\sqrt[4]{7 \cdot 25a}}{\sqrt[4]{5^4 a^4}} = \frac{\sqrt[4]{175a}}{5a}$$

Written Exercises

Simplify each expression. Assume that no denominator has the value of 0.

(A)
1. $\sqrt[3]{-27}$ -3
2. $\sqrt[4]{1}$ 1
3. $\sqrt[3]{64}$ 4
4. $-\sqrt[4]{81}$ -3

5. $\sqrt[4]{10,000}$ 10
6. $\sqrt[3]{-125}$ -5
7. $\sqrt[4]{625}$ 5
8. $-\sqrt[3]{1,000}$ -10

9. $\sqrt[3]{x^9}$ x^3
10. $\sqrt[4]{y^8}$ y^2
11. $\sqrt[4]{y^{20}}$ y^5
12. $\sqrt[3]{x^3 y^6}$ xy^2

13. $\sqrt[4]{32}$ $2\sqrt[4]{2}$
14. $\sqrt[3]{-40}$ $-2\sqrt[3]{5}$
15. $\sqrt[4]{128}$ $4\sqrt[4]{2}$
16. $\sqrt[4]{243}$ $3\sqrt[4]{3}$

17. $\sqrt[3]{a^5}$ $a\sqrt[3]{a^2}$
18. $\sqrt[4]{b^7}$ $b\sqrt[4]{b^3}$
19. $\sqrt[3]{x^{10}}$ $x^3\sqrt[3]{x}$
20. $\sqrt[4]{y^9}$ $y^2\sqrt[4]{y}$

21. $\sqrt[4]{8} + \sqrt[4]{8}$ $2\sqrt[4]{8}$
22. $6\sqrt[3]{4} + \sqrt[3]{4}$ $7\sqrt[3]{4}$
23. $\sqrt[4]{32} + 3\sqrt[4]{2}$ $5\sqrt[4]{2}$
24. $\sqrt[3]{54} + \sqrt[3]{2}$ $4\sqrt[3]{2}$

25. $\sqrt[3]{-64x^6}$ $-4x^2$
26. $\sqrt[4]{81y^{16}}$ $3y^4$
27. $\sqrt[3]{250a^7}$ $5a^2\sqrt[3]{2a}$
28. $\sqrt[4]{162b^{19}}$ $3b^4\sqrt[4]{2b^3}$

29. $\sqrt[4]{7a^2} \cdot \sqrt[4]{3a^2}$ $a\sqrt[4]{21}$
30. $\sqrt[3]{4a} \cdot \sqrt[3]{16a}$ $4\sqrt[3]{a^2}$
31. $\sqrt[4]{8x^3} \cdot \sqrt[4]{20x^6}$ $2x^2\sqrt[4]{10x}$
32. $\sqrt[3]{25y^4} \cdot \sqrt[3]{10y}$ $5y\sqrt[3]{2y^2}$

33. $\dfrac{2}{\sqrt[3]{7}}$ $\dfrac{2\sqrt[3]{49}}{7}$
34. $\dfrac{6x}{\sqrt[4]{3}}$ $2x\sqrt[4]{27}$
35. $\dfrac{7\sqrt[3]{32}}{\sqrt[3]{4}}$ 14
36. $\dfrac{3\sqrt[4]{144}}{5\sqrt[4]{9}}$ $\dfrac{6}{5}$ or $1\dfrac{1}{5}$

37. $\sqrt[4]{\dfrac{1}{5}}$ $\dfrac{\sqrt[4]{125}}{5}$
38. $\sqrt[3]{\dfrac{5}{6}}$ $\dfrac{\sqrt[3]{180}}{6}$
39. $\sqrt[4]{\dfrac{11}{8}}$ $\dfrac{\sqrt[4]{22}}{2}$
40. $\sqrt[3]{\dfrac{10}{9}}$ $\dfrac{\sqrt[3]{30}}{3}$

(B)
41. $\sqrt[3]{216}$ 6
42. $\sqrt[4]{256}$ 4
43. $\sqrt[5]{-243}$ -3

44. $\sqrt[4]{2,000x^7 y^{22}}$ $2xy^5\sqrt[4]{125x^3 y^2}$
45. $5ab\sqrt[3]{270a^5 b^{10}}$ $15a^2 b^4\sqrt[3]{10a^2 b}$
46. $\sqrt[5]{64m^{20}n^{14}}$ $2m^4 n^2\sqrt[5]{2n^4}$

47. $8\sqrt[3]{4} - \sqrt[3]{32} + \sqrt[3]{108}$ $9\sqrt[3]{4}$
48. $\sqrt[4]{2} + 3\sqrt[4]{32} - \sqrt[4]{162}$ $4\sqrt[4]{2}$
49. $\sqrt[5]{2} - \sqrt[5]{64} + \sqrt[5]{486}$ $2\sqrt[5]{2}$

50. $\sqrt[4]{16c^7} + \sqrt[4]{81c^7}$ $5c\sqrt[4]{c^3}$
51. $\sqrt[3]{8a^5} + \sqrt[3]{27a^5}$ $5a\sqrt[3]{a^2}$
52. $\sqrt[5]{32y^9} - \sqrt[5]{243y^9}$ $-y\sqrt[5]{y^4}$

53. $\sqrt[3]{2x^2} \cdot \sqrt[3]{8x^2} \cdot \sqrt[3]{4x^2}$ $4x^2$
54. $\sqrt[4]{3y^3} \cdot \sqrt[4]{6y^3} \cdot \sqrt[4]{9y^3}$ $3y^2\sqrt[4]{2y}$
55. $\sqrt[5]{3n^4} \cdot \sqrt[5]{8n^3} \cdot \sqrt[5]{4n^2}$ $2n\sqrt[5]{3n^4}$

56. $\sqrt[3]{\dfrac{5}{4y^2}}$ $\dfrac{\sqrt[3]{10y}}{2y}$
57. $\dfrac{6a^2}{\sqrt[4]{8a^2}}$ $3a\sqrt[4]{2a^2}$
58. $\dfrac{12n}{\sqrt[3]{9n^7}}$ $\dfrac{4\sqrt[3]{3n^2}}{n^2}$

(C)
59. $\sqrt[3]{x^{6n}}$ x^{2n}
60. $\sqrt[4]{y^{4n+12}}$ y^{n+3}
61. $\sqrt[3]{x^{2n+1}} \cdot \sqrt[3]{x^{4n+2}}$ x^{2n+1}
62. $y^n\sqrt[4]{y^{3n}} + \sqrt[4]{y^{7n}}$ $2y^n\sqrt[4]{y^{3n}}$

63. $\sqrt[n]{x^{4n}}$ x^4
64. $\sqrt[n]{x^{3n+2}}$ $x^3\sqrt[n]{x^2}$
65. $\sqrt[n]{a^n x^{5n+1}}$ $ax^5\sqrt[n]{x}$
66. $\sqrt[n]{ab^{2n}x^{2n+3}}$ $b^2 x^2\sqrt[n]{ax^3}$

A Challenge To You

Simplify $\sqrt{\sqrt[3]{\sqrt[4]{4,096x^{24}y^{36}}}}$. $xy\sqrt{2y}$

6.6 Rational Number Exponents

OBJECTIVES ▶ **To write a radical expression in exponential form**
To write an exponential expression in radical form
To evaluate an expression containing rational number exponents

Each of the properties and definitions for integral exponents can be extended to rational number exponents. Using the Product of Powers property, $3^{\frac{1}{2}} \cdot 3^{\frac{1}{2}} = 3^1 = 3$. But you know that $\sqrt{3} \cdot \sqrt{3} = 3$. Thus, since $3^{\frac{1}{2}}$ and $\sqrt{3}$ are two different symbols for the same number, $3^{\frac{1}{2}} = \sqrt{3}$.

Similarly, $5^{\frac{1}{3}} = \sqrt[3]{5}$ since $5^{\frac{1}{3}} \cdot 5^{\frac{1}{3}} \cdot 5^{\frac{1}{3}} = 5$ and $\sqrt[3]{5} \cdot \sqrt[3]{5} \cdot \sqrt[3]{5} = 5$. Notice that $3^{\frac{1}{2}}$ and $5^{\frac{1}{3}}$ are written in *exponential form* and that $\sqrt{3}$ and $\sqrt[3]{5}$ are written in *radical form*.

Definition:
$x^{\frac{1}{n}}$

For all integers $n > 1$ and all real numbers x,
$$x^{\frac{1}{n}} = \sqrt[n]{x},$$
except when n is even and $x < 0$.

You will use the definition of $x^{\frac{1}{n}}$ to write radical expressions in exponential form, to write exponential expressions in radical form, and to evaluate expressions containing rational number exponents.

Example 1 Write $7\sqrt[4]{a}$ and $\sqrt[4]{7a}$ in exponential form.

$$7\sqrt[4]{a} = 7 \cdot \sqrt[4]{a} = 7a^{\frac{1}{4}} \qquad \qquad \sqrt[4]{7a} = (7a)^{\frac{1}{4}}$$

Example 2 Write $5y^{\frac{1}{3}}$ and $(5y)^{\frac{1}{3}}$ in radical form.

$$5y^{\frac{1}{3}} = 5 \cdot y^{\frac{1}{3}} = 5\sqrt[3]{y} \qquad \qquad (5y)^{\frac{1}{3}} = \sqrt[3]{5y}$$

Example 3 Find the value of $36^{\frac{1}{2}}$ and $10 \cdot 81^{\frac{1}{4}}$.

$$36^{\frac{1}{2}} = \sqrt{36} = 6 \qquad \qquad 10 \cdot 81^{\frac{1}{4}} = 10 \cdot \sqrt[4]{81} = 10 \cdot 3 = 30$$

Since $\frac{2}{3} = 2 \cdot \frac{1}{3}$, you can rewrite $8^{\frac{2}{3}}$ as $(8^2)^{\frac{1}{3}}$ or $(8^{\frac{1}{3}})^2$, using the Power of a Power property. Then, $(8^2)^{\frac{1}{3}} = \sqrt[3]{8^2}$ and $(8^{\frac{1}{3}})^2 = (\sqrt[3]{8})^2$. Notice that $\sqrt[3]{8^2} = \sqrt[3]{64} = 4$ and $(\sqrt[3]{8})^2 = (2)^2 = 4$. Thus, $\sqrt[3]{8^2} = (\sqrt[3]{8})^2$.

Definition:
$x^{\frac{m}{n}}$

For all integers m and n, with $n > 1$, and all nonzero real numbers x,
$$x^{\frac{m}{n}} = (\sqrt[n]{x})^m = \sqrt[n]{x^m},$$
except when n is even and $x < 0$.

Example 4 Write $\sqrt[5]{x^4}$ and $(\sqrt[4]{15})^3$ in exponential form.

$$\sqrt[5]{x^4} = x^{\frac{4}{5}} \quad \blacktriangleleft \quad \sqrt[n]{x^m} = x^{\frac{m}{n}} \qquad\qquad (\sqrt[4]{15})^3 = 15^{\frac{3}{4}} \quad \blacktriangleleft \quad (\sqrt[n]{x})^m = x^{\frac{m}{n}}$$

Example 5 Write $5y^{\frac{2}{3}}$ and $(5y)^{\frac{2}{3}}$ in radical form.

$$5y^{\frac{2}{3}} = 5 \cdot y^{\frac{2}{3}} = 5\sqrt[3]{y^2} \qquad\qquad (5y)^{\frac{2}{3}} = \sqrt[3]{(5y)^2} = \sqrt[3]{25y^2}$$

Example 6 Find the value of $2 \cdot 81^{\frac{5}{4}}$ and $8^{-\frac{2}{3}}$.

$$2 \cdot 81^{\frac{5}{4}} = 2(\sqrt[4]{81})^5 = 2 \cdot 3^5 = 2 \cdot 243 = 486$$
$$8^{-\frac{2}{3}} = \frac{1}{8^{\frac{2}{3}}} = \frac{1}{(\sqrt[3]{8})^2} = \frac{1}{2^2} = \frac{1}{4} \quad \blacktriangleleft \quad x^{-n} = \frac{1}{x^n}$$

Notice in Example 6 how an expression containing a negative rational number exponent is changed into an equivalent expression containing a positive rational number exponent.

Written Exercises

Write each expression in exponential form.

(A) **1.** $\sqrt{5}$ $5^{\frac{1}{2}}$ **2.** $\sqrt[3]{30}$ $30^{\frac{1}{3}}$ **3.** $\sqrt[4]{21}$ $21^{\frac{1}{4}}$ **4.** $7\sqrt[3]{a}$ $7a^{\frac{1}{3}}$ **5.** $\sqrt{3b}$ $(3b)^{\frac{1}{2}}$ **6.** $3\sqrt[5]{9c}$ $3(9c)^{\frac{1}{5}}$

Write each expression in radical form.

7. $17^{\frac{1}{2}}$ $\sqrt{17}$ **8.** $a^{\frac{1}{5}}$ $\sqrt[5]{a}$ **9.** $6c^{\frac{1}{3}}$ $6\sqrt[3]{c}$ **10.** $(6c)^{\frac{1}{3}}$ $\sqrt[3]{6c}$ **11.** $(7n)^{\frac{1}{4}}$ $\sqrt[4]{7n}$ **12.** $7n^{\frac{1}{4}}$ $7\sqrt[4]{n}$

Find the value of each expression.

13. $25^{\frac{1}{2}}$ 5 **14.** $27^{\frac{1}{3}}$ 3 **15.** $81^{\frac{1}{4}}$ 3 **16.** $20 \cdot 32^{\frac{1}{5}}$ **17.** $-7 \cdot 64^{\frac{1}{2}}$ **18.** $-10 \cdot 625^{\frac{1}{4}}$
19. $8^{-\frac{1}{3}}$ $\frac{1}{2}$ **20.** $36^{-\frac{1}{2}}$ $\frac{1}{6}$ **21.** $16^{-\frac{1}{4}}$ $\frac{1}{2}$ **22.** $6 \cdot 9^{-\frac{1}{2}}$ 2 **23.** $8^{\frac{1}{3}} \cdot 16^{\frac{1}{4}}$ **24.** $-8 \cdot 32^{-\frac{1}{5}}$

16. 40　　17. −56　　18. −50　　23. 4　　24. −4

(B) **25.** $64^{\frac{2}{3}}$ 16 **26.** $16^{\frac{5}{4}}$ 32 **27.** $243^{\frac{2}{5}}$ 9 **28.** $11 \cdot 25^{\frac{3}{2}}$ **29.** $5 \cdot 81^{\frac{3}{4}}$ **30.** $9 \cdot 100^{\frac{5}{2}}$
31. $625^{-\frac{3}{4}}$ $\frac{1}{125}$ **32.** $4^{-\frac{5}{2}}$ $\frac{1}{32}$ **33.** $27^{-\frac{5}{3}}$ $\frac{1}{243}$ **34.** $12 \cdot 8^{-\frac{4}{3}}$ $\frac{3}{4}$ **35.** $10 \cdot 16^{-\frac{5}{4}}$ $\frac{5}{16}$ **36.** $25^{-\frac{3}{2}} \cdot 16^{\frac{3}{4}}$ $\frac{8}{125}$

28. 1,375　　29. 135　　30. 900,000

Write each expression in exponential form.

37. $\sqrt[5]{c^3}$ $c^{\frac{3}{5}}$ **38** $(\sqrt[3]{10})^5$ $10^{\frac{5}{3}}$ **39.** $\sqrt[6]{x^5}$ $x^{\frac{5}{6}}$ **40.** $(\sqrt[4]{23})^3$ $23^{\frac{3}{4}}$ **41.** $\sqrt{n^7}$ $n^{\frac{7}{2}}$ **42.** $(\sqrt{53})^9$ $53^{\frac{9}{2}}$

Write each expression in simplest radical form.

43. $5^{\frac{3}{2}}$ $5\sqrt{5}$ **44.** $2^{\frac{5}{3}}$ $2\sqrt[3]{4}$ **45.** $10x^{\frac{2}{3}}$ $10\sqrt[3]{x^2}$ **46.** $(10x)^{\frac{2}{3}}$ $\sqrt[3]{100x^2}$ **47.** $(6t)^{\frac{3}{4}}$ $\sqrt[4]{216t^3}$ **48.** $6t^{\frac{3}{4}}$ $6\sqrt[4]{t^3}$

156

6.7 Expressions With Rational Number Exponents

OBJECTIVES ▶ **To simplify an expression containing rational number exponents**
To solve an exponential equation using properties of rational number exponents

To simplify an expression containing rational number exponents, the properties for integral exponents and radicals should be used. Notice that a given expression is not in *simplest form* until each exponent is a positive number.

Example 1 Simplify $8^{\frac{2}{7}} \cdot 4a^{-1} \cdot 8^{-\frac{5}{7}} \cdot 6a^{\frac{3}{5}}$.

$$8^{\frac{2}{7}} \cdot 4 \cdot a^{-1} \cdot 8^{-\frac{5}{7}} \cdot 6 \cdot a^{\frac{3}{5}} = 8^{\frac{2}{7}} \cdot 8^{-\frac{5}{7}} \cdot 4 \cdot 6 \cdot a^{-1} \cdot a^{\frac{3}{5}}$$

$$= 8^{\frac{2}{7}+(-\frac{5}{7})} \cdot 24 \cdot a^{-\frac{5}{5}+\frac{3}{5}} \qquad \blacktriangleleft \ x^m \cdot x^n = x^{m+n}$$

$$= 8^{-\frac{3}{7}} \cdot 24 \cdot a^{-\frac{2}{5}}$$

$$= \frac{24}{8^{\frac{3}{7}}a^{\frac{2}{5}}} \qquad \blacktriangleleft \ x^{-n} = \frac{1}{x^n}$$

Example 2 Simplify $(a^{\frac{1}{2}}b^{\frac{2}{3}})^6$ and $(27c^6d^{-3})^{\frac{2}{3}}$.

$(xy)^n = x^n y^n \blacktriangleright$ $\quad (a^{\frac{1}{2}}b^{\frac{2}{3}})^6 = (a^{\frac{1}{2}})^6(b^{\frac{2}{3}})^6$

$(x^m)^n = x^{mn} \blacktriangleright$ $\qquad = a^3 b^4$

$\qquad (27c^6d^{-3})^{\frac{2}{3}} = 27^{\frac{2}{3}}(c^6)^{\frac{2}{3}}(d^{-3})^{\frac{2}{3}}$

$\qquad = (\sqrt[3]{27})^2 c^4 d^{-2} \qquad \blacktriangleleft \ x^{\frac{m}{n}} = (\sqrt[n]{x})^m$

$\qquad = \frac{9c^4}{d^2}$

The Quotient of Powers and Power of a Quotient properties are used in simplifying expressions in Examples 3 and 4, respectively.

Example 3 Simplify $\dfrac{t^{\frac{1}{2}}v^{-\frac{1}{5}}}{t^{\frac{2}{3}}v^{-\frac{4}{5}}}$.

$$\frac{x^m}{x^n} = x^{m-n} \blacktriangleright \qquad \frac{t^{\frac{1}{2}}v^{-\frac{1}{5}}}{t^{\frac{2}{3}}v^{-\frac{4}{5}}} = t^{\frac{1}{2}-\frac{2}{3}}v^{-\frac{1}{5}-(-\frac{4}{5})} = t^{-\frac{1}{6}}v^{\frac{3}{5}} = \frac{v^{\frac{3}{5}}}{t^{\frac{1}{6}}}$$

Example 4 Simplify $\left(\dfrac{8a^{12}}{27b^9}\right)^{\frac{2}{3}}$.

$$\left(\frac{x}{y}\right)^n = \frac{x^n}{y^n} \blacktriangleright \qquad \left(\frac{8a^{12}}{27b^9}\right)^{\frac{2}{3}} = \frac{(8a^{12})^{\frac{2}{3}}}{(27b^9)^{\frac{2}{3}}} = \frac{8^{\frac{2}{3}}(a^{12})^{\frac{2}{3}}}{27^{\frac{2}{3}}(b^9)^{\frac{2}{3}}} = \frac{(\sqrt[3]{8})^2 a^8}{(\sqrt[3]{27})^2 b^6} = \frac{4a^8}{9b^6}$$

You have solved an exponential equation like $3^{2x-1} = 3^7$ by setting the exponents equal to each other and solving the equation $2x - 1 = 7$. This method of solving an exponential equation is based upon the property that if $a^m = a^n$, then $m = n$. As shown in Example 5, some exponential equations that involve rational number exponents can be solved in a similar way.

Example 5 Solve each equation.

$8^x = 16$
Write 8 and 16 as powers of 2.
$(8)^x = 16$
$(2^3)^x = 2^4$
$2^{3x} = 2^4$
$3x = 4$ ◀ *If $a^m = a^n$, then $m = n$.*
$x = \dfrac{4}{3}$

Thus, the solution is $\dfrac{4}{3}$.

$3^{8x} = \dfrac{1}{81}$

Write $\dfrac{1}{81}$ as a power of 3.

$3^{8x} = 3^{-4}$ ◀ $\dfrac{1}{81} = \dfrac{1}{3^4} = 3^{-4}$
$8x = -4$
$x = -\dfrac{1}{2}$

Thus, the solution is $-\dfrac{1}{2}$.

Written Exercises

Simplify each expression.

(A)

1. $6^{\frac{3}{8}} \cdot 6^{-\frac{1}{8}} \cdot 6^{\frac{5}{8}}$ $6^{\frac{7}{8}}$

2. $x^{\frac{4}{3}} \cdot x^{\frac{5}{3}} \cdot x^{-\frac{7}{3}}$ $x^{\frac{2}{3}}$

3. $y^3 \cdot y^{-\frac{1}{2}}$ $y^{\frac{5}{2}}$

4. $5a^2 \cdot 6a^{-\frac{3}{8}}$ $30a^{\frac{13}{8}}$

5. $(x^{\frac{2}{5}})^{10}$ x^4

6. $(y^{12})^{\frac{2}{3}}$ y^8

7. $(n^{10})^{\frac{3}{5}}$ n^6

8. $(b^{-\frac{2}{3}})^{-9}$ b^6

9. $(x^{\frac{1}{4}}y^{\frac{3}{4}})^8$ x^2y^6

10. $(25a^2b^8)^{\frac{1}{2}}$ $5ab^4$

11. $(-4m^{\frac{1}{2}}n^{\frac{3}{2}})^2$ $16mn^3$

12. $(16c^{12}d^8)^{\frac{3}{4}}$ $8c^9d^6$

13. $\dfrac{a^{\frac{9}{7}}}{a^{\frac{3}{7}}}$ $a^{\frac{6}{7}}$

14. $\dfrac{x^{\frac{4}{5}}}{x^{-\frac{2}{5}}}$ $x^{\frac{6}{5}}$

15. $\dfrac{n^{-\frac{1}{3}}}{n^{-\frac{5}{3}}}$ $n^{\frac{4}{3}}$

16. $\dfrac{b^3}{b^{\frac{3}{4}}}$ $b^{\frac{9}{4}}$

17. $\left(\dfrac{x^{\frac{3}{4}}}{y^{\frac{1}{2}}}\right)^8$ $\dfrac{x^6}{y^4}$

18. $\left(\dfrac{a^{\frac{2}{3}}}{b^{\frac{3}{5}}}\right)^{15}$ $\dfrac{a^{10}}{b^9}$

19. $\left(\dfrac{25m^6}{9n^8}\right)^{\frac{1}{2}}$ $\dfrac{5m^3}{3n^4}$

20. $\left(\dfrac{27c^6}{8d^{12}}\right)^{\frac{2}{3}}$ $\dfrac{9c^4}{4d^8}$

Solve each equation.

21. $9^x = 27$ $\dfrac{3}{2}$

22. $3^{9x} = \dfrac{1}{27}$ $-\dfrac{1}{3}$

23. $125^x = 25$ $\dfrac{2}{3}$

24. $4^{6x} = \dfrac{1}{64}$ $-\dfrac{1}{2}$

(B)

25. $25^{2x+1} = 125$ $\dfrac{1}{4}$

26. $2^{2x+2} = \dfrac{1}{16}$ -3

27. $32^{3x-2} = 16$ $\dfrac{14}{15}$

28. $10^{3x-1} = \dfrac{1}{10,000}$ -1

Simplify each expression.

29. $x^{\frac{2}{5}} \cdot x^{\frac{1}{5}} \cdot x^{-\frac{4}{5}}$ $\dfrac{1}{x^{\frac{1}{5}}}$

30. $b^{-6} \cdot b^{\frac{5}{8}}$ $\dfrac{1}{b^{\frac{43}{8}}}$

31. $7a^{\frac{3}{5}} \cdot 6a^{\frac{1}{2}} \cdot 5a^{\frac{3}{4}}$ $210a^{\frac{37}{20}}$

32. $-10n^{-\frac{3}{4}} \cdot 2n^{-\frac{5}{8}}$ $\dfrac{-20}{n^{\frac{11}{8}}}$

33. $(x^{\frac{2}{3}})^{-9}$ $\dfrac{1}{x^6}$

34. $(x^{\frac{1}{2}}y^{-\frac{3}{4}})^8$ $\dfrac{x^4}{y^6}$

35. $(8m^9n^{-6})^{\frac{1}{3}}$ $\dfrac{2m^3}{n^2}$

36. $(125a^{-9}b^{12})^{-\frac{2}{3}}$ $\dfrac{a^6}{25b^8}$

37. $\dfrac{x^{\frac{1}{3}}y^{\frac{5}{4}}}{x^{\frac{2}{3}}y^{\frac{3}{4}}}\quad \dfrac{y^{\frac{1}{2}}}{x^{\frac{1}{3}}}$
  38. $\dfrac{a^{\frac{2}{5}}b^{\frac{1}{6}}}{a^{\frac{3}{10}}b^{\frac{1}{4}}}\quad \dfrac{a^{\frac{1}{10}}}{b^{\frac{1}{12}}}$
  39. $\dfrac{m^{-\frac{2}{3}}n^{-4}}{m^{-\frac{1}{3}}n^{-5}}\quad \dfrac{n}{m^{\frac{1}{3}}}$
  40. $\dfrac{27^{\frac{3}{4}}x^{-\frac{1}{2}}y^{\frac{1}{4}}}{27^{\frac{1}{12}}x^{\frac{3}{4}}y^{-\frac{1}{6}}}\quad \dfrac{9y^{\frac{5}{12}}}{x^{\frac{5}{4}}}$

41. $\left(\dfrac{x^{-\frac{3}{4}}}{y^{-\frac{1}{4}}}\right)^8\quad \dfrac{y^2}{x^6}$
  42. $\left(\dfrac{-2a^{-\frac{1}{3}}}{3b^{-\frac{2}{3}}}\right)^3\quad \dfrac{-8b^2}{27a}$
  43. $\left(\dfrac{64m^{-3}}{27n^{-6}}\right)^{\frac{2}{3}}\quad \dfrac{16n^4}{9m^2}$
  44. $\left(\dfrac{4c^{-6}}{25d^{-4}}\right)^{\frac{3}{2}}\quad \dfrac{8d^6}{125c^9}$

Simplify and write each expression with the least possible number of radical signs.

Example   Simplify $\sqrt[3]{x}\cdot\sqrt[4]{x}$ and $(\sqrt[4]{x^3}+\sqrt[6]{y})(\sqrt[4]{x^3}-\sqrt[6]{y})$.

Two radical signs ▶ $\sqrt[3]{x}\cdot\sqrt[4]{x}=x^{\frac{1}{3}}\cdot x^{\frac{1}{4}}$ ◀ $\sqrt[n]{x}=x^{\frac{1}{n}}$

$\qquad\qquad\qquad\qquad\quad = x^{\frac{7}{12}}$ ◀ $x^m\cdot x^n = x^{m+n}$

One radical sign ▶ $\qquad = \sqrt[12]{x^7}$ ◀ $x^{\frac{m}{n}} = \sqrt[n]{x^m}$

Four radical signs ▶ $(\sqrt[4]{x^3}+\sqrt[6]{y})(\sqrt[4]{x^3}-\sqrt[6]{y})$

$\qquad\qquad\qquad\quad (x^{\frac{3}{4}}+y^{\frac{1}{6}})(x^{\frac{3}{4}}-y^{\frac{1}{6}})$ ◀ $\sqrt[n]{x^m}=x^{\frac{m}{n}}$

$\qquad\qquad\qquad\quad (x^{\frac{3}{4}})^2-(y^{\frac{1}{6}})^2$ ◀ $(a+b)(a-b)=a^2-b^2$

$\qquad\qquad\qquad\quad x^{\frac{3}{2}}-y^{\frac{1}{3}}$

$\qquad\qquad\qquad\quad \sqrt{x^3}-\sqrt[3]{y}$

Two radical signs ▶ $x\sqrt{x}-\sqrt[3]{y}$

Ⓒ **45.** $\sqrt{x}\cdot\sqrt[5]{x}\quad\sqrt[10]{x^7}$
  46. $\sqrt[6]{y}\cdot\sqrt{y}\quad\sqrt[3]{y^2}$
  47. $\sqrt[3]{z}\cdot\sqrt[4]{z}\cdot\sqrt[6]{z}\quad\sqrt[4]{z^3}$

48. $\sqrt[3]{x^2}\cdot\sqrt[4]{x^3}\quad x\sqrt[12]{x^5}$
  49. $\sqrt{a}\cdot\sqrt[3]{b}\cdot\sqrt[4]{c}\quad\sqrt[12]{a^6b^4c^3}$
  50. $\sqrt[6]{m^5}\cdot\sqrt[3]{n^2}\quad\sqrt[6]{m^5n^4}$

51. $(\sqrt[3]{x}+\sqrt[4]{x})(\sqrt[3]{x}-\sqrt[4]{x})$
  52. $(\sqrt{x}-\sqrt[5]{y^2})(\sqrt{x}+\sqrt[5]{y^2})$
  53. $(\sqrt[4]{x^3}+\sqrt[8]{y^5})(\sqrt[4]{x^3}-\sqrt[8]{y^5})$

54. $(\sqrt{x}+\sqrt[4]{x})^2$
  55. $(3\sqrt{x}-2\sqrt[6]{y})^2$
  56. $(\sqrt[4]{x}+\sqrt[4]{y})(\sqrt[4]{x}+\sqrt[4]{y})$

57. $\dfrac{\sqrt{x}}{\sqrt[3]{x}}\quad\sqrt[6]{x}$
  58. $\dfrac{\sqrt[4]{x^3}}{\sqrt[5]{x^2}}\quad\sqrt[20]{x^7}$
  59. $\dfrac{\sqrt[5]{x}}{\sqrt[4]{x}}\quad\dfrac{\sqrt[20]{x^{19}}}{x}$

60. $(\sqrt[3]{x}-\sqrt[3]{2})(\sqrt[3]{x^2}+\sqrt[3]{2x}+\sqrt[3]{4})$
  61. $(\sqrt[3]{x}+\sqrt[3]{y})(\sqrt[3]{x^2}-\sqrt[3]{xy}+\sqrt[3]{y^2})\quad x+y$

51. $\sqrt[3]{x^2}-\sqrt{x}$
  52. $x-\sqrt[5]{y^4}$
  53. $x\sqrt{x}-y\sqrt[4]{y}$
  54. $x+2\sqrt[4]{x^3}+\sqrt{x}$
  55. $9x-12\sqrt[6]{x^3y}+4\sqrt[3]{y}$

56. $\sqrt{x}+2\sqrt[4]{xy}+\sqrt{y}$

A Challenge To You

$$1.\ \dfrac{x-\sqrt[3]{x^2y}+\sqrt[3]{xy^2}}{x+y}$$

Use one of the special products, $(a+b)(a^2-ab+b^2)=a^3+b^3$ or $(a-b)(a^2+ab+b^2)=a^3-b^3$, to rationalize each denominator.

1. $\dfrac{\sqrt[3]{x}}{\sqrt[3]{x}+\sqrt[3]{y}}\cdot\dfrac{\sqrt[3]{x^2}-\sqrt[3]{xy}+\sqrt[3]{y^2}}{\sqrt[3]{x^2}-\sqrt[3]{xy}+\sqrt[3]{y^2}}$ above
  2. $\dfrac{\sqrt[3]{x^2y^2}}{\sqrt[3]{x}-\sqrt[3]{y}}\quad\dfrac{xy+x\sqrt[3]{xy^2}+y\sqrt[3]{x^2y}}{x-y}$

Chapter Six Review

Vocabulary
conjugates [6.4]
index [6.5]
irrational number [6.1]
like radicals [6.3]
nth root, $\sqrt[n]{k}$ [6.5]
radical [6.1]
radical sign [6.1]
radicand [6.1]
rational number exponent, $x^{\frac{1}{n}}, x^{\frac{m}{n}}$ [6.6]
real number [6.1]
simplest radical form [6.4]
square root, $\sqrt{k}$ [6.1]

Solve each equation. Approximate the solutions to the nearest hundredth. [6.1]
1. $5y^2 + 24 = 174$ **−5.48, 5.48**
2. $n^2 - 7 = 18 - 3n^2$ **−2.50, 2.50**

Determine whether each number is rational or irrational. [6.1]
3. $8.43843843\ldots$ **R** 4. $\sqrt{160}$ **I**
5. $-\sqrt{1600}$ **R** 6. $\sqrt{0.16}$ **R**

Simplify each expression. Assume that no denominator has the value of 0. **$-10y^5\sqrt{2y}$**
7. $\sqrt{20c^2}$ **$2c\sqrt{5}$** 8. $-5y\sqrt{8y^9}$ [6.2]
9. $m^2n\sqrt{32m^7n^3}$ **$4m^5n^2\sqrt{2mn}$**
10. $\sqrt{8} + \sqrt{50} - \sqrt{18}$ **$4\sqrt{2}$** [6.3]
11. $(5\sqrt{x} + 6\sqrt{y})(\sqrt{x} - \sqrt{y})$ **$5x + \sqrt{xy} - 6y$**
12. $(4\sqrt{3} - 2\sqrt{5})^2$ **$68 - 16\sqrt{15}$**
13. $6\sqrt{c^5d} + c\sqrt{16c^3d}$ **$10c^2\sqrt{cd}$**
14. $\dfrac{\sqrt{27a^8}}{\sqrt{3a^3}}$ **$3a^2\sqrt{a}$** 15. $\dfrac{-5\sqrt{2}}{3\sqrt{7}}$ **$\dfrac{-5\sqrt{14}}{21}$** [6.4]
16. $\dfrac{\sqrt{2}}{2\sqrt{7} + \sqrt{10}}$ **$\dfrac{\sqrt{14} - \sqrt{5}}{9}$**
18. **$2c^2$**
17. $\sqrt[3]{-16x^{12}}$ **$-2x^4\sqrt[3]{2}$** 18. $\sqrt[5]{2c^2} \cdot \sqrt[5]{16c^8}$ [6.5]
19. $\sqrt[4]{32x^8y^{11}}$ 20. $\sqrt[3]{27a^7} + \sqrt[3]{64a^7}$
21. $\sqrt[3]{\dfrac{7}{9}}$ **$\dfrac{\sqrt[3]{21}}{3}$** 22. $\dfrac{2c^2}{\sqrt[4]{4c^3}}$ **$c\sqrt[4]{4c}$**
19. **$2x^2y^2\sqrt[4]{2y^3}$** 20. **$7a^2\sqrt[3]{a}$**

Write each expression in exponential form. [6.6]
23. $(\sqrt[3]{17})^2$ **$17^{\frac{2}{3}}$** 24. $6\sqrt[4]{3a}$ **$6(3a)^{\frac{1}{4}}$**
25. $\sqrt{c^5}$ **$c^{\frac{5}{2}}$**

Write each expression in radical form. [6.6]
26. $2a^{\frac{5}{3}}$ 27. $4y^{\frac{3}{5}}$ **$4\sqrt[5]{y^3}$**
28. $(4y)^{\frac{3}{5}}$ **$\sqrt[5]{64y^3}$, or $2\sqrt[5]{2y^3}$**
26. **$2\sqrt[3]{a^5}$, or $2a\sqrt[3]{a^2}$**

Find the value of each expression. [6.6]
29. $-15 \cdot 32^{\frac{1}{5}}$ **−30** 30. $125^{\frac{4}{3}}$ **625**
31. $20 \cdot 625^{\frac{3}{4}}$ **2,500** 32. $32^{-\frac{2}{5}}$ **$\dfrac{1}{4}$**

Simplify each expression. [6.7]
33. $-9a^{\frac{3}{4}} \cdot 2a^{-\frac{1}{2}}$ 34. $(49a^2b^{10})^{\frac{1}{2}}$ **$7ab^5$**
35. $(a^{\frac{1}{3}}b^{-\frac{2}{3}})^{-9}$ **$\dfrac{b^6}{a^3}$** 36. $\dfrac{x^{\frac{1}{4}}y^{-\frac{1}{5}}}{x^{\frac{3}{8}}y^{-\frac{3}{5}}}$ **$\dfrac{y^{\frac{2}{5}}}{x^{\frac{1}{8}}}$**
37. $\left(\dfrac{8x^9}{27y^{-12}}\right)^{\frac{2}{3}}$ **$\dfrac{4x^6y^8}{9}$** 33. **$-18a^{\frac{1}{4}}$**

Solve each equation. [6.7]
38. $4^x = 8$ **$\frac{3}{2}$** 39. $27^{2x-1} = 9$ **$\frac{5}{6}$**
40. $3^{10x} = \dfrac{1}{9}$ **$-\frac{1}{5}$** 41. $5^{4x+1} = \dfrac{1}{125}$ **−1**
★42. Solve $\dfrac{2x^2 - 3}{4} + \dfrac{x^2 + 5}{6} = \dfrac{5x^2 + 4}{8}$.
Approximate the solutions to the nearest hundredth. [6.1] **−3.16, 3.16**

Simplify each expression.
★43. $x^m y^{2n}\sqrt{x^{4m+5}y^{6n}}$ [6.3] **$x^{3m+2}y^{5n}\sqrt{x}$**
★44. $\dfrac{4\sqrt{x-y}}{\sqrt{x-y}+3}$ [6.4] **$\dfrac{4x - 4y - 12\sqrt{x-y}}{x - y - 9}$**
★45. $\sqrt[n]{x^{2n}y^{3n+5}}$ [6.7] **$x^2y^3\sqrt[n]{y^5}$**
★46. Factor $9x - 4y$ as a difference of two squares. [6.3] **$(3\sqrt{x} - 2\sqrt{y})(3\sqrt{x} + 2\sqrt{y})$**
★47. Write $(x^{2n}y^{n+2})^{\frac{a}{n}}$ in simplest radical form. [6.6] **$x^{2a}y^a\sqrt[n]{y^{2a}}$**

Chapter Six Test

Solve each equation. Approximate the solutions to the nearest hundredth.

1. $7a^2 + 19 = 236$ **−5.57, 5.57**

2. $3y^2 - 11 = 7y^2 - 60$ **−3.50, 3.50**

Determine whether each number is rational or irrational.

3. $\sqrt{90}$ **I**

4. $-\sqrt{900}$ **R**

Simplify each expression. Assume that no denominator has the value of 0.

5. $\sqrt{27n^8}$ **$3n^4\sqrt{3}$**

6. $8\sqrt{16x^5y^9}$

7. $5\sqrt{12x} - 6\sqrt{48x} + \sqrt{75x}$ **$-9\sqrt{3x}$**

8. $(3\sqrt{2} + \sqrt{5})(5\sqrt{2} - \sqrt{5})$ **$25 + 2\sqrt{10}$**

9. $\sqrt[3]{9x^4} \cdot \sqrt[3]{3x^5}$ **$3x^3$**   6. $32x^2y^4\sqrt{xy}$

10. $(-4\sqrt{13})^2$ **208**

11. $m\sqrt[4]{2n^5} + mn\sqrt[4]{32n}$ **$3mn\sqrt[4]{2n}$**

12. $\dfrac{\sqrt{24x^7}}{\sqrt{2x}}$ **$2x^3\sqrt{3}$**

13. $\dfrac{2x}{\sqrt[3]{5x^2}}$ **$\dfrac{2\sqrt[3]{25x}}{5}$**   14. $\sqrt[4]{\dfrac{3}{8}}$ **$\dfrac{\sqrt[4]{6}}{2}$**

15. $\dfrac{8}{5\sqrt{12c^3}}$ **$\dfrac{4\sqrt{3c}}{15c^2}$**   16. $\dfrac{4}{3\sqrt{5} + \sqrt{30}}$

17. $(27x^6y^{12})^{\frac{2}{3}}$ **$9x^4y^8$**   16. $\dfrac{12\sqrt{5} - 4\sqrt{30}}{15}$

18. $\dfrac{x^{\frac{5}{7}}y^{-\frac{1}{4}}}{x^{-\frac{1}{7}}y^{\frac{1}{2}}}$ **$\dfrac{x^{\frac{6}{7}}}{y^{\frac{3}{4}}}$**   19. $\left(\dfrac{c^{\frac{2}{3}}}{d^{\frac{1}{2}}}\right)^{12}$ **$\dfrac{c^8}{d^6}$**

20. Write $\sqrt[4]{a^3}$ in exponential form. **$a^{\frac{3}{4}}$**

21. Write $(2x)^{\frac{4}{5}}$ in radical form. **$\sqrt[5]{16x^4}$**

Find the value of each expression.

22. $25^{\frac{3}{2}}$ **125**   23. $6 \cdot 81^{-\frac{3}{4}}$ **$\frac{2}{9}$**

Solve each equation.

24. $25^{2x+1} = 125$ **$\frac{1}{4}$**   25. $2^{4x-1} = \dfrac{1}{32}$ **−1**

★26. Solve $\dfrac{x^2 - 10}{5} + \dfrac{x^2}{10} = \dfrac{x^2 + 10}{4}$.
Approximate the solutions to the nearest hundredth. **−9.49, 9.49**

Simplify each expression.

★27. $x^{2c}y^d\sqrt{x^{2c+3}y^{6d+5}}$ **$x^{3c+1}y^{4d+2}\sqrt{xy}$**

★28. $\dfrac{\sqrt{x+y}}{\sqrt{x+y}+6}$ **$\dfrac{x+y-6\sqrt{x+y}}{x+y-36}$**

★29. Simplify and write $(\sqrt{x} + \sqrt[6]{y})(\sqrt{x} + \sqrt[6]{y})$ with the least possible number of radical signs. **$x + 2\sqrt[6]{x^3y} + \sqrt[3]{y}$**

Computer Activities

To Be Rational or NOT!

The rational numbers and irrational numbers together make up the real numbers. Sometimes it is helpful to know if a given real number is rational or irrational.

You know already that a square root expression that is equivalent to a nonterminating, nonrepeating decimal is irrational. The square root of certain fractions may also be irrational, as shown in the computer program below.

PROGRAM

```
10 PRINT "PROGRAM DETERMINES IF THE SQUARE ROOT"
20 PRINT "OF A GIVEN FRACTION IS RATIONAL OR IRRATIONAL"
30 PRINT "ENTER NUMERATOR, DENOMINATOR OF FRACTION"
40 PRINT "FOR WHICH YOU WANT THE SQUARE ROOT"
50 INPUT N, D
60 LET N1 = SQR(N)
70 LET D1 = SQR(D)
80 IF N1 = INT(N1) THEN 110
90 PRINT "GIVEN NUMBER IS IRRATIONAL"
100 GO TO 160
110 IF D1 = INT(D1) THEN 140
120 PRINT "GIVEN NUMBER IS IRRATIONAL"
130 GO TO 160
140 PRINT "GIVEN NUMBER IS RATIONAL"
150 PRINT "AND CAN BE WRITTEN AS"; N1; "/"; D1
160 END
```

Exercises

Run the program above to determine if the square root of each of the following fractions is rational or irrational.

1. $\frac{22}{7}$ irrational

2. $\frac{25}{4}$ rational

3. $\frac{144}{3}$ irrational

4. $\frac{9}{64}$ rational

5. Add instructions to the program above to indicate the reasons why the square root of a given fraction is irrational.
   95 PRINT N; "/"; D; "IS NOT A PERFECT SQUARE"
   125 PRINT N; "/"; D; "IS NOT A PERFECT SQUARE"

College Prep Test

Directions: In each item, you are to compare a quantity in Column 1 with a quantity in Column 2. Write the letter of the correct answer from these choices:

A The quantity in Column 1 is greater than the quantity in Column 2.
B The quantity in Column 2 is greater than the quantity in Column 1.
C The quantity in Column 1 is equal to the quantity in Column 2.
D The relationship cannot be determined from the given information.

Notes: Information centered over both columns refers to one or both of the quantities to be compared.

A symbol that appears in both columns has the same meaning in each column.

All variables represent real numbers.

SAMPLE ITEMS AND ANSWERS

Column 1	Column 2

S1. $x = 8$ and $y = 9$

$\sqrt{2x}$ $\qquad$ $\sqrt[3]{3y}$

The answer is **A** because $\sqrt{2 \cdot 8} = \sqrt{16} = 4$, $\sqrt[3]{3 \cdot 9} = \sqrt[3]{27} = 3$, and $4 > 3$.

S2. $0 < x < y$

$\sqrt{2x}$ $\qquad$ $\sqrt{y}$

The answer is **D**. If $x = 8$ and $y = 9$, then $\sqrt{2x} > \sqrt{y}$. If $x = 2$ and $y = 4$, then $\sqrt{2x} = \sqrt{y}$.

	Column 1	Column 2	
1.	$\sqrt[3]{65}$	4	A
2.	$\dfrac{1}{3}$	$\sqrt[3]{\dfrac{2}{27}}$	B
3.	$\sqrt[4]{x + y}$	$\sqrt[4]{x - y}$	D
4.	The sum of the two solutions of $x^2 = 10$	The sum of the two solutions of $x^4 = 16$	C

	Column 1	Column 2	
	$x = 12$ and $y = 9$		
5.	$\sqrt{xy}$	$\sqrt{6x + 4y}$	C
	$x = y = 50$		
6.	$7 + \sqrt{x}$	$\sqrt{x} + \sqrt{y}$	B
	$x > 0$ and $y > 0$		
7.	$\sqrt{x^2 + y^2}$	$x + y$	B
	$x = -2$ and $y = 2$		
8.	$\sqrt{8x^2y^3}$	$2xy\sqrt{2y}$	A

Items 9 and 10 refer to Rectangles I and II below. The rectangles are not drawn to scale.

$\sqrt{2}$ [I] $\sqrt{50}$ $\qquad$ $\sqrt{5}$ [II] $\sqrt{20}$

	Column 1	Column 2	
9.	Area of Rectangle I	Area of Rectangle II	C
10.	Perimeter of Rectangle I	Perimeter of Rectangle II	A

QUADRATIC FORMULA

Can You Answer?

Puzzle: A pharmacist has only 5-ounce beakers and 8-ounce beakers available for measuring liquids. How can these beakers be used to measure exactly 22 oz of water? $8 + 8 + (8 - 5) + (8 - 5) = 22$

Puzzle: There are five bronze pellets that weigh 1 oz, 2 oz, 4 oz, 8 oz, and 16 oz, respectively. How many different masses can be weighed using *one or more* of the five pellets on a balance scale? 31

Puzzle: Find the next letter in the sequence of letters. *T* for "Ten."

O, T, T, F, F, S, S, E, N, ⋯

 PROJECT Among $\sqrt[3]{2}$, $\sqrt[10]{10}$, and $\sqrt[15]{30}$, which is the greatest? Justify your answer. $\sqrt[3]{2}$

7.1 Completing the Square

OBJECTIVE ▶ **To solve a quadratic equation by completing the square**

As shown below, you can solve a *quadratic equation* like $y^2 = 49$ or $(n + 3)^2 = 16$ by using the definition of square root: if $x^2 = k$, then $x = \sqrt{k}$ or $x = -\sqrt{k}$.

$$y^2 = 49$$
$$y = \sqrt{49} \quad \text{or} \quad y = -\sqrt{49}$$
$$y = 7 \qquad\qquad y = -7$$
Solutions: 7, −7

$$(n + 3)^2 = 16$$
$$n + 3 = \sqrt{16} \quad \text{or} \quad n + 3 = -\sqrt{16}$$
$$n + 3 = 4 \qquad \text{or} \quad n + 3 = -4$$
$$n = 1 \qquad\qquad n = -7$$
Solutions: 1, −7

The equation $y^2 + 10y = 3$ can be solved in a similar way.

Example 1 Solve $y^2 + 10y = 3$.

$$y^2 + 10y \qquad\;\; = 3$$
$$y^2 + 10y + 25 = 3 + 25 \qquad \blacktriangleleft \textit{Add 25 to each side.}$$
$$(y + 5)^2 = 28$$
$$y + 5 = \pm\sqrt{28} \qquad \blacktriangleleft \textit{If } x^2 = k, \textit{ then } x = \pm\sqrt{k}.$$
$$y + 5 = \pm 2\sqrt{7}$$
$$y = -5 \pm 2\sqrt{7} \qquad \blacktriangleleft \textit{Add −5 to each side.}$$

Thus, the solutions are $-5 + 2\sqrt{7}$ and $-5 - 2\sqrt{7}$.

The procedure used to solve the quadratic equation in Example 1 is called **completing the square.** By adding 25 to each side of the equation, the left side becomes a *perfect square trinomial*, $y^2 + 10y + 25$, that can be factored into the square of a binomial, $(y + 5)^2$.

To solve a quadratic equation of the form $x^2 + bx = c$ by completing the square, you divide b by 2, square the result, then add $\left(\dfrac{b}{2}\right)^2$ to each side.

Example 2 Solve $n^2 - 3n = 10$ by completing the square.

$$n^2 - 3n \qquad\;\; = 10 \qquad \blacktriangleleft \textit{b = −3}$$
$$n^2 - 3n + \frac{9}{4} = 10 + \frac{9}{4} \qquad \blacktriangleleft \textit{Add } \left(\frac{-3}{2}\right)^2, \textit{ or } \frac{9}{4}, \textit{ to each side.}$$
$$\left(n - \frac{3}{2}\right)^2 = \frac{49}{4}$$
$$n - \frac{3}{2} = \pm\sqrt{\frac{49}{4}} \qquad \blacktriangleleft \textit{If } x^2 = k, \textit{ then } x = \pm\sqrt{k}.$$
$$n = \frac{3}{2} \pm \frac{7}{2}, \textit{ or } \frac{3 \pm 7}{2}$$

Thus, the solutions are 5 and −2.

COMPLETING THE SQUARE

To solve $9y^2 + 12y - 8 = 0$ by completing the square, you must rewrite the equation in the general form of $y^2 + by = c$.

Example 3 Solve $9y^2 + 12y - 8 = 0$ by completing the square.

$$9y^2 + 12y - 8 = 0$$
$$9y^2 + 12y = 8 \qquad \blacktriangleleft \text{ Add 8 to each side.}$$
$$y^2 + \frac{12}{9}y = \frac{8}{9} \qquad \blacktriangleleft \text{ Divide each side by 9.}$$
$$y^2 + \frac{4}{3}y = \frac{8}{9} \qquad \blacktriangleleft \frac{12}{9} = \frac{4}{3}, \text{ so } b = \frac{4}{3}.$$
$$y^2 + \frac{4}{3}y + \frac{4}{9} = \frac{8}{9} + \frac{4}{9} \qquad \blacktriangleleft \text{ Add } \left(\frac{1}{2} \cdot \frac{4}{3}\right)^2, \text{ or } \frac{4}{9}, \text{ to each side.}$$
$$\left(y + \frac{2}{3}\right)^2 = \frac{12}{9}$$
$$y + \frac{2}{3} = \pm\sqrt{\frac{12}{9}}$$
$$y = -\frac{2}{3} \pm \frac{2\sqrt{3}}{3} \qquad \blacktriangleleft \pm\sqrt{\frac{12}{9}} = \pm\frac{\sqrt{12}}{\sqrt{9}} = \pm\frac{2\sqrt{3}}{3}$$

Thus, the solutions are $\dfrac{-2 + 2\sqrt{3}}{3}$ and $\dfrac{-2 - 2\sqrt{3}}{3}$.

Oral Exercises

Find the number to be added to each expression to complete the square.

1. $a^2 + 14a$ 49 2. $n^2 - 8n$ 16 3. $x^2 + 5x$ $\frac{25}{4}$ 4. $y^2 - y$ $\frac{1}{4}$ 5. $b^2 + \frac{3}{2}b$ $\frac{9}{16}$ 6. $c^2 - \frac{2}{5}c$ $\frac{1}{25}$

Written Exercises

Solve each equation by completing the square.

Ⓐ 1. $x^2 + 4x = 21$ −7, 3   2. $y^2 - 8y = 33$ −3, 11   3. $n^2 + 12n = -20$ −10, −2

4. $a^2 - 6a = 5$ $3 \pm \sqrt{14}$ 5. $b^2 + 10b = -5$ $-5 \pm 2\sqrt{5}$ 6. $c^2 - 2c = 74$ $1 \pm 5\sqrt{3}$

7. $y^2 + 3y - 6 = 0$ $\frac{-3 \pm \sqrt{33}}{2}$ 8. $t^2 - 5t + 2 = 0$ $\frac{5 \pm \sqrt{17}}{2}$ 9. $x^2 - x - 7 = 0$ $\frac{1 \pm \sqrt{29}}{2}$

10. $5x^2 + 3x - 2 = 0$ $-1, \frac{2}{5}$ 11. $2a^2 - 7a - 4 = 0$ $-\frac{1}{2}, 4$ 12. $3y^2 + 10y + 3 = 0$ $-3, -\frac{1}{3}$

13. $a^2 - 5a - 5 = 0$ $\frac{5 \pm 3\sqrt{5}}{2}$ 14. $y^2 + 7y = 0$ −7, 0   15. $n^2 = n$ 1, 0

Ⓑ 16. $2n^2 = 5 - 5n$ $\frac{-5 \pm \sqrt{65}}{4}$ 17. $7x - 1 = 5x^2$ $\frac{7 \pm \sqrt{29}}{10}$ 18. $3a^2 + 4a = 3$ $\frac{-2 \pm \sqrt{13}}{3}$

19. $\frac{1}{3}y^2 - 2y - 1 = 0$ $3 \pm 2\sqrt{3}$ 20. $\frac{1}{8}n^2 - n = \frac{1}{2}$ $4 \pm 2\sqrt{5}$ 21. $\frac{5}{3}x^2 - \frac{5}{2}x - \frac{5}{6} = 0$ $\frac{3 \pm \sqrt{17}}{4}$

22. $\frac{x^2 + 12x}{24} = \frac{1}{12}$ $-6 \pm \sqrt{38}$ 23. $\frac{y^2 + 15}{10} = y$ $5 \pm \sqrt{10}$ 24. $2n = \frac{3 - n^2}{4}$ $-4 \pm \sqrt{19}$

Ⓒ 25. $x^2 + (2\sqrt{3})x - 24 = 0$ $-4\sqrt{3}, 2\sqrt{3}$ 26. $y^2 - 4\sqrt{2} \cdot y + 8 = 0$ $2\sqrt{2}$ 27. $n^2 + 6n\sqrt{5} + 45 = 0$ $-3\sqrt{5}$

28. $a^2 - 2a\sqrt{3} + 1 = 0$ $\sqrt{3} \pm \sqrt{2}$ 29. $b^2 - 6b\sqrt{2} + 15 = 0$ $3\sqrt{2} \pm \sqrt{3}$ 30. $4x^2 + 4x\sqrt{5} + 3 = 0$ $\frac{-\sqrt{5} \pm \sqrt{2}}{2}$

Applications

Read → Plan → Solve → Interpret

The quadratic polynomial $-5t^2 + 40t$ has a **maximum value** for a certain value of its variable, t. The table below shows a pattern in the values of $-5t^2 + 40t$ as t assumes various increasing values.

t	0	1	2	3	4	5	6	7	8
$-5t^2 + 40t$	0	35	60	75	80	75	60	35	0

As the value of t increases from 0 to 8, the value of $-5t^2 + 40t$ increases from 0 to 80 and then decreases from 80 to 0. It seems reasonable to infer that $-5t^2 + 40t$ has a maximum value for some value of t between 3 and 5.

Example 1 Find the maximum value of $-5t^2 + 40t$ and the corresponding value of t.

$-5t^2 + 40t$
$-5(t^2 - 8t \qquad)$ ◀ *Factor out -5.*
$-5(t^2 - 8t + 16) + 5(16)$ ◀ *Complete the square. Add $-5(16) + 5(16)$, or 0.*
$-5(t - 4)^2 + 80$

Value of variable   Maximum value

Check: $t = 4$	Check: $t \neq 4$ (Let $t = 5$.)
$-5 \cdot 4^2 + 40 \cdot 4$	$-5 \cdot 5^2 + 40 \cdot 5$
$-80 + 160$	$-125 + 200$
80	75

Thus, the maximum value is 80 and this occurs when $t = 4$.

Example 2 Find the maximum value of $-10x^2 + 100x + 6000$ and the corresponding value of x.

$-10x^2 + 100x \qquad + 6000$
$-10(x^2 - 10x \qquad) + 6000$ ◀ *Factor out -10 from $-10x^2 + 100x$.*
$-10(x^2 - 10x + 25) + 6000 + 10(25)$ ◀ *Complete the square. Add $-10(25) + 10(25)$, or 0.*
$-10(x - 5)^2 + 6250$

Thus, the maximum value is 6,250 and this occurs when $x = 5$.

In Chapter 1, you learned a method for finding the maximum height of an object that is shot upward from the earth's surface with a given initial velocity. The maximum height can also be found by the method of completing the square.

Example 3 Find the maximum height and the corresponding time of an object shot upward from the earth's surface at an initial velocity of 40 m/s.

$h = -5t^2 + vt = -5t^2 + 40t = -5(t - 4)^2 + 80$ ◀ *See Example 1 for the steps.*

Thus, the maximum height is 80 m at the end of 4 s.

Example 4

An orange grove has 20 trees per acre, and the average yield is 300 oranges per tree. For each additional tree per acre, the average yield will be reduced by 10 oranges per tree. How many trees per acre will yield the maximum number of oranges per acre, and what is the maximum number of oranges per acre?

Additional trees-per-acre	Trees per acre × Oranges per tree	= Oranges per acre
2 ▶	$(20 + 2)(300 - 10 \cdot 2)$	= 6160
3 ▶	$(20 + 3)(300 - 10 \cdot 3)$	= 6210
⋮	⋮ ⋮	
x ▶	$(20 + x)(300 - 10x)$	$= 6000 + 100x - 10x^2$
		$= -10x^2 + 100x + 6000$
	See Example 2 for the steps. ▶	$= -10(x - 5)^2 + 6250$

The maximum value is 6,250 and this occurs when $x = 5$.
Thus, $20 + 5$, or 25 trees per acre, will yield the maximum number of 6,250 oranges per acre.

Find the maximum value of each polynomial and the corresponding value of x.
(Exercises 1–6)

1. $-2x^2 + 12x$ **18; $x = 3$**
2. $64x - 16x^2$ **64; $x = 2$**
3. $10 + 6x - x^2$ **19; $x = 3$**
4. $-3x^2 + 6x + 25$ **28; $x = 1$**
5. $625 + 200x - 20x^2$ **1,125; $x = 5$**
6. $-2x^2 + 5x + 20$ **$23\frac{1}{8}$; $x = \frac{5}{4}$**

7. An arrow is shot upward at 60 m/s. Find the maximum height of the arrow and the corresponding time. Use the method of completing the square and the formula $h = -5t^2 + vt$. **180 m, 6 s**

8. A chartered bus ride costs $30 per ticket if there are 20 passengers. The ticket price is reduced by $1 for each additional passenger beyond 20. How many passengers will produce the maximum income, and what is the maximum income? **25 passengers; $625**

9. A rectangular chicken pen next to a barn wall is enclosed by 120 m of chicken wire on three sides and the barn wall on the fourth side. Find the maximum area that can be enclosed in this way. Find the dimensions of the pen. **1,800 m²; 30 m by 60 m**

10. A rectangular field adjacent to the straight bank of a river is to be fenced, but there is to be no fencing along the riverbank. If 180 m of fencing is available, what is the maximum area that can be enclosed? **4,050 m²**

11. Four-hundred people will attend a sidewalk display if tickets cost $1 each. Attendance will decrease by 20 people for each 10-cent increase in ticket price. What ticket price will yield the maximum income, and what is the maximum income from ticket sales? **$1.50; $450**

12. A publishing company can get 1,000 subscribers for a new magazine if the monthly subscription rate is $5. It will get 100 more subscribers for each 10-cent decrease in the monthly rate. What monthly rate will produce the maximum monthly income and what will that income be? **$3; $9,000**

APPLICATIONS

7.2 The Quadratic Formula

OBJECTIVE ▶ **To solve a quadratic equation by using the quadratic formula**

Every quadratic equation can be written in the standard form of $ax^2 + bx + c = 0$, where $a \neq 0$. You can solve this general equation for x by the method of completing the square. The result is called **the quadratic formula.**

$$ax^2 + bx + c = 0$$
$$ax^2 + bx = -c$$
$$x^2 + \frac{b}{a}x = \frac{-c}{a} \qquad \text{Divide each side by } a.$$
$$x^2 + \frac{b}{a}x + \left(\frac{b}{2a}\right)^2 = \frac{-c}{a} + \left(\frac{b}{2a}\right)^2 \qquad \text{Add } \left(\frac{b}{2a}\right)^2 \text{ to each side.}$$
$$x^2 + \frac{b}{a}x + \frac{b^2}{4a^2} = \frac{-c}{a} + \frac{b^2}{4a^2}$$
$$\left(x + \frac{b}{2a}\right)^2 = \frac{-4ac + b^2}{4a^2}$$
$$x + \frac{b}{2a} = \pm \sqrt{\frac{b^2 - 4ac}{4a^2}} \qquad \text{If } x^2 = k, \text{ then } x = \pm\sqrt{k}.$$
$$x = \frac{-b}{2a} \pm \frac{\sqrt{b^2 - 4ac}}{2a}$$
$$x = \frac{-b \pm \sqrt{b^2 - 4ac}}{2a}$$

The Quadratic Formula

> The solutions of a quadratic equation of the form $ax^2 + bx + c = 0$, $a \neq 0$, are given by the formula $x = \dfrac{-b \pm \sqrt{b^2 - 4ac}}{2a}$.

The quadratic formula can be used to solve any quadratic equation. You must first identify the values of a, b, and c. Then, you substitute these values in the formula, as shown in Example 1 below.

Example 1 Solve $3x^2 + 5x - 4 = 0$ by using the quadratic formula.

$$ax^2 + bx + c = 0$$
$$\downarrow \quad \downarrow \quad \downarrow$$
$$3x^2 + 5x - 4 = 0$$

$$a = 3, b = 5, c = -4$$

$$x = \frac{-b \pm \sqrt{b^2 - 4ac}}{2a}$$
$$= \frac{-(5) \pm \sqrt{5^2 - 4 \cdot 3 \cdot (-4)}}{2 \cdot 3}$$
$$= \frac{-5 \pm \sqrt{25 + 48}}{6}$$
$$= \frac{-5 \pm \sqrt{73}}{6}$$

Thus, the solutions are $\dfrac{-5 + \sqrt{73}}{6}$ and $\dfrac{-5 - \sqrt{73}}{6}$.

If a quadratic equation is not given in standard form, you should rewrite it in standard form in order to identify the values of *a, b,* and *c.*

Example 2 **Solve $4x^2 = 11 + 4x$ by using the quadratic formula.**

$$4x^2 - 4x - 11 = 0$$ ◀ *Write the equation in the standard form of $ax^2 + bx + c = 0$.*

$$a = 4, b = -4, c = -11$$ ◀ *Identify the values of a, b, and c.*

$$x = \frac{-b \pm \sqrt{b^2 - 4ac}}{2a}$$

$$= \frac{-(-4) \pm \sqrt{(-4)^2 - 4 \cdot 4 \cdot (-11)}}{2 \cdot 4}$$ ◀ *Substitute.*

$$= \frac{4 \pm \sqrt{192}}{8}$$

$$= \frac{4 \pm 8\sqrt{3}}{8}$$ ◀ $\sqrt{192} = \sqrt{64 \cdot 3}$

$$= \frac{4(1 \pm 2\sqrt{3})}{4 \cdot 2}$$

$$= \frac{1 \pm 2\sqrt{3}}{2}$$ ◀ *Divide numerator and denominator by 4.*

Thus, the solutions are $\dfrac{1 + 2\sqrt{3}}{2}$ and $\dfrac{1 - 2\sqrt{3}}{2}$.

An equation of the form $ax^2 + bx + c = 0$, where $a = 0$, is *not* a quadratic equation since the square term is eliminated: $0 \cdot x^2 = 0$. However, there is no such restriction on the value of b or c. The standard form of the quadratic equation $5x^2 - 9x = 0$ is $5x^2 - 9x + 0 = 0$, where $c = 0$. The standard form of the quadratic equation $y^2 - 150 = 0$ is $y^2 + 0y - 150 = 0$. Equations of either type can be solved by using the quadratic formula.

Example 3 **Solve $5x^2 - 9x = 0$ and $y^2 - 150 = 0$ by using the quadratic formula.**

$$5x^2 - 9x = 0$$
$$5x^2 - 9x + 0 = 0$$
$$a = 5, b = -9, c = 0$$

$$x = \frac{-(-9) \pm \sqrt{(-9)^2 - 4 \cdot 5 \cdot 0}}{2 \cdot 5}$$

$$= \frac{9 \pm \sqrt{81 - 0}}{10}$$

$$= \frac{9 \pm 9}{10}, \text{ or } \frac{9 + 9}{10} \text{ and } \frac{9 - 9}{10}$$

The solutions are $\dfrac{9}{5}$ and 0.

$$y^2 - 150 = 0$$
$$1y^2 + 0y - 150 = 0$$
$$a = 1, b = 0, c = -150$$

$$y = \frac{-(0) \pm \sqrt{0^2 - 4 \cdot 1 \cdot (-150)}}{2 \cdot 1}$$

$$= \frac{0 \pm \sqrt{0 + 600}}{2}$$

$$= \frac{\pm 10\sqrt{6}}{2}, \text{ or } \pm 5\sqrt{6}$$

The solutions are $5\sqrt{6}$ and $-5\sqrt{6}$.

Reading In Algebra

For each equation in the left column, identify every correct description in the right column.

1. $9x + 5^2 = 0$ **C**
2. $x^2 - 14 = 0$ **A, D, E**
3. $3x - 5 = x^2$ **B, D**
4. $5x^2 - 9x = 0$ **A, F**
5. $2x^2 - 7x - 6 = 0$ **A**

A A quadratic equation in standard form
B A quadratic equation not in standard form
C Not a quadratic equation
D $a = 1$ **E** $b = 0$
F $c = 0$

6. Identify three different methods for solving the quadratic equation $x^2 - 3x - 10 = 0$.
factoring; completing the square; quadratic formula

Oral Exercises

Identify the values of a, b, and c for each quadratic equation.

1. $6x^2 + 3x - 2 = 0$
   $a = 6, b = 3, c = -2$
2. $y^2 - 8y + 7 = 0$
   $a = 1, b = -8, c = 7$
3. $-2n^2 - n = 0$
   $a = -2, b = -1, c = 0$
4. $z^2 - 8 = 0$
   $a = 1, b = 0, c = -8$

Give each quadratic equation in standard form.

5. $x^2 - 6x = 7$
   $x^2 - 6x - 7 = 0$
6. $4 + 3y^2 = -y$
   $3y^2 + y + 4 = 0$
7. $-3 = t - 4t^2$
   $4t^2 - t - 3 = 0$
8. $5x = -10x^2$
   $10x^2 + 5x + 0 = 0$

Written Exercises

Simplify each expression.

(A)

1. $\dfrac{-5 \pm \sqrt{8}}{2}$ $\dfrac{-5 \pm 2\sqrt{2}}{2}$
2. $\dfrac{6 \pm \sqrt{20}}{4}$ $\dfrac{3 \pm \sqrt{5}}{2}$
3. $\dfrac{-10 \pm \sqrt{32}}{2}$ $-5 \pm 2\sqrt{2}$
4. $\dfrac{8 \pm \sqrt{12}}{4}$ $\dfrac{4 \pm \sqrt{3}}{2}$
5. $\dfrac{10 \pm \sqrt{36 - 36}}{4}$ $\dfrac{5}{2}$
6. $\dfrac{0 \pm \sqrt{24}}{6}$ $\pm \dfrac{\sqrt{6}}{3}$

Solve each equation by using the quadratic formula.

7. $4x^2 + x - 2 = 0$ $\dfrac{-1 \pm \sqrt{33}}{8}$
8. $3y^2 + 7y + 3 = 0$ $\dfrac{-7 \pm \sqrt{13}}{6}$
9. $2n^2 - n - 2 = 0$ $\dfrac{1 \pm \sqrt{17}}{4}$
10. $2y^2 - 4y + 1 = 0$ $\dfrac{2 \pm \sqrt{2}}{2}$
11. $t^2 + 4t - 1 = 0$ $-2 \pm \sqrt{5}$
12. $2x^2 + 6x + 3 = 0$ $\dfrac{-3 \pm \sqrt{3}}{2}$
13. $4n^2 + 7 = 12n$ $\dfrac{3 \pm \sqrt{2}}{2}$
14. $0 = 4x^2 + 8x + 1$ $\dfrac{-2 \pm \sqrt{3}}{2}$
15. $9y^2 = 6y + 7$ $\dfrac{1 \pm 2\sqrt{2}}{3}$
16. $3x^2 + 6x = 2$ $\dfrac{-3 \pm \sqrt{15}}{3}$
17. $2y^2 = 6y - 1$ $\dfrac{3 \pm \sqrt{7}}{2}$
18. $5n^2 = 1 - 2n$ $\dfrac{-1 \pm \sqrt{6}}{5}$
19. $y^2 - 8y + 16 = 0$ 4
20. $x^2 - 6x = 0$ $0, 6$
21. $t^2 - 11 = 0$ $\pm\sqrt{11}$
22. $t^2 - 20 = 0$ $\pm 2\sqrt{5}$
23. $0 = 9y^2 + 12y + 4$ $-\dfrac{2}{3}$
24. $3x^2 + 2x = 0$ $-\dfrac{2}{3}, 0$
25. $4x^2 = 7x$ $0, \dfrac{7}{4}$
26. $5t^2 - 11 = 0$ $\pm \dfrac{\sqrt{55}}{5}$
27. $4y^2 = 20y - 25$ $\dfrac{5}{2}$

(B)

28. $\dfrac{3}{2}x^2 + \dfrac{1}{2}x - 3 = 0$ $\dfrac{-1 \pm \sqrt{73}}{6}$
29. $\dfrac{1}{2}y^2 - \dfrac{3}{2}y + \dfrac{5}{6} = 0$ $\dfrac{9 \pm \sqrt{21}}{6}$
30. $\dfrac{1}{4}n^2 = \dfrac{1}{2}n + \dfrac{3}{8}$ $\dfrac{2 \pm \sqrt{10}}{2}$
31. $\dfrac{y^2}{15} + \dfrac{5}{3} = \dfrac{2y}{3}$ 5 $\dfrac{-4 \pm \sqrt{7}}{3}$
32. $\dfrac{n^2}{4} = \dfrac{n}{2} - \dfrac{1}{6}$ $\dfrac{3 \pm \sqrt{3}}{3}$
33. $\dfrac{x^2}{3} - \dfrac{1}{2} = \dfrac{x}{3}$ $\dfrac{1 \pm \sqrt{7}}{2}$
34. $6\left(2x^2 + \dfrac{4}{3}x\right) = 3(3x^2 - 1)$ $-\sqrt{2}, 3\sqrt{2}$
35. $\dfrac{y + 3}{2y - 1} = \dfrac{2y + 3}{y + 5}$ $\dfrac{2 \pm \sqrt{58}}{3}$
36. $\dfrac{n^2 + 1}{n} + \dfrac{n - 2}{2n} = \dfrac{1}{3n}$ $\dfrac{-3 \pm \sqrt{57}}{12}$

(C)

37. $x^2 - (2\sqrt{2})x - 6 = 0$ $-\sqrt{2}, 3\sqrt{2}$
38. $x^2\sqrt{6} - 4x - 2\sqrt{6} = 0$ $\dfrac{-\sqrt{6}}{3}, \sqrt{6}$
39. $5x^2 + 2x\sqrt{10} - 1 = 0$ $\dfrac{-\sqrt{10} \pm \sqrt{15}}{5}$
40. $(y + 2)^2 + 7(y + 2) - 3 = 0$ [Hint: Let $x = y + 2$.] $\dfrac{-11 \pm \sqrt{61}}{2}$
41. $(n + \sqrt{5})^2 - 5(n + \sqrt{5}) - 5 = 0$ [Hint: Let $x = n + \sqrt{5}$.] $\dfrac{5 - 5\sqrt{5}}{2}, \dfrac{5 + \sqrt{5}}{2}$
42. $(n^2)^2 - 3n^2\sqrt{2} + 4 = 0$ [Hint: Let $x = n^2$.] $\pm\sqrt[4]{2}, \pm\sqrt[4]{8}$
43. $x^{-2} - 6x^{-1} + 4 = 0$ $\dfrac{3 \pm \sqrt{5}}{4}$
44. $(x^{\frac{1}{2}})^2 - (3\sqrt{3})x^{\frac{1}{2}} + 6 = 0$ $3, 12$
45. $8x^{-4} - 6x^{-2} + 1 = 0$ $-2, 2, -\sqrt{2}, \sqrt{2}$

THE QUADRATIC FORMULA **171**

7.3 Problem Solving: The Quadratic Formula

OBJECTIVE ▶ **To solve a word problem by using the quadratic formula**

Sometimes a statement about the relationships between two numbers is in the form of a quadratic equation. Since a given quadratic equation may have two real number solutions, there may be two values for each of the numbers.

Example 1

A second number is 6 more than twice a first number. If the second number is multiplied by 3 more than the first number, the product is 9. Find the two numbers.

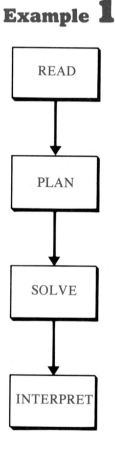

READ

PLAN

SOLVE

INTERPRET

Let $\quad f$ = first number.
$\quad\quad 2f + 6$ = second number
$\quad$ (second number) · (3 more than first number) = 9
$$(2f + 6)(f + 3) = 9$$
$$2f^2 + 12f + 18 = 9$$
$$2f^2 + 12f + 9 = 0$$

Use the quadratic formula: $a = 2$, $b = 12$, and $c = 9$.

$$f = \frac{-12 \pm \sqrt{12^2 - 4 \cdot 2 \cdot 9}}{2 \cdot 2}$$
$$= \frac{-12 \pm \sqrt{72}}{4}$$
$$= \frac{-12 \pm 6\sqrt{2}}{4}, \text{ or } \frac{-6 \pm 3\sqrt{2}}{2}$$

If $f = \dfrac{-6 + 3\sqrt{2}}{2}$, then $2f + 6 = 2 \cdot \dfrac{-6 + 3\sqrt{2}}{2} + 6 = 3\sqrt{2}$.

If $f = \dfrac{-6 - 3\sqrt{2}}{2}$, then $2f + 6 = 2 \cdot \dfrac{-6 - 3\sqrt{2}}{2} + 6 = -3\sqrt{2}$.

Each pair of answers checks in the problem.

Thus, the two numbers are $\dfrac{-6 + 3\sqrt{2}}{2}$, $3\sqrt{2}$ or $\dfrac{-6 - 3\sqrt{2}}{2}$, $-3\sqrt{2}$.

Some problems involve the use of formulas so that when values are substituted for the variables, a quadratic equation is obtained. The resulting quadratic equation can then be solved using the quadratic formula. One formula of this type is $h = vt - 5t^2$, which you used earlier in this chapter. It is used again in Example 2 on page 173.

Example 2

An object is to be shot upward from the earth's surface with an initial velocity of 25 m/s. To the nearest tenth of a second, when will the height of the object be 15 m?

$$h = vt - 5t^2$$
$$15 = 25t - 5t^2 \quad \blacktriangleleft \text{ Substitute 15 for } h \text{ and 25 for } v.$$
$$3 = 5t - t^2$$

$$t^2 - 5t + 3 = 0$$
$$t = \frac{5 \pm \sqrt{25 - 12}}{2} = \frac{5 \pm \sqrt{13}}{2}$$
$$\doteq \frac{5 \pm 3.606}{2}, \text{ or } 4.303 \text{ and } 0.697$$

Check the irrational solutions, $\frac{5 \pm \sqrt{13}}{2}$, in the original equation.

Check: $\frac{5 + \sqrt{13}}{2}$

15	$25t - 5t^2$
15	$25 \cdot \frac{5 + \sqrt{13}}{2} - 5\left(\frac{5 + \sqrt{13}}{2}\right)^2$
	$\frac{125 + 25\sqrt{13}}{2} - 5\left(\frac{25 + 10\sqrt{13} + 13}{4}\right)$
	$\frac{125 + 25\sqrt{13}}{2} - \frac{95 + 25\sqrt{13}}{2}$
	$\frac{30}{2}$, or 15

Check: $\frac{5 - \sqrt{13}}{2}$

15	$25t - 5t^2$
15	$25 \cdot \frac{5 - \sqrt{13}}{2} - 5\left(\frac{5 - \sqrt{13}}{2}\right)^2$
	$\frac{125 - 25\sqrt{13}}{2} - 5\left(\frac{25 - 10\sqrt{13} + 13}{4}\right)$
	$\frac{125 - 25\sqrt{13}}{2} - \frac{95 - 25\sqrt{13}}{2}$
	$\frac{30}{2}$, or 15

Thus, the height will be 15 m at the end of 0.7 s and again at the end of 4.3 s, to the nearest 0.1 s.

Written Exercises

1. $1 - \sqrt{5}, -1 - \sqrt{5}$ or $1 + \sqrt{5}, -1 + \sqrt{5}$ 2. $-2 - \sqrt{5}, 2 - \sqrt{5}$ or $-2 + \sqrt{5}, 2 + \sqrt{5}$

Solve each problem. Give the answers in simplest radical form.

(A) 1. A second number is 2 less than a first number. Their product is 4. Find the numbers.

2. The product of two numbers is 1. Find the numbers if one of them is 4 more than the other.

3. One number is 2 less than twice another number. Find these numbers if their product is 3. $\frac{1 - \sqrt{7}}{2}, -1 - \sqrt{7}$ or $\frac{1 + \sqrt{7}}{2}, -1 + \sqrt{7}$

4. Find two numbers such that their product is -2 and one number is 6 more than 3 times the other number.
$\frac{-3 - \sqrt{3}}{3}, 3 - \sqrt{3}$ or $\frac{-3 + \sqrt{3}}{3}, 3 + \sqrt{3}$

Solve each problem using the formula $h = vt - 5t^2$. Approximate each answer to the nearest 0.1 s, unless directed otherwise.

5. An object is shot upward from the earth's surface with an initial velocity of 50 m/s. When will the height of the object be 100 m? **2.8 s, 7.2 s**

6. If a pellet is launched straight up from the surface of the earth with an initial velocity of 75 m/s, when will the altitude of the pellet be 225 m? **4.1 s, 10.9 s**

(B) 7. A certain baseball pitcher can throw a ball with an initial velocity of 40 m/s. If the ball is thrown straight up, when will its height be 15 m? **0.4 s, 7.6 s**

PROBLEM SOLVING: THE QUADRATIC FORMULA   **173**

8. An archer shot an arrow upward with an initial velocity of 125 m/s. When will its height be 755 m on its upward flight? When will its height be 755 m on its downward flight? **10.2 s, 14.8 s**

9. An object was shot upward from the earth with an initial velocity of 38 m/s. When did it return to earth? **7.6 s**

10. The *maximum value* of h in the formula $h = vt - 5t^2$ is $\dfrac{v^2}{20}$. What initial velocity is needed for an object to reach a maximum height of 400 m? Give the answer to the nearest meter per second. **89 m/s**

Solve each problem. Give the answers in simplest radical form.

11. A second number is 4 more than 3 times a first number. If the second number is multiplied by 2 more than the first number, the product is 2. Find the numbers.
$\dfrac{-5 - \sqrt{7}}{3}, -1 - \sqrt{7}$ or $\dfrac{-5 + \sqrt{7}}{3}, -1 + \sqrt{7}$

12. The smaller of two numbers is 3 less than twice the greater number. The product of the smaller number and 8 more than 4 times the greater number is -16. Find the numbers. $\dfrac{-1 - \sqrt{17}}{4}, \dfrac{-7 - \sqrt{17}}{2}$ or $\dfrac{-1 + \sqrt{17}}{4}, \dfrac{-7 + \sqrt{17}}{2}$

Solve each problem using the formula $h = d + vt - 5t^2$. Approximate each answer to the nearest 0.1 s. (See explanation on page 24, if necessary.)

©
13. An object is launched upward from the top of a tower 80 m tall with an initial velocity of 40 m/s. When will the object be 130 m above the earth's surface? **1.6 s, 6.4 s**

14. A pellet was sent up from the top of a tower 60 m tall with an initial velocity of 35 m/s. When will it be 115 m above the earth? **2.4 s, 4.6 s**

15. When will the pellet in Exercise 14 return to earth? **8.4 s**

16. When would the pellet in Exercise 14 be 35 m above the surface if it were launched from 20 m below the surface? **2.4 s, 4.6 s**

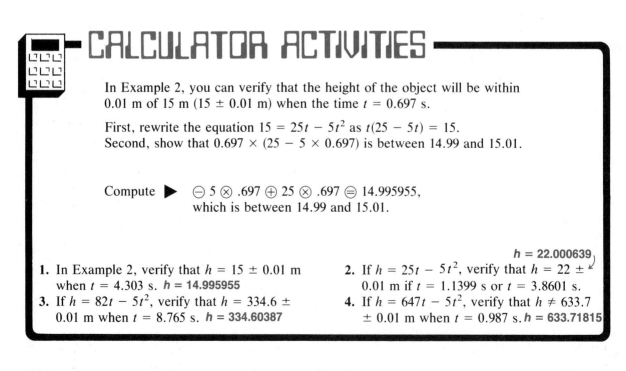

CALCULATOR ACTIVITIES

In Example 2, you can verify that the height of the object will be within 0.01 m of 15 m (15 ± 0.01 m) when the time $t = 0.697$ s.

First, rewrite the equation $15 = 25t - 5t^2$ as $t(25 - 5t) = 15$.
Second, show that $0.697 \times (25 - 5 \times 0.697)$ is between 14.99 and 15.01.

Compute ▶ $\ominus$ 5 $\otimes$ .697 $\oplus$ 25 $\otimes$ .697 $\ominus$ 14.995955,
which is between 14.99 and 15.01.

$h = 22.000639$

1. In Example 2, verify that $h = 15 \pm 0.01$ m when $t = 4.303$ s. **h = 14.995955**

2. If $h = 25t - 5t^2$, verify that $h = 22 \pm$ 0.01 m if $t = 1.1399$ s or $t = 3.8601$ s.

3. If $h = 82t - 5t^2$, verify that $h = 334.6 \pm$ 0.01 m when $t = 8.765$ s. **h = 334.60387**

4. If $h = 647t - 5t^2$, verify that $h \neq 633.7$ ± 0.01 m when $t = 0.987$ s. **h = 633.71815**

7.4 Problem Solving: Irrational Measurements

OBJECTIVE ▶ **To solve a word problem involving a geometric figure with irrational dimensions**

You can use the Pythagorean relation, $a^2 + b^2 = c^2$, and the quadratic formula to solve some problems involving a right triangle. As shown in Example 1, measurements may be given as irrational numbers in simplest radical form.

Example 1

One leg of a right triangle is twice as long as the other leg. The hypotenuse is 3 cm longer than the longer leg. Find the length of each side of the triangle.

Let w = length of the shorter leg.
         $2w$ = length of the longer leg
   $2w + 3$ = length of the hypotenuse

$$a^2 + b^2 = c^2$$
$$\blacktriangledown \qquad \blacktriangledown \qquad \blacktriangledown$$
$$w^2 + (2w)^2 = (2w + 3)^2$$
$$w^2 + 4w^2 = 4w^2 + 12w + 9$$
$$w^2 - 12w - 9 = 0 \quad \blacktriangleleft \quad \textit{Quadratic equation: } a = 1, b = -12, c = -9$$

$$w = \frac{-(-12) \pm \sqrt{(-12)^2 - 4 \cdot 1(-9)}}{2 \cdot 1}$$
$$= \frac{12 \pm \sqrt{180}}{2}$$
$$= \frac{12 \pm 6\sqrt{5}}{2}, \text{ or } 6 \pm 3\sqrt{5}$$

One solution of the quadratic equation is $6 - 3\sqrt{5}$, but it is *not* a solution to the problem. The length of a side of a triangle cannot be a negative number: $(6 - 3\sqrt{5}) < 0$ since $6 - 3 \cdot 2.236 < 0$.

$$w = 6 + 3\sqrt{5} \qquad 2w = 12 + 6\sqrt{5} \qquad 2w + 3 = 15 + 6\sqrt{5}$$

Check:

$a^2 + b^2$	c^2
$(6 + 3\sqrt{5})^2 + (12 + 6\sqrt{5})^2$	$(15 + 6\sqrt{5})^2$
$36 + 36\sqrt{5} + 45 + 144 + 144\sqrt{5} + 180$	$225 + 180\sqrt{5} + 180$
$405 + 180\sqrt{5}$	$405 + 180\sqrt{5}$

Thus, the lengths of the two legs and the hypotenuse are $6 + 3\sqrt{5}$ cm, $12 + 6\sqrt{5}$ cm, and $15 + 6\sqrt{5}$ cm, respectively.

───────────────── • ─────────────────

Sometimes measurements in the form of irrational numbers may have to be changed into decimal form. This is shown in Example 2 on page 176.

Example 2

A 10-cm square (10 cm by 10 cm) is cut from each corner of a rectangular piece of cardboard that is 4 times as long as it is wide. The flaps are folded up to form an open carton with a volume of 7,000 cm³. Find the dimensions of the original piece of cardboard to the nearest 0.1 cm.

Let x be the width and $4x$ the length of the original piece of cardboard.

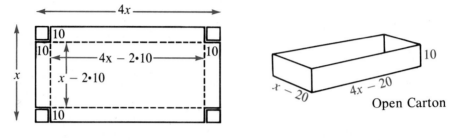

Open Carton

length × width × height = volume

$$(4x - 20)(x - 20) \cdot 10 = 7{,}000$$
$$(4x - 20)(x - 20) = 700$$
$$4x^2 - 100x + 400 = 700$$
$$4x^2 - 100x - 300 = 0$$
$$x^2 - 25x - 75 = 0$$

$$x = \frac{-(-25) \pm \sqrt{(-25)^2 - 4 \cdot 1(-75)}}{2}$$

$$= \frac{25 \pm \sqrt{925}}{2}$$

$$= \frac{25 \pm 5\sqrt{37}}{2}$$

$$\doteq \frac{25 \pm 5(6.083)}{2}$$

$$= 27.7075 \quad \text{or} \quad -2.7075$$

The width cannot be negative, so $x = 27.7075$.
The length, $4x = 4 \cdot 27.7075$, or 110.8300.

Check: See A CHALLENGE TO YOU on page 177.

Thus, the width of the original piece of cardboard was 27.7 cm, and the length was 110.8 cm, to the nearest 0.1 cm.

Written Exercises

Solve each problem. Give the answers in simplest radical form, unless directed otherwise.

(A) **1.** One leg of a right triangle is twice as long as the other leg and the hypotenuse is 6 m long. Find the length of each leg of the triangle. $\frac{6\sqrt{5}}{5}$ m; $\frac{12\sqrt{5}}{5}$ m

2. In a certain right triangle, one leg is 1 cm shorter than the other leg and the hypotenuse is 3 cm longer than the shorter leg. Find the length of each side of the triangle.
$3 + 2\sqrt{3}$ cm; $2 + 2\sqrt{3}$ cm; $5 + 2\sqrt{3}$ cm

3. A 2-cm square is cut from each corner of a rectangular piece of cardboard that is 20 cm longer than it is wide. The four flaps are turned up to form an open box with a volume of 50 cm³. Find the dimensions of the original piece of cardboard to the nearest 0.1 cm. **5.2 cm by 25.2 cm**

4. A rectangular piece of plastic is 3 times as long as it is wide. After a 6-cm square is cut from each corner, the flaps are pressed upward to form an open pan with a volume of 720 cm³. To the nearest 0.1 cm, find the length and the width of the original piece of plastic. **15.5 cm; 46.5 cm**

5. A diagonal of a square is 8 cm long. Find the width of the square. **4√2 cm**

6. Find the width of a square if one diagonal is 3√22 mm long. **3√11 mm**

7. A rectangular lawn measures 20 m by 40 m and is surrounded by a sidewalk of uniform width. The outer edge of the sidewalk is a rectangle with an area of 1,000 m². Find the width of a strip of the sidewalk to the nearest 0.1 m. **1.6 m**

8. A rectangular piece of mirror glass measures 40 cm by 60 cm. It is surrounded by a uniform frame whose outer edge is a rectangle with an area of 3,200 cm². To the nearest 0.1 cm, find the width of a strip of the frame. **3.7 cm**

9. A rectangle is 2 dm longer than it is wide. A diagonal of the rectangle is 1 dm longer than the rectangle's length. Find the length of the diagonal and the area of the rectangle. **4 + √6 dm; 9 + 4√6 dm²**

10. A rectangle's length is 1 mm more than 3 times its width. The length of one of its diagonals is 1 mm more than the rectangles' length. Find the length, the width, and the area of the rectangle. **10 + 6√3 mm; 3 + 2√3 mm; 66 + 38√3 mm²**

11. A diagonal of a square is 2 m longer than a side of the square. Find the length of the diagonal and the area of the square. **4 + 2√2 m; 12 + 8√2 m²**

12. One side of a square is 3 dm shorter than one diagonal of the square. Find the length of the side and the area of the square. **3 + 3√2 dm; 27 + 18√2 dm²**

CALCULATOR ACTIVITIES

1. 11,950.653, which is within 11,950 ± 1   **2. 2,238.4375, which is not within 2,250 ± 1**

In Example 2 on page 176, the open carton measures $4x - 20$ cm by $x - 20$ cm by 10 cm and the volume is 7,000 cm³. Determine whether the volume is within $7,000 \pm 1$ cm³ if $x = 27.7075$ cm.

If $x = 27.7075$, then $4x - 20 = 90.8300$ and $x - 20 = 7.7075$.

$$90.83 \otimes 7.7075 \otimes 10 \ominus 7000.7222, \text{ which is within } 7000 \pm 1.$$

A certain box measures $x - 10$ cm by $3x - 10$ cm by 20 cm. Determine whether the volume of the box is within 1 cm³ of the given volume for the given value of x.

1. 11,950 cm³ if $x = 21.168$ cm
2. 2,250 cm³ if $x = 13.625$ cm
3. 39,240 cm³ if $x = 32.456$ cm
4. 1,270 cm³ if $x = 12.347$ cm
3. 39,238.716, which is not within 39,240 ± 1
4. 1,269.3045, which is within 1,270 ± 1

→ A Challenge To You

Show that $10(x - 20)(4x - 20) = 7,000$ if $x = \dfrac{25 + 5\sqrt{37}}{2}$. **See TE Answer Section.**

PROBLEM SOLVING: IRRATIONAL MEASUREMENTS

7.5 Radical Equations

OBJECTIVE ▶ **To solve a radical equation**

Equations like $\sqrt[3]{6x + 10} = -2$ and $3\sqrt{2y + 2} = 2\sqrt{5y - 1}$ contain a variable in a radicand. They are called **radical equations.**

Example 1 Solve $\sqrt[3]{6x + 10} = -2$.

$$\sqrt[3]{6x + 10} = -2$$
$$(\sqrt[3]{6x + 10})^3 = (-2)^3 \quad ◀ \text{ If } a = b, \text{ then } a^3 = b^3.$$
$$6x + 10 = -8$$
$$6x = -18$$
$$x = -3$$

Check in the original equation.

$\sqrt[3]{6x + 10}$	-2
$\sqrt[3]{6(-3) + 10}$	$-2.$
$\sqrt[3]{-18 + 10}$	
$\sqrt[3]{-8}$	
-2	

Thus, the solution is -3.

Example 2 Solve $3\sqrt{2y + 2} = 2\sqrt{5y - 1}$.

$$3\sqrt{2y + 2} = 2\sqrt{5y - 1}$$
$$(3\sqrt{2y + 2})^2 = (2\sqrt{5y - 1})^2 \quad ◀ \text{ If } a = b, \text{ then } (a)^2 = (b)^2.$$
$$9(2y + 2) = 4(5y - 1)$$
$$18y + 18 = 20y - 4$$
$$22 = 2y$$
$$11 = y$$

Check in the original equation.

$3\sqrt{2y + 2}$	$2\sqrt{5y - 1}$
$3\sqrt{2 \cdot 11 + 2}$	$2\sqrt{5 \cdot 11 - 1}$
$3\sqrt{24}$	$2\sqrt{54}$
$3 \cdot 2\sqrt{6}$	$2 \cdot 3\sqrt{6}$
$6\sqrt{6}$	$6\sqrt{6}$

Thus, the solution is 11.

It is necessary to check the apparent solutions of a radical equation since raising each side of an equation to the same power may introduce *extraneous solutions*.

Example 3 Solve $3 + \sqrt{3x + 1} = x$.

"Isolate" the radical. Rewrite the equation so that the term containing the radical is alone on one side.

$$\sqrt{3x + 1} = x - 3$$
$$(\sqrt{3x + 1})^2 = (x - 3)^2$$
$$3x + 1 = x^2 - 6x + 9$$
Quadratic equation ▶ $\quad 0 = x^2 - 9x + 8$
$$0 = (x - 1)(x - 8)$$
$$x = 1 \text{ or } x = 8$$

1 does *not* check. ▶

Check:

	$3 + \sqrt{3x + 1}$	x
$x = 1$	$3 + \sqrt{3 \cdot 1 + 1}$	1
	$3 + \sqrt{4}$	
	$3 + 2, \text{ or } 5$	

Check:

	$3 + \sqrt{3x + 1}$	x
$x = 8$	$3 + \sqrt{3 \cdot 8 + 1}$	8
	$3 + \sqrt{25}$	
	$3 + 5, \text{ or } 8$	

Thus, the solution is 8.

In some radical equations, the radicand contains an exponent.

Example 4 Solve $\sqrt[3]{2y^{-1}} = -4$.

$$(\sqrt[3]{2y^{-1}})^3 = (-4)^3$$
$$2y^{-1} = -64$$
$$y^{-1} = -32$$
$$\frac{1}{y} = -32$$
$$y = \frac{1}{-32}, \text{ or } -\frac{1}{32}$$

Check:

$$\begin{array}{c|c} \sqrt[3]{2y^{-1}} & -4 \\ \hline \sqrt[3]{2 \cdot \left(\frac{1}{-32}\right)^{-1}} & -4 \\ \sqrt[3]{2(-32)} & \\ \sqrt[3]{-64}, \text{ or } -4 & \end{array}$$

Thus, the solution is $-\dfrac{1}{32}$.

Example 5 Solve $\sqrt[4]{x^2 - 8} = 2$.

$$(\sqrt[4]{x^2 - 8})^4 = 2^4$$
$$x^2 - 8 = 16$$
$$x^2 = 24$$
$$x = \pm 2\sqrt{6}$$

Check:

$$\begin{array}{c|c} \sqrt[4]{x^2 - 8} & 2 \\ \hline \sqrt[4]{(\pm 2\sqrt{6})^2 - 8} & 2 \\ \sqrt[4]{24 - 8} & \\ \sqrt[4]{16}, \text{ or } 2 & \end{array}$$

Thus, the solutions are $2\sqrt{6}$ and $-2\sqrt{6}$.

An equation such as $\sqrt{5x + 1} - \sqrt{3x - 5} = 2$ in Example 6 contains two radicals and a third term. To solve this equation, you need to isolate the radicals, one at a time.

Example 6 Solve $\sqrt{5x + 1} - \sqrt{3x - 5} = 2$.

Isolate one of the two radicals.
$$\sqrt{5x + 1} = 2 + \sqrt{3x - 5}$$
$$(\sqrt{5x + 1})^2 = (2 + \sqrt{3x - 5})^2$$
$$5x + 1 = 4 + 4\sqrt{3x - 5} + 3x - 5$$
Isolate the other radical.
$$2x + 2 = 4\sqrt{3x - 5}$$
$$x + 1 = 2\sqrt{3x - 5}$$
$$(x + 1)^2 = (2\sqrt{3x - 5})^2$$
$$x^2 + 2x + 1 = 4(3x - 5)$$
$$x^2 + 2x + 1 = 12x - 20$$
$$x^2 - 10x + 21 = 0$$
$$(x - 3)(x - 7) = 0$$
$$x = 3 \quad \text{or} \quad x = 7$$

Check:

$$\begin{array}{r|c} \sqrt{5x + 1} - \sqrt{3x - 5} & 2 \\ \hline x = 3 \quad \sqrt{5 \cdot 3 + 1} - \sqrt{3 \cdot 3 - 5} & 2 \\ \sqrt{16} - \sqrt{4} & \\ 4 - 2, \text{ or } 2 & \end{array}$$

$$\begin{array}{r|c} \sqrt{5x + 1} - \sqrt{3x - 5} & 2 \\ \hline x = 7 \quad \sqrt{5 \cdot 7 + 1} - \sqrt{3 \cdot 7 - 5} & 2 \\ \sqrt{36} - \sqrt{16} & \\ 6 - 4, \text{ or } 2 & \end{array}$$

Thus, the solutions are 3 and 7.

RADICAL EQUATIONS

Oral Exercises

For each equation, the only apparent solutions are 3 and 5. Check 3 and 5 in each equation to find the solution, or solutions, of the equation.

1. $\sqrt{x-1} = 2$ **5**   2. $\sqrt{x+1} = x-1$ **3**   3. $\sqrt{x+1} = -2$ **neither**   4. $\sqrt{x-1} = x-3$ **5**   5. $\sqrt{2x-6} = x-3$ **3, 5**

Written Exercises

Solve each equation.

(A)

1. $\sqrt{x-2} = 7$ **51**
2. $\sqrt{2y-6} = 6$ **21**
3. $\sqrt{3c} = \sqrt{c+6}$ **3**
4. $\sqrt[3]{2a} = 4$ **32**
5. $\sqrt[3]{7x-1} = \sqrt[3]{5x+7}$ **4**
6. $\sqrt[4]{5x+1} - \sqrt[4]{6x-2} = 0$ **3**
7. $2\sqrt{x} = \sqrt{3x+5}$ **5**
8. $\sqrt{12y+3} - 3\sqrt{2y} = 0$ $\frac{1}{2}$
9. $3\sqrt{2a-4} = 2\sqrt{a-2}$ **2**
10. $2\sqrt[3]{4y} = -1$ $-\frac{1}{32}$
11. $3\sqrt[4]{2x} = 2$ $\frac{8}{81}$
12. $2\sqrt[3]{3n} = 3\sqrt[3]{n-1}$ **9**
13. $x - 4 = \sqrt{2x}$ **8**
14. $y - 5 = \sqrt{y-3}$ **7**
15. $\sqrt{2w-3} = w-3$ **6**
16. $\sqrt[3]{y^{-1}} = 5$ $\frac{1}{125}$
17. $\sqrt[3]{c^2} = 2$ $\pm 2\sqrt{2}$
18. $\sqrt[3]{x^2+9} = 3$ $\pm 3\sqrt{2}$
19. $\sqrt[4]{x^3} = 2$ $2\sqrt[3]{2}$
20. $\sqrt[4]{y^{-2}} = 3$ $\pm\frac{1}{9}$
21. $\sqrt[4]{a^2+16} = 4$ $\pm 4\sqrt{15}$
22. $\sqrt{8y} = \sqrt{2y} + 2$ **2**
23. $\sqrt{x+7} = \sqrt{x} + 1$ **9**
24. $\sqrt{3n} - 2 = \sqrt{n-2}$ **3**

(B)

25. $\sqrt[3]{3y^{-1}} = -6$ $-\frac{1}{72}$
26. $\sqrt[4]{2y^{-2}} = \frac{1}{3}$ $\pm 9\sqrt{2}$
27. $\sqrt{(x-3)^{-2}} = \frac{1}{4}$ **-1, 7**
28. $3 + \sqrt{2t+5} = 0$ **no solution**
29. $-2 + \sqrt{4x+3} = 0$ $\frac{1}{4}$
30. $-5 - \sqrt{7y-3} = 0$ **no solution**
31. $6 + \sqrt{3x} = x$ **12**
32. $y - \sqrt{4y-3} = 2$ **7**
33. $2 + \sqrt{5x+6} = 3x$ **2**
34. $4 - \sqrt{10-3a} = a$ **2, 3**
35. $2\sqrt{3x-2} = x+2$ **2, 6**
36. $3\sqrt{2n+3} = 2n+5$ $-1, \frac{1}{2}$
37. $\sqrt{x^2+x-3} = 3$ **-4, 3**
38. $\sqrt[3]{y^2-12y} = 4$ **-4, 16**
39. $\sqrt[4]{5x^2+3} = 2\sqrt[4]{x}$ $\frac{1}{5}, 3$
40. $\sqrt{2y+3} = 1 + \sqrt{y+1}$
41. $\sqrt{4x-3} = 2 + \sqrt{2x-5}$ **3, 7**
42. $\sqrt{3a+1} - \sqrt{a-4} = 3$ **5, 8**
43. $\sqrt{\dfrac{x-3}{x+2}} = \dfrac{2}{3}$ **7**   **-1, 3**
44. $\sqrt{\dfrac{2}{y+3}} = \sqrt{\dfrac{3}{2y+2}}$ **5**
45. $\dfrac{\sqrt{x-2}}{x-2} = \dfrac{x-5}{\sqrt{x-2}}$ **6**
46. $\sqrt{y+15} - \sqrt{2y+7} = 1$ **1**
47. $\sqrt{3x-5} + \sqrt{x-1} = 2$ **2**
48. $\sqrt{3x+9} - \sqrt{2x+7} = 1$ **9**

(C)

49. The time T for one period of a simple pendulum is determined by the formula $T = 2\pi\sqrt{\dfrac{l}{g}}$. Solve for l, the length of the pendulum's string. $l = \frac{T^2 g}{4\pi^2}$

50. The time t on an upward launch is found from the formula $t = \dfrac{v \pm \sqrt{v^2 + 20(d-h)}}{10}$. Solve for h, the height at the time t.

51. Solve $\sqrt{x-1} = \sqrt[4]{8x+1}$ for x.   **10**

52. Solve $\sqrt[3]{x+6} = \sqrt[6]{32x}$ for x.   **2, 18**

53. The radius r of a sphere is given by the formula $r = \sqrt[3]{\dfrac{3V}{4\pi}}$. Solve for V, the volume of the sphere. $V = \frac{4\pi r^3}{3}$

54. One side s of an equilateral triangle is given by the formula $s = \dfrac{2\sqrt{A}}{\sqrt[4]{3}}$. Solve for A, the area of the triangle. $A = \frac{s^2}{4}\sqrt{3}$

55. Solve $x = \dfrac{N \pm \sqrt{N^2 - 4M(T-D)}}{2M}$ for T. $T = -Mx^2 + Nx + D$

56. Solve $2Lx + R = \sqrt{R^2 - \dfrac{4L}{C}}$ for $\dfrac{-1}{C}$. $\frac{-1}{C} = Lx^2 + Rx$

50. $h = -5t^2 + tv + d$

Cumulative Review

Simplify each expression.

1. $5\sqrt{72}$ $30\sqrt{2}$
2. $3x^2y\sqrt{24x^7y^8}$ $6x^5y^5\sqrt{6x}$
3. $5\sqrt{2} + 2\sqrt{18} + 3\sqrt{2}$ $14\sqrt{2}$
4. $(2\sqrt{7} - \sqrt{10})(2\sqrt{7} + \sqrt{10})$ **18**

Applications

If a weight is suspended on a string, the result is a simple pendulum. Ideally, the motion of a pendulum is **periodic.** If the weight on the pendulum is pulled to one side and released, it will swing away and back. One such back-and-forth motion is called a **vibration.**

The action of some clocks is based on the periodic motion of a pendulum. Of course, some mechanical contrivance is usually employed to keep the periodic motion stable. The time, T, for one period of a simple pendulum is given by the radical equation

$$T = 2\pi\sqrt{\frac{l}{g}}$$

where l is the length of the string, and g is the acceleration due to gravity. Notice that the period, T, depends on the length, l, of the string and not upon the amount of weight that is used.

The formula above can be solved for l.

$$\left(\frac{T}{2\pi}\right)^2 = \left(\sqrt{\frac{l}{g}}\right)^2 \qquad \frac{l}{g} = \frac{T^2}{4\pi^2} \qquad \text{So, } l = \frac{gT^2}{4\pi^2}.$$

Solve each problem.

1. Find the length, l, if $T = 1.57$ s. Use 10 m/s^2 for g and 3.14 for π.   **0.625 m**

2. How should the length of the string be changed in order to double the period of a given pendulum? [Hint: Replace T by $2T$ in the formula.]

   4 times as long

Chapter Seven Review

Vocabulary
completing the square [7.1]
quadratic formula [7.2]
radical equation [7.5]

Solve each equation by completing the square.
[7.1]

1. $x^2 - 6x = 3$ $3 \pm 2\sqrt{3}$

2. $2n^2 = 1 - 5n$ $\dfrac{-5 \pm \sqrt{33}}{4}$

3. $\dfrac{c^2 - 6}{5} = c$ $-1, 6$

★ 4. $x^2 + 2x\sqrt{2} - 48 = 0$ $-6\sqrt{2}, 4\sqrt{2}$

Solve each equation by using the quadratic formula. [7.2]

5. $3y^2 + 2y = 2$ $\dfrac{-1 \pm \sqrt{7}}{3}$

6. $5c^2 = 7$ $\dfrac{\pm\sqrt{35}}{5}$

7. $\dfrac{x^2}{8} = \dfrac{x}{2} - \dfrac{1}{4}$ $2 \pm \sqrt{2}$

★ 8. $x^{-2} - 8x^{-1} + 3 = 0$ $\dfrac{4 \pm \sqrt{13}}{3}$

9. A second number is 2 more than 4 times a first number. Find the numbers if their product is 5. [7.3]
$\dfrac{-1 - \sqrt{21}}{4}, 1 - \sqrt{21}$ or $\dfrac{-1 + \sqrt{21}}{4}$ $1 + \sqrt{21}$

10. An object is shot upward from the earth's surface with an initial velocity of 60 m/s. To the nearest 0.1 s, when will its height be 150 m? Use the formula $h = vt - 5t^2$.
[7.3] **3.6 s, 8.4 s**

11. A 4-cm square is cut from each corner of a rectangular piece of sheet metal that is twice as long as it is wide. Find the dimensions of the original rectangle if the flaps are turned up to form a pan with a volume of 800 cm^3. Express each dimension in simplest radical form. [7.4]
$6 + 2\sqrt{26}$ cm, $12 + 4\sqrt{26}$ cm

12. A rectangle is 1 m longer than it is wide. The length of one of its diagonals is 3 m more than the rectangle's width. Find the length of the diagonal and the area of the rectangle. Give the answers in simplest radical form. [7.4]
$5 + 2\sqrt{3}$ m; $18 + 10\sqrt{3}$ m^2

★13. A pellet is sent up from the top of a tower 50 m tall with an initial velocity of 45 m/s. To the nearest 0.1 s, when will its height be 125 m? Use the formula $h = d + vt - 5t^2$. [7.3] **2.2 s, 6.8 s**

Solve each equation. [7.5]

14. $3\sqrt{2x + 4} = 12$ **6**

15. $x - 1 = \sqrt{x + 5}$ **4**

16. $\sqrt[4]{5y^{-1}} = \dfrac{1}{2}$ **80**

17. $\sqrt[3]{n^2 - 6n} = 3$ **$-3, 9$**

18. $\sqrt{3x - 5} - \sqrt{x - 2} = 1$ **2, 3**

★19. $\sqrt[3]{4x + 6} = 2\sqrt[6]{2x}$ $\dfrac{1}{2}, \dfrac{9}{2}$

Chapter Seven Test

Solve each equation by completing the square.

1. $x^2 - 8x - 4 = 0$ $4 \pm 2\sqrt{5}$

2. $3c^2 = -7c - 1$ $\dfrac{-7 \pm \sqrt{37}}{6}$

Solve each equation by using the quadratic formula.

3. $2y^2 + 3y = 3$ $\dfrac{-3 \pm \sqrt{33}}{4}$

4. $5x^2 = 11x$ $0, \dfrac{11}{5}$

5. $\dfrac{x^2}{4} = \dfrac{x}{2} - \dfrac{1}{6}$ $\dfrac{3 \pm \sqrt{3}}{3}$

6. One leg of a right triangle is 3 times as long as the other leg and 2 cm shorter than the hypotenuse. Find the length of the hypotenuse. Give the answer in simplest radical form. $20 + 6\sqrt{10}$ cm

7. A second number is 2 less than 4 times a first number. If the second number is multiplied by 1 less than the first number, the product is 1. Find the numbers.

$$\dfrac{3 - \sqrt{5}}{4}, 1 - \sqrt{5} \text{ or } \dfrac{3 + \sqrt{5}}{4}, 1 + \sqrt{5}$$

8. To the nearest 0.1 s, when will an object reach a height of 15 m if it is sent up from the earth with an initial velocity of 25 m/s? Use the formula $h = vt - 5t^2$.

0.7 s, 4.3 s

9. A 3-cm square is cut from each corner of a rectangular piece of plastic that is 3 times as long as it is wide. Find the dimensions of the original rectangle if the four flaps are turned up to form an open box with a volume of 270 cm³. Express each dimension in simplest radical form.

$4 + \sqrt{34}$ cm, $12 + 3\sqrt{34}$ cm

Solve each equation.

10. $\sqrt[4]{7x + 4} = 3$ **11**

11. $y - \sqrt{2y - 1} = 2$ **5**

12. $\sqrt[3]{n^2 - 2n} = 2$ **−2, 4**

13. $\sqrt{3x + 1} - \sqrt{x - 1} = 2$ **1, 5**

★**14.** Solve $x^2 + 4x\sqrt{5} + 15 = 0$ by completing the square. $-3\sqrt{5}, -\sqrt{5}$

★**15.** Solve $\sqrt{x - 1} = \sqrt[4]{3x + 1}$.   **5**

Computer Activities

Will It Fit?

A kite designer wants to package her kites in boxes so that the sticks for each kite are placed along a diagonal of the box. In order to do this, she must decide which length sticks will fit in which boxes. The computer program below uses the given formula to help make the decision. In the formula, D is the length of a diagonal of the box, X is the length of the box, and Y is its width.

Diagonal (D) = Square Root of $(X \uparrow 2 + Y \uparrow 2)$

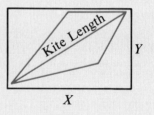

PROGRAM

```
10 PRINT "ENTER LENGTH OF BOX, WIDTH OF BOX, AND LENGTH OF
   KITE"
20 INPUT X, Y, K
30 LET D = SQR(X ↑ 2 + Y ↑ 2)
40 IF D > = K THEN 70
50 PRINT "KITE STICKS WON'T FIT"
60 GO TO 80
70 PRINT "KITE STICKS WILL FIT, DIAGONAL IS"; D
80 END
```

Exercises

Type in the program above and run it for the following sets of values:

1. $X = 14$ $Y = 15$ $K = 18$ **KITE STICKS WILL FIT, DIAGONAL IS 20.51828**

2. $X = 10$ $Y = 18$ $K = 22$ **KITE STICKS WON'T FIT**

3. $X = 25$ $Y = 16$ $K = 25$ **KITE STICKS WILL FIT, DIAGONAL IS 29.68164**

4. Alter the program above to get a program for finding the minimum length of a diagonal of the box in order for a given kite stick to fit in the box. Choose from four lengths. **For Ex. 4, see TE Answer Section.**

5. Write a program to find the box with the least perimeter in which a given kite stick will fit. Choose from four boxes. **For Ex. 5, see TE Answer Section.**

6. Write a program to use to solve equations of the form $ax^2 + bx + c = 0 (a \neq 0)$ by the quadratic formula. **For Ex. 6, see TE Answer Section.**

College Prep Test

DIRECTIONS: Choose the *one* best answer to each question or problem.

1. One diagonal of a rectangle is 10 cm long. The rectangle's length is 8 cm. Find the area of the rectangle. **C**

   (A) 24 cm^2 (B) 36 cm^2 (C) 48 cm^2
   (D) 80 cm^2 (E) None of these

2. Which equation has two different positive integers as its solutions? **D**

   (A) $(x - 5)^2 = 0$ (B) $(x - 1)^2 = 4$
   (C) $(x + 4)^2 = 9$ (D) $(x - 6)^2 = 16$
   (E) None of these

3. For which pair of numbers is the product of *2 more than the first* and *3 less than the second* greatest? **D**

   (A) 9 and 7 (B) 8 and 8
   (C) 7 and 9 (D) −12 and −3
   (E) All products are the same.

4. If $x = -2$, then **D**

   (A) $\sqrt{x^2} = x$ (B) $\sqrt[3]{x^3} = -x$
   (C) $\sqrt[4]{x^4} = x$ (D) $\sqrt[3]{x^3} = x$
   (E) All of these

5. For which equation is the sum of its two solutions greater than their product? **B**

   (A) $x^2 - 7x + 12 = 0$
   (B) $x^2 + 9x - 10 = 0$
   (C) $x^2 + 8x = 0$
   (D) $x^2 + 4 = 0$
   (E) None of these

6. Find a solution of
   $\sqrt{4x} + \sqrt{2x} = \sqrt{4x - 12} + \sqrt{2x + 12}$. **C**

   (A) 2 (B) 4 (C) 6 (D) 8
   (E) None of these

7. A rectangular piece of cardboard is 70 cm by 50 cm. A 10-cm square is cut from each corner and the four flaps are folded up to form an open box. Find the volume of the box. **B**

   (A) 1,500 cm^3 (B) 15,000 cm^3
   (C) 24,000 cm^3 (D) 35,000 cm^3
   (E) None of these

8. Choose the number that is not equal to the other three? **E**

   (A) $4 + 2\sqrt{3}$ (B) $\dfrac{8 + \sqrt{48}}{2}$
   (C) $6 + \sqrt{48} - 2 - \sqrt{12}$
   (D) $\sqrt{2}(\sqrt{8} + \sqrt{6})$
   (E) They are all equal.

9. The formula, $h = 5t(20 - t)$, gives the height h of an object at t seconds. The greatest height is achieved at which time?
   C

   (A) 0 s (B) 5 s (C) 10 s (D) 20 s
   (E) All heights are the same.

10. Find an equation with integral coefficients having $3 - 2\sqrt{3}$ as a solution. **B**

    (A) $x^2 = 9x - 12$ (B) $x^2 - 6x = 3$
    (C) $x^2 - 6x + 15 = 0$ (D) $x^2 = 21$
    (E) None of these

8 COMPLEX NUMBERS
Maria Gaetana Agnesi

Maria Gaetana Agnesi was born in 1782 into a wealthy family of Milan, Italy where her father was a professor of mathematics at the university. She was educated privately and showed outstanding ability at a very early age. At age nine she published a paper defending the right of women to have a liberal arts education, and by the age of thirteen, she knew seven languages.

In her early adult life, much of Maria's time was spent in the study of mathematics. She is most famous for an equation and its corresponding graph that she formulated in her work in analytic geometry. The graph, or curve, is known as "the witch of Agnesi."

In the first figure below,

(1) the circle of radius a is tangent to the horizontal lines $\overleftrightarrow{AC}$ and $\overleftrightarrow{OR}$,

(2) the line $\overleftrightarrow{OC}$ intersects the circle at B, and

(3) $P(x, y)$ is the point of intersection of the horizontal line $\overleftrightarrow{BP}$ and the vertical line $\overleftrightarrow{CP}$.

As C moves along the line $\overleftrightarrow{AC}$, the point P traces the curve called **the witch of Agnesi** (second figure). An equation of the witch of Agnesi is $x^2 y = 4a^2(2a - y)$.

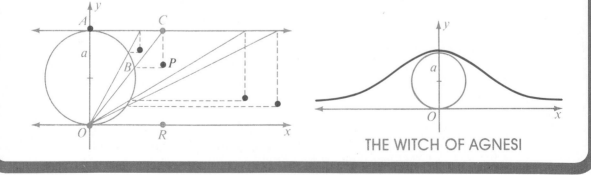

THE WITCH OF AGNESI

8.1 Sums and Differences of Complex Numbers

OBJECTIVES ▶ To simplify a square root expression where the radicand is a negative real number
To solve a quadratic equation whose solutions are imaginary numbers
To simplify an expression containing a sum or difference of complex numbers

The equation $x^2 = -1$ does not have a real number solution since there is no real number whose square is negative. In order to solve equations of this type, mathematicians invented the numbers i and $-i$.
If $x^2 = -1$, then x would have to be $\sqrt{-1}$ or $-\sqrt{-1}$, where $(\sqrt{-1})^2 = -1$ and $(-\sqrt{-1})^2 = -1$. The number $\sqrt{-1}$ is represented by i and the number $-\sqrt{-1}$ is represented by $-i$.

Definition:
i and $-i$

$$i = \sqrt{-1} \quad \text{and} \quad i^2 = -1$$
$$-i = -\sqrt{-1} \quad \text{and} \quad (-i)^2 = -1$$

Notice that i and $-i$ are *not* variables; each of them names one specific number. You can use the definition of i to simplify a square root expression where the radicand is a negative real number.

Example 1 Simplify $\sqrt{-16}$, $\sqrt{-7}$, and $\sqrt{-12}$.

$$\begin{aligned} \sqrt{-16} &= \sqrt{-1(16)} \\ &= \sqrt{-1} \cdot \sqrt{16} \\ &= 4i \end{aligned} \qquad \begin{aligned} \sqrt{-7} &= \sqrt{-1(7)} \\ &= \sqrt{-1} \cdot \sqrt{7} \\ &= i\sqrt{7} \end{aligned} \qquad \begin{aligned} \sqrt{-12} &= \sqrt{-1(12)} \\ &= \sqrt{-1} \cdot \sqrt{12} \\ &= i \cdot 2\sqrt{3} \\ &= 2i\sqrt{3} \end{aligned}$$

In Example 1, the property $\sqrt{xy} = \sqrt{x} \cdot \sqrt{y}$ for $x \geq 0$, $y \geq 0$, was extended to include $\sqrt{-1 \cdot y} = \sqrt{-1} \cdot \sqrt{y}$ for $y \geq 0$. In general, $\sqrt{-y} = i\sqrt{y}$ for $y \geq 0$.

Example 2 Simplify each expression.

$$\begin{aligned} -3 &+ \sqrt{-4} \\ -3 &+ i\sqrt{4} \\ -3 &+ i \cdot 2 \\ -3 &+ 2i \end{aligned} \qquad \begin{aligned} -5&\sqrt{-8} \\ -5 &\cdot i\sqrt{8} \\ -5 &\cdot i \cdot 2\sqrt{2} \\ -10&i\sqrt{2} \end{aligned} \qquad \begin{aligned} 2 &- \sqrt{-10} \\ 2 &- i\sqrt{10} \end{aligned}$$

The numbers $-3 + 2i$, $-10i\sqrt{2}$ and $2 - i\sqrt{10}$ are examples of **complex numbers.** A complex number is one that can be written in the form $a + bi$, where a and b are real numbers. Note that $-10i\sqrt{2} = 0 + (-10\sqrt{2})i$, where $a = 0$, $b = -10\sqrt{2}$, and $2 - i\sqrt{10} = 2 + (-\sqrt{10})i$, where $a = 2$, $b = -\sqrt{10}$.

Definition:
Complex
Number

> A *complex number* is a number that can be written in the form $a + bi$ where a and b are real numbers and $i = \sqrt{-1}$.

Complex numbers like $-3 + 2i$ and $-10i\sqrt{2}$, where $b \neq 0$, are called **imaginary numbers.** A complex number like $-10i\sqrt{2}$, where $a = 0$, is called a **pure imaginary number.** Notice that every *real number* is also a complex number. For example, the real number -5 can be written as $-5 + 0i$, where $b = 0$.

You can solve equations like $x^2 = -25$ and $2y^2 + 16 = 0$ if imaginary numbers are permitted as solutions.

Example 3

Solve $x^2 = -25$.

$$x^2 = -25$$
$$x = \pm\sqrt{-25}$$
$$= \pm 5i$$

The solutions are $5i$ and $-5i$.

Solve $2y^2 + 16 = 0$.

$$2y^2 = -16$$
$$y^2 = -8$$
$$y = \pm\sqrt{-8} = \pm 2i\sqrt{2}$$

The solutions are $2i\sqrt{2}$ and $-2i\sqrt{2}$.

An expression containing a sum of two complex numbers can be simplified by combining the like terms as you would with a pair of binomials. For example,

$$(3 + 5i) + (2 - 8i) = (3 + 2) + (5i - 8i) = (3 + 2) + (5 - 8)i = 5 - 3i.$$

This leads to the following property:

Sum of
Complex
Numbers

> For all real numbers a, b, c, and d,
> $$(a + bi) + (c + di) = (a + c) + (b + d)i.$$

To simplify an expression containing a difference of two complex numbers, $(a + bi) - (c + di)$, add the additive inverse (opposite) of $c + di$, which is $-c - di$.

Example 4

Simplify each expression.

$$(8 - 9i) - (6 - 4i)$$

$$(8 - 9i) + (-6 + 4i)$$
$$(8 - 6) + (-9 + 4)i$$
$$2 - 5i$$

$$(-9 + \sqrt{-2}) + (6 - \sqrt{-18})$$

$$(-9 + i\sqrt{2}) + (6 - 3i\sqrt{2})$$
$$(-9 + 6) + (\sqrt{2} - 3\sqrt{2})i$$
$$-3 - 2i\sqrt{2}$$

Reading In Algebra

Which of the words at the right apply to each complex number?

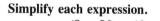

1. $5i$ **A, E**
2. $8 - 4i$ **A**
3. -25 **B, D**
4. i **A, E**
5. i^2 **B, D**
6. $5 + 6\sqrt{2}$ **B, C**

A imaginary   B real   C irrational
D rational   E pure imaginary

CHAPTER EIGHT

Oral Exercises

Show that each number is a complex number $a + bi$ by identifying the real numbers a and b.

$a = 0, b = 6$
1. $6i$
$a = 7, b = 0$
2. 7
$a = 0, b = 1$
3. i
$a = -\sqrt{10}, b = 0$
4. $-\sqrt{10}$
$a = 0, b = -9$
5. $-9i$

6. $i\sqrt{3}$
$a = 0, b = \sqrt{3}$
7. -2.5
$a = -2.5, b = 0$
8. $-i$
$a = 0, b = -1$
9. $-i\sqrt{5}$
$a = 0, b = -\sqrt{5}$
10. $7 - 12i$
$a = 7, b = -12$

Written Exercises

Simplify each expression.

(A) **1.** $\sqrt{-36}$ $6i$
2. $-\sqrt{-81}$ $-9i$
3. $\sqrt{-64}$ $8i$

4. $\sqrt{-15}$ $i\sqrt{15}$
5. $\sqrt{-22}$ $i\sqrt{22}$
6. $-\sqrt{-7}$ $-i\sqrt{7}$

7. $\sqrt{-40}$ $2i\sqrt{10}$
8. $-\sqrt{-27}$ $-3i\sqrt{3}$
9. $2\sqrt{-45}$ $6i\sqrt{5}$

10. $-5\sqrt{-4}$ $-10i$
11. $-6\sqrt{-20}$ $-12i\sqrt{5}$
12. $10\sqrt{-90}$ $30i\sqrt{10}$

13. $4 + \sqrt{-9}$ $4 + 3i$
14. $-20 - \sqrt{-30}$ $-20 - i\sqrt{30}$
15. $8 - \sqrt{-50}$ $8 - 5i\sqrt{2}$

Solve each equation.

16. $x^2 = -49$ $\pm 7i$
17. $y^2 = -3$ $\pm i\sqrt{3}$
18. $z^2 = -48$ $\pm 4i\sqrt{3}$

19. $3y^2 = -30$ $\pm i\sqrt{10}$
20. $x^2 = -100$ $\pm 10i$
21. $4a^2 = -200$ $\pm 5i\sqrt{2}$

Simplify each expression.

22. $(3 + 6i) + (4 + 3i)$ $7 + 9i$
23. $(7 + 8i) - (3 + 6i)$ $4 + 2i$
24. $(-2 - 5i) + (8 + 12i)$ $6 + 7i$

25. $(6 + 12i) - (-3 + 8i)$ $9 + 4i$
26. $(5 + i) + (-6 - 3i)$ $-1 - 2i$
27. $(-7 + i) - (5 - i)$ $-12 + 2i$

28. $(7 - i) + (-10 + 10i)$ $-3 + 9i$
29. $(-14 + 6i) - (-6 - 6i)$ $-8 + 12i$
30. $(-8 + 4i) + (-8 - 4i)$ -16

(B) **31.** $7 + 8\sqrt{-16}$ $7 + 32i$
32. $-5 - 5\sqrt{-25}$ $-5 - 25i$
33. $\sqrt{60} - 4\sqrt{-15}$ $2\sqrt{15} - 4i\sqrt{15}$

34. $20 - 10\sqrt{-12}$ $20 - 20i\sqrt{3}$
35. $-1 + 4\sqrt{-80}$ $-1 + 16i\sqrt{5}$
36. $-\sqrt{8} - 2\sqrt{-32}$ $-2\sqrt{2} - 8i\sqrt{2}$

Solve each equation.

37. $x^2 + 81 = 0$ $\pm 9i$
38. $y^2 + 45 = 0$ $\pm 3i\sqrt{5}$
39. $0 = n^2 + 65$ $\pm i\sqrt{65}$

40. $5t^2 + 21 = t^2 - 43$ $\pm 4i$
41. $4x^2 + 21 = 3 - 2x^2$ $\pm i\sqrt{3}$
42. $8y^2 + 12 = 8 - y^2$ $\pm \frac{2}{3}i$

Simplify each expression.

43. $(3 + \sqrt{-36}) + (-8 - \sqrt{-16})$ $-5 + 2i$
44. $(-9 + 2\sqrt{-25}) - (7 - 3\sqrt{-49})$ $-16 + 31i$

45. $(6 - 5\sqrt{-3}) - (1 - 2\sqrt{-3})$ $5 - 3i\sqrt{3}$
46. $(-10 + 6\sqrt{-20}) + (-4 - 4\sqrt{-5})$ **below**

47. $(12 + \sqrt{-18}) + (-4 + 4\sqrt{-2})$ $8 + 7i\sqrt{2}$
48. $(7 - 3\sqrt{-8}) - (17 - 2\sqrt{-50})$ $-10 + 4i\sqrt{2}$

46. $-14 + 8i\sqrt{5}$

Solve each equation for $x + yi$. Then answer the question.   **49.** $0; 0 + 0i$ **50.** $-a - bi$

(C) **49.** $(3 - 2i) + (x + yi) = (3 - 2i)$. Which complex number is the additive identity? **above**
50. $(a + bi) + (x + yi) = 0 + 0i$. What is the additive inverse of $a + bi$? **above**

51. $(x + yi) + (3 + 3i) = (3 + 3i) + (5 - 5i)$. What property of addition is suggested?
52. $[7 + (x + yi)] + 2i = 7 + [(4 + 6i) + 2i]$. What property of addition is suggested?

5 − 5i; Commutative property of addition
4 + 6i; Associative property of addition

Cumulative Review

Simplify each expression.

1. $(2\sqrt{5} + \sqrt{3})(3\sqrt{5} - 4\sqrt{3})$ $18 - 5\sqrt{15}$
2. $\dfrac{6}{5\sqrt{3}}$ $\dfrac{2\sqrt{3}}{5}$
3. $\dfrac{2}{3\sqrt{3} - \sqrt{5}}$ $\dfrac{3\sqrt{3} + \sqrt{5}}{11}$

SUMS AND DIFFERENCES OF COMPLEX NUMBERS

8.2 Products and Quotients of Complex Numbers

OBJECTIVES ▶ **To simplify an expression containing a product of complex numbers**
To simplify an expression containing a quotient of complex numbers

The fact that $i^2 = -1$ permits you to simplify products that involve imaginary numbers. Before multiplying two pure imaginary numbers, each number should be written as the product of i and a real number.

Example 1 Simplify each product.

$$6i \cdot 4i \qquad\qquad -\sqrt{-6} \cdot 5\sqrt{-3}$$

$$
\begin{aligned}
& 6i \cdot 4i \\
&= 24i^2 \\
i^2 = -1 \blacktriangleright \quad &= 24(-1) \\
&= -24
\end{aligned}
\qquad
\begin{aligned}
-\sqrt{-6} \cdot 5\sqrt{-3} &= -i\sqrt{6} \cdot 5i\sqrt{3} \qquad \blacktriangleleft \sqrt{-y} = i\sqrt{y}\\
&= -5i^2\sqrt{18} \\
&= -5(-1) \cdot 3\sqrt{2} \\
&= 15\sqrt{2}
\end{aligned}
$$

In Example 1, notice that $\sqrt{-6} \cdot \sqrt{-3}$ is *not* equal to $\sqrt{-6(-3)}$, or $\sqrt{18}$. The correct way to simplify this product is shown below.

$$\sqrt{-6} \cdot \sqrt{-3} = i\sqrt{6} \cdot i\sqrt{3} = i^2\sqrt{18} = (-1) \cdot 3\sqrt{2} = -3\sqrt{2}$$

The Product of Square Roots property on page 145, $\sqrt{x} \cdot \sqrt{y} = \sqrt{x \cdot y}$, applies only when each radicand is a positive real number or 0. The following property is used to multiply two pure imaginary numbers.

Product of Pure Imaginary Numbers

$$\sqrt{-x} \cdot \sqrt{-y} = i\sqrt{x} \cdot i\sqrt{y} = i^2\sqrt{x \cdot y} = -\sqrt{xy},$$
where $-x$ and $-y$ are negative real numbers.

The multiplication in Example 2 involves both real and imaginary numbers.

Example 2 Simplify each product.

$$5\sqrt{10} \cdot 6\sqrt{-2} \qquad\qquad 2\sqrt{5}(3\sqrt{10} - 4i\sqrt{15})$$

$$
\begin{aligned}
&= 5\sqrt{10} \cdot 6\sqrt{-2} \\
&= 5\sqrt{10} \cdot 6i\sqrt{2} \\
&= 30i\sqrt{20} \\
&= 30i \cdot 2\sqrt{5} \\
&= 60i\sqrt{5}
\end{aligned}
\qquad
\begin{aligned}
& 2\sqrt{5}(3\sqrt{10} - 4i\sqrt{15}) \qquad \blacktriangleleft \textit{Use the}\\
&= 6\sqrt{50} - 8i\sqrt{75} \qquad\qquad\quad \textit{Distributive Property.}\\
&= 6 \cdot 5\sqrt{2} - 8i \cdot 5\sqrt{3} \\
&= 30\sqrt{2} - 40i\sqrt{3}
\end{aligned}
$$

You should notice in Example 1 that the product of two pure imaginary numbers is a real number, whereas in Example 2 the product of a real number and an imaginary number is an imaginary number.

To simplify a product that involves complex numbers that are imaginary numbers, but not pure imaginary, the FOIL method of multiplying two binomials can be used.

Example 3 Simplify $(3 + 2i)(5 + 4i)$.

$$
\begin{array}{cccc}
\text{F} & \text{O} & \text{I} & \text{L}
\end{array}
$$
$$
\begin{aligned}
(3 + 2i)(5 + 4i) &= 3 \cdot 5 + 3 \cdot 4i + 2i \cdot 5 + 2i \cdot 4i \\
&= 15 + 12i + 10i + 8i^2 \\
&= 7 + 22i \quad \blacktriangleleft \; 8i^2 = 8(-1) = -8
\end{aligned}
$$

In Example 3, notice that the product of the two imaginary numbers is an imaginary number. This is not always the case, however. Two numbers of the form $a + bi$ and $a - bi$ are imaginary, but $(a + bi)(a - bi)$ is a real number.

Definition:
Conjugate
Complex
Numbers

> Two complex numbers of the form $a + bi$ and $a - bi$ are *conjugates*. Their product, $(a + bi)(a - bi)$, is a real number, $a^2 + b^2$.

Example 4 Simplify $(-2 + 3i)(-2 - 3i)$.

$$(-2 + 3i)(-2 - 3i) = (-2)^2 + (3)^2 = 4 + 9 = 13 \quad \blacktriangleleft \; (a + bi)(a - bi) = a^2 + b^2$$

Recall that $\dfrac{2}{3\sqrt{5}} = \dfrac{2}{3\sqrt{5}} \cdot \dfrac{\sqrt{5}}{\sqrt{5}} = \dfrac{2\sqrt{5}}{15}$ and

$\dfrac{7}{4 - \sqrt{6}} = \dfrac{7}{4 - \sqrt{6}} \cdot \dfrac{4 + \sqrt{6}}{4 + \sqrt{6}} = \dfrac{7(4 + \sqrt{6})}{16 - 6} = \dfrac{28 + 7\sqrt{6}}{10}$.

You can simplify quotients of complex numbers by rationalizing the denominators in a similar way.

Example 5 Simplify $-5 \div (6i)$ by rationalizing the denominator.

Write the quotient as a fraction.
$$\frac{-5}{6i} = \frac{-5}{6i} \cdot \frac{i}{i} = \frac{-5i}{6i^2} = \frac{-5i}{6(-1)} = \frac{-5i}{-6} = \frac{5i}{6}$$

Example 6 Simplify $\dfrac{2 - 4i}{5 + 3i}$ by rationalizing the denomiantor.

$$\frac{2 - 4i}{5 + 3i} = \frac{2 - 4i}{5 + 3i} \cdot \frac{5 - 3i}{5 - 3i} = \frac{10 - 6i - 20i + 12i^2}{25 + 9} = \frac{-2 - 26i}{34} = \frac{-1 - 13i}{17}$$

Powers of i can be simplified by using i^2 as a factor as many times as needed. For example,
$$i^9 = i^2 \cdot i^2 \cdot i^2 \cdot i^2 \cdot i = (-1)(-1)(-1)(-1)i = i.$$

PRODUCTS AND QUOTIENTS OF COMPLEX NUMBERS

Example 7 Simplify $(2i)^7$.

$$(2i)^7 = 2^7 \cdot i^7 = 2^7 \cdot i^4 \cdot i^2 \cdot i = 128 \cdot 1(-1) \cdot i = -128i \quad \blacktriangleleft \quad i^4 = i^2 \cdot i^2 = 1$$

Reading In Algebra

Determine whether each statement is always true (A), sometimes true (S), or never true (N).

1. The product of two pure imaginary numbers is an imaginary number. **N**

2. The product of two imaginary numbers is a real number. **S**

3. The product of a real number and an imaginary number is an imaginary number. **A**

4. The quotient of two imaginary numbers is an imaginary number. **S**

Written Exercises

Simplify each product.

(A)
1. $6i \cdot 7i$ **-42**
2. $-i\sqrt{3} \cdot i\sqrt{5}$ **$\sqrt{15}$**
3. $i\sqrt{3} \cdot i\sqrt{2} \cdot i\sqrt{6}$ **$-6i$**
4. $\sqrt{-5} \cdot \sqrt{-6}$ **$-\sqrt{30}$**
5. $-3\sqrt{-2} \cdot 4\sqrt{-11}$ **$12\sqrt{22}$**
6. $2\sqrt{3} \cdot 3\sqrt{-2}$ **$6i\sqrt{6}$**
7. $2\sqrt{-6} \cdot 4\sqrt{-2}$ **$-16\sqrt{3}$**
8. $-4\sqrt{-15} \cdot 2\sqrt{6}$ **$-24i\sqrt{10}$**
9. $\sqrt{-5} \cdot \sqrt{-10} \cdot \sqrt{-2}$ **$-10i$**
10. $\sqrt{3}(2\sqrt{6} + i\sqrt{15})$
11. $3\sqrt{6}(\sqrt{2} - \sqrt{-10})$
12. $\sqrt{-6}(\sqrt{11} + \sqrt{-3})$
13. $(4 + 3i)(5 + 6i)$ **$2 + 39i$**
14. $(3 - 4i)(2 + 2i)$ **$14 - 2i$**
15. $(6 - 5i(-3 + i)$ **$-13 + 21i$**
16. $(9 + 11i)(9 - 11i)$ **202**
17. $(-7 - 6i)(-7 + 6i)$ **85**
18. $(-3 + 4i)(-3 - 4i)$ **25**
19. $(4 + 5i)^2$ **$-9 + 40i$**
20. $(6 - 2i)^2$ **$32 - 24i$**
21. $(-5 - i)^2$ **$24 + 10i$**
22. $(-4i)^3$ **$64i$**
23. $(i\sqrt{3})^4$ **9**
24. $(-2i)^5$ **$-32i$**
10. $6\sqrt{2} + 3i\sqrt{5}$
11. $6\sqrt{3} - 6i\sqrt{15}$
12. $i\sqrt{66} - 3\sqrt{2}$

Simplify each quotient by rationalizing the denominator.

25. $7 \div (4i)$ **$\frac{7i}{-4}$**
26. $-3 \div (5i)$ **$\frac{3i}{5}$**
27. $8 \div (-6i)$ **$\frac{4i}{3}$**
28. $-10 \div (-10i)$ **$-i$**
29. $\frac{-2}{5i}$ **$\frac{2i}{5}$**
30. $\frac{1}{-9i}$ **$\frac{i}{9}$**
31. $\frac{7}{i}$ **$-7i$**
32. $\frac{-8}{12i}$ **$\frac{2i}{3}$**
33. $\frac{5}{3 + 2i}$ **$\frac{15 - 10i}{13}$**
34. $-3 \div (4 - 2i)$ **$\frac{-6 - 3i}{10}$**
35. $\frac{i}{-1 + i}$ **$\frac{1 - i}{2}$**
36. $5i \div (-3 - i)$ **$\frac{-1 - 3i}{2}$**

(B)
37. $\frac{2 + 3i}{3 - 4i}$ **$\frac{-6 + 17i}{25}$**
38. $\frac{5 - 3i}{1 - i}$ **$4 + i$**
39. $\frac{1 - 3i}{-2 - 4i}$ **$\frac{1 + i}{2}$**
40. $\frac{50}{3\sqrt{5} + \sqrt{-5}}$ ⤵
$3\sqrt{5} - i\sqrt{5}$

Simplify each product. (Exercises 41–52)

41. $(10i)^6$ **$-1{,}000{,}000$**
42. $(-2i)^8$ **256**
43. i^{11} **$-i$**
44. $(2i)^{10}$ **$-1{,}024$**
45. $(4 + 2i\sqrt{3})^2$
46. $(6 - 2\sqrt{-6})^2$
47. $(2i\sqrt{7} + 3i\sqrt{2})^2$
48. $(\sqrt{-17} - \sqrt{-10})^2$
49. $(3i\sqrt{7})^4$ **$3{,}969$**
50. $(-2\sqrt{-2})^{10}$ **$-32{,}768$**
51. $(1 - i\sqrt{3})^3$ **-8**
52. $(2 + 2i\sqrt{3})^3$ **-64**
45. $4 + 16i\sqrt{3}$
46. $12 - 24i\sqrt{6}$
47. $-46 - 12\sqrt{14}$
48. $-27 + 2\sqrt{170}$

Let $a + bi$ and $a - bi$ represent conjugate complex numbers, where a and b are real numbers.

(C)
53. Prove that the product of two conjugate complex numbers is a real number. **below**

54. Prove that the sum of two conjugate complex numbers is a real number. **below**

55. Prove that the quotient of two conjugate complex numbers is *not* a real number if $a \neq 0$.

56. Prove that the difference of two conjugate complex numbers is a pure imaginary number. **$(a + bi) - (a - bi) = 2bi$**

53. $(a + bi)(a - bi) = a^2 - abi + abi - b^2i^2 = a^2 + b^2$

54. $(a + bi) + (a - bi) = 2a$

192
55. $\frac{a + bi}{a - bi} = \frac{a + bi}{a - bi} \cdot \frac{a + bi}{a + bi} = \frac{a^2 + abi + abi + b^2i^2}{a^2 + abi - abi - b^2i^2} = \frac{a^2 + 2abi - b^2}{a^2 + b^2}$

CHAPTER EIGHT

8.3 Equations with Imaginary Number Solutions

OBJECTIVES ▶ To solve an equation whose solutions are imaginary numbers
To find the three cube roots of a nonzero integer that is a perfect cube

You have used the quadratic formula, $x = \dfrac{-b \pm \sqrt{b^2 - 4ac}}{2a}$, to find the real number solutions of a given quadratic equation. As shown in Example 1, the formula can also be used when the solutions are imaginary numbers.

Example 1 Solve $3x^2 + 2 = 4x$.

Write the equation in standard form and use the quadratic formula.
$$3x^2 - 4x + 2 = 0$$

$a = 3, b = -4, c = 2$ ▶ $x = \dfrac{-(-4) \pm \sqrt{(-4)^2 - 4 \cdot 3 \cdot 2}}{2 \cdot 3} = \dfrac{4 \pm \sqrt{-8}}{6} = \dfrac{4 \pm 2i\sqrt{2}}{6} = \dfrac{2 \pm i\sqrt{2}}{3}$

Thus, the solutions are $\dfrac{2 + i\sqrt{2}}{3}$ and $\dfrac{2 - i\sqrt{2}}{3}$.

A fourth-degree equation may have imaginary number solutions. One such equation is solved by factoring in Example 2. Notice that two of the solutions of the equation are imaginary numbers and two are real numbers.

Example 2 Solve $2x^4 + 3x^2 - 20 = 0$.

$$2x^4 + 3x^2 - 20 = 0$$
$$(x^2 + 4)(2x^2 - 5) = 0$$

$$
\begin{array}{llll}
x^2 + 4 = 0 & \quad \text{or} \quad & 2x^2 - 5 = 0 \\
x^2 = -4 & & 2x^2 = 5 \\
x = \pm\sqrt{-4} & & x^2 = \dfrac{5}{2} \\
x = \pm 2i & & x = \pm \sqrt{\dfrac{5}{2}} = \pm \dfrac{\sqrt{5}}{\sqrt{2}} \cdot \dfrac{\sqrt{2}}{\sqrt{2}} = \pm \dfrac{\sqrt{10}}{2}
\end{array}
$$

Thus, the four solutions are $2i$, $-2i$, $\dfrac{\sqrt{10}}{2}$, and $-\dfrac{\sqrt{10}}{2}$.

Every real number, except 0, has two different square roots and three different cube roots. However, some of the roots may be imaginary numbers. You can use a third-degree equation to find the three cube roots of a nonzero integer that is a perfect cube, such as -8.

Example **3** Find the three cube roots of -8.

The cube roots of -8 are the solutions of the equation $x^3 = -8$.

$$x^3 = -8$$
$$x^3 + 8 = 0 \qquad \blacktriangleleft \; x^3 + 8 \text{ is a sum of two cubes.}$$
$$x^3 + 2^3 = 0$$
$$(x + 2)(x^2 - 2x + 4) = 0 \qquad \blacktriangleleft \; m^3 + n^3 = (m + n)(m^2 - mn + n^2)$$

$$x + 2 = 0 \quad \text{or} \quad x^2 - 2x + 4 = 0$$

$$x = -2 \qquad x = \frac{2 \pm \sqrt{4 - 16}}{2} = \frac{2 \pm \sqrt{-12}}{2} = \frac{2 \pm 2i\sqrt{3}}{2} = 1 \pm i\sqrt{3}$$

Thus, the three cube roots of -8 are -2, $1 + i\sqrt{3}$, and $1 - i\sqrt{3}$.

In Example 3, the three cube roots of -8 were found as solutions of the equation $x^3 = -8$. You can check these roots by showing that the third power of each number is -8.

$$-2: \qquad (-2)^3 = (-2)(-2)(-2) = -8$$
$$1 + i\sqrt{3}: \; (1 + i\sqrt{3})^3 = (1 + i\sqrt{3})(1 + i\sqrt{3})^2 = (1 + i\sqrt{3})(1 + 2i\sqrt{3} + 3i^2)$$
$$= (1 + i\sqrt{3})(-2 + 2i\sqrt{3}) = -2 + 6i^2, \text{ or } -8$$
$$1 - i\sqrt{3}: \text{ See exercise 51 on page 192.}$$

Written **Exercises**

Solve each equation.

(A) 1. $x^2 - 3x + 3 = 0$ $\frac{3 \pm i\sqrt{3}}{2}$

2. $2y^2 + 3y + 3 = 0$ $\frac{-3 \pm i\sqrt{15}}{4}$

3. $3n^2 - 3n + 1 = 0$ $\frac{3 \pm i\sqrt{3}}{6}$

4. $2y^2 + 4 = 5y$ $\frac{5 \pm i\sqrt{7}}{4}$

5. $c^2 + 4 = 3c$ $\frac{3 \pm i\sqrt{7}}{2}$

6. $3x^2 = x - 2$ $\frac{1 \pm i\sqrt{23}}{6}$

7. $x^2 - 4x + 5 = 0$ $2 \pm i$

8. $n^2 + 2n + 2 = 0$ $-1 \pm i$

9. $y^2 - 8y + 20 = 0$ $4 \pm 2i$

10. $2y^2 - 2y + 13 = 0$ $\frac{1 \pm 5i}{2}$

11. $3t^2 + 2 = 2t$ $\frac{1 \pm i\sqrt{5}}{3}$

12. $4x^2 = 2x - 1$ $\frac{1 \pm i\sqrt{3}}{4}$

13. $x^4 + 7x^2 - 18 = 0$

14. $x^4 - 16 = 0$ $\pm 2i, \pm 2$

15. $y^4 = 7y^2 + 8$ $\pm i, \pm 2\sqrt{2}$

16. $y^4 + 2y^2 - 15 = 0$

17. $c^4 = 10c^2 + 24$

18. $x^4 = 24 - 5x^2$

13. $\pm 3i, \pm\sqrt{2}$ $\quad \pm i\sqrt{5}, \pm\sqrt{3}$ $\quad\quad \pm i\sqrt{2}, \pm 2\sqrt{3}$ $\quad\quad\quad \pm 2i\sqrt{2}, \pm\sqrt{3}$

Find the three cube roots of each number.

19. -1 $-1, \dfrac{1 + i\sqrt{3}}{2}, \dfrac{1 - i\sqrt{3}}{2}$

20. 8 $2, -1 + i\sqrt{3}, -1 - i\sqrt{3}$

21. -27 $-3, \dfrac{3 + 3i\sqrt{3}}{2}, \dfrac{3 - 3i\sqrt{3}}{2}$

(B) 22. 64 $4, -2 + 2i\sqrt{3}, -2 - 2i\sqrt{3}$

23. -125 $-5, \dfrac{5 + 5i\sqrt{3}}{2}, \dfrac{5 - 5i\sqrt{3}}{2}$

24. $1,000$

$10, -5 + 5i\sqrt{3}, -5 - 5i\sqrt{3}$

Solve each equation.

28. $\pm 2i, \pm 3i$ $\quad\quad$ **29.** $\pm i\sqrt{2}, \pm 2i\sqrt{2}$

25. $\frac{1}{2}x^2 = x - \frac{3}{4}$ $\dfrac{2 \pm i\sqrt{2}}{2}$

26. $\frac{1}{3}x^2 + \frac{3}{2} = \frac{1}{3} - x$ $\dfrac{-3 \pm i\sqrt{5}}{2}$

27. $\frac{5x}{12} - \frac{x^2}{6} = \frac{1}{2}$ $\dfrac{5 \pm i\sqrt{23}}{4}$

28. $y^4 + 13y^2 + 36 = 0$

29. $n^4 + 10n^2 + 16 = 0$

30. $c^4 + 16c^2 + 64 = 0$ $\pm 2i\sqrt{2}$

31. $4x^4 + 19x^2 + 12 = 0$

32. $16x^4 + 16x^2 + 3 = 0$

33. $2x^4 + 11x^2 + 9 = 0$

$\pm\dfrac{i\sqrt{3}}{2}, \pm 2i$ $\quad\quad\quad \pm\dfrac{i}{2}, \pm\dfrac{i\sqrt{3}}{2}$ $\quad\quad\quad\quad \pm\dfrac{3i\sqrt{2}}{2}, \pm i$

(C) 34. $x^2 + 2ix + 3 = 0$ $-3i, i$

35. $x^2 - 6ix + 8 = 0$ $3i \pm i\sqrt{17}$

36. $2ix^2 + 5x - 2i = 0$ $\frac{1}{2}, 2i$

37. $\sqrt{x} = 3i$ -9

38. $\sqrt{x - 1} = 2i$ -3

39. $\sqrt{x + 8} = 3 - i$ $-6i$

Find the three cube roots of each number. Then raise each cube root to the third power.

40. $\frac{1}{8}$ $\frac{1}{2}, \dfrac{-1 + i\sqrt{3}}{4}, \dfrac{-1 - i\sqrt{3}}{4}$

41. $-\frac{8}{27}$ $-\frac{2}{3}, \dfrac{1 + i\sqrt{3}}{3}, \dfrac{1 - i\sqrt{3}}{3}$

42. $\frac{125}{64}$ $\frac{5}{4}, \dfrac{-5 + 5i\sqrt{3}}{8}, \dfrac{-5 - 5i\sqrt{3}}{8}$

8.4 The Discriminant

OBJECTIVES ▶ To determine the nature of the solutions of a quadratic equation by examining its discriminant

To find the coefficients of a quadratic equation having exactly one solution by using the value of its discriminant

The quadratic formula, $x = \dfrac{-b \pm \sqrt{b^2 - 4ac}}{2a}$, can be used to find the solutions of any quadratic equation. However, it is not necessary to solve a given quadratic equation in order to tell the *number* and *type* of solutions that it will have. All of this information about the nature of the solutions can be obtained from the value of $b^2 - 4ac$, the radicand in the quadratic formula.

Equation	Solutions	$b^2 - 4ac$	Nature of Solutions
$6x^2 - x - 2 = 0$	$\dfrac{1 \pm \sqrt{49}}{12} = \dfrac{1 \pm 7}{12}$	49: positive perfect square	Two real number solutions: rational
$x^2 + 3x - 5 = 0$	$\dfrac{-3 \pm \sqrt{29}}{2}$	29: positive	Two real number solutions: irrational
$\dfrac{3}{2}x^2 - 2x + \dfrac{2}{3} = 0$	$\dfrac{2 \pm \sqrt{0}}{3} = \dfrac{2}{3}$	0: perfect square	One real number solution: rational
$2x^2 + 3x + 3 = 0$	$\dfrac{-3 \pm \sqrt{-15}}{4} = \dfrac{-3 \pm i\sqrt{15}}{4}$	−15: negative	Two imaginary number solutions

The expression $b^2 - 4ac$ is called the **discriminant** because its value determines the nature of the solutions of a quadratic equation.

Nature of Solutions of Quadratic Equation

If $ax^2 + bx + c = 0$, where a, b, and c are real numbers ($a \neq 0$), then $x = \dfrac{-b \pm \sqrt{b^2 - 4ac}}{2a}$, and $b^2 - 4ac$ is the discriminant of the equation.

The nature of the solutions of the equation is determined as follows:
(1) if $b^2 - 4ac > 0$, there are two real number solutions.
(2) if $b^2 - 4ac = 0$, there is exactly one real number solution.
(3) if $b^2 - 4ac < 0$, there are two imaginary number solutions.

If a, b, and c are rational numbers and $b^2 - 4ac \geq 0$, the solutions are *rational* when $b^2 - 4ac$ is a perfect square, and the solutions are *irrational* when $b^2 - 4ac$ is not a perfect square.

Example 1

Determine the nature of the solutions of $x^2 + 5x - 3 = 0$ without solving the equation.

Identify a, b, and c and compute the value of $b^2 - 4ac$.

$$a = 1, b = 5, c = -3$$
$$b^2 - 4ac = 5^2 - 4(1)(-3) = 25 + 12 = 37$$

$b^2 - 4ac = 37$; positive but not a perfect square.
Thus, $x^2 + 5x - 3 = 0$ has two real number solutions that are irrational.

Example 2

Determine the nature of the solutions of $3y^2 = 4y - 2$ without solving the equation.

$$3y^2 = 4y - 2$$
$$3y^2 - 4y + 2 = 0 \qquad \blacktriangleleft \text{ } \textit{Rewrite the equation in standard form.}$$
$$a = 3, b = -4, c = 2 \qquad \blacktriangleleft \text{ } \textit{Identify a, b, and c.}$$
$$b^2 - 4ac = (-4)^2 - 4(3)(2) = 16 - 24 = -8$$

$b^2 - 4ac = -8$; negative
Thus, $3y^2 = 4y - 2$ has two imaginary number solutions.

Example 3

Determine the nature of the solutions of $\frac{1}{9}n^2 + \frac{2}{3}n + 1 = 0$ without solving the equation.

$$\frac{1}{9}n^2 + \frac{2}{3}n + 1 = 0$$
$$a = \frac{1}{9}, b = \frac{2}{3}, c = 1$$
$$b^2 - 4ac = \left(\frac{2}{3}\right)^2 - 4\left(\frac{1}{9}\right)(1) = \frac{4}{9} - \frac{4}{9} = 0$$

$b^2 - 4ac = 0$; a perfect square
Thus, $\frac{1}{9}n^2 + \frac{2}{3}n + 1 = 0$ has exactly one real number solution that is rational.

Example 4

For what values of k will $2x^2 + (k + 2)x + 8 = 0$ have exactly one solution?

If $b^2 - 4ac = 0$, there is exactly one solution to the equation.
$$b^2 - 4ac = 0 \qquad a = 2, b = k + 2, c = 8$$
$$(k + 2)^2 - 4(2)(8) = 0$$
$$k^2 + 4k + 4 - 64 = 0$$
$$k^2 + 4k - 60 = 0$$
$$(k - 6)(k + 10) = 0$$
$$k = 6 \quad \text{or} \quad k = -10$$
Thus, the equation will have exactly one solution if $k = 6$ or $k = -10$.

Reading in **Algebra**

You are given a quadratic equation $ax^2 + bx + c = 0$, where a, b, and c are real numbers ($a \neq 0$). Match each expression or statement at the left to exactly one phrase at the right.

1. $b^2 - 4ac < 0$ **C**
2. $b^2 - 4ac > 0$ **D**
3. $b^2 - 4ac = 0$ **B**
4. $b^2 - 4ac$ **A**
5. $\sqrt{b^2 - 4ac}$ **F**
6. $b^2 - 4ac$ is a positive number but not a perfect square. **E**

A the discriminant
B exactly one solution
C two imaginary solutions
D two real solutions
E two irrational solutions
F the radical in the quadratic formula

(In exercises 1–12 and 19–30 below, R = real, IM = imaginary, Rt = rational, and Ir = irrational.)

Written **Exercises**

1. two R:Rt   2. two R:Ir   3. two Im   4. one R:Rt   5. one R:Rt
6. two Im   7. two R:Rt   8. two R:Ir   9. two Im   10. two R:Rt   11. two R:Ir   12. one R:Rt

Determine the nature of the solutions without solving the equation.

(A)
1. $x^2 + 6x - 16 = 0$ 2. $y^2 - 8y + 2 = 0$ 3. $n^2 + 2n + 3 = 0$ 4. $z^2 + 16 = 8z$
5. $4y^2 + 12y + 9 = 0$ 6. $3n^2 - 4n + 3 = 0$ 7. $6x^2 = 4 - 5x$ 8. $15d^2 - 25d + 9 = 0$
9. $9x^2 + 0x + 4 = 0$ 10. $4y^2 - 5y = 0$ 11. $n^2 = 15$ 12. $25t^2 = 0$

For what value(s) of k will each quadratic equation have exactly one solution?

13. $x^2 - 20x + k^2 = 0$ $-10, 10$ 14. $25y^2 + 10ky + 16 = 0$ $-4, 4$ 15. $9ky^2 + 1 = 2ky$ 9

(B)
16. $x^2 - 16x + (k - 1)^2 = 0$ $-7, 9$ 17. $4y^2 - (k - 3)y + 9 = 0$ $-9, 15$ 18. $(2k + 1)x^2 = 12x - k$ $-\frac{9}{2}, 4$

Determine the nature of the solutions without solving the equation.

19. $\frac{1}{3}x^2 - \frac{5}{6}x - 2 = 0$ two R:Rt   20. $\frac{5}{2}y^2 + 2y + \frac{2}{5} = 0$ one R:Rt   21. $\frac{2}{9}n^2 = \frac{4}{3}n - 2$ one R:Rt

22. $(2y - 3)(3y + 4) = -10$ 23. $(5x + 1)(2x + 1) = 2$ 24. $(t - 5)(t - 3) + 3 = 0$ two Im
25. $-5n^2 + 8n - 3 = 0$ 26. $-3y^2 - 3y - 108 = 0$ 27. $-2x(3x + 4) + 4 = 0$

22. two R:Rt   23. two R:Ir   25. two R:Rt   26. two Im   27. two R:Ir

Determine the nature of the solutions without solving the equation. The coefficient of x in each equation is an irrational number.

(C)
28. $x^2 + 2\sqrt{2}x - 6 = 0$ two R:Ir   29. $x^2 - 2\sqrt{3}x + 3 = 0$ one R:Ir   30. $x^2 + 4\sqrt{5}x + 4 = 0$ two R:Ir

31. For what values of k will $2x^2 + kx + 8 = 0$ have two real solutions? $k < -8$ or $k > 8$
32. For what values of k will $2x^2 + (k + 1)x + 18 = 0$ have two imaginary solutions? $-13 < k < 11$

→ A Challenge To You

Given a pair of quadratic equations,
  (1) $px^2 + qx + r = 0$ and   (2) $ptx^2 + qtx + rt = 0$,
prove that the discriminant of equation (2) is t^2 times the discriminant of equation (1). **discriminant of (1) $q^2 - 4pr$; discriminant of (2) $(qt)^2 - 4(pt)(rt)$, or $q^2t^2 - 4prt^2$, or $t^2(q^2 - 4pr)$**

THE DISCRIMINANT

8.5 Sum and Product of Solutions

OBJECTIVES ▶ **To find the sum and the product of the solutions of a quadratic equation**
To write a quadratic equation, given its solutions

The solutions of the quadratic equation $3x^2 - 4x - 20 = 0$ are -2 and $\frac{10}{3}$.

The equation is in the standard form of $ax^2 + bx + c = 0$, where $a = 3$, $b = -4$, and $c = -20$. Let r and s represent the solutions of $3x^2 - 4x - 20 = 0$. Then,

$$(1) \quad r + s = -2 + \frac{10}{3} = \frac{4}{3} = \frac{-b}{a} \quad \text{and}$$

$$(2) \quad r \cdot s = -2 \cdot \frac{10}{3} = \frac{-20}{3} = \frac{c}{a}.$$

The *sum*, $r + s$, and the *product*, $r \cdot s$, of the solutions of $3x^2 - 4x - 20 = 0$ are related to the value of the coefficients a, b, and c.

$$3x^2 - 4x - 20 = 0 \qquad\qquad ax^2 + bx + c = 0$$

$$x^2 - \frac{4}{3}x - \frac{20}{3} = 0 \qquad\qquad x^2 + \frac{b}{a}x + \frac{c}{a} = 0$$

Notice that $\qquad r + s = \frac{4}{3} = -\frac{b}{a} \qquad$ or $\qquad \frac{b}{a} = -(r + s)$, and

$$r \cdot s = -\frac{20}{3} = \frac{c}{a}.$$

These relationships remain true for any quadratic equation.

Sum and Product of Solutions of a Quadratic Equation

> If r and s are the solutions of $ax^2 + bx + c = 0$ $(a \neq 0)$, then
> $$r + s = -\frac{b}{a} \qquad \text{and} \qquad r \cdot s = \frac{c}{a}.$$

Example 1 Find the sum and the product of the solutions of $4x^2 + 7x + 3 = 0$.

$$4x^2 + 7x + 3 = 0$$

$$x^2 + \frac{7}{4}x + \frac{3}{4} = 0 \quad \blacktriangleleft \text{ Divide each side by } a, \text{ or } 4.$$

$$\frac{b}{a} = \frac{7}{4}, \text{ or } -\frac{b}{a} = -\frac{7}{4}, \text{ and } \frac{c}{a} = \frac{3}{4}.$$

Thus, the sum of the solutions is $-\frac{7}{4}$ and the product is $\frac{3}{4}$.

If you are given two numbers, either real or imaginary, you can write a quadratic equation that has the two numbers as its solutions.

Example 2 Write a quadratic equation, in standard form, that has $-\frac{3}{4}$ and $\frac{2}{3}$ as its solutions.

Let $r = -\frac{3}{4}$ and $s = \frac{2}{3}$. Find $\frac{b}{a}$ and $\frac{c}{a}$.

$$\frac{b}{a} = -(r + s) = -\left(-\frac{3}{4} + \frac{2}{3}\right) \qquad\qquad \frac{c}{a} = r \cdot s$$

$$= -\left(-\frac{9}{12} + \frac{8}{12}\right) \qquad\qquad\qquad = -\frac{3}{4} \cdot \frac{2}{3}$$

$$= \frac{1}{12} \qquad\qquad\qquad\qquad\qquad = -\frac{1}{2}$$

$$x^2 + \frac{b}{a}x + \frac{c}{a} = 0$$

Substitute. ▶ $x^2 + \left(\frac{1}{12}\right)x + \left(-\frac{1}{2}\right) = 0$

Write in standard form. ▶ $12x^2 + x - 6 = 0$

Thus, $12x^2 + x - 6 = 0$ is a quadratic equation, in standard form, whose solutions are $-\frac{3}{4}$ and $\frac{2}{3}$.

A similar procedure is used to write a quadratic equation that has exactly one given real number solution. You begin by letting $r = s$.

Example 3 Write a quadratic equation, in standard form, that has $\frac{3}{7}$ as its only solution.

Let $r = s = \frac{3}{7}$.

$$\frac{b}{a} = -(r + s) = -\left(\frac{3}{7} + \frac{3}{7}\right) = -\frac{6}{7} \qquad\qquad \frac{c}{a} = r \cdot s = \frac{3}{7} \cdot \frac{3}{7} = \frac{9}{49}$$

$$x^2 + \frac{b}{a}x + \frac{c}{a} = 0$$

Substitute. ▶ $x^2 + \left(-\frac{6}{7}\right)x + \left(\frac{9}{49}\right) = 0$

Write in standard form. ▶ $49x^2 - 42x + 9 = 0$

Thus, the required equation is $49x^2 - 42x + 9 = 0$.

The two numbers represented by $\dfrac{4 \pm 2\sqrt{3}}{3}$ are a pair of conjugate irrational numbers, $\dfrac{4 + 2\sqrt{3}}{3}$ and $\dfrac{4 - 2\sqrt{3}}{3}$. As shown in Example 4 on page 200, a quadratic equation can be written that has these two numbers as its solutions.

SUM AND PRODUCT OF SOLUTIONS

Example 4 Write a quadratic equation, in standard form, that has $\dfrac{4 \pm 2\sqrt{3}}{3}$ as its solutions.

Let $r = \dfrac{4 + 2\sqrt{3}}{3}$ and $s = \dfrac{4 - 2\sqrt{3}}{3}$.

$$\dfrac{b}{a} = -\left(\dfrac{4 + 2\sqrt{3}}{3} + \dfrac{4 - 2\sqrt{3}}{3}\right) = -\dfrac{4 + 2\sqrt{3} + 4 - 2\sqrt{3}}{3} = -\dfrac{8}{3}$$

$$\dfrac{c}{a} = \dfrac{4 + 2\sqrt{3}}{3} \cdot \dfrac{4 - 2\sqrt{3}}{3} = \dfrac{4^2 - (2\sqrt{3})^2}{3 \cdot 3} = \dfrac{16 - 12}{9} = \dfrac{4}{9}$$

$$x^2 - \dfrac{8}{3}x + \dfrac{4}{9} = 0$$

Thus, $9x^2 - 24x + 4 = 0$ is the required equation.

9. $x^2 - 8x + 15 = 0$ 10. $x^2 + 4x - 12 = 0$ 12. $x^2 + 9x = 0$ 13. $8x^2 - 6x + 1 = 0$

Written Exercises For complete solutions, see TE Answer Section.

1. sum: $-\frac{9}{2}$, prod.: -3 2. sum: $-\frac{4}{3}$, prod.: $-\frac{1}{3}$ 3. sum: 3, prod.: $-\frac{1}{2}$ 4. sum: -9, prod.: 14

Without solving the equation, find the sum and the product of its solutions.

(A) 1. $2x^2 + 9x - 6 = 0$ 2. $3y^2 + 4y - 1 = 0$ 3. $4n^2 - 12n - 2 = 0$ 4. $x^2 + 9x + 14 = 0$
  5. $6t^2 + 5t = 0$ 6. $3x^2 - 9 = 0$ 7. $y^2 = 6y - 9$ 8. $12 = 6n + 3n^2$
sum: $-\frac{5}{6}$, prod.: 0   sum: 0, prod.: -3 sum: 6, prod.: 9   sum: -2, prod.: -4

Write a quadratic equation, in standard form, that has the given solution(s).

9. 3 and 5 above   10. -6 and 2 above   11. 0 and 4 $x^2 - 4x = 0$ 12. -9 and 0 above

13. $\dfrac{1}{4}$ and $\dfrac{1}{2}$ above   14. $-\dfrac{3}{4}$ and $-\dfrac{5}{8}$ below   15. -6 and $\dfrac{2}{3}$ below   16. $\dfrac{9}{10}$ and 2 below

17. 7 $x^2 - 14x + 49 = 0$ 18. -8 19. $-\dfrac{1}{2}$ 20. $\dfrac{10}{7}$
  $x^2 - 7 = 0$ $x^2 + 16x + 64 = 0$
  $4x^2 + 4x + 1 = 0$ $49x^2 - 140x + 100 = 0$

(B) 21. $-\sqrt{7}$ and $\sqrt{7}$ 22. $-4\sqrt{3}$ and $4\sqrt{3}$ 23. $-i\sqrt{10}$ and $i\sqrt{10}$ 24. $-2i\sqrt{6}$ and $2i\sqrt{6}$
  25. $4 \pm \sqrt{5}$ 26. $-3 \pm 2\sqrt{10}$ 27. $5 \pm 2i\sqrt{7}$ 28. $-6 \pm 3i\sqrt{5}$ below
  29. $\dfrac{2 \pm \sqrt{3}}{2}$ 30. $\dfrac{-2 \pm 3\sqrt{2}}{3}$ 31. $\dfrac{-3 \pm 2i\sqrt{3}}{3}$ 32. $\dfrac{4 \pm 2i\sqrt{5}}{3}$
  $4x^2 - 8x + 1 = 0$ $9x^2 + 12x - 14 = 0$ $3x^2 + 6x + 7 = 0$ $3x^2 - 8x + 12 = 0$

Without solving the equation, find the sum and the product of its solutions.

33. $4x^2 + \dfrac{1}{3}x - \dfrac{1}{2} = 0$ sum: $-\dfrac{1}{12}$, prod.: $-\dfrac{1}{8}$ 34. $\dfrac{1}{3}y^2 - 3y + 1 = 0$ sum: 9, prod.: 3

35. $2.5x^2 + 5x - 10 = 0$ sum: -2, prod.: -4 36. $0.2y^2 - 4y + 0.6 = 0$ sum: 20, prod.: 3

(C) 37. Show that the following statement is true for all real numbers a, b, and c, if $a \neq 0$.

If $r = \dfrac{-b + \sqrt{b^2 - 4ac}}{2a}$ and $s = \dfrac{-b - \sqrt{b^2 - 4ac}}{2a}$, then $r + s = -\dfrac{b}{a}$ and $r \cdot s = \dfrac{c}{a}$. $-\frac{1}{2}, \frac{3}{2}$

38. For what values of k will the *sum* of the solutions of $x^2 - (k^2 - 2k)x + 12 = 0$ be 8? -2, 4
39. For what values of k will the *product* of the solutions of $2x^2 + x + (4k^2 - 4k - 3) = 0$ be 0?

40. Prove: If a, b, and c are odd integers, then $ax^2 + bx + c = 0$ has no integral solutions. [Hint: First prove that there are no *even* integral solutions and then that there are no *odd* integral solutions.]   14. $32x^2 + 44x + 15 = 0$ 15. $3x^2 + 16x - 12 = 0$ 16. $10x^2 - 29x + 18 = 0$

22. $x^2 - 48 = 0$ 23. $x^2 + 10 = 0$ 24. $x^2 + 24 = 0$ 25. $x^2 - 8x + 11 = 0$

26. $x^2 + 6x - 31 = 0$ 27. $x^2 - 10x + 53 = 0$ 28. $x^2 + 12x + 81 = 0$ **CHAPTER EIGHT**

8.6 Problem Solving: Mixed Types (Optional)

OBJECTIVE ▶ **To solve word problems of various types**

Solve each problem.

1. In a bag of coins, there are 12 more quarters than dimes and 4 times as many nickels as quarters. The nickels and dimes together have the same value as the quarters. Find the number of each kind of coin. **nickels: 96, dimes: 12, quarters: 24**

2. Ben is twice as old as Al and Carol is two years older than Ben. Five years ago, the sum of the two younger ages was the same as the age of the oldest. Find the present age of all three people.
   Ben: 14, Al: 7, Carol: 16

3. Some 50¢ red pens and some 30¢ blue pens are mixed to make a package of 20 pens. If the package is worth $8.40, how many red pens and how many blue pens are in the package? **red pens: 12, blue pens: 8**

4. Machine A can do a job in 15 h. If machines A and B work together, the job can be done in 10 h. How many hours would it take machine B to do the job if it works alone? **30 h**

5. Find four consecutive multiples of 4 such that the product of the second and the third numbers is 192. **8, 12, 16, 20 or −20, −16, −12, −8**

6. How much water must be added to 4 L of a 30% iodine solution to dilute it to a 10% iodine solution? **8 L**

7. The height of a triangle is 6 cm more than 4 times the length of its base. Find the length of the base and the height if the area of the triangle is 27 cm^2.
   base: 3 cm, height: 18 cm

8. Melvin is 15 years older than Phyllis. Two years from now, he will be 4 times as old as she will be. How old is each person now? **Melvin: 18, Phyllis: 3**

9. Machine C can do a job in 20 h and machine D can do the same job in 15 h. If C works alone for 2 h and then D works alone for 3 h, how many additional hours are needed to complete the job with both machines at work? **6 h**

10. At 10:00 A.M., Mrs. Conrad drove from her home to a city at an average speed of 90 km/h. After shopping for $2\frac{1}{2}$ h, she returned home at an average speed of 60 km/h. If she arrived home at 2:30 P.M., how far does Mrs. Conrad live from the city? **72 km**

11. A rowing crew traveled 10.5 km downstream in the same time that it took to travel 7.5 km upstream. Find the rate of the current if the crew can travel 30 km/h in still water. **5 km/h**

12. With the help of a tailwind, a plane flew 568 km in $\frac{2}{3}$ of the time that a second plane flew 828 km against the wind. Find the rate of the wind if each plane can fly 700 km/h in still air. **10 km/h**

Chapter Eight Review

Vocabulary

complex number [8.1]
conjugate complex numbers [8.2]
discriminant [8.4]
imaginary number [8.1]
pure imaginary number [8.1]

Simplify each expression.

1. $5\sqrt{-12}$ [8.1] **$10i\sqrt{3}$**
2. $(-3 + 4i) - (5 - i)$ **$-8 + 5i$**
3. $(9 - 4\sqrt{-18}) + (-2 + 3\sqrt{-50})$ **$7 + 3i\sqrt{2}$**
4. $2\sqrt{-6} \cdot 3\sqrt{-15}$ [8.2] **$-18\sqrt{10}$**
5. $(2i)^{11}$ **$-2,048i$**
6. $(7 - 2i)(-6 + 3i)$ **$-36 + 33i$**
7. $(4 - \sqrt{-10})^2$ **$6 - 8i\sqrt{10}$**

Simplify each quotient by rationalizing the denominator. [8.2]

8. $-3 \div (4i)$ **$\frac{3i}{4}$**
9. $4i \div (5 - 3i)$ **$\frac{-6 + 10i}{17}$**
10. $\dfrac{3 + 2i}{-2 + i}$ **$\dfrac{-4 - 7i}{5}$**

Solve each equation. (Exercises 11–16)

11. $x^2 = -60$ [8.1] **$\pm 2i\sqrt{15}$**
12. $4y^2 + 100 = 0$ **$\pm 5i$**
13. $x^2 + 4x + 6 = 0$ [8.3] **$-2 \pm i\sqrt{2}$**
14. $2x^2 + 13 = 2x$ **$\frac{1 \pm 5i}{2}$**
15. $y^4 + 12y^2 + 32 = 0$ **$\pm 2i,\ \pm 2i\sqrt{2}$**
★16. $x^2 - 2ix + 15 = 0$ **$-3i,\ 5i$**

17. Find the three cube roots of 27. [8.3]

$$3,\ \frac{-3 + 3i\sqrt{3}}{2},\ \frac{-3 - 3i\sqrt{3}}{2}$$

Determine the nature of the solutions without solving the equation. [8.4]

18. $2x^2 + 5x + 2 = 0$ **two R:Rt**
19. $4y^2 + 25 = 0$ **two Im**
20. $\frac{1}{2}n^2 - n = \frac{2}{3}$ **two R:Ir**
★21. $x^2 - 6x\sqrt{2} - 14 = 0$ **two R:Ir**

22. For what values of k will $2kx^2 + 12x + (4k + 1) = 0$ have exactly one solution? [8.4] **$-\frac{9}{4},\ 2$**

Without solving the equation, find the sum and the product of its solutions. [8.5]

23. $4x^2 + 3x - 2 = 0$ **sum: $-\frac{3}{4}$, prod.: $-\frac{1}{2}$**
24. $\frac{1}{6}y^2 - \frac{4}{3}y + 2 = 0$ **sum: 8, prod.: 12**

Write a quadratic equation, in standard form, that has the given pair of numbers as its solutions. [8.5]

25. -8 and 5 **$x^2 + 3x - 40 = 0$**
26. $\frac{1}{6}$ and $\frac{3}{4}$ **$24x^2 - 22x + 3 = 0$**
27. $-5 \pm 2\sqrt{7}$ **$x^2 + 10x - 3 = 0$**
28. $\dfrac{1 \pm 2i\sqrt{5}}{2}$ **$4x^2 - 4x + 21 = 0$**

★29. For what values of k will the sum of the solutions of $x^2 - (k^2 - 3k)x + 24 = 0$ be 10? [8.5] **$-2,\ 5$**

Chapter Eight Test

Simplify each expression.

1. $-8 + 4\sqrt{-20}$ **$-8 + 8i\sqrt{5}$**

2. $(12 - 10i) - (-3 + 4i)$ **$15 - 14i$**

3. $5\sqrt{-3} \cdot 2\sqrt{-6}$ **$-30\sqrt{2}$**

4. $(6 - 5i)(6 + 5i)$ **61**

5. $(3 + 2i\sqrt{5})^2$ **$-11 + 12i\sqrt{5}$**

Simplify each quotient by rationalizing the denominator.

6. $-7 \div (10i)$ **$\frac{7i}{10}$**

7. $\dfrac{3i}{4 + 3i}$ **$\dfrac{9 + 12i}{25}$**

Solve each equation. (Exercises 8–11)

8. $2x^2 + 24 = 0$ **$\pm 2i\sqrt{3}$**

9. $y^2 - 6y + 10 = 0$ **$3 \pm i$**

10. $3x^2 + 5 = 2x$ **$\dfrac{1 \pm i\sqrt{14}}{3}$**

11. $t^4 + 7t^2 + 12 = 0$ **$\pm 2i, \pm i\sqrt{3}$**

12. Find the three cube roots of 125.
   $5, \dfrac{-5 + 5i\sqrt{3}}{2}, \dfrac{-5 - 5i\sqrt{3}}{2}$

Determine the nature of the solutions without solving the equation. (Exercises 13–15)

13. $3x^2 + 4x = 4$ **two R:Rt**

14. $2y^2 - 3y + 4 = 0$ **two Im**

15. $\dfrac{5}{3}x^2 + 2x + \dfrac{3}{5} = 0$ **one R:Rt**

16. For what values of k will $y^2 + (k + 2)y + 16 = 0$ have exactly one solution? **$-10, 6$**

17. Without solving the equation, find the sum and the product of the solutions of $12x^2 + 2 = 3x$. **sum: $\frac{1}{4}$, prod.: $\frac{1}{6}$**

Write a quadratic equation, in standard form, that has the given pair of numbers as its solutions. (Exercises 18–19)

18. $-\dfrac{1}{3}$ and $\dfrac{2}{3}$ **$9x^2 - 3x - 2 = 0$**

19. $-2 \pm i\sqrt{6}$ **$x^2 + 4x + 10 = 0$**

★ 20. Compute the value of the discriminant for $x^2 - 2x\sqrt{3} - 24 = 0$ and determine the nature of the solutions. **108; two R:Ir**

★ 21. For what values of k will $5x^2 - kx + 5 = 0$ have two real number solutions.
   $k < -10$ or $k > 10$

★ 22. Factor $x^2 + 9$ as a difference of two squares. [Hint: Use the fact that $i^2 = -1$.] **$(x + 3i)(x - 3i)$**

Computer Activities

Adding Complex Numbers

Recall that complex numbers can be written in the form $a + bi$, where a and b are real numbers and $i = \sqrt{-1}$.

You can perform calculations with complex numbers on the computer if you supply the real numbers. The program below finds the sum of complex numbers using the following property:

$$(a + bi) + (c + di) = (a + c) + (b + d)i.$$

PROGRAM

```
10 PRINT "PROGRAM FINDS THE SUM OF TWO"
20 PRINT "COMPLEX NUMBERS"
30 PRINT "ENTER THE COEFFICIENTS A AND B"
40 PRINT "OF THE FIRST ADDEND"
50 INPUT A, B
60 PRINT "ENTER THE COEFFICIENTS C AND D"
70 PRINT "OF THE SECOND ADDEND"
80 INPUT C, D
90 LET A1 = A + C
100 LET B1 = B + D
110 PRINT "THE COEFFICIENTS OF THE SUM ARE"
120 PRINT "A IS"; A1; "B IS"; B1
130 END
```

Exercises

Run the program above for the following values:

1. $A = 2, B = 3, C = 2, D = 4$ **A is 4, B is 7**

2. $A = 6, B = -3, C = -2, D = -2$ **A is 4, B is −5**

3. $A = -2, B = 3, C = 1, D = -6$ **A is −1, B is −3**

4. Alter the program above to get a program for finding the difference of two complex numbers. **For Ex, 4, see TE Answer Section.**

5. Write a program to find the product of a pair of conjugate complex numbers, $a + bi$ and $a - bi$, given the values of a and b.
   For Ex, 5, see TE Answer Section.

College Prep Test

DIRECTIONS: Choose the *one* best answer to each question or problem.

1. Let x and y represent two imaginary numbers. Which statement(s) could be true? **E**

   I xy is a real number.
   II xy is an imaginary number.
   III $x + y$ is a real number.

   (A) I only   (B) II only
   (C) I or II only   (D) II or III only
   (E) I, II, or III

2. If $i = \sqrt{-1}$ and $i^2 = -1$, which statement is *false*? **E**

   (A) $i^4 = 1$ (B) $i^6 = i^2$ (C) $i^3 = -i$
   (D) $i^5 = i$ (E) None of these

3. For what value(s) of k will
   $$kx^2 + 2x + k = 0$$
   have exactly one solution? **A**

   (A) $-1, 0,$ and 1 (B) 0 and 1 only
   (C) -1 and 1 only   (D) 1 only
   (E) None of these

4. If $n \div 7$ gives a remainder of 5, then $(n + 3) \div 7$ gives what remainder? **A**

   (A) 1   (B) 2   (C) 3   (D) 4   (E) 5

5. For which equation(s) is the sum of the solutions greater than the product of the solutions? **C**

   (A) $7x^2 - 28x + 28 = 0$
   (B) $8x^2 + 12x - 8 = 0$
   (C) $9x^2 - 3x - 2 = 0$
   (D) All of these
   (E) None of these

6. The conjugate of $-(-2i + 3)$ is **B**

   (A) $3 - 2i$ (B) $-3 - 2i$ (C) $3 + 2i$
   (D) $-3 + 2i$ (E) None of these

7. For every complex number x, $x\bigstar$ is defined to be x^2. Find the value of $[(-2i)\bigstar]\bigstar$. **B**

   (A) $16i$ (B) 16 (C) $-16i$
   (D) -16 (E) None of these

8. Which equation does *not* have two imaginary number solutions? **C**

   (A) $x^2 + 4 = 0$ (B) $\dfrac{x}{2} + \dfrac{2}{x} = 0$

   (C) $(x + 2)^2 = 0$ (D) $\dfrac{(-x)^2}{3} + \sqrt{\dfrac{16}{9}} = 0$

   (E) None of these

9. If $-2i \cdot 3i \cdot 4i \cdot N = 3i \cdot 4i$, then $N =$ **C**

   (A) $-\dfrac{i}{2}$ (B) $-\dfrac{1}{2}$ (C) $\dfrac{i}{2}$

   (D) $\dfrac{1}{2}$ (E) None of these

10. For what value(s) of k will
    $$x^2 + kx + 1 = 0$$
    have two imaginary number solutions? **B**

    (A) $k < -2$ or $k > 2$ (B) $-2 < k < 2$
    (C) $-4 < k < 4$ (D) 0 only
    (E) None of these

11. If $x = a + bi$ and $y = a - bi$, where a and b are real numbers and $i = \sqrt{-1}$, which statement(s) is (are) true? **E**

    I xy is always an imaginary number.
    II xy is always a real number.
    III $x + y$ is always a real number.

    (A) I only   (B) II only   (C) III only
    (D) I and III only   (E) II and III only

Cumulative Review (Chapters 1–8)

DIRECTIONS: Choose the *one* best answer to each question or problem. (Exercises 1–12)

1. Factor $3x^3 - 4x^2 + 15x - 20$ completely by grouping pairs of terms. **D**

   (A) $(3x^2 + 5)(x - 4)$ (B) $(x^2 - 4)(3x + 5)$
   (C) $(3x^2 - 4)(x + 5)$ (D) $(x^2 + 5)(3x - 4)$

2. If $x^2 - 5x - 14 > 0$, then **B**

   (A) $-2 < x < 7$ (B) $x < -2$ or $x > 7$
   (C) $-7 < x < 2$ (D) $x < -7$ or $x > 2$

3. Multiply: $\dfrac{8x^2 - 72y^2}{10a^{-4}b^{-3}c^2} \cdot \dfrac{-6a^{-2}b^3c^{-6}}{6x^2 + 3xy - 45y^2}$. **A**

   (A) $-\dfrac{8a^2b^6(x - 3y)}{5c^8(2x - 5y)}$ (B) $\dfrac{5(x + 3y)}{16a^2bc^3(2x - 5y)}$
   (C) $\dfrac{-8a^2b^6(x - 3y)}{5c^8(2x + 5y)}$ (D) $\dfrac{8(x + 3y)}{-5a^2c^4(2x + 5y)}$

4. Machine X can do a certain job in 4 h and machine Y can do the same job in 6 h. If machines X, Y, and Z can do the job in 2 h working together, how long would it take Z to do the job working alone? **A**

   (A) 12 h   (B) 10 h   (C) 8 h   (D) 6 h

5. Solve $\dfrac{x + 1}{3x - 1} = \dfrac{x + 4}{2x + 6}$. **D**

   (A) $\dfrac{3}{5}, \dfrac{1}{4}$ (B) 2, 5
   (C) $-2, 5$ (D) $-5, 2$

6. Solve $32^{2x+1} = 8$ for x. **C**

   (A) 1   (B) $\dfrac{7}{2}$ (C) $-\dfrac{1}{5}$ (D) $\dfrac{1}{4}$

7. Solve $a(bx - c) = x - 2(x + c)$ for x. **C**

   (A) $\dfrac{ac - 2c - x}{ab}$ (B) $\dfrac{ac - 2c}{ab}$
   (C) $\dfrac{ac - 2c}{ab + 1}$ (D) $\dfrac{2c - ac}{ab + 1}$

8. Use synthetic division to find the value of $3x^4 + 20x^3 - 2x + 20$ if $x = -6$. **A**

   (A) -400 (B)   32
   (C)   104   (D) 8,216

9. Find the value of $\dfrac{81^{-\frac{5}{4}}}{9^{-\frac{3}{2}}}$. **C**

   (A) 9   (B) $\dfrac{1}{4}$ (C) $\dfrac{1}{9}$ (D) $\dfrac{5}{2}$

10. Solve $n - 1 = \sqrt{3n + 7}$. **B**

    (A) -1 (B) 6
    (C) $-1, 6$ (D) None of these

11. Factor $4x^2 - 12x + 9 - 25y^2$ as a difference of squares. **B**

    (A) $(2x - 3 - 5y)^2$
    (B) $(2x + 5y - 3)(2x - 5y - 3)$
    (C) $(2x - 3 - 5y)(2x - 3 - 5y)$
    (D) $(2x - 5y + 3)(2x - 5y - 3)$

12. Find the three cube roots of 64. **A**

    (A) $4, -2 + 2i\sqrt{3}, -2 - 2i\sqrt{3}$
    (B) $4, -2 + 4i\sqrt{3}, -2 - 4i\sqrt{3}$
    (C) $-4, 2 + 2i\sqrt{3}, 2 - 2i\sqrt{3}$
    (D) $4, 2 + 4i\sqrt{3}, 2 - 4i\sqrt{3}$

Solve each equation.

13. $|5x - 4| = 26$ $-\frac{22}{5}, 6$

14. $\dfrac{5}{x + 4} = \dfrac{3x - 4}{x^2 + 2x - 8} + \dfrac{1}{2x - 4}$ $\dfrac{16}{3}$

15. $\dfrac{y + 5}{2y + 2} = \dfrac{y - 4}{y - 3}$ 1, 7   16. $\dfrac{9}{n - 2} - \dfrac{6}{n} = 3$ −1, 4

17. $8^{3x-1} = 4$ $\dfrac{5}{9}$ 18. $5^{2x-3} = \dfrac{1}{25}$ $\dfrac{1}{2}$

19. $n + 1 = \sqrt{n + 7}$ 2

20. $\sqrt[3]{y^2 - 3y + 10} = 4$ −6, 9

21. $n^4 + 16n^2 + 48 = 0$ $\pm 2i, \pm 2i\sqrt{3}$

22. $x^2 + 13 = 6x$ $3 \pm 2i$

Solve each equation for x.

23. $a(3x + t) = b + c(4x - v)$ $x = \dfrac{b - cv - at}{3a - 4c}$

24. $\dfrac{6}{m} = \dfrac{4}{n} + \dfrac{2}{x}$ $x = \dfrac{mn}{3n - 2m}$

Factor each polynomial completely.

25. $2n^3 - 54$ 26. $6x^3 - 3x^2 + 10x - 5$
$2(n - 3)(n^2 + 3n + 9)$ $(3x^2 + 5)(2x - 1)$

Find the solution set of each inequality. Graph the solutions on a number line.

27. $8(2x - 3) - (14x - 19) \leq 3x - 2$ $\{x | x \geq -3\}$

28. $y^2 - 2y - 24 > 0$ $\{y | y < -4 \text{ or } y > 6\}$

29. $n^4 - 26n^2 + 25 < 0$
$\{n | -5 < n < -1 \text{ or } 1 < n < 5\}$

Simplify each expression. Assume that no divisor has the value of 0.

30. $(-3a^{-5}b^2)^{-4}$ $\dfrac{a^{20}}{81b^8}$ 31. $\dfrac{-14x^{-2}y^3}{28x^6y^{-6}}$ $\dfrac{-y^9}{2x^8}$

32. $\dfrac{40mn^2 - 90m}{30n^2 + 75n + 45}$ $\dfrac{2m(2n - 3)}{3(n + 1)}$

33. $\dfrac{6 - 2a}{3a^2 + 12a} \div \dfrac{a^2 - 9}{a^3 + 3a^2 - 4a}$ $\dfrac{-2(a - 1)}{3(a + 3)}$

34. $\dfrac{4}{x + 4} - \dfrac{x + 1}{16 - x^2} + \dfrac{2}{12 - 3x}$ $\dfrac{13x - 53}{3(x + 4)(x - 4)}$

35. $\dfrac{4x + 6y}{\dfrac{4}{x} + \dfrac{6}{y}}$ $\dfrac{xy(2x + 3y)}{2y + 3x}$

36. $-5a^2b\sqrt{80a^7b^9c^{11}}$ $-20a^5b^5c^5\sqrt{5abc}$

37. $\sqrt{8c^3d} + c\sqrt{50cd} - 4\sqrt{18c^3d}$ $-5c\sqrt{2cd}$

38. $\sqrt{\dfrac{25a^5}{12b^3}}$ $\dfrac{5a^2\sqrt{3ab}}{6b^2}$ 39. $\dfrac{6c^2}{\sqrt[4]{8c^2}}$ $3c\sqrt[4]{2c^2}$

40. $\sqrt[3]{-8x^7} + \sqrt[3]{125x^7}$ $3x^2\sqrt[3]{x}$

41. $(-5 + \sqrt{-27}) - (4 - 2\sqrt{-3})$
$-9 + 5i\sqrt{3}$ 42. $\dfrac{6i}{1 + 7i}$ $\dfrac{1 + 7i}{}$
$\dfrac{21 + 3i}{25}$

Use synthetic division in Exercises 43–45.

43. $(5x^3 + 8 - 77x) \div (x + 4)$

44. Is $x + 4$ a factor of $5x^3 - 77x + 8$? (See Exercise 43.) **No**

45. Evaluate $2n^3 - 15n^2 - 10n + 33$ if $n = 8$. **17**
43. $5x^2 - 20x + 3 + \dfrac{-4}{x + 4}$

Determine whether each number is rational or irrational.

46. $\sqrt{40}$ **I**   47. $83.43434\ldots$ **R**

48. $-\sqrt{400}$ **R**   49. $9.29929992\ldots$ **I**

Find the value of each expression.

50. $-10 \cdot 32^{\frac{3}{5}} \cdot 36^{\frac{1}{2}}$ **−480**   51. $\dfrac{5^{-3}}{8^{-\frac{2}{3}}}$ $\dfrac{4}{125}$

52. Write $4\sqrt[3]{x^2}$ in exponential form. $4x^{\frac{2}{3}}$

53. Write $(5y)^{\frac{3}{4}}$ in radical form. $\sqrt[4]{125y^3}$

54. How many liters of a 20% salt solution must be added to 8 L of a 60% salt solution to obtain a 50% salt solution? $2\frac{2}{3}$ **L**

55. Machines A, B, and C can complete a certain job in 30 min, 40 min, and 1 h, respectively. How long will the job take if the machines work together? $13\frac{1}{3}$ **min**

56. One plane flew 390 km with a tailwind in the same time that another plane flew 360 km against the wind. Find the rate of the wind if each plane can fly at 500 km/h in still air. **20 km/h**

57. The length of a rectangle is twice its width and 5 m less than the length of one of its diagonals. Find the length of the diagonal and the area of the rectangle.
$25 + 10\sqrt{5}$ **m,** $450 + 200\sqrt{5}$ **m²**

58. Without solving $5y^2 + 3y - 10 = 0$, find the sum and the product of its solutions.
sum: $-\frac{3}{5}$**, prod.:** **−2**

9 COORDINATE GEOMETRY

Careers: Computer Programming

If you are organized in your work, consider alternative ways to solve difficult problems, pay attention to details, look for shortcuts, and enjoy mathematics and problem solving, then you may want to consider a career in the field of computer programming.

The person who writes a computer program is called a **computer programmer.** In addition to the high school mathematics program, a computer programmer must also receive further education. This additional training may be taken at a college that offers courses in computer science or at a vocational school that specializes in computer programming.

9.1 The Coordinate Plane

OBJECTIVES ▶ **To graph an ordered pair of real numbers in a coordinate plane**
To give the coordinates of a point in a coordinate plane
To draw the graph of a linear equation in two variables

When a horizontal number line is perpendicular to a vertical number line, a **coordinate plane** is formed. The horizontal line is called the **x-axis** and the vertical line is called the **y-axis.** The two axes intersect in a point called the **origin** and they separate the plane into four sections called **quadrants.** The four quadrants are numbered in a counterclockwise direction, as shown in the figure.

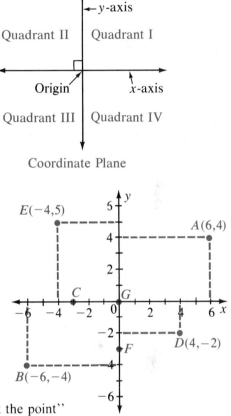

Coordinate Plane

Each point in a coordinate plane is assigned a unique **ordered pair** of real numbers, (x, y). The two numbers paired with a given point are called the **coordinates** of that point. In the second figure, the coordinates of point A are written as the ordered pair of numbers, $(6, 4)$. [The order is important; $(6, 4)$ and $(4, 6)$ are two different ordered pairs.] For each ordered pair of real numbers, there is a unique point in the coordinate plane. The point is called the **graph** of the ordered pair. Thus, the point A is the graph of $(6, 4)$.

You can "graph the ordered pair of numbers" $(6, 4)$ or "plot the point" A $(6, 4)$ in the following way. Starting at the origin, move to the right 6 units and then up 4 units. Place a dot in the coordinate plane to represent the graph. In general, the x-coordinate, or **abscissa,** indicates the direction and distance to move horizontally from the origin along the x-axis. The y-coordinate, or **ordinate,** indicates the direction and distance to move vertically, or parallel to the y-axis.

In the second figure, notice that the points C, F, and G are not located in a quadrant. Each point falls on one of the axes. Point C is the graph of $(-3, 0)$ and point F is the graph of $(0, -3)$. Point G is at the origin, so it is the graph of $(0, 0)$.

An equation of the form $ax + by = c$, where a, b, and c are real numbers with a and b both not equal to 0, is called a **linear equation in two variables** x and y. One solution of a linear equation in two variables is an ordered pair of real numbers that satisfies the equation. For example, $(0, 4)$ is a solution of $-2x + y = 4$ since $-2 \cdot 0 + 4 = 0 + 4 = 4$.

The graph of a given linear equation in two variables is the set of all the points whose coordinates (ordered pairs) satisfy the equation. As shown in the examples, the graph of any linear equation in two variables is a line.

Example 1 Draw the graph of $-2x + y = 4$.

First, solve the equation for y in terms of x.

$$-2x + y = 4$$
$$y = 2x + 4$$

Second, make a table by choosing values for x and finding corresponding values for y.

Third, plot the points and draw the graph.

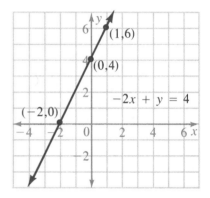

x	$2x + 4$	y	ordered pair
0	$2 \cdot 0 + 4$	4	$(0, 4)$
1	$2 \cdot 1 + 4$	6	$(1, 6)$
-2	$2 \cdot -2 + 4$	0	$(-2, 0)$

Example 2 Draw the graph of $3x + 2y = 5$.

$$3x + 2y = 5$$
$$2y = -3x + 5$$
$$y = -\frac{3}{2}x + \frac{5}{2}$$

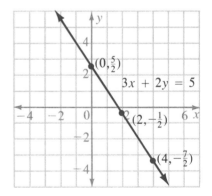

x	$-\dfrac{3}{2}x + \dfrac{5}{2}$	y	ordered pair
0	$-\dfrac{3}{2} \cdot 0 + \dfrac{5}{2}$	$\dfrac{5}{2}$	$\left(0, \dfrac{5}{2}\right)$
2	$-\dfrac{3}{2} \cdot 2 + \dfrac{5}{2}$	$-\dfrac{1}{2}$	$\left(2, -\dfrac{1}{2}\right)$
4	$-\dfrac{3}{2} \cdot 4 + \dfrac{5}{2}$	$-\dfrac{7}{2}$	$\left(4, -\dfrac{7}{2}\right)$

You could have used different values than those used for x in the tables. Although only two points are needed to determine the graph of a linear equation, it is wise to plot a third point as a check.

Reading In Algebra

Let $P(x, y)$ represent any point in a coordinate plane. Match each term at the left to exactly one description at the right.

1. Quadrant I **G**
2. Quadrant II **C**
3. Quadrant III **E**
4. Quadrant IV **A**
5. x-axis **F**
6. y-axis **B**
7. origin **D**

A $x > 0$ and $y < 0$
B $x = 0$ and y is a real number
C $x < 0$ and $y > 0$
D $(0, 0)$
E $x < 0$ and $y < 0$
F $y = 0$ and x is a real number
G $x > 0$ and $y > 0$

Written Exercises

On the same coordinate plane, graph each ordered pair. **Check student graphs.**

Ⓐ
1. $(-3, 2)$
2. $(4, -1)$
3. $(0, 1)$
4. $(-1, -3)$
5. $(4, 3)$
6. $(0, 0)$
7. $(-1, 4)$
8. $(5, 0)$
9. $(-3, 0)$
10. $(0, -5)$

Use the coordinate system at the right for Exercises 11–13.

11. Give the coordinates of each of the labeled points.

12. Which of the labeled points do not lie in a quadrant? **A and E**

13. In which quadrant does each of the other labeled points lie?
I: D; II: B, F; III: C, G; IV: H, I

Draw the graph of each equation. **Check student graphs. See TE Answer Section.**

14. $y = -3x - 1$
15. $y = -2x + 3$
16. $y = 3x + 2$
17. $y - 4x = -2$
18. $y = 4x + 3$
19. $y = 2x + 4$
20. $y = -2x - 3$
21. $x - y = 5$
22. $3x + 3y = 9$
23. $4x - 2y = 10$
24. $-4x - 2y = 10$
25. $10x - 5y = 15$
26. $x - y = 0$
27. $6x + 3y = 9$
28. $6x - 3y = 15$
29. $4x + 2y = 8$

Ⓑ
30. $2x - 4y = 12$
31. $3x + 2y = 12$
32. $-3x - y = 5$
33. $5x + 3y = 9$
34. $x - 2y + 5 = 0$
35. $-x + 2y - 3 = 0$
36. $-4x - 3y = 9$
37. $4x - 3y = 8$
38. $\frac{2}{3}x + \frac{1}{6}y = 4$
39. $-\frac{1}{5}x + \frac{3}{10}y = 2$
40. $\frac{1}{5}x + \frac{2}{3}y = -1$
41. $\frac{1}{3}x + 3y = 8$
42. $-1.2x + 3.6y = 2.4$
43. $0.2x + 0.3y = 1.2$
44. $0.12x - 0.02y = 0.06$

Ⓒ
45. $\sqrt{2}x + 3y = 9$
46. $x - \sqrt{3}y = 10$
47. $\sqrt{3}x + \sqrt{2}y = -2$

THE COORDINATE PLANE

9.2 Slope of a Line

OBJECTIVES ▶ **To find the length of a vertical or a horizontal segment, given the coordinates of its endpoints**
To find the slope of a line, given the coordinates of any two points on the line

If you are given the coordinates of the endpoints of a vertical or horizontal segment in a coordinate plane, you can find the *length* of the segment.

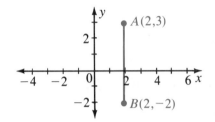

Notice that $\overline{AB}$ (read: segment AB) in the figure at the right is vertical and that the points A and B have the same x-coordinate. You can find AB (read: the length of $\overline{AB}$) by subtracting the y-coordinates of the two points A and B and then taking the absolute value of the difference.

$AB = |y\text{-coord. of } A - y\text{-coord. of } B| = |3 - (-2)| = 5$

It is necessary to use absolute value since a length cannot be negative.

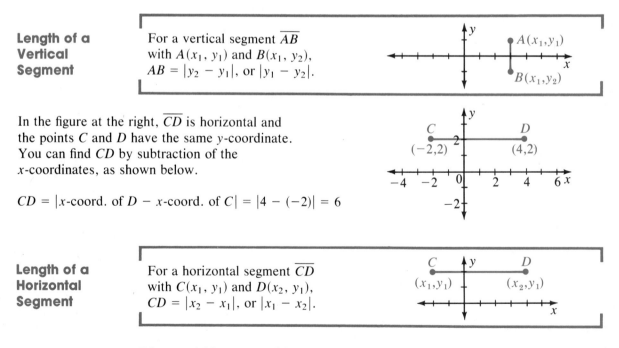

Length of a Vertical Segment

For a vertical segment $\overline{AB}$ with $A(x_1, y_1)$ and $B(x_1, y_2)$,
$AB = |y_2 - y_1|$, or $|y_1 - y_2|$.

In the figure at the right, $\overline{CD}$ is horizontal and the points C and D have the same y-coordinate. You can find CD by subtraction of the x-coordinates, as shown below.

$CD = |x\text{-coord. of } D - x\text{-coord. of } C| = |4 - (-2)| = 6$

Length of a Horizontal Segment

For a horizontal segment $\overline{CD}$ with $C(x_1, y_1)$ and $D(x_2, y_1)$,
$CD = |x_2 - x_1|$, or $|x_1 - x_2|$.

When variables are used for coordinates in this chapter, you should assume that the variables represent real numbers.

Example 1 Find the length of $\overline{BC}$ and $\overline{AC}$ in the figure.

Then find the ratio $\dfrac{BC}{AC}$.

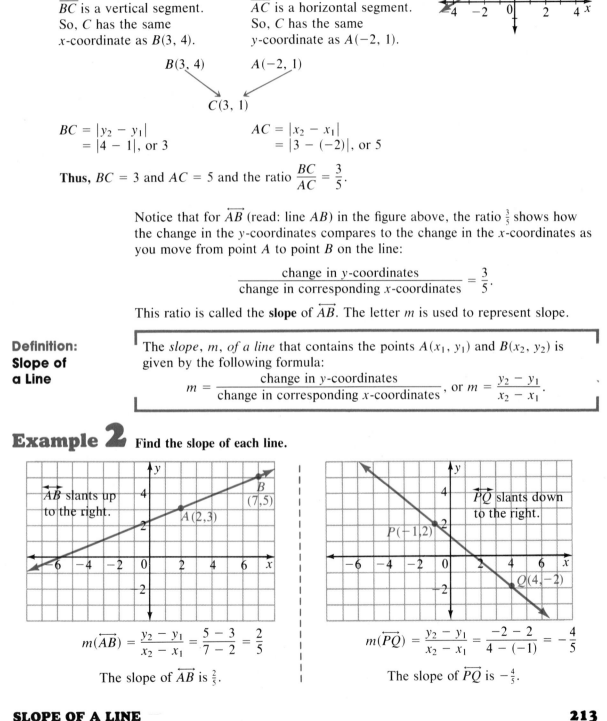

Find the coordinates of C.

$\overline{BC}$ is a vertical segment. So, C has the same x-coordinate as $B(3, 4)$.

$\overline{AC}$ is a horizontal segment. So, C has the same y-coordinate as $A(-2, 1)$.

$B(3, 4)$ $A(-2, 1)$

$C(3, 1)$

$BC = |y_2 - y_1|$
$\quad = |4 - 1|$, or 3

$AC = |x_2 - x_1|$
$\quad = |3 - (-2)|$, or 5

Thus, $BC = 3$ and $AC = 5$ and the ratio $\dfrac{BC}{AC} = \dfrac{3}{5}$.

Notice that for $\overrightarrow{AB}$ (read: line AB) in the figure above, the ratio $\frac{3}{5}$ shows how the change in the y-coordinates compares to the change in the x-coordinates as you move from point A to point B on the line:

$$\frac{\text{change in } y\text{-coordinates}}{\text{change in corresponding } x\text{-coordinates}} = \frac{3}{5}.$$

This ratio is called the **slope** of $\overrightarrow{AB}$. The letter m is used to represent slope.

**Definition:
Slope of
a Line**

The *slope, m, of a line* that contains the points $A(x_1, y_1)$ and $B(x_2, y_2)$ is given by the following formula:

$$m = \frac{\text{change in } y\text{-coordinates}}{\text{change in corresponding } x\text{-coordinates}}, \text{ or } m = \frac{y_2 - y_1}{x_2 - x_1}.$$

Example 2 Find the slope of each line.

$\overrightarrow{AB}$ slants up to the right.

$A(2, 3)$ $B(7, 5)$

$m(\overrightarrow{AB}) = \dfrac{y_2 - y_1}{x_2 - x_1} = \dfrac{5 - 3}{7 - 2} = \dfrac{2}{5}$

The slope of $\overrightarrow{AB}$ is $\frac{2}{5}$.

$\overrightarrow{PQ}$ slants down to the right.

$P(-1, 2)$ $Q(4, -2)$

$m(\overrightarrow{PQ}) = \dfrac{y_2 - y_1}{x_2 - x_1} = \dfrac{-2 - 2}{4 - (-1)} = -\dfrac{4}{5}$

The slope of $\overrightarrow{PQ}$ is $-\frac{4}{5}$.

The slope of a line is a measure of its "steepness." In Example 2, you have seen that if a line slants up to the right it has a positive slope and that if a line slants down to the right it has a negative slope. You will now see what happens when different pairs of points on the same line are used to compute its slope.

Example 3

Find the slope of the line in the figure, using points A and B, B and C, C and D.

$$m = \frac{y_2 - y_1}{x_2 - x_1}$$

$$m(\overrightarrow{AB}) = \frac{0 - (-1)}{-3 - (-6)} = \frac{1}{3}$$

$$m(\overrightarrow{BC}) = \frac{2 - 0}{3 - (-3)} = \frac{2}{6}, \text{ or } \frac{1}{3}$$

$$m(\overrightarrow{CD}) = \frac{3 - 2}{6 - 3} = \frac{1}{3}$$

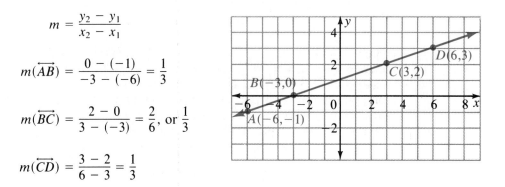

Thus, the slope of the line is $\frac{1}{3}$ using all three pairs of points.

Example 3 shows you that the slope of a given line is uniform. That is, for any two points on the line, the slope is the same.

Example 4

Find the slope of each line.

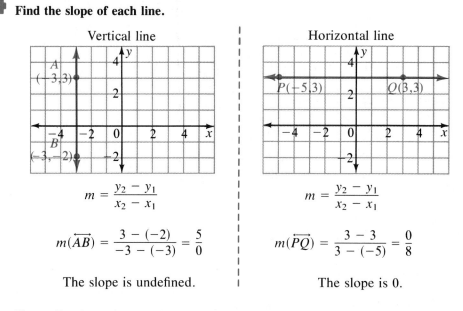

| Vertical line | Horizontal line |

$$m = \frac{y_2 - y_1}{x_2 - x_1}$$

$$m(\overrightarrow{AB}) = \frac{3 - (-2)}{-3 - (-3)} = \frac{5}{0}$$

The slope is undefined.

$$m = \frac{y_2 - y_1}{x_2 - x_1}$$

$$m(\overrightarrow{PQ}) = \frac{3 - 3}{3 - (-5)} = \frac{0}{8}$$

The slope is 0.

Since all points of a vertical line have the same x-coordinates, the slope of any vertical line is *undefined*. Similarly, since all points of a horizontal line have the same y-coordinates, the slope of any horizontal line is *0*.

Reading In Algebra

Match each sentence to exactly one of the statements at the right.
1. Points A, B, C, and D are on the same line. **C**
2. The coordinates of P and Q are $P(3, 1)$ and $Q(5, 1)$. **E**
3. The length of segment PQ is 2. **D**
4. The slope of line PQ is 2. **A**
5. A line is vertical. **H**
6. The coordinates of four points are $A(1, 5)$, $B(6, 5)$, $C(1, 1)$ and $D(4, 1)$. **B**
7. A line slants up to the right. **G**
8. A line slants down to the right. **F**

A $m(\overrightarrow{PQ}) = 2$
B $m(\overrightarrow{AB}) = m(\overrightarrow{CD})$
C $m(\overrightarrow{AB}) = m(\overrightarrow{BC}) = m(\overrightarrow{CD})$
D $PQ = 2$
E $m = 0$
F $m < 0$
G $m > 0$
H m is undefined

Written Exercises

1. 5   2. 3   3. 5   4. 2   5. 4   6. 2   7. 10   8. 12

Find the length of $\overline{AB}$ for the given coordinates.
Ⓐ 1. $A(3, 2)$, $B(3, -3)$ 2. $A(1, -4)$, $B(-2, -4)$ 3. $A(2, 3)$, $B(-3, 3)$ 4. $A(-2, 1)$, $B(-2, 3)$
5. $A(2, -4)$, $B(-2, -4)$ 6. $A(5, -1)$, $B(5, 1)$ 7. $A(-2, 5)$, $B(-2, -5)$ 8. $A(6, -4)$, $B(-6, -4)$

UR = up to the right, DR = down to the right, H = horizontal, V = vertical, UN = undefined

Find the slope of $\overrightarrow{AB}$ for the given coordinates. Tell whether the line slants up to the right, slants down to the right, is horizontal, or is vertical.
9. $A(-6, 1)$, $B(4, 4)$ $\frac{3}{10}$, **UR**   10. $A(-1, -4)$, $B(-3, 2)$ -3, **DR** 11. $A(-2, 9)$, $B(1, -3)$ -4, **DR**
12. $A(3, 8)$, $B(-3, 8)$ 0, **H**   13. $A(2, -3)$, $B(2, 3)$ **UN, V**   14. $A(6, 5)$, $B(-4, -5)$ 1, **UR**
15. $A(7, 8)$, $B(1, 11)$ $-\frac{1}{2}$, **DR**   16. $A(-4, -1)$, $B(-2, 4)$ $\frac{5}{2}$, **UR** 17. $A(-4, -7)$, $B(3, -7)$ 0, **H**
18. $A(-3, -1)$, $B(-6, -4)$ 1, **UR** 19. $A(-9, -7)$, $B(10, 8)$ $\frac{15}{19}$, **UR** 20. $A(6, 2)$, $B(-1, -4)$ $\frac{6}{7}$, **UR**
21. $A(-4, -2)$, $B(-1, 7)$ 3, **UR**   22. $A(4, -2)$, $B(8, -6)$ -1, **DR**   23. $A(-3, -5,)$, $B(-5, -5)$ 0, **H**
24. $A(6, 0)$, $B(0, -8)$ $\frac{4}{3}$, **UR**

Show that $m(\overrightarrow{AB}) = m(\overrightarrow{BC}) = m(\overrightarrow{AC})$ for the given coordinates.
25. $A(-2, -4)$, $B(0, 0)$, $C(4, 8)$ $m = 2$ 26. $A(-6, -4)$, $B(-4, -3)$, $C(-2, -2)$ $m = \frac{1}{2}$
27. $A(3, 6)$, $B(0, 4)$, $C(-3, 2)$ $m = \frac{2}{3}$ 28. $A(5, -1)$, $B(0, -1)$, $C(-6, -1)$ $m = 0$

Find the slope of $\overrightarrow{PQ}$ for the given coordinates.
Ⓑ 29. $P(-2, -3)$, $Q(-\frac{1}{2}, -\frac{1}{3})$ $\frac{16}{9}$ 30. $P(-\frac{1}{3}, \frac{1}{2})$, $Q(\frac{5}{6}, 4)$ 3 31. $P(\frac{1}{5}, \frac{1}{4})$, $Q(\frac{3}{5}, \frac{3}{4})$ $\frac{5}{4}$
32. $P(-\frac{1}{6}, \frac{1}{4})$, $Q(\frac{1}{2}, \frac{1}{2})$ $\frac{3}{8}$ 33. $P(\frac{2}{3}, \frac{3}{4})$, $Q(\frac{1}{6}, -\frac{1}{2})$ $\frac{5}{2}$ 34. $P(\frac{2}{5}, -\frac{1}{3})$, $Q(-\frac{1}{3}, \frac{1}{3})$ $-\frac{10}{11}$
35. $P(a, -b)$, $Q(-a, b)$ $-\frac{b}{a}$ 36. $P(4x, 5y)$, $Q(-2x, -7y)$ $\frac{2y}{x}$
37. $P(6a, -2b)$, $Q(7a, 5b)$ $\frac{7b}{a}$ 38. $P(-10a, 12b)$, $Q(-2a, -7b)$ $-\frac{19b}{8a}$
Ⓒ 39. $P(x_1, y_1)$, $Q(x_1 + t, y_1 + s)$ $\frac{s}{t}$ 40. $P(2m - 5n, t + v)$, $Q(-n, 3v - t)$ $\frac{v - t}{2n - m}$

Find the missing coordinate for the given data.
41. $A(4, y)$, $B(5, 0)$, $m(\overrightarrow{AB}) = -2$ 2 42. $M(-3, 2)$, $N(x, -4)$, $m(\overrightarrow{MN}) = -\frac{1}{2}$ 9
43. $P(-\frac{1}{3}, -\frac{1}{2})$, $Q(\frac{4}{3}, y)$, $m(\overrightarrow{PQ}) = \frac{1}{5}$ $-\frac{1}{6}$ 44. $F(x, -\frac{1}{5})$, $G(\frac{2}{5}, -\frac{4}{5})$, $m(\overrightarrow{FG}) = -\frac{3}{4}$ $-\frac{2}{5}$

Cumulative Review

Solve each equation.
1. $3x - 2(1 - x) = 13$ 3 2. $\dfrac{x - 5}{2} = \dfrac{x - 3}{5}$ $\frac{19}{3}$ 3. $\dfrac{3}{x^2 - 7x + 12} - \dfrac{x}{x - 3} = \dfrac{2x - 1}{x - 4}$ $0, \frac{11}{3}$

SLOPE OF A LINE

9.3 Equation of a Line

OBJECTIVES ▶ To write an equation of a line, given its slope and the coordinates of a point on the line
To write an equation of a line, given its slope and *y*-intercept
To find the slope and the *y*-intercept of a line, given an equation of the line
To write an equation of a line, given the coordinates of two points on the line

The line in the figure passes through the points $P(x_1, y_1)$ and $Q(x_2, y_2)$. Let $R(x, y)$ be any other point on $\overrightarrow{PQ}$. You can find an equation of this line by applying the definition of slope. Consider the points P and R.

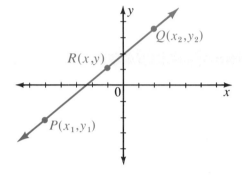

$$P(x_1, y_1) \qquad R(x, y) \qquad m = \frac{y_2 - y_1}{x_2 - x_1}$$
$$\quad \uparrow \ \uparrow \qquad \qquad \uparrow \ \uparrow \qquad m = \frac{y - y_1}{x - x_1}$$
$$\quad x_1 \ y_1 \qquad \quad x_2 \ y_2$$
$$y - y_1 = m(x - x_1)$$

Point-slope Form of an Equation of a Line

$y - y_1 = m(x - x_1)$ is an equation of a nonvertical line whose slope is a real number, m, and passes through the point $P(x_1, y_1)$.

The point-slope form enables you to write an equation of a nonvertical line when its slope and the coordinates of one point of the line are known. The process is shown in Example 1.

Example 1 Write an equation of the line that passes through the point $P(3, -4)$ and whose slope is $-\frac{2}{3}$.

$$y - y_1 = m(x - x_1) \qquad \blacktriangleleft \textit{Use the point-slope form.}$$
$$y - (-4) = -\frac{2}{3}(x - 3)$$
$$y + 4 = -\frac{2}{3}(x - 3)$$
$$3y + 12 = -2x + 6 \qquad \blacktriangleleft \textit{Multiply each side by 3.}$$
$$2x + 3y = -6$$

Thus, an equation of the line is $2x + 3y = -6$.

An equation of a line is a *linear equation in two variables*. The **standard form** is $ax + by = c$, where a, b, and c are integers, and a and b both not equal to 0. Notice that the equation in Example 1 is written in this standard form.

The **y-intercept** of a line is the y-coordinate of the point where the line intersects the y-axis. Generally, the letter b is used to represent the y-intercept of a line.

In the figure at the right, the point $P(0, b)$ is the point where the given line intersects the y-axis, with b the y-intercept. Let $R(x, y)$ be any other point on the line. You can find an equation of the line by using the point-slope form of an equation.

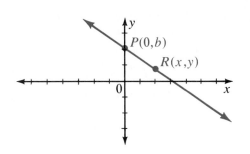

$$
\begin{array}{cc}
P(0, b) & R(x, y) \\
\uparrow \ \uparrow & \uparrow \ \uparrow \\
x_1 \ y_1 & x \ \ y
\end{array}
\qquad
\begin{aligned}
y - y_1 &= m(x - x_1) \\
y - b &= m(x - 0) \\
y - b &= mx \\
y &= mx + b
\end{aligned}
$$

Slope-intercept Form of an Equation of a Line

$y = mx + b$ is an equation of a nonvertical line whose slope is a real number, m, and whose y-intercept is b.

Example 2 Write an equation, in standard form, of the line whose slope is $-\dfrac{5}{2}$ and whose y-intercept is -3.

$$
\begin{aligned}
y &= mx + b & &\blacktriangleleft \text{ Use the slope-intercept form.} \\
y &= -\frac{5}{2}x + (-3) & &\blacktriangleleft \ m = -\frac{5}{2},\ b = -3 \\
2y &= -5x - 6 & &\blacktriangleleft \text{ Multiply each side by 2.} \\
5x + 2y &= -6
\end{aligned}
$$

Thus, an equation of the line is $5x + 2y = -6$.

Given an equation of a line, you can find the slope and the y-intercept of the line.

Example 3 Find the slope and the y-intercept of the line whose equation is $3x + 2y = 9$.

Rewrite the equation in the form $y = mx + b$.

$$
\begin{aligned}
3x + 2y &= 9 \\
2y &= -3x + 9 \\
y &= -\frac{3}{2}x + \frac{9}{2} & &\blacktriangleleft \text{ Divide each side by 2.}
\end{aligned}
$$

Thus, the slope is $-\dfrac{3}{2}$ and the y-intercept is $\dfrac{9}{2}$.

Example 4 on page 218 shows you how to find an equation of a line when the coordinates of two points of the line are known.

EQUATION OF A LINE

Example 4 Write an equation, in standard form, of the line that passes through the points $P(-3, 1)$ and $Q(5, -4)$.

Find the slope of $\overleftrightarrow{PQ}$. ▶ $m = \dfrac{y_2 - y_1}{x_2 - x_1} = \dfrac{-4 - 1}{5 - (-3)} = -\dfrac{5}{8}$

Use the point-slope form. ▶ $y - y_1 = m(x - x_1)$

$$y - 1 = -\frac{5}{8}[x - (-3)]$$

$$y - 1 = -\frac{5}{8}(x + 3)$$

$$8y - 8 = -5x - 15$$

$$5x + 8y = -7$$

Thus, an equation of the line is $5x + 8y = -7$.

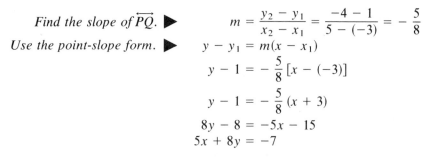

In the figure at the right, $\overleftrightarrow{AB}$ is a horizontal line and $\overleftrightarrow{PQ}$ is a vertical line. You can write an equation of $\overleftrightarrow{AB}$ and an equation of $\overleftrightarrow{PQ}$ as shown below. Recall that the slope of a horizontal line is 0 and the slope of a vertical line is undefined.

The y-intercept of $(\overleftrightarrow{AB})$ is 4 and $m(\overleftrightarrow{AB})$ is 0.

$$y = mx + b$$
$$y = 0 \cdot x + 4$$
$$y = 4$$

For each point C on $\overleftrightarrow{AB}$, the y-coordinate is 4 and the x-coordinate is a real number. Therefore, $y = 4$ is an equation of $\overleftrightarrow{AB}$.

$\overleftrightarrow{PQ}$ does not intersect the y-axis, so there is no y-intercept; $m(\overleftrightarrow{PQ})$ is undefined. Let $R(x, y)$ be any point on $\overleftrightarrow{PQ}$. Then $m(\overleftrightarrow{PQ}) = m(\overleftrightarrow{PR}) = \dfrac{y - 3}{x - 2}$, which is undefined only for $x = 2$. For each point R on $\overleftrightarrow{PQ}$, the x-coordinate is 2 and the y-coordinate is a real number. Therefore, $x = 2$ is an equation of $\overleftrightarrow{PQ}$.

Example 5 For the given data, write an equation of each line.

Data	Equation
Line passes through $A(7, 3)$ and $B(7, -2)$	$x = 7$
Line passes through $C(-5, -4)$ and $D(6, -4)$	$y = -4$
Line passes through $T(-10, 8)$ and m is undefined	$x = -10$
Line with $m = 0$ and $b = 6$	$y = 6$

The linear equations $y = c$ and $x = c$, where c is a constant, represent the *standard form* of the equation of a horizontal line and a vertical line, respectively.

Reading In Algebra

A description of each of five lines is given at the left. Match each description to the *one best* form to use to find an equation of each line.

1. $P(-1, -5)$ is on the line and its slope is $-\frac{3}{5}$. **D**
2. The line is vertical and $P(-2, 3)$ is on the line. **B**
3. The y-intercept of the line is -4 and its slope is 3. **A**
4. The line is horizontal and $P(-2, 3)$ is on the line. **C**
5. $P(-3, 5)$ and $Q(2, -1)$ are on the line. **D**

A $y = mx + b$
B $x = c$
C $y = c$
D $y - y_1 = m(x - x_1)$

Written Exercises

A line has the given slope, y-intercept, or contains the indicated point(s). Write an equation, in standard form, of each line. 4. $x + y = -5$ 14. $3x - 5y = 15$ 18. $9x - 2y = -19$

Ⓐ
1. $P(2, -5)$, $m = \frac{2}{3}$ $2x - 3y = 19$ 2. $Q(2, -2)$, $m = -\frac{1}{2}$ $x + 2y = -2$ 3. $R(-1, 6)$, $m = \frac{5}{6}$ $5x - 6y = -41$
4. $A(-2, -3)$, $m = -1$ **above** 5. $M(-2, 4)$, $m = -4$ $4x + y = -4$ 6. $R(3, -2)$, $m = -3$ $3x + y = 7$
7. $m = -\frac{4}{3}$, $b = 2$ $4x + 3y = 6$ 8. $m = \frac{3}{5}$, $b = -10$ $3x - 5y = 50$ 9. $m = -\frac{5}{8}$, $b = -\frac{3}{8}$ $5x + 8y = -3$
10. $m = 2$, $b = 3$ $2x - y = -3$ 11. $m = -4$, $b = -4$ $4x + y = -4$ 12. $m = -3$, $b = \frac{7}{3}$ $9x + 3y = 7$
13. $A(-1, 3)$, $B(0, 4)$ $x - y = -4$ 14. $A(0, -3)$, $B(-5, -6)$ **above** 15. $A(2, -3)$, $B(0, 4)$ $7x + 2y = 8$
16. $M(-1, 6)$, $N(-4, 2)$ **below** 17. $M(7, 3)$, $N(-3, 6)$ **below** 18. $M(-1, 5)$, $N(-3, -4)$ **above**
19. $P(7, 5)$, $Q(-3, 5)$ $y = 5$ 20. $P(5, -4)$, $Q(-2, -4)$ $y = -4$ 21. $P(8, 4)$, $Q(8, 9)$ $x = 8$
22. $A(0, 7)$, $B(4, 0)$ $7x + 4y = 28$ 23. $M(-5, 0)$, $N(0, 9)$ **below** 24. $R(0, -6)$, $Q(10, 0)$ $3x - 5y = 30$
25. $R(8, 12)$, $m = 0$ $y = 12$ 26. $S(-6, -4)$, m is undefined 27. $T(7, -3)$, line is horizontal
16. $4x - 3y = -22$ 23. $9x - 5y = -45$ $x = -6$ $3x + 10y = 51$ $y = -3$

Find the slope and the y-intercept of the line described by the given equation.

28. $2x + 3y = 9$ $-\frac{2}{3}, 3$ 29. $3x - 5y = 10$ $\frac{3}{5}, -2$ 30. $7x + 3y = -21$ $-\frac{7}{3}, -7$
31. $5x - 3y - 15 = 0$ $\frac{5}{3}, -5$ 32. $5y - x + 20 = 0$ $\frac{1}{5}, -4$ 33. $3x + 4y - 40 = 0$ $-\frac{3}{4}, 10$
34. $7x - 3(4 - y) = 0$ $-\frac{7}{3}, 4$ 35. $15 - 4(-2x - 3y) = 39$ $-\frac{2}{3}, 2$ 36. $3y - (18 + 6x) = 0$ $2, 6$
$-8, -15$ $\frac{3}{2}, -2$ $0, 2$

Ⓑ
37. $y - (4x + 5) = -4(3x + 5)$ 38. $3x + 5(x - y) - (y - x) = 12$ 39. $2(x + 3y) - (2x - y) = 14$
40. $-2(3y + 4x) - 5(2x - 3y) = 15$ $2, \frac{15}{9}$ 41. $7y + 5(-3y - 4x) = -(7 - 3x) + 2y$ $-\frac{23}{10}, \frac{7}{10}$
42. $\frac{4}{5}(10y - 20x) - \frac{2}{3}(6x - 15y) = 0$ $\frac{10}{9}, 0$ 43. $-\frac{1}{2}(6x - 8y) + \frac{4}{5}(10x + 15y) = 6$ $-y$ $-\frac{5}{17}, \frac{6}{17}$

Ⓒ
44. $4x - 5[2(6x - 3) - 4(6y - 3)] = 6$ $\frac{7}{15}, \frac{3}{10}$ 45. $-8 - 3[-(4 - 3y) - 2(5x + 2y)] = x - y$
46. $0.3x - 4.3[-(x - 2) - 2.1(4 - y)] = 1.8$ 47. $1.6y - 3.1[(y + 5) - 1.6(4 - x)] = 7.3$ $-\frac{248}{75}, -\frac{148}{75}$
46. $\frac{460}{903}, \frac{2,572}{903}$ 45. $-\frac{29}{4}, -1$

Write an equation, in standard form, of each line.

48. The line having an x-intercept of -2 and a y-intercept of 3 $3x - 2y = -6$

49. The line having an x-intercept of 4 and a y-intercept of -4 $x - y = 4$

50. The line having an x-intercept of $\frac{1}{A}$ and a y-intercept of $\frac{1}{B}$ $Ax + By = 1$

51. The line having an x-intercept of $\frac{C}{A}$ and a y-intercept of $\frac{C}{B}$ $Ax + By = C$

52. If $P(a, 0)$ and $Q(0, b)$ are the x- and y-intercepts, respectively, of $\overleftrightarrow{PQ}$ $(a \neq 0, b \neq 0)$, prove that $\frac{x}{a} + \frac{y}{b} = 1$ is an equation of $\overleftrightarrow{PQ}$.

For Ex. 52, see TE Answer Section.

EQUATION OF A LINE

9.4 Slope-Intercept Method of Drawing Graphs

OBJECTIVES ▶ **To draw the graph of a linear equation in two variables, using the slope-intercept method**
To determine whether a point is on a line, given the coordinates of the point and an equation of the line

To draw the graph of $y = \frac{3}{5}x + 1$ using its slope and y-intercept, proceed as follows:

First, determine the slope and the y-intercept of the line.

$$y = \frac{3}{5}x + 1$$
$$\uparrow \qquad \uparrow$$
$$m \qquad b$$

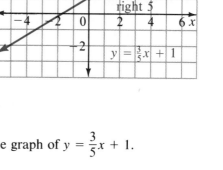

Then, plot the point whose y-intercept is 1. From this point, move to the right 5 units and up 3 units to locate a second point.

Draw the line that contains the two points. The line is the graph of $y = \frac{3}{5}x + 1$.

Example 1 Draw the graph of $2x + 3y = -9$.

Solve for y in terms of x.
$$2x + 3y = -9$$
$$3y = -2x - 9$$
$$y = -\frac{2}{3}x - 3$$

$m = \frac{-2}{3}$ or $\frac{2}{-3}$, and $b = -3$.

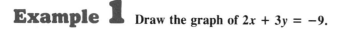

Plot the point whose y-intercept is -3. From this point, move to the right 3 units and down 2 units *or* move to the left 3 units and up 2 units.

Recall that $m = \frac{y_2 - y_1}{x_2 - x_1}$. Thus, whenever the slope, m, is written as a fraction, the denominator indicates the change in the x-coordinates (distance and direction to move horizontally), and the numerator indicates the change in the y-coordinates (distance and direction to move vertically) as you move from one point to another point. Even though two points determine a line, when drawing graphs it is wise to locate a third point as a check.

Example 2 — Draw the graph of $y = 4$ and the graph of $x = -3$.

$y = c$, where c is a constant, determines a horizontal line.

$x = c$, where c is a constant, determines a vertical line.

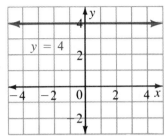
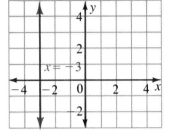

Given the coordinates of a point and an equation of a line, you can determine whether the point is on the line. The process involves substituting the x- and y- coordinate values of the point into the equation and checking to see if a true equation results.

Example 3 — Determine whether each point having the given coordinates is on the line described by the given equation.

$P(-4, 7)$, $5x + 3y - 1 = 0$　|　$Q(8, -2)$, $4y - x = 34$

Substitute -4 for x and 7 for y.

$$\begin{array}{c|c} 5x + 3y - 1 & 0 \\ \hline 5(-4) + 3(7) - 1 & 0 \\ -20 + 21 - 1 & \\ 0 & \end{array}$$

Thus, $(-4, 7)$ satisfies the equation and so P is a point on the line.

$$\begin{array}{c|c} 4y - x & 34 \\ \hline 4(-2) - (8) & 34 \\ -8 - 8 & \\ -16 & \end{array}$$

Substitute 8 for x and -2 for y.

Thus, $(8, -2)$ does not satisfy the equation and so Q is not a point on the line.

Point on a Line

Each point $P(x, y)$ whose coordinates satisfy an equation of a given line is a point on the line.
Each point $P(x, y)$ on a given line has coordinates that satisfy an equation of the line.

Oral Exercises

Match each equation to exactly one group of ordered pairs.

1. $3x - 8y = 24$ **B**
2. $6x + 4y = -24$ **C**
3. $x - 24y = 24$ **A**
4. $12x + 2y = -24$ **D**

A $(0, -1)$	B $(8, 0)$	C $(-2, -3)$	D $(-1, -6)$
$(24, 0)$	$(-8, -6)$	$(0, -6)$	$(-2, 0)$
$(-24, -2)$	$(0, -3)$	$(-4, 0)$	$(0, -12)$

Tell whether each equation describes a horizontal line, a vertical line, or neither.

    5. $y = 5$ H   **6.** $x = -4$ V   **7.** $2y = 7$ H   **8.** $y = 0$ H   **9.** $-x = -6$ V **10.** $y = 7 + x$ N

Written Exercises _____

Draw the graph of each equation. **Check student's graphs. See TE Answer Section.**

Ⓐ **1.** $y = \frac{2}{3}x + 3$ **2.** $y = -\frac{2}{3}x - 2$ **3.** $y = \frac{1}{3}x + 1$ **4.** $y = -\frac{1}{2}x + 4$

    5. $y = -2x - 1$ **6.** $y = -2x + 1$ **7.** $y = -3x - 2$ **8.** $y = 5x + 3$

    9. $y = -2x + 4$ **10.** $y = -3x - 1$ **11.** $y = 4x - 3$ **12.** $y = -x + 5$

    13. $3x + 2y = 4$ **14.** $x - 3y - 9 = 0$ **15.** $3y = 15$ **16.** $3x - 4y = 12$

    17. $x + y - 4 = 0$ **18.** $x = 4$ **19.** $5x + 20 = 0$ **20.** $2x + 5y + 15 = 0$

Determine whether a point having the given coordinates is on the line described by the given equation.

    21. $(1, 2)$, $3x + 2y = 7$ yes   **22.** $(2, 3)$, $x - 3y = -7$ yes   **23.** $(-3, -2)$, $3x - 2y = -6$ no

    24. $(-2, 1)$, $2x - y = -5$ yes   **25.** $(-1, -2)$, $-2x + y + 4 = 0$, **26.** $(-2, 1)$, $-2x + y - 5 = 0$ yes
                                                        no

Ⓑ **27.** $(2, 3)$, $\frac{2}{3}y - \frac{1}{2}x = 1$ yes   **28.** $(-6, -4)$, $-\frac{1}{3}x + \frac{3}{4}y = -1$ **29.** $(-2, 2)$, $\frac{3}{4}x - \frac{3}{4}y = -3$ yes

    30. $(-5, -6)$, $\frac{3}{5}x + \frac{1}{3}y = 5$ no   **31.** $(8, 4)$, $\frac{3}{4}y - \frac{7}{8}x = -4$ yes   **32.** $(10, -6)$, $\frac{2}{5}x + \frac{5}{3}y = 6$ no

                                   28. yes

Draw the graph of each equation. **For Ex 33–38, see TE Answer Section.**

    33. $2(x - 3) - 4(3 - 2y) = 8$ **34.** $6x - 2(5 - 3y) = 12$ **35.** $-4x - 3(2y - 1) = 6$

    36. $2y - (5 - 2x) = -2x - 3y$ **37.** $-4(3 - 2x) - (8 - 2y) = x - y$ **38.** $-(x - 3y) - 2(x + y) = -10$

Find the coordinates of a point on the line that satisfies the given conditions. Do not draw a graph.

Ⓒ **39.** An equation of the line is $x + 4y = 18$ and the ordinate of the point is twice the abscissa of the point. **(2, 4)**

    40. An equation of the line is $3x - 2y = 12$ and the ordinate of the point is one-half the abscissa of the point. **(6, 3)**

Find each equation that satisfies the given description. Draw the graph of each equation.

    41. A set of points equidistant from both axes
        x − y = 0 or x + y = 0

    42. The set of all points whose ordinate is two more than three times its abscissa
        −3x + y = 2

➤ A Challenge To You ═══════════

What number does the sequence of numbers below seem to approach?

$$\left(1 - \frac{1}{2^2}\right), \left(1 - \frac{1}{3^2}\right), \left(1 - \frac{1}{4^2}\right), \left(1 - \frac{1}{5^2}\right), \ldots \text{ 1}$$

9.5 The Distance Between Two Points

OBJECTIVES ▶ To find the length of each side of a right triangle in a coordinate plane
To find the distance between any two points in a coordinate plane
To determine if a triangle with given lengths for its sides is a right triangle

Recall that the square of the length of the hypotenuse of a right triangle is equal to the sum of the squares of the lengths of the two legs: That is, for right triangle ABC with right angle C, $c^2 = a^2 + b^2$, where c is the length of the hypotenuse and a and b are the lengths of the legs. This relationship, known as the *Pythagorean relation*, is illustrated below.

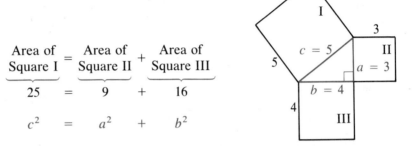

$$\underbrace{\text{Area of Square I}}_{25} = \underbrace{\text{Area of Square II}}_{9} + \underbrace{\text{Area of Square III}}_{16}$$

$$c^2 = a^2 + b^2$$

The Pythagorean relation can be used to find the length of the hypotenuse of a right triangle where the coordinates of the vertices of the triangle are given.

Example 1 The vertices of right triangle PRS are $P(-1, 2)$, $R(6, 5)$, and $S(6, 2)$. Find the length of $\overline{PR}$.

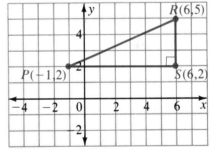

Let $c = PR$, $a = RS$, and $b = PS$.

$$c^2 = a^2 + b^2$$
$$(PR)^2 = (RS)^2 + (PS)^2$$

$\overline{RS}$ is vertical. ▶
$\overline{PS}$ is horizontal.

$$= |5 - 2|^2 + |6 - (-1)|^2$$
$$= 3^2 + 7^2$$
$$= 9 + 49$$
$$(PR)^2 = 58$$
$$PR = \pm\sqrt{58} \quad ◀ \text{ A length cannot be negative.}$$

Thus, the length of PR is $\sqrt{58}$.

In Example 1, notice that for $P(x_1, y_1)$, $R(x_2, y_2)$, and $S(x_2, y_1)$, $(PS)^2 = (x_2 - x_1)^2$ and $(RS)^2 = (y_2 - y_1)^2$. Therefore, $(PR)^2 = (x_2 - x_1)^2 + (y_2 - y_1)^2$, or $PR = \sqrt{(x_2 - x_1)^2 + (y_2 - y_1)^2}$. On page 224, it is shown that this relationship remains true for any two points in a coordinate plane.

In the figure at the right, points $A(x_1, y_1)$ and $B(x_2, y_2)$ determine $\overline{AB}$. A horizontal ray from A and a vertical ray from B intersect at a point C. Then, C has the same x-coordinate as B and the same y-coordinate as A. Since ABC is a right triangle,

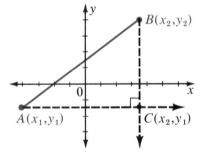

$(AB)^2 = (AC)^2 + (BC)^2$ by the Pythagorean relation.

$\quad = |x_2 - x_1|^2 + |y_2 - y_1|^2$ by the definition of length of a horizontal and a vertical segment.

$\quad = (x_2 - x_1)^2 + (y_2 - y_1)^2$ since $|a - b|^2 = (a - b)^2$.

So, $AB = \sqrt{(x_2 - x_1)^2 + (y_2 - y_1)^2}$ by the definition of square root.

Distance Formula

> The distance d between any two points $A(x_1, y_1)$ and $B(x_2, y_2)$ in a coordinate plane is given by the formula
> $$d = \sqrt{(x_2 - x_1)^2 + (y_2 - y_1)^2}.$$

Notice that the distance between any two points A and B is the length of the segment connecting the two points. The symbol d or AB may be used to indicate this distance.

Example 2 Find the distance between $A(2, -4)$ and $B(4, 6)$.

Let $A(2, -4) = A(x_1, y_1)$ and $B(4, 6) = B(x_2, y_2)$.
$$d = \sqrt{(x_2 - x_1)^2 + (y_2 - y_1)^2}$$
$$= \sqrt{(4 - 2)^2 + [6 - (-4)]^2}$$
$$= \sqrt{4 + 100} = \sqrt{104}, \text{ or } 2\sqrt{26}$$

Thus, the distance between A and B is $2\sqrt{26}$.

The converse of the Pythagorean relation is also true. If $c^2 = a^2 + b^2$ where a, b, and c are the lengths of the sides of a triangle, then the triangle is a right triangle.

Example 3 A triangle has sides of lengths 5, $\sqrt{7}$, and $4\sqrt{2}$. Is the triangle a right triangle?

The hypotenuse is the longest side, so $c = 4\sqrt{2}$. ▶

c^2	$a^2 + b^2$
$(4\sqrt{2})^2$	$(5)^2 + (\sqrt{7})^2$
$16 \cdot 2$	$25 + 7$
32	32

Thus, since $c^2 = a^2 + b^2$, the triangle is a right triangle.

Written Exercises

1. $AB = \sqrt{82}$, $BC = 1$, $AC = 9$ 2. $AB = 2\sqrt{26}$, $BC = 10$, $AC = 2$ 3. $AB = \sqrt{85}$, $BC = 7$, $AC = 6$

Find the length of each side of right triangle ABC with the given coordinates for its vertices. C is the vertex of the right angle.

(A)
1. $A(-3, 4)$, $B(6, 5)$, $C(6, 4)$
2. $A(2, -4)$, $B(4, 6)$, $C(4, -4)$
3. $A(4, 1)$, $B(10, 8)$, $C(10, 1)$
4. $A(-5, -1)$, $B(-2, 5)$, $C(-2, -1)$
5. $A(-6, -4)$, $B(-2, -1)$, $C(-2, -4)$
6. $A(8, 10)$, $B(10, 15)$, $C(10, 10)$

4. $AB = 3\sqrt{5}$, $BC = 6$, $AC = 3$ 5. $AB = 5$, $BC = 3$, $AC = 4$ 6. $AB = \sqrt{29}$, $BC = 5$, $AC = 2$

Find the distance between the given points. Give each answer in simplest radical form.

7. $A(2, 4)$, $B(6, 6)$
8. $R(-2, -3)$, $S(-7, 5)$
9. $P(-2, 4)$, $Q(7, 8)$
10. $M(7, 8)$, $N(-2, -4)$
11. $A(6, -2)$, $B(-3, 4)$
12. $A(5, 1)$, $B(-2, 4)$
13. $M(8, 4)$, $N(-2, -3)$
14. $A(0, 3)$, $B(4, 0)$
15. $M(0, -4)$, $N(5, 0)$
16. $M(9, 1)$, $N(-2, -1)$
17. $A(5, 1)$, $B(7, -3)$
18. $P(10, 2)$, $Q(-1, -3)$
19. $R(-5, -4)$, $S(-2, -3)$
20. $P(-1, 4)$, $Q(5, -3)$
21. $R(-2, -2)$, $S(-4, -4)$
22. $R(-10, 12)$, $S(2, -5)$

7. $2\sqrt{5}$ 8. $\sqrt{89}$ 9. $\sqrt{97}$

(B)
23. $P(1, -3)$, $Q(\frac{2}{3}, -\frac{1}{2})$
24. $A(\frac{1}{2}, \frac{1}{4})$, $B(-3, 2)$
25. $A(1, 2)$, $B(\frac{1}{6}, -\frac{1}{3})$
26. $A(\frac{1}{3}, \frac{1}{4})$, $B(-\frac{2}{3}, \frac{3}{4})$
27. $P(\frac{1}{5}, -\frac{1}{4})$, $Q(\frac{3}{5}, \frac{1}{2})$
28. $A(\frac{2}{3}, \frac{1}{3})$, $B(\frac{1}{3}, \frac{2}{3})$
29. $M(a, b)$, $N(3a, 2b)$
30. $M(2x, 3y)$, $N(-3, y)$
31. $M(s, p)$, $N(-3s, -2p)$
32. $P(0, 0)$, $Q(a, 0)$
33. $A(b, c)$, $B(a + b, c)$
34. $P(\frac{b}{2}, \frac{c}{2})$, $Q(\frac{2+a}{2}, \frac{c}{2})$
35. $A(\frac{a}{2}, \frac{b}{3})$, $B(\frac{a}{6}, \frac{b}{4})$
36. $M(\frac{c}{5}, \frac{d}{3})$, $N(\frac{c}{3}, -\frac{d}{2})$
37. $M(\frac{a}{3}, -\frac{b}{2})$, $N(-\frac{a}{6}, \frac{b}{8})$

The lengths of the sides of a triangle are given. Is the triangle a right triangle?

38. 6, 8, 11 **no**   39. $\sqrt{5}$, 1, 2 **yes**   40. 18, $3\sqrt{5}$, 19   41. 15, 12, 9 **yes**   42. $2\sqrt{3}$, $4\sqrt{3}$, 6
43. 4, 6, 9 **no**   44. 6, $2\sqrt{3}$, $2\sqrt{6}$ 45. 12, 20, 16 **yes**   46. 10, 24, 26 **yes**   47. $\sqrt{19}$, $3\sqrt{5}$, 8

40. **no**   42. **yes**   44. **yes**   47. **yes**

For each of the following, find the values of x, if any, that make the distance from A to B equal to the given distance.

(C)
48. $A(x, 4)$, $B(-2, 3)$; $d = 4$ **below**
49. $A(3, x)$, $B(6, 2)$; $d = 5$ **6, −2**
50. $A(3, -1)$, $B(-x, 4)$; $d = 3$ **no values**
51. $A(-2, 1)$, $B(-4, x)$; $d = 6$ **$1 + 4\sqrt{2}$, $1 - 4\sqrt{2}$**

48. $-2 + \sqrt{15}$, $-2 - \sqrt{15}$

Find the perimeter of each polygon with the given coordinates for its vertices. Give each answer in simplest radical form. For complete solutions, see TE Answer Section.

52. $P(3, -1)$, $Q(6, -5)$, $R(-4, -5)$ $15 + \sqrt{65}$
53. $P(-b, 0)$, $Q(c, 0)$, $R(c - d, e)$
54. $P(-a, 0)$, $Q(a, 0)$, $R(0, a)$ $2a + 2a\sqrt{2}$
55. $P(-\frac{2}{3}, -\frac{1}{2})$, $Q(2, -\frac{4}{5})$, $R(\frac{5}{6}, -5)$
56. $P\left(\frac{a + c}{2}, \frac{b + d}{2}\right)$, $Q\left(\frac{c + e}{2}, \frac{f + d}{2}\right)$, $R\left(\frac{g + e}{2}, \frac{h + f}{2}\right)$, $S\left(\frac{a + g}{2}, \frac{h + b}{2}\right)$

Cumulative Review

1. One number is 8 more than another number. Their product is 20. Find the numbers. **−10, −2 or 2, 10**

2. Find three consecutive integers so that 5 times the second, decreased by the third, is 15. **3, 4, 5**

THE DISTANCE BETWEEN TWO POINTS

9.6 The Midpoint of a Segment

OBJECTIVES ▶ To determine the coordinates of the midpoint of a segment
To determine the coordinates of an endpoint of a segment, given the coordinates of the other endpoint and the midpoint

In the figure at the right, M is the **midpoint** of $\overline{AB}$ since $AM = MB = \frac{1}{2}(AB)$.

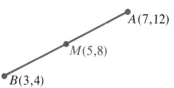

$AM = \sqrt{(7-5)^2 + (12-8)^2} = \sqrt{4+16} = \sqrt{20}$, or $2\sqrt{5}$
$MB = \sqrt{(5-3)^2 + (8-4)^2} = \sqrt{4+16} = \sqrt{20}$, or $2\sqrt{5}$
$AB = \sqrt{(7-3)^2 + (12-4)^2} = \sqrt{16+64} = \sqrt{80}$, or $4\sqrt{5}$

Notice that $M(5,8) = M\left(\dfrac{7+3}{2}, \dfrac{12+4}{2}\right)$. In other words, the x-coordinate of M is the average (arithmetic mean) of the x-coordinates of A and B, and the y-coordinate of M is the average of the y-coordinates of A and B.

Midpoint Formula

Given $P(x_1, y_1)$ and $Q(x_2, y_2)$, the midpoint of $\overline{PQ}$ is
$$M\left(\frac{x_1 + x_2}{2}, \frac{y_1 + y_2}{2}\right).$$

Example 1 Determine the coordinates of M, the midpoint of $\overline{PQ}$, given $P(6, -3)$ and $Q(-14, 9)$.

$$M\left(\frac{x_1 + x_2}{2}, \frac{y_1 + y_2}{2}\right) = M\left(\frac{6 + (-14)}{2}, \frac{-3 + 9}{2}\right) = M(-4, 3)$$

Thus, $(-4, 3)$ are the coordinates of M.

If the coordinates of one endpoint of a segment and the coordinates of its midpoint are known, you can find the coordinates of the other endpoint.

Example 2 Determine the coordinates of Q, the other endpoint of $\overline{PQ}$, given $P(2, 3)$ and its midpoint $M(4, -7)$.

$P(2, 3)$, $M(4, -7)$, $Q(x_2, y_2)$

x-coordinate of the midpoint. ▶

$$x_m = \frac{x_1 + x_2}{2}$$
$$4 = \frac{2 + x_2}{2}$$
$$8 = 2 + x_2$$
$$x_2 = 6$$

$$y_m = \frac{y_1 + y_2}{2}$$
$$-7 = \frac{3 + y_2}{2}$$
$$-14 = 3 + y_2$$
$$y_2 = -17$$

◀ *y-coordinate of the midpoint.*

$P(2,3)$
$M(4,-7)$
$Q(x_2, y)$

Thus, the coordinates of the other endpoint are $(6, -17)$.

Oral Exercises

Determine the coordinates (x, y) of M, the midpoint of $\overline{AB}$.

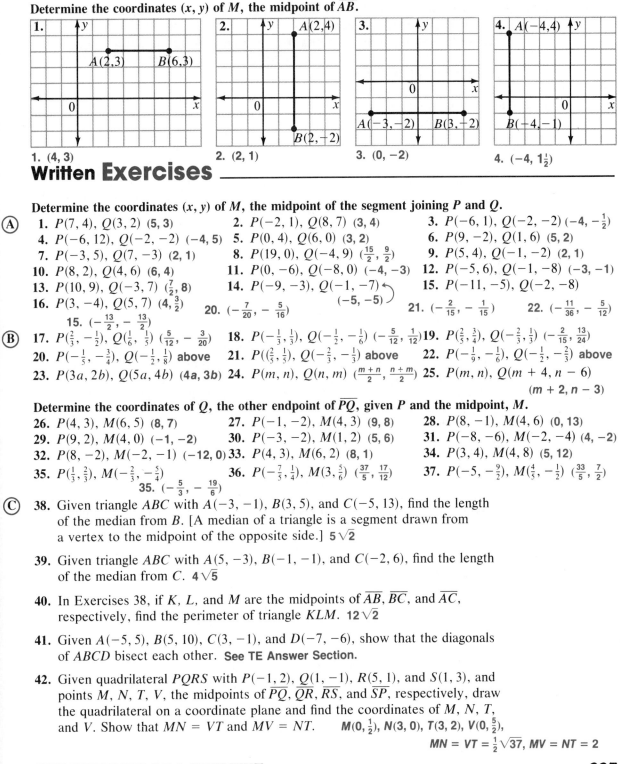

1. $A(2,3)$ $B(6,3)$

2. $A(2,4)$ $B(2,-2)$

3. $A(-3,-2)$ $B(3,-2)$

4. $A(-4,4)$ $B(-4,-1)$

1. **(4, 3)**   2. **(2, 1)**   3. **(0, −2)**   4. **(−4, $1\frac{1}{2}$)**

Written Exercises

Determine the coordinates (x, y) of M, the midpoint of the segment joining P and Q.

(A)

1. $P(7, 4)$, $Q(3, 2)$ **(5, 3)**
2. $P(-2, 1)$, $Q(8, 7)$ **(3, 4)**
3. $P(-6, 1)$, $Q(-2, -2)$ **(−4, −$\frac{1}{2}$)**

4. $P(-6, 12)$, $Q(-2, -2)$ **(−4, 5)**
5. $P(0, 4)$, $Q(6, 0)$ **(3, 2)**
6. $P(9, -2)$, $Q(1, 6)$ **(5, 2)**

7. $P(-3, 5)$, $Q(7, -3)$ **(2, 1)**
8. $P(19, 0)$, $Q(-4, 9)$ **($\frac{15}{2}$, $\frac{9}{2}$)**
9. $P(5, 4)$, $Q(-1, -2)$ **(2, 1)**

10. $P(8, 2)$, $Q(4, 6)$ **(6, 4)**
11. $P(0, -6)$, $Q(-8, 0)$ **(−4, −3)**
12. $P(-5, 6)$, $Q(-1, -8)$ **(−3, −1)**

13. $P(10, 9)$, $Q(-3, 7)$ **($\frac{7}{2}$, 8)**
14. $P(-9, -3)$, $Q(-1, -7)$ **(−5, −5)**
15. $P(-11, -5)$, $Q(-2, -8)$

16. $P(3, -4)$, $Q(5, 7)$ **(4, $\frac{3}{2}$)**
20. $(-\frac{7}{20}, -\frac{5}{16})$
21. $(-\frac{2}{15}, -\frac{1}{15})$
22. $(-\frac{11}{36}, -\frac{5}{12})$

     15. $(-\frac{13}{2}, -\frac{13}{2})$

(B)

17. $P(\frac{2}{3}, -\frac{1}{2})$, $Q(\frac{1}{6}, \frac{1}{5})$ **($\frac{5}{12}$, −$\frac{3}{20}$)**
18. $P(-\frac{1}{3}, \frac{1}{3})$, $Q(-\frac{1}{2}, -\frac{1}{6})$ **(−$\frac{5}{12}$, $\frac{1}{12}$)**
19. $P(\frac{2}{5}, \frac{3}{4})$, $Q(-\frac{2}{3}, \frac{1}{3})$ **(−$\frac{2}{15}$, $\frac{13}{24}$)**

20. $P(-\frac{1}{5}, -\frac{3}{4})$, $Q(-\frac{1}{2}, \frac{1}{8})$ **above**
21. $P((\frac{2}{5}, \frac{1}{5})$, $Q(-\frac{2}{3}, -\frac{1}{3})$ **above**
22. $P(-\frac{1}{9}, -\frac{1}{6})$, $Q(-\frac{1}{2}, -\frac{2}{3})$ **above**

23. $P(3a, 2b)$, $Q(5a, 4b)$ **(4a, 3b)**
24. $P(m, n)$, $Q(n, m)$ **($\frac{m+n}{2}$, $\frac{n+m}{2}$)**
25. $P(m, n)$, $Q(m + 4, n - 6)$

                                                                (m + 2, n − 3)

Determine the coordinates of Q, the other endpoint of $\overline{PQ}$, given P and the midpoint, M.

26. $P(4, 3)$, $M(6, 5)$ **(8, 7)**
27. $P(-1, -2)$, $M(4, 3)$ **(9, 8)**
28. $P(8, -1)$, $M(4, 6)$ **(0, 13)**

29. $P(9, 2)$, $M(4, 0)$ **(−1, −2)**
30. $P(-3, -2)$, $M(1, 2)$ **(5, 6)**
31. $P(-8, -6)$, $M(-2, -4)$ **(4, −2)**

32. $P(8, -2)$, $M(-2, -1)$ **(−12, 0)**
33. $P(4, 3)$, $M(6, 2)$ **(8, 1)**
34. $P(3, 4)$, $M(4, 8)$ **(5, 12)**

35. $P(\frac{1}{3}, \frac{2}{3})$, $M(-\frac{2}{3}, -\frac{5}{4})$
36. $P(-\frac{7}{5}, \frac{1}{4})$, $M(3, \frac{5}{6})$ **($\frac{37}{5}$, $\frac{17}{12}$)**
37. $P(-5, -\frac{9}{2})$, $M(\frac{4}{5}, -\frac{1}{2})$ **($\frac{33}{5}$, $\frac{7}{2}$)**

         35. $(-\frac{5}{3}, -\frac{19}{6})$

(C)

38. Given triangle ABC with $A(-3, -1)$, $B(3, 5)$, and $C(-5, 13)$, find the length of the median from B. [A median of a triangle is a segment drawn from a vertex to the midpoint of the opposite side.] **$5\sqrt{2}$**

39. Given triangle ABC with $A(5, -3)$, $B(-1, -1)$, and $C(-2, 6)$, find the length of the median from C. **$4\sqrt{5}$**

40. In Exercises 38, if K, L, and M are the midpoints of $\overline{AB}$, $\overline{BC}$, and $\overline{AC}$, respectively, find the perimeter of triangle KLM. **$12\sqrt{2}$**

41. Given $A(-5, 5)$, $B(5, 10)$, $C(3, -1)$, and $D(-7, -6)$, show that the diagonals of $ABCD$ bisect each other. **See TE Answer Section.**

42. Given quadrilateral $PQRS$ with $P(-1, 2)$, $Q(1, -1)$, $R(5, 1)$, and $S(1, 3)$, and points M, N, T, V, the midpoints of $\overline{PQ}$, $\overline{QR}$, $\overline{RS}$, and $\overline{SP}$, respectively, draw the quadrilateral on a coordinate plane and find the coordinates of M, N, T, and V. Show that $MN = VT$ and $MV = NT$. **$M(0, \frac{1}{2})$, $N(3, 0)$, $T(3, 2)$, $V(0, \frac{5}{2})$,**
                                           $MN = VT = \frac{1}{2}\sqrt{37}$, $MV = NT = 2$

9.7 Parallel and Perpendicular Lines

OBJECTIVES ▶ To determine whether two lines are parallel, perpendicular, or neither, using their slopes

To write an equation of a line that passes through a point whose coordinates are given and is parallel, or perpendicular, to a line whose equation is given

Recall that **parallel lines** are lines that lie in the same plane but do not intersect. In the figure at the right, $\overleftrightarrow{MN} \parallel \overleftrightarrow{PQ} \parallel \overleftrightarrow{RS}$.

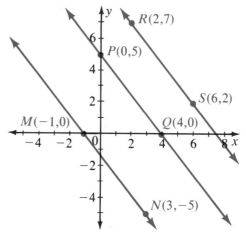

$$m(\overleftrightarrow{MN}) = \frac{-5 - 0}{3 - (-1)} = -\frac{5}{4}$$

$$m(\overleftrightarrow{PQ}) = \frac{0 - 5}{4 - 0} = -\frac{5}{4}$$

$$m(\overleftrightarrow{RS}) = \frac{7 - 2}{2 - 6} = -\frac{5}{4}$$

Notice that each line has the same slope, $-\frac{5}{4}$.

Slope of Parallel Lines

In a plane, if two or more different nonvertical lines are parallel, then the lines have the same slope.
If two or more different nonvertical lines have the same slope, then the lines are parallel.

Notice that the statements above about the slope of parallel lines refer only to *nonvertical* lines. The slope of any vertical line is undefined, but all vertical lines in the same plane are parallel.

You can use slope to find an equation of a line that is parallel to a second line.

Example 1 Write an equation, in standard form, of the line that passes through the point $P(4, 2)$ and is parallel to a line whose equation is $2y - 3x = 6$.

First, find the slope.

$$2y - 3x = 6$$
$$2y = 3x + 6$$
$$m = \frac{3}{2} \blacktriangleright \quad y = \frac{3}{2}x + 3$$

The slope of each line is $\frac{3}{2}$ since the lines are parallel.

Then, use the point-slope form.

$$y - y_1 = m(x - x_1)$$
$$y - 2 = \frac{3}{2}(x - 4) \quad \blacktriangleleft (x_1, y_1) = (4, 2)$$
$$2y - 4 = 3x - 12$$
$$3x - 2y = 8 \quad \blacktriangleleft \textit{Standard form}$$

Thus, an equation of the line is $3x - 2y = 8$,

Recall that two lines are **perpendicular** if they intersect to form a right angle. In the figure, $\overleftrightarrow{PQ} \perp \overleftrightarrow{RS}$.

$$m(\overleftrightarrow{PQ}) = \frac{4 - 1}{3 - 1} = \frac{3}{2}$$

$$m(\overleftrightarrow{RS}) = \frac{-4 - 2}{2 - (-7)} = \frac{-6}{9}, \text{ or } -\frac{2}{3}$$

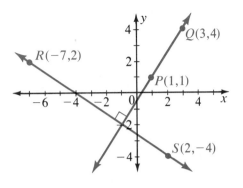

Notice that the product of their slopes is $\frac{3}{2} \cdot -\frac{2}{3}$, or -1. Hence, their slopes are *negative reciprocals* of each other.

Slope of Perpendicular Lines

> If two lines are perpendicular, then the slopes of the lines are negative reciprocals.
> If the slopes of two lines are negative reciprocals, then the lines are perpendicular.

The statements above about the slope of perpendicular lines do not refer to horizontal or vertical lines. A vertical line and a horizontal line in the same plane are always perpendicular to each other.

Example 2 Write an equation, in standard form, of the line that passes through the point $Q(4, 2)$ and is perpendicular to a line whose equation is $2y - 3x = 6$.

First, find the slope.

$$2y - 3x = 6$$

$$m = \frac{3}{2} \blacktriangleright \qquad y = \frac{3}{2}x + 3$$

The slope of the given line is $\frac{3}{2}$ and so the slope of the line perpendicular to it is $-\frac{2}{3}$.

Then, use the point-slope form.

$$y - y_1 = m(x - x_1)$$

$$y - 2 = -\frac{2}{3}(x - 4)$$

$$3y - 6 = -2x + 8$$

$$2x + 3y = 14 \qquad \blacktriangleleft \text{ Standard form}$$

Thus, $2x + 3y = 14$ is an equation of the line.

Example 3 Determine whether the lines with equations of $3x = -4y + 7$ and $6x + 8y = 11$ are parallel, perpendicular, or neither.

Rewrite in slope-intercept form. $\blacktriangleright$

$$3x = -4y + 7$$
$$4y = -3x + 7$$
$$y = -\frac{3}{4}x + \frac{7}{4}$$
$$m = -\frac{3}{4}$$

$$6x + 8y = 11$$
$$8y = -6x + 11$$
$$y = -\frac{6}{8}x + \frac{11}{8}$$
$$m = -\frac{6}{8}, \text{ or } -\frac{3}{4}$$

Thus, the lines are parallel since their slopes are the same.

PARALLEL AND PERPENDICULAR LINES   **229**

Example 4 Write an equation, in standard form, of the line that passes through the point $B(-3, 4)$ and is perpendicular to a line whose equation is $y = 2$.

$y = 2$ is the equation of a horizontal line.
A line perpendicular to this line is vertical. A vertical line has an equation of the form $x = c$, where c is a constant.

Thus, $x = -3$ is an equation of the line.

Written Exercises

Write an equation, in standard form, of the line that passes through the given point and is parallel to the line described by the given equation.

Ⓐ   **1.** $A(5, 7)$, $x + 4y = 5$ **2.** $B(6, 3)$, $5x + 4y = 16$ **3.** $C(-3, -4)$, $2x - 5y = 15$
   4. $D(3, -4)$, $y = 6$ $y = -4$ **5.** $E(-3, -8)$, $x = -5$ $x = -3$ **6.** $F(6, -10)$, $y = x$ $x - y = 16$
   1. $x + 4y = 33$ **2.** $5x + 4y = 42$ **3.** $2x - 5y = 14$

Determine whether the lines whose equations are given are parallel, perpendicular, or neither.

   7. $y = 2x + 3$; $2y = 4x + 7$ **8.** $6x - 4y = 3$; $8y - 12x = -7$ **9.** $x = 5$; $y = 4$ **perp.**
  10. $4x - 5y + 3 = 0$; $x = 2$ **11.** $7x + 3y = 7$; $8x + 4y = 6$ **12.** $y = 2$; $x = 0$ **perp.**
   7. par.   **10.** neither   **8.** par.   **11.** neither

Write an equation, in standard form, of the line that passes through the given point and is perpendicular to the line described by the given equation.

  13. $G(6, -2)$, $x = 5$ $y = -2$ **14.** $H(3, -4)$, $y = -4$ $x = 3$ **15.** $I(6, -10)$, $y = -x$ $x - y = 16$
  16. $J(-3, 2)$, $2x - 5y = 4$ **17.** $K(-5, -8)$, $3x + 2y + 7 = 0$ **18.** $L(8, 0)$, $3y + 5 = 0$ $x = 8$
  $5x + 2y = -11$ $2x - 3y = 14$

Write an equation, in standard form, of the line that is perpendicular to $\overline{AB}$ at point B.

Ⓑ   **19.** $A(-3, 5)$, $B(6, -2)$ **20.** $A(-2, -3)$, $B(-1, 4)$ **21.** $A(6, -1)$, $B(8, 2)$
  22. $A(-6, -4)$, $B(10, -3)$ **23.** $A(8, -7)$, $B(6, -4)$ **24.** $A(-3, -5)$, $B(0, 0)$
  19. $9x - 7y = 68$ $16x + y = 157$ **20.** $x + 7y = 27$ $2x - 3y = 24$ **21.** $2x + 3y = 22$ $3x + 5y = 0$

Write an equation, in standard form, of the line that is the perpendicular bisector of the segment joining P and Q.

  25. $P(-3, -4)$, $Q(6, 5)$ $x + y = 2$ **26.** $P(7, -3)$, $Q(-8, 2)$ **27.** $P(-7, -3)$, $Q(4, 8)$ $x + y = 1$
  28. $P(-2, 3)$, $Q(4, 7)$ **29.** $P(1, 5)$, $Q(7, -3)$ **30.** $P(6, -3)$, $Q(4, 7)$ $x - 5y = -5$
  $3x + 2y = 13$ **26.** $3x - y = -1$ $3x - 4y = 8$

Ⓒ   **31.** Given $P(a, 2b)$, $Q(2a, b)$ and $R(a, b)$, write an equation, in standard form, of the line through R that is parallel to $\overline{PQ}$ if $a \neq 0$.
                       $bx + ay = 2ab$

       32. Given $P(a, b)$, $Q(3a, 3b)$, $a \neq 0$ and $b \neq 0$, write an equation, in standard form, of the line through P that is perpendicular to $\overline{PQ}$. $ax + by = a^2 + b^2$

  33. Given $P(2a, 2b)$, $Q(2c, 2d)$, $a \neq c$, and $b \neq d$, write an equation, in standard form, of the line that is the perpendicular bisector of $\overline{PQ}$.
  $(a - c)x + (b - d)y = a^2 - c^2 - d^2 + b^2$

       34. Given triangle PQR with $P(2a, 2b)$, $Q(2a + 2c, 2b)$, and $R(2a + c, 2d)$, write an equation of the line that contains the median from R. $x = 2a + c$

Cumulative Review

Solve each equation for x.

  1. $ax + b = c$ $\dfrac{c - b}{a}$ **2.** $ax - bx = c$ $\dfrac{c}{a - b}$ **3.** $\dfrac{1}{a} - \dfrac{1}{b} = \dfrac{1}{x}$ $\dfrac{ab}{b - a}$

9.8 Using Coordinate Geometry

OBJECTIVE ▶ **To show that a given property of a geometric figure is true, by using the slope, distance, or midpoint formula**

Coordinate geometry can often be used to show that a given property of a geometric figure is true. The geometric figure is drawn on a coordinate plane, usually with coordinates assigned to each of the vertices of the figure. The slope, distance, or midpoint formula can then be applied.

Example 1 **Show that the segments joining the points $A(-3, -4)$, $B(2, 5)$ and $C(-5, 3)$ form a right triangle.**

Draw a diagram and find the slopes.

$$m(\overline{AB}) = \frac{-4 - 5}{-3 - 2} = \frac{9}{5}$$

$$m(\overline{AC}) = \frac{-4 - 3}{-3 - (-5)} = -\frac{7}{2}$$

$$m(\overline{BC}) = \frac{5 - 3}{2 - (-5)} = \frac{2}{7}$$

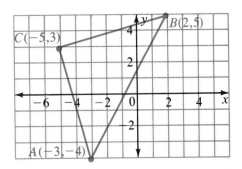

Since the slopes of $\overline{AC}$ and $\overline{BC}$ are negative reciprocals, $\overline{AC} \perp \overline{BC}$ and angle C is a right angle.

Thus, $\triangle ABC$ is a right triangle.

Points that lie on the same line are said to be *collinear*. You can use the slope formula to show that certain points are collinear. Recall that the coordinates of any two points of a line can be used to find its slope, and that the slope should be the same regardless of which points are used.

Example 2 **Show that the points $A(-3, -2)$, $B(0, 0)$, and $C(6, 4)$ are collinear.**

$$m(\overleftrightarrow{AB}) = \frac{0 - (-2)}{0 - (-3)} = \frac{2}{3}$$

$$m(\overleftrightarrow{BC}) = \frac{4 - 0}{6 - 0} = \frac{4}{6}, \text{ or } \frac{2}{3}$$

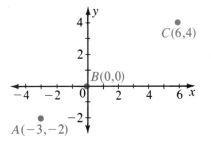

Thus, $m(\overleftrightarrow{AB}) = m(\overleftrightarrow{BC})$ and so the points A, B, and C are collinear.

USING COORDINATE GEOMETRY **231**

If you studied geometry, you may have proved that the line connecting the midpoints of two sides of a triangle is parallel to the third side of the triangle. This can be shown algebraically using coordinate geometry.

Example 3 **In triangle ABC, D is the midpoint of $\overline{AB}$ and E is the midpoint of $\overline{BC}$. Show that $\overleftrightarrow{DE} \parallel \overline{AC}$.**

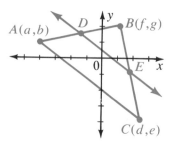

First, find the coordinates of the midpoints.

$$D(x, y) = D\left(\frac{a + f}{2}, \frac{b + g}{2}\right) \qquad E(x, y) = E\left(\frac{f + d}{2}, \frac{g + e}{2}\right)$$

Next, find the slope of $\overleftrightarrow{DE}$ and $\overline{AC}$.

$$m = \frac{y_1 - y_2}{x_1 - y_2}$$

$$m(\overleftrightarrow{DE}) = \frac{\dfrac{g + e}{2} - \dfrac{b + g}{2}}{\dfrac{f + d}{2} - \dfrac{a + f}{2}} = \frac{\dfrac{g + e - b - g}{2}}{\dfrac{f + d - a - f}{2}} = \frac{e - b}{d - a}$$

$$m(\overline{AC}) = \frac{e - b}{d - a}$$

Thus, $m(\overleftrightarrow{DE}) = m(\overline{AC})$, and so $\overleftrightarrow{DE} \parallel \overline{AC}$.

In the next example, you will use the slope formula to show that a given quadrilateral is a parallelogram. Recall that if both pairs of opposite sides of a quadrilateral are parallel, then the quadrilateral is a parallelogram.

Example 4 **The vertices of a quadrilateral are $A(-1, 3)$, $B(0, 0)$, $C(6, 1)$, and $D(5, 4)$. Show that $ABCD$ is a parallelogram.**

$$m(\overline{AB}) = \frac{0 - 3}{0 - (-1)} = -3; \ m(\overline{DC}) = \frac{1 - 4}{6 - 5} = -3$$

$$m(\overline{BC}) = \frac{1 - 0}{6 - 0} = \frac{1}{6}; \ m(\overline{AD}) = \frac{4 - 3}{5 - (-1)} = \frac{1}{6}$$

So, $\overline{AB} \parallel \overline{DC}$ and $\overline{BC} \parallel \overline{AD}$.

Thus, $ABCD$ is a parallelogram.

Written Exercises _____

For Ex. 1–14, see TE Answer Section.
For each of the following, show that the segments joining the points A, B, and C form a right triangle.

(A)
1. $A(1, 2)$, $B(2, 5)$, $C(-1, 6)$
3. $A(5, -5)$, $B(7, 3)$, $C(-1, 5)$

2. $A(-1, -2)$, $B(5, 1)$, $C(3, 5)$
4. $A(2, 3)$, $B(4, -1)$, $C(8, 1)$

5. Show that the points $A(1, 2)$, $B(-1, -8)$, and $C(0, -3)$ are collinear.

6. The vertices of a quadrilateral are $A(0, 0)$, $B(1, 2)$, $C(6, 5)$, and $D(5, 3)$. Show that $ABCD$ is a parallelogram.

7. The vertices of triangle ABC are $A(2, 1)$, $B(8, 3)$, and $C(4, 5)$. Show that the segment joining the midpoints of $\overline{AB}$ and $\overline{BC}$ is one-half the length of $\overline{AC}$.

8. The vertices of a triangle are $A(2, 1)$, $B(7, 4)$, and $C(2, 7)$. Show that triangle ABC is isosceles.

(B)
9. The vertices of a quadrilateral are $A(0, 0)$, $B(a, 0)$, $C(a, b)$, and $D(0, b)$. Show that $ABCD$ is a rectangle by showing that $\overline{AB} \perp \overline{BC}$, $\overline{AB} \perp \overline{AD}$, $\overline{CD} \perp \overline{AD}$ and $\overline{CD} \perp \overline{BC}$.

10. Show that the midpoints of the sides of a rectangle determine a rhombus. [A rhombus is an equilateral quadrilateral.]

11. Show that the diagonals of a rectangle bisect each other.

(C)
12. Show that the midpoints of the sides of trapezoid $ABCD$ determine a parallelogram. The coordinates of the vertices are $A(0, 0)$, $B(a, 0)$, $C(b + d, c)$ and $D(b, c)$.

13. Show that the diagonals of rhombus $STUV$ are perpendicular to each other. The coordinates of the vertices are $S(0, 0)$, $T(a, 0)$, $U(a + \sqrt{a^2 - b^2}, b)$, and $V(\sqrt{a^2 - b^2}, b)$.

14. Given $A(0, 0)$, $B(2a, 0)$, and $C(2b, 2c)$, show that the three medians of triangle ABC intersect at $T\left(\dfrac{2a + 2b}{3}, \dfrac{2c}{3}\right)$. [Hint: Use the point-slope form to write an equation of each median and then solve each equation for y.]

USING COORDINATE GEOMETRY   **233**

Applications

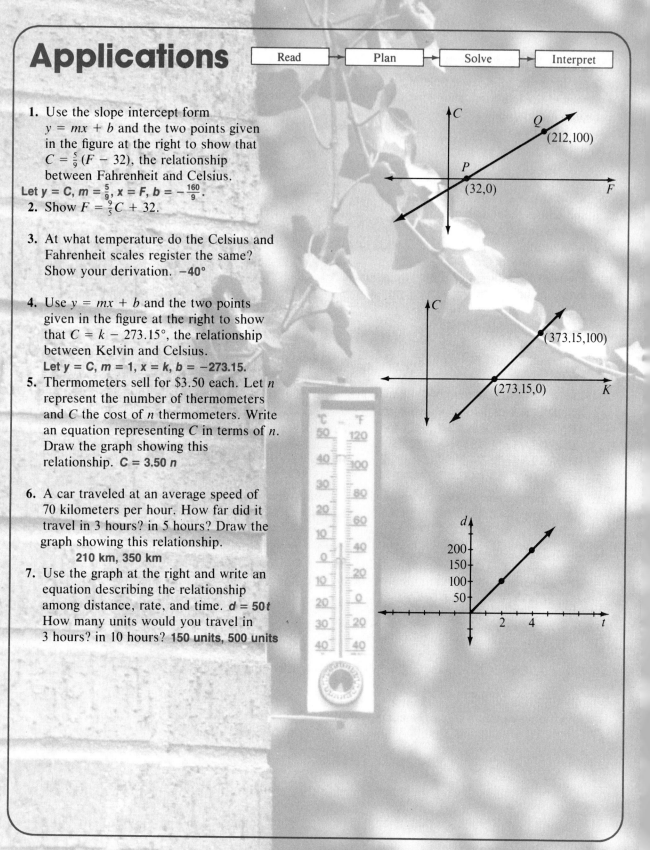

1. Use the slope intercept form
   $y = mx + b$ and the two points given
   in the figure at the right to show that
   $C = \frac{5}{9}(F - 32)$, the relationship
   between Fahrenheit and Celsius.
   Let $y = C$, $m = \frac{5}{9}$, $x = F$, $b = -\frac{160}{9}$.

2. Show $F = \frac{9}{5}C + 32$.

3. At what temperature do the Celsius and
   Fahrenheit scales register the same?
   Show your derivation. **−40°**

4. Use $y = mx + b$ and the two points
   given in the figure at the right to show
   that $C = k - 273.15°$, the relationship
   between Kelvin and Celsius.
   Let $y = C$, $m = 1$, $x = k$, $b = -273.15$.

5. Thermometers sell for $3.50 each. Let n
   represent the number of thermometers
   and C the cost of n thermometers. Write
   an equation representing C in terms of n.
   Draw the graph showing this
   relationship. **$C = 3.50\,n$**

6. A car traveled at an average speed of
   70 kilometers per hour. How far did it
   travel in 3 hours? in 5 hours? Draw the
   graph showing this relationship.
   210 km, 350 km

7. Use the graph at the right and write an
   equation describing the relationship
   among distance, rate, and time. **$d = 50t$**
   How many units would you travel in
   3 hours? in 10 hours? **150 units, 500 units**

APPLICATIONS

Computer Activities

The Way the Crow Flies

When flying an airplane, the pilot usually follows the shortest path between two cities. This is not possible when you drive an automobile. You must follow the way the road is built.

It is sometimes helpful to draw a coordinate diagram to assist in making decisions about the most appropriate route to travel. Coordinates are assigned to various cities in the coordinate plane, and the necessary distances are computed. The program below may be used to find the distance between two cities in a coordinate plane.

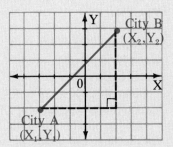

$$D = \sqrt{(X_2 - X_1)^2 + (Y_2 - Y_1)^2}$$

PROGRAM

```
10 PRINT "PROGRAM FINDS SHORTEST"
20 PRINT "PATH BETWEEN A AND B"
30 PRINT "ENTER COORDINATES OF A AND B AS"
40 PRINT "X1, Y1, X2, Y2"
50 INPUT X1, Y1, X2, Y2
60 LET D = SQR((X2 - X1) ↑ 2 + (Y2 - Y1) ↑ 2)
70 PRINT "THE DISTANCE FROM A TO B IS"; D; "KILOMETERS"
80 END
```

Exercises

Type in the program above and run it for the following coordinates:

1. $A(117, 129)$ $B(405, 325)$ **348.3674 kilometers**

2. $A(585, 405)$ $B(620, 475)$ **78.26237 kilometers**

3. $A(5, 230)$ $B(1785, 2352)$ **2769.708 kilometers**

4. Write a program to determine if a triangle is a right triangle, given the measures of the three sides. **For Ex. 4, see TE Answer Section.**

5. Write a program to find the area of a rectangle, given the length of a diagonal and the length of one side of the rectangle. **For Ex. 5, see TE Answer Section.**

Chapter Nine Review

Vocabulary

abscissa [9.1]
coordinate plane [9.1]
coordinates [9.1]
linear equation [9.1]
  point-slope form of [9.3]
  slope-intercept form of [9.3]

ordered pair [9.1]
ordinate [9.1]
origin [9.1]
quadrant [9.1]
slope [9.2]
y-intercept [9.3]

On the same coordinate plane, graph each ordered pair. [9.1]

1. $(-2, -3)$ 2. $(4, -6)$ 3. $(-7, 0)$
4. $(0, -3)$ 5. $(5, -5)$ 6. $(0, 2)$

Give the coordinates of each point. [9.1]

7. A **(−2, −3)**
8. B **(4, −1)**
9. C **(1, 3)**
10. D **(−3, 2)**
11. E **(1, 0)**

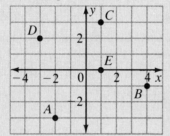

Draw the graph of each equation.

12. $2x + 4y = 12$ [9.1]
13. $-(x - y) - 3(x - y) = 6$ [9.4]

Find the length of $\overline{AB}$. [9.2]

14. $A(2, -3), B(-6, -3)$ **8**
15. $A(-4, 1), B(-4, 5)$ **4**

Find the slope of $\overleftrightarrow{PQ}$. [9.2]

16. $P(6, 4), Q(-2, 3)$ $\frac{1}{8}$
17. $P(-2, -2), Q(-3, -4)$ **2**
18. $P(\frac{1}{2}, \frac{1}{4}), Q(-\frac{3}{4}, \frac{2}{3})$ $-\frac{1}{3}$
★ 19. $P(2x, -3y), Q(-3x, 2y)$ $-\frac{y}{x}$

Find the missing coordinate for the given data. [9.2]

★ 20. $A(-3, y), B(6, -8), m(\overline{AB}) = -2$ **10**

A line has the given slope, y-intercept, or contains the indicated point(s). Write an equation, in standard form, of each line. [9.3]

21. $P(2, 5), m = \frac{2}{3}$ 22. $m = 3, b = 7$
23. $A(-3, 4), B(-1, 5)$ $x - 2y = -11$
21. $2x - 3y = -11$ 22. $3x - y = -7$

Find the slope and the y-intercept of the line described by each given equation. [9.3]

24. $y = -\frac{2}{3}x + 4$ 25. $y - 2(3 - 2x) = 7$
★ 26. $6 - (3 - 2y) - 2[-3(2x - 1)] = 5$ **−6, 4**
24. $-\frac{2}{3}, 4$ 25. $-4, 13$

Is the given point on the line described by the given equation? [9.4]

27. $P(-1, -3), 2x - 3y = 7$ **yes**
28. $Q(-4, 2), \frac{3}{5}x + \frac{2}{3}y = 1$ **no**

Find the distance between the given points. Answer in simplest radical form. [9.5]

29. $P(-1, 2), Q(7, 4)$ $2\sqrt{17}$
30. $M(3, 0), N(10, 8)$ $\sqrt{113}$
31. $P(\frac{1}{2}, -\frac{1}{3}), Q(\frac{2}{3}, \frac{5}{6})$ $\frac{5}{6}\sqrt{2}$

The lengths of the sides of a triangle are given. Is the triangle a right triangle?

32. $8, 12, 4\sqrt{13}$ [9.5] **yes**

Determine the coordinates (x, y) of M, the midpoint of $\overline{PQ}$. [9.6]

33. $P(4, -3), Q(7, 4)$ $(\frac{11}{2}, \frac{1}{2})$
34. $P(-\frac{1}{4}, \frac{1}{2}), Q(\frac{2}{5}, -\frac{1}{3})$ $(\frac{3}{40}, \frac{1}{12})$

Determine the coordinates of Q, the other endpoint of $\overline{PQ}$, given P and the midpoint, M. [9.6]

35. $P(-3, 6), M(1, 2)$ **(5, −2)**

Write an equation, in standard form, of the line that passes through the given point and is parallel to the given line. [9.7]

36. $C(1, 2), 3x - 5y = 15$ $3x - 5y = -7$
37. $D(4, -1), -2x - 3y = 10$ $2x + 3y = 5$

Write an equation, in standard form, of the line that passes through the given point and is perpendicular to the given line. [9.7]

38. $A(-1, -3), 2x + 5y = 7$ $5x - 2y = 1$
39. $B(2, -7), 3y + 6x = 8$ $x - 2y = 16$

40. The vertices of a quadrilateral are $A(-5, 3), B(4, 0), C(6, 6),$ and $D(-3, 9)$. Show that $ABCD$ is a parallelogram. [9.8]

For Ex. 40, see TE Answer Section.

Chapter Nine Test

Give the coordinates of each point.

1. A **(1, 0)**
2. B **(3, 1)**
3. C **(−3, −1)**
4. D **(−4, 3)**

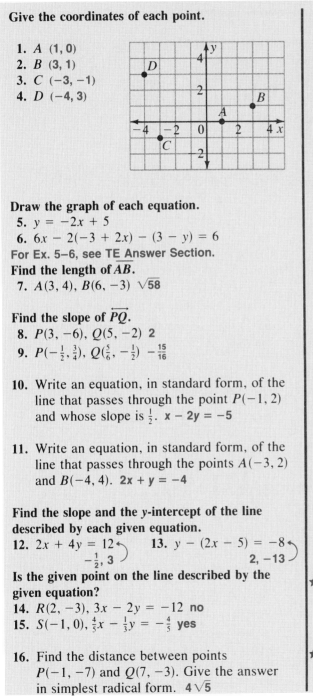

Draw the graph of each equation.

5. $y = -2x + 5$
6. $6x - 2(-3 + 2x) - (3 - y) = 6$

For Ex. 5–6, see TE Answer Section.

Find the length of $\overline{AB}$.

7. $A(3, 4), B(6, -3)$ $\sqrt{58}$

Find the slope of $\overrightarrow{PQ}$.

8. $P(3, -6), Q(5, -2)$ **2**
9. $P(-\frac{1}{2}, \frac{3}{4}), Q(\frac{5}{6}, -\frac{1}{2})$ $-\frac{15}{16}$

10. Write an equation, in standard form, of the line that passes through the point $P(-1, 2)$ and whose slope is $\frac{1}{2}$. **x − 2y = −5**

11. Write an equation, in standard form, of the line that passes through the points $A(-3, 2)$ and $B(-4, 4)$. **2x + y = −4**

Find the slope and the y-intercept of the line described by each given equation.

12. $2x + 4y = 12$ $-\frac{1}{2}, 3$
13. $y - (2x - 5) = -8$ $2, -13$

Is the given point on the line described by the given equation?

14. $R(2, -3), 3x - 2y = -12$ **no**
15. $S(-1, 0), \frac{4}{5}x - \frac{1}{3}y = -\frac{4}{5}$ **yes**

16. Find the distance between points $P(-1, -7)$ and $Q(7, -3)$. Give the answer in simplest radical form. $4\sqrt{5}$

17. The lengths of the sides of a triangle are $4\sqrt{3}$, $8\sqrt{3}$, and 12. Is the triangle a right triangle? **yes**

18. Determine the coordinates of M, the midpoint of $\overline{PQ}$, given $P(4, -3)$ and $Q(6, -7)$. **(5, −5)**

19. Determine the coordinates of Q, the other endpoint of $\overline{PQ}$, given $P(-2, -3)$ and its midpoint $M(3, -1)$. **(8, 1)**

20. Write an equation, in standard form, of the line the passes through the point $A(-1, -2)$ and is parallel to a line whose equation is $3x + 5y = 15$. **3x + 5y = −13**

21. Write an equation, in standard form, of the line that passes through the point $N(-4, 1)$ and is perpendicular to a line whose equation is $5x - 2y = 10$. **2x + 5y = −3**

22. The vertices of a quadrilateral are $A(3, 0)$, $B(9, 4)$, $C(6, 9)$, and $D(0, 5)$. Show that $ABCD$ is a parallelogram.

For Ex. 22, see TE Answer Section.

★ 23. Find the missing coordinate for the given data: $P(x, -3), Q(9, 6), m(\overline{PQ}) = 3$. **6**

★ 24. Show that the midpoints of the sides of an isosceles triangle determine an isosceles triangle.

For Ex. 24, see TE Answer Section.

College Prep Test

DIRECTIONS: Choose the *one* best answer to each question or problem.

1. In the figure, the coordinates of M are $(6, 0)$ and the area of triangle MON is 24. What are the coordinates of N? **C**

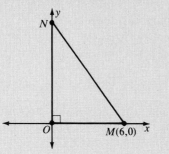

   (**A**) $(4, 0)$ (**B**) $(0, 4)$ (**C**) $(0, 8)$
   (**D**) $(8, 0)$ (**E**) None of these

2. In the figure, triangles PQR and PMN are isosceles right triangles. If the areas of the triangles are the same, what are the coordinates of point M? **B**

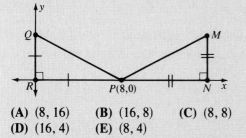

   (**A**) $(8, 16)$ (**B**) $(16, 8)$ (**C**) $(8, 8)$
   (**D**) $(16, 4)$ (**E**) $(8, 4)$

3. The distance between $R(-5, 0)$ and S is 4. The coordinates of point S could be any of the following except **D**

   (**A**) $(-5, 4)$ (**B**) $(-5, -4)$ (**C**) $(-9, 0)$
   (**D**) $(0, -1)$ (**E**) $(-1, 0)$

4. The point $(a, -b)$ is on the line described by which linear equation in x and y? **D**

   (**A**) $x + y = a + b$ (**B**) $x - y = a - b$

   (**C**) $2x - b = 2a - y$ (**D**) $x - \dfrac{y + b}{2} = a$

   (**E**) None of these

5. Which point is the farthest away from the origin? **E**

   (**A**) $P(7, -5)$ (**B**) $Q(5, -7)$
   (**C**) $R(8, -3)$ (**D**) $S(2, 8)$
   (**E**) $T(0, -9)$

6. Find the area of right triangle PQR, with right angle R, if the equation of $\overleftrightarrow{PQ}$ is $y = 3x + 9$ and the coordinates of R are $(7, 0)$. **C**

   (**A**) 70   (**B**) 100   (**C**) 150
   (**D**) 300   (**E**) None of these

7. Choose the table of ordered pairs (x, y) for which $5ay - 10bx = 15ab$. **B**

(**A**)

x	y
$3b$	0
b	$-a$
$-b$	$-2a$

(**B**)

x	y
a	$5b$
$-3a$	$-3b$
$-a$	b

(**C**)

x	y
0	$3b$
a	b
$-a$	$-b$

(**D**)

x	y
$-2a$	$-b$
$-a$	b
a	$-2b$

   (**E**) None of these

8. Given $P(a, b)$, $Q(3a, 3b)$, $R(-c, -d)$, and $S(c, d)$, where a, b, c, and d are nonzero real numbers, which statement is true? **A**

   (**A**) $PQ = RS$ if $a = d$ and $b = c$.
   (**B**) $\overline{PQ} \parallel \overline{RS}$ if $a = b = c$.
   (**C**) $\overline{PQ} \perp \overline{RS}$ if $ac = bd$.
   (**D**) $\overline{PQ}$ and $\overline{RS}$ have the same midpoint if $a = b$.
   (**E**) None of these

LINEAR SYSTEMS, MATRICES, AND DETERMINANTS

10

Best Buy?

Solving consumer-related problems often requires reading with comprehension and computing with accuracy. See if you can solve these problems.

1. Which size jar of tomato sauce is the best buy per ounce? **C**

   A. Small **B.** Medium **C.** Large
   D. Extra Large

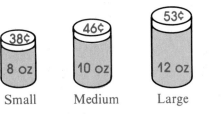

Small	Medium	Large	Extra Large
38¢	46¢	53¢	94¢
8 oz	10 oz	12 oz	20 oz

2. A sports store is having a sale featuring a 25% discount on all baseball equipment. Find the total cost of the four items, before tax. **C**

   A. $6.10 **B.** $24.60 **C.** $26.70
   D. $32.80

ITEM	REG. PRICE
Baseball bat	$ 6.20
Golf ball	3.80
Box of baseballs ..	18.20
Table-tennis set ...	4.60

3. What is the cost for carpeting this L-shaped floor at $6 per square yard? **A**

   A. $192 **B.** $576 **C.** $640
   D. $1920

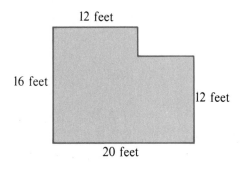

12 feet

16 feet

12 feet

20 feet

PROJECT

Stores *P* and *Q* each have automobile tires on sale. If you want to buy four tires, identify some of the considerations you would need to make in order to decide which store has the better buy.

10.1 Solving Linear Systems Graphically

OBJECTIVES ▶ **To solve a system of two linear equations in two variables graphically**
To determine whether a system of two linear equations is consistent, inconsistent, dependent, or independent

A pair of linear equations in two variables is called a **system of equations.** A solution of a system of two linear equations is an ordered pair of real numbers that makes both equations true. You can solve a system of linear equations by graphing each equation. You should draw the graph of each equation in the same coordinate plane and then locate the point of intersection of the two graphs, if any. The ordered pair associated with this point is a solution of the system.

Example 1 Solve the system $2x - y = 5$ graphically.
$$-x + y = -3$$

Write each equation in slope-intercept form.

$$2x - y = 5 \qquad\qquad -x + y = -3$$
$$y = 2x - 5 \qquad\qquad y = x - 3$$

Graph each equation in the same coordinate plane.

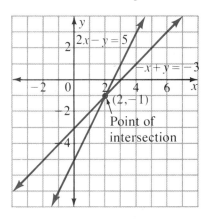

Check that the ordered pair $(2, -1)$ is a solution of both equations.

Thus, $(2, -1)$ is the solution of the system.

In Example 1, the two lines have exactly one point in common, and so the two equations have one common solution. When a system of linear equations has exactly one solution, the system is called an **independent system.** When a system has at least one solution, the system is called a **consistent system.**

Example 2

Solve the system $5x - 3(y + x) = -6$ graphically.
$$2x - 3y = 3$$

$$5x - 3(y + x) = -6$$
$$5x - 3y - 3x = -6$$
$$-3y = -2x - 6$$
$$y = \frac{2}{3}x + 2$$

$$2x - 3y = 3$$
$$-3y = -2x + 3$$
$$y = \frac{2}{3}x - 1$$

The slopes of the two lines are the same but their y-intercepts are different. The lines are parallel. There is no point of intersection of the graphs.

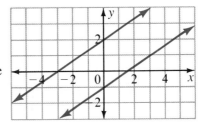

Thus, there is no solution of the system.

A system of linear equations which has no solution is called an **inconsistent system.**

Example 3

Solve the system $3x + y = 1$ graphically.
$$2y = 2 - 6x$$

$$3x + y = 1$$
$$y = -3x + 1$$

$$2y = 2 - 6x$$
$$y = -3x + 1$$

The slopes of the two lines and their y-intercepts are the same. The lines coincide. The two graphs have all of their points in common.

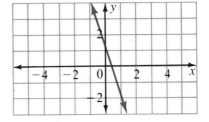

Thus, all (x, y) such that $y = -3x + 1$ are solutions of the system.

In Example 3, the two lines have all of their points in common and so each solution of one equation is also a solution of the other. A system of linear equations that has all solutions in common is called a **dependent system.** A dependent system has infinitely many solutions.

Reading In Algebra _____

True or false? Give a reason for your answer.
1. A system of two linear equations has at least one solution. **F**
2. A system of two linear equations has at most one solution. **F**
3. An inconsistent system of equations is one that has more than one solution. **F**
4. A dependent system of equations is also a consistent system. **T**

SOLVING LINEAR SYSTEMS GRAPHICALLY   **241**

Written Exercises

(Note: con = consistent, inc = inconsistent, dep = dependent, ind = independent)

Solve each system of equations graphically. Indicate whether the system is consistent, inconsistent, dependent, or independent.

(A) 1. $2x + y = 3$ $(2, -1)$;
     $y - x = -3$ con, ind

2. $3x + 2y = 8$
     $3x = 10 - 2y$
       no solution; inc

3. $4x - y + 3 = 0$
     $x - y = 0$
     $(-1, -1)$; con, ind

4. $y = 2 - 3x$
     $x = \dfrac{2}{3} - \dfrac{y}{3}$
 all $(x, y)|y = 2 - 3x$; con, dep

5. $\dfrac{x}{2} = \dfrac{y}{3}$
     $y - x = 1$
     $(2, 3)$; con, ind

6. $\dfrac{x + 2y}{2} = x$
     $2y = x$
 all $(x, y)|y = \frac{1}{2}x$; con, dep

7. $3y + 4 = 5x$
     $10x - 3 = 6y$
 no solution; inc

8. $-4x + 2y - 3 = 0$
     $6y - 9 = 12x$
 all $(x, y)|y = 2x + \frac{3}{2}$; con, dep

9. $2x + y = 3$
     $2y - 3x = 6$
     $(0, 3)$; con, ind

(B) 10. $2(x + y) = x + 2$
     $2y + 3(x - 2y + 8) = 0$
   $(-4, 3)$; con, ind

11. $x + 2(y + 5) = 3(x + y + 1)$
     $0 = 5y - 3(x - 10)$
   $(5, -3)$; con, ind

12. $-3(x - y) = 2(y - x) + 8$
     $-(2x - y) = 3(y + 3x - 1)$
   $(-1, 7)$; con, ind

13. $-x - 3y = 2(x - 3y) + 4$
     $y - x - 2(x - y) = -3$
     no solution; inc

14. $0.2x - 0.3y = -0.8$
     $0.3x + 0.5y = 0.7$
   $(-1, 2)$; con, ind

15. $0.3x - 0.2y = 0.7$
     $0.4x - 0.1y = 0.6$
   $(1, -2)$; con, ind

Write a system of two linear equations in two variables that has the given number of solutions. (Answers may vary.)   18. any two equations with $m_1 = m_2$, $b_1 = b_2$

(C) 16. exactly one solution
   any two equations with $m_1 \neq m_2$

17. no solution
   any two equations with $m_1 = m_2$, $b_1 \neq b_2$

18. infinitely many solutions

Find the value(s) of k, if any, that satisfies the given condition for each system.

19. $\left.\begin{array}{l} y = kx + 8 \\ y = 3x - 1 \end{array}\right\}$ is inconsistent **3**

20. $\left.\begin{array}{l} kx - 3y = 9 \\ 2x + 3y = 12 \end{array}\right\}$ is consistent
        all values except $k = -2$

21. $\left.\begin{array}{l} 4x - 2y = 7 \\ 12x - ky = 21 \end{array}\right\}$ has infinitely many solutions **6**

22. $\left.\begin{array}{l} 2x + ky = 6 \\ 3x - 4y = -8 \end{array}\right\}$ has exactly one solution
       all values except $k = -\frac{8}{3}$

CALCULATOR ACTIVITIES

To check to see if $(1.3, 2.5)$ is a solution of the system
$12.6x + 15.7y = 55.63$,
$-5.3x + 11.8y = 22.61$
substitute 1.3 for x and 2.5 for y in each equation.

$12.6 \otimes 1.3$ $15.7 \otimes 2.5$ $-5.3 \otimes 1.3$ $11.8 \otimes 2.5$

  $\ominus$ $\ominus$ $\ominus$ $\ominus$

16.38 $\oplus$ 39.25 -6.89 $\oplus$ 29.50

     55.63   22.61

Check to determine if the given ordered pair is a solution of the system of equations.

1. $4.6x + 3.5y = 29.23$
     $5.1x - 1.7y = 17.34$, $(4.3, 2.7)$ **yes**

2. $15.9x - 13.3y = 21.44$
     $-18.1x + 21.7y = 13.64$, $(6.2, 5.8)$
                   yes

10.2 Solving Linear Systems Algebraically

OBJECTIVES ▶ **To solve a system of two linear equations by the substitution method**
To solve a system of two linear equations by the addition method

A system of two linear equations can be solved algebraically. In this lesson, you will use two algebraic methods, *substitution* and *addition*.

You can solve a system of two linear equations in two variables by substitution using the following procedure:
(1) Solve one of the equations for either variable;
(2) Substitute this value in the other equation;
(3) Solve for the other variable;
(4) Substitute in either original equation to find the value of the second variable.
(5) Check the ordered pair in both original equations.

Example 1 **Solve the system $2x - y = 5$ by substitution.**
$$-x + y = -3$$

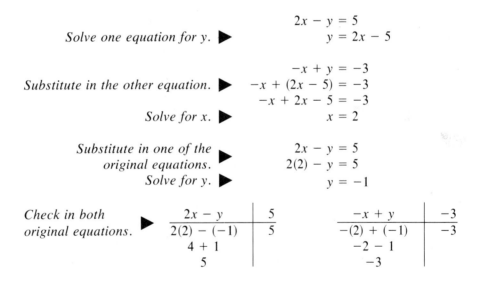

Solve one equation for y. ▶
$$2x - y = 5$$
$$y = 2x - 5$$

Substitute in the other equation. ▶
$$-x + y = -3$$
$$-x + (2x - 5) = -3$$
$$-x + 2x - 5 = -3$$

Solve for x. ▶
$$x = 2$$

Substitute in one of the original equations. ▶
Solve for y. ▶
$$2x - y = 5$$
$$2(2) - y = 5$$
$$y = -1$$

Check in both original equations. ▶

$2x - y$	5
$2(2) - (-1)$	5
$4 + 1$	
5	

$-x + y$	-3
$-(2) + (-1)$	-3
$-2 - 1$	
-3	

Thus, $(2, -1)$ is the solution of the system.

Notice that Example 1 above is an algebraic solution to Example 1 of the preceding lesson.
A system of two linear equations can also be solved algebraically by addition, as shown on page 244.

Example 2 Solve the system $2x + 3y = 9$ by addition.
$$-2x - 5y = 1$$

Add the two equations and solve for y.

$$
\begin{array}{rcl}
2x + 3y &=& 9 \\
-2x - 5y &=& 1 \\
\hline
-2y &=& 10 \\
y &=& -5
\end{array}
$$

Substitute -5 for y in either equation. Solve for x.

$$
\begin{array}{rcl}
2x + 3y &=& 9 \\
2x + 3(-5) &=& 9 \\
2x - 15 &=& 9 \\
2x &=& 24 \\
x &=& 12
\end{array}
$$

Check in both original equations. Substitute 12 for x and -5 for y.

$2x + 3y$	9
$2(12) + 3(-5)$	9
$24 - 15$	
9	

$-2x - 5y$	1
$-2(12) - 5(-5)$	1
$-24 + 25$	
1	

Thus, $(12, -5)$ is the solution of the system.

In Example 2, notice that the coefficients of x in the original equations are additive inverses. Thus, when the equations are added the x-variable is eliminated.

Sometimes it is necessary to multiply one or both of the linear equations by some number or numbers so that the coefficients of one variable are additive inverses. This is shown in Examples 3 and 4 which follow.

Example 3 Solve the system $5x - 2y = 20$ by addition.
$$7x + 4y = 11$$

Multiply the first equation by 2. ▶
$$
\begin{array}{rcl}
5x - 2y &=& 20 \\
2(5x - 2y) &=& 2(20)
\end{array}
$$

Add the equations. ▶
$$
\begin{array}{rcl}
10x - 4y &=& 40 \\
7x + 4y &=& 11 \\
\hline
17x &=& 51 \\
x &=& 3
\end{array}
$$

Substitute 3 for x in one of the original equations. ▶
$$
\begin{array}{rcl}
5x - 2y &=& 20 \\
5(3) - 2y &=& 20 \\
-2y &=& 5
\end{array}
$$

Solve for y. ▶
$$y = -\frac{5}{2}$$

Check $(3, -\frac{5}{2})$ in both original equations.

Thus, $(3, -\frac{5}{2})$ is the solution of the system.

CHAPTER TEN

Example 4 Solve the system $3x + 2y = 5$ by addition.
$$4x - 5y = 22$$

First Way

Eliminate x. Use $12x$ and $-12x$.

$$\begin{array}{ll} 4(3x + 2y) = 4(5) & \quad 12x + 8y = 20 \\ -3(4x - 5y) = -3(22) & \quad \underline{-12x + 15y = -66} \\ & \quad 23y = -46 \\ & \quad y = -2 \end{array}$$

Solve for x.

$$\begin{array}{l} 3x + 2y = 5 \\ 3x + 2(-2) = 5 \\ 3x = 9 \\ x = 3 \end{array}$$

Second Way

Eliminate y. Use $10y$ and $-10y$.

$$\begin{array}{ll} 5(3x + 2y) = 5(5) & \quad 15x + 10y = 25 \\ 2(4x - 5y) = 2(22) & \quad \underline{8x - 10y = 44} \\ & \quad 23x = 69 \\ & \quad x = 3 \end{array}$$

Solve for y.

$$\begin{array}{l} 3x + 2y = 5 \\ 3(3) + 2y = 5 \\ 2y = -4 \\ y = -2 \end{array}$$

Check in both original equations. Substitute 3 for x and -2 for y.

$3x + 2y$	5
$3(3) + 2(-2)$	5
$9 - 4$	
5	

$4x - 5y$	22
$4(3) - 5(-2)$	22
$12 + 10$	
22	

Thus, $(3, -2)$ is the solution of the system.

When you solve a system of two linear equations either by the method of substitution or addition, sometimes both variables are eliminated. If the resulting equation is a false statement, the system is inconsistent and has no solution. If the resulting equation is a true statement, the system is dependent and has infinitely many solutions.

Example 5 Solve each system by addition.

$$\begin{array}{l} 2x - 4y = 5 \\ -x + 2y = 8 \end{array} \qquad\qquad \begin{array}{l} -3x + 2y = 4 \\ 9x - 6y = -12 \end{array}$$

Multiply the second equation by 2. ▶

$$\begin{array}{l} -x + 2y = 8 \\ 2(-x + 2y) = 2(8) \\ -2x + 4y = 16 \end{array}$$

$$\begin{array}{l} -3x + 2y = 4 \\ 3(-3x + 2y) = 3(4) \\ -9x + 6y = 12 \end{array}$$ ◀ *Multiply the first equation by 3.*

Add the equations. ▶

$$\begin{array}{l} 2x - 4y = 5 \\ \underline{-2x + 4y = 16} \\ 0 + 0 = 21 \\ \quad 0 = 21 \text{ False} \end{array}$$

$$\begin{array}{l} -9x + 6y = 12 \\ \underline{9x - 6y = -12} \\ 0 + 0 = 0 \\ \quad 0 = 0 \text{ True} \end{array}$$ ◀ *Add the equations.*

Thus, there is no solution.

Thus, all (x, y) such that $-3x + 2y = 4$ are the solutions.

SOLVING LINEAR SYSTEMS ALGEBRAICALLY

Example 6

A riverboat travels downstream 16 km in 2 h and returns the same distance upstream in 3 h. Find the rate of the boat in still water and the rate of the current.

READ

PLAN

Let x = rate of boat in still water and y = rate of current

	rate(r)	time(t)	distance(d)
Downstream	$x + y$	2	$2(x + y)$
Upstream	$x - y$	3	$3(x - y)$

◀ *Use* $d = rt$.

$$\begin{matrix} 2(x + y) = 16 \\ 3(x - y) = 16 \end{matrix} \Rightarrow \begin{matrix} 2x + 2y = 16 \\ 3x - 3y = 16 \end{matrix} \Rightarrow \begin{matrix} x + y = 8 \\ 3x - 3y = 16 \end{matrix}$$

SOLVE

Multiply the first equation by 3. Then add the equations.

$$\begin{matrix} 3x + 3y = 24 \\ 3x - 3y = 16 \\ \hline 6x = 40 \\ x = 6\frac{2}{3} \end{matrix} \qquad \begin{matrix} 2(x + y) = 16 \\ 2(6\frac{2}{3} + y) = 16 \\ 6\frac{2}{3} + y = 8 \\ y = 1\frac{1}{3} \end{matrix}$$

INTERPRET

Check to see that distance downstream, $2(x + y)$, is equal to distance upstream, $3(x - y)$.

Thus, the rate of the boat in still water is $6\frac{2}{3}$ km/h and the rate of the current is $1\frac{1}{3}$ km/h.

Written Exercises

Solve each system of equations by substitution.

(A)
1. $4x - 3y = 2$
$2x + y = -4$
$(-1, -2)$

2. $5x + 6y = 14$
$4x - y = 17$
$(4, -1)$

3. $2a - b + 1 = 0$
$3b - 5a + 1 = 0$
$(-4, -7)$

4. $2r - 3s = 1.3$
$s - r = -0.5$
$(0.2, -0.3)$

5. $2x - 4y = -6$
$-x + 2y = 3$
all (x, y) such that $x = 2y - 3$

6. $2y - z = 8$
$-4y + 6z = -16$
$(4, 0)$

7. $2 = x + 4y$
$8y = 7 + x$
$(-1, \frac{3}{4})$

8. $5x - 2y = 0$
$2x + y = 3$
$(\frac{2}{3}, \frac{5}{3})$

Solve each system of equations by addition.

9. $2x + 2y = 3$
$-5x + 4y = 15$
$(-1, \frac{5}{2})$

10. $3x - 2y = 10$
$5x + 3y = -15$
$(0, -5)$

11. $7c + 9d - 3 = 0$
$9c - 7d - 2 = 0$
$(\frac{3}{10}, \frac{1}{10})$

12. $2y + 3x - 8.1 = 0$
$2x - 3y + 3.7 = 0$
$(1.3, 2.1)$

13. $4t - 7u = -13$
$-3u - 5 = -7t$
$(2, 3)$

14. $5x - 7y + 16 = 0$
$x + 4y - 13 = 0$
$(1, 3)$

15. $9m = 21 - 7n$
$12n = 36 - m$
$(0, 3)$

16. $3x - 5y + 10 = 0$
$-9x + 15y = -30$
no solution

Solve each problem by using a system of two linear equations in two variables.

(B)
17. An airplane flew 112 km in 21 min with a tailwind and returned the same distance in 24 min against the wind. What was the rate of the tailwind? **20 km/h**

18. A first number is 10 less than 4 times a second number. The first number, decreased by the second number, is −19. Find the numbers. **−22, −3**

19. Alicia is 4 years older than Bill. Two years ago, she was $1\frac{1}{2}$ times as old as he was. Find their present ages. ◀ **Alicia: 14, Bill: 10**

20. How many milliliters of a 25% iodine solution must be added to 90 mL of a 65% iodine solution to obtain a 55% iodine solution? **30 mL**

10.3 Solving Systems of Three Linear Equations

OBJECTIVE ▶ **To solve a system of three linear equations**

You have learned that a system of two linear equations may have no solution, infinitely many solutions, or exactly one solution. A solution of an independent system of two linear equations is always an ordered pair of real numbers. In this lesson, you will learn to solve a system containing three linear equations. The equations in the system contain three variables, and so a solution of an independent system is an **ordered triple** of real numbers.

Example

Solve the system:
$$x + 2y - z = 1$$
$$2x + y + 3z = 5$$
$$3x + y + 2z = 8.$$

Choose *any two* equations and eliminate one of the variables.

$$\begin{array}{l} x + 2y - z = 1 \\ 2x + y + 3z = 5 \end{array} \Rightarrow \begin{array}{l} 3x + 6y - 3z = 3 \\ \underline{2x + y + 3z = 5} \\ 5x + 7y \quad\;\; = 8 \end{array}$$

Next, choose a *different* pair of equations and eliminate the same variable.

$$\begin{array}{l} x + 2y - z = 1 \\ 3x + y + 2z = 8 \end{array} \Rightarrow \begin{array}{l} 2x + 4y - 2z = 2 \\ \underline{3x + y + 2z = 8} \\ 5x + 5y \quad\;\; = 10 \end{array}$$

A system of 2 linear equations in x and y remains. Solve the system.

$$\begin{array}{l} 5x + 7y = 8 \\ 5x + 5y = 10 \end{array} \Rightarrow \begin{array}{l} 5x + 7y = \quad\; 8 \\ \underline{-5x - 5y = -10} \\ 2y = -2 \\ \boxed{y = -1} \end{array}$$

Substitute for y in either equation to find x.

$$5x + 5y = 10$$
$$5x + 5(-1) = 10$$
$$5x = 15$$
$$\boxed{x = 3}$$

Substitute for x and y in one of the original equations to find z.

$$x + 2y - z = 1$$
$$3 + 2(-1) - z = 1$$
$$1 - z = 1$$
$$-z = 0$$
$$\boxed{z = 0}$$

Check by substituting 3 for x, -1 for y, and 0 for z in the original equations.

$x + 2y - z$	1	$2x + y + 3z$	5	$3x + y + 2z$	8
$3 + 2(-1) - 0$	1	$2(3) + (-1) + 3(0)$	5	$3(3) + (-1) + 2(0)$	8
$3 - 2$		$6 - 1$		$9 - 1$	
1		5		8	

Thus, $(3, -1, 0)$ is the solution of the system.

Example 2 Solve the system: $x + 2y = -6$
$$y + 2z = 11$$
$$2x + z = 16.$$

Use the addition method with the second and third original equations. Eliminate z. ▶

$$y + 2z = 11$$
$$2x + z = 16$$

$$\Rightarrow$$

$$\begin{array}{rrr} y + 2z = & 11 \\ -4x \quad - 2z = & -32 \\ \hline -4x + y \quad = & -21 \end{array}$$

The equation $-4x + y = -21$ and the first original equation, $x + 2y = -6$, form a linear system in two variables. Eliminate x and solve for y. ▶

$$x + 2y = -6$$
$$-4x + y = -21$$

$$\Rightarrow$$

$$\begin{array}{rr} 4x + 8y = & -24 \\ -4x + y = & -21 \\ \hline 9y = & -45 \\ \boxed{y = -5} \end{array}$$

Substitute -5 for y in the first original equation. ▶

$$x + 2y = -6$$
$$x + 2(-5) = -6$$
$$\boxed{x = 4}$$

Substitute 4 for x in the third original equation. ▶

$$2x + z = 16$$
$$2(4) + z = 16$$
$$\boxed{z = 8}$$

Check in all three original equations.

Thus, $(4, -5, 8)$ is the solution of the system.

———————◆◆———————

A system of linear equations in three variables may be inconsistent.

Example 3 Solve the system: $2x + 3y - 2z = 4$
$$3x - 3y + 2z = 16$$
$$6x - 12y + 8z = 5.$$

Use the addition method with the first and third original equations. Two variables, y and z, are eliminated. ▶

$$2x + 3y - 2z = 4$$
$$6x - 12y + 8z = 5$$

$$\Rightarrow$$

$$\begin{array}{rr} 8x + 12y - 8z = & 16 \\ 6x - 12y + 8z = & 5 \\ \hline 14x \quad = & 21 \\ x = & \frac{3}{2} \end{array}$$

Use the addition method with the first and second original equations. Two variables, y and z, are eliminated. ▶

$$\begin{array}{rr} 2x + 3y - 2z = & 4 \\ 3x - 3y + 2z = & 16 \\ \hline 5x \quad = & 20 \\ x = & 4 \end{array}$$

Two different values are obtained for x, which is a contradiction. The system is inconsistent.

Thus, there is no solution of the system.

Reading in Algebra

True or false? Give a reason for your answer.

1. A system of three linear equations in three variables has at least one solution. **F**
2. A solution of a system of three linear equations in three variables is an ordered triple of real numbers. **T**
3. A system of three linear equations in three variables may be independent, inconsistent, or dependent. **T**
4. If an ordered triple of real numbers is a solution of one of the linear equations in a system, it is a solution of all equations in the system. **F**

Written Exercises

Solve each system of equations.

(A)
1. $-x + 3y + z = -10$
   $3x + 2y - 2z = 3$
   $2x - y - 4z = -7$
   (7, -3, 6)

2. $a + b - 3c = 8$
   $3a + 4b - 2c = 20$
   $2a - 3b + c = -6$
   (2, 3, -1)

3. $m + n + p = 1$
   $m + 3n + 7p = 13$
   $m + 2n + 3p = 4$
   (1, -3, 3)

4. $x + 2y + 3z = 9$
   $-3x + 5y - 4z = -7$
   $3x - y + 2z = -1$
   (-3, 0, 4)

5. $a + b + c = 2$
   $2a + b + 2c = 3$
   $3a - b + c = 4$
   (2, 1, -1)

6. $2m + 2n + 6p = 9$
   $m - 3n + 2p = 5$
   $-m - 5n - 4p = 4$
   no solution

(B)
7. $x - 2y = 14$
   $y + 2z = 11$
   $2x + z = 16$
   (4, -5, 8)

8. $y + z = -3$
   $-x - 2z = 5$
   $3x + 2y = -5$
   (-1, -1, -2)

9. $2x + 3y = -5$
   $4y - 5z = -32$
   $3x + 2z = 14$
   (2, -3, 4)

Solve each problem by using a system of three linear equations in three variables.

10. Find three numbers in decreasing order such that their sum is 3, the difference of the first two numbers is 4, and the sum of the smallest number and the greatest number is 2. **5, 1, -3**

11. Find three positive numbers in increasing order such that the difference of the first two numbers is 2, the difference of the first and the last numbers is 4, and the quotient of the last two numbers is $1\frac{1}{5}$. **8, 10, 12**

12. A coin box contains pennies, nickels, and dimes. The pennies and nickels are worth 35¢, the nickels and dimes are worth 80¢, and the value of the dimes and the pennies is 75¢. Find the number of each kind of coin in the box.
    pennies: 15, nickels: 4, dimes: 6

13. Find the number of nickels, dimes, and quarters in a collection of 80 such coins if the nickels and the quarters are worth $4.50 and the value of the quarters and the dimes is $5.50.
    nickels: 40, dimes: 30, quarters: 10

Solve each system of equations.

(C)
14. $\dfrac{m}{4} - \dfrac{3n}{2} + \dfrac{p}{2} = -6$
    $\dfrac{m}{6} - \dfrac{n}{4} - \dfrac{p}{3} = 1$
    $\dfrac{m}{3} + \dfrac{n}{2} - p = 7$ **(6, 4, -3)**

15. $\dfrac{1}{a} + \dfrac{1}{b} - \dfrac{2}{c} = 9$
    $\dfrac{3}{a} - \dfrac{2}{b} + \dfrac{1}{c} = -1$
    $\dfrac{2}{a} - \dfrac{1}{b} + \dfrac{3}{c} = 7$ $(\frac{14}{65}, \frac{2}{17}, \frac{14}{29})$

16. $\dfrac{3}{x} - \dfrac{1}{y} + \dfrac{4}{z} = -3$
    $\dfrac{2}{x} + \dfrac{3}{y} - \dfrac{1}{z} = 6$
    $-\dfrac{1}{x} + \dfrac{2}{y} - \dfrac{3}{z} = 2$ **no solution**

SOLVING SYSTEMS OF THREE LINEAR EQUATIONS

10.4 Two by Two Determinants

OBJECTIVES ▶ **To find the value of a 2 by 2 determinant**
To solve a system of two linear equations in two variables using determinants

A **matrix** is an array of numbers or other elements arranged in rows and columns. A matrix that has the same number of rows as columns is called a **square matrix.** Each square matrix has a corresponding real number assigned to it called a **determinant.**

The square matrix $\begin{bmatrix} 3 & 7 \\ 2 & 8 \end{bmatrix}$ contains four elements, which are arranged in 2 rows and 2 columns. It is called a 2×2 (read: two by two) matrix. The determinant of the matrix is written in the same form as the matrix but with vertical bars instead of brackets. The value of the 2×2 determinant $\begin{vmatrix} 3 & 7 \\ 2 & 8 \end{vmatrix}$ is found in the following way.

$$\begin{vmatrix} 3 & 7 \\ 2 & 8 \end{vmatrix} = 3 \cdot 8 - 2 \cdot 7 = 10$$

Definition:
2 × 2
Determinant

The determinant of $\begin{bmatrix} a & b \\ c & d \end{bmatrix}$ is $\begin{vmatrix} a & b \\ c & d \end{vmatrix}$. Its value is $ad - cb$.

Example 1 Find the value of each determinant.

$$\begin{vmatrix} 2 & 1 \\ -3 & -5 \end{vmatrix} \qquad \begin{vmatrix} m+n & m-n \\ -3 & 5 \end{vmatrix}$$

$\begin{vmatrix} 2 & 1 \\ -3 & -5 \end{vmatrix} = 2(-5) - (-3)(1)$
$= -10 + 3$
$= -7$

$\begin{vmatrix} m+n & m-n \\ -3 & 5 \end{vmatrix} = (m+n)(5) - (-3)(m-n)$
$= 5m + 5n + 3m - 3n$
$= 8m + 2n$

Thus, the value is -7.

Thus, the value is $8m + 2n$.

You can use 2×2 determinants to solve a system of two linear equations such as $5x + 2y = 4$
$\qquad 2x - 3y = 13.$

$$\begin{array}{c} 5x + 2y = 4 \\ 2x + -3y = 13 \end{array}$$

$$x = \frac{\begin{vmatrix} 4 & 2 \\ 13 & -3 \end{vmatrix}}{\begin{vmatrix} 5 & 2 \\ 2 & -3 \end{vmatrix}} = \frac{\begin{vmatrix} 4 & 2 \\ 13 & -3 \end{vmatrix}}{\begin{vmatrix} 5 & 2 \\ 2 & -3 \end{vmatrix}} = \frac{4(-3) - 13(2)}{5(-3) - 2(2)} = \frac{-12 - 26}{-15 - 4} = \frac{-38}{-19} = 2$$

$$y = \frac{\begin{vmatrix} 5 & 4 \\ 2 & 13 \end{vmatrix}}{\begin{vmatrix} 5 & 2 \\ 2 & -3 \end{vmatrix}} = \frac{\begin{vmatrix} 5 & 4 \\ 2 & 13 \end{vmatrix}}{\begin{vmatrix} 5 & 2 \\ 2 & -3 \end{vmatrix}} = \frac{5(13) - 2(4)}{5(-3) - 2(2)} = \frac{65 - 8}{-15 - 4} = \frac{57}{-19} = -3$$

So, $x = 2$ and $y = -3$. The solution of the system is $(2, -3)$.

The solutions of a system of linear equations of the form $a_1x + b_1y = c_1$
$$a_2x + b_2y = c_2,$$
where all coefficients are real numbers, are found as follows:

$$x = \frac{\begin{vmatrix} c_1 & b_1 \\ c_2 & b_2 \end{vmatrix}}{\begin{vmatrix} a_1 & b_1 \\ a_2 & b_2 \end{vmatrix}} = \frac{c_1b_2 - c_2b_1}{a_1b_2 - a_2b_1} \qquad y = \frac{\begin{vmatrix} a_1 & c_1 \\ a_2 & c_2 \end{vmatrix}}{\begin{vmatrix} a_1 & b_1 \\ a_2 & b_2 \end{vmatrix}} = \frac{a_1c_2 - a_2c_1}{a_1b_2 - a_2b_1} \qquad [a_1b_2 - a_2b_1 \neq 0]$$

Each solution is an ordered pair (x, y) of real numbers.

Example 2

Solve the system $2x + 3y = 3$ using determinants.
$$6x = y - 11$$

Write each equation in the general form.

$$\underset{\substack{\uparrow \\ a_1}}{2x} + \underset{\substack{\uparrow \\ b_1}}{3y} = \underset{\substack{\uparrow \\ c_1}}{3} \qquad\qquad \underset{\substack{\uparrow \\ a_2}}{6x} + \underset{\substack{\uparrow \\ b_2}}{(-1)y} = \underset{\substack{\uparrow \\ c_2}}{-11}$$

$$x = \frac{\begin{vmatrix} c_1 & b_1 \\ c_2 & b_2 \end{vmatrix}}{\begin{vmatrix} a_1 & b_1 \\ a_2 & b_2 \end{vmatrix}} \qquad\qquad y = \frac{\begin{vmatrix} a_1 & c_1 \\ a_2 & c_2 \end{vmatrix}}{\begin{vmatrix} a_1 & b_1 \\ a_2 & b_2 \end{vmatrix}}$$

$$= \frac{\begin{vmatrix} 3 & 3 \\ -11 & -1 \end{vmatrix}}{\begin{vmatrix} 2 & 3 \\ 6 & -1 \end{vmatrix}} \qquad\qquad = \frac{\begin{vmatrix} 2 & 3 \\ 6 & -11 \end{vmatrix}}{\begin{vmatrix} 2 & 3 \\ 6 & -1 \end{vmatrix}}$$

$$= \frac{3(-1) - (-11)(3)}{2(-1) - 6(3)} \qquad\qquad = \frac{2(-11) - 6(3)}{2(-1) - 6(3)}$$

$$= \frac{-3 + 33}{-2 - 18} \qquad\qquad\qquad = \frac{-22 - 18}{-2 - 18}$$

$$= \frac{30}{-20}, \text{ or } -\frac{3}{2} \qquad\qquad = \frac{-40}{-20}, \text{ or } 2$$

Check in the original equations.

Thus, $\left(-\dfrac{3}{2}, 2\right)$ is the solution of the system.

TWO BY TWO DETERMINANTS

Oral Exercises

30. $\left(\dfrac{11}{3m+2n}, \dfrac{4m-n}{3m+2n}\right)$ 31. $\left(\dfrac{nr+ms}{n+2m}, \dfrac{s-2r}{n+2m}\right)$

To solve the system $2x - 3y = -4$ using determinants, state the determinant that
$$-4x + 5y = 7$$
you would use for each of the following. Do not find the value.

1. the denominator for x **below**   **2.** the numerator for x **below**
3. the numerator for y **below**   **4.** the denominator for y **below**

Written Exercises

1. $\begin{vmatrix} 2 & -3 \\ -4 & 5 \end{vmatrix}$ **2.** $\begin{vmatrix} -4 & -3 \\ 7 & 5 \end{vmatrix}$ **3.** $\begin{vmatrix} 2 & -4 \\ -4 & 7 \end{vmatrix}$ **4.** $\begin{vmatrix} 2 & -3 \\ -4 & 5 \end{vmatrix}$

Find the value of each determinant.

Ⓐ **1.** $\begin{vmatrix} 2 & 3 \\ -2 & 5 \end{vmatrix}$ **16**   **2.** $\begin{vmatrix} 6 & -1 \\ 4 & 8 \end{vmatrix}$ **52**   **3.** $\begin{vmatrix} -3 & -2 \\ 5 & 3 \end{vmatrix}$ **1**   **4.** $\begin{vmatrix} -8 & 6 \\ 4 & -2 \end{vmatrix}$ **-8**

5. $\begin{vmatrix} -10 & 3 \\ -4 & 5 \end{vmatrix}$ **-38**   **6.** $\begin{vmatrix} 1 & 0 \\ 0 & 1 \end{vmatrix}$ **1**   **7.** $\begin{vmatrix} -3 & 5 \\ -9 & -2 \end{vmatrix}$ **51**   **8.** $\begin{vmatrix} -2 & 0 \\ 4 & 2 \end{vmatrix}$ **-4**

9. $\begin{vmatrix} 3\sqrt{2} & 5 \\ -2 & 2\sqrt{2} \end{vmatrix}$ **22**   **10.** $\begin{vmatrix} 0 & 7 \\ 0 & 9 \end{vmatrix}$ **0**   **11.** $\begin{vmatrix} \frac{1}{4} & \frac{5}{6} \\ \frac{1}{2} & \frac{2}{3} \end{vmatrix}$ $-\frac{1}{4}$ **12.** $\begin{vmatrix} \frac{1}{3} & \frac{1}{6} \\ -\frac{1}{5} & \frac{3}{10} \end{vmatrix}$ $\frac{2}{15}$

13. $\begin{vmatrix} m+n & 3 \\ m-n & 5 \end{vmatrix}$ **2m + 8n**   **14.** $\begin{vmatrix} c-d & c+d \\ 3 & 4 \end{vmatrix}$ **c - 7d**   **15.** $\begin{vmatrix} -r & p+r \\ 6 & 10 \end{vmatrix}$ **-6p - 16r**

Solve each system of linear equations using determinants.

16. $2x + 3y = 7$
$x + 2y = 3$
$(5, -1)$

17. $5x - 12y = 4$
$4x - 7y = -2$
$(-4, -2)$

18. $3x - 4y = 7$
$4x + 6y = 15$
$(3, \frac{1}{2})$

19. $2x + 3y = 4$
$4x + y = -2$
$(-1, 2)$

20. $3x + 2y = 1$
$3x - 2y = -5$
$(-\frac{2}{3}, \frac{3}{2})$

21. $-x + y = 1$
$3x - 4y = -3$
$(-1, 0)$

22. $4x + y = 0$
$6x - y = 5$
$(\frac{1}{2}, -2)$

23. $2x + 3y = -2$
$x + 5y = 3$
$(-\frac{19}{7}, \frac{8}{7})$

Ⓑ **24.** $2x - 3y = 2.5$
$-x - 2y = 0.5$ **(0.5, -0.5)**

25. $5x - y = 0.4$
$x - y = 0.2$ **(0.05, -0.15)**

26. $0.6x - 0.1y = -1$
$-4x - 0.5y = 2$ **(-1, 4)**

Find the value of each determinant.

27. $\begin{vmatrix} p+r & -r \\ r & p-r \end{vmatrix}$ **p²**   **28.** $\begin{vmatrix} m+n & m+n \\ m+n & m-n \end{vmatrix}$ **-2n² - 2mn**   **29.** $\begin{vmatrix} m^2 - n^2 & 1 \\ m+n & \frac{1}{m+n} \end{vmatrix}$ **-2n**

Solve each system of linear equations for (x, y) using determinants. Assume that all variables represent real numbers.

Ⓒ **30.** $mx - 2y = 1$ **above**
$nx + 3y = 4$

31. $x - my = r$ **above**
$2x + ny = s$

32. $a_1x + b_1y = 1$
$a_2x + b_2y = 1$

33. $a_1x + b_1y = c_1$
$a_2x + b_2y = c_2$

252   **32.** $\left(\dfrac{b_2 - b_1}{a_1b_2 - a_2b_1}, \dfrac{a_1 - a_2}{a_1b_2 - a_2b_1}\right)$ **33.** $\left(\dfrac{c_1b_2 - c_2b_1}{a_1b_2 - a_2b_1}, \dfrac{a_1c_2 - a_2c_1}{a_1b_2 - a_2b_1}\right)$ **CHAPTER TEN**

10.5 Three by Three Determinants

OBJECTIVES ▶ **To find the value of a 3 by 3 determinant**
To solve a system of three linear equations in three variables using determinants

The 3×3 square matrix $\begin{bmatrix} 3 & -2 & 1 \\ -1 & 4 & 10 \\ 2 & -3 & 5 \end{bmatrix}$ contains 3 rows and 3 columns. You can find the value of its corresponding determinant as shown below.

(1) Repeat columns 1 and 2 as columns 4 and 5.

(2) Multiply on the *down* diagonals.

(3) Multiply on the *up* diagonals.

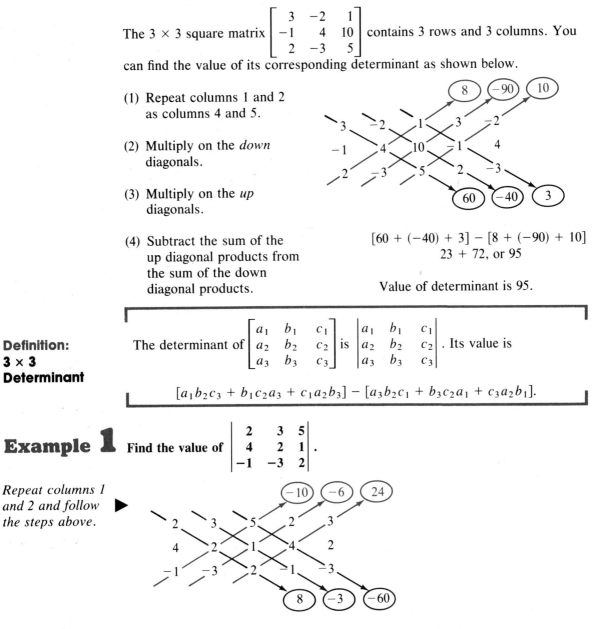

(4) Subtract the sum of the up diagonal products from the sum of the down diagonal products.

$$[60 + (-40) + 3] - [8 + (-90) + 10]$$
$$23 + 72, \text{ or } 95$$

Value of determinant is 95.

Definition:
3 × 3
Determinant

The determinant of $\begin{bmatrix} a_1 & b_1 & c_1 \\ a_2 & b_2 & c_2 \\ a_3 & b_3 & c_3 \end{bmatrix}$ is $\begin{vmatrix} a_1 & b_1 & c_1 \\ a_2 & b_2 & c_2 \\ a_3 & b_3 & c_3 \end{vmatrix}$. Its value is

$$[a_1 b_2 c_3 + b_1 c_2 a_3 + c_1 a_2 b_3] - [a_3 b_2 c_1 + b_3 c_2 a_1 + c_3 a_2 b_1].$$

Example 1 Find the value of $\begin{vmatrix} 2 & 3 & 5 \\ 4 & 2 & 1 \\ -1 & -3 & 2 \end{vmatrix}$.

Repeat columns 1 and 2 and follow the steps above. ▶

$$[8 + (-3) + (-60)] - [-10 + (-6) + 24] = (-55) - (8) = -63$$

Thus, the value of the determinant is -63.

The solutions of a system of linear equations of the form
$a_1x + b_1y + c_1z = d_1$
$a_2x + b_2y + c_2z = d_2$
$a_3x + b_3y + c_3z = d_3$ where all coefficients are real numbers, are found
as follows.

$$x = \frac{\begin{vmatrix} d_1 & b_1 & c_1 \\ d_2 & b_2 & c_2 \\ d_3 & b_3 & c_3 \end{vmatrix}}{\begin{vmatrix} a_1 & b_1 & c_1 \\ a_2 & b_2 & c_2 \\ a_3 & b_3 & c_3 \end{vmatrix}} \qquad y = \frac{\begin{vmatrix} a_1 & d_1 & c_1 \\ a_2 & d_2 & c_2 \\ a_3 & d_3 & c_3 \end{vmatrix}}{\begin{vmatrix} a_1 & b_1 & c_1 \\ a_2 & b_2 & c_2 \\ a_3 & b_3 & c_3 \end{vmatrix}} \qquad z = \frac{\begin{vmatrix} a_1 & b_1 & d_1 \\ a_2 & b_2 & d_2 \\ a_3 & b_3 & d_3 \end{vmatrix}}{\begin{vmatrix} a_1 & b_1 & c_1 \\ a_2 & b_2 & c_2 \\ a_3 & b_3 & c_3 \end{vmatrix}}$$

Each solution is an ordered triple (x, y, z) of real numbers. The value of the
determinant in the denominator must not be equal to 0.

Example 2 Solve the system $2x + 3y + 4z = 4$ using determinants.
$$5x + 7y + 8z = 9$$
$$3x - 2y - 6z = 7$$

$$x = \frac{\begin{vmatrix} 4 & 3 & 4 \\ 9 & 7 & 8 \\ 7 & -2 & -6 \end{vmatrix}\begin{matrix} 4 & 3 \\ 9 & 7 \\ 7 & -2 \end{matrix}}{\begin{vmatrix} 2 & 3 & 4 \\ 5 & 7 & 8 \\ 3 & -2 & -6 \end{vmatrix}\begin{matrix} 2 & 3 \\ 5 & 7 \\ 3 & -2 \end{matrix}} = \frac{[-168 + 168 + (-72)] - [196 + (-64) + (-162)]}{[-84 + 72 + (-40)] - [84 + (-32) + (-90)]}$$

$$= \frac{-42}{-14}, \text{ or } 3$$

$$y = \frac{\begin{vmatrix} 2 & 4 & 4 \\ 5 & 9 & 8 \\ 3 & 7 & -6 \end{vmatrix}\begin{matrix} 2 & 4 \\ 5 & 9 \\ 3 & 7 \end{matrix}}{\begin{vmatrix} 2 & 3 & 4 \\ 5 & 7 & 8 \\ 3 & -2 & -6 \end{vmatrix}\begin{matrix} 2 & 3 \\ 5 & 7 \\ 3 & -2 \end{matrix}} = \frac{[-108 + 96 + 140] - [108 + 112 + (-120)]}{-14}$$

$$= \frac{28}{-14}, \text{ or } -2$$

$$z = \frac{\begin{vmatrix} 2 & 3 & 4 \\ 5 & 7 & 9 \\ 3 & -2 & 7 \end{vmatrix}\begin{matrix} 2 & 3 \\ 5 & 7 \\ 3 & -2 \end{matrix}}{\begin{vmatrix} 2 & 3 & 4 \\ 5 & 7 & 8 \\ 3 & -2 & -6 \end{vmatrix}\begin{matrix} 2 & 3 \\ 5 & 7 \\ 3 & -2 \end{matrix}} = \frac{[98 + 81 + (-40)] - [84 + (-36) + 105]}{-14}$$

$$= \frac{-14}{-14}, \text{ or } 1 \quad \text{Check in the original equations.}$$

Thus, $(3, -2, 1)$ is the solution of the system.

Written Exercises

Find the value of each determinant.

(A) 1. $\begin{vmatrix} 2 & -4 & -3 \\ 4 & -1 & -2 \\ -3 & 4 & -2 \end{vmatrix}$ 2. $\begin{vmatrix} -3 & 2 & -5 \\ 4 & -1 & 2 \\ -1 & -2 & -3 \end{vmatrix}$ 3. $\begin{vmatrix} 4 & -1 & -2 \\ -3 & 2 & -1 \\ 2 & -1 & 3 \end{vmatrix}$ 4. $\begin{vmatrix} -2 & -3 & 2 \\ -1 & 2 & -2 \\ 3 & -2 & 1 \end{vmatrix}$

           −75   44   15   11

5. $\begin{vmatrix} 2 & 3 & 5 \\ 4 & 2 & 1 \\ -1 & -3 & 2 \end{vmatrix}$ 6. $\begin{vmatrix} -3 & 1 & 5 \\ -2 & 0 & 2 \\ 6 & 3 & 4 \end{vmatrix}$ 7. $\begin{vmatrix} 1 & 3 & -2 \\ 1 & -4 & 5 \\ 1 & 2 & 3 \end{vmatrix}$ 8. $\begin{vmatrix} 1 & -1 & 4 \\ 0 & 1 & -7 \\ 0 & 0 & 1 \end{vmatrix}$

           −63   8   −28   1

Solve each system of linear equations using determinants.

(B) 9.
$$2x - 3y + z = 7$$
$$3x - 2y + 2z = 9$$
$$-2x - y + 2z = 3$$
$$(1, -1, 2)$$

10.
$$-x + 2y - 3z = 11$$
$$2x + y + 2z = -4$$
$$3x + 3y - z = 5$$
$$(-1, 2, -2)$$

11.
$$3x - 2y + 4z = 11$$
$$-2x + 4y + z = -10$$
$$2x - y + 3z = 7$$
$$(3, -1, 0)$$

12.
$$-3x + 2y - 2z = -10$$
$$2x + 3y + z = -1$$
$$-x - y + 2z = -8$$
$$(4, -2, -3)$$

13.
$$-3x + 4y + 5z = 3$$
$$x - y + 3z = 8$$
$$-2x + 3y - z = -7$$
$$(1, -1, 2)$$

14.
$$4x - 3y + 2z = 0$$
$$-2x + y - 3z = 4$$
$$5x - 6y + 2z = 1$$
$$(1, 0, -2)$$

15.
$$a + b + c = -1$$
$$2a - b + c = 19$$
$$3a - 2b - 4c = 16$$
$$(4, -8, 3)$$

16.
$$3x - 4z = 7$$
$$2y + 5z = 2$$
$$6x + 5y = 10$$
$$(5, -4, 2)$$

17.
$$5n + 10d = 70$$
$$5n + 25q = 270$$
$$10d + 25q = 300$$
$$(5, 4, 10)$$

(C) 18.
$$0.6x + 0.4y - 0.6z = 5.8$$
$$0.8x - 1y - 0.4z = 16$$
$$1.5x - 1.5y = 19.5$$
$$(5, -8, -10)$$

19.
$$\frac{2x}{5} + \frac{3y}{4} - \frac{2z}{3} = -\frac{9}{10}$$
$$-\frac{x}{3} - \frac{2y}{5} + \frac{3z}{5} = \frac{4}{3}$$
$$\frac{3x}{2} - \frac{3y}{5} - \frac{z}{5} = -\frac{33}{10}$$
$$(-1, 2, 3)$$

20.
$$a_1 x + b_1 y = d_1$$
$$b_2 y + c_2 z = d_2$$
$$a_3 x + c_3 z = d_3$$

20. $\left(\dfrac{b_2 c_3 d_1 + b_1 c_2 d_3 - b_1 c_3 d_2}{a_1 b_2 c_3 + a_3 b_1 c_2}, \dfrac{a_1 c_2 d_2 + a_3 c_2 d_1 - a_1 c_2 d_3}{a_1 b_2 c_3 + a_3 b_1 c_2}, \dfrac{a_1 b_2 d_3 + a_3 b_1 d_2 - a_3 b_2 d_1}{a_1 b_2 c_3 + a_3 b_1 c_2} \right)$

➔ A Challenge To You

Let $M = x^2 - x + 1$; $N = x^2 + x + 1$; $P = -x^2 + x + 1$; and $Q = -x^2 - x + 1$. Q can also be expressed as $aM + bN + cP$ where a, b, and c are real numbers.

Solve for the ordered triple (a, b, c). **See TE Answer Section.**

Cumulative Review

Graph the solution set of each inequality. **See TE Answer Section.**

1. $-2x + 5 > 20$ 2. $3x - 2 \le 16$ 3. $|a - 2| < 4$

10.6 Matrix Addition

OBJECTIVES ▶ **To find the sum of two matrices**
To determine the properties of matrix addition

Recall that a matrix (pl. matrices) is an array of real numbers or other elements enclosed by brackets.

$$\begin{bmatrix} a_{11} & a_{12} & a_{13} \\ a_{21} & a_{22} & a_{23} \\ a_{31} & a_{32} & a_{33} \end{bmatrix} \qquad \begin{bmatrix} a_{11} & a_{12} \\ a_{21} & a_{22} \\ a_{31} & a_{32} \end{bmatrix} \qquad \begin{bmatrix} a_{11} \\ a_{21} \\ a_{31} \end{bmatrix} \qquad \begin{bmatrix} a_{11} & a_{12} & a_{13} \end{bmatrix}$$

3 by 3 square	3 by 2	3 by 1	1 by 3
matrix	matrix	matrix	matrix
3 rows, 3 columns	3 rows, 2 columns	3 rows, 1 column	1 row, 3 columns

In the matrices above, the first number of the subscript indicates the row and the second number of the subscript indicates the column; a_{32} means the number or element in the third row and second column position.

The number of rows and columns determines the **dimensions** of a matrix. The dimensions of the matrices above, in order, are 3×3, 3×2, 3×1, and 1×3.

It is possible for two matrices to be equal. The matrix $\begin{bmatrix} 1 & -2 \\ -1 & 4 \end{bmatrix}$ is equal to

the matrix $\begin{bmatrix} \dfrac{2}{2} & -\dfrac{4}{2} \\ -\dfrac{6}{6} & \dfrac{12}{3} \end{bmatrix}$ since they have the same dimensions, 2×2, and their

corresponding elements are equal.

Equality of Matrices

> Two matrices are equal if they have the same dimensions and the elements in corresponding positions are equal.

Example 1 Determine which pairs of matrices are equal, if any.

$$\begin{bmatrix} -2 & 1 & 6 \\ 3 & -1 & 2 \end{bmatrix} \quad \begin{bmatrix} -\dfrac{6}{3} & \dfrac{7}{7} & \dfrac{-12}{-2} \\ \dfrac{12}{4} & -\dfrac{8}{8} & \dfrac{4}{2} \end{bmatrix} \qquad \qquad \begin{bmatrix} 1 & -3 & 2 \end{bmatrix} \quad \begin{bmatrix} 1 \\ -3 \\ 2 \end{bmatrix}$$

Dimensions of each matrix is 3×2.
Elements in corresponding positions are equal:

$$-2 = -\frac{6}{3} \qquad 1 = \frac{7}{7} \qquad 6 = \frac{-12}{-2}$$

$$3 = \frac{12}{4} \qquad -1 = -\frac{8}{8} \qquad 2 = \frac{4}{2}$$

Dimensions of one matrix is 1×3.
Dimensions of other matrix is 3×1.

Thus, the first pair are equal; the second pair are not.

You can find the sum of two matrices with the same dimensions, using the following property.

Sum of Two Matrices

The *sum* of two matrices, A and B, having the same dimensions is a matrix whose elements are the sums of the corresponding elements of A and B.

If $A = \begin{bmatrix} a_{11} & a_{12} \\ a_{21} & a_{22} \end{bmatrix}$ and $B = \begin{bmatrix} b_{11} & b_{12} \\ b_{21} & b_{22} \end{bmatrix}$, then

$$A + B = \begin{bmatrix} a_{11} + b_{11} & a_{12} + b_{12} \\ a_{21} + b_{21} & a_{22} + b_{22} \end{bmatrix}.$$

Example 2 If $A = \begin{bmatrix} -3 & -2 \\ 5 & 6 \end{bmatrix}$, $B = \begin{bmatrix} 4 & 8 \\ -7 & -3 \end{bmatrix}$, and $C = \begin{bmatrix} 4 \\ -7 \\ 1 \end{bmatrix}$, find $A + B$ and $A + C$, if possible.

A and B have the same dimensions. ▶ $A + B = \begin{bmatrix} -3 + 4 & -2 + 8 \\ 5 + (-7) & 6 + (-3) \end{bmatrix} = \begin{bmatrix} 1 & 6 \\ -2 & 3 \end{bmatrix}$

Since A and C do not have the same dimensions, they cannot be added.

Thus, $A + B = \begin{bmatrix} 1 & 6 \\ -2 & 3 \end{bmatrix}$, but $A + C$ is not defined.

Recall that the *additive identity* is 0 since $a + 0 = a$ for any real number a. Also, the *additive inverse* of any real number a is $-a$ since $a + (-a) = 0$. Similarly, identities and inverses exist for matrix addition.

Additive Identity Matrix
Additive Inverse Matrix

I is called the *additive identity* (or *zero*) *matrix* for any matrix A if A and I have the same dimensions and $A + I = A$.
$-A$ is called the *additive inverse matrix* of any matrix A if A and $-A$ have the same dimensions and $A + (-A) = I$.

Example 3 If $A = \begin{bmatrix} 2 & -3 \\ 5 & -7 \end{bmatrix}$, $I = \begin{bmatrix} 0 & 0 \\ 0 & 0 \end{bmatrix}$, and $-A = \begin{bmatrix} -2 & 3 \\ -5 & 7 \end{bmatrix}$, show that $A + I = A$ and $A + (-A) = I$.

A and I have the same dimensions. ▶ $A + I = \begin{bmatrix} 2 + 0 & -3 + 0 \\ 5 + 0 & -7 + 0 \end{bmatrix} = \begin{bmatrix} 2 & -3 \\ 5 & -7 \end{bmatrix} = A$

A and -A have the same dimensions. ▶ $A + (-A) = \begin{bmatrix} 2 + -2 & -3 + 3 \\ 5 + -5 & -7 + 7 \end{bmatrix} = \begin{bmatrix} 0 & 0 \\ 0 & 0 \end{bmatrix} = I$

Thus, $A + I = A$ and $A + (-A) = I$.

Matrix addition is *associative* and *commutative*.

Associative and Commutative Property of Addition

For any matrices A, B, and C having the same dimensions,
$(A + B) + C = A + (B + C)$ and $A + B = B + A$.

Example 4

If $A = \begin{bmatrix} -3 & 2 \\ -1 & 4 \end{bmatrix}$, $B = \begin{bmatrix} 5 & -3 \\ 3 & -6 \end{bmatrix}$, and $C = \begin{bmatrix} -1 & 8 \\ 4 & -2 \end{bmatrix}$, show that

$(A + B) + C = A + (B + C)$ and that $A + B = B + A$.

$$(A + B) + C = \left(\begin{bmatrix} -3 + 5 & 2 + -3 \\ -1 + 3 & 4 + -6 \end{bmatrix}\right) + \begin{bmatrix} -1 & 8 \\ 4 & -2 \end{bmatrix} = \begin{bmatrix} 2 + -1 & -1 + 8 \\ 2 + 4 & -2 + -2 \end{bmatrix} = \begin{bmatrix} 1 & 7 \\ 6 & -4 \end{bmatrix}$$

$$A + (B + C) = \begin{bmatrix} -3 & 2 \\ -1 & 4 \end{bmatrix} + \begin{bmatrix} 5 + -1 & -3 + 8 \\ 3 + 4 & -6 + -2 \end{bmatrix} = \begin{bmatrix} -3 + 4 & 2 + 5 \\ -1 + 7 & 4 + -8 \end{bmatrix} = \begin{bmatrix} 1 & 7 \\ 6 & -4 \end{bmatrix}$$

$$A + B = \begin{bmatrix} -3 + 5 & 2 + -3 \\ -1 + 3 & 4 + -6 \end{bmatrix} = \begin{bmatrix} 2 & -1 \\ 2 & -2 \end{bmatrix}$$

$$B + A = \begin{bmatrix} 5 + -3 & -3 + 2 \\ 3 + -1 & -6 + 4 \end{bmatrix} = \begin{bmatrix} 2 & -1 \\ 2 & -2 \end{bmatrix}$$

5. $\begin{bmatrix} 7 & 0 & 10 \\ 4 & -2 & -1 \\ 6 & -6 & -3 \end{bmatrix}$

Written **Exercises**

Determine if the pairs of matrices are equal.

(A)

1. $\begin{bmatrix} -1 & 0 \\ 3 & -2 \end{bmatrix}$, $\begin{bmatrix} -\frac{2}{2} & 5 - 5 \\ \frac{-6}{-2} & 2 - 4 \end{bmatrix}$ **yes**

2. $\begin{bmatrix} -2 & 3 \\ 1 & -2 \\ -3 & 4 \end{bmatrix}$, $\begin{bmatrix} -\frac{4}{2} & \frac{6}{2} \\ \frac{3}{3} & -\frac{8}{4} \\ \frac{9}{-3} & 2^2 \end{bmatrix}$ **yes**

3. $\begin{bmatrix} \frac{1}{2} \\ \frac{1}{3} \\ \frac{1}{4} \end{bmatrix}$, $\begin{bmatrix} -\frac{4}{8} & -\frac{3}{9} & -\frac{5}{20} \end{bmatrix}$ **no**

Find each sum, if possible.

4. $\begin{bmatrix} -2 & -3 \\ 4 & -6 \\ -5 & 1 \end{bmatrix} + \begin{bmatrix} 4 & 6 \\ -1 & 7 \\ 8 & -2 \end{bmatrix}$ $\begin{bmatrix} 2 & 3 \\ 3 & 1 \\ 3 & -1 \end{bmatrix}$

5. $\begin{bmatrix} -1 & 2 & 3 \\ -2 & 3 & -4 \\ 7 & -6 & 5 \end{bmatrix} + \begin{bmatrix} 8 & -2 & 7 \\ 6 & -5 & 3 \\ -1 & 0 & -8 \end{bmatrix}$ **above**

6. $\begin{bmatrix} 4 & -2 & 1 \\ 3 & -6 & -4 \end{bmatrix} + \begin{bmatrix} 3 & 8 \\ 1 & 7 \\ 5 & -2 \end{bmatrix}$ **not possible**

7. $\begin{bmatrix} 7 & -3 & 6 \\ -1 & 4 & -8 \end{bmatrix} + \begin{bmatrix} -7 & 3 & -6 \\ 1 & -4 & 8 \end{bmatrix}$ $\begin{bmatrix} 0 & 0 & 0 \\ 0 & 0 & 0 \end{bmatrix}$

8. $[9 \ 8 \ -7] + \begin{bmatrix} 6 \\ -3 \\ -2 \end{bmatrix}$ **not possible**

9. $\begin{bmatrix} 0 & -8 \\ 9 & -1 \end{bmatrix} + \begin{bmatrix} -9 & -7 \\ -6 & -5 \end{bmatrix}$ $\begin{bmatrix} -9 & -15 \\ 3 & -6 \end{bmatrix}$

Let $A = \begin{bmatrix} 3 & 5 \\ -2 & -6 \end{bmatrix}$, $B = \begin{bmatrix} 8 & -3 \\ -7 & -6 \end{bmatrix}$, and $C = \begin{bmatrix} 1 & -2 \\ 7 & -9 \end{bmatrix}$.

10. Find $-A$, $-B$, and $-C$. **above**

10. $\begin{bmatrix} -3 & -5 \\ 2 & 6 \end{bmatrix}$, $\begin{bmatrix} -8 & 3 \\ 7 & 6 \end{bmatrix}$, $\begin{bmatrix} -1 & 2 \\ -7 & 9 \end{bmatrix}$

(B)

11. Show that $B + I = B$.
12. Show that $B + C = C + B$.
13. Show that $(B + C) + A = B + (C + A)$.
14. Show that $C + A = A + C$.
15. Show that $(C + A) + B = C + (A + B)$.
16. Show that $(A + C) + B = A + (C + B)$.

For Ex. 11–16, see TE Answer Section.

10.7 Matrix Multiplication

OBJECTIVES ▶ **To find the product of a scalar and a matrix**
To find the product of two matrices
To determine the properties of matrix multiplication

When working with matrices, any real number is called a **scalar.** You will now learn how to find the product of a scalar and a matrix.

Product of Scalar and Matrix

The product of a scalar k and a matrix A is the matrix kA obtained by multiplying each element of A by k.

If $A = \begin{bmatrix} a_{11} & a_{12} & a_{13} \\ a_{21} & a_{22} & a_{23} \\ a_{31} & a_{32} & a_{33} \end{bmatrix}$, then $kA = \begin{bmatrix} ka_{11} & ka_{12} & ka_{13} \\ ka_{21} & ka_{22} & ka_{23} \\ ka_{31} & ka_{32} & ka_{33} \end{bmatrix}$.

Example 1 Find kA if $k = -3$ and $A = \begin{bmatrix} -1 & 2 & -3 \\ 13 & -5 & 4 \end{bmatrix}$.

$$kA = \begin{bmatrix} -3(-1) & -3(2) & -3(-3) \\ -3(13) & -3(-5) & -3(4) \end{bmatrix} = \begin{bmatrix} 3 & -6 & 9 \\ -39 & 15 & -12 \end{bmatrix}$$

Thus, $kA = \begin{bmatrix} 3 & -6 & 9 \\ -39 & 15 & -12 \end{bmatrix}$.

Two matrices can be multiplied if the number of columns of one matrix equals the number of rows of the other.

Product of Two Matrices

The *product* of two matrices, A and B, where the number of columns of A equals the number of rows of B, is a matrix whose elements are obtained by multiplying the row elements of A by the column elements of B in the following manner.

If $A = \begin{bmatrix} a_{11} & a_{12} & a_{13} \\ a_{21} & a_{22} & a_{23} \end{bmatrix}$ and $B = \begin{bmatrix} b_{11} & b_{12} \\ b_{21} & b_{22} \\ b_{31} & b_{32} \end{bmatrix}$, then

$A \cdot B = \begin{bmatrix} a_{11}b_{11} + a_{12}b_{21} + a_{13}b_{31} & a_{11}b_{12} + a_{12}b_{22} + a_{13}b_{32} \\ a_{21}b_{11} + a_{22}b_{21} + a_{23}b_{31} & a_{21}b_{12} + a_{22}b_{22} + a_{23}b_{32} \end{bmatrix}$.

In general, $A_{m \times n} \cdot B_{n \times r} = AB_{m \times r}$ where $m \times n$, $n \times r$, and $m \times r$ are the dimensions of the matrices.

Example 2 If $A = \begin{bmatrix} -1 & 2 & -6 \\ 3 & -1 & 4 \end{bmatrix}$ and $B = \begin{bmatrix} -6 & 4 \\ -2 & 3 \\ 1 & -4 \end{bmatrix}$, find AB, if possible.

$$AB = \begin{bmatrix} (-1)(-6) + 2(-2) + (-6)(1) & (-1)(4) + 2(3) + (-6)(-4) \\ 3(-6) + (-1)(-2) + 4(1) & 3(4) + (-1)(3) + 4(-4) \end{bmatrix} = \begin{bmatrix} -4 & 26 \\ -12 & -7 \end{bmatrix}$$

Thus, $AB = \begin{bmatrix} -4 & 26 \\ -12 & -7 \end{bmatrix}$.

Recall that the *multiplicative identity* is 1 since $a \cdot 1 = a$ for any real number a. Also, the *multiplicative inverse* of any nonzero real number a is $\frac{1}{a}$ since $a \cdot \frac{1}{a} = 1$. Similarly, identities and inverses exist for matrix multiplication.

Multiplicative Identity Matrix

I is called the *multiplicative identity matrix* for any square matrix A if $A \cdot I = A$.

Multiplicative Inverse Matrix

A^{-1} is called the *multiplicative inverse matrix* of any square matrix A if $A \cdot A^{-1} = I$.

For a 3 × 3 square matrix, the multiplicative identity matrix is $\begin{vmatrix} 1 & 0 & 0 \\ 0 & 1 & 0 \\ 0 & 0 & 1 \end{vmatrix}$.

Example 3 If $A = \begin{bmatrix} -1 & 2 & 3 \\ -2 & 4 & -1 \\ 5 & -3 & 2 \end{bmatrix}$ and $I = \begin{bmatrix} 1 & 0 & 0 \\ 0 & 1 & 0 \\ 0 & 0 & 1 \end{bmatrix}$, show that $AI = A$.

$$AI = \begin{bmatrix} -1(1) + 2(0) + 3(0) & -1(0) + 2(1) + 3(0) & -1(0) + 2(0) + 3(1) \\ -2(1) + 4(0) + (-1)(0) & -2(0) + 4(1) + (-1)(0) & -2(0) + 4(0) + (-1)(1) \\ 5(1) + (-3)(0) + 2(0) & 5(0) + (-3)(1) + 2(0) & 5(0) + (-3)(0) + 2(1) \end{bmatrix}$$

$$= \begin{bmatrix} -1 & 2 & 3 \\ -2 & 4 & -1 \\ 5 & -3 & 2 \end{bmatrix} = A$$

Thus, $AI = A$.

Example 4 If $A = \begin{bmatrix} 1 & 4 \\ 2 & 9 \end{bmatrix}$ and $B = \begin{bmatrix} 9 & -4 \\ -2 & 1 \end{bmatrix}$, show that B is the multiplicative inverse of A by showing that $A \cdot B = I$.

$$A \cdot B = \begin{bmatrix} 1(9) + 4(-2) & 1(-4) + 4(1) \\ 2(9) + 9(-2) & 2(-4) + 9(1) \end{bmatrix} = \begin{bmatrix} 1 & 0 \\ 0 & 1 \end{bmatrix} = I.$$

Thus, B is the multiplicative inverse of A, or $B = A^{-1}$.

260

The next example shows you how to find the multiplicative inverse matrix for a given square matrix.

Example 5 If $A = \begin{bmatrix} -3 & -2 \\ -2 & 1 \end{bmatrix}$, find A^{-1}.

Let $A^{-1} = \begin{bmatrix} b_{11} & b_{12} \\ b_{21} & b_{22} \end{bmatrix}$.

$\begin{bmatrix} 3 & -2 \\ -2 & 1 \end{bmatrix} \cdot \begin{bmatrix} b_{11} & b_{12} \\ b_{21} & b_{22} \end{bmatrix} = \begin{bmatrix} 1 & 0 \\ 0 & 1 \end{bmatrix}$ ◄ $A \cdot A^{-1} = I$

$\begin{bmatrix} 3b_{11} - 2b_{21} & 3b_{12} - 2b_{22} \\ -2b_{11} + b_{21} & -2b_{12} + b_{22} \end{bmatrix} = \begin{bmatrix} 1 & 0 \\ 0 & 1 \end{bmatrix}$

Since the two matrices are equal, the corresponding elements are equal.

$3b_{11} - 2b_{21} = 1$ $3b_{12} - 2b_{22} = 0$
$-2b_{11} + b_{21} = 0$ $-2b_{12} + b_{22} = 1$

Solve each system of equations.

$\begin{array}{l} 3b_{11} - 2b_{21} = 1 \\ \underline{-4b_{11} + 2b_{21} = 0} \\ \quad -b_{11} \qquad\quad = 1 \end{array}$ $\begin{array}{l} 3b_{12} - 2b_{22} = 0 \\ \underline{-4b_{12} + 2b_{22} = 2} \\ \quad -b_{12} \qquad\quad = 2 \end{array}$

$\boxed{b_{11} = -1}$ $\boxed{b_{12} = -2}$

$\begin{array}{l} -2b_{11} + b_{21} = 0 \\ -2(-1) + b_{21} = 0 \end{array}$ $\begin{array}{l} 3b_{12} - 2b_{22} = 0 \\ 3(-2) - 2b_{22} = 0 \end{array}$

$\boxed{b_{21} = -2}$ $\boxed{b_{22} = -3}$

Thus, $A^{-1} = \begin{bmatrix} -1 & -2 \\ -2 & -3 \end{bmatrix}$.

Matrix multiplication is *associative*.

Associative Property of Multiplication

> For any matrices A, B, and C, if the products exist,
> $(A \cdot B) \cdot C = A \cdot (B \cdot C)$.

As shown in Example 6, matrix multiplication is *not commutative*.

Example 6 If $A = \begin{bmatrix} 2 & 1 \\ -1 & 3 \end{bmatrix}$ and $B = \begin{bmatrix} -1 & 5 \\ 4 & -2 \end{bmatrix}$, show that $A \cdot B \neq B \cdot A$.

$A \cdot B = \begin{bmatrix} 2(-1) + 1(4) & 2(5) + 1(-2) \\ -1(-1) + 3(4) & -1(5) + 3(-2) \end{bmatrix} = \begin{bmatrix} 2 & 8 \\ 13 & -11 \end{bmatrix}$

$B \cdot A = \begin{bmatrix} -1(2) + 5(-1) & -1(1) + 5(3) \\ 4(2) + -2(-1) & 4(1) + -2(3) \end{bmatrix} = \begin{bmatrix} -7 & 14 \\ 10 & -2 \end{bmatrix}$

Thus, $A \cdot B \neq B \cdot A$.

Written Exercises

Which of the following pairs of matrices can be multiplied? Why or why not?

(A) **1.** $[3 \quad 2 \quad -1]$, $\begin{bmatrix} 2 \\ -1 \\ 5 \end{bmatrix}$ yes

2. $\begin{bmatrix} 2 & -1 & 3 \\ 4 & 6 & -1 \end{bmatrix}$, $\begin{bmatrix} 1 & -3 \\ -5 & 4 \\ 6 & -2 \end{bmatrix}$ yes

3. $\begin{bmatrix} 4 & 5 & -6 \\ 3 & -1 & 7 \end{bmatrix}$, $\begin{bmatrix} -1 & 4 & -6 \\ 5 & 9 & -2 \end{bmatrix}$ no

4. $\begin{bmatrix} -1 & -5 \\ 6 & -3 \\ -4 & 7 \end{bmatrix}$, $\begin{bmatrix} 3 & -1 & 5 \\ -7 & 6 & -7 \end{bmatrix}$ yes

For Ex. 5–21, see TE Answer Section.

Find each product, if possible.

5. $-3 \begin{bmatrix} -2 & 3 & 5 \\ -6 & 10 & 6 \\ 8 & 12 & -4 \end{bmatrix}$

6. $9 \begin{bmatrix} -8 & -2 \\ 5 & -1 \\ 9 & 3 \end{bmatrix}$

7. $-1 \begin{bmatrix} 7 & 6 & 9 \\ 8 & -1 & -5 \end{bmatrix}$

8. $\begin{bmatrix} -2 & 1 \\ 4 & -3 \end{bmatrix} \cdot \begin{bmatrix} 4 & -5 \\ -1 & 2 \end{bmatrix}$

9. $\begin{bmatrix} -2 & 3 & 8 \\ 4 & -1 & -3 \end{bmatrix} \cdot \begin{bmatrix} 4 & 6 & 1 \\ -1 & 7 & -2 \\ 2 & -1 & 2 \end{bmatrix}$

10. $\begin{bmatrix} 1 & -3 & 2 \\ -1 & 2 & -4 \\ -2 & 5 & -3 \end{bmatrix} \cdot \begin{bmatrix} 1 & 4 & -1 \\ -2 & 5 & -4 \end{bmatrix}$

11. $\begin{bmatrix} 1 & -8 & -9 \\ 7 & 6 & -3 \end{bmatrix} \cdot \begin{bmatrix} -1 & 0 & 1 \\ 0 & 1 & -1 \\ -1 & 0 & 1 \end{bmatrix}$

Find the multiplicative identity and the multiplicative inverse for each matrix, if possible.

(B) **12.** $\begin{bmatrix} 6 & -7 \\ -4 & 5 \end{bmatrix}$

13. $\begin{bmatrix} -8 & 2 \\ -6 & -1 \end{bmatrix}$

14. $\begin{bmatrix} -1 & 2 & -3 \\ -2 & 4 & 2 \end{bmatrix}$

15. $\begin{bmatrix} 7 & -3 & 2 \\ -1 & -2 & 5 \\ 6 & -4 & 8 \end{bmatrix}$

$A = \begin{bmatrix} -3 & 1 \\ -2 & -4 \end{bmatrix}$, $B = \begin{bmatrix} 1 & -6 \\ 3 & -2 \end{bmatrix}$ and $C = \begin{bmatrix} 7 & -3 \\ 2 & 5 \end{bmatrix}$. Show that each of the following statements is true.

16. $(A \cdot B) \cdot C = A \cdot (B \cdot C)$

17. $B \cdot C \neq C \cdot B$

18. $A \cdot B \neq B \cdot A$

19. $A \cdot (B + C) = A \cdot B + A \cdot C$

20. $A \cdot I = I \cdot A$

21. $B \cdot B^{-1} = I$

$A = \begin{bmatrix} a_{11} & a_{12} \\ a_{21} & a_{22} \end{bmatrix}$, $B = \begin{bmatrix} b_{11} & b_{12} \\ b_{21} & b_{22} \end{bmatrix}$ and $C = \begin{bmatrix} c_{11} & c_{12} \\ c_{21} & c_{22} \end{bmatrix}$. All elements represent real numbers.

Determine which are true. Justify your answer by performing the computations.

(C) **22.** $A \cdot B = B \cdot A$ False

23. $I \cdot A = A \cdot I = A$ True

24. $(A \cdot B)^{-1} = B^{-1} \cdot A^{-1}$ True

25. $A \cdot (B + C) = A \cdot B + A \cdot C$ True

26. $(A \cdot B)^2 = A^2 \cdot B^2$ False

27. $A \cdot A^{-1} = A^{-1} \cdot A = I$ True

Cumulative Review

1. Solve $\sqrt{x - 8} + \sqrt{x} = 4$. 9

2. Find the distance from $A(3, 5)$ to $B(-6, 4)$. $\sqrt{82}$

10.8 Matrix Transformations

OBJECTIVE ▶ **To solve a system of three linear equations in three variables using matrix transformations**

The general system of two linear equations $\begin{matrix} a_1x + b_1y = c_1 \\ a_2x + b_2y = c_2 \end{matrix}$ can be written in matrix form as

$$\begin{bmatrix} a_1 & b_1 \\ a_2 & b_2 \end{bmatrix} \begin{bmatrix} x \\ y \end{bmatrix} = \begin{bmatrix} c_1 \\ c_2 \end{bmatrix}.$$

Multiplying the two matrices on the left side, you get

$$\begin{bmatrix} a_1x + b_1y \\ a_2x + b_2y \end{bmatrix} = \begin{bmatrix} c_1 \\ c_2 \end{bmatrix}.$$

By the definition of equality of matrices, the elements are equal, so

$$a_1x + b_1y = c_1$$
$$a_2x + b_2y = c_2.$$

Similarly, the general system of three linear equations $\begin{matrix} a_1x + b_1y + c_1z = d_1 \\ a_2x + b_2y + c_2z = d_2 \\ a_3x + b_3y + c_3z = d_3 \end{matrix}$

can be written in matrix form as $\begin{bmatrix} a_1 & b_1 & c_1 \\ a_2 & b_2 & c_2 \\ a_3 & b_3 & c_3 \end{bmatrix} \begin{bmatrix} x \\ y \\ z \end{bmatrix} = \begin{bmatrix} d_1 \\ d_2 \\ d_3 \end{bmatrix}.$

Example 1 Multiply and solve for x, y, and z.

$$\begin{bmatrix} 1 & -2 & 1 \\ 0 & 1 & 0 \\ 0 & 0 & 1 \end{bmatrix} \begin{bmatrix} x \\ y \\ z \end{bmatrix} = \begin{bmatrix} 1 \\ 5 \\ -2 \end{bmatrix}$$

Multiply on the left side. ▶ $\begin{bmatrix} 1x - 2y + 1z \\ 0x + 1y + 0z \\ 0x + 0y + 1z \end{bmatrix} = \begin{bmatrix} 1 \\ 5 \\ -2 \end{bmatrix}$

$\begin{matrix} 1x - 2y + 1z = 1 \\ 0x + 1y + 0z = 5 \\ 0x + 0y + 1z = -2 \end{matrix}$ ◀ *Solve the system.*

$$y = 5 \qquad z = -2$$
$$1x - 2(5) + 1(-2) = 1$$
$$x - 10 - 2 = 1$$
$$x = 13$$

Thus, $x = 13$, $y = 5$, and $z = -2$.

A system of linear equations such as the one at the right is said to be in **triangular form.** The value of one of the variables in the system is given. The value of each of the other two variables can be found by substitution.

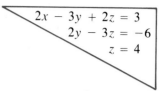

$$2x - 3y + 2z = 3$$
$$2y - 3z = -6$$
$$z = 4$$

In Example 2, a system of three linear equations is transformed into triangular form so that the solution of the system is easily obtained.

Example 2 Solve the system of equations by transforming it into triangular form:

$$2x - 3y - 3z = -1$$
$$-x + 2y + 4z = 5$$
$$3x - 4y - 5z = -3.$$

Step 1 Interchange the first two equations.

$$-x + 2y + 4z = 5$$
$$2x - 3y - 3z = -1$$
$$3x - 4y - 5z = -3$$

Step 2 Multiply the 1st equation by 2.
Add it to the 2nd equation.
Multiply the 1st equation by 3.
Add it to the 3rd equation.

$$-x + 2y + 4z = 5$$
$$0 + y + 5z = 9$$
$$0 + 2y + 7z = 12$$

Step 3 Multiply the 2nd equation of the new system by 2. Subtract it from the 3rd equation.
The system is in triangular form.

$$-x + 2y + 4z = 5$$
$$y + 5z = 9$$
$$- 3z = -6$$

Step 4 Solve for y. Substitute 2 for z in the 2nd equation.
Substitute -1 for y and 2 for z in the 1st equation.
Solve for x.

$\boxed{z = 2}$

$$y + 5z = 9$$
$$y + 5(2) = 9$$
$$\boxed{y = -1}$$
$$-x + 2y + 4z = 5$$
$$-x + 2(-1) + 4(2) = 5$$
$$\boxed{x = 1}$$

Thus, $(1, -1, 2)$ is the solution of the system.

Example 2 suggests that by applying a series of steps, called **transformations,** the coefficients and constants of a system of three linear equations can be changed until the system is in triangular form. **Matrix transformations** can be used in a similar way.
The matrix form of the system in Example 2 is

$$\begin{bmatrix} 2 & -3 & -3 \\ -1 & 2 & 4 \\ 3 & -4 & -5 \end{bmatrix} \begin{bmatrix} x \\ y \\ z \end{bmatrix} = \begin{bmatrix} -1 \\ 5 \\ -3 \end{bmatrix}.$$

The matrix of coefficients is sometimes called the **matrix of detached coefficients.**

264

In working with matrix transformations, it is convenient to write the matrix of detached coefficients and the matrix of constants in one combined matrix, called an **augmented matrix.** The augmented matrix for

$$\begin{bmatrix} 2 & -3 & -3 \\ -1 & 2 & 4 \\ 3 & -4 & -5 \end{bmatrix} \begin{bmatrix} x \\ y \\ z \end{bmatrix} = \begin{bmatrix} -1 \\ 5 \\ -3 \end{bmatrix} \text{ is } \begin{bmatrix} 2 & -3 & -3 & -1 \\ -1 & 2 & 4 & 5 \\ 3 & -4 & -5 & -3 \end{bmatrix}.$$

There are three elementary transformations that can be used to change an augmented matrix into an equivalent augmented matrix.

Elementary Matrix Transformations

Two augmented matrices are equivalent if one is obtained from the other by
(1) interchanging any two rows;
(2) multiplying each element of any row by a nonzero number; or
(3) adding the elements of any row to the corresponding elements of another row.

You can solve a system of three linear equations by using elementary matrix transformations. Begin by writing an augmented matrix. Then, transform it to an equivalent augmented matrix in triangular form with ones in the main diagonal.

$$\begin{bmatrix} 1 & b_1 & c_1 & d_1 \\ 0 & 1 & c_2 & d_2 \\ 0 & 0 & 1 & d_3 \end{bmatrix}$$
Augmented matrix
in triangular form

Example 3 Solve the system by matrix transformations:

$$5x - 2y + 3z = -7$$
$$-2x + 4y + z = 4$$
$$3x - 3y + 4z = 2.$$

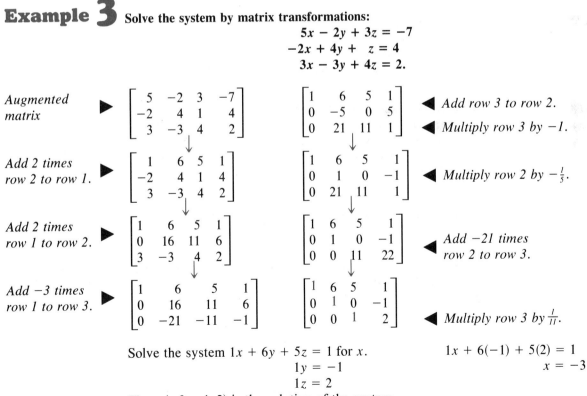

Augmented matrix
$$\begin{bmatrix} 5 & -2 & 3 & -7 \\ -2 & 4 & 1 & 4 \\ 3 & -3 & 4 & 2 \end{bmatrix}$$

$$\begin{bmatrix} 1 & 6 & 5 & 1 \\ 0 & -5 & 0 & 5 \\ 0 & 21 & 11 & 1 \end{bmatrix}$$ ◀ *Add row 3 to row 2.*
◀ *Multiply row 3 by −1.*

Add 2 times row 2 to row 1.
$$\begin{bmatrix} 1 & 6 & 5 & 1 \\ -2 & 4 & 1 & 4 \\ 3 & -3 & 4 & 2 \end{bmatrix}$$

$$\begin{bmatrix} 1 & 6 & 5 & 1 \\ 0 & 1 & 0 & -1 \\ 0 & 21 & 11 & 1 \end{bmatrix}$$ ◀ *Multiply row 2 by −$\frac{1}{5}$.*

Add 2 times row 1 to row 2.
$$\begin{bmatrix} 1 & 6 & 5 & 1 \\ 0 & 16 & 11 & 6 \\ 3 & -3 & 4 & 2 \end{bmatrix}$$

$$\begin{bmatrix} 1 & 6 & 5 & 1 \\ 0 & 1 & 0 & -1 \\ 0 & 0 & 11 & 22 \end{bmatrix}$$ ◀ *Add −21 times row 2 to row 3.*

Add −3 times row 1 to row 3.
$$\begin{bmatrix} 1 & 6 & 5 & 1 \\ 0 & 16 & 11 & 6 \\ 0 & -21 & -11 & -1 \end{bmatrix}$$

$$\begin{bmatrix} 1 & 6 & 5 & 1 \\ 0 & 1 & 0 & -1 \\ 0 & 0 & 1 & 2 \end{bmatrix}$$ ◀ *Multiply row 3 by $\frac{1}{11}$.*

Solve the system $1x + 6y + 5z = 1$ for x. $1x + 6(-1) + 5(2) = 1$
$$1y = -1$$ $x = -3$
$$1z = 2$$

Thus, $(-3, -1, 2)$ is the solution of the system.

Whenever a matrix can be transformed into an augmented matrix of the form

$\begin{bmatrix} 1 & 0 & 0 & d_1 \\ 0 & 1 & 0 & d_2 \\ 0 & 0 & 1 & d_3 \end{bmatrix}$, it is even easier to solve.

If you continue to transform the augmented matrix in Example 3 on page 265,

you get $\begin{bmatrix} 1 & 0 & 0 & -3 \\ 0 & 1 & 0 & -1 \\ 0 & 0 & 1 & 2 \end{bmatrix}$, which is equivalent to $\begin{bmatrix} 1 & 0 & 0 \\ 0 & 1 & 0 \\ 0 & 0 & 1 \end{bmatrix} \begin{bmatrix} x \\ y \\ z \end{bmatrix} = \begin{bmatrix} -3 \\ -1 \\ 2 \end{bmatrix}$.

So, $x = -3$, $y = -1$, and $z = 2$.

Written Exercises

Multiply and solve for x, y, and z.

(A) **1.** $\begin{bmatrix} 1 & 3 & -1 \\ 0 & 1 & -4 \\ 0 & 0 & 1 \end{bmatrix} \begin{bmatrix} x \\ y \\ z \end{bmatrix} = \begin{bmatrix} 40 \\ 14 \\ -3 \end{bmatrix}$
2. $\begin{bmatrix} 1 & -2 & 3 \\ 0 & 1 & 2 \\ 0 & 0 & 1 \end{bmatrix} \begin{bmatrix} x \\ y \\ z \end{bmatrix} = \begin{bmatrix} -6 \\ 10 \\ 4 \end{bmatrix}$
3. $\begin{bmatrix} 1 & 5 & -3 \\ 0 & 1 & 4 \\ 0 & 0 & 1 \end{bmatrix} \begin{bmatrix} x \\ y \\ z \end{bmatrix} = \begin{bmatrix} -8 \\ 16 \\ -3 \end{bmatrix}$

$x = 31, y = 2, z = -3$ $x = -14, y = 2, z = 4$ $x = -157, y = 28, z = -3$

Solve by using matrix transformations.

4. $-x + 2y - 3z = -8$
$2x + 3y + z = -3$
$-2x - y + 2z = 2$
$(1, -2, 1)$

5. $3x - 2y + 2z = -1$
$-2x + 3y - 3z = -1$
$-x - y + 4z = 8$
$(-1, 1, 2)$

6. $-2x + 3y - 2z = -1$
$-3x + 2y - z = -5$
$4x - 3y + 2z = 5$
$(2, -1, -3)$

7. $4x - 2y + z = 2$
$-x - 3y + 2z = -5$
$2x + y + 3z = -4$
$(1, 0, -2)$

8. $-3x + 4y + z = 5$
$2x + 5y + 3z = 0$
$-4x - 2y + 2z = 16$
$(-2, -1, 3)$

9. $2x - 3y + z = 10$
$-x + 2y + 3z = 1$
$-3x + y - 2z = -9$
$(1, -2, 2)$

Solve by using matrix transformations. Transform to get ones in the main diagonal and zeros in all other positions except the constants column.

(B) **10.** $-3x + 2y + 3z = 7$
$2x + 3y - z = -7$
$-x - y + z = 4$
$(-1, -1, 2)$

11. $2x - 3y + 3z = -12$
$3x - 2y - 2z = 4$
$-3x + 2y - z = 5$
$(0, 1, -3)$

12. $-4x + 5y + 2z = 2$
$3x + 2y + 3z = -4$
$-3x - 5y + 2z = 20$
$(-2, -2, 2)$

13. $6x - 3y + 4z = -4$
$-2x + 5y + 3z = 2$
$3x - 2y - 2z = -9$
$(-3, -2, 2)$

14. $5x + 2y + 3z = 12$
$3x - 5y + 2z = 13$
$-2x + 3y + 4z = -19$
$(4, -1, -2)$

15. $-3x - 4y + 5z = 4$
$2x + 5y + 3z = -1$
$-4x - y + 2z = -8$
$(3, -2, 1)$

Solve by using matrix transformations.

(C) **16.** $-2a + 3b - c + 2d = -11$
$3a - 2b + 3c + d = 9$
$-4a + 5b - 3c - 3d = -9$
$4a - 3b + 4c + 4d = 7$ $(1, -1, 2, -2)$

17. $5a + 2b + 3c - 2d = 4$
$-3a + 3b - 2c + 4d = 9$
$-2a - 3b + 4c - 2d = -14$
$3a + 4b - 5c + 3d = 19$ $(1, 2, -1, 1)$

18. $3r + 2s - 2t + 4v = 4$
$-2r - 3s + 4t - 3v = 4$
$4r + 2s - 3t + v = 1$
$-3r - 4s + 3t + 5v = 9$ $(2, -1, 2, 1)$

19. $-2r + 6s - 3t + 3v = -5$
$4r - 3s + 2t - v = -3$
$-3r - 4s - 3t + 4v = -15$
$5r + 2s - 2t + 3v = -20$ $(-2, 1, 3, -2)$

10.9 Problem Solving Using Linear Systems

OBJECTIVES ▶ **To solve a digit problem using a system of linear equations**
To solve various types of word problems using systems of linear equations

A two-digit number like 76 can be written as follows:
$$76 = 70 + 6$$
$$= 10(7) + 1(6),$$
where 7 is the *tens digit* and 6 is the *units digit*.

To *reverse the digits* of a two-digit number, interchange the positions of the tens and units digits as follows: $76 = 10(7) + 6$; its reverse, $67 = 10(6) + 7$.

The *sum of the digits* of a two-digit number like 76 is $7 + 6$, or 13.

Two-Digit Number

Tens digit	Units digit	Original number	Sum of the digits	Number with its digits reversed
t	u	$10t + u$	$t + u$	$10u + t$

Systems of linear equations can often be used to solve problems involving two-digit numbers.

Example 1

In a certain two-digit number, the units digit is 24 less than 3 times the sum of the digits. If the digits are reversed, the new number is 18 more than the original number. Find the two-digit number.

READ

PLAN

Let t = tens digit and u = units digit.
The units digit is 24 less than 3 times the sum of the digits.

$$u = 3(t + u) - 24 \quad \text{or} \quad 2u + 3t = 24$$

When the digits are reversed, the new number is 18 more than the original.

$$10u + t = 10t + u + 18 \quad \text{or} \quad u - t = 2$$

SOLVE

Solve the system $2u + 3t = 24$.
$\qquad\qquad\qquad\qquad u - t = 2$

$$
\begin{array}{l}
2u + 3t = 24 \\
\underline{3u - 3t = 6} \\
 5u = 30 \\
\boxed{u = 6}
\end{array}
$$

$$
\begin{array}{l}
u - t = 2 \\
6 - t = 2 \\
\boxed{t = 4}
\end{array}
$$

INTERPRET

The two-digit number is $10t + u = 10 \cdot 4 + 6$, or 46. (Check the answer in the problem.)

Thus, the two-digit number is 46.

A three-digit number like 658 can be written as follows:

$$658 = 600 + 50 + 8$$
$$= 100(6) + 10(5) + 1(8),$$ where 6 is the hundreds digit,

5 is the tens digit, and 8 is the units digit.

When the digits are reversed, you get

$$856 = 100(8) + 10(5) + 6.$$

The sum of the digits of the number is $6 + 5 + 8$, or 19.

Three-Digit Number

Hundreds digit	Tens digit	Units digit	Original number	Sum of the digits	Number with its digits reversed
h	t	u	$100h + 10t + u$	$h + t + u$	$100u + 10t + h$

Example 2

In a certain three-digit number, if the sum of the digits is doubled, the result is 16 more than 3 times the tens digit. One more than twice the hundreds digit is the units digit. The hundreds digit is 11 decreased by twice the tens digit. Find the three-digit number.

Represent the data.

Let h = hundreds digit, t = tens digit, and u = units digit.

Write a system of equations.

$$(1)\quad 2(h + t + u) = 3t + 16 \qquad (2)\ 2h + 1 = u \qquad (3)\ h = 11 - 2t$$
$$2h + 2t + 2u = 3t + 16$$
$$2h - t + 2u = 16 \qquad\qquad\qquad 2h - u = -1 \qquad\qquad h + 2t = 11$$

$$
\begin{aligned}
2h - t + 2u &= 16 \\
2h \quad\ - u &= -1 \\
h + 2t \quad &= 11
\end{aligned}
$$

Solve the system.

Solve the system for h using determinants.

$$
h = \frac{\begin{vmatrix} 16 & -1 & 2 \\ -1 & 0 & -1 \\ 11 & 2 & 0 \end{vmatrix}\begin{matrix} 16 & -1 \\ -1 & 0 \\ 11 & 2 \end{matrix}}{\begin{vmatrix} 2 & -1 & 2 \\ 2 & 0 & -1 \\ 1 & 2 & 0 \end{vmatrix}\begin{matrix} 2 & -1 \\ 2 & 0 \\ 1 & 2 \end{matrix}} = \frac{[0 + 11 + (-4)] - [0 + (-32) + 0]}{[0 + 1 + 8] - [0 + (-4) + 0]} = \frac{39}{13}, \text{ or } 3
$$

$$
\begin{aligned}
2h + 1 &= u \qquad\qquad h + 2t = 11 \\
2 \cdot 3 + 1 &= u \qquad\qquad 3 + 2t = 11
\end{aligned}
$$

$$\boxed{h = 3} \qquad \boxed{7 = u} \qquad \boxed{t = 4}$$

Check the answer.

The three-digit number is $100h + 10t + u = 100 \cdot 3 + 10 \cdot 4 + 7$, or 347. (Check the answer in the problem.)

Thus, the three-digit number is 347.

In Chapter 2, you learned how to solve various types of mixture problems by writing and then solving one equation in one variable. Many of these same problems can be solved by using a system of two equations in two variables.

Example 3

Some dried fruit worth $3.45/kg is to be mixed with some raisins worth $2.10/kg to make a mixture worth $2.64/kg. How many kilograms of dried fruit and how many kilograms of raisins should be used to make 10.5 kg of the mixture?

Represent the data.

Represent the data in a table. Use two variables.

	No. of kg	Value/kg	Value in ¢
Dried fruit	x	345	$345x$
Raisins	y	210	$210y$
Mixture	10.5	264	$264(10.5)$

Write a system of equations.

$$\text{(kg of fruit)} + \text{(kg of raisins)} = \text{(kg of mixture)}$$
$$x \qquad + \qquad y \qquad = \qquad 10.5$$

$$\text{(Value of fruit)} + \text{(Value of raisins)} = \text{(Value of mixture)}$$
$$345x \qquad + \qquad 210y \qquad = \qquad 264(10.5)$$

Solve the system.

Solve the system $x + y = 10.5$ by substitution.
$$345x + 210y = 2772$$

$$x + y = 10.5 \qquad\qquad 345x + 210y = 2772 \qquad\qquad y = 10.5 - x$$
$$y = 10.5 - x \qquad\quad 345x + 210(10.5 - x) = 2772 \qquad y = 10.5 - 4.2$$
$$345x + 2205 - 210x = 2772 \qquad\quad \boxed{y = 6.3}$$
$$135x = 567$$
$$\boxed{x = 4.2}$$

Check the answer.

(4.2 kg at $3.45/kg) + (6.3 kg at $2.10/kg)	(10.5 kg at $2.64/kg)
$14.49 + $13.23	$27.72
$27.72	

Thus, 4.2 kg of dried fruit and 6.3 kg of raisins should be used.

In the exercises on page 270, you will be asked to solve a variety of word problems using a system of two (three) linear equations in two (three) variables.

PROBLEM SOLVING USING LINEAR SYSTEMS

Written Exercises _____

Use a system of two (three) linear equations in two (three) variables to solve each problem.

(A)

1. The tens digit of a two-digit number is 3 more than twice the units digit. If the digits are reversed, the resulting number is 45 less than the original number. Find the original number. **72**

2. A two-digit number is 9 less than 4 times the sum of its digits. If the digits are reversed, the new number is 54 more than the original number. Find the original number. **39**

3. A two-digit number is 27 more than the number obtained by reversing the digits. The number is also 38 more than twice the sum of the digits. Find the two-digit number. **52**

4. The sum of the digits of a two-digit number is 8. If the digits are reversed, the new number is 18 more than the original number. Find the two-digit number. **35**

5. Brand A coffee worth $5.60/kg is to be mixed with Brand B coffee worth $6.10/kg to make 15 kg of a mixture worth $5.90/kg. How many kilograms of each brand should be mixed? **brand A: 6 kg, brand B: 9 kg**

6. Powdered milk worth $3.60/kg and cocoa worth $5.20/kg are to be mixed so that their combination is worth $82.40. How many kilograms of milk should be used if the weight of the milk is 10 times that of the cocoa? **20 kg**

(B)

7. The tens digit of a three-digit number is 7 less than 3 times the units digit. Twice the hundreds digit is 10 less than 3 times the tens digit. Three times the sum of the three digits is 4 more than 8 times the hundreds digit. Find the three-digit number. **785**

8. A three-digit number is 198 less than the number obtained by reversing the digits. Twice the sum of the digits is 5 more than 7 times the tens digit. The tens digit is 5 less than twice the hundreds digit. Find the original number. **436**

9. Ralph is 8 years younger than Lisa but 6 years ago, she was three times as old as he was. How old is each now? **Ralph: 10, Lisa: 18**

10. A certain boat can travel 24 km downstream in 48 minutes and 21 km upstream in 72 minutes. Find the rate of the boat in still water and the rate of the current in kilometers per hour. **boat: 23.75 km/h, current: 6.25 km/h**

11. Mrs. Brown invested a total of $6,400, one part at 9% per year and the rest at 8% per year. At the end of 2 years 6 months, she had earned a total of $1,380 in simple interest. How much did she invest at each rate? **$4,000 at 9%, $2,400 at 8%**

12. Sunflower seeds worth $2.90/kg, peanuts worth $2.50/kg, and almonds worth $3.30/kg are to be mixed to make 40 kg worth $3.00/kg. If the combined weight of the peanuts and the almonds is triple that of the seeds, how many kilograms of each should be used? **sunflower: 10 kg, peanut: 10 kg, almond: 20 kg**

(C)

13. A chemist mixed iodine solutions of 25%, 40%, and $37\frac{1}{2}$% to obtain 15 L of a $33\frac{1}{3}$% iodine solution. Find the volume of each solution if the volume of the 25% solution was $1\frac{1}{2}$ times the volume of the $37\frac{1}{2}$% solution. **25%: 6 L, 40%: 5 L, $37\frac{1}{2}$%: 4 L**

Computer Activities

Gasoline Prices

Computers are often used to find optimum energy values for consumers, oil companies, and automobile manufacturers. The program below produces a 3 by 4 matrix of comparison values for three automobile samples, including the miles per gallon and the cost per mile for each sample.

PROGRAM

```
10 PRINT "PROGRAM FORMS A 3 BY 4 MATRIX GIVING SAMPLE"
20 PRINT "NUMBER, TOTAL MILES, MILES PER GALLON AND"
30 PRINT "COST PER MILE FOR THREE SAMPLES"
40 DIM M(3), R(3), T(3)
50 FOR I = 1 TO 3
60 PRINT "ENTER COST OF GALLON OF GAS"
70 INPUT C
80 PRINT "ENTER MILEAGE BEFORE FILL-UP"
90 INPUT S
100 PRINT "ENTER MILEAGE AT NEXT FILL-UP"
110 INPUT E
120 PRINT "ENTER AMOUNT OF GALLONS OF GAS BOUGHT"
130 INPUT G
140 LET M(I) = E - S
150 REM MILES PER GALLON IS R
160 LET R(I) = M(I)/G
170 REM COST PER MILE IS T
180 LET T(I) = C/R(I)
190 NEXT I
200 REM PRINT OUT MATRIX
210 PRINT "SAMPLE NUMBER", "TOTAL MILES"
220 PRINT "MILES PER GALLON", "CENTS PER MILE"
230 FOR I = 1 TO 3
240 PRINT I, M(I), R(I), T(I)
250 NEXT I
260 END
```

Exercises See TE Answer Section.

Type in the above program and run it for the following values:

Sample 1	C = $1.15	S = 36,352	E = 36,930	G = 15
Sample 2	C = $1.50	S = 40,132	E = 40,350	G = 12
Sample 3	C = $1.75	S = 25,625	E = 25,978	G = 20

ACTIVITY: GASOLINE PRICES

Vocabulary
determinant [10.4]
  2 by 2 [10.4]   3 by 3 [10.5]
matrix [10.4]
  additive identity [10.6]
  additive inverse [10.6]
  augmented [10.8]
  dimensions of [10.6]
  multiplicative identity [10.7]
  multiplicative inverse [10.7]
  square [10.4]
ordered triple [10.3]   scalar [10.7]
system of equations [10.1]
  consistent [10.1]   dependent [10.1]
  inconsistent [10.1]   independent [10.1]

Solve each system of equations graphically. Classify each system as consistent, inconsistent, dependent, or independent. [10.1]

1. $3x + 2y - 14 = 0$
    $2y - 3x + 10 = 0$

2. $5y - 2x = 15$
    $2x - 5y = 15$ **below**

3. $3(x + 2y) = 2y + 8$ **all (x, y) such that**
    $4y = 8 - 3x$ $y = -\frac{3}{4}x + 2$; con, dep

4. $-2(y - 3x) = (y + 5x) + 9$ **(−3, −4); con, ind**
    $2(3x - 2y) = -(5x - 7y) + 11$

Solve each system of equations by substitution. [10.2]

5. $5x + 2y = 7$ **6.** $4x + 5y = 12$ **(3, 0)**
    $4x - y = 3$ **(1, 1)** $6x - y = 18$

Solve each system of equations by addition. [10.2]

7. $4x - 3y - 10 = 0$ **8.** $5x + 4y + 8 = 0$
    $5x + 6y + 7 = 0$ **(1, −2)** $7y = 3x + 33$ **(−4, 3)**

9. $4x - 6y = 11$ **★ 10.** $c_1x + d_1y = e_1$
    $-2x + 3y = 9$ $c_2x + d_2y = e_2$

Solve each system of equations. [10.3]

11. $x + 3y + 2z = 11$ **1. (4, 1) con, ind**
    $4x + 2y + 5z = 15$ **2. no solution; inc**
    $-2x + 3y - z = 5$ **(−1, 2, 3)**

12. $-3x + 4y = -6$
    $5x - 3z = -22$ **9. no solution**
    $3y + 2z = -1$ **(−2, −3, 4)**

Find the value of each determinant. [10.4]

13. $\begin{vmatrix} 3 & -2 \\ 4 & 8 \end{vmatrix}$ **32**   **14.** $\begin{vmatrix} a - b & -b \\ -3 & 2 \end{vmatrix}$

15. $\begin{vmatrix} m + n & m \\ m & m - n \end{vmatrix}$ **16.** $\begin{vmatrix} a - b & a + b \\ a - b & a - b \end{vmatrix}$

14. $2a - 5b$ **15.** $-n^2$ **16.** $2b^2 - 2ab$

17. $\begin{vmatrix} -2 & 1 & 2 \\ 3 & -1 & 4 \\ 5 & 2 & 3 \end{vmatrix}$ **55**   **18.** $\begin{vmatrix} a & 0 & b \\ 0 & 1 & 0 \\ c & 0 & d \end{vmatrix}$ [10.5] **ad − bc**

Solve each system of equations by using determinants. [10.4]

19. $-2x + 5y = 19$ **20.** $2x - y = 0.7$
    $4x - 7y = -29$ $3x - 4y = -0.2$
        (−2, 3)   **(0.6, 0.5)**

21. $3x + 2y - 5z = 5$ [10.5]
    $2x - y + z = 6$
    $x + 4y - 6z = -4$ **(2, −3, −1)**

For Ex. 10, 22–25, see TE Answer Section.

22. Find the sum, if possible: [10.6]

$$\begin{bmatrix} -1 & 2 & 3 \\ 2 & 3 & -1 \\ 4 & -2 & 5 \end{bmatrix} + \begin{bmatrix} 6 & -1 & 2 \\ -3 & 4 & 5 \\ 2 & -1 & -3 \end{bmatrix}$$

23. Find the product, if possible: [10.7]

$$\begin{bmatrix} -2 & 3 & 1 \\ 4 & -1 & 2 \end{bmatrix} \cdot \begin{bmatrix} 1 & -1 & 2 \\ -3 & 4 & 1 \\ 2 & -2 & 3 \end{bmatrix}$$

Find the multiplicative identity, additive inverse, and the multiplicative inverse for each, if possible. [10.6], [10.7]

24. $\begin{bmatrix} 7 & -3 \\ 2 & 1 \end{bmatrix}$ **25.** $\begin{bmatrix} 3 & -1 & 2 \\ 2 & 1 & 2 \\ -3 & 2 & -1 \end{bmatrix}$

Solve by using matrix transformations. [10.8]

26. $3x - 2y + 2z = 10$
    $-2x + y - 3z = -8$
    $x + 3y - 2z = -3$ **(2, −1, 1)**

Use a system of two (three) equations in two (three) variables to solve each problem. [10.9]

27. A two-digit number is 45 less than the number obtained by reversing the digits. Find the original number if twice the sum of the digits is 1 more than 7 times the tens digit. **38**

28. The sum of a three-digit number and the number obtained by reversing the digits is 1,655. In the original number, the sum of its digits is 1 more than 3 times the tens digit, and the tens digit is 5 less than twice the units digit. Find the original number. **976**

Chapter Ten Test

Solve each system graphically. Classify each system as consistent, inconsistent, dependent, or independent.

1. $4y - 3x - 8 = 0$
   $x + 2y + 6 = 0$
   $(-4, -1)$; con, ind

2. $4y - 5x = 8$
   $5x - 4y = 12$
   no solution; inc

3. Solve the system by substitution.
   $4x - 3y = 3$
   $x - 2y = -8$ $(6, 7)$

4. Solve the system by addition.
   $2x + 3y = 10$
   $3x + 5y = 19$ $(-7, 8)$

Solve each system of equations.

5. $2x - 3y + 5z = 13$
   $-3x + 3y - 2z = -8$
   $5x - 2y + 4z = 2$ $(-2, -4, 1)$

6. $2x + 5y = -2$
   $5x - 2z = 14$
   $3y + 4z = 6$ $(4, -2, 3)$

Find the value of each determinant.

7. $\begin{vmatrix} -3 & 4 \\ 6 & -2 \end{vmatrix}$ -18

8. $\begin{vmatrix} a + b & 2a + b \\ b & a + b \end{vmatrix}$ a^2

9. $\begin{vmatrix} 3 & -1 & 2 \\ -2 & 3 & 4 \\ 2 & 1 & -2 \end{vmatrix}$ -50

Solve each system of equations by using determinants.

10. $3x + 5y = 1$
   $-2x + 3y = 12$ $(-3, 2)$

11. $3x + 2y + 2z = -3$
   $2x + 3y + 3z = -2$
   $-3x - 5y + z = -9$ $(-1, 2, -2)$

12. Find the sum, if possible:

$\begin{bmatrix} 3 & -1 & 2 \\ 4 & 5 & 3 \\ -2 & -6 & -1 \end{bmatrix} + \begin{bmatrix} -2 & 3 & 4 \\ -3 & -2 & 1 \\ 4 & 6 & -5 \end{bmatrix}$

12. $\begin{bmatrix} 1 & 2 & 6 \\ 1 & 3 & 4 \\ 2 & 0 & -6 \end{bmatrix}$

13. Find the product, if possible:

$\begin{bmatrix} 2 & 1 & 3 \\ -3 & 2 & -4 \end{bmatrix} \cdot \begin{bmatrix} -1 & 4 & 6 \\ 2 & -1 & -3 \\ 3 & -2 & 1 \end{bmatrix}$

13. $\begin{bmatrix} 9 & 1 & 12 \\ -5 & -6 & -28 \end{bmatrix}$

14. $\begin{bmatrix} -3 & -2 \\ 1 & -2 \end{bmatrix}, \begin{bmatrix} 1 & 0 \\ 0 & 1 \end{bmatrix}$

Find the additive inverse and the multiplicative identity for each, if possible.

14. $\begin{bmatrix} 3 & 2 \\ -1 & 2 \end{bmatrix}$

15. $\begin{bmatrix} 4 & -1 & 6 \\ -3 & 2 & 1 \\ 2 & -4 & -3 \end{bmatrix}$

16. Solve by using matrix transformations.
   $4x - 3y + z = -8$
   $-3x + 2y - 5z = -11$
   $2x - 4y + 3z = 9$ $(-\frac{58}{15}, -\frac{17}{15}, \frac{61}{15})$

15. $\begin{bmatrix} -4 & 1 & -6 \\ 3 & -2 & -1 \\ -2 & 4 & 3 \end{bmatrix}, \begin{bmatrix} 1 & 0 & 0 \\ 0 & 1 & 0 \\ 0 & 0 & 1 \end{bmatrix}$

Use a system of two linear equations in two variables to solve each problem.

17. If 3 more than a first number is divided by a second number and if 5 less than the second number is divided by 1 more than the first number, both quotients are $\frac{3}{4}$. Find the numbers. 1st: 3; 2nd: 8

18. A certain two-digit number is 27 less than the number obtained by reversing the digits. Three times the sum of the digits is 3 more than 7 times the tens digit. Find the two-digit number. 69

★**19.** Solve this system using matrix transformations:
   $3a + 4b - 2c + 5d = -5$
   $-2a - 3b + c + 2d = 14$
   $4a + 2b + 3c - 3d = -8$
   $-5a - 2b + 4c + 3d = 23$ $(-1, -2, 2, 2)$

College Prep Test

DIRECTIONS: Choose the *one* best answer to each question or problem.

1. Which ordered pair (x, y) is a solution of
   $ax + by = 7ab$? **B**
   $3ax - 2by = 6ab$

   (A) $(3b, 4a)$ (B) $(4b, 3a)$
   (C) $(2b, 0)$ (D) all of these
   (E) None of these

2. The equation of
   the graph shown is
   D 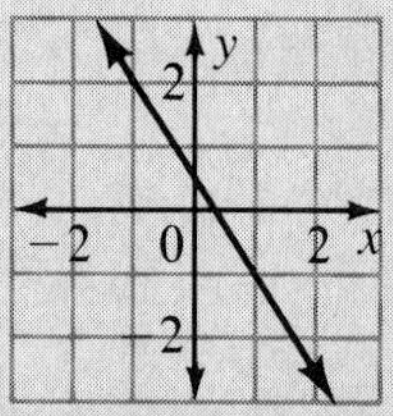
   (A) $y = -\frac{1}{2}x + \frac{1}{2}$
   (B) $y = -\frac{2}{3}x + \frac{1}{2}$
   (C) $y = \frac{1}{2}x - 1$
   (D) $y = -\frac{3}{2}x + \frac{1}{2}$
   (E) $y = \frac{1}{2}x - \frac{3}{2}$

3. $\dfrac{\begin{vmatrix} a & b \\ c & d \end{vmatrix}}{\begin{vmatrix} 2b & -a \\ 2d & -c \end{vmatrix}} =$ **C**

   (A) $-\frac{1}{2}$ (B) $-\frac{1}{4}$ (C) $\frac{1}{2}$
   (D) $\frac{1}{4}$ (E) None of these

4. If the value of $\begin{vmatrix} 2x & -4 \\ x & x \end{vmatrix}$ is 6, then x
   equals **E**

   (A) 1   (B) -1 (C) -1 or 3
   (D) -3 (E) 1 or -3

5. The solution of the system
   $\frac{x}{2} + y + z = 6$
   $x + \frac{y}{3} - z = 6$
   $x + y + 2z = 5$ is **E**

   (A) $(4, 1, 1)$ (B) $(6, 3, 1)$ (C) $(4, 3, -1)$
   (D) $(1, 1, 2)$ (E) None of these

6. In a collection of pennies, nickels, and
   dimes, the pennies and nickels are worth
   35¢, the nickels and dimes are worth 80¢,
   and the pennies and dimes are worth 75¢.
   What is the value of the collection? **D**

   (A) \$1.90   (B) \$1.55   (C) \$1.15
   (D) 95¢   (E) None of these

7. Which of the following matrices are
   equivalent? **A**

   $$R = \begin{bmatrix} 1 & 5 & 6 \\ 2 & 3 & -1 \end{bmatrix} \qquad S = \begin{bmatrix} 2 & 3 & -1 \\ 1 & 5 & 6 \end{bmatrix}$$

   $$T = \begin{bmatrix} 3 & 8 & -5 \\ 2 & 3 & -1 \end{bmatrix} \qquad U = \begin{bmatrix} 2 & 6 & 7 \\ 2 & 3 & -1 \end{bmatrix}$$

   (A) R and S (B) R and T
   (C) T and U (D) R, S, and T
   (E) R, S, T, and U

8. Consider square matrices A, B, C, and I,
   each having the same dimensions and with
   I the multiplicative identity element. Which
   of the following statements is false? **B**

   (A) $A + B = B + A$
   (B) $AB = BA$
   (C) $AI = IA = A$
   (D) $A + (B + C) = (A + B) + C$
   (E) $(A \cdot B) \cdot C = A \cdot (B \cdot C)$

11 FUNCTIONS

Careers: Pharmacy

The primary responsibility of a pharmacist is to dispense prescribed medicines. Although the pharmacist may be called upon to mix ingredients in order to obtain a certain form of a given medicine, most medicines prescribed today are produced in consumable form by the drug manufacturers. When situations require the pharmacist to mix ingredients, he or she must possess a clear understanding of the mathematics that is needed to obtain the precise results.

All states require pharmacists to obtain a license to practice. Five years of study and a degree from an accredited college or university are usually the minimum requirements. Most pharmacists study sciences, such as chemistry, biology, and social sciences as well as mathematics.

11.1 Relations and Functions

OBJECTIVES ▶ **To determine the domain and the range of a relation**
To determine whether a relation is a function

The points shown on the coordinate plane at the right are associated with the following set of ordered pairs of real numbers:

$$A = \{(-1, -2), (-1, 1), (2, -1), (3, 2)\}$$

A set of ordered pairs is called a **relation**. The set of all first coordinates of the ordered pairs is called the **domain** of the relation, and the set of all second coordinates is called the **range** of the relation.

The domain of relation A above is $\{-1, 2, 3\}$ and the range is $\{-2, 1, -1, 2\}$. Notice that even though -1 is the first coordinate of two different points, it is listed only once in the domain.

Definition:
Relation

A *relation* is a set of ordered pairs of real numbers.

Domain

The *domain* of a relation is the set of all first coordinates of the ordered pairs.

Range

The *range* of a relation is the set of all second coordinates of the ordered pairs.

Example 1

Write the relation G whose graph is given. Determine the domain and the range of G.

$$G = \{(-3, -2), (-1, 3), (3, 2), (4, 1)\}$$

The domain of G is $\{-3, -1, 3, 4\}$.
The range of G is $\{-2, 3, 2, 1\}$.

For relation G in Example 1, notice that each ordered pair has a different first coordinate. However, this is not true for all relations. When it is true, the relation is called a **function**.

Definition:
Function

A *function* is a relation in which different ordered pairs have different first coordinates.

Example 2 Determine which of the following relations is a function.

$A = \{(-1, 2), (2, 2), (3, -1)\}$ $B = \{(2, 3), (3, 4), (2, 6)\}$

All ordered pairs have
different first coordinates.

Thus, relation A is a function.

Two ordered pairs have a first
coordinate of 2.

Thus, relation B is not a function.

A given relation may contain infinitely many ordered pairs (x, y) of real
numbers. A graph of one such relation is shown in Example 3.

Example 3 Determine the domain and the range of the
relation C whose graph is given. Is the
relation a function?

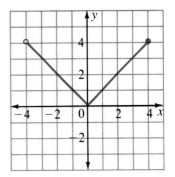

The domain is $\{x | -4 < x \le 4\}$.
The range is $\{y | 0 \le y \le 4\}$.

For each value of x, there is exactly one
value for y. All ordered pairs (x, y) have
different first coordinates.

Thus, relation C is a function.

The open circle on the segment in the figure above indicates that this point is
not a point of the graph. Notice that -4 is not included in the domain of the
relation.

You can tell whether a given relation is a function by examining its graph. If
any vertical line intersects the graph of a relation in more than one point, the
relation is not a function.

Example 4 Determine which graphs are the graphs of functions.
**Draw vertical lines. Check to see if any of the lines intersect the graph in more
than one point.**

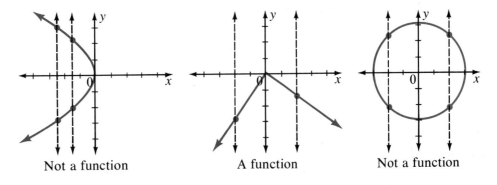

Not a function   A function   Not a function

RELATIONS AND FUNCTIONS   **277**

Oral Exercises

State the domain and the range of each relation.

1. $\{(2, -1), (3, 2), (2, -5)\}$ **2.** $\{(-2, -2), (6, -4), (5, 2)\}$ **3.** $\{(-2, 3), (2, -3), (3, -2), (-3, 2)\}$

D = {2, 3}, R = {−5, −1, 2}   D = {−2, 5, 6}, R = {−4, −2, 2}   D = {−3, −2, 2, 3}, R = {−3, −2, 2, 3}

Written Exercises

(A) Determine the domain and the range of each relation. Is the relation a function?

1. $\{(3, 1), (2, -3), (-1, 5), (-2, -2), (0, 2)\}$ **2.** $\{(8, 7), (7, 8), (-7, 8), (-8, 7), (5, -2)\}$

3. $\{(0, 0), (8, 7), (-3, 6), (4, -1), (5, -1)\}$ **4.** $\{(3, -3), (4, -4), (5, -5), (-3, 3), (-4, 4)\}$

5. $\{(3, 2), (4, 2), (-4, -2), (-3, 2), (2, -3)\}$ **6.** $\{(0, 1), (3, 1), (0, 4), (1, -3), (2, -3)\}$

7. $\{(1, -2), (-1, 0), (2, -4), (-2, 3), (3, 0)\}$ **8.** $\{(9, 8), (7, 9), (8, 9), (-9, 8), (-8, 7)\}$

9. $\{(4, -1), (-1, 4), (-1, 3), (4, -3), (-3, 0)\}$ **10.** $\{(6, -3), (-3, 3), (-6, -3), (6, 5), (-3, 6)\}$

Write the relation G whose graph is given. Determine the domain and the range of G.

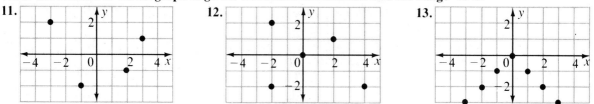

11.   **12.**   **13.**

Determine the domain and the range of each relation whose graph is given. Is the relation a function?

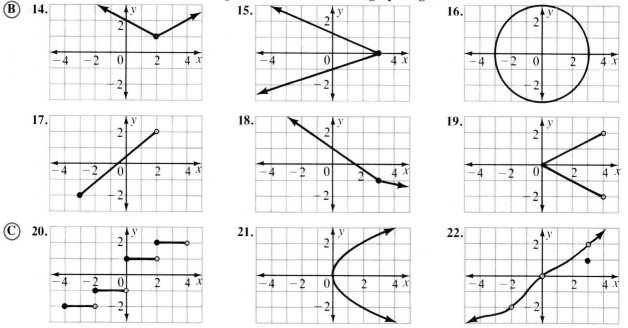

(B) **14.**   **15.**   **16.**

17.   **18.**   **19.**

(C) **20.**   **21.**   **22.**

Determine the domain and the range of each relation. Is the relation a function?

23. $\{\ldots, (-4, -2), (-2, -1), (0, 0), (2, 1), \ldots\}$ **24.** $\{(2, 4), (3, 9), (4, 16), (5, 25), \ldots\}$

25. $\{(4, 2), (9, 3), (16, 4), (25, 5), (36, 6), \ldots\}$ **26.** $\{\ldots, (-2, -1), (-1, 1), (0, 3), (1, 5), (2, 7), \ldots\}$

For all Written Exercises on this page, see TE Answer Section.

11.2 Values and Composition of Functions

▶ **To find the value of a function, given an element in the domain of the function**
To find the range of a function, given its domain
To determine the domain of a function having infinitely many elements
To find a value of a function that is composed of two other functions

The graph of the function, $f = \{(-3, -2),$ $(-2, 3), (3, 2), (4, 1)\}$, is shown at the right. A lowercase letter is usually used to name a function. Notice that each element of the domain is paired with exactly one element of the range.

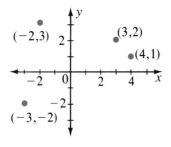

Domain of f: $\{-3, -2, 3, 4\}$
$\quad\quad\quad \updownarrow \quad \updownarrow \; \updownarrow \; \updownarrow$
Range of f: $\{-2, \quad 3, 2, 1\}$

Each element of the range is called a **value of the function.** The expression $f(-3) = -2$ is read "the value of f at negative 3 equals negative two," or "f at negative three equals negative two," or "f of negative three equals negative two." In general, the notation $f(x)$ means the value of f at x.

Definition:
Value of a Function

> For any ordered pair, (x, y), of a function, f,
> $f(x) = y$. The *value of f* at x equals y.

Example 1 Let $g = \{(-1, -2), (0, 3), (2, 3), (3, -1)\}$. Find $g(-1)$, $g(0)$, $g(2)$ and $g(3)$.

$$(-1, -2) \quad\quad (0, 3) \quad\quad (2, 3) \quad\quad (3, -1)$$
$$\nearrow \quad\quad\quad\quad \nearrow \quad\quad\quad \nearrow \quad\quad\quad \nearrow$$
$$g(-1) \quad\quad\quad g(0) \quad\quad\quad g(2) \quad\quad\quad g(3)$$

Thus, $g(-1) = -2$, $g(0) = 3$, $g(2) = 3$, and $g(3) = -1$.

A function f is often defined by giving an equation or formula for its range.

Example 2 If $f(x) = 2x - 3$, find $f(1)$, $f(-2)$, and $f(-a)$.

Substitute for x in $f(x) = 2x - 3$.

$$f(x) = 2x - 3 \quad\quad\quad f(x) = 2x - 3 \quad\quad\quad f(x) = 2x - 3$$
$$f(1) = 2(1) - 3 \quad\quad\quad f(-2) = 2(-2) - 3 \quad\quad\quad f(-a) = 2(-a) - 3$$
$$= -1 \quad\quad\quad\quad\quad\quad = -7 \quad\quad\quad\quad\quad\quad = -2a - 3$$

Example 3 If $f(x) = 3x + 2$, find $f(2a - 5)$, $f(a + b)$, and $f(a + h) - f(a)$.

$$f(x) = 3x + 2$$
$$f(2a - 5) = 3(2a - 5) + 2$$
$$= 6a - 15 + 2$$
$$= 6a - 13$$

$$f(x) = 3x + 2$$
$$f(a + b) = 3(a + b) + 2$$
$$= 3a + 3b + 2$$

$$f(x) = 3x + 2$$
$$f(a + h) - f(a) = 3(a + h) + 2 - [3(a) + 2]$$
$$= 3a + 3h + 2 - 3a - 2$$
$$= 3h$$

Example 4 If $h(x) = -x^2 + 3$, find the range of h for D (domain) $= \{-2, 0, 1\}$.

$$h(x) = -x^2 + 3$$
$$h(-2) = -(-2)^2 + 3$$
$$= -4 + 3$$
$$= -1$$

$$h(x) = -x^2 + 3$$
$$h(0) = -(0)^2 + 3$$
$$= 0 + 3$$
$$= 3$$

$$h(x) = -x^2 + 3$$
$$h(1) = -(1)^2 + 3$$
$$= -1 + 3$$
$$= 2$$

Thus, R (range) $= \{-1, 3, 2\}$.

The domain or the range of a given function may contain infinitely many elements. For example, sometimes the domain, the range, or both the domain and the range are defined for all real numbers. You should always check to see if there are any values for which the domain or the range is undefined. Unless told otherwise, you should assume that the domain contains all of the real numbers that produce real number values for the function.

Example 5 If $g(x) = \dfrac{1}{x(x - 2)}$, determine the domain of g.

All real numbers in the domain give real-number values for $g(x)$ in the range except those numbers that make the denominator of $\dfrac{1}{x(x - 2)}$ equal to 0.
If $(x)(x - 2) = 0$, then $x = 0$ or $x - 2 = 0$
$$x = 2$$

Thus, the domain is {all real numbers except 0 and 2}.

Sometimes a function is composed of other functions. Given an element in the domain, you can find a value of the function as shown in Example 6.

Example 6 If $f(x) = x + 2$ and $g(x) = 2x^2 - 3$, find $f(g(-4))$ and $g(f(-4))$.

$$g(x) = 2x^2 - 3$$
$$g(-4) = 2(-4)^2 - 3$$
$$= 2 \cdot 16 - 3$$
$$= 29$$

$$f(g(-4)) = f(29)$$
$$f(29) = 29 + 2$$
$$= 31$$

$$f(x) = x + 2$$
$$f(-4) = -4 + 2$$
$$= -2$$

$$g(f(-4)) = g(-2)$$
$$g(-2) = 2(-2)^2 - 3$$
$$= 5$$

Thus, $f(g(-4)) = 31$ and $g(f(-4)) = 5$.

Written Exercises _____

(A)
Let $g = \{(2, -3), (-1, 5), (-4, -2), (0, 5), (8, -1), (-7, 9)\}$. Find each of the following function values.
1. $g(2)$ -3 2. $g(-1)$ 5   3. $g(-4)$ -2 4. $g(0)$ 5   5. $g(8)$ -1 6. $g(-7)$ 9

Let $f(x) = -2x + 5$. Find each of the following function values.
7. $f(2)$ 1   8. $f(-1)$ 7   9. $f(0)$ 5   10. $f(-2)$ 9   11. $f(5)$ -5 12. $f(-a)$ $2a + 5$ 13. $f(b)$ $-2b + 5$

Let $t(x) = x^2 + 3x - 1$. Find each of the following function values.
14. $t(0)$ -1 15. $t(-1)$ -3 16. $t(-5)$ 9   17. $t(a + b)$ $a^2 + 2ab + b^2 + 3a + 3b - 1$ 18. $t(2a + 3)$ $4a^2 + 18a + 17$

Find the range of each function for the given domain.
19. $h(x) = x + 5$; $D = \{-1, 0, 2\}$ {4, 5, 7}   20. $f(x) = -3x + 2$; $D = \{-2, 2, 3\}$ {8, -4, -7}
21. $t(x) = 2x - 3$; $D = \{0, 1, 3\}$ {-3, -1, 3}   22. $g(x) = 4x + 3$; $D = \{-3, 2, 0\}$ {-9, 11, 3}
23. $g(x) = x^2 - 3$; $D = \{-2, 0, 2\}$ {1, -3}   24. $t(x) = (x - 2)^2$; $D = \{-1, 0, 2\}$ {9, 4, 0}
25. $f(x) = |x|$; $D = \{-3, -2, 0, 1, 2\}$ {3, 2, 1, 0}   26. $h(x) = \sqrt{x}$; $D = \{0, 1, 4, 9\}$ {0, 1, 2, 3}

Let $f(x) = x - 1$ and $g(x) = 2x$. Find each of the following.
27. $f(g(2))$ 3   28. $g(f(2))$ 2   29. $g(f(-3))$ -8 30. $f(g(-3))$ -7
31. {all real numbers except 0} 32. {all real numbers except 0 and -2} 33. {all real numbers except 3 and 4}
Find the domain of each function. 36. {all real numbers except 7 and -2}

(B)
31. $h(x) = \dfrac{1}{x}$ 32. $t(x) = \dfrac{1}{x(x + 2)}$ 33. $f(x) = \dfrac{3x}{(x - 3)(x - 4)}$

34. $g(x) = -\dfrac{4x^2 - 3x}{(x + 1)(x + 3)}$ 35. $f(x) = \dfrac{2x}{x^2 + 4x - 12}$ 36. $t(x) = \dfrac{-3x^2}{x^2 - 5x - 14}$

34. {all real numbers except -1 and -3}   35. {all real numbers except -6 and 2}
Let $f(x) = 2x - 3$ and $g(x) = x^2 - 2$. Find each of the following.
Assume that no denominator has the value of 0.
37. $f(2) - g(3)$ -6 38. $g(-1) - f(-2)$ 6   39. $f(-3) - g(0)$ -7 40. $f(a) + g(b)$
41. $f(a + h) - f(a)$ $2h$ 42. $g(a + h) - g(a)$ 43. $f(a) - f(t)$ $2a - 2t$ 44. $g(a) - f(b)$
45. $f(g(a))$ $2a^2 - 7$ 46. $g(f(a))$ 47. $g(f(-3a))$ 48. $f(g(-3a))$ $18a^2 - 7$

(C)
49. $\dfrac{f(a + h) - f(a)}{h}$ 2   50. $\dfrac{g(a) - g(b)}{a - b}$ $a + b$ 51. $\dfrac{f(b) - f(a)}{b - a}$ 2   52. $\dfrac{g(c + h) - g(c)}{h}$ $2c + h$

40. $2a + b^2 - 5$ 42. $2ah + h^2$ 44. $a^2 - 2b + 1$ 46. $4a^2 - 12a + 7$ 47. $36a^2 + 36a + 7$

53. If $s(x) = -x + 2$ and $t(x) = -x - 2$, find $t(s(x))$ and $s(t(x))$. Does $t(s(x)) = s(t(x))$?

   $x - 4$, $x + 4$, no

54. If $f(x) = 3x - 4$ and $g(x) = \dfrac{x + 4}{3}$, find $f(g(x))$ and $g(f(x))$. Does $f(g(x)) = g(f(x))$? x, x, yes

55. If $f(x) = x^2 - 3$, $g(x) = 5x + 2$, and $h(x) = 4 - x$, find $f(g(h(3)))$ and $h(g(f(-2)))$. 46, -3

56. If $t(x) = x^2 - 3x + 2$ and $s(x) = -x - 3$, and $v(x) = 5 - x$, find $t(s(v(-a)))$ and $s(v(t(a + 3)))$. $a^2 + 19a + 90$, $a^2 + 3a - 6$

➤ A Challenge To You

If $f(x) = x^2 - 3$, $g(x) = 5x + 2$, and $h(x) = 4 - x$, find
(1) $f(g(h(a)))$ and (2) $h(g(f(c)))$. $25a^2 - 220a + 481$; $17 - 5c^2$

11.3 Linear and Constant Functions

OBJECTIVES ▶ To determine whether a given function is a linear function or a constant function, given either an equation of the function or a graph of the function
To draw the graphs of some special functions

As shown in the figures below, the graph of a **linear function** may be a line, a ray, or a segment, depending upon the domain of the function.

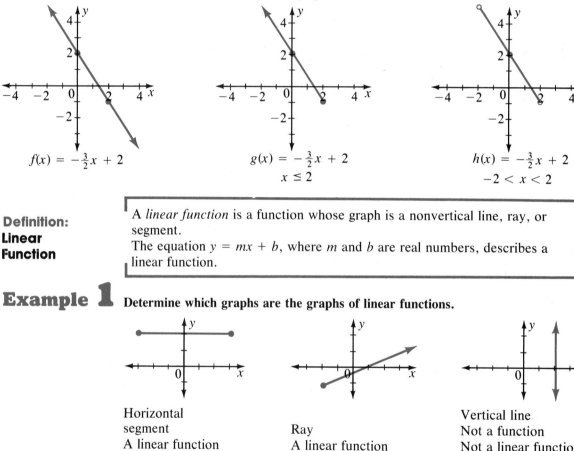

$$f(x) = -\tfrac{3}{2}x + 2$$

$$g(x) = -\tfrac{3}{2}x + 2$$
$$x \leq 2$$

$$h(x) = -\tfrac{3}{2}x + 2$$
$$-2 < x < 2$$

Definition:
Linear Function

A *linear function* is a function whose graph is a nonvertical line, ray, or segment.
The equation $y = mx + b$, where m and b are real numbers, describes a linear function.

Example 1 Determine which graphs are the graphs of linear functions.

Horizontal
segment
A linear function

Ray
A linear function

Vertical line
Not a function
Not a linear function

The graph of a linear function described by the equation $y = mx + b$, where $m = 0$, is a horizontal line, ray, or segment, depending upon the domain of the function. A function of this type is called a **constant function.**

Definition:
Constant Function

A constant function is a linear function whose graph is a horizontal line, ray, or segment.
The equation $y = mx + b$, where $m = 0$ and b is a real number, or $y = b$, describes a constant function.

Example 2 Determine which graphs are the graphs of constant functions.

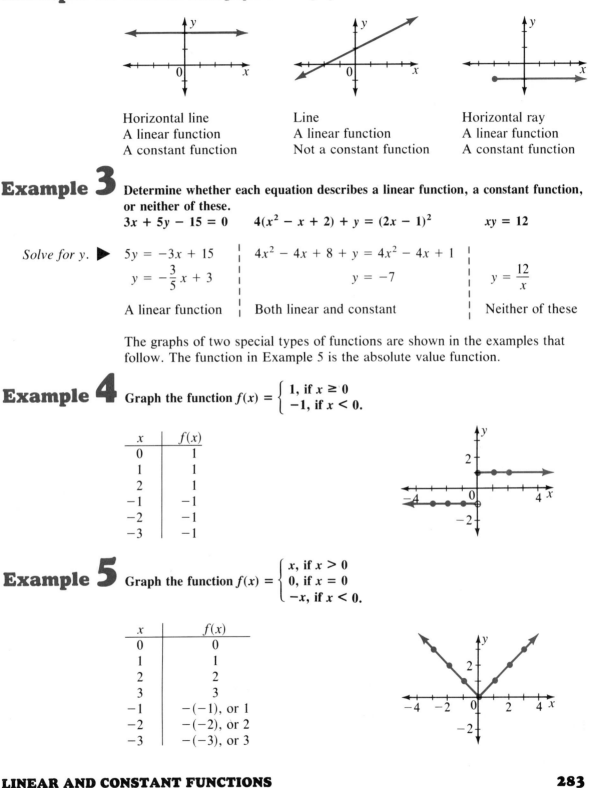

Horizontal line
A linear function
A constant function

Line
A linear function
Not a constant function

Horizontal ray
A linear function
A constant function

Example 3 Determine whether each equation describes a linear function, a constant function, or neither of these.

$$3x + 5y - 15 = 0 \qquad 4(x^2 - x + 2) + y = (2x - 1)^2 \qquad xy = 12$$

Solve for y. ▶

$$5y = -3x + 15 \qquad\qquad 4x^2 - 4x + 8 + y = 4x^2 - 4x + 1$$

$$y = -\frac{3}{5}x + 3 \qquad\qquad\qquad y = -7 \qquad\qquad\qquad y = \frac{12}{x}$$

A linear function $\quad$ Both linear and constant $\quad$ Neither of these

The graphs of two special types of functions are shown in the examples that follow. The function in Example 5 is the absolute value function.

Example 4 Graph the function $f(x) = \begin{cases} 1, \text{ if } x \geq 0 \\ -1, \text{ if } x < 0. \end{cases}$

x	$f(x)$
0	1
1	1
2	1
-1	-1
-2	-1
-3	-1

Example 5 Graph the function $f(x) = \begin{cases} x, \text{ if } x > 0 \\ 0, \text{ if } x = 0 \\ -x, \text{ if } x < 0. \end{cases}$

x	$f(x)$
0	0
1	1
2	2
3	3
-1	$-(-1)$, or 1
-2	$-(-2)$, or 2
-3	$-(-3)$, or 3

LINEAR AND CONSTANT FUNCTIONS

Reading in Algebra

True or false?
1. A constant function is a linear function. **True**
2. A vertical line is the graph of a function that is not a linear function. **False**
3. The equation $f(x) = b$, where b is a real number, describes a constant function. **True**
4. The equation $x = 0$ describes a linear function. **False**

Written Exercises

Determine whether each of the following describes a linear function, a constant function, or neither of these.

(A)
1. $y = 2x - 5$ **L**
2. $y = -2x$ **L**
3. $y = -5$ **C, L**
4. $f(x) = 3x + 1$ **L**
5. $h(x) = x^2$ **N**
6. $t(x) = \frac{x}{2}$ **L**
7. $x = -7$ **N**
8. $g(x) = 3$ **C, L**
9. $y = x$ **L**
10. $x = y + 2$ **L**
11. $xy = 9$ **N**
12. $h(x) = 6, -2 \leq x \leq 2$ **C, L**
13. $5(7x - 2y) - 15x = 20x - 4$
14. $(2x + 3)^2 + 5 = (2x - 3)^2 + 4$ **N**
15. $h(x) = 3x - 2, x \geq 1$ **L**

(B)
16. $(x + 5)^2 - y = 10x$ **N**
17. $(x - 3)^2 + y = (x + 1)^2$ **L**
18. $2x - 3y - 6 = 3(-2y + x)$

13. **C, L**

19. $\{(5, 3), (7, 3), (9, 3), \ldots\}$ **C, L**
20. $\{(1, 7), (2, 9), (3, 11), (4, 13), \ldots\}$ **L**
21. $\{(3, 9), (4, 16), (5, 25)\}$ **N**

18. **L**

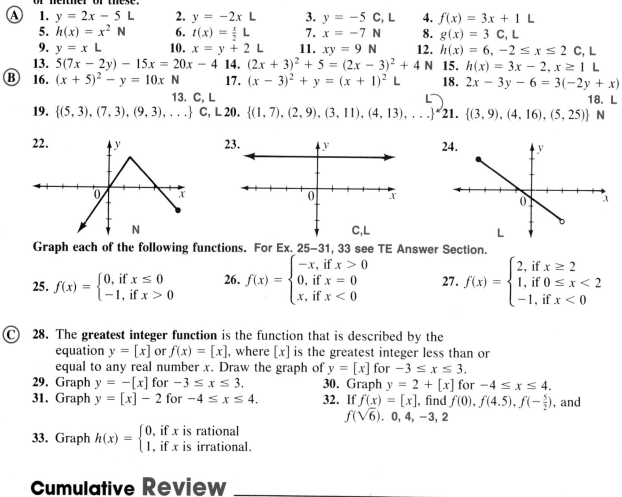

22.   **N**

23.   **C,L**

24.   **L**

Graph each of the following functions. For Ex. 25–31, 33 see TE Answer Section.

25. $f(x) = \begin{cases} 0, & \text{if } x \leq 0 \\ -1, & \text{if } x > 0 \end{cases}$

26. $f(x) = \begin{cases} -x, & \text{if } x > 0 \\ 0, & \text{if } x = 0 \\ x, & \text{if } x < 0 \end{cases}$

27. $f(x) = \begin{cases} 2, & \text{if } x \geq 2 \\ 1, & \text{if } 0 \leq x < 2 \\ -1, & \text{if } x < 0 \end{cases}$

(C)
28. The **greatest integer function** is the function that is described by the equation $y = [x]$ or $f(x) = [x]$, where $[x]$ is the greatest integer less than or equal to any real number x. Draw the graph of $y = [x]$ for $-3 \leq x \leq 3$.
29. Graph $y = -[x]$ for $-3 \leq x \leq 3$.
30. Graph $y = 2 + [x]$ for $-4 \leq x \leq 4$.
31. Graph $y = [x] - 2$ for $-4 \leq x \leq 4$.
32. If $f(x) = [x]$, find $f(0), f(4.5), f(-\frac{5}{2})$, and $f(\sqrt{6})$. **0, 4, −3, 2**

33. Graph $h(x) = \begin{cases} 0, & \text{if } x \text{ is rational} \\ 1, & \text{if } x \text{ is irrational.} \end{cases}$

Cumulative Review

Solve each proportion.

1. $\dfrac{5}{n + 4} = \dfrac{3}{n - 2}$ **11**

2. $\dfrac{4a + 3}{3} = \dfrac{2a + 5}{4}$ **$\frac{3}{10}$**

3. $\dfrac{5}{n - 7} = \dfrac{5}{7 - n}$ **no solution**

11.4 Inverse Relations and Functions

OBJECTIVES ▶ To find the inverse of a relation
To draw the graph of a function and its inverse
To determine whether the inverse of a function is a function

If you reverse the order of the elements of each ordered pair in a relation A, you will obtain the **inverse** of relation A, or A^{-1}.
For example, if $A = \{(1, 2), (2, -3), (5, 2)\}$,

then $A^{-1} = \{(2, 1), (-3, 2), (2, 5)\}$.

Notice that the domain of A is the range of A^{-1}, and the range of A is the domain of A^{-1}. Also, A is a function, but A^{-1} is not a function.

Definition:
Inverse
Relations

> The inverse of a relation A is the relation A^{-1} obtained by reversing the order of the elements of each ordered pair in A.
> A and A^{-1} are called *inverse relations*.

When both a relation and its inverse are functions, they are called **inverse functions.**

Example 1 Let $A = \{(-3, -2), (-1, 2), (3, -5)\}$. Find A^{-1}. Is A^{-1} a function?

Interchange the elements of each ordered pair in A.

$$A^{-1} = \{(-2, -3), (2, -1), (-5, 3)\}$$

All ordered pairs in A^{-1} have different first coordinates.

Thus, A^{-1} is a function.

When the inverse of a given function f is a function, the symbol f^{-1} is used to denote it. If a function is defined by an equation, the equation of the inverse is obtained by interchanging x and y in the original equation.

Example 2 A function f is defined by $y = -\frac{2}{3}x + 4$. Find an equation of f^{-1}.

$$y = -\frac{2}{3}x + 4$$
$$x = -\frac{2}{3}y + 4 \quad \blacktriangleleft \text{ } Interchange \text{ } x \text{ } and \text{ } y.$$
$$3x = -2y + 12$$
$$2y = -3x + 12$$
$$y = -\frac{3}{2}x + 6$$

Thus, an equation of f^{-1} is $y = -\frac{3}{2}x + 6$.

In the next two examples, you will learn how to graph the inverse of a function, and to determine whether the inverse is a function by using the vertical line test.

Example 3

Graph the function defined by $y = |x|$ and its inverse. Determine if the inverse is a function.

Make a table of ordered pairs of the function and its inverse.

x	$|x|$	function	inverse
0	0	$(0, 0)$	$(0, 0)$
1	1	$(1, 1)$	$(1, 1)$
2	2	$(2, 2)$	$(2, 2)$
-1	1	$(-1, 1)$	$(1, -1)$
-2	2	$(-2, 2)$	$(2, -2)$

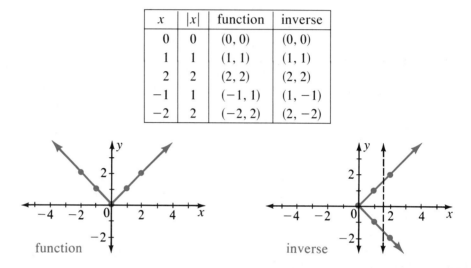

Since a vertical line intersects the graph of the inverse in two points, the inverse is not a function.

Example 4

Graph the function defined by $4x - 2y = 8$ and its inverse in the same coordinate plane. Determine if the inverse is a function.

$$4x - 2y = 8$$
$$-2y = -4x + 8$$
$$y = 2x - 4$$

x	$2x - 4$	function	inverse
0	-4	$(0, -4)$	$(-4, 0)$
1	-2	$(1, -2)$	$(-2, 1)$
2	0	$(2, 0)$	$(0, 2)$

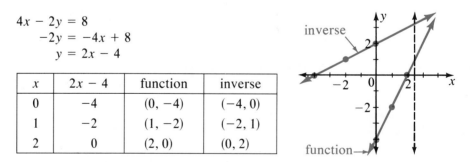

Since no vertical line intersects the graph of the inverse in more than one point, the inverse is a function.

An equation of the inverse function in Example 4 is $x = 2y - 4$, or $y = \frac{1}{2}x + 2$. If a function is defined by an equation of the form $y = mx + b$, $m \neq 0$, then its inverse can be written in the same form, and the inverse is a function.

Reading in Algebra

True or false? Give a reason for your answer.
1. Each relation A has an inverse relation, A^{-1}. **True**
2. Each function f has an inverse function, f^{-1}. **False**
3. If $G = \{(3, 7), (5, 5), (7, 3)\}$, then $G = G^{-1}$. **True**
4. For any relations A and B, if $B = A^{-1}$, then $A = B^{-1}$. **True**
5. For any relation A, $(A^{-1})^{-1} = A$. **True**

Written Exercises

(F = function, N = not a function)

1. $\{(3, -2), (3, -1), (-1, 3)\}$, **N**　　2. $\{(6, 0), (-3, 1), (4, 1)\}$, **F**　　3. $\{(-1, 4), (-2, 5), (-3, 6)\}$, **F**

Find the inverse of each relation. Determine if the inverse is a function.

(A) 1. $\{(-2, 3), (-1, 3), (3, -1)\}$　　2. $\{(0, 6), (1, -3), (1, 4)\}$　　3. $\{(4, -1), (5, -2), (6, -3)\}$
4. $\{(4, 9), (5, -1), (6, 9)\}$　　5. $\{(7, 11), (8, 10), (9, 9)\}$　　6. $\{(5, -2), (-6, -6), (-2, 5)\}$
$\{(9, 4), (-1, 5), (9, 6)\}$, **N**　　$\{(11, 7), (10, 8), (9, 9)\}$, **F**　　$\{(-2, 5), (-6, -6), (5, -2)\}$, **F**

Graph each function and its inverse in the same coordinate plane. Determine if the inverse is a function.

7. $x + y = 6$ **F**　　　　　8. $x - y = 6$ **F**　　　　　9. $5x - 2y = 10$ **F**
10. $2y - 3x = 4$ **F**　　　11. $3x + 4y = -8$ **F**　　12. $4y - x - 10 = 0$ **F**
13. $y = 6$ **N**　　　　　　14. $x = y$ **F**　　　　　　15. $y = 0.5x - 10$ **F**
16. $y = |x| - 2$ **N**　　　17. $y = 2|x| - 1$ **N**　　　18. $y = |x| + 3$ **N**
19. $y = \frac{9}{10}x + 15$; **F**　　20. $y = -\frac{5}{3}x + 16$; **F**　　21. $y = \frac{2}{21}x + \frac{8}{7}$; **F**

A relation is defined by each given equation. Find an equation of the inverse of each relation. Determine if the inverse is a function.

(B) 19. $\frac{2}{3}x - \frac{3}{5}y = 10$　**above**　　20. $\frac{5}{4}y + \frac{3}{4}x = 12$　**above**　　21. $7x - \frac{2}{3}y - 8 = 0$　**above**
22. $x^2 + y^2 = 1$　**below**　　23. $x^2 - y^2 = 4$　**below**　　24. $y = x^2$　$y = \pm\sqrt{x}$; **N**
25. $y = x^2 + 5$　**below**　　26. $x = y^2$　$y = x^2$; **F**　　27. $xy = 9$　$y = \frac{9}{x}$; **F**
22. $y = \pm\sqrt{1 - x^2}$; **N**　　23. $y = \pm\sqrt{x^2 + 4}$; **N**　　25. $y = \pm\sqrt{x - 5}$; **N**

(C) 28. Show that the graph of $y = mx + b$ and the graph of its inverse are symmetric with respect to the line determined by the equation $y = x$.
[Hint: Select points $P(x, y)$ and $Q(y, x)$ on the graphs. Show that the line determined by $y = x$ is the perpendicular bisector of $\overline{PQ}$.]
For Ex. 28, see TE Answer Section.

If $f(x) = 3x - 5$, find each of the following function values.

29. $f^{-1}(1)$ **2**　　　30. $f^{-1}(4)$ **3**　　　31. $f^{-1}(-5)$ **0**　　　32. $f^{-1}(16)$ **7**
33. $f^{-1}(2.5)$ **2.5**　　34. $f^{-1}(3a - 5)$ **a**　　35. $f(f^{-1}(10))$ **10**　　36. $f^{-1}(f(30))$ **30**
37. $f(f^{-1}(a))$ **a**　　38. $f^{-1}(f(a))$ **a**

→ A Challenge To You

If f is any linear function, is the following statement true or false? Prove your answer.
For each real number x, $f(x + 2) - f(x + 1) = f(x + 1) - f(x)$.
For answer to the Challenge, see TE Answer Section.

11.5 Direct Variation

▶ **To determine whether a relation expresses direct variation**
To solve a word problem using direct variation

Frequently in mathematics, one variable is related to another variable in such a way that a change in the value of one produces a corresponding change in the other. For example, if you drive an automobile at a constant speed of 60 km/h, the distance traveled is directly related to the time traveled. When the time increases, the distance traveled increases. In the table, notice that the ratio $\frac{d}{t}$ is 60 in each case.

Time in hours(t)	1	2	3	4	5
Distance in kilometers(d)	60	120	180	240	300

The table determines a set of ordered pairs with coordinates (t, d) that expresses **direct variation** between the variables t and d.

Definition:
Direct
Variation

A linear function defined by an equation of the form $y = kx$, or $\frac{y}{x} = k$, where k is a nonzero constant, is called a *direct variation*.
The constant k is called the *constant of variation*.

The equation $\frac{y}{x} = k$, or $y = kx$, is read, "y varies directly as x," or "y varies directly with x."

Example 1

Determine if the table expresses a direct variation between the variables y and x. If so, find the constant of variation and an equation that defines the function.

x	y	ordered pair
1	-6	$(1, -6)$
-2	12	$(-2, 12)$
3	-18	$(3, -18)$

$$\frac{y}{x} = \frac{-6}{1} = \frac{12}{-2} = \frac{-18}{3} = -6$$

$$\frac{y}{x} = -6, \text{ or } y = -6x$$

The ratio $\frac{y}{x} = -6$ for each ordered pair in the function.

Thus, y varies directly as x, the constant of variation is -6, and an equation of the function is $y = -6x$.

Example 2 Determine if the equation expresses a direct variation between the variables y and x, in each case.

$y = 2x$ $y = 3x + 4$

| The equation is of the form $y = kx$. | | The equation is not of the form $y = kx$. |

Thus, $y = 2x$ expresses a direct variation; $y = 3x + 4$ does not.

Notice that an equation of a function that expresses direct variation is an equation of the form $y = mx + b$, where m is a constant and $b = 0$.

Example 3 The voltage V of a given electrical circuit varies directly as the current I. If V is 120 volts when I is 9 amperes, find the voltage V when the current I is 15 amperes.

(1) Write a formula and find the value of k.

$$V = kI$$
$$120 = k \cdot 9$$
$$k = \frac{120}{9} = \frac{40}{3}$$

(2) Substitute for k and I. Find the value of V.

$$V = kI$$
$$V = \frac{40}{3} \cdot 15 = 200$$

Thus, the voltage is 200 volts when the current is 15 amperes.

A direct variation problem may be solved by using a proportion. If (x_1, y_1) and (x_2, y_2) are any two ordered pairs of a direct variation and neither is $(0, 0)$, then $\frac{y_1}{x_1} = k$ and $\frac{y_2}{x_2} = k$ for some constant $k \neq 0$. Thus, $\frac{y_1}{x_1} = \frac{y_2}{x_2}$.

The constant k is called the **constant of proportionality,** and y is said to be "directly proportional to" x.

Example 4 If y varies directly as the cube of x, and $y = 54$ when $x = 3$, find y when $x = 5$.

y varies directly as the cube of x means that y is directly proportional to the cube of x. Write a proportion.

$$\frac{54}{3^3} = \frac{y}{5^3}$$
$$\frac{54}{27} = \frac{y}{125}$$
$$\frac{2}{1} = \frac{y}{125} \quad \blacktriangleleft \quad \textit{In a proportion, product of means equals product of extremes.}$$
$$1 \cdot y = 2 \cdot 125$$
$$y = 250$$

Thus, $y = 250$ when $x = 5$.

Oral Exercises

If c is a constant, determine whether each equation expresses a direct variation.

1. $\dfrac{a}{b} = c$ **Yes** **2.** $m = nc$ **Yes** **3.** $mn = c$ **No** **4.** $x = cy$ **Yes** **5.** $xy = c$ **No**

6. $p = cq$ **Yes** **7.** $\dfrac{1}{p} = \dfrac{c}{q}$ **Yes** **8.** $\dfrac{c}{1} = \dfrac{q}{p}$ **Yes** **9.** $x = \dfrac{c}{y}$ **No** **10.** $\dfrac{y}{x} - c = 0$ **Yes**

Written Exercises

Determine if the table expresses a direct variation between the variables. If so, find the constant of variation and an equation that defines the function.

(A)

1. x	y
-3	1
-9	3
3	-1
6	-2

Yes; $-\frac{1}{3}$; $y = -\frac{1}{3}x$

2. c	d
7	3
14	6
-21	-9
28	-12

No

3. A	r
-15	-3
10	2
-20	-4
25	5

Yes, 5; $A = 5r$

4. R	S
2	1
3	2
4	3
5	4

No

5. M	N
1	1
2	2
3	3
-4	-4

Yes; 1; $M = 1N$

Determine if the equation expresses a direct variation between the variables. If so, find the constant of variation. **6.** Yes; -1 **7.** Yes; 3   **8.** No   **9.** Yes; 2   **10.** Yes, 2π

6. $y = -x$ **7.** $y = 3x$ **8.** $y = -2x + 5$ **9.** $c = 2d$ **10.** $c = 2\pi r$

11. $A = 3r + 6$ No **12.** $A = \dfrac{4}{l}$ No **13.** $\dfrac{y}{x} - 6 = 0$ Yes; 6 **14.** $y = \dfrac{4}{x}$ No **15.** $3y = 2x$ Yes, $\frac{2}{3}$

In Exercises 16–23, y varies directly as x. Find the value as indicated.

16. If $y = 12$ when $x = 4$, find y when $x = 12$. **36**

17. If $y = -81$ when $x = 9$, find y when $x = 7$. **-63**

18. If $y = 16$ when $x = -4$, find y when $x = 8$. **-32**

19. If $y = -3$ when $x = -15$, find x when $y = 2$. **10**

20. If $y = -12$ when $x = -3$, find y when $x = -8$. **-32**

21. If $y = 5$ when $x = 25$, find y when $x = 30$. **6**

22. If $y = 3$ when $x = 10$, find x when $y = 1.2$. **4**

23. If $y = 3$ when $x = 10$, find x when $y = \frac{1}{2}$. **$\frac{5}{3}$**

(B) **24.** If y varies directly as the square of x, and $y = 25$ when $x = 3$, find y when $x = 6$. **100**

25. If y is directly proportional to $\sqrt{x}$, and $y = 3.5$ when $x = 4$, find x when $y = 8.75$.

26. If y is directly proportional to $\sqrt[3]{x}$, and $x = 27$ when $y = 7.2$, find x when $y = 12$.

27. If y varies directly as the cube of x, and $x = 0.2$ when $y = 16$, find y when $x = 0.5$.

28. If you earn $22.75 for 7 hours work, how long must you work to earn $39.65? **12.2 h**

29. If a batter averages 81 hits for each 216 times at bat, approximately how many hits will he get in 400 times at bat? **150**

30. The scale on a certain blueprint is $3'' = 8'$. Find the dimensions of a floor that is $5\frac{1}{2}''$ by $7\frac{3}{4}''$ on the blueprint. **14′ 8″ by 20′ 8″**

31. The stretch S in a spring balance varies directly as the applied weight w. If $S = 5$ in. when $w = 15$ lb, find the weight needed for a stretch of $7\frac{1}{2}$ in. **22.5 lb**

(C) **32.** In a statement of direct variation in which y varies directly as x, if the value of y remains constant, $(y > 0)$, what happens to the value of k when x increases? when x decreases? **k decreases; k increases**

33. If A varies directly as B, and if A is multiplied by c, how is the corresponding value of B affected? **B is multiplied by c.**

25. 25   **26.** 125   **27.** 250

11.6 Inverse Variation

OBJECTIVES ▶ **To determine whether a relation expresses inverse variation**
To solve a word problem using inverse variation

In some mathematical situations, when the value of one variable increases, the value of a second variable decreases. For example, if you drive an automobile a distance of 180 km, the time required for the trip decreases as the speed increases. In the table, notice that the product rt is 180 in each case.

Speed in kilometers per hour (r)	90	72	60	45	40	36	30
Time in hours (t)	2	2.5	3	4	4.5	5	6

The table determines a set of ordered pairs with coordinates (r, t) that expresses **inverse variation** between the variables r and t.

Definition:
Inverse Variation

> A function defined by an equation of the form $xy = k$, or $y = \frac{k}{x}$, where k is a nonzero constant, is called an *inverse variation*.
> The constant k is called the *constant of variation*.

The equation $xy = k$, or $y = \frac{k}{x}$, is read, "y varies inversely as x," or "y varies inversely with x."

Example 1 Determine if the table expresses an inverse variation between the variables y and x. If so, find the constant of variation and an equation that defines the function.

x	4	8	1	-1	-2	$-\frac{1}{2}$
y	-2	-1	-8	8	4	16

$$\underset{-8}{4 \cdot (-2)} \quad \underset{-8}{8 \cdot (-1)} \quad \underset{-8}{1 \cdot (-8)} \quad \underset{-8}{-1 \cdot 8} \quad \underset{-8}{-2 \cdot 4} \quad \underset{-8}{-\tfrac{1}{2} \cdot 16}$$

$x \cdot y = -8$ for each ordered pair (x, y) in the function.

Thus, y varies inversely as x, the constant of variation is -8, and an equation of the function is $xy = -8$.

Example 2 Determine if the equation expresses an inverse variation between the variables y and x, in each case.

$y = 5x - 3$ $xy = -12$

The equation is not of the form $xy = k$.

The equation is of the form $xy = k$.

Thus, $y = 5x - 3$ does not express an inverse variation; $xy = -12$ does.

Example 3 The height h of a triangle varies inversely as the length of the base b. If $h = 10$ cm when $b = 4.8$ cm, find h when $b = 9$ cm.

(1) Write a formula and find the value of k.

$$bh = k$$
$$4.8 \cdot 10 = k$$
$$48 = k$$

(2) Substitute for k and b. Find the value of h.

$$bh = k$$
$$9 \cdot h = 48$$
$$h = 5\frac{1}{3}, \text{ or } 5.3$$

Thus, $h = 5.3$ cm when $b = 9$ cm.

If (x_1, y_1) and (x_2, y_2) are any two ordered pairs of an inverse variation and neither is $(0, 0)$, then $x_1 y_1 = k$ and $x_2 y_2 = k$. Thus, $x_1 y_1 = x_2 y_2$. This equation is often written as a proportion of the form $\frac{x_1}{x_2} = \frac{y_2}{y_1}$; y is said to be "inversely proportional to" x.

Example 4 If y varies inversely as the square of x, and $y = 10$ when $x = 4$, find x when $y = 5$.

y varies inversely as the square of x means that y is inversely proportional to the square of x. Write a proportion.

$$\frac{4^2}{x^2} = \frac{5}{10}$$
$$\frac{16}{x^2} = \frac{1}{2}$$
$$x^2 \cdot 1 = 16 \cdot 2 \qquad \blacktriangleleft \quad \textit{In a proportion, product of means}$$
$$x^2 = 32 \qquad\qquad\qquad \textit{equals product of extremes.}$$
$$x = \pm\sqrt{32}, \text{ or } \pm4\sqrt{2}$$

Thus, $x = \pm4\sqrt{2}$ when $y = 5$.

Example 5 If y is inversely proportional to $\sqrt[3]{x}$ and $y = 2.7$ when $x = 8$, find y when $x = 27$.

$$\sqrt[3]{8} \cdot 2.7 = \sqrt[3]{27} \cdot y \qquad \blacktriangleleft \quad \textit{Write an equation in the}$$
$$2 \cdot 2.7 = 3 \cdot y \qquad\qquad \textit{product form.}$$
$$5.4 = 3y$$
$$1.8 = y$$

Thus, $y = 1.8$ when $x = 27$.

Oral Exercises

If c is a constant, determine whether each equation expresses an inverse variation.

1. $\dfrac{x}{y} = c$ **No**   2. $xc = y$ **No**   3. $x = \dfrac{c}{y}$ **Yes**   4. $x = \dfrac{y}{c}$ **No**   5. $y = cx + x$ **No**

6. $\dfrac{1}{c} = \dfrac{x}{y}$ **No**   7. $\dfrac{c}{x} = \dfrac{1}{y}$ **No**   8. $1 = \dfrac{c}{xy}$ **Yes**   9. $xc = \dfrac{c}{y}$ **Yes**   10. $\dfrac{c}{x} = \dfrac{y}{c}$ **Yes**

Written Exercises

Determine if the table expresses an inverse variation between the variables. If so, find the constant of variation and an equation that defines the function.

(A)

1. s	t
12	3 **No**
16	4
20	5
24	6

2. x	y
-3	-4 **Yes;**
-2	-6 **12;**
4	3 **xy = 12**
12	1

3. c	d
-4	6 **No**
8	-3
-12	$--2$
-24	-1

4. x	y
1.0	0.32 **Yes;**
0.4	0.80 **0.32;**
0.2	1.60 **xy =**
0.1	3.20 **0.32**

5. a	b
$\frac{1}{2}$	$\frac{1}{6}$ **Yes;**
$\frac{1}{3}$	$\frac{1}{4}$ $\frac{1}{12}$
$-\frac{1}{6}$	$-\frac{1}{2}$ **ab =**
$-\frac{1}{12}$	-1 $\frac{1}{12}$

Determine if the equation expresses an inverse variation between the variables. If so, find the constant of variation.

6. $x = 10y$ **No**   7. $xy = 12$ **Yes; 12**   8. $5st = 12$ **Yes;** $\frac{12}{5}$ 9. $c = 5r$ **No**   10. $a \cdot b = \pi$ **Yes;** π

11. $A = 6.28r$ **No**   12. $\dfrac{r}{4} = t$ **No**   13. $6m = \dfrac{4}{n}$ **Yes;** $\frac{2}{3}$ 14. $x = \dfrac{10}{y}$ **Yes; 10**   15. $y = \dfrac{10}{x}$ **Yes; 10**

In Exercises 16–19, y varies inversely as x. Find the value as indicated.

16. If $y = 27$ when $x = 3$, find y when $x = 9$. **9**   17. If $y = 15$ when $x = -2$, find y when $x = -5$. **6**

18. If $y = 9$ when $x = 4$, find y when $x = 6$. **6**   19. If $y = 81$ when $x = -9$, find x when $y = 27$. **−27**

20. The illumination i from a light varies inversely as the square of its distance d from an object. If $i = 8$ foot-candles when $d = 3$ ft, find i when $d = 4$ ft. **$4\frac{1}{2}$ foot-candles**

21. The pressure P of a gas at a constant temperature varies inversely as the volume V. If $V = 450$ in.^{3} when $P = 30$ lb/in.^{2}, find P when $V = 750$ in.^{3}. **18 lb/in.²**

(B)

22. If y varies inversely as the square of x, and $y = 3$ when $x = 4$, find y when $x = 2$. **12**

23. If y is inversely proportional to $\sqrt{x}$, and $y = 6$ when $x = 9$, find y when $x = 16$. **$4\frac{1}{2}$**

24. If x is inversely proportional to $\sqrt[3]{y}$, and $x = 1.8$ when $y = 64$, find x when $y = 27$. **2.4**

25. If x varies inversely as the cube of y, and $x = 3$ when $y = 2$, find x when $y = 5$. **$\frac{24}{125}$**

26. The frequency of a radio wave is inversely proportional to its wave length. If a radio wave, 30 m long, has a frequency of 1200 kilocycles per second, what is the length of a wave with a frequency of 900 kilocycles per second?
    40 m

INVERSE VARIATION

11.7 Joint and Combined Variation

OBJECTIVES ▶ **To determine whether a relation expresses joint variation or combined variation**
To solve a word problem using joint variation or combined variation

In some mathematical situations, one variable is a constant multiple of the product of two or more variables. For example, simple interest, i, received on an investment of a specific amount of money is related to both the rate of interest, r, and the time, t, that the money was invested. Specifically, as the value of $r \cdot t$ increases, the value of i increases. The variation of the variables is called a **joint variation.**

Definition:
Joint
Variation

A function defined by an equation of the form $y = kxz$, or $\frac{y}{xz} = k$, where k is a nonzero constant, is called a *joint variation.*
The constant k is called the *constant of variation.*

The equation $\frac{y}{xz} = k$, or $y = kxz$, is read, "y varies jointly as x and z," or "y varies jointly with x and z." The variation in this case is a direct variation between y and the product xz.

Example 1 Determine if the equation expresses a joint variation between the variables, in each case.
$A = \frac{1}{2}bh$ $\qquad\qquad\qquad\qquad$ $m = \frac{3}{4}n + \frac{1}{3}$

The equation is of the form $y = kxz$. $\qquad$ The equation is not of the form $y = kxz$.

Thus, $A = \frac{1}{2}bh$ expresses a joint variation; $m = \frac{3}{4}n + \frac{1}{3}$ does not.

Example 2 If y varies jointly as x and z and if $y = -24$ when $x = 4$ and $z = 3$, find y when $x = -6$ and $z = 2$.

First Method: $\qquad$ Second Method:

Use the equation $y = kxz$. ▶
$$-24 = k \cdot 4 \cdot 3$$
$$-24 = 12k$$
$$-2 = k$$

$$\frac{-24}{4 \cdot 3} = \frac{y}{-6 \cdot 2}$$
$$\frac{-2}{1} = \frac{y}{-12}$$

◀ *Use a proportion of the form $\frac{y_1}{x_1 z_1} = \frac{y_2}{x_2 z_2}$.*

$$y = -2(-6)(2) \qquad 1 \cdot y = -2(-12)$$
$$y = 24 \qquad\qquad\quad y = 24$$

Thus, $y = 24$ when $x = -6$ and $z = 2$.

Example 3 The area A of a triangle varies jointly as the length of a base b and the length of a corresponding altitude h. If $A = 15$ cm when $b = 10$ cm and $h = 3$ cm, find A when $b = 25$ cm and $h = 6$ cm.

$$A = kbh$$
$$15 = k \cdot 10 \cdot 3$$
$$15 = 30k$$
$$\tfrac{1}{2} = k$$
◀ *Write a formula and solve for k.*

$$A = kbh$$
$$A = \tfrac{1}{2} \cdot 25 \cdot 6$$
$$A = 75$$
◀ *Substitute for k, b, and h. Find the value of A.*

Thus, A is 75 cm^2 when $b = 25$ cm and $h = 6$ cm.

In some mathematical applications, both direct variation and inverse variation occur at the same time. This type of variation is called **combined variation.**

Definition:
Combined
Variation

A function defined by an equation of the form $y = \dfrac{kxz}{w}$, or $\dfrac{yw}{xz} = k$, where k is a nonzero constant, is called a *combined variation.*
The constant k is called the *constant of variation.*

In the equation $y = \dfrac{kxz}{w}$, or $\dfrac{yw}{xz} = k$, the variable y varies jointly with the variables x and z and inversely with the variable w.

Example 4 If y varies jointly as x and z and inversely as $\sqrt{w}$, and $y = 12$ when $x = 2$, $z = 6$, and $w = 9$, find y when $x = 5$, $z = 7$, and $w = 25$.

Use an equation of the form
$$y = \frac{kxz}{\sqrt{w}}.$$
▶

First Method:

$$12 = \frac{k \cdot 2 \cdot 6}{\sqrt{9}} \qquad y = \frac{3 \cdot 5 \cdot 7}{\sqrt{25}}$$

$$12 = \frac{12k}{3} \qquad y = \frac{3 \cdot 5 \cdot 7}{5}$$

$$12 = 4k \qquad y = 21$$

$$3 = k$$

Second Method:

$$\frac{12 \cdot \sqrt{9}}{2 \cdot 6} = \frac{y \cdot \sqrt{25}}{5 \cdot 7}$$

$$\frac{12 \cdot 3}{2 \cdot 6} = \frac{y \cdot 5}{5 \cdot 7}$$

$$\frac{3}{1} = \frac{y}{7}$$

$$1 \cdot y = 3 \cdot 7$$

$$y = 21$$

◀ *Use a proportion of the form*
$$\frac{y_1 \sqrt{w_1}}{x_1 z_1} = \frac{y_2 \sqrt{w_2}}{x_2 z_2}.$$

Thus, $y = 21$ when $x = 5$, $z = 7$, and $w = 25$.

Written Exercises

Determine whether each equation expresses a joint variation, a combined variation, or neither. If either joint or combined variation exists, find the constant of variation.

(A) **1.** $x = \dfrac{-2}{y}$ **N**

2. $mn = 5$ **N**

3. $\dfrac{r}{s} = \dfrac{6t}{v}$ **C; 6**

4. $-6x = \dfrac{y}{z}$ **J; −6**

5. $w = 4u$ **N**

6. $a \cdot b \cdot c = 15$ **N**

7. $m = \dfrac{5n^2}{2p}$ **J;** $\dfrac{5}{2}$

8. $y = \dfrac{8x}{\sqrt{t}}$ **J; 8**

In Exercises 9–15, y varies jointly as x and z. Find the value as indicated.

9. If $y = 12$ when $x = 4$ and $z = 3$, find y when $x = 9$ and $z = 8$. **72**

10. If $y = 72$ when $x = 3$ and $z = 8$, find y when $x = -2$ and $z = -3$. **18**

11. If $y = 24$ when $x = 2$ and $z = 3$, find y when $x = 4$ and $z = 7$. **112**

12. If $y = 18$ when $x = 1$ and $z = 6$, find y when $x = 4$ and $z = 10$. **120**

13. If $y = 30$ when $x = 3$ and $z = 15$, find y when $x = -5$ and $z = -12$. **40**

14. If y varies directly as the square of x and inversely as z, and if $y = 12$ when $x = 2$ and $z = 7$, find y when $x = 3$ and $z = 9$. **21**

15. If y varies directly as $\sqrt[3]{x}$ and inversely as the square of z, and if $y = 3$ when $x = 8$ and $z = 4$, find y when $x = 27$ and $z = 6$. **2**

16. The area A, of a parallelogram varies jointly as the length of a base, b, and the length of a corresponding altitude, h. If $A = 16$ when $b = 2$ and $h = 8$, find A when $b = 8$ and $h = 16$. **128**

17. The distance, D, traveled at a uniform rate varies jointly as the rate, r, and the time, t. If $D = 120$ when $r = 60$ and $t = 2$, find D when $r = 80$ and $t = 3$. **240**

(B) **18.** If y varies jointly as x and $\sqrt{z}$ and inversely as the cube of w, and if $y = 6$ when $x = 3$, $z = 9$, and $w = 3$, find y when $x = 4$, $z = 36$, and $w = 4$. $\dfrac{27}{4}$

19. If y varies jointly as x and z and inversely as the square of w, and if $y = 6$ when $x = 3$, $z = 4$, and $w = 49$, find y when $x = 6$, $z = 8$, and $w = 4$. $\dfrac{7{,}203}{2}$

20. Interest i varies jointly as the principal p, the rate r, and the time t. If the value of r is halved, what happens to the value of i? **The value of i is halved.**

21. The volume V of a cube varies directly as the cube of its edge e. If the value of e is doubled, what happens to the value of V? **The value of V is multiplied by 8.**

(C) **22.** If r varies directly as the square of s and inversely as t, what happens to the value of r if the value of s is doubled and the value of t is tripled? **The value of r is multiplied by $\dfrac{4}{3}$.**

23. If t varies directly as s and inversely as the square of r, how is the value of t affected if the value of r is increased by 25%? **The value of t is multiplied by $\dfrac{16}{25}$.**

24. If 6 people take 14 days to assemble 18 computers, how many days will it take 10 people to assemble 30 computers? **14 days**

25. If y varies directly as x and inversely as z, how is the value of y affected if the value of z is decreased by 25%? **The value of z is multiplied by $\dfrac{4}{3}$.**

Cumulative Review

Solve each equation.

1. $\sqrt{x - 3} + \sqrt{x} = 3$ **4**

2. $\sqrt{x} + \sqrt{x - 5} = 5$ **9**

3. $\sqrt{2x} - \sqrt{\dfrac{x}{2}} = 2$ **8**

Applications

1. The frequency of a string under constant tension is inversely proportional to its length. If a string, 40 cm long, vibrates 680 times per second, what length must the string be to vibrate 850 times per second under the same tension? **32 cm**

2. The frequency of a radio wave is inversely proportional to its wavelength. If a radio wave, 30 m long, has a frequency of 1,200 kilocycles per second, what is the length of a wave with a frequency of 900 kilocycles per second? **40 m**

3. Boyle's Law states that the volume of a given mass of gas varies inversely as the absolute pressure, provided the temperature remains constant. If the volume of a gas is 40 in.^{3} when the absolute pressure is 50 lb/in.^{2}, what will be the volume when the pressure is 70 lb/in.^{2}? **$28\frac{4}{7}$ in.^{3}**

4. The kinetic energy, E, of a body varies jointly as its weight, w, and the square of its velocity, V. If a 10-lb body moving at 6 ft/s has 3 ft-lb of kinetic energy, what will the kinetic energy be of a 4-T truck traveling at 50 mi/h? **$83\frac{1}{3}$ mi/T**

5. The load, l, that a beam of fixed length can support varies jointly as its width, w, and the square of its depth, d. A beam with $w = 4$ and $d = 2$ can support a load of 1,760 kg. Find l when $w = 4$ and $d = 8$. **28,160 kg**

6. The pressure, P, of a gas varies directly as the temperature, T, and inversely as the volume, V. If $P = 50$ when $T = 25$ and $V = 2$, find P when $T = 40$ and $V = 4$. **40**

7. The force of attraction, F, between two objects varies jointly as their masses, m_1 and m_2, and inversely as the square of the distance, d, between them. When $m_1 = 1$ g, $m_2 = 500$ g, and $d = 5$ cm, then $F = 1.33 \times 10^{-6}$ dynes. Find F when $m_1 = 2$ g, $m_2 = 600$ g, and $d = 6$ cm. **2.216×10^{-6} dynes**

8. Refer to Exercise 7. What is the effect on the force of attraction between the two objects if the mass of each is doubled and the distance between them is halved? **force is multiplied by $\frac{1}{16}$**

9. The speed, V, at which a motorcycle must travel on the inside cylinder in order not to fall varies as the square root of the radius of the cylinder. If the motorcycle must travel at least 45 km/h to stay on the side of the cylinder with a radius of 12 m, how fast must it travel on a cylinder with radius of 30 m? **71.15 km/h**

10. A conservationist can approximate the number of deer in a forest. Suppose 650 deer are caught, tagged and released. Suppose later 216 deer are caught and 54 of them were tagged. How many deer are in the forest? Assume that the number of tagged deer caught varies directly as the number of deer caught later. **2,600 deer**

Chapter Eleven Review

Vocabulary
combined variation [11.7]
constant function [11.3]
direct variation [11.5]
domain [11.1] function [11.1]
inverse function [11.4]
inverse relation [11.4]
inverse variation [11.6]
joint variation [11.7]
range [11.1] relation [11.1]

Determine the domain and the range of each relation. Is the relation a function? [11.1]
1. $\{(-2, 3), (0, -7), (8, -3), (4, 3)\}$ **F**
2. $\{(0, 6), (1, -3), (4, -6), (0, 0)\}$ **N**
★ 3. $\{\ldots(-1, 1), (0, 0), (1, 1), (2, 4), (3, 9), \ldots\}$**F**
4.

5.

Let $f = \{(2, -3), (1, 0), (-3, 5), (-1, -2)\}$. **Find each of these function values.** [11.2]
6. $f(1)$ **0**　7. $f(-1)$ **-2**　8. $f(-3)$ **5**　9. $f(2)$ **-3**

Let $h(x) = x^2 - 2$. **Find each of the following function values.** [11.2]
10. $h(0)$ **-2**　11. $h(-4)$ **14**　12. $h(a - 1)$ $a^2 - 2a - 1$

Find the range of each function for the given domain. [11.2]　15. {all real numbers except 1}
13. $h(x) = 2x + 3, D = \{0, 1, -2\}$ **{3, 5, -1}**
14. $g(x) = x^2 + 1, D = \{-1, 0, 4\}$ **{2, 1, 17}**
16. {all real numbers except −2 and 5}

Find the domain of each function. [11.2]
15. $h(x) = \dfrac{x}{x - 1}$ **above**　16. $t(x) = \dfrac{-4}{(x + 2)(x - 5)}$

Let $f(x) = 3x - 5$ **and** $g(x) = x^2 + 6$. **Find each of the following.** [11.2]
17. $f(-7)$ **-26**　18. $g(2\sqrt{3})$ **18**　19. $g(f(\frac{2}{3}))$ **15**
20. $\dfrac{f(a) - f(b)}{a - b}; a \neq b$ **3**　21. $\dfrac{g(c + h) - g(c)}{h}; h \neq 0$ **2c + h**

Determine whether each equation describes a linear function, a constant function, or neither of these. [11.3]
22. $2x - 3y = 6$ **L**　23. $y = 2$　24. $x = -3$ **N**
25. $-3(2x - 3y) - 8x = 3(2x - 1)$ **L**　23. **C, L**

Find the inverse of each relation. Determine if the inverse is a function. [11.4]
26. $\{(-1, -2), (6, -2), (1, 2)\}$
27. $\{(3, 1), (3, 6), (3, 9)\}$ **{(1, 3), (6, 3), (9, 3)}, F**

Graph each function and its inverse in the same coordinate plane. Determine if the inverse is a function. [11.4]　26. {(−2, 1), (−2, 6), (2, 1)}; N
28. $3x - 2y = 8$ **F**　29. $y = |x| - 1$ **N**
30. $xy = 4$ **F**　31. $x^2 = y - 1$ **N**

Determine if the table expresses a direct variation or an inverse variation. Find the constant of variation. [11.5–11.6]

32.	x	y	33.	s	t	34.	m	n
	8	3		−6	2		12	1
	12	2		−3	1		6	2
	−6	−4		6	−2		−4	−3

inverse; 24　　direct; −3　　inverse; 12

In Exercises 35–36, y varies directly as x. [11.5]
35. If $y = 18$ when $x = 3$, find y when $x = 5$. **30**
36. If $y = -8$ when $x = 2$, find y when $x = -4$. **16**

In Exercises 37–38, y varies inversely as x. [11.6]
37. If $y = 12$ when $x = 2$, find y when $x = 12$. **2**
38. If $y = -3$ when $x = 5$, find y when $x = -3$. **5**
39. If y varies jointly as x and z, and $y = -12$ when $x = 3$ and $z = -1$, find y when $x = 5$ and $z = 6$. [11.7] **120**
40. If y varies directly as the square of x and inversely as the positive square root of z, and if $y = 9$ when $x = 3$ and $z = 16$, find y when $x = -1$ and $z = 4$. [11.7] **2**

Chapter Eleven Test

Determine the domain and the range of each relation. Is the relation a function?

1. $\{(-2, -1), (3, -2), (4, -3), (2, 1)\}$ **F**
2. $\{(2, 5), (3, 0), (1, 3), (-2, 0)\}$ **F**

Let $h = \{(-1, 4), (0, -3), (1, 4), (2, -6)\}$. Find each of these function values.

3. $h(-1)$ **4**   4. $h(0)$ **−3**   5. $h(2)$ **−6**   6. $h(1)$ **4**

Let $f(x) = x^2 + 3$. Find each of the following function values.

7. $f(-1)$ **4**   8. $f(0)$ **3**   9. $f(a + 2)$ **$a^2 + 4a + 7$**

Find the range of each function for the given domain.

10. $h(x) = x^2 + 2$, $D = \{-1, 0, 4\}$ **{3, 2, 18}**
11. $g(x) = 3x - 5$, $D = \{0, -1, 2\}$ **{−5, −8, 1}**

Find the domain of each function.

12. $g(x) = \dfrac{x}{x - 2}$ 13. $t(x) = \dfrac{4}{x^2 - 4x - 5}$

Let $f(x) = 2x + 4$ and $g(x) = x^2 - 1$. Find each of the following.

14. $f(-1)$ **2**   15. $g(3\sqrt{2})$ **17**   16. $f(g(\tfrac{1}{3}))$ **$\tfrac{20}{9}$**
17. $\dfrac{f(a) - f(b)}{a - b}$; $a \neq b$ **2**

Determine whether each equation describes a linear function, a constant function, or neither of these.   **19. C, L**

18. $-2x + 3y = 12$ **L** 19. $y = -6$ **20.** $x = 0$ **N**
21. $-2(-2y - x) - 3x = 2(3x - 1)$ **L**

1. $D = \{4, 3, 2, -2\}$; $R = \{1, -1, -2, -3\}$; function
2. $D = \{3, 2, 1, -2\}$; $R = \{5, 3, 0\}$; function
12. $D = \{$all real numbers except 2$\}$
13. $D = \{$all real numbers except 5 and $-1\}$

Graph each function and its inverse in the same coordinate plane. Determine if the inverse is a function.   function

22. $y = x^2 + 2$ **not a function** 23. $xy = -2$

Determine if the table expresses a direct variation or an inverse variation. Find the constant of variation.

24.

x	y
-4	-5
-5	-4
1	20

inverse; 20

25.

r	s
-2	8
16	-1
-32	$\frac{1}{2}$

inverse; −16

26.

m	n
2	24
-3	-36
$\frac{1}{2}$	6

direct; 12

In Exercises 27–28, y varies directly as x.

27. If $y = 10$ when $x = 2$, find y when $x = 6$. **30**
28. If $y = -10$ when $x = 5$, find y when $x = -6$. **12**

In Exercises 29–30, y varies inversely as x.

29. If $y = 5$ when $x = 6$, find y when $x = 15$. **2**
30. If $y = 8$ when $x = 3$, find y when $x = 12$. **2**

31. If r varies directly as the square of s and if $r = 32$ when $s = 4$, find r when $s = 6$. **72**

32. If x varies jointly as s and t, and $x = 24$ when $s = 4$ and $t = 2$, find x when $s = -2$ and $t = -3$. **18**

33. If x varies directly as the positive square root of y and inversely as the square of z, and if $x = 2$ when $y = 4$ and $z = 5$, find x when $y = 9$ and $z = 6$. **$2\frac{1}{12}$**

Computer Activities

Centripetal Force

A 1500 kg automobile is turning a curve at a speed of 7 m/sec. The curve is part of a circle with a radius of 10 m. You can use the computer program below to find the amount of force that must be exerted by the road on the tires to keep the automobile on the circular path. As shown in the equation, the force (F) required varies directly with the mass (m) of the automobile and the square of its velocity (v) and inversely with the length of the radius (r) of the circle.

$$F = \frac{mv^2}{r}$$

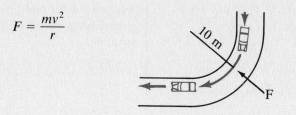

PROGRAM

```
10 PRINT "PROGRAM FINDS FORCE"
20 PRINT "ENTER MASS OF CAR"
30 INPUT M
40 PRINT "ENTER VELOCITY OF CAR"
50 INPUT V
60 PRINT "ENTER RADIUS OF CIRCLE"
70 INPUT R
80 LET F = (M * (V ↑ 2))/R
90 PRINT "THE FORCE REQUIRED IS"; F
100 PRINT "KILOGRAM-METERS PER SECOND PER SECOND"
110 END
```

Exercises

Type in and run the above program for the following values:

1. $m = 1{,}500$ kg $v = 7$ m/sec $r = 10$ m
   7,350 kilogram-meters per second per second
2. $m = 2{,}000$ kg $v = 15$ m/sec $r = 5$ m
   90,000 kilogram-meters per second per second
3. $m = 1{,}500$ kg $v = 12$ m/sec $r = 15$ m
   14,400 kilogram-meters per second per second
4. Alter the program to find the radius of a curve, given F, m, and v.
   For Ex. 4, see TE Answer Section.

300

College Prep Test

DIRECTIONS: Choose the *one* best answer to each question or problem.

1. A bag of rabbit food will feed 24 rabbits for 72 days. How long will it feed 16 rabbits? **A**

    (A) 108   (B) 48   (C) 71
    (D) 49   (E) 96

2. Which of the following equations gives the relationship between x and y in the table? **E**

x	1	2	3	4	5	6
y	3	7	11	15	19	23

    (A) $y = 3x$ (B) $y = x^2 + 2$
    (C) $y = x^2 + 3$ (D) $y = 3x + 5$
    (E) $y = 4x - 1$

3. In making egg salad, a recipe calls for 4 cups of diced eggs to $\frac{1}{4}$ cup of chopped onions. How much onion should be used for 16 cups of egg salad? **E**

    (A) $\frac{1}{4}$ (B) $\frac{1}{8}$ (C) $\frac{3}{4}$
    (D) 4   (E) 1

4. A person sews m boxes of shirts in n days. If there are p shirts in a box, how many shirts does the person sew in a day? **D**

    (A) $\frac{m}{pn}$ (B) $\frac{n}{pm}$ (C) $\frac{pn}{m}$
    (D) $\frac{pm}{n}$ (E) $\frac{mn}{p}$

5. A bell chimes every c minutes and a horn blasts every b minutes. Assume c and b are prime numbers and the bell and horn start simultaneously. In how many minutes will they sound simultaneously? **C**

    (A) $\frac{b}{c}$ (B) $\frac{c}{b}$ (C) bc
    (D) $\frac{cb}{2}$ (E) $2bc$

6. If $2y - 6$ varies directly as the square of $x + 2$ and inversely as $z - 3$, and if $y = 1$ when $x = 2$ and $z = 11$, find y when $x = 4$ and $z = 9$. **C**

    (A) -213 (B) $\frac{17}{6}$ (C) -3
    (D) $\frac{18 - \sqrt{6}}{6}$ (E) None of these

7. A machine can produce 140 valves in 20 seconds. At this rate, how many valves will it produce in 30 minutes? **B**

    (A) 210   (B) 12,600   (C) 114
    (D) 93   (E) None of these

8. If the tax on a $125 bike is $10, at the same rate, what is the tax on a $300 bike? **D**

    (A) $30   (B) $21   (C) $27
    (D) $24

12 CONIC SECTIONS

Sufficient, Insufficient, and Extraneous Information

To solve mathematical problems that are stated for you or ones that must be formulated, one of your first tasks is to identify what information is given. To solve some problems, you can be given

I just enough, but not too much, information.

II not enough information.

III some information that is not needed.

IV a combination of II and III above.

In every problem-solving situation, you should systematically examine the information that is provided. One four-step approach is shown below.

Problem: Ms. Brown used 760 yd of barbed-wire fencing to enclose a herd of 45 cows in a rectangular pasture. The length of the pasture is about 20 yd less than triple the width. What is the approximate area of the pasture?

Step 1 What question is asked? ⟶ What is the approximate area of the pasture?

Step 2 What information is needed ⟶ The approximate measures to answer the question? of the length and width

Step 3 Is there enough information ⟶ (YES) or NO to solve the problem?

Step 4 Is there more information ⟶ (YES) or NO than what is needed?

Conclusion: If x = width of pasture, $3x - 20$ = length. The equation $2(x) + 2(3x - 20) = 760$ can be used to find the width and the length. Then use $A = lw$ to find the area.
The number of cows, 45, is not needed.

12.1 Symmetric Points in a Coordinate Plane

To determine whether two given points are symmetric with respect to the *x*-axis, the *y*-axis, or the origin

Two points in a coordinate plane are **symmetric** with respect to a given line, *l*, in the plane if *l* is the perpendicular bisector of the segment connecting the two points. Line *l* is called the **line of symmetry** or the **axis of symmetry** for the two points.

In the figure at the right, the two pairs of points $P(-5, 4)$ and $Q(-5, -4)$, $R(4, 3)$ and $S(4, -3)$ are symmetric with respect to the *x*-axis. The *x*-axis, whose equation is $y = 0$, is the axis of symmetry. Notice that the points $T(1, 2)$ and $U(2, -1)$ are not symmetric with respect to the *x*-axis.

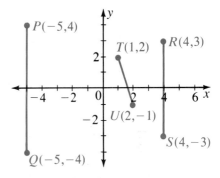

Symmetric Points with Respect to the *x*-Axis

> Two points, $P(x, y)$ and $Q(x, -y)$, in a coordinate plane are *symmetric with repect to the x-axis*. Their *x*-coordinates are the same and their *y*-coordinates are additive inverses.

Example 1

Determine whether the two points are symmetric with respect to the *x*-axis.
$C(2, -3)$ $D(2, 3)$ **$E(5, -4)$ $F(-5, -4)$**

Points *C* and *D* have the same *x*-coordinates. Their *y*-coordinates are additive inverses.
Thus, *C* and *D* are symmetric with respect to the *x*-axis.

Points *E* and *F* have different *x*-coordinates.

Thus, *E* and *F* are not symmetric with respect to the *x*-axis.

In the figure at the right, the two pairs of points $G(-4, 3)$ and $H(4, 3)$, $I(-5, -2)$ and $J(5, -2)$ are symmetric with respect to the *y*-axis. The *y*-axis, whose equation is $x = 0$, is the axis of symmetry. Notice that the points $K(-1, 2)$ and $L(2, 1)$ are not symmetric with respect to the *y*-axis.

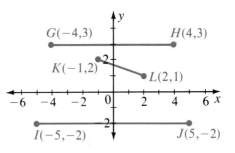

Symmetric Points with Respect to the y-Axis

> Two points, $P(x, y)$ and $Q(-x, y)$, in a coordinate plane are *symmetric with respect to the y-axis*. Their x-coordinates are additive inverses and their y-coordinates are the same.

Example 2

Determine whether the two points are symmetric with respect to the y-axis.

$A(5, -6)$ $B(-5, -6)$ $M(-4, 6)$ $N(-4, -6)$

The x-coordinates of points A and B are additive inverses. Their y-coordinates are the same.

The x-coordinates of points M and N are not additive inverses.

Thus, A and B are symmetric with respect to the y-axis.

Thus, M and N are not symmetric with respect to the y-axis.

It is possible for two given points in a coordinate plane to be symmetric with respect to the origin.
In the figure at the right, the two pairs of points, the endpoints of the diameters of the circle, $P(-3, 2)$ and $Q(3, -2)$, $R(3, 2)$ and $S(-3, -2)$ are symmetric with respect to the origin, whose coordinates are $(0, 0)$. The origin is a **point of symmetry.**

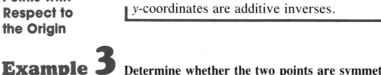

Symmetric Points with Respect to the Origin

> Two points, $P(x, y)$ and $Q(-x, -y)$, in a coordinate plane are *symmetric with respect to the origin*. Their x-coordinates are additive inverses and their y-coordinates are additive inverses.

Example 3

Determine whether the two points are symmetric with respect to the origin.

$W(5, -9)$ $X(-5, 9)$ $Y(2, \sqrt{5})$ $Z(-2, \sqrt{5})$

The x-coordinates of points W and X are additive inverse. Their y-coordinates are additive inverses.
Thus, W and X are symmetric with respect to the origin.

The y-coordinates of points Y and Z are not additive inverses.

Thus, Y and Z are not symmetric with respect to the origin.

Example 4

For $P(3, -5)$, find the coordinates of the corresponding point symmetric with respect to the x-axis, the y-axis, and the origin.

x-axis	y-axis	origin
(3, 5)	(-3, -5)	(-3, 5)

Oral Exercises

Determine which point, A, B, C, or D, is symmetric to each given point with respect to the x-axis, y-axis, and the origin.

1. $P(7, -4)$: $A(-7, -4)$ $B(0, 0)$ $C(-7, 4)$ $D(7, 4)$ **x-axis: D, y-axis: A, origin: C**
2. $Q(-2, 3)$: $A(-2, 0)$ $B(-2, -3)$ $C(2, -3)$ $D(2, 3)$ **x-axis: B, y-axis: D, origin: C**
3. $R(6, 1)$: $A(-6, -1)$ $B(0, 1)$ $C(-6, 1)$ $D(6, -1)$ **x-axis: D, y-axis: C, origin: A**
4. $S(-1, -5)$: $A(1, -5)$ $B(1, 5)$ $C(-1, 5)$ $D(5, 0)$ **x-axis: C, y-axis: A, origin: B**

10. $(6, 4), (-6, -4), (-6, 4)$ 11. $(-4, 5), (4, -5), (4, 5)$ 12. $(6, 6), (-6, -6), (-6, 6)$

25. $(\frac{5}{6}, \frac{1}{3}), (-\frac{5}{6}, -\frac{1}{3}), (-\frac{5}{6}, \frac{1}{3})$

26. $(\frac{2}{3}, -\frac{5}{7}), (-\frac{2}{3}, \frac{5}{7}), (-\frac{2}{3}, -\frac{5}{7})$ 27. $(-1, \frac{2}{3}), (1, -\frac{2}{3}), (1, \frac{2}{3})$

Written Exercises

13. $(-3, -5), (3, 5), (3, -5)$ 14. $(-1, 3), (1, -3), (1, 3)$ 15. $(-2, -5), (2, 5), (2, -5)$

Determine whether P and Q are symmetric with respect to the x-axis, the y-axis, the origin, or none of these. 16. $(-7, 2), (7, -2), (7, 2)$ 17. $(5, -4), (-5, 4), (-5, -4)$ 18. $(7, 2), (-7, -2), (-7, 2)$

(A)
1. $P(-3, 2); Q(3, -2)$ **origin**   2. $P(-5, -4); Q(5, 4)$ **origin**   3. $P(-4, -3); Q(4, -3)$ **y-axis**
4. $P(7, 3); Q(7, -3)$ **x-axis**   5. $P(6, 8); Q(-6, 8)$ **y-axis**   6. $P(-4, -5); Q(4, 5)$ **origin**
7. $P(0, 5); Q(0, -5)$ **x-axis and origin**   8. $P(8, 0); Q(-8, 0)$ **y-axis and origin**   9. $P(-7, 6); Q(6, -7)$ **none of these**

For each point, find the coordinates of the corresponding point symmetric with respect to the x-axis, the y-axis, and the origin. 19. $(-3, 4), (3, -4), (3, 4)$ 20. $(2, 2), (-2, -2), (-2, 2)$ 21. $(-8, 8), (8, -8), (8, 8)$

10. $A(6, -4)$ 11. $B(-4, -5)$ 12. $C(6, -6)$ 13. $D(-3, 5)$ 14. $E(-1, -3)$ 15. $F(-2, 5)$
16. $G(-7, -2)$ 17. $H(5, 4)$ 18. $I(7, -2)$ 19. $J(-3, -4)$ 20. $K(2, -2)$ 21. $L(-8, -8)$

22. $(\frac{1}{3}, \frac{1}{4}), (-\frac{1}{3}, -\frac{1}{4}), (-\frac{1}{3}, \frac{1}{4})$ 23. $(-\frac{2}{3}, -\frac{4}{5}), (\frac{2}{3}, \frac{4}{5}), (\frac{2}{3}, -\frac{4}{5})$ 24. $(-\frac{1}{2}, \frac{1}{3}), (\frac{1}{2}, -\frac{1}{3}), (\frac{1}{2}, \frac{1}{3})$

(B)
22. $M(\frac{1}{3}, -\frac{1}{4})$ 23. $N(-\frac{2}{3}, \frac{4}{5})$ 24. $O(-\frac{1}{2}, -\frac{1}{3})$ 25. $P(\frac{5}{6}, -\frac{1}{3})$ 26. $Q(\frac{2}{3}, \frac{5}{7})$ 27. $R(-1, -\frac{2}{3})$
28. $S(a, -b)$ 29. $T(-a, -b)$ 30. $U(-a, b)$ 31. $V(x, -y)$ 32. $W(-x, y)$ 33. $Z(-x, -y)$

28. $(a, b), (-a, -b), (-a, b)$ 29. $(-a, b), (a, -b), (a, b)$ 30. $(-a, -b), (a, b), (a, -b)$ 31. $(x, y), (-x, -y), (-x, y)$

For the given point on each circle, find the coordinates of the corresponding point symmetric with respect to the x-axis, the y-axis, and the origin. 32. $(-x, -y), (x, y), (x, -y)$ 33. $(-x, y), (x, -y), (x, y)$

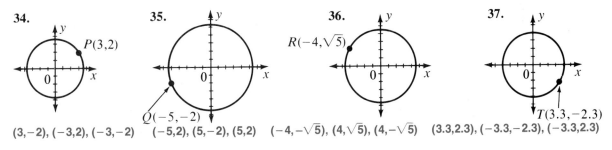

34. $P(3, 2)$
$(3, -2), (-3, 2), (-3, -2)$

35. $Q(-5, -2)$
$(-5, 2), (5, -2), (5, 2)$

36. $R(-4, \sqrt{5})$
$(-4, -\sqrt{5}), (4, \sqrt{5}), (4, -\sqrt{5})$

37. $T(3.3, -2.3)$
$(3.3, 2.3), (-3.3, -2.3), (-3.3, 2.3)$

Determine if the graph of each equation is symmetric with respect to the x-axis, y-axis, or the origin. [Hint: For all real numbers a and b, if (a, b) and $(-a, -b)$ satisfy the equation, the graph is symmetric with respect to the origin.] 37. $(3.3, 2.3), (-3.3, -2.3), (-3.3, 2.3)$

(C)
38. $x^2 + y^2 = 7$ **x-axis, y-axis, and origin**   39. $y = x^2$ **y-axis**   40. $x^2 + (-y)^2 = 7$ **x-axis, y-axis, and origin**   41. $-y = x^2$ **y-axis**   42. $-y = (-x)^2$ **y-axis**

A function is said to be *even* if its graph has y-axis symmetry and *odd* if it has origin symmetry. Which of the following are odd? even?

43. $y = x^2$ **even**   44. $y = \frac{1}{x}$ **odd**   45. $y = |x|$ **even**   46. $xy = 4$ **odd**   47. $y = x^3$ **odd**

SYMMETRIC POINTS IN A COORDINATE PLANE   **305**

12.2 The Parabola

OBJECTIVES ▶ **To draw the graph of a quadratic function (parabola)**
To determine the coordinates of the vertex of a parabola
To find an equation of the axis of symmetry of a parabola
To estimate graphically the *x*-intercepts of a parabola

The graph of a quadratic function is called a **parabola.** Examples of parabolas are shown in the diagrams below.

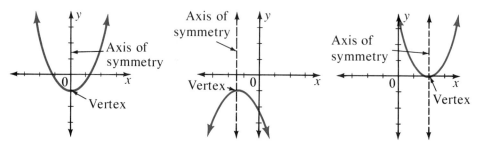

Every parabola has an axis of symmetry. Recall that an axis of symmetry is the perpendicular bisector of any segment connecting two symmetric points on the parabola. A parabola intersects its axis of symmetry at a point called the **vertex** or **turning point.**

You can graph a quadratic function determined by the equation $y = x^2 - 6x + 8$ as follows. First, make a table by choosing values for x and finding corresponding values for y. Then, plot as many points as needed to determine the parabola.

x	$x^2 - 6x + 8$	y
-1	$(-1)^2 - 6(-1) + 8$	15
0	$0^2 - 6(0) + 8$	8
1	$1^2 - 6(1) + 8$	3
2	$2^2 - 6(2) + 8$	0
3	$3^2 - 6(3) + 8$	-1
4	$4^2 - 6(4) + 8$	0
5	$5^2 - 6(5) + 8$	3
6	$6^2 - 6(6) + 8$	8
7	$7^2 - 6(7) + 8$	15

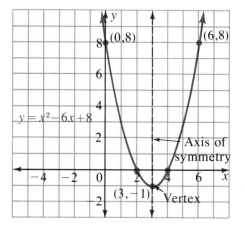

In general, any equation of the form $y = ax^2 + bx + c$, where a, b, and c are real numbers with $a \neq 0$, describes a parabola.

The vertex of the parabola above is the point whose coordinates are $(3, -1)$. The axis of symmetry passes through the vertex and is parallel to the y-axis. Therefore, an equation of the axis of symmetry is $x = 3$.

Example 1 Draw the graph of $y = -x^2 + 2x + 3$. Find the coordinates of the vertex and an equation of the axis of symmetry.

x	$-x^2 + 2x + 3$	y
-1	$-(-1)^2 + 2(-1) + 3$	0
0	$-(0)^2 + 2(0) + 3$	3
1	$-(1)^2 + 2(1) + 3$	4
2	$-(2)^2 + 2(2) + 3$	3
3	$-(3)^2 + 2(3) + 3$	0

Thus, $(1, 4)$ are the coordinates of the vertex and $x = 1$ is an equation of the axis of symmetry.

In Example 1, the graph intersects the x-axis in two points with coordinates of $(-1, 0)$ and $(3, 0)$. The x-coordinates of these points, -1 and 3, are the solutions of the corresponding quadratic equation, $-x^2 + 2x + 3 = 0$. Notice that the equation of the axis of symmetry, $x = 1$, can be found from the x-coordinates of the midpoint of the segment connecting these two points. That is, $x = \dfrac{-1 + 3}{2} = 1$. In general, if r and s are the solutions of the quadratic equation, then an equation of the axis of symmetry is $x = \dfrac{r + s}{2}$.

Recall that the sum $(r + s)$ of the solutions of a quadratic equation is $-\dfrac{b}{a}$.

Since $x = \dfrac{r + s}{2}$ and $r + s = -\dfrac{b}{a}$, then $x = \dfrac{-\dfrac{b}{a}}{2} = -\dfrac{b}{2a}$.

Equation of Axis of Symmetry

For a parabola with equation $y = ax^2 + bx + c$, $a \neq 0$, an equation of the axis of symmetry is $x = -\dfrac{b}{2a}$.

Example 2 Find an equation of the axis of symmetry of the parabola with equation $y = 4x + x^2 - 3$.

Write the equation in the form $y = ax^2 + bx + c$. ▶ $y = 1x^2 + 4x - 3$
$\qquad\qquad\qquad\qquad\qquad\qquad\qquad\qquad\qquad\qquad\qquad\quad a \qquad b$

Determine a and b. ▶ $a \qquad b$

Substitute 1 for a and 4 for b. ▶ $x = -\dfrac{b}{2a} = -\dfrac{4}{2 \cdot 1}$, or -2

Thus, an equation of the axis of symmetry is $x = -2$.

If a graph intersects the x-axis, the x-coordinate of each point of intersection is called an **x-intercept**.

Example 3

Estimate graphically, to the nearest tenth, the x-intercepts of the parabola determined by the function $y = x^2 - 3x - 5$.

x	$x^2 - 3x - 5$	y
-2	$(-2)^2 - 3(-2) - 5$	5
-1	$(-1)^2 - 3(-1) - 5$	-1
0	$0^2 - 3(0) - 5$	-5
1	$1^2 - 3(1) - 5$	-7
2	$2^2 - 3(2) - 5$	-7
3	$3^2 - 3(3) - 5$	-5
4	$4^2 - 3(4) - 5$	-1
5	$5^2 - 3(5) - 5$	5

Thus, the x-intercepts of the parabola are approximately -1.2 and 4.2.

You can find the coordinates of the vertex of the parabola in Example 3 algebraically. First, find an equation of the axis of symmetry.

$$x = -\frac{b}{2a} = -\frac{-3}{2 \cdot 1} = \frac{3}{2} \quad \text{The equation is } x = \frac{3}{2}.$$

The axis of symmetry is a line that passes through the vertex. Let $\left(\frac{3}{2}, y\right)$ be the coordinates of the vertex. Then,

$$y = x^2 - 3x - 5 = \left(\frac{3}{2}\right)^2 - 3 \cdot \frac{3}{2} - 5, \text{ or } -\frac{29}{4}.$$

Therefore, the coordinates of the vertex are $\left(\frac{3}{2}, -\frac{29}{4}\right)$.

Example 4

Draw the graphs of $y = \frac{1}{2}x^2$, $y = x^2$, and $y = 2x^2$ on the same coordinate axes. Find an equation of the axis of symmetry and the coordinates of the vertex of each parabola.

x	x^2	$\frac{1}{2}x^2$	$2x^2$
-2	4	2	8
-1	1	$.5$	2
0	0	0	0
1	1	$.5$	2
2	4	2	8

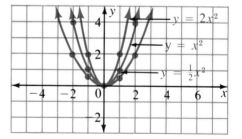

Thus, for each parabola, $x = 0$ is an equation of the axis of symmetry and $(0, 0)$ are the coordinates of the vertex.

CHAPTER TWELVE

In Example 4 on page 308, notice that each parabola intersects the x-axis at the point whose coordinates are $(0, 0)$. Since there is only one point of intersection, the single x-intercept of each graph is 0. This means also that the corresponding quadratic equations each have exactly one real number solution.

Sometimes a parabola of the form $y = ax^2 + bx + c$ does not intersect the x-axis. In this case, there is no x-intercept and the corresponding quadratic equation has no real number solution. The solutions of such quadratic equations are imaginary numbers.

Written Exercises

Graph each quadratic function. Draw the axis of symmetry and label the coordinates of the vertex.

Ⓐ
1. $y = x^2 + 2x - 4$ $(-1, -5)$
2. $y = 2x^2 + 8x - 1$ $(-2, -9)$
3. $y = -2x^2 + 4x + 1$ $(1, 3)$
4. $y = x^2 - 4$ $(0, -4)$
5. $y = -x^2$ $(0, 0)$
6. $y = x^2 - 5x + 6$ $(\frac{5}{2}, -\frac{1}{4})$

7. $x = 1$, $(1, 2)$
8. $x = \frac{3}{2}$, $(\frac{3}{2}, \frac{5}{4})$
9. $x = -\frac{3}{2}$, $(-\frac{3}{2}, -\frac{25}{2})$

Find an equation of the axis of symmetry of each parabola with the given equation. Determine the coordinates of the vertex. Do not draw the graphs.

7. $y = x^2 - 2x + 3$
8. $y = -x^2 + 3x - 1$
9. $y = 6x + 2x^2 - 8$
10. $y = -5x + 6x^2 - 4$
   $x = \frac{5}{12}$, $(\frac{5}{12}, -\frac{121}{24})$
11. $y = -4x^2 - x + 7$
   $x = -\frac{1}{8}$, $(-\frac{1}{8}, \frac{113}{16})$
12. $y = -10x^2 + 4x - 6$
   $x = \frac{1}{5}$, $(\frac{1}{5}, -\frac{28}{5})$

Graph each quadratic function. Estimate, to the nearest tenth, the x-intercept(s) of each parabola.

Ⓑ
13. $y = -2x^2 - 5x + 2$ $-2.9, 0.4$
14. $y = 5x^2 + 7x - 7$ $-2.1, 0.7$
15. $y = -5x^2 - 3x + 1$ $-0.8, 0.2$
16. $y = 2x^2 + 7x - 3$ $-3.9, 0.4$
17. $y = -4x^2 + 6x + 1$ $-0.2, 1.7$
18. $y = 4x - x^2 + 2$ $-0.4, 4.4$
19. $y = -\frac{1}{4}x^2$ 0
20. $y = 3x^2 - x + 4$
   no x-intercept
21. $y = 9x + 3x^2 + 2$ $-2.8, -0.2$

Graph each set of functions on the same coordinate axes. Find an equation of the axis of symmetry and the coordinates of the vertex.

22. $y = -\frac{1}{4}x^2$, $y = -x^2$, $y = -4x^2$ $x = 0$, $(0, 0)$
23. $y = \frac{1}{4}x^2 - 2$, $y = x^2 - 2$, $y = 4x^2 - 2$
24. $y = x^2$, $y = 2x^2$, $y = 4x^2$ $x = 0$, $(0, 0)$
25. $y = x^2 + 1$, $y = 2x^2 + 1$, $y = 4x^2 + 1$
23. $x = 0$, $(0, -2)$ 25. $x = 0$, $(0, 1)$

Find the inverse of the function determined by each given equation. Draw the graph of each inverse. Is the inverse an inverse function? Find an equation of the axis of symmetry for the inverse relation.

Ⓒ
26. $y = x^2 - 3x - 4$
27. $y = x^2 + 2x - 6$
28. $y = -x^2 - 4x + 3$
29. $y = -2x^2 - 4x + 5$
30. $y = -3x^2 + 6x + 1$
31. $y = 4x^2 - 5x - 2$
26. $x = y^2 - 3y - 4$; No; $y = \frac{3}{2}$ 27. $x = y^2 + 2y - 6$; No; $y = -1$ 28. $x = -y^2 - 4y + 3$; No; $y = -2$
29. $x = -2y^2 - 4y + 5$; No; $y = -1$ 30. $x = -3y^2 + 6y + 1$; No; $y = 1$ 31. $x = 4y^2 - 5y - 2$; No; $y = \frac{5}{8}$
32. Show that the coordinates of the vertex of the parabola with equation

$y = ax^2 + bx + c$ are $\left(-\dfrac{b}{2a}, \dfrac{4ac - b^2}{4a}\right)$. **For Ex. 32, see TE Answer Section.**

THE PARABOLA

12.3 The Circle

OBJECTIVES ▶ To find an equation of a circle whose center is at the origin
To find the length of a radius of a circle from its equation
To draw a graph of the equation of a circle
To find an equation of a circle whose center is not at the origin

A **circle** can be defined as a set of points as follows.

Definition:
Circle

A *circle* is the set of all points in a coordinate plane that are a given distance from a given point in the plane. The given distance is the *radius* of the circle and the given point is the *center* of the circle.

For simplicity, the term "radius" is used to mean "length of the radius." That is, radius 6 means a radius has a length of 6 units.

You can write an equation of a circle with radius r and center at the origin. Let $P(x, y)$ be any point on a circle.

Use the distance formula to find the distance from P to the center of the circle.

$$d = \sqrt{(x_2 - x_1)^2 + (y_2 - y_1)^2}$$
$$r = \sqrt{(x - 0)^2 + (y - 0)^2}$$

Squaring both sides and simplifying, you get $x^2 + y^2 = r^2$

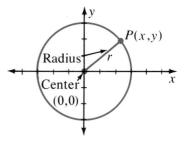

Standard Form
of Equation
of Circle

The standard form of the equation of a circle with center at the origin $(0, 0)$ and radius of length r is $x^2 + y^2 = r^2$.

Example 1

Find an equation of a circle whose center is at the origin and whose radius is 4.

Use the standard form of the equation of a circle.

$$x^2 + y^2 = r^2$$
Substitute 4 for r. ▶ $\quad x^2 + y^2 = 4^2$
$$x^2 + y^2 = 16$$

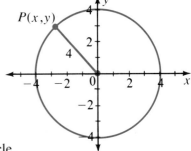

Thus, $x^2 + y^2 = 16$ is an equation of the circle.

Example 2 Find the radius of a circle whose equation is $x^2 + y^2 = 64$.

Use the standard form of the equation of a circle.
$$x^2 + y^2 = r^2$$
$$x^2 + y^2 = 64$$
$$r^2 = 64$$
$$r = \pm\sqrt{64}, \text{ or } \pm 8$$

Since r is a length and a length is always positive, r is always positive.

Thus, the radius of the circle is 8.

Example 3 Find an equation of a circle whose center is at the origin and which passes through the point $P(5, 12)$.

Let $P(x, y) = P(5, 12)$. Find r.
$$x^2 + y^2 = r^2$$
$$5^2 + 12^2 = r^2$$
$$25 + 144 = r^2$$
$$169 = r^2$$

Thus, $x^2 + y^2 = 169$ is an equation of the circle.

The next example shows how to draw the graph of an equation of the form $x^2 + y^2 = r^2$.

Example 4 Draw the graph of each equation.
$$x^2 + y^2 = 9 \qquad\qquad x^2 + y^2 = 21$$

Use $x^2 + y^2 = r^2$. ▶

$x^2 + y^2 = 9$	$x^2 + y^2 = 21$
$r^2 = 9$	$r^2 = 21$
$r = 3$	$r = \sqrt{21} \doteq 4.6$

Plot some points 3 units from the origin.

Plot some points 4.6 units from the origin.

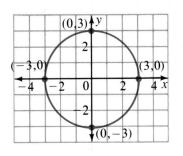

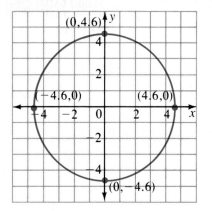

You have learned how to find an equation of a circle with its center at the origin. You can use a similar approach to find an equation of a circle with its center at any point in the coordinate plane.

Let $P(x, y)$ be any point on a circle and $C(h, k)$ be the center of the circle. Use the distance formula to find the distance from P to C.

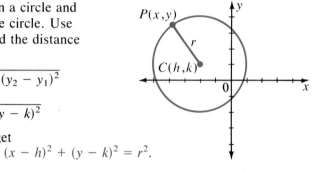

$$d = \sqrt{(x_2 - x_1)^2 + (y_2 - y_1)^2}$$

$$r = \sqrt{(x - h)^2 + (y - k)^2}$$

Squaring both sides, you get
$$(x - h)^2 + (y - k)^2 = r^2.$$

This equation is the standard form of the equation of a circle with center $C(h, k)$ and radius of length r.

Example 5

Find an equation of a circle whose center is at $C(7, -6)$ and whose radius is 8.

Use $(x - h)^2 + (y - k)^2 = r^2.$
        $(x - 7)^2 + [y - (-6)]^2 = 8^2$ ◀ *Substitute 7 for h, −6 for k, and 8 for r.*

Thus, $(x - 7)^2 + (y + 6)^2 = 64$ is an equation of the circle.

Example 6

Find an equation of a circle whose center is at $C(-3, 5)$ and which passes through the point $P(7, -3)$.

Let $P(x, y) = P(7, -3)$ and $C(h, k) = C(-3, 5)$. Find r^2.

$$(x - h)^2 + (y - k)^2 = r^2$$
$$[7 - (-3)]^2 + (-3 - 5)^2 = r^2$$
$$100 + 64 = r^2$$
$$164 = r^2$$

Thus, $(x + 3)^2 + (y - 5)^2 = 164$ is an equation of the circle.

Oral Exercises

Find the radius of each circle whose equation is given.
  1. $x^2 + y^2 = 100$ **10**   2. $x^2 + y^2 = 4$ **2**   3. $x^2 + y^2 = 7$ **$\sqrt{7}$**   4. $(x - 3)^2 + (y + 2)^2 = 3$ **$\sqrt{3}$**

Reading in **Algebra**

Select the one ordered pair, or number, that does not belong with the equation at the left. Give a reason for your answer.

1. $x^2 + y^2 = 8$ **A** $(2, 2)$ **B** $(-2, -2)$ **C** $(6, 2)$ **D** $2\sqrt{2}$ **C**
2. $x^2 + y^2 = 5$ **A** $(0, 0)$ **B** $(2, 1)$ **C** $(3, -2)$ **D** $\sqrt{5}$ **C**
3. $x^2 + y^2 = 25$ **A** $(-3, 4)$ **B** $(4, -3)$ **C** $(3, 4)$ **D** -5 **D**

Written **Exercises**

Answers for Ex. 1–28 are of the form $x^2 + y^2 = r^2$. The value of r^2 is given for each exercise.

Find an equation of each circle whose center is at the origin and which has the given radius.

(A)
1. 1   1   2. 12   144   3. 3   9   4. 15   225   5. 2   4   6. 13   169
7. 9   81   8. 8   64   9. 5   25   10. 20   400   11. 17   289   12. 11   121
13. 7   49   14. 4   16   15. $\sqrt{2}$ 2   16. $\sqrt{5}$ 5   17. $\sqrt{3}$ 3   18. $\sqrt{7}$ 7

Find an equation of each circle whose center is at the origin and which passes through the given point.

19. $P(3, -4)$ 25   20. $P(-1, 2)$ 5   21. $P(2, -3)$ 13   22. $P(8, 0)$ 64   23. $P(0, -2)$ 4
24. $P(5, 12)$ 169   25. $P(-6, -5)$ 61   26. $P(8, -7)$ 113   27. $P(3, -13)$ 178   28. $P(-7, -9)$ 130

Draw the graph of each equation. For Ex. 29–36, see TE Answer Section.

29. $x^2 + y^2 = 25$ 30. $x^2 + y^2 = 16$ 31. $x^2 + y^2 = 81$ 32. $x^2 + y^2 = 100$
33. $x^2 + y^2 = 36$ 34. $x^2 + y^2 = 3$ 35. $x^2 + y^2 = 12$ 36. $x^2 + y^2 = 6$

37. $(x - 5)^2 + (y - 6)^2 = 49$ 38. $(x + 2)^2 + (y - 8)^2 = 81$ 39. $(x - 11)^2 + (y + 7)^2 = \frac{49}{4}$ 40. $(x + 10)^2 + y^2 = \frac{16}{9}$

Find an equation of each circle whose center C is given, and with the given radius r or with the given point P on the circle.

(B)
37. $C(5, 6); r = 7$ 38. $C(-2, 8); r = 9$ 39. $C(11, -7); r = 3\frac{1}{2}$ 40. $C(-10, 0); r = 1\frac{1}{3}$
41. $C(2, -3); P(4, 6)$ 42. $C(7, 0); P(5, 2)$ 43. $C(-6, -3); P(4, -1)$ 44. $C(-4, -3); P(-3, -4)$
$(x - 2)^2 + (y + 3)^2 = 85$ $(x - 7)^2 + y^2 = 8$ $(x + 6)^2 + (y + 3)^2 = 104$ $(x + 4)^2 + (y + 3)^2 = 2$

Determine which of the following is an equation of a circle. Find the radius of each circle.

45. $7x^2 + 7y^2 = 49$ **Yes;** $\sqrt{7}$ 46. $5x^2 + 5y^2 = 20$ **Yes; 2**   47. $6x^2 + 6y^2 = 36$ **Yes;** $\sqrt{6}$
48. $8x^2 + 8y^2 = 72$ **Yes; 3**   49. $7x^2 - 7y^2 = 49$ **No**   50. $3x^2 + 3y^2 = 10$ **Yes;** $\frac{\sqrt{30}}{3}$
51. $10x^2 + 10y^2 = 25$ **Yes;** $\frac{\sqrt{10}}{2}$ 52. $-15x^2 + 15y^2 = 30$ **No**   53. $-3x^2 - 3y^2 = -10$ **Yes;** $\frac{\sqrt{30}}{3}$

Find the coordinates of the center of each circle, and the radius of each circle, from the given equation. [Hint: Use the method of completing the square.]

(C)
54. $x^2 - 6x + y^2 + 8y = -9$ $(3, -4); 4$ 55. $x^2 + 4x + y^2 - 2y = 4$ $(-2, 1); 3$
56. $x^2 - 2x + y^2 - 6y = -1$ $(1, 3); 3$ 57. $x^2 - 10x + y^2 - 8y = 59$ $(5, 4); 10$

THE CIRCLE

12.4 The Ellipse

OBJECTIVES ▶ **To find an equation of an ellipse whose center is at the origin, given the *x*- and *y*-intercepts**
To determine the *x*- and *y*-intercepts of an ellipse
To draw a graph of the equation of an ellipse

The orbit of the earth around the sun is in the shape of an **ellipse**. An ellipse can be defined as a set of points as follows.

Definition:
Ellipse

> An *ellipse* is the set of all points in a coordinate plane such that for each point of the set, the sum of its distances from two fixed points is constant. Each of the fixed points is called a *focus* (plural: foci).

You can write an equation of an ellipse whose center is at the origin, foci are $F_1(-3, 0)$ and $F_2(3, 0)$, and where the sum of the distances from any point on the ellipse to the foci is 10.

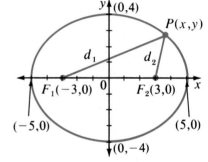

Let $P(x, y)$ be any point on the ellipse. Then find the distance d_1 from $P(x, y)$ to $F_1(-3, 0)$ and d_2 from $P(x, y)$ to $F_2(3, 0)$. Use the distance formula.

$$d_1 = \sqrt{[x - (-3)]^2 + (y - 0)^2}$$
$$d_2 = \sqrt{(x - 3)^2 + (y - 0)^2}$$

The sum of the distances is 10. Use this fact to write one radical equation. Then simplify the radical equation by squaring each side.

$$\sqrt{(x + 3)^2 + y^2} + \sqrt{(x - 3)^2 + y^2} = 10$$
$$\sqrt{x^2 + 6x + 9 + y^2} = 10 - \sqrt{x^2 - 6x + 9 + y^2}$$
$$(\sqrt{x^2 + 6x + 9 + y^2})^2 = (10 - \sqrt{x^2 - 6x + 9 + y^2})^2$$
$$x^2 + 6x + 9 + y^2 = 100 - 20\sqrt{x^2 - 6x + 9 + y^2} + x^2 - 6x + 9 + y^2$$
$$12x - 100 = -20\sqrt{x^2 - 6x + 9 + y^2}$$
$$3x - 25 = -5\sqrt{x^2 - 6x + 9 + y^2}$$
$$(3x - 25)^2 = (-5\sqrt{x^2 - 6x + 9 + y^2})^2$$
$$9x^2 - 150x + 625 = 25x^2 - 150x + 225 + 25y^2$$
$$400 = 16x^2 + 25y^2$$

Divide each side by 400 to get the following equation of the ellipse.

$$\frac{x^2}{25} + \frac{y^2}{16} = 1$$

Notice that the *x*-intercepts of the ellipse in the figure above are $\pm\sqrt{25}$, or ± 5, and the *y*-intercepts are $\pm\sqrt{16}$, or ± 4.

314

Standard Form of Equation of Ellipse

> The standard form of the equation of an ellipse with center at the origin $(0, 0)$ and whose x- and y-intercepts are $\pm a$ and $\pm b$, respectively, is
> $$\frac{x^2}{a^2} + \frac{y^2}{b^2} = 1; \; a \neq 0, \, b \neq 0.$$

Example 1 Write an equation, in standard form, of an ellipse whose center is at the origin and whose x-intercepts are ± 9 and whose y-intercepts are ± 7.

Use the standard form of the equation of an ellipse.
$$\frac{x^2}{a^2} + \frac{y^2}{b^2} = 1$$

Substitute ± 9 for a and ± 7 for b. ▶ $\dfrac{x^2}{(\pm 9)^2} + \dfrac{y^2}{(\pm 7)^2} = 1$

Thus, $\dfrac{x^2}{81} + \dfrac{y^2}{49} = 1$ is an equation of the ellipse.

Example 2 Draw the graph of $\dfrac{x^2}{25} + \dfrac{y^2}{16} = 1$.

Use $\dfrac{x^2}{a^2} + \dfrac{y^2}{b^2} = 1$. ▶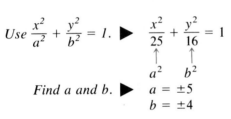

Find a and b. ▶ $a = \pm 5$
$b = \pm 4$

The x-intercepts are ± 5 and the y-intercepts are ± 4.

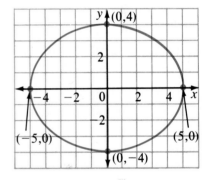

Plot the points with coordinates $(5, 0)$, $(-5, 0)$, $(0, 4)$, and $(0, -4)$. Then draw a smooth curve.

Example 3 Draw the graph of $6x^2 + 9y^2 = 27$.

Write $6x^2 + 9y^2 = 27$ in standard form.

Divide by 27. ▶ $\dfrac{6x^2}{27} + \dfrac{9y^2}{27} = \dfrac{27}{27}$

$$\frac{x^2}{\frac{27}{6}} + \frac{y^2}{3} = 1$$

$$\frac{x^2}{\frac{9}{2}} + \frac{y^2}{3} = 1$$

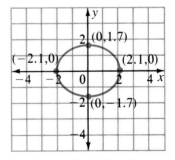

$a = \pm \dfrac{3\sqrt{2}}{2} \doteq \pm 2.1 \qquad b = \pm\sqrt{3} \doteq \pm 1.7$

THE ELLIPSE

Written Exercises _____

Write an equation, in standard form, of an ellipse whose center is at the origin and whose intercepts are given.

Ⓐ 1. x-intercepts ±3; y-intercepts ±2 $\frac{x^2}{9} + \frac{y^2}{4} = 1$ 2. x-intercepts $\pm\sqrt{8}$; y-intercepts ±3 $\frac{x^2}{8} + \frac{y^2}{9} = 1$

3. x-intercepts ±2; y-intercepts $\pm\sqrt{3}$ $\frac{x^2}{4} + \frac{y^2}{3} = 1$ 4. x-intercepts $\pm\sqrt{3}$; y-intercepts $\pm\sqrt{5}$ $\frac{x^2}{3} + \frac{y^2}{5} = 1$

5. x-intercepts ±8; y-intercepts ±6 $\frac{x^2}{64} + \frac{y^2}{36} = 1$ 6. x-intercepts ±7; y-intercepts $\pm\sqrt{3}$

7. $a = \pm4, b = \pm3$ 8. $a = \pm6, b = \pm5$ 9. $a = \pm5, b = \pm2$ 10. $a = \pm9, b = \pm3$ $\frac{x^2}{49} + \frac{y^2}{3} = 1$

Find the x- and y-intercepts of the ellipse whose equation is given. Then draw the graph.

7. $\dfrac{x^2}{16} + \dfrac{y^2}{9} = 1$ above   8. $\dfrac{x^2}{36} + \dfrac{y^2}{25} = 1$ above   9. $\dfrac{x^2}{25} + \dfrac{y^2}{4} = 1$ above   10. $\dfrac{x^2}{81} + \dfrac{y^2}{9} = 1$ above

11. $\dfrac{x^2}{4} + \dfrac{y^2}{16} = 1$ 12. $\dfrac{x^2}{100} + \dfrac{y^2}{25} = 1$ 13. $\dfrac{x^2}{9} + \dfrac{y^2}{100} = 1$ 14. $\dfrac{x^2}{4} + \dfrac{y^2}{25} = 1$

15. $4x^2 + y^2 = 100$ 16. $3x^2 + y^2 = 75$ 17. $x^2 + 9y^2 = 36$ 18. $4x^2 + 25y^2 = 100$

11. $a = \pm2, b = \pm4$ 12. $a = \pm10, b = \pm5$ 13. $a = \pm3, b = \pm10$ 14. $a = \pm2, b = \pm5$

15. $a = \pm5, b = \pm10$ 16. $a = \pm5, b = \pm5\sqrt{3}$ 17. $a = \pm6, b = \pm2$ 18. $a = \pm5, b = \pm2$

Determine which of the following is an equation of an ellipse. Find the x- and y-intercepts of each ellipse. 19. $a = \pm\sqrt{5}, b = \pm1$ 20. $a = \pm5\sqrt{3}, b = \pm5$ 21. $a = \pm4, b = \pm4\sqrt{2}$

Ⓑ 19. $5x^2 + 25y^2 = 25$ 20. $x^2 + 3y^2 = 75$ 21. $2x^2 + y^2 = 32$ 22. $3x^2 + 2y^2 = 18$

23. $3x^2 - 2y^2 = 30$ 24. $4x^2 + 5y^2 = 16$ 25. $16x^2 + 16y^2 = 64$ 26. $7x^2 + 5y^2 = 35$

27. $5x^2 + 6y^2 = 30$ 28. $5x^2 + 3y^2 = 16$ 29. $3x^2 - 5y^2 = 45$ 30. $5x^2 + 2y^2 = 40$

22. $a = \pm\sqrt{6}, b = \pm3$ 23. not an ellipse   24. $a = \pm2, b = \pm\frac{4}{5}\sqrt{5}$ 25. $a = \pm2, b = \pm2$

27. $a = \pm\sqrt{6}, b = \pm\sqrt{5}$ 28. $a = \pm\frac{4}{5}\sqrt{5}, b = \pm\frac{4}{3}\sqrt{3}$ 29. not an ellipse   30. $a = \pm2\sqrt{2}, b = \pm2\sqrt{5}$

Write an equation, in standard form, of each ellipse with center at the origin, F_1 and F_2 the foci, and where c is the *sum of the distances* from any point on the ellipse to the foci.

Ⓒ 31. $F_1(-3, 0), F_2(3, 0); c = 8$ $\frac{x^2}{16} + \frac{y^2}{7} = 1$ 32. $F_1(-2, 0), F_2(2, 0); c = 12$ $\frac{x^2}{36} + \frac{y^2}{32} = 1$

33. $F_1(-4, 0), F_2(4, 0); c = 10$ $\frac{x^2}{25} + \frac{y^2}{9} = 1$ 34. $F_1(-5, 0), F_2(5, 0); c = 14$ $\frac{x^2}{49} + \frac{y^2}{24} = 1$

Find the domain and range of the function defined by the given equation by solving the equation for each variable in terms of the other variable. [The *extent* of the graph of the equation is the set of all possible values of x and the set of all possible values of y. This is the region of the coordinate plane that the graph occupies.]

35. $\dfrac{x^2}{9} + \dfrac{y^2}{16} = 1$ 36. $\dfrac{x^2}{36} + \dfrac{y^2}{25} = 1$ 37. $\dfrac{x^2}{4} + \dfrac{y^2}{81} = 1$

$\{x \mid -3 \le x \le 3\}, \{y \mid -4 \le y \le 4\}$ $\{x \mid -6 \le x \le 6\}, \{y \mid -5 \le y \le 5\}$ $\{x \mid -2 \le x \le 2\}, \{y \mid -9 \le y \le 9\}$

Draw the graph of each equation. Determine the extent of the graph.

38. $y = \pm\dfrac{1}{3}\sqrt{81 - x^2}$ 39. $y = \pm\dfrac{1}{2}\sqrt{16 - x^2}$ 40. $y = \pm\dfrac{3}{2}\sqrt{4 - x^2}$

$\{x \mid -9 \le x \le 9 \text{ and } y \mid -3 \le y \le 3\}$ $\{x \mid -4 \le x \le 4 \text{ and } y \mid -2 \le y \le 2\}$ $\{x \mid -2 \le x \le 2 \text{ and } y \mid -3 \le y \le 3\}$

26. $a = \pm\sqrt{5}, b = \pm\sqrt{7}$

12.5 The Hyperbola

OBJECTIVES ▶ **To find an equation of a hyperbola whose center is at the origin**
To determine the intercepts of a hyperbola
To find the equations of the asymptotes of a hyperbola
To draw a graph of the equation of a hyperbola

Another curve that can be defined as a set of points is a **hyperbola.**

Definition:
Hyperbola

A *hyperbola* is the set of all points in a coordinate plane such that for each point of the set, the difference of its distances from two fixed points is constant. The fixed points are called the *foci.*

You can write an equation of a hyperbola whose center is at the origin, foci are $F_1(-5, 0)$ and $F_2(5, 0)$, and where the difference of the distances from any point on the hyperbola to the foci is 8.

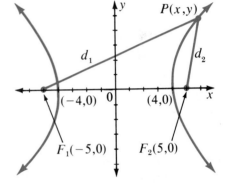

Let $P(x, y)$ be any point on the hyperbola. Then find the distance d_1 from $P(x, y)$ to $F_1(-5, 0)$ and d_2 from $P(x, y)$ to $F_2(5, 0)$. Use the distance formula.

$$d_1 = \sqrt{[x - (-5)]^2 + (y - 0)^2}$$
$$d_2 = \sqrt{(x - 5)^2 + (y - 0)^2}$$

The difference of the distances is 8. Use this fact to write one radical equation. Then simplify the radical equation by squaring each side.

$$\sqrt{(x + 5)^2 + y^2} - \sqrt{(x - 5)^2 + y^2} = 8$$
$$\sqrt{x^2 + 10x + 25 + y^2} = 8 + \sqrt{x^2 - 10x + 25 + y^2}$$
$$(\sqrt{x^2 + 10x + 25 + y^2})^2 = (8 + \sqrt{x^2 - 10x + 25 + y^2})^2$$
$$x^2 + 10x + 25 + y^2 = 64 + 16\sqrt{x^2 - 10x + 25 + y^2} + x^2 - 10x + 25 + y^2$$
$$20x - 64 = 16\sqrt{x^2 - 10x + 25 + y^2}$$
$$5x - 16 = 4\sqrt{x^2 - 10x + 25 + y^2}$$
$$(5x - 16)^2 = (4\sqrt{x^2 - 10x + 25 + y^2})^2$$
$$25x^2 - 160x + 256 = 16x^2 - 160x + 400 + 16y^2$$
$$9x^2 - 16y^2 = 144$$

An equation of the hyperbola is $\dfrac{x^2}{16} - \dfrac{y^2}{9} = 1$.

In the figure above, notice that a hyperbola has two branches. In this case, the x-intercepts are $\pm\sqrt{16}$, or ± 4. A hyperbola of this type has no y-intercepts since the curve does not intersect the y-axis.

Standard Form of Equation of Hyperbola with x-Intercepts

The standard form of the equation of a hyperbola with center at the origin $(0, 0)$ and whose x-intercepts are $\pm a$ is $\dfrac{x^2}{a^2} - \dfrac{y^2}{b^2} = 1; a \neq 0, b \neq 0$.

Example 1 Draw the graph of $\dfrac{x^2}{25} - \dfrac{y^2}{9} = 1$.

Use $\dfrac{x^2}{a^2} - \dfrac{y^2}{b^2} = 1$. ▶ $\underset{\underset{a^2}{\uparrow} \quad \underset{b^2}{\uparrow}}{\dfrac{x^2}{25} - \dfrac{y^2}{9}} = 1$

Find a and b. ▶ $a = \pm 5 \quad b = \pm 3$

Draw a rectangle using $(5, 0)$, $(-5, 0)$, $(0, 3)$ and $(0, -3)$ as the coordinates of the midpoints of the sides.

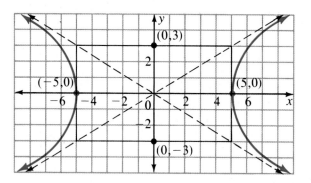

Use the extended diagonals of the rectangle and the x-intercepts. Draw a smooth curve.

The extended diagonal lines in Example 1 are called the **asymptotes** of the hyperbola. A hyperbola approaches but never intersects its asymptotes.

The graph of $\dfrac{x^2}{a^2} - \dfrac{y^2}{b^2} = 1$ is shown at the right. The y-intercept of each of the asymptotes is 0 and the slopes are $\dfrac{b}{a}$ and $-\dfrac{b}{a}$, respectively. Therefore, $y = \dfrac{b}{a}x$ and $y = -\dfrac{b}{a}x$ are the equations of the asymptotes, where a and b are positive real numbers.

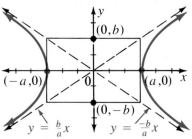

In Example 1, the equations of the asymptotes are $y = \dfrac{3}{5}x$ and $y = -\dfrac{3}{5}x$.

**Standard Form
of Equation
of Hyperbola
with y-Intercepts**

The standard form of the equation of a hyperbola with center at the origin $(0, 0)$ and whose y-intercepts are $\pm a$ is $\dfrac{y^2}{a^2} - \dfrac{x^2}{b^2} = 1; a \neq 0, b \neq 0$.

The equations of the asymptotes for a hyperbola of this type are $y = \frac{a}{b}x$ and $y = -\frac{a}{b}x$

Example 2 **Draw the graph of $4y^2 - x^2 = 16$. Find the equations of the asymptotes.**

Write $4y^2 - x^2 = 16$ in standard form.

$$\frac{4y^2}{16} - \frac{x^2}{16} = \frac{16}{16}, \text{ or } \frac{y^2}{4} - \frac{x^2}{16} = 1$$

$Use \dfrac{y^2}{a^2} - \dfrac{x^2}{b^2} = 1.$ ▶ $\quad \begin{array}{ll} a^2 = 4 & b^2 = 16 \\ a = \pm 2 & b = \pm 4 \end{array}$

Draw a rectangle using $(0, 2)$, $(0, -2)$, $(4, 0)$ and $(-4, 0)$ as the coordinates of the midpoints of the sides.

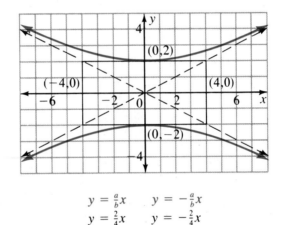

$$\begin{array}{ll} y = \frac{a}{b}x & y = -\frac{a}{b}x \\ y = \frac{2}{4}x & y = -\frac{2}{4}x \end{array}$$

Thus, the equations of the asymptotes are $y = \frac{1}{2}x$ and $y = -\frac{1}{2}x$.

The graph of an equation of the form $xy = k\,(k \neq 0)$ is a hyperbola that does not intersect the x- or y-axis. A hyperbola of this type is called a **rectangular hyperbola.** The asymptotes of the hyperbola are the x- and y-axes. If $k > 0$, the branches of the hyperbola lie in Quadrants I and III. If $k < 0$, the branches lie in Quadrants II and IV.

**Standard Form
of Equation
of Rectangular
Hyperbola**

The standard form of the equation of a hyperbola with center at the origin $(0, 0)$ and which does not intersect the x-axis or y-axis is $xy = k$, where k is a nonzero real number. The hyperbola is called a *rectangular hyperbola.*

THE HYPERBOLA

Example 3

Draw the graph of $xy = 4$. Find the equations of the asymptotes.

Solve for y in terms of x and make a table.

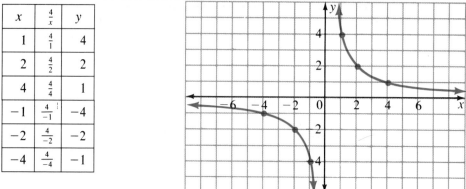

x	$\frac{4}{x}$	y
1	$\frac{4}{1}$	4
2	$\frac{4}{2}$	2
4	$\frac{4}{4}$	1
-1	$\frac{4}{-1}$	-4
-2	$\frac{4}{-2}$	-2
-4	$\frac{4}{-4}$	-1

Thus, the equations of the asymptotes are $x = 0$ and $y = 0$.

Written Exercises

For complete solutions, see TE Answer Section.

Draw a graph of each equation. Find the equations of the asymptotes.

(A)

1. $\frac{x^2}{16} - \frac{y^2}{4} = 1$ $y = \frac{1}{2}x,$ $y = -\frac{1}{2}x$
2. $\frac{x^2}{25} - \frac{y^2}{9} = 1$
3. $\frac{x^2}{4} - \frac{y^2}{16} = 1$
4. $\frac{x^2}{36} - \frac{y^2}{49} = 1$

5. $\frac{x^2}{9} - \frac{y^2}{16} = 1$ $y = \frac{4}{3}x,$ $y = -\frac{4}{3}x$
6. $\frac{x^2}{49} - \frac{y^2}{81} = 1$
7. $\frac{x^2}{49} - \frac{y^2}{4} = 1$
8. $\frac{x^2}{100} - \frac{y^2}{64} = 1$

9. $\frac{x^2}{4} - \frac{y^2}{9} = 1$
10. $\frac{x^2}{81} - \frac{y^2}{64} = 1$
11. $\frac{x^2}{100} - \frac{y^2}{81} = 1$
12. $\frac{x^2}{121} - \frac{y^2}{36} = 1$

13. $xy = 4$ $x = 0, y = 0$
14. $xy = 1$ $x = 0, y = 0$
15. $xy = 7$ $x = 0, y = 0$
16. $4xy = 16$ $x = 0, y = 0$

17. $\frac{y^2}{16} - \frac{x^2}{9} = 1$
18. $\frac{y^2}{25} - \frac{x^2}{16} = 1$
19. $\frac{y^2}{81} - \frac{x^2}{25} = 1$
20. $\frac{y^2}{36} - \frac{x^2}{4} = 1$

(B)

21. $xy = -6$
22. $xy = -9$
23. $-xy = 12$
24. $-3xy = 12$

25. $4x^2 - y^2 = 36$
26. $4x^2 - 9y^2 = 36$
27. $16x^2 - 9y^2 = 144$
28. $12x^2 - 3y^2 = 48$

29. $4y^2 - 16x^2 = 64$ $y = 2x, y = -2x$
30. $5y^2 - 9x^2 = 45$ $y = \frac{3\sqrt{5}}{5}x, y = -\frac{3\sqrt{5}}{5}x$
31. $16y^2 - 4x^2 = 64$ $y = \frac{1}{2}x, y = -\frac{1}{2}x$
32. $4y^2 - 5x^2 = 100$ $y = \frac{\sqrt{5}}{2}x, y = -\frac{\sqrt{5}}{2}x$

Write an equation, in standard form, of each hyperbola with center at the origin, F_1 and F_2 the foci, and where c is the *difference of the distances* from any point on the hyperbola to the foci.

(C)

33. $F_1(-13, 0), F_2(13, 0); c = 24$
34. $F_1(-10, 0), F_2(10, 0); c = 16$
35. $F_1(-6, 0), F_2(6, 0); c = 10$ $\frac{x^2}{25} - \frac{y^2}{11} = 1$
36. $F_1(-10, 0), F_2(10, 0); c = 18$ $\frac{x^2}{81} - \frac{y^2}{19} = 1$

The standard form of the equation of a hyperbola with center at $C(h, k)$ and whose x-intercepts are $\pm a$ is $\dfrac{(x - h)^2}{a^2} - \dfrac{(y - k)^2}{b^2} = 1; a \neq 0, b \neq 0$. Write an equation, in standard form, of each hyperbola whose center C is given, and with the given values for a and b. Draw a graph of each equation.

37. $C(-3, 5); a = \pm 3, b = \pm 2$ $\frac{(x+3)^2}{9} - \frac{(y-5)^2}{4} = 1$
38. $C(4, -1); a = \pm 5, b = \pm 3$ $\frac{(x-4)^2}{25} - \frac{(y+1)^2}{9} = 1$
39. $C(1, 7); a = \pm 8, b = \pm 5$ $\frac{(x-1)^2}{64} - \frac{(y-7)^2}{25} = 1$
40. $C(-8, -2); a = \pm 10, b = \pm 8$ $\frac{(x+8)^2}{100} - \frac{(y+2)^2}{64} = 1$

2. $y = \frac{3}{5}x, y = -\frac{3}{5}x$ 3. $y = 2x, y = -2x$ 4. $y = \frac{7}{6}x, y = -\frac{7}{6}x$ 6. $y = \frac{9}{7}x, y = -\frac{9}{7}x$ 7. $y = \frac{2}{7}x, y = -\frac{2}{7}x$

8. $y = \frac{4}{5}x, y = -\frac{4}{5}x$ 9. $y = \frac{3}{2}x, y = -\frac{3}{2}x$ 10. $y = \frac{8}{9}x, y = -\frac{8}{9}x$ 11. $y = \frac{9}{10}x, y = -\frac{9}{10}x$ 12. $y = \frac{6}{11}x, y = -\frac{6}{11}x$

12.6 Identifying Conic Sections

OBJECTIVE ▶ **To identify an equation of a parabola, circle, ellipse, and hyperbola**

As shown below, a parabola, circle, ellipse, or a hyperbola can be formed by passing a plane through a hollow double cone. Therefore, each of these curves is called a **conic section.**

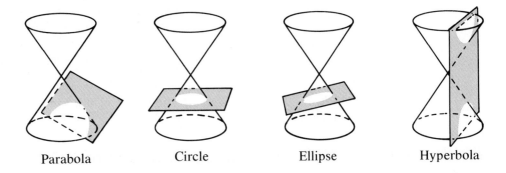

Parabola   Circle   Ellipse   Hyperbola

An equation of a conic section can be written in the form $Ax^2 + Bxy + Cy^2 + Dx + Ey + F = 0$, where A, B, and C are not all zero. To identify the curve that is described by a given quadratic equation of this form, you should rewrite the equation so that it is expressed in one of the standard forms which you have studied.

Example 1 **Determine whether $9x^2 - 16y^2 = 144$ is an equation of a parabola, a circle, an ellipse, or a hyperbola.**

$$9x^2 - 16y^2 = 144$$

Divide each term by the constant. ▶ $\dfrac{9x^2}{144} - \dfrac{16y^2}{144} = \dfrac{144}{144}$

Standard form: $\dfrac{x^2}{a^2} - \dfrac{y^2}{b^2} = 1.$ ▶ $\dfrac{x^2}{16} - \dfrac{y^2}{9} = 1$

Thus, $9x^2 - 16y^2 = 144$ is an equation of a hyperbola.

Example 2 **Determine whether $17 + 3x^2 = y + 5x$ is an equation of a parabola, a circle, an ellipse, or a hyperbola.**

There is no y^2 term. ▶ $17 + 3x^2 = y + 5x$
Solve for y. ▶ $3x^2 - 5x + 17 = y$ ◀ *Standard form:* $y = ax^2 + bx + c.$

Thus, $17 + 3x^2 = y + 5x$ is an equation of a parabola.

When the x-intercepts and y-intercepts of an ellipse are equal, the standard form of the equation of the ellipse becomes $\dfrac{x^2}{a^2} + \dfrac{y^2}{a^2} = 1$. Multiplying by a^2, you get $x^2 + y^2 = a^2$. This is an equation of a circle with radius a. Thus, a circle can be considered to be a special type of ellipse.

Example 3 Identify each conic section whose equation is given.

$$9x^2 = 36 - 4y^2 \qquad\qquad 8x^2 + 8y^2 = 56$$

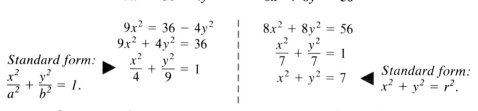

$$\begin{array}{c|c}
9x^2 = 36 - 4y^2 & 8x^2 + 8y^2 = 56 \\
9x^2 + 4y^2 = 36 & \dfrac{x^2}{7} + \dfrac{y^2}{7} = 1 \\
\end{array}$$

Standard form: ▶ $\dfrac{x^2}{4} + \dfrac{y^2}{9} = 1$ $\quad|\quad$ $x^2 + y^2 = 7$ ◀ *Standard form:*

$\dfrac{x^2}{a^2} + \dfrac{y^2}{b^2} = 1$. $\qquad\qquad\qquad\qquad x^2 + y^2 = r^2$.

Thus, $9x^2 = 36 - 4y^2$ is an equation of an ellipse and $8x^2 + 8y^2 = 56$ is an equation of a circle.

Written Exercises

(In Exercises 1–47, let P = parabola, C = circle, E = ellipse, and H = hyperbola.)

Identify each conic section whose equation is given.

(A) **1.** $\dfrac{x^2}{16} + \dfrac{y^2}{4} = 1$ E **2.** $\dfrac{x^2}{14} + \dfrac{y^2}{14} = 1$ C **3.** $\dfrac{x^2}{16} - \dfrac{y^2}{16} = 1$ H **4.** $\dfrac{x^2}{12} + \dfrac{y^2}{3} = 1$ E

5. $\dfrac{y^2}{4} - \dfrac{x^2}{16} = 1$ H **6.** $x = \dfrac{-3}{y}$ H **7.** $\dfrac{x^2}{50} + \dfrac{y^2}{50} = 1$ C **8.** $y = \dfrac{8}{x}$ H

9. $6x^2 + 4y^2 = 24$ E **10.** $x^2 = 4 + y$ P **11.** $7x^2 - 3x = -3 + y$ P **12.** $5x^2 - 6y^2 = 30$ H

13. $15x^2 + 15y^2 = 225$ C **14.** $5x^2 - 3y^2 = 15$ H **15.** $y - 3x^2 = 6 + x$ P **16.** $30x^2 = -3y^2 + 15$

17. $y + x^2 = 3x + 2$ P **18.** $x^2 + 2y^2 = 8$ E **19.** $9x^2 - 4y^2 = 36$ H **20.** $-y - 3x = x^2 + 5$

21. $3x^2 + 4y^2 = 48$ E **22.** $7x^2 - 8y^2 = 35$ H **23.** $4x^2 + 4y^2 = 15$ C **24.** $2x^2 + 3y^2 = 45$ E

(B) **25.** $16x^2 - 16y^2 = 5$ H **26.** $12x^2 + 16y^2 = 17$ **27.** $19y^2 + 9x^2 = 5$ E **28.** $6x^2 - 6y^2 = 8$ H

29. $(x + 3y)(x - 3y) = 4$ **30.** $y - 3 = (x - 2)^2$ P **31.** $(3x - 2y)(3x + 2y) = 1$ **32.** $\dfrac{x}{9} = \dfrac{1}{y}$ H

33. $x^2 - 6x + y^2 + 8y = 24$ C **34.** $x^2 - 2x + y^2 - 6y = 26$ C **35.** $x^2 + 10x + y^2 + 12y = 60$ C

16. E 20. P 26. E 29. H 31. H

Identify each conic section whose equation is given. Determine whether the graph is symmetric with respect to the x-axis, the y-axis, the origin, or none of these.

36. $5x^2 - 6y^2 = 30$ **37.** $x^2 + 3y^2 = 12$ **38.** $4x^2 + 4y^2 = 16$ **39.** $y - x^2 - 2x = 8$

40. $\dfrac{x^2}{16} + \dfrac{y^2}{16} = 1$ **41.** $\dfrac{x^2}{4} - \dfrac{y^2}{16} = 1$ **42.** $\dfrac{y^2}{25} - \dfrac{x^2}{4} = 1$ **43.** $\dfrac{x^2}{16} + \dfrac{y^2}{4} = 1$

44. $7y = \dfrac{-16}{x}$ H; origin **45.** $x^2 - 16 = y$ **46.** $\dfrac{16}{y} = \dfrac{-x}{7}$ H; origin **47.** $\dfrac{x^2}{18} + \dfrac{y^2}{18} = 23$

Cumulative Review

Find the slope of a line perpendicular to each line whose equation is given.

1. $-3x + 5y = 8$ $-\frac{5}{3}$ **2.** $7x + 2y = 10$ $\frac{2}{7}$ **3.** $x = -4$ 0 **4.** $y = 6$ undefined

36. H; x-axis, y-axis, origin 37. E; x-axis, y-axis, origin 38. C; x-axis, y-axis, origin 39. P; none of these
40. C; x-axis, y-axis, origin 41. H; x-axis, y-axis, origin 42. H; x-axis, y-axis, origin

43. E; x-axis, y-axis, origin 45. P; y-axis 47. C; x-axis, y-axis, origin **CHAPTER TWELVE**

12.7 Translations

To draw a graph of the equation of an absolute value function or a conic section whose vertex or center is not at the origin

The graph of the absolute value function, $y = |x|$, is shown at the right. Compare the graphs of $y = |x - 2|$ and $y = |x + 2|$ below with this basic graph.

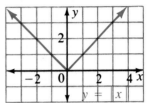

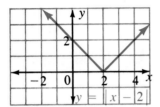

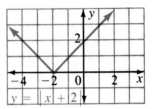

The basic graph is moved 2 units to the right.

The basic graph is moved 2 units to the left.

Example 1 Graph $y = |x| + 2$ and $y = |x| - 2$. Use the basic graph of $y = |x|$ for reference.

Move the basic graph 2 units up.

Move the basic graph 2 units down.

You have just seen how to draw the graph of $y = |x \pm h|$ or $y = |x| \pm k$ for some real number constants h and k.

The graph of an equation of the form $y = (x - h)^2$, $y = (x + h)^2$, $y = x^2 + k$, or $y = x^2 - k$ can be drawn by using the basic graph of $y = x^2$ for reference. Each graph is a parabola whose vertex is not at the origin. The graph of $y = x^2$ is translated so that the vertex is moved h or k units horizontally or vertically.

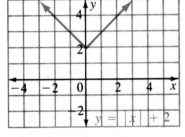

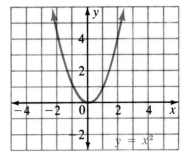

TRANSLATIONS

Example 1

Graph $y = (x - 2)^2$ and $y = (x + 2)^2$. Use the graph of $y = x^2$ for reference.

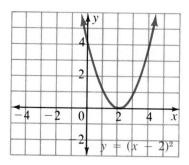

Move the basic graph two units to the right.

Move the basic graph two units to the left.

Example 2

Graph $y = x^2 + 2$ and $y = x^2 - 2$. Use the basic graph of $y = x^2$ for reference.

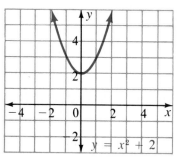

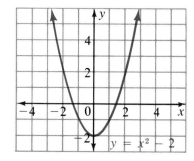

Move the basic graph two units up.

Move the basic graph two units down.

Translation of a Parabola

The graph of $y = (x - h)^2 + k$ is a parabola whose vertex has the coordinates (h, k).

Example 3

Graph $y = x^2 + 8x + 6$. Use the basic graph of $y = x^2$ for reference.

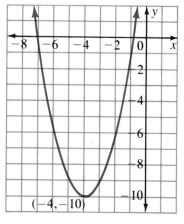

$$y = x^2 + 8x + 6$$
$$y - 6 = x^2 + 8x$$

Complete the square on the right side. ▶

$$y - 6 + 16 = x^2 + 8x + 16$$
$$y + 10 = (x + 4)^2$$
$$y = (x + 4)^2 - 10$$
$$y = [x - (-4)]^2 - 10$$

The vertex has coordinates of $(-4, -10)$.
Move the basic graph four units to the left and ten units down.

324

Recall that the standard form of the equation of a circle whose center is at $C(h, k)$ is $(x - h)^2 + (y - k)^2 = r^2$.

Example 4 Graph $(x + 2)^2 + (y - 1)^2 = 10$. Use the basic graph of $x^2 + y^2 = 10$ for reference.

The circle defined by $x^2 + y^2 = 10$ has center at the origin and radius $\sqrt{10}$.
The circle defined by $(x + 2)^2 + (y - 1)^2 = 10$ has center at $C(-2, 1)$ and radius $\sqrt{10}$.

Move the basic graph two units to the left and one unit up.

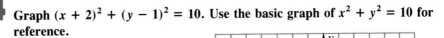

The standard form of the equation of an ellipse whose center is at $C(h, k)$ is $\dfrac{(x - h)^2}{a^2} + \dfrac{(y - k)^2}{b^2} = 1$, and the standard form of the equation of a hyperbola whose center is at $C(h, k)$ is $\dfrac{(x - h)^2}{a^2} - \dfrac{(y - k)^2}{b^2} = 1$. $(a \neq 0, b \neq 0)$

Example 5 Graph $\dfrac{(x - 3)^2}{16} + \dfrac{(y + 2)^2}{4} = 1$. Use the basic graph of $\dfrac{x^2}{16} + \dfrac{y^2}{4} = 1$ for reference.

The ellipse defined by $\dfrac{x^2}{16} + \dfrac{y^2}{4} = 1$ has center at the origin, x-intercepts of ± 4 and y-intercepts of ± 2.
The ellipse defined by $\dfrac{(x - 3)^2}{16} + \dfrac{(y + 2)^2}{4} = 1$ has center at $C(3, -2)$.

Move the basic graph three units to the right and two units down.

Example 6 Graph $\dfrac{(x + 1)^2}{9} - \dfrac{(y + 2)^2}{4} = 1$. Use the basic graph of $\dfrac{x^2}{9} - \dfrac{y^2}{4} = 1$ for reference.

The hyperbola defined by $\dfrac{x^2}{9} - \dfrac{y^2}{4} = 1$ has center at the origin and x-intercepts of ± 3.
The hyperbola defined by $\dfrac{(x + 1)^2}{9} - \dfrac{(y + 2)^2}{4} = 1$ has center at $C(-1, -2)$.

Move the basic graph one unit to the left and two units down.

TRANSLATIONS

Oral Exercises

Describe how the graph of each equation compares with its basic graph.

1. $y = (x - 1)^2$ **2.** $y = (x + 2)^2$ **3.** $y = x^2 + 5$ **4.** $y = x^2 - 6$

5. $y = (x + 2)^2 + 1$ **6.** $y = (x - 3)^2 - 2$ **7.** $y = |x - 3|$ **8.** $y = |x| + 7$

9. $(x - 3)^2 + (y + 2)^2 = 16$ **10.** $\dfrac{(x + 5)^2}{36} - \dfrac{(y - 3)^2}{81} = 1$ **11.** $\dfrac{(x - 8)^2}{4} + \dfrac{(y + 9)^2}{100} = 1$

Written Exercises

Draw a graph of each of the following equations. Use a basic graph for reference.

(A)
1. $y = (x + 1)^2$ **2.** $y = (x - 3)^2$ **3.** $y = (x - 1)^2$ **4.** $y = (x + 3)^2$

5. $y = x^2 + 1$ **6.** $y = x^2 - 2$ **7.** $y = x^2 - 4$ **8.** $y = x^2 + 3$

9. $y = (x - 2)^2 + 1$ **10.** $y = (x + 2)^2 - 1$ **11.** $y = (x - 1)^2 - 2$ **12.** $y = (x - 1)^2 + 2$

13. $y = |x + 3|$ **14.** $y = |x - 3|$ **15.** $y = |x| + 1$ **16.** $y = |x| - 1$

17. $y = |x - 1| + 2$ **18.** $y = |x + 2| - 3$ **19.** $y = |x - 3| - 1$ **20.** $y = |x + 3| + 2$

(B)
21. $y = x^2 - 2x + 1$ **22.** $y = x^2 + 4x + 4$ **23.** $y = x^2 - 4x + 4$ **24.** $y = x^2 + 6x + 9$

25. $y = x^2 + 10x + 5$ **26.** $y = x^2 - 6x + 4$ **27.** $y = x^2 + 6x + 5$ **28.** $y = x^2 - 8x - 4$

29. $(x - 1)^2 + (y + 2)^2 = 16$ **30.** $(x + 1)^2 + (y - 3)^2 = 4$ **31.** $(x + 2)^2 + (y + 1)^2 = 25$

32. $\dfrac{(x + 2)^2}{16} + \dfrac{(y - 1)^2}{4} = 1$ **33.** $\dfrac{(x + 1)^2}{25} - \dfrac{(y + 2)^2}{4} = 1$ **34.** $\dfrac{(x - 3)^2}{4} + \dfrac{(y + 2)^2}{4} = 1$

35. $\dfrac{(x - 4)^2}{25} - \dfrac{(y - 3)^2}{9} = 1$ **36.** $\dfrac{(x - 3)^2}{9} - \dfrac{(y + 2)^2}{25} = 1$ **37.** $\dfrac{(x - 3)^2}{100} + \dfrac{(y - 4)^2}{81} = 1$

(C)
38. $x^2 + 8x + y^2 + 4y = 19$ **39.** $2(x + 1)^2 + (y + 2)^2 = 32$ **40.** $3(x + 2)^2 + 2(y - 1)^2 = 48$

41. $9x^2 - 54x + 4y^2 + 16y = -61$ **42.** $3x^2 - 2y^2 + 12x + 4y - 14 = 18$

43. $9x^2 - 54x + y^2 - 4y = -49$ **44.** $-9x^2 + 4y^2 + 36x + 8y = 68$

> ## ➤ A Challenge To You
>
> Two years ago, the salaries of Martin and Melanie were the same. Last year, he received a raise of 20% while she had a salary cut of 20%. This year, Melanie got a raise of 20% and Martin got a salary cut of 20%. Who is earning more now? **The salaries are the same.**

12.8 Equations of Conic Sections

OBJECTIVES ▶ **To find an equation of a parabola, using the coordinates of the focus and the equation of the directrix**
To draw the graph of an equation of a parabola
To find an equation of an ellipse, using the coordinates of the foci, length of major axis, or length of minor axis

In the figure at the right, the distance from the point P to the fixed point F is the same as the distance from P to the fixed line l. Notice that the curve traced by all such points P is a parabola.

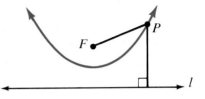

Definition: Parabola

A *parabola* is the set of all points in a coordinate plane that are equidistant from a fixed point and a fixed line in the plane. The fixed point is called the *focus* and the fixed line is called the *directrix*.

Let $P(x, y)$ be any point on a parabola with $F(0, p)$ the focus, and $y = -p$ the equation of the directrix. You can use the distance formula to find an equation of the parabola. Let d_1 = distance from P to F and d_2 = distance from P to A.

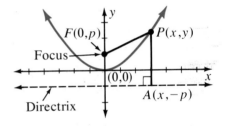

$$d_1 = d_2$$
$$\sqrt{(x - 0)^2 + (y - p)^2} = \sqrt{(x - x)^2 + [y - (-p)]^2}$$
$$\sqrt{x^2 + y^2 - 2py + p^2} = \sqrt{y^2 + 2py + p^2}$$
$$x^2 + y^2 - 2py + p^2 = y^2 + 2py + p^2$$
$$x^2 = 4py$$

There are three other types of parabolas with vertex at the origin. Information on all four types is presented in the table.

Coordinates of Focus	$(0, p)$	$(0, -p)$	$(p, 0)$	$(-p, 0)$
Equation of directrix	$y = -p$	$y = p$	$x = -p$	$x = p$
Opening	Up	Down	Right	Left
Equation of the Parabola	$x^2 = 4py$ $p > 0$	$x^2 = -4py$ $p > 0$	$y^2 = 4px$ $p > 0$	$y^2 = -4px$ $p > 0$

Example 1 Find an equation of a parabola with $F(-3, 0)$ the focus, and $x = 3$ the equation of the directrix.

The coordinates of the vertex are of the form $(-p, 0)$.
Use $y^2 = -4px$ from the table on page 327.
$$y^2 = -4px$$
Substitute 3 for p. ▶ $\quad y^2 = -4 \cdot 3x$

Thus, $y^2 = -12x$ is an equation of the parabola.

Example 2 Draw a graph of the equation $x^2 = -6y$.

The equation $x^2 = -6y$ is of the form $x^2 = -4py$.

$$x^2 = -6y$$
$$-4p = -6$$
$$p = \frac{3}{2}$$

The coordinates of the focus are $(0, -\frac{3}{2})$.
The equation of the directrix is $y = \frac{3}{2}$.
The graph opens down.

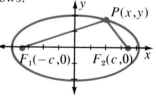

Recall that an ellipse is the set of all points in a plane the sum of whose distances from two fixed points called the foci is a constant. $\dfrac{x^2}{a^2} + \dfrac{y^2}{b^2} = 1$ is the standard form of the equation of an ellipse with center at the origin and foci on the x-axis. This equation is derived as follows.

Let $P(x, y)$ be any point on an ellipse with $F_1(-c, 0)$ and $F_2(c, 0)$ the foci. Let $d_1 = $ distance from P to F_1 and $d_2 = $ distance from P to F_2.
Then, $d_1 + d_2 = 2a$, a constant.

$$\sqrt{[x - (-c)]^2 + (y - 0)^2} + \sqrt{(x - c)^2 + (y - 0)^2} = 2a$$
$$\sqrt{(x + c)^2 + y^2} = 2a - \sqrt{(x - c)^2 + y^2}$$
$$x^2 + 2cx + c^2 + y^2 = 4a^2 - 4a\sqrt{(x - c)^2 + y^2} + x^2 - 2cx + c^2 + y^2$$
$$cx - a^2 = -a\sqrt{(x - c)^2 + y^2}$$
$$c^2x^2 - 2a^2cx + a^4 = a^2x^2 - 2a^2cx + a^2c^2 + a^2y^2$$
$$a^2(a^2 - c^2) = x^2(a^2 - c^2) + a^2y^2$$

$$\frac{x^2\cancel{(a^2 - c^2)}}{a^2\cancel{(a^2 - c^2)}} + \frac{\cancel{a^2}y^2}{\cancel{a^2}(a^2 - c^2)} = \frac{\cancel{a^2}\cancel{(a^2 - c^2)}}{\cancel{a^2}\cancel{(a^2 - c^2)}}$$

Let $a^2 - c^2 = b^2$.

Therefore, $\dfrac{x^2}{a^2} + \dfrac{y^2}{b^2} = 1$ is an equation of the ellipse.

CHAPTER TWELVE

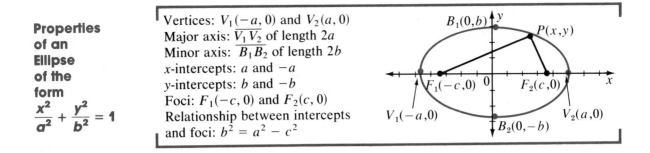

Properties of an Ellipse of the form
$$\frac{x^2}{a^2} + \frac{y^2}{b^2} = 1$$

Vertices: $V_1(-a, 0)$ and $V_2(a, 0)$
Major axis: $\overline{V_1 V_2}$ of length $2a$
Minor axis: $\overline{B_1 B_2}$ of length $2b$
x-intercepts: a and $-a$
y-intercepts: b and $-b$
Foci: $F_1(-c, 0)$ and $F_2(c, 0)$
Relationship between intercepts and foci: $b^2 = a^2 - c^2$

Example 3

Write an equation, in standard form, of an ellipse whose center is at the origin, coordinates of vertices are $(\pm 4, 0)$, and coordinates of foci are $(\pm 3, 0)$.

The major axis of the ellipse is on the x-axis. Use $\dfrac{x^2}{a^2} + \dfrac{y^2}{b^2} = 1$.

$$b^2 = a^2 - c^2$$
$$b^2 = 4^2 - 3^2$$
$$b^2 = 16 - 9$$
$$b^2 = 7$$

◀ *Substitute 4 for a and 3 for c.*

Thus, $\dfrac{x^2}{16} + \dfrac{y^2}{7} = 1$ is an equation of the ellipse.

Example 4

Write an equation, in standard form, of an ellipse whose center is at the origin, coordinates of foci are $(\pm 4, 0)$ and the length of the minor axis is 6.

Use $\dfrac{x^2}{a^2} + \dfrac{y^2}{b^2} = 1$.   ◀ *Major axis is on the x-axis.*

Length of minor axis = 2b = 6. Substitute 3 for b.   ▶

$$b^2 = a^2 - c$$
$$3^2 = a^2 - 4^2$$
$$9 = a^2 - 16$$
$$25 = a^2$$

◀ *The foci has coordinates $(\pm c, 0)$. Substitute 4 for c.*

Thus, $\dfrac{x^2}{25} + \dfrac{y^2}{9} = 1$ is an equation of the ellipse.

When the major axis of an ellipse is on the y-axis, the general form of the equation of the ellipse becomes $\dfrac{x^2}{b^2} + \dfrac{y^2}{a^2} = 1$.

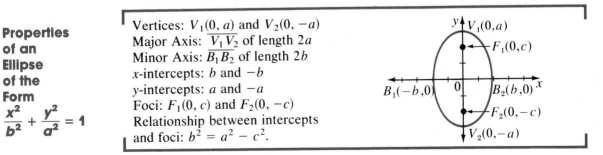

Properties of an Ellipse of the Form
$$\frac{x^2}{b^2} + \frac{y^2}{a^2} = 1$$

Vertices: $V_1(0, a)$ and $V_2(0, -a)$
Major Axis: $\overline{V_1 V_2}$ of length $2a$
Minor Axis: $\overline{B_1 B_2}$ of length $2b$
x-intercepts: b and $-b$
y-intercepts: a and $-a$
Foci: $F_1(0, c)$ and $F_2(0, -c)$
Relationship between intercepts and foci: $b^2 = a^2 - c^2$.

EQUATIONS OF CONIC SECTIONS

Example 5

Write an equation, in standard form, of an ellipse whose center is at the origin and whose x-intercepts are ± 3 and y-intercepts are ± 4. Find the coordinates of the foci.

The major axis of the ellipse is on the y-axis.

$$\text{Use } \frac{x^2}{b^2} + \frac{y^2}{a^2} = 1.$$

$$b = 3; \; b^2 = 9 \qquad\qquad b^2 = a^2 - c^2$$
$$a = 4; \; a^2 = 16 \qquad\qquad 9 = 16 - c^2$$
$$\qquad\qquad\qquad\qquad c^2 = 7, \text{or } c = \sqrt{7}$$

Thus, $\frac{x^2}{9} + \frac{y^2}{16} = 1$ is an equation of the ellipse and $(0, \sqrt{7})$ and $(0, -\sqrt{7})$ are the coordinates of the foci.

Written Exercises

Find an equation of each parabola.

(A)
1. Focus $(2, 0)$, directrix $x = -2$ $y^2 = 8x$
2. Focus $(0, -2)$, directrix $y = 2$ $x^2 = -8y$
3. Focus $(-2, 0)$, directrix $x = 2$ $y^2 = -8x$
4. Focus $(0, 3)$, directrix $y = -3$ $x^2 = 12y$
5. Focus $(0, -1)$, directrix $y = 1$ $x^2 = -4y$
6. Focus $(4, 0)$, directrix $x = -4$ $y^2 = 16x$
7. Focus $(0, 2)$, directrix $y = -2$ $x^2 = 8y$
8. Focus $(-4, 0)$, directrix $x = 4$ $y^2 = -16x$

Draw the graph of each equation. For Ex. 9–16, see TE Answer Section.

9. $x^2 = -4y$
10. $y^2 = -3x$
11. $y^2 = 4x$
12. $x^2 = 10y$
13. $y^2 = 20x$
14. $x^2 = 6y$
15. $-x^2 = 3y$
16. $-y^2 = 2x$

Write an equation, in standard form, of an ellipse with center at the origin and which satisfies the following conditions.

17. Vertices $(\pm 5, 0)$, Foci $(\pm 4, 0)$ $\frac{x^2}{25} + \frac{y^2}{9} = 1$
18. Vertices $(\pm 7, 0)$, Foci $(\pm 5, 0)$ $\frac{x^2}{49} + \frac{y^2}{24} = 1$
19. Vertices $(\pm 4, 0)$, Foci $(\pm 2, 0)$ $\frac{x^2}{16} + \frac{y^2}{12} = 1$
20. Vertices $(\pm \sqrt{7}, 0)$, Foci $(\pm 2, 0)$ $\frac{x^2}{7} + \frac{y^2}{3} = 1$
21. Vertices $(0, \pm 6)$, Foci $(0, \pm 5)$ $\frac{x^2}{11} + \frac{y^2}{36} = 1$
22. Vertices $(0, \pm 8)$, Foci $(0, \pm 4)$ $\frac{x^2}{48} + \frac{y^2}{64} = 1$
23. Foci $(\pm 4, 0)$, length of minor axis 6 $\frac{x^2}{25} + \frac{y^2}{9} = 1$
24. Foci $(0, \pm 6)$, length of minor axis 8 $\frac{x^2}{16} + \frac{y^2}{52} = 1$
25. x-intercepts ± 7, y-intercepts ± 9 $\frac{x^2}{49} + \frac{y^2}{81} = 1$
26. x-intercepts ± 11, y-intercepts ± 10 $\frac{x^2}{121} + \frac{y^2}{100} = 1$

(B)
27. length of major axis 10 $\frac{x^2}{25} + \frac{y^2}{9} = 1$
    length of minor axis 6 or $\frac{x^2}{9} + \frac{y^2}{25} = 1$
28. length of major axis 8 $\frac{x^2}{16} + \frac{y^2}{4} = 1$
    length of minor axis 4 or $\frac{x^2}{4} + \frac{y^2}{16} = 1$

29. length of major axis 6 $\frac{x^2}{9} + \frac{y^2}{4} = 1$
    length of minor axis 4 or $\frac{x^2}{4} + \frac{y^2}{9} = 1$
30. length of major axis 12 $\frac{x^2}{36} + \frac{y^2}{25} = 1$
    length of minor axis 10 or $\frac{x^2}{25} + \frac{y^2}{36} = 1$

For Ex. 31–32, see TE Answer Section.

(C)
31. A *latus rectum* of an ellipse is a chord that is perpendicular to the major axis through one of the foci. Show that the length of a latus rectum for the ellipse defined by $\frac{x^2}{a^2} + \frac{y^2}{b^2} = 1$ is $\frac{2b^2}{a}$.

32. The standard form of the equation of a hyperbola with x-intercepts is $\frac{x^2}{a^2} - \frac{y^2}{b^2} = 1$.

    Let $P(x, y)$ be any point on a hyperbola with $F_1(-c, 0)$ and $F_2(c, 0)$ the foci. Show how the standard form of the equation is derived.

Computer Activities

Graphing a Quadratic Function

The computer is a useful tool for graphing a quadratic function. Substituting different values for one of the variables, it can compute coordinates of points of the graph, and actually print out a graph. Various graphs may be generated and compared to see what effect changing the value of a constant in the basic equation has on the resulting graphs.

The program below involves a function P defined by the following statement:

$$\text{DEF FNP(X)} = X \uparrow 2$$

PROGRAM

```
 10  PRINT "PROGRAM GRAPHS A FUNCTION"
 20  DEF FN P(X) = X ↑ 2
 30  REM NEXT TWO LOOPS DEFINE X AND Y RANGE
 40  FOR X = -7 TO 7
 50  PRINT
 60  FOR Y = 0 TO 70
 70  IF Y = FN P(X) THEN 110
 80  REM IF NOT EQUAL PRINT BLANK SPACE
 90  PRINT " "
100  NEXT Y
110  PRINT "*"
120  NEXT X
130  END
```

Exercises

1. Type in the above program and run it. What is unusual about the graph?
   It is rotated 90° clockwise from the conventional system.
2. Alter the program above to graph the function defined by $y = 4x^2$.
   20 DEF FNP(X) = 4*X ↑ 2   40 FOR X = -4 to 4
3. Alter the program above to graph the function defined by $y = \frac{1}{4}x^2$. You must change statements 20, 40, and 60.
   20 DEF FNP(X) = .25*X ↑ 2   40 FOR X = -8 TO 8   60 FOR Y = 0 TO 16 STEP .25
4. Write a program to find an equation of the axis of symmetry and the coordinates of the vertex of a parabola, given an equation of the parabola.
   For Ex. 4, see TE Answer Section.

ACTIVITY: GRAPHING A QUADRATIC EQUATION

Chapter Twelve Review

Vocabulary

asymptotes	[12.5]	axis of symmetry	[12.1]
circle	[12.3]	conic section	[12.6]
ellipse	[12.4]	hyperbola	[12.5]
parabola	[12.2]	rectangular hyperbola	
symmetric points	[12.1]		[12.5]

For complete solutions, see TE Answer Section.

Determine whether P and Q are symmetric with respect to the x-axis, the y-axis, the origin, or none of these. [12.1]

1. origin 2. y-axis 3. x-axis 4. none of these

1. $P(-2, 6)$; $Q(2, -6)$ 2. $P(-3, 5)$; $Q(3, 5)$
3. $P(8, -1)$; $Q(8, 1)$ 4. $P(-5, 3)$; $Q(3, -5)$

5. $(-5, -1), (5, 1), (5, -1)$ 6. $(7, 2), (-7, -2), (-7, 2)$

For each point find the coordinates of the corresponding point symmetric with respect to the x-axis, the y-axis, and the origin. [12.1]

5. $A(-5, 1)$ 6. $B(7, -2)$ 7. $C(-3, -8)$
8. $D\left(-\frac{1}{7}, -\frac{1}{8}\right)$ 9. $E(m, -n)$ 10. $F(-r, -s)$

7. $(-3, 8), (3, -8), (3, 8)$ 8. $(-\frac{1}{7}, \frac{1}{8}), (\frac{1}{7}, -\frac{1}{8}), (\frac{1}{7}, \frac{1}{8})$

Determine which of the following functions are odd, even, or neither. [12.1]

★ **11.** $y = x^2$ **even**   ★ **12.** $x - 4y^2 = 1$ **neither**

Graph each quadratic function. Draw the axis of symmetry and label the coordinates of the vertex. Find an equation of the axis of symmetry. [12.2]

13. $y = x^2 - 6x + 12$ 14. $y = -2x^2 + 8x + 3$
15. $y = -\frac{1}{3}x^2$ $\begin{matrix}(0, 0);\\ x = 0\end{matrix}$ 16. $y = 2x^2 + 6x + 9$

13. $(3, 3)$; $x = 3$ 14. $(2, 11)$; $x = 2$ 16. $(-\frac{3}{2}, \frac{9}{2})$; $x = -\frac{3}{2}$

Graph each function. Estimate, to the nearest tenth, the x-intercepts of each parabola. [12.2]

17. $y = x^2 + 4x - 3$ $-4.6, 0.6$ 18. $y = -2x^2 + 7x + 1$ $-0.1, 3.6$

Find an equation of each circle whose center is at the origin and which has the given radius. [12.3]

19. 13   20. 17   21. $\sqrt{8}$
$x^2 + y^2 = 169$ $x^2 + y^2 = 289$ $x^2 + y^2 = 8$

Find an equation of each circle whose center C is at the origin and which passes through P. [12.3]

22. $P(-2, -1)$ 23. $P(7, -3)$ 24. $P(-5, -2)$
$x^2 + y^2 = 5$ $x^2 + y^2 = 58$ $x^2 + y^2 = 29$

Find an equation of each circle whose center C is given and which passes through point P. [12.3]

25. $C(-6, -5)$, $P(5, -1)$ $(x + 6)^2 + (y + 5)^2 = 137$
26. $C(1, -8)$, $P(-1, -6)$ $(x - 1)^2 + (y + 8)^2 = 8$

Draw the graph of each equation. [12.3]

27. $x^2 + y^2 = 49$ 28. $x^2 + y^2 = 27$

29. Write an equation, in standard form, of an ellipse whose center is at the origin and whose x-intercepts are ± 5 and whose y-intercepts are ± 3. [12.4] $\frac{x^2}{25} + \frac{y^2}{9} = 1$

Find the x- and y-intercepts of the ellipse whose equation is given. Then draw the graph. [12.4]

30. $\frac{x^2}{36} + \frac{y^2}{4} = 1$ 31. $\frac{x^2}{16} + \frac{y^2}{49} = 1$
32. $9x^2 + y^2 = 36$ 33. $5x^2 + 3y^2 = 30$
$a = \pm 2, b = \pm 6$ $a = \pm\sqrt{6}, b = \pm\sqrt{10}$

Draw the graph of each equation. Find the equations of the asymptotes. [12.5]

34. $\frac{x^2}{9} - \frac{y^2}{4} = 1$ 35. $xy = -6$
$y = \frac{2}{3}x, y = -\frac{2}{3}x$ $x = 0, y = 0$

Identify each conic section. [12.6]

36. $\frac{x^2}{16} - \frac{y^2}{4} = 1$ 37. $\frac{x^2}{8} + \frac{y^2}{8} = 1$ **circle**
38. $4x^2 + 5y^2 = 20$ 39. $10x^2 + 20y^2 = 20$

36. hyperbola 38. ellipse 39. ellipse

Graph each of the following equations. [12.7]

40. $y = |x| - 4$ 41. $y = (x - 2)^2 - 3$
42. $y = -2 + |x + 3|$ 43. $y = x^2 + 4$
44. $y = x^2 + 6x + 4$ 45. $(x - 1)^2 + (y + 2)^2 = 16$
46. $\frac{(x - 3)^2}{16} + \frac{(y + 5)^2}{4} = 1$
47. $\frac{(x - 5)^2}{9} + \frac{(y - 1)^2}{16} = 1$

48. Find an equation of a parabola with $F(-4, 0)$ the focus, and $x = 4$ the equation of the directrix. Draw a graph of the equation. [12.8] $y^2 = -16x$

Write an equation, in standard form, of an ellipse with center at the origin and which satisfies the following conditions. [12.8]

49. Vertices $(\pm 6, 0)$, Foci $(\pm 5, 0)$
50. Foci $(0, \pm 7)$, length of minor axis 12

Chapter Twelve Test

Determine whether P and Q are symmetric with respect to the x-axis, the y-axis, the origin, or none of these.

1. $P(3, -4)$; $Q(3, 4)$
   x-axis

2. $P(-2, -1)$; $Q(2, 1)$
   origin

For each point, find the coordinates of the corresponding point symmetric with respect to the x-axis the y-axis, and the origin.

3. $A(-8, 1)$ 4. $B(-2, -3)$ 5. $C(-c, d)$
   $(-8, -1), (8, 1), (8, -1)$ $(-c, -d), (c, d), (c, -d)$

Graph each quadratic function. Draw the axis of symmetry and label the coordinates of the vertex. Find an equation of the axis of symmetry.

4. $(-2, 3), (2, -3), (2, 3)$

6. $y = x^2 + 8x + 3$
   $(-4, -13); x = -4$

7. $y = -\frac{2}{3}x^2$
   $(0, 0); x = 0$

Graph each quadratic function. Estimate, to the nearest tenth, the x-intercepts of each parabola.

8. $y = x^2 + 6x + 2$
   $-5.6, -0.4$

9. $y = -2x^2 + 6x + 3$
   $-0.4, 3.4$

Find an equation of each circle whose center is at the origin and which has the given radius.

10. 6 $x^2 + y^2 = 36$ 11. $\sqrt{20}$ $x^2 + y^2 = 20$

Find an equation of each circle whose center is at the origin and which passes through the given point.

12. $P(-1, 2)$
   $x^2 + y^2 = 5$

13. $P(-4, -3)$
   $x^2 + y^2 = 25$

14. Find an equation of a circle whose center is at $C(-8, -5)$ and which passes through the point $P(3, -2)$. $(x + 8)^2 + (y + 5)^2 = 130$

15. Write an equation, in standard form, of an ellipse whose center is at the origin and whose x-intercepts are ± 3 and whose y-intercepts are ± 2. $\frac{x^2}{9} + \frac{y^2}{4} = 1$

Find the x- and y-intercepts of the ellipse whose equation is given. Then draw the graph.

16. $\frac{x^2}{16} + \frac{y^2}{4} = 1$ 17. $\frac{x^2}{4} + \frac{y^2}{36} = 1$

18. $9x^2 + 4y^2 = 36$ $a = \pm 2, b = \pm 3$
16. $a = \pm 4, b = \pm 2$ 17. $a = \pm 2, b = \pm 6$

Draw the graph of each equation. Find the equations of the asymptotes.

19. $\frac{x^2}{16} - \frac{y^2}{4} = 1$
   $y = -\frac{1}{2}x, y = \frac{1}{2}x$

20. $xy = -2$
   $x = 0, y = 0$

Identify each conic section whose equation is given. **21. circle**   **22. ellipse**

21. $\frac{x^2}{4} + \frac{y^2}{4} = 1$ 22. $\frac{x^2}{49} + \frac{y^2}{81} = 1$

23. $5x^2 + 3y^2 = 30$ 24. $4x^2 - 5y^2 = 20$
   ellipse   **hyperbola**

Graph each of the following equations.

25. $y = |x| + 3$ 26. $y = |x - 1| + 2$
27. $y = (x + 3)^2 - 2$ 28. $y = x^2 + 4x - 1$
29. $(x - 3)^2 + (y + 1)^2 = 16$
30. $\frac{(x + 5)^2}{16} + \frac{(y - 2)^2}{4} = 1$

For Ex. 25–30, see TE Answer Section.

31. Find an equation of a parabola with $F(0, 3)$ the focus, and $y = -3$ the equation of the directrix. $x^2 = 12y$

Write an equation, in standard form, of the ellipse with center at the origin and which satisfies the following conditions.

32. Foci $(0, \pm 10)$, length of minor axis 8
   $\frac{x^2}{16} + \frac{y^2}{116} = 1$

Determine which of the following functions are odd, even, or neither.

★33. $y = 7x^2$ **even**   34. $x^2 + 16y^2 = 1$
   even and odd

★35. Find the coordinates of the center of a circle and the radius of the circle whose equation is $x^2 - 10x + y^2 + 6y = -33$.
   $(5, -3); 1$

College Prep Test

DIRECTIONS: Choose the *one* best answer to each question or problem.

1.

   Each circle in the above figure has a diameter of 4. What is the area of the rectangle? **E**

   (A) 64   (B) 32   (C) 80
   (D) 16   (E) 40

2. The circumference of a circle in a coordinate plane is 18π units. The center of the circle is at the origin. Which point is on the circle? **A**

   (A) $P(9, 0)$ (B) $P(-3, -3)$ (C) $P(0, -3)$
   (D) $P(3, 0)$ (E) $P(9, 9)$

3. The area of a circle is 36π square units. The center of the circle is at $C(-2, 3)$. Which point does the circle not pass through? **E**

   (A) $P(-2, -3)$ (B) $P(4, 3)$ (C) $P(-2, 9)$
   (D) $P(-8, 3)$ (E) $P(-2, 3)$

4. $\overline{AB}$ is a diameter of a circle whose center is point O. The diameter is 6, C is a point on the circle, and the measure of $\angle BOC$ is $60°$. What is the length of chord $\overline{AC}$? **B**

   (A) 3   (B) $3\sqrt{3}$ (C) 6
   (D) $3\sqrt{2}$ (E) None of these

5. A radius of a given circle measures 10 cm. If the length of the radius is decreased by 2 cm, what is the percent of area decrease? **D**

   (A) 81   (B) 19   (C) 64
   (D) 36   (E) None of these

6. The set of all points in a coordinate plane 10 units from the origin is represented by which of the following equations? **D**

   (A) $x = 10$ (B) $x^2 + y^2 = 10$
   (C) $x^2 + y^2 = \sqrt{10}$ (D) $x^2 + y^2 = 100$
   (E) $y = 10$

7. An equation of a circle with center at $C(-3, 4)$, and radius 5 is **B**

   (A) $(x - 3)^2 + (y + 4)^2 = 25$
   (B) $(x + 3)^2 + (y - 4)^2 = 25$
   (C) $x^2 + y^2 = 25$
   (D) $x^2 + y^2 = 1$ (E) None of these

8. The *x*- and *y*-intercepts of the ellipse defined by $\dfrac{x^2}{9} + \dfrac{y^2}{16} = 1$ are **C**

   (A) 3 and 4   (B) 4 and 3
   (C) ± 3 and ± 4 (D) ± 4 and ± 3
   (E) None of these

9. The equations of the asymptotes of a hyperbola defined by $\dfrac{x^2}{9} - \dfrac{y^2}{4} = 1$ are **A**

   (A) $y = \pm\dfrac{2}{3}x$ (B) $y = \pm 2x$
   (C) $y = \pm 3x$ (D) $y = \pm\dfrac{3}{2}x$
   (E) None of these

10. The one equation whose graph is not a conic section is **B**

    (A) $(x + 2)^2 + (y - 6)^2 = 4$
    (B) $\dfrac{x}{4} + \dfrac{y}{9} = 16$ (C) $\dfrac{x^2}{4} + \dfrac{y^2}{16} = 1$
    (D) $\dfrac{x^2}{9} - \dfrac{y^2}{25} = 1$ (E) $xy = 4$

DIRECTIONS: Choose the *one* best answer to each question or problem.

1. Factor $2x^3 - 5x^2 - 3x$ completely.

   (A) $(x^2 - 3x)(2x + 1)$
   (B) $(2x^2 + x)(x - 3)$
   (C) $x(x - 3)(2x + 1)$
   (D) $x(x + 3)(2x - 1)$ **C**

2. Solve $16^{x-2} = 64$.

   (A) $\frac{7}{2}$ (B) 6   (C) 3   (D) $\frac{9}{4}$ **A**

3. Solve $-3(x - 2c) = 2 + a(bx + c)$ for x.

   (A) $\dfrac{-(ac + 6c + 2)}{ab + 3}$ (B) $\dfrac{6c - ac - 2}{ab + 3}$

   (C) $\dfrac{6c - ac - 2}{3ab}$ (D) $\dfrac{5ac - 2}{ab + 3}$ **B**

4. Find the value of $2 \cdot 27^{-\frac{4}{3}}$.

   (A) $\dfrac{2}{81}$ (B) 162   (C) $\dfrac{1}{6}$ (D) $-\dfrac{2}{3}$ **A**

5. Solve $n + 2 = \sqrt{2n + 12}$

   (A) -4 (B) 2
   (C) -4 and 2   (D) 10 **B**

6. Factor $9x^2 + 6x + 1 - 16y^2$ as a difference of two squares.

   (A) $(3x - 1 + 4y)(3x - 1 - 4y)$
   (B) $(3x - 2x + 1 - 4y)^2$
   (C) $(3x + 1 + 4y)(3x + 1 - 4y)$
   (D) $(3x - 4y - 1)(3x - 4y + 1)$ **C**

7. Find the slope of $\overleftrightarrow{PQ}$ for $P(-3, 5)$ and $Q(6, -2)$.

   (A) $-\dfrac{9}{7}$ (B) $-\dfrac{1}{3}$
   (C) $-\dfrac{7}{9}$ (D) $-\dfrac{7}{3}$ **C**

8. Write an equation, in standard form, of the line that passes through the point $P(-2, 1)$ and is parallel to the line described by the equation $3x - 2y = 4$.

   (A) $2x + 3y = -1$ (B) $2x - 3y = 1$ **C**
   (C) $3x - 2y = -8$ (D) $3x - 2y = -2$

9. Find the product, if possible.

   $$\begin{bmatrix} -3 & 1 & -2 \\ 2 & 5 & -1 \end{bmatrix} \cdot \begin{bmatrix} 1 & -2 & 2 \\ 2 & 3 & 1 \\ -1 & 2 & -2 \end{bmatrix}$$

   (A) $\begin{bmatrix} -2 & -1 & 0 \\ 4 & 8 & 0 \\ -1 & 2 & -2 \end{bmatrix}$ (B) $\begin{bmatrix} 1 & 13 \\ 5 & 9 \\ -1 & 11 \end{bmatrix}$

   (C) $\begin{bmatrix} 1 & 5 & -1 \\ 13 & 9 & 11 \end{bmatrix}$ (D) None of these **C**

10. Find the domain of the function defined by
    $t(x) = \dfrac{-2x}{x^2 + 2x - 3}.$ **D**

    (A) {all real numbers}
    (B) {all real numbers except 0}
    (C) {all real numbers except -3, 0, and 1}
    (D) {all real numbers except -3 and 1}

11. Let $f(x) = 3x - 1$ and $g(x) = x^2 + 1$. Find $f(g(-2))$.

    (A) 14   (B) -10 (C) 50   (D) 5 **A**

12. Find an equation of the inverse of the function defined by $y = 3x - 2$.

    (A) $y = -3x + 2$ (B) $x - 3y = -2$
    (C) $3y = x - 2$ (D) $-3x + y = -2$ **B**

13. Which of the following is an equation of a parabola?

    (A) $y = x^3$ (B) $y = x^2 + 2$
    (C) $y = x^3 + 3$ (D) $y^2 + x^2 = 2$ **B**

14. Which of the following is an equation of a hyperbola? **C**

    (A) $5x^2 + 4y^2 = 20$ (B) $4x^2 + 5y^2 = 20$
    (C) $16x^2 - 16y^2 = 1$ (D) $8x^2 + 8y^2 = 8$

15. Find an equation of a parabola with $F(-2, 0)$ the focus and $x = 2$ the equation of the directrix.

    (A) $x^2 = -8y$ (B) $x^2 = 8y$
    (C) $y^2 = 8x$ (D) $y^2 = -8x$ **D**

Solve each equation.

16. $|3x - 2| = 13$ **5, $-\frac{11}{3}$**

17. $\frac{10}{n - 1} - \frac{3}{n} = 4$ **3, $-\frac{1}{4}$**

18. $3^{x - 5} = \frac{1}{9}$ **3**

19. $n^2 - 9 = -5n$ $\frac{-5 \pm \sqrt{61}}{2}$

20. Solve $\frac{-4}{a} = \frac{3}{b} + \frac{1}{x}$ for x. $\frac{-ab}{3a + 4b}$

Factor each polynomial completely.

21. $36a^2 - 49b^2$ 22. $2x^3 - 16$

   $(6a - 7b)(6a + 7b)$ $2(x - 2)(x^2 + 2x + 4)$

Simplify and write each expression with positive exponents.

23. $(-2a^{-3}b^4)^2$ $\frac{4b^8}{a^6}$ 24. $\frac{-25x^{-3}y^4}{15x^{-2}y^6}$ $\frac{-5}{3xy^2}$

25. Divide: $\frac{8 - 2n}{4n^2 + 8n} \div \frac{n^2 - 16}{n^3 - n^2 - 6n}$. $\frac{-2(n + 4)}{n - 3}$ ↙

26. Simplify: $ab\sqrt{18ab^3} - 2b\sqrt{8a^3b^3} + a\sqrt{32ab^5}$. $3ab^2\sqrt{2ab}$

27. Simplify: $-2 - \sqrt{-8} - (5 - 3\sqrt{-2})$. $-7 + i\sqrt{2}$

28. Some sunflower seeds worth \$3.80/kg are mixed with some raisins worth \$3.20/kg to make 12 kg of a mixture worth \$3.60/kg. How many kg of each kind are there in the mixture? **sunflower: 8 kg, raisins: 4 kg**

29. A second number is 6 more than 3 times a first number. Find the numbers if their difference is 26. **10, 36**

Draw the graph of each equation.

30. $3x - 2y = 8$ 31. $\frac{2}{3}y = \frac{1}{2}x + 4$

For Ex. 30–31, see TE Answer Section.

A line has the given slope, y-intercept, or contains the indicated point(s). Write an equation, in standard form, of each line.

32. $A(-1, 2)$, $m = -\frac{3}{5}$ **$3x + 5y = 7$**

33. $m = \frac{2}{3}$, $b = -1$ **$2x - 3y = 3$**

34. $P(4, -1)$, $Q(-5, 2)$ **$x + 3y = 1$**

35. The vertices of a quadrilateral are $A(2, -3)$, $B(5, 6)$, $C(3, 2)$ and $D(-2, -1)$. Show that the segments connecting the midpoints of $ABCD$ form a parallelogram.

For Ex. 35, see TE Answer Section.

Solve each system of equations.

36. $3(x - 2) = 2y - 7$ **$\left(-2, -\frac{5}{2}\right)$**

    $-2(y + 4) = -(x + 5)$

37. $2x - 3y + z = 7$

    $-x + 2y - 3z = -9$

    $3x - y + 2z = 8$ **$(1, -1, 2)$**

38. A two-digit number is 54 less than the number obtained by reversing the digits. Find the original number if 4 times the sum of the digits is 3 more than 5 times the units digit. **39**

Let $g(x) = x^2 - 2x + 3$. Find each of the following function values.

39. $g(-2)$ **11**   40. $g(2n)$ **$4n^2 - 4n + 3$**

41. If y varies inversely as x, and if $y = 6$ when $x = 5$, find y when $x = 10$. **3**

42. If y varies directly as the positive square root of x and inversely as the cube of z, and if $y = 6$ when $x = 9$ and $z = 2$, find y when $x = 4$ and $z = 3$. $\frac{32}{27}$

43. For the point whose coordinates are $(-6, 1)$, find the corresponding point symmetric with respect to the x-axis, the y-axis, and the origin.

   $(-6, -1)$, $(6, 1)$, $(6, -1)$

44. Draw the graph of $y = 2x^2 + 6x - 1$.

For Ex. 44, see TE Answer Section.

45. Find an equation of a circle whose center is at $C(3, -1)$ and which passes through $P(5, 4)$. **$(x - 3)^2 + (y + 1)^2 = 29$**

Graph each of the following equations.

46. $y = |x| - 3$ 47. $y = (x + 2)^2 - 3$

48. $\frac{(x - 1)^2}{9} + \frac{(y + 2)^2}{4} = 1$

49. $(x + 2)^2 + (y - 2)^2 = 9$

For Ex. 46–49, see TE Answer Section.

13

LINEAR-QUADRATIC SYSTEMS

Karl Wilhelm Theodor Weierstrass

Karl Wilhelm Theodor Weierstrass was born on October 31, 1815, at Ostenfelde, Germany. At age 19, he graduated from the Catholic Gymnasium (school) at Pearborn with honors in German, Latin, Greek, and mathematics. Against Karl's wishes, his father sent him to study business and law at the University of Bonn. Karl rebelled at this school and refused to study; his interest was mathematics.

At age 24 Karl enrolled at the Academy of Munster to prepare for the state teacher's examination to pursue a career as a secondary school teacher of mathematics. Two years later, at age 26, he passed the examination. The test was given in two parts, one written and the other oral. For the written part, Karl was alloted 6 months to write 3 essays on topics approved by the commission of examiners. His test is one of the most unusual of its kind ever given to certify a person for teaching secondary school mathematics.

For the next 15 years, Karl taught in various small villages during the day and did mathematical research at night. This after-school work resulted in his being recognized as the leading mathematical analyst in Europe. The years 1864–1897 Karl spent at the University of Berlin as Professor of Mathematics, where he became one of the great scholars in the study of the theory of functions and in the development of the theory of irrational numbers. At age 55 Karl accepted a 20-year-old private pupil, Sonya Kovalevsky, who would later become one of the foremost mathematicians of modern times. (See page 454.)

13.1 Solving Linear-Quadratic Systems of Equations

OBJECTIVE ▶ **To find the real number solutions of a system of one quadratic and one linear equation graphically and algebraically**

The general form of the quadratic equations of some conic sections you have studied are given below.

Parabola: $y = ax^2 + bx + c$ Circle: $x^2 + y^2 = r^2$

Hyperbola: $\dfrac{x^2}{a^2} - \dfrac{y^2}{b^2} = 1$ and $xy = k$ Ellipse: $\dfrac{x^2}{a^2} + \dfrac{y^2}{b^2} = 1$

You have also learned that the general form of a linear equation in two variables is $ax + by = c$, and that the graph of each such equation is a line.

A system of equations may contain one quadratic equation and one linear equation. Such a system is called a **linear-quadratic system.** A common solution of a linear-quadratic system of equations is an ordered pair of real numbers corresponding to a point of intersection of their graphs. As illustrated by the graphs below, a system of one quadratic and one linear equation may have 0, 1, or 2 solutions.

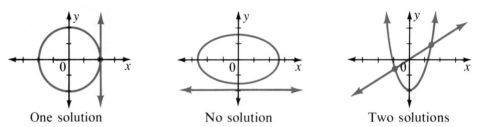

One solution   No solution   Two solutions

The solutions of a linear-quadratic system may be found graphically.

Example 1   Solve the system $\dfrac{x^2}{16} + \dfrac{y^2}{9} = 1$ **graphically.**

$$2x - 3y = 6$$

Estimate the solutions to the nearest tenth.

Ellipse ▶
$\dfrac{x^2}{16} + \dfrac{y^2}{9} = 1$
$a^2 = 16 \quad b^2 = 9$
$a = \pm 4, b = \pm 3$

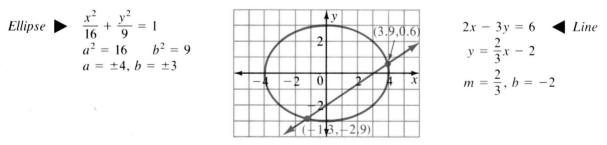

$2x - 3y = 6$ ◀ *Line*
$y = \dfrac{2}{3}x - 2$
$m = \dfrac{2}{3}, b = -2$

Thus, $(-1.3, -2.9)$ and $(3.9, 0.6)$ are the solutions of the system.

Example 2

Solve the system $x^2 + y^2 = 13$ **algebraically.**
$$-2x + y = -1$$

Step 1   Solve the linear equation for one of its variables.

$$-2x + y = -1$$
$$y = 2x - 1$$

Step 2   Substitute this result in the quadratic equation.

$$x^2 + y^2 = 13$$
$$x^2 + (2x - 1)^2 = 13$$
$$x^2 + 4x^2 - 4x + 1 = 13$$

Step 3   Solve the resulting quadratic equation by factoring, completing the square, or using the quadratic formula.

$$5x^2 - 4x - 12 = 0 \quad \blacktriangleleft \; \textit{Solve by factoring.}$$
$$(5x + 6)(x - 2) = 0$$
$$\boxed{x = -\tfrac{6}{5}} \quad \text{or} \quad \boxed{x = 2}$$

Step 4   Find the value of the other variable by substituting in the linear equation.

$$-2x + y = -1 \qquad\qquad -2x + y = -1$$
$$-2\left(-\tfrac{6}{5}\right) + y = -1 \qquad\qquad -2(2) + y = -1$$
$$\tfrac{12}{5} + y = -1 \qquad\qquad -4 + y = -1$$
$$\boxed{y = -\tfrac{17}{5}} \qquad\qquad \boxed{y = 3}$$

Step 5   Check by substituting each ordered pair in both equations.

$x^2 + y^2 = 13$		$-2x + y = -1$	
$\left(-\tfrac{6}{5}\right)^2 + \left(-\tfrac{17}{5}\right)^2$	13	$-2\left(-\tfrac{6}{5}\right) + \left(-\tfrac{17}{5}\right)$	-1
$\tfrac{36}{25} + \tfrac{289}{25}$		$\tfrac{12}{5} - \tfrac{17}{5}$	
$\tfrac{325}{25}$		$-\tfrac{5}{5}$	
13		-1	

$x^2 + y^2 = 13$		$-2x + y = -1$	
$2^2 + 3^2$	13	$-2(2) + 3$	-1
$4 + 9$		$-4 + 3$	
13		-1	

Thus, $\left(-\dfrac{6}{5}, -\dfrac{17}{5}\right)$ and $(2, 3)$ are the solutions of the system.

Oral Exercises

State the number of solutions of each system of equations whose graphs are given.
Give the solution(s) of each system, if any.

1.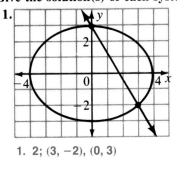

1. 2; (3, −2), (0, 3)

2.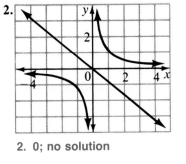

2. 0; no solution

3.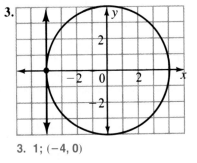

3. 1; (−4, 0)

SOLVING LINEAR-QUADRATIC SYSTEMS OF EQUATIONS

Written Exercises

20. $(\frac{19 + \sqrt{973}}{18}, \frac{-26 + \sqrt{973}}{27})$, $(\frac{19 - \sqrt{973}}{18}, \frac{-26 - \sqrt{973}}{27})$ 21. $(-\frac{11}{19}, \frac{63}{19})$, $(1, -3)$

Solve each system of equations graphically. Estimate the decimal solutions to the nearest tenth.

Ⓐ 1. $\frac{x^2}{16} + \frac{y^2}{9} = 1$
$2x - 3y = 6$
$(-1.2, -2.8)$, $(3.9, 0.6)$

2. $\frac{x^2}{25} - \frac{y^2}{4} = 1$
$x = 5$ **(5, 0)**

3. $\frac{x^2}{16} + \frac{y^2}{16} = 1$
$x + y = 2$
$(3.6, -1.6)$, $(-1.7, 3.7)$

4. $xy = 4$
$2x + 3y = 9$
no solution

5. $y = x^2 - 6x + 8$
$x - 2y = 2$
$(2, 0)$, $(4.5, 1.3)$

6. $x^2 + y^2 = 16$
$3x - 2y = 4$
$(-1.2, -3.8)$, $(3.1, 2.7)$

7. $\frac{x^2}{4} + \frac{y^2}{4} = 1$
$2x - 6y = 12$
$(1.2, -1.6)$, $(0, -2)$

8. $y = x^2 - 9$
$x + y = 3$
$(-4, 7)$, $(3, 0)$

For complete solutions, see TE Answer Section.

Solve each system of equations algebraically. Give the irrational solutions in simplest radical form.

9. $xy = 8$
$y = x + 2$
$(-4, -2)$, $(2, 4)$

10. $y = x^2 - 7x - 3$
$2x - y = 3$
$(0, -3)$, $(9, 15)$

11. $y = 5(x - 3)$
$2y = x^2 - 6$
$(4, 5)$, $(6, 15)$

12. $\frac{x^2}{10} + \frac{y^2}{40} = 1$
$y = \frac{2}{3}x$
$(-3, -2)$, $(3, 2)$

13. $y = 3(x - 3)$
$2y = x^2 - 10$
$(2, -3)$, $(4, 3)$

14. $y = 2x - 3$
$x = -\frac{y^2}{4} + \frac{21}{4}$
$(-1, -5)$, $(3, 3)$

15. $y - 2x = 5$
$x^2 + y^2 = 25$
$(-4, -3)$, $(0, 5)$

16. $\frac{x^2}{1} - \frac{y^2}{2} = 1$
$y = 2x - 2$
$(1, 0)$, $(3, 4)$

Ⓑ 17. $y = -\frac{x}{2} + \frac{1}{2}$
$x = -3y^2 - 12y + 8$
$(\frac{25 + \sqrt{493}}{6}, \frac{-5 + \sqrt{493}}{18})$,

18. $y = x^2 - 8x + 2$
$x - 3y = 5$
$(\frac{25 + \sqrt{493}}{6}, \frac{-5 + \sqrt{493}}{18})$,

19. $3x - 2y = 8$
$y = 2x^2 - 5x - 3$
$(\frac{25 - \sqrt{493}}{6}, \frac{-5 - \sqrt{493}}{18})$

$(\frac{13 + \sqrt{137}}{8}, \frac{-25 + 3\sqrt{137}}{16})$,

20. $3y - 2x = -5$
$y = -3x^2 + 7x + 4$
above

$(\frac{13 - \sqrt{137}}{8}, \frac{-25 - 3\sqrt{137}}{16})$

21. $4x + y = 1$
$3x^2 + y^2 = 12$

22. $y = 2x + 3$
$x^2 + y^2 = 25$

23. $x^2 + (y - 5)^2 = 49$
$y - x = -2$
$(0, -2)$, $(7, 5)$

24. $\frac{x^2}{16} + \frac{y^2}{3} = 1$
$y = x - 1$

22. $(\frac{-6 + 2\sqrt{29}}{5}, \frac{3 + 4\sqrt{29}}{5})$, $(\frac{-6 - 2\sqrt{29}}{5}, \frac{3 - 4\sqrt{29}}{5})$

Ⓒ 25. $(x - 2)^2 + (y + 3)^2 = 96$
$y = 2x$
$(\frac{-4 + \sqrt{431}}{5}, \frac{-8 + 2\sqrt{431}}{5})$, $(\frac{-4 - \sqrt{431}}{5}, \frac{-8 - 2\sqrt{431}}{5})$

26. $x^2 + 4x + y^2 - 6y = 12$
$y = -x + 3$

27. $2x^2 + y^2 = 8x + 4y + 3$
$2x - 3y = 7$
$(\frac{31 + 3\sqrt{42}}{11}, \frac{-5 + 2\sqrt{42}}{11})$, $(\frac{31 - 3\sqrt{42}}{11}, \frac{-5 - 2\sqrt{42}}{11})$

28. $3x^2 - 2y^2 - 6x + 5y = -12$
$3x - 2y = -8$
$(0, 4)$, $(-15, -\frac{37}{2})$

➤ A Challenge To You

The number of distinct points in the coordinate plane common to the graphs of
$(2x - y + 1)(2x + 3y - 11) = 0$ and $(x + 2y - 7)(3x - 2y + 3) = 0$ is **B**
(A) 0   (B) 1   (C) 2   (D) 3   (E) 4   (F) infinitely many

Cumulative Review

Simplify.

1. $3a^3 b(-2a^4 b^5)$ $-6a^7 b^6$

2. $\frac{16x^6 yz^2}{-4xy^5 z^2}$ $-\frac{4x^5}{y^4}$

3. $(-3a^2 b^3 c)^3$ $-27a^6 b^9 c^3$

13.2 Solving Quadratic Systems of Equations

OBJECTIVE ▶ **To find the real number solutions of a system of two quadratic equations graphically and algebraically**

A system of equations may contain two quadratic equations. A system of this type is called a **quadratic system.** As illustrated by the graphs below, a system of two quadratic equations may have 4, 3, 2, 1, or 0 solutions.

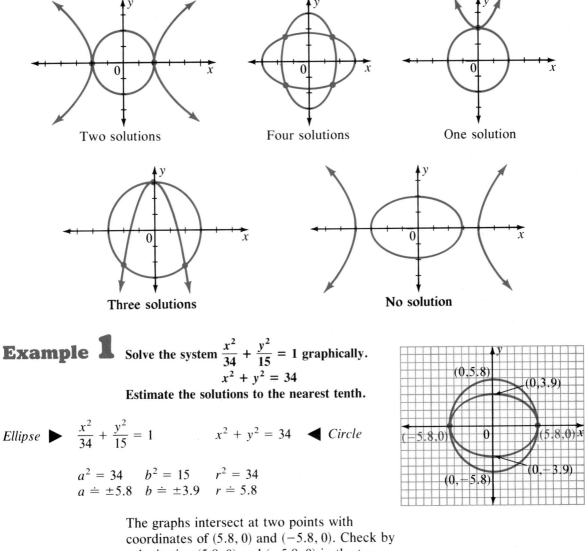

Two solutions   Four solutions   One solution

Three solutions   No solution

Example **1** Solve the system $\dfrac{x^2}{34} + \dfrac{y^2}{15} = 1$ graphically.

$$x^2 + y^2 = 34$$

Estimate the solutions to the nearest tenth.

Ellipse ▶ $\dfrac{x^2}{34} + \dfrac{y^2}{15} = 1$ $x^2 + y^2 = 34$ ◀ *Circle*

$a^2 = 34 \quad b^2 = 15 \quad r^2 = 34$
$a \doteq \pm 5.8 \quad b \doteq \pm 3.9 \quad r \doteq 5.8$

The graphs intersect at two points with coordinates of $(5.8, 0)$ and $(-5.8, 0)$. Check by substituting $(5.8, 0)$ and $(-5.8, 0)$ in the two equations.

Thus, $(5.8, 0)$ and $(-5.8, 0)$ are the solutions of the system.

The next examples show you how to find the solutions of a system of two quadratic equations algebraically. Notice that either the addition method or substitution method may be used.

Example 2 Solve the system $\dfrac{x^2}{36} + \dfrac{y^2}{25} = 1$ algebraically.

$$x^2 + y^2 = 25$$

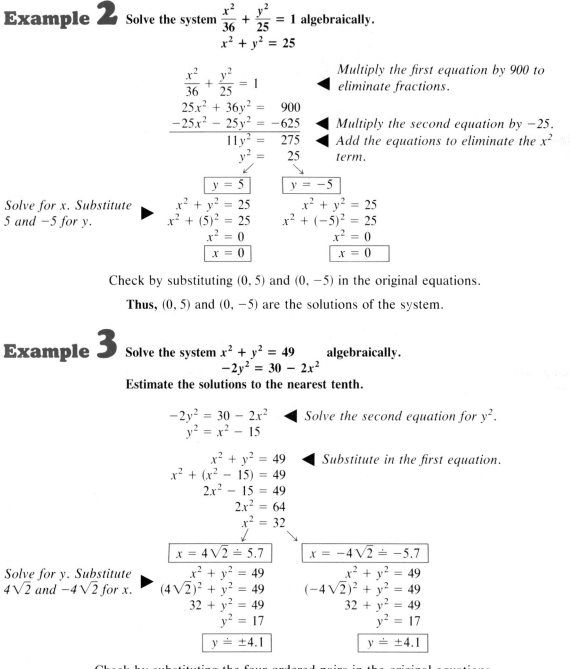

$\dfrac{x^2}{36} + \dfrac{y^2}{25} = 1$ ◀ *Multiply the first equation by 900 to eliminate fractions.*

$$\begin{aligned}25x^2 + 36y^2 &= 900\\ -25x^2 - 25y^2 &= -625 \quad \blacktriangleleft \ \textit{Multiply the second equation by } -25.\\ 11y^2 &= 275 \quad \blacktriangleleft \ \textit{Add the equations to eliminate the } x^2\\ y^2 &= 25 \qquad \textit{term.}\end{aligned}$$

$$\boxed{y = 5} \qquad \boxed{y = -5}$$

Solve for x. Substitute 5 and −5 for y. ▶

$$\begin{aligned}x^2 + y^2 &= 25 & x^2 + y^2 &= 25\\ x^2 + (5)^2 &= 25 & x^2 + (-5)^2 &= 25\\ x^2 &= 0 & x^2 &= 0\\ \boxed{x = 0} & & \boxed{x = 0}\end{aligned}$$

Check by substituting $(0, 5)$ and $(0, -5)$ in the original equations.

Thus, $(0, 5)$ and $(0, -5)$ are the solutions of the system.

Example 3 Solve the system $x^2 + y^2 = 49$ algebraically.

$$-2y^2 = 30 - 2x^2$$

Estimate the solutions to the nearest tenth.

$$\begin{aligned}-2y^2 &= 30 - 2x^2 \quad \blacktriangleleft \ \textit{Solve the second equation for } y^2.\\ y^2 &= x^2 - 15\end{aligned}$$

$$\begin{aligned}x^2 + y^2 &= 49 \quad \blacktriangleleft \ \textit{Substitute in the first equation.}\\ x^2 + (x^2 - 15) &= 49\\ 2x^2 - 15 &= 49\\ 2x^2 &= 64\\ x^2 &= 32\end{aligned}$$

$$\boxed{x = 4\sqrt{2} \doteq 5.7} \qquad \boxed{x = -4\sqrt{2} \doteq -5.7}$$

Solve for y. Substitute $4\sqrt{2}$ and $-4\sqrt{2}$ for x. ▶

$$\begin{aligned}x^2 + y^2 &= 49 & x^2 + y^2 &= 49\\ (4\sqrt{2})^2 + y^2 &= 49 & (-4\sqrt{2})^2 + y^2 &= 49\\ 32 + y^2 &= 49 & 32 + y^2 &= 49\\ y^2 &= 17 & y^2 &= 17\\ \boxed{y \doteq \pm 4.1} & & \boxed{y \doteq \pm 4.1}\end{aligned}$$

Check by substituting the four ordered pairs in the original equations.

Thus, $(5.7, 4.1)$, $(5.7, -4.1)$, $(-5.7, 4.1)$, and $(-5.7, -4.1)$ are the solutions of the system.

Oral Exercises

12. $(\frac{6\sqrt{430}}{43}, \frac{2\sqrt{129}}{43})$, $(\frac{6\sqrt{430}}{43}, \frac{-2\sqrt{129}}{43})$, $(\frac{-6\sqrt{430}}{43}, \frac{2\sqrt{129}}{43})$, $(\frac{-6\sqrt{430}}{43}, \frac{-2\sqrt{129}}{43})$

State the number of solutions of each system of equations whose graphs are given. Give the solution(s) of each system, if any.

1.

2.

3.

1. 4; (2, 2), (2, −2), (−2, 2), (−2, −2)

2. 2; (1.5, 1.5), (−1.5, 1.5)

3. 2; (3, 0), (−3, 0)

Written Exercises

2. (3.1, 2.4), (3.1, −2.4), (−3.1, 2.4), (−3.1, −2.4)   7. (5, 3.6), (5, −3.6), (−5, 3.6), (−5, −3.6)

Solve each system of equations graphically. Estimate the decimal solutions to the nearest tenth.

(A)

1. $\dfrac{x^2}{16} + \dfrac{y^2}{4} = 1$
$x^2 + y^2 = 16$
(−4, 0), (4, 0)

2. $\dfrac{x^2}{25} + \dfrac{y^2}{9} = 1$
$x^2 - y^2 = 4$
above

3. $\dfrac{x^2}{9} - \dfrac{y^2}{4} = 1$
$xy = 5$
(3.6, 1.4), (−3.6, −1.4)

4. $\dfrac{x^2}{16} + \dfrac{y^2}{25} = 1$
$x^2 + y^2 = 4$
no solution

Solve each system of equations algebraically. Give the irrational solutions as decimals to the nearest tenth.
9. $(2\sqrt{5}, 2)$, $(2\sqrt{5}, -2)$, $(-2\sqrt{5}, 2)$, $(-2\sqrt{5}, -2)$ 11. $(\frac{\sqrt{3}}{3}, 4)$, $(\frac{\sqrt{3}}{3}, -4)$, $(-\frac{\sqrt{3}}{3}, 4)$, $(-\frac{\sqrt{3}}{3}, -4)$

5. $x^2 + y^2 = 16$
$x^2 - y^2 = 16$
(−4, 0), (4, 0)

6. $x^2 + y^2 = 1$
$y = x^2 + 5$
no solution

7. $x^2 + y^2 = 38$
$x^2 - y^2 = 12$
above

8. $x^2 + y^2 = 13$
$xy = -6$
(−3, 2), (3, −2), (−2, 3), (2, −3)

Solve each system of equations algebraically. Give the irrational solutions in simplest radical form.

(B)

9. $\dfrac{x^2}{36} + \dfrac{y^2}{9} = 1$
$x^2 - y^2 = 16$
above

10. $\dfrac{x^2}{2} + \dfrac{y^2}{4} = 1$
$8x^2 + 3y^2 = 12$
(0, 2), (0, −2)

11. $3x^2 + 2y^2 = 33$
$3x^2 + y^2 = 17$ above

12. $\dfrac{x^2}{9} + \dfrac{y^2}{4} = 1$
$3x^2 - 4y^2 = 24$

14. $(\frac{4\sqrt{5}}{3}, \frac{2}{3})$, $(\frac{4\sqrt{5}}{3}, -\frac{2}{3})$, $(\frac{-4\sqrt{5}}{3}, \frac{2}{3})$, $(\frac{-4\sqrt{5}}{3}, -\frac{2}{3})$

13. $\dfrac{x^2}{16} + \dfrac{y^2}{4} = 1$
$\dfrac{x^2}{4} - \dfrac{y^2}{3} = 1$
$(\sqrt{7}, \frac{3}{2})$, $(\sqrt{7}, -\frac{3}{2})$, $(-\sqrt{7}, \frac{3}{2})$, $(-\sqrt{7}, -\frac{3}{2})$

14. $\dfrac{x^2}{10} + \dfrac{y^2}{4} = 1$
$2y^2 = x^2 - 8$

15. $x^2 + y^2 = 13$
$\dfrac{x^2}{5} - \dfrac{y^2}{5} = 1$ below

16. $\dfrac{x^2}{5} + \dfrac{y^2}{25} = 1$
$x^2 + y^2 = 9$
$(2, \sqrt{5})$, $(2, -\sqrt{5})$, $(-2, \sqrt{5})$, $(-2, -\sqrt{5})$

Solve each system of equations graphically. Give the solutions as decimals to the nearest tenth.

(C)

17. $\dfrac{(x - 3)^2}{9} + \dfrac{(y + 2)^2}{4} = 1$
$(x + 1)^2 + (y - 3)^2 = 16$
(1.0, −0.5)

18. $\dfrac{(x + 2)^2}{9} - \dfrac{(y - 3)^2}{4} = 1$
$\dfrac{(x - 1)^2}{25} + \dfrac{(y + 2)^2}{16} = 1$
(1.2, 2.0), (6.0, −2.3)

19. $(x - 3)^2 + (y + 4)^2 = 25$
$\dfrac{(x + 2)^2}{9} + \dfrac{(y - 1)^2}{16} = 1$
(1.0, 0.6), (−1.9, −3.0)

15. (3, 2), (3, −2), (−3, 2), (−3, −2)

SOLVING QUADRATIC SYSTEMS OF EQUATIONS   **343**

Applications

There are many applications that use a system of equations to determine a solution. The equations can be both linear, both quadratic, or one of each. The following example illustrates such an application using one linear and one quadratic equation.

Example

Find the length of each side of both squares if the sum of the perimeters is 56 cm and the sum of the areas is 106 cm².

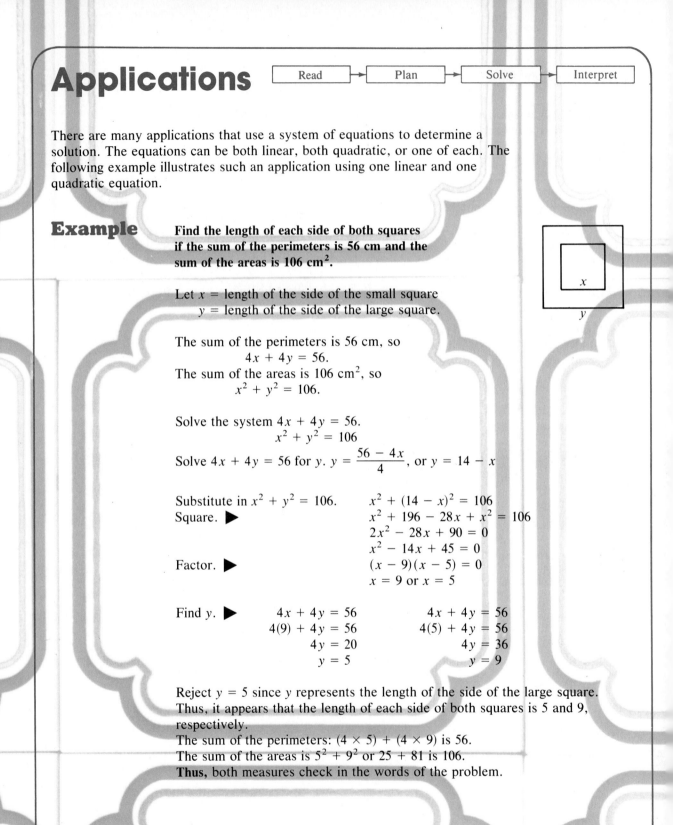

Let x = length of the side of the small square
y = length of the side of the large square.

The sum of the perimeters is 56 cm, so
$$4x + 4y = 56.$$
The sum of the areas is 106 cm², so
$$x^2 + y^2 = 106.$$

Solve the system $4x + 4y = 56.$
$$x^2 + y^2 = 106$$

Solve $4x + 4y = 56$ for y. $y = \dfrac{56 - 4x}{4}$, or $y = 14 - x$

Substitute in $x^2 + y^2 = 106.$

Square. ▶

$$x^2 + (14 - x)^2 = 106$$
$$x^2 + 196 - 28x + x^2 = 106$$
$$2x^2 - 28x + 90 = 0$$
$$x^2 - 14x + 45 = 0$$

Factor. ▶

$$(x - 9)(x - 5) = 0$$
$$x = 9 \text{ or } x = 5$$

Find y. ▶

$4x + 4y = 56$	$4x + 4y = 56$
$4(9) + 4y = 56$	$4(5) + 4y = 56$
$4y = 20$	$4y = 36$
$y = 5$	$y = 9$

Reject $y = 5$ since y represents the length of the side of the large square. Thus, it appears that the length of each side of both squares is 5 and 9, respectively.
The sum of the perimeters: $(4 \times 5) + (4 \times 9)$ is 56.
The sum of the areas is $5^2 + 9^2$ or $25 + 81$ is 106.
Thus, both measures check in the words of the problem.

Solve.

1. The perimeter of a rectangular lot is 26 cm. The area is 36 cm². Find the lengths of the sides. **4 cm, 9 cm**

2. Find the length of each side of two squares if the sum of their perimeters is 56 cm and the sum of their areas is 100 cm². **6 cm, 8 cm**

3. The area of a right triangle is 25 cm². The length of its hypotenuse is $5\sqrt{5}$ cm. Find the lengths of the legs. **5 cm, 10 cm**

4. The difference of the squares of two numbers is 84. The first number is 2 more than twice the second. What are the numbers? **10, 4**

5. Senior Girl Scout Troop 195 hiked 8 km to the top of High Peak and hiked the same distance down in a total time of 6 hours and 40 minutes. Their rate of ascent was 10 km/h slower than their rate of descent. What was their rate of ascent? **1.3 km/h**

6. Ms. Stanton received $480 interest on an investment for one year. If the interest rate had been $1\frac{1}{2}\%$ higher and the principal $1,000 less, she would have received the same amount of interest. Find the principal and the rate of interest. **$6,178.91, 7.77%**

7. A rectangular sheet of metal has 4 squares with sides 8 cm long cut from the corners of the sheet. The edges are bent up to form an open box with a volume of 12,672 cm³. The area of the sheet is 3,120 cm². Find the dimensions of the box. **8 cm, 36 cm, 44 cm**

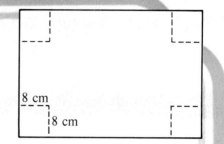

8. Find two numbers whose product is 18 and the sum of their reciprocals is $\frac{1}{2}$. **3, 6**

9. The sum of the squares of two numbers is 80 and their product is 32. What are the numbers? **8, 4 or −8, −4**

10. If the numerator of a fraction is increased by 3 and the denominator is decreased by 3, the resulting fraction is the reciprocal of the original fraction. The numerator of the original fraction is 1 more than one half its denominator. What was the original fraction? $\frac{5}{8}$

11. The product of a two-digit number and the number obtained by reversing its digits is 2,268. If the difference of the numbers is 27, find the numbers. **63, 36**

13.3 Solving Linear Inequality Systems

OBJECTIVES ▶ **To draw the graph of a linear inequality in two variables**
To find the real number solutions of a system of two linear inequalities graphically

The general form of a **linear inequality** in two variables, x and y, is $ax + by > c$ or $ax + by < c$, where a and b are not both equal to 0.

The graph of the linear inequality $3x - 2y < 2$ is a region of the coordinate plane above the line determined by the equation $3x - 2y = 2$. You should use the following steps to draw the graph of $3x - 2y < 2$:

(1) Solve for y. Division by a negative number reverses the order of the inequality.

$$3x - 2y < 2$$
$$-2y < -3x + 2$$
$$y > \tfrac{3}{2}x - 1$$

(2) Draw the graph of the equation $y = \tfrac{3}{2}x - 1$. Use a dashed line with $m = \tfrac{3}{2}$ and $b = -1$.

(3) Shade the region above the line.

(4) Check. Pick a point in the shaded region and one below the line. Test $(-2, 1)$ and $(4, -2)$.

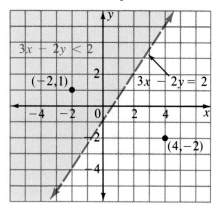

$3x - 2y < 2$		$3x - 2y < 2$	
$3(-2) - 2(1)$	2	$3(4) - 2(-2)$	2
$-6 - 2$		$12 + 4$	
-8		16	
$-8 < 2$		$16 < 2$	
True		False	

Notice that since $y > \tfrac{3}{2}x - 1$, the region *above* the line is shaded. Also notice that a dashed line is used to indicate that the line is not part of the graph. The graph would include the line if the inequality contained the symbol $\geq$. When the line is part of the graph, a solid line should be used.

Example 1 Draw the graph of $-x - 2y \geq 4$.

Solve for y. ▶
$$-x - 2y \geq 4$$
$$-2y \geq x + 4$$
$$y \leq -\tfrac{1}{2}x - 2$$

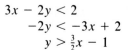

Graph the equation. Use a solid line. ▶
$$y = -\tfrac{1}{2}x - 2$$
$$m = -\tfrac{1}{2}, \ b = -2$$

Shade the region below the line.

Example 2 Draw the graph of $y \le -2$.

Graph the equation $y = -2$.
Use a solid line.

Shade the region below the line.

Check. Pick a point in the shaded region and one above the line.

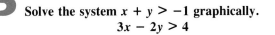

The next two examples show you how to solve a system of two linear inequalities graphically.

Example 3 Solve the system $x + y > -1$ graphically.
$$3x - 2y > 4$$

Graph $x + y > -1$ or $y > -x - 1$:
(a) Graph $y = -x - 1$. Use a dashed line.
(b) Shade above the line.

Graph $3x - 2y > 4$ or $y < \frac{3}{2}x - 2$:
(a) Graph $y = \frac{3}{2}x - 2$. Use a dashed line.
(b) Shade below the line with a different color.

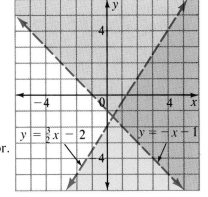

Check. Pick a point in the double-shaded region and one not in the region.

Thus, the solution set is the set of all ordered pairs for the points in the double-shaded region.

Example 4 Solve the system $2x - y \le -3$ graphically.
$$x \le -2$$

Graph $2x - y \le -3$ or $y \ge 2x + 3$:
(a) Graph $y = 2x + 3$. Use a solid line.
(b) Shade above the line.

Graph $x \le -2$:
(a) Graph $x = -2$. Use a solid line.
(b) Shade to the left of the line with a different color.

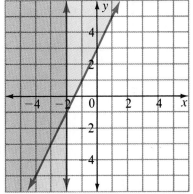

Check. Pick a point in the double-shaded region and one not in the region.

Thus, the solution set is the set of all ordered pairs for the points in the double-shaded region.

SOLVING LINEAR INEQUALITY SYSTEMS

Reading in Algebra

Examine the inequalities on the left and the expressions describing the graphs of the inequalities on the right. Match each inequality with one or more of the descriptions.

1. $x \le 3$ **A, F**
2. $y > -4$ **B, C**
3. $y \le 2x + 3$ **A, D, E**
4. $y > 3x + 5$ **B, C, F**
5. $y \le -7$ **A, D**
6. $x \ge -8$ **A, E**
7. $y < x + 8$ **B, D, E**
8. $y \ge -2x + 1$ **A, C, E**

A includes the line
B excludes the line
C above the line
D below the line
E right of the line
F left of the line

Written Exercises

For all Written Exercises, see TE Answer Section.

Draw the graph of each of the following inequalities. Check.

(A)
1. $3x - 2y \le 6$
2. $2y - 3x + 4 \ge 0$
3. $2x + 5y < 10$
4. $5x - 3y > 15$
5. $7x - 3y \ge 21$
6. $2x - 7y > 35$
7. $-y \le 2x - 8$
8. $-5x - 2y \le 12$
9. $3x < -y + 8$
10. $-5x > 4y + 8$
11. $-8 + x \ge 2y$
12. $y - 2x < -7$
13. $x \ge 8$
14. $y \ge 4$
15. $y < -4$
16. $x < 5$

Solve each system of inequalities graphically. Check.

17. $y \le -2x + 3$
    $y > 4x - 1$
18. $y \le 3x - 1$
    $y > -2x + 4$
19. $2x + 3y \ge 6$
    $2y - x < -4$
20. $5x + 2y \ge 12$
    $3x + 4y \le 8$

21. $2x + 3y \ge 9$
    $-3x + 4y \ge -4$
22. $5x + 6y < 30$
    $4x + 3y \ge 9$
23. $-4x + 5y \le 15$
    $4y \ge 5x + 12$
24. $-9 \le 2x + 3y$
    $3y + 4x \le 6$

(B)
25. $-2x - 3y \ge 6$
    $-2y + x > -4$
26. $x - 2y > 6$
    $x + 2y \le 4$
27. $2x - 3y \ge 9$
    $-2y + x > 6$
28. $-3x - y \ge 6$
    $y - 2x > 1$

29. $2x + y > 3$
    $y \ge x$
30. $y \le 2$
    $x \le 4$
31. $y \ge -3$
    $x \le -2$
32. $y \ge 5$
    $x \ge -3$

Solve each system of three inequalities graphically. Check.

(C)
33. $x + y \le 3$
    $4x - 5y \ge 10$
    $-2x + y > 2$
34. $2x - y \ge -4$
    $x + 3y < 6$
    $x + 2y \ge 4$
35. $-x + 3y < 5$
    $3x - 2y \ge 6$
    $-4x + y < 3$
36. $4x - 2y \le 2$
    $-4x + y \ge 1$
    $2x - y \le -3$

348

13.4 Solving Linear-Quadratic Inequality Systems

OBJECTIVES ▶ **To draw the graph of a quadratic inequality**
To find the real number solutions of a system of one linear and one quadratic inequality graphically
To find the real number solutions of a system of two quadratic inequalities graphically

The graph of the **quadratic inequality** $x^2 + y^2 < 16$ is a region of the coordinate plane in the interior of the circle determined by the equation $x^2 + y^2 = 16$. You should use the following steps to draw the graph of $x^2 + y^2 < 16$:

(1) Draw the graph of the equation $x^2 + y^2 = 16$. The graph is a circle. Use a dashed curve.

(2) Shade the region in the interior of the circle.

(3) Check. Pick a point in the shaded region, one not in the region, and one on the circle.
Test $(2, 3)$, $(4, -3)$, and $(4, 0)$.

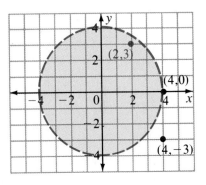

Notice that since $x^2 + y^2 < 16$, the region *in the interior of* the circle is shaded. The dashed curve is used to show that the circle is not part of the graph of the inequality. The graph would include the circle if the inequality contained the symbol $\leq$. The graph of $x^2 + y^2 > 16$ is the region *in the exterior of* the circle.

Example 1 Draw the graph of $xy \geq 4$.

Make a table of x and y values for $xy = 4$.

Graph the equation $xy = 4$. Use a solid curve.

Shade the region in the interior of each branch of the hyperbola.

Check. Pick a point in the shaded region, one not in the region, and one on the hyperbola.

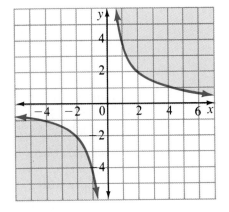

SOLVING LINEAR-QUADRATIC INEQUALITY SYSTEMS   **349**

Systems containing linear or quadratic inequalities can be solved graphically.

Example 2

Solve the system $x^2 + y^2 \leq 9$ graphically.
$$y \geq 3x - 2$$

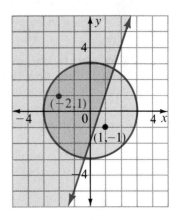

Graph $x^2 + y^2 \leq 9$:
(a) Graph $x^2 + y^2 = 9$. The graph is a circle. Use a solid curve.
(b) Shade the region in the interior of the circle.

Graph $y \geq 3x - 2$:
(a) Graph $y = 3x - 2$. Use a solid line.
(b) Shade the region above the line with a different color.

Check. Pick a point in the double-shaded region and one not in the region. Test $(-2, 1)$ and $(1, -1)$ in both inequalities.

$x^2 + y^2 \leq 9$		$y \geq 3x - 2$		$x^2 + y^2 \leq 9$		$y \geq 3x - 2$	
$(-2)^2 + 1^2$	9	1	$3(-2) - 2$	$1^2 + (-1)^2$	9	-1	$3 \cdot 1 - 2$
5			-8	2			1
$5 \leq 9$		$1 \geq -8$		$2 \leq 9$		$-1 \geq 1$	
True		True		True		False	

Thus, the solution set is the set of all ordered pairs for the points in the double-shaded region, including the points of the boundary of the region.

Example 3

Solve the system $x^2 + y^2 \geq 4$ graphically.
$$\frac{x^2}{9} + \frac{y^2}{4} \leq 1$$

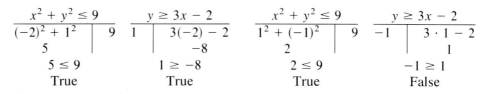

Graph $x^2 + y^2 \geq 4$:
(a) Graph $x^2 + y^2 = 4$. The graph is a circle. Use a solid curve.
(b) Shade the region in the exterior of the circle.

Graph $\dfrac{x^2}{9} + \dfrac{y^2}{4} \leq 1$:

(a) Graph $\dfrac{x^2}{9} + \dfrac{y^2}{4} = 1$. The graph is an ellipse. Use a solid curve.
(b) Shade the region in the interior of the ellipse with a different color.

Check. Pick a point in the double-shaded region and one not in the region.

Thus, the solution set is the set of all ordered pairs for the points in the double-shaded region, including the points of the boundary of the region.

CHAPTER THIRTEEN

Oral Exercises

State the inequality that describes the shaded region.

1.
$$\frac{x^2}{9} + \frac{y^2}{4} = 1$$

2.
$$y = 3x - 2$$

3.
$$\frac{x^2}{4} - \frac{y^2}{9} = 1$$

Written Exercises

1. $\dfrac{x^2}{9} + \dfrac{y^2}{4} \leq 1$ 2. $y \geq 3x - 2$ 3. $\dfrac{x^2}{4} - \dfrac{y^2}{9} > 1$

For solutions to all Written Exercises, see TE Answer Section.

Draw the graph of each of the following inequalities. Check.

(A)
1. $x^2 + y^2 \leq 9$ **2.** $x^2 + y^2 \geq 4$ **3.** $x^2 + y^2 < 25$ **4.** $x^2 + y^2 > 16$

5. $xy \geq 6$ **6.** $xy < 8$ **7.** $xy > 3$ **8.** $xy \leq -2$

9 $\dfrac{x^2}{25} + \dfrac{y^2}{4} \leq 1$ **10.** $\dfrac{x^2}{36} + \dfrac{y^2}{16} \geq 1$ **11.** $\dfrac{x^2}{100} + \dfrac{y^2}{9} < 1$ **12.** $\dfrac{x^2}{16} + \dfrac{y^2}{1} > 1$

13. $\dfrac{x^2}{9} - \dfrac{y^2}{4} \leq 1$ **14.** $\dfrac{x^2}{25} - \dfrac{y^2}{8} \geq 1$ **15.** $\dfrac{x^2}{4} - \dfrac{y^2}{9} < 1$ **16.** $\dfrac{x^2}{25} - \dfrac{y^2}{81} > 1$

(B)
17. $2x^2 + 3y^2 \geq 18$ **18.** $3x^2 + 9y^2 \leq 27$ **19.** $9x^2 - 4y^2 < 36$ **20.** $16x^2 - 8y^2 \geq 64$

21. $27x^2 + 9y^2 \geq 81$ **22.** $25x^2 - 4y^2 > 100$ **23.** $36x^2 - 18y^2 \leq 72$ **24.** $25x^2 + 4y^2 < 100$

Solve each system of inequalities graphically. Check.

25. $x^2 + y^2 \leq 16$ **26.** $x^2 + y^2 > 25$ **27.** $xy \geq 1$ **28.** $xy < -5$
$\quad\ \ 2x - 3y \leq 6$ $\quad\ \ -3x + 4y > 12$ $\quad\ \ 4x + 5y \geq 15$ $\quad\ \ -2x - 3y \leq 6$

29. $\dfrac{x^2}{16} + \dfrac{y^2}{4} \geq 1$ **30.** $\dfrac{x^2}{4} - \dfrac{y^2}{2} \leq 2$ **31.** $\dfrac{x^2}{25} + \dfrac{y^2}{81} \leq 1$ **32.** $\dfrac{x^2}{9} - \dfrac{y^2}{16} \geq 3$
$\quad\ \ -2x - 3y \leq 2$ $\quad\ \ 3x - y > 2$ $\quad\ \ 2x + 4y \leq -3$ $\quad\ \ -x - 4y \geq -5$

(C)
33. $x^2 + y^2 \geq 25$ **34.** $x^2 - y^2 \leq 12$ **35.** $25x^2 + 4y^2 \geq 100$ **36.** $3x^2 - 27y^2 \leq 81$
$\quad\ \ xy < -5$ $\quad\ \ x^2 + y^2 \leq 36$ $\quad\ \ x^2 + \ y^2 \leq 36$ $\quad\ \ 4x^2 + 25y^2 \geq 100$

37. $4x^2 + 16y^2 \geq 64$ **38.** $-3x^2 + 4y^2 \leq 36$ **39.** $4x^2 + 6y^2 \geq 24$ **40.** $2x^2 + 4y^2 \leq 12$
$\quad\ \ 3x^2 - \ 9y^2 \leq 27$ $\quad\ \ x^2 + 5y^2 \geq 25$ $\quad\ \ -x^2 - \ y^2 \geq -9$ $\quad\ \ 3x^2 - 5y^2 \geq 15$

Cumulative Review

1. Denine has nickels, dimes, and quarters in her coin collection. The number of quarters is 4 less than twice the number of dimes. The number of dimes is 3 times the number of nickels. If the value of her collection is $8.25, how many nickels, dimes, and quarters does she have?

5 nickels, 15 dimes, 26 quarters

2. Some dry peanuts worth $2.20/kg are mixed with sunflower seeds worth $3.80/kg to make 30 kg of a mixture worth $3.00/kg. How many kilograms of peanuts and how many kilograms of sunflower seeds are there in the mixture?

peanuts: 15 kg, sunflower seeds: 15 kg

Chapter Thirteen Review

Vocabulary
linear inequality [13.3]
quadratic inequality   [13.4]
system of equations
  linear-quadratic   [13.1]
  quadratic [13.2]
system of inequalities
  linear-quadratic   [13.4]
  quadratic   [13.4]

Solve each system of equations graphically. Estimate the decimal solutions to the nearest tenth.

1. $\frac{x^2}{25} + \frac{y^2}{4} = 1$
   $y = 2x + 1$
   (0.5, 2.0), (−1.5, −1.9)

2. $x^2 - y^2 = 9$ [13.1]
   $x - 3y = 6$
   (3.1, −1.0), (−4.6, −3.5)

3. $4x^2 + 9y^2 = 100$
   $2x - 9y = -10$
   (4, 2), (−5, 0) [13.1]

4. $\frac{x^2}{9} + \frac{y^2}{4} = 1$ [13.2]
   $xy = 2$
   (2.8, 0.7), (−2.8, −0.7)
   (1.1, 1.8), (−1.1, −1.8)

5. $\frac{x^2}{8} - \frac{y^2}{4} = 1$ [13.2]
   $x^2 + 4y^2 = 10$
   (2.9, 0.6), (2.9, −0.6), (−2.9, 0.6), (−2.9, −0.6)

★6. $(x - 1)^2 + (y - 3)^2 = 9$ [13.2]
   $\frac{(x - 2)^2}{4} + \frac{(y + 2)^2}{9} = 1$ (0.5, 0), (2.9, 0.7)

Solve each system of equations algebraically. Give the irrational solutions in simplest radical form.

7. $y = x^2 + 7x - 3$
   $x + 2y = -3$

8. $x^2 - y^2 = -5$ [13.1]
   $2x + y = -1$
   (−2, 3), ($\frac{2}{3}$, −$\frac{7}{3}$)

★9. $x^2 + 2x + y^2 - 4y = 8$ [13.1]
   $x - y = 2$ (2, 0), (1, −1)

10. $y = 2x^2 - x - 5$ [13.2]
    $y = x^2 + 1$ (3, 10), (−2, 5)

7. $\left(\frac{-15 - \sqrt{249}}{4}, \frac{3 + \sqrt{249}}{8}\right)$, $\left(\frac{-15 + \sqrt{249}}{4}, \frac{3 - \sqrt{249}}{8}\right)$

11. $x^2 + y^2 = 10$
    $xy = 3$
    (3, 1), (−3, −1),
    (1, 3), (−1, −3)

12. $\frac{x^2}{16} + \frac{y^2}{16} = 1$ [13.2]
    $\frac{x^2}{16} - \frac{y^2}{9} = 1$
    (4, 0), (−4, 0)

Draw the graph of each of the following inequalites. Check.   [13.3]

13. $y \geq 2x - 3$

14. $y < -3x + 5$

15. $3x - 2y \leq 8$

16. $y > -3$

17. $x^2 + y^2 \leq 4$

18. $xy > 4$ [13.4]

19. $xy \leq -5$

20. $3x^2 + 6y^2 \geq 18$

21. $\frac{x^2}{36} - \frac{y^2}{45} \leq 1$

22. $9x^2 + 4y^2 > 36$

Solve each system of inequalities graphically. Check.

23. $y \geq -x + 3$
    $y < 3x - 4$

24. $5x - 2y < 4$ [13.3]
    $x \geq y$

25. $y - 3x < 5$
    $2x + 4y \geq 15$

26. $3x + 3y > 7$
    $5x - 2y \leq 10$

★27. $2x - y \leq 2$
    $x + y \geq 4$
    $-2x + 3y \leq 6$ [13.3]

28. $x^2 + y^2 \leq 25$
    $-x + 2y > 6$ [13.4]

29. $xy < 6$
    $y \geq x$

30. $\frac{x^2}{36} + \frac{y^2}{4} \geq 1$ [13.4]
    $-3x + 2y \leq 8$

31. $4x^2 - 25y^2 < 100$
    $x + 2y \leq 4$

★32. $4x^2 + 5y^2 \geq 60$
    $2x^2 - 3y^2 \leq 18$

Check student graphs for Ex. 13–32.
See TE Answer Section.

Chapter Thirteen Test

For complete solutions, see TE Answer Section.

Solve each system of equations graphically. Estimate the decimal solutions to the nearest tenth.

1. $\dfrac{x^2}{4} - \dfrac{y^2}{9} = 1$

   $-2x + 3y = 6$

   $(3.5, 4.3), (-2.0, 0.6)$

2. $x^2 + y^2 = 25$

   $-2y = 8 - 4x$

   $(3.7, 3.4), (-0.5, -5.0)$

3. $x^2 + y^2 = 16$

   $xy = 6$

   $(3.6, 1.7), (1.7, 3.6),$
   $(-3.6, -1.7), (-1.7, -3.6)$

4. $\dfrac{x^2}{25} + \dfrac{y^2}{36} = 1$

   $x^2 - y^2 = 9$

   below

Solve each system of equations algebraically. Give the irrational solutions in simplest radical form.

5. $x^2 - y^2 = 36$

   $y = 6 - x$ **(6, 0)**

6. $y = x^2 - 2x + 5$

   $4x - y = 4$ **(3, 8)**

7. $x^2 + y^2 = 16$

   $\dfrac{x^2}{16} + \dfrac{y^2}{4} = 1$

   $(4, 0), (-4, 0)$

8. $x^2 + 2y^2 = 24$

   $x^2 - y^2 = 3$

   $(\sqrt{10}, \sqrt{7}), (\sqrt{10}, -\sqrt{7}),$
   $(-\sqrt{10}, \sqrt{7}), (-\sqrt{10}, -\sqrt{7})$

Draw the graph of each of the following inequalities. Check.

9. $y \le 3x + 5$

10. $2x - 3y \ge 9$

11. $x > -1$

12. $x^2 - y^2 \ge 6$

13. $xy > 2$

14. $\dfrac{x^2}{36} + \dfrac{y^2}{4} \le 1$

Check student graphs for Ex. 9–14.

4. $(-4.3, -3.1), (4.3, 3.1), (4.3, -3.1), (-4.3, 3.1)$

Solve each system of inequalities graphically. Check.

15. $y < 2x - 1$

    $y \ge -3x + 2$

16. $3x - 4y \le -8$

    $y - x \le 2$

17. $2x - 5y \ge 10$

    $3x + 7y < 14$

18. $x^2 - y^2 \ge 4$

    $2x - 3y \le 6$

19. $\dfrac{x^2}{16} + \dfrac{y^2}{4} \le 1$

    $4x + 5y \ge 10$

20. $xy \le 4$

    $-y \le x$

Check student graphs for Ex. 15–20.

★ 21. Solve the system $(x - 2)^2 + (y + 1)^2 = 16$

   $y = x + 1$

   algebraically. $(2, 3)(-2, -1)$

Solve each system of inequalities graphically. Check.

★ 22. $3x + y \ge 4$

   $x - 2y \le 6$

   $-2x + 3y < 9$

★ 23. $5x^2 + 25y^2 \le 125$

   $3x^2 - 9y^2 \ge 27$

Check student graphs for Ex. 22–23.

Computer Activities

Landscape Design

Landscape architects design parks, recreation areas, school yards, and other city public areas. In designing a school yard, for example, a landscape architect has to plan which playing fields may overlap and which will require a border of free space.

A designer has to paint two circles on the blacktop of a fenced-in school yard. If the circles have a given radii, will they intersect at two points, one point, or no points? The following program determines in which configuration the circles will fit in the school yard.

PROGRAM

```
10 PRINT "PROGRAM TO FIND CIRCLE INTERSECTIONS"
20 PRINT "AND FIT IN GIVEN RECTANGLE"
30 PRINT "ENTER LENGTH AND WIDTH OF SCHOOL YARD"
40 INPUT L, W
50 PRINT "ENTER RADIUS OF CIRCLE 1 AND CIRCLE 2"
60 INPUT R1, R2
70 IF W < 2 * R1 THEN 180
80 IF W < 2 * R2 THEN 190
90 IF L = 2 * R1 + 2 * R2 THEN 140
100 IF L > 2 * R1 + 2 * R2 THEN 160
110 PRINT "CIRCLES WILL FIT IF THEY INTERSECT IN TWO PLACES"
120 PRINT "BUT THEY MAY COINCIDE"
130 GO TO 190
140 PRINT "CIRCLES WILL FIT IF THEY INTERSECT IN ONE POINT"
150 GO TO 190
160 PRINT "CIRCLES WILL FIT AND THEY WILL NOT INTERSECT"
170 GO TO 190
180 PRINT "CIRCLE IS TOO LARGE FOR WIDTH OF YARD"
190 END
```

Exercises

Enter and run the above program for the following radii and field measurements.

1. R1 = 6 m   R2 = 8 m   L = 15 m   W = 16 m
   INTERSECT IN TWO PLACES
2. R1 = 3 m   R2 = 5 m   L = 16 m   W = 10 m
   ONE INTERSECTION
3. R1 = 4.5 m   R2 = 3.25 m   L = 18 m   W = 9 m
   NO INTERSECTION

College Prep Test

DIRECTIONS: Choose the *one* best answer to each question or problem.

1. Find the area of the region described by $\frac{x^2}{2} + \frac{y^2}{2} \le 8$. **C**

   (A) 4π (B) 8π (C) 16π
   (D) 32π (E) None of these

2. The graph of $2(x + y) < y - 3$ does not pass through **A**

   (A) quadrant I   (B) quadrant II
   (C) quadrant III   (D) quadrant IV
   (E) None of these

3. Find the area of the region determined by the graph of the solutions of the system
   $x^2 + y^2 \ge 4$
   $x^2 + y^2 \le 25$. **B**

   (A) 4π (B) 21π (C) 25π
   (D) 29π (E) None of these

4. Find a solution of the system
   $3x + 2y < 12$
   $4x + y > 11$. **E**

   (A) $(2, 3)$ (B) $(3, 2)$ (C) $(2, 2)$
   (D) $(3, 3)$ (E) None of these

5. Find the area of the region determined by the graph of the solutions of the system
   $y \le x$
   $x \le 6$
   $y \ge 0$. **B**

   (A) 12   (B) 18   (C) 24
   (D) 30   (E) 36

6. Two distinct parallel lines may intersect another two distinct parallel lines in the same plane in exactly **D**

   (A) one point   (B) two points
   (C) three points   (D) four points
   (E) None of these

7. The system $x^2 + y^2 \ge a^2$
   $\qquad\qquad x^2 + y^2 \le b^2$
   has no solution if **A**

   (A) $a^2 > b^2$ (B) $a^2 < b^2$ (C) $a^2 = b^2$
   (D) All of these   (E) None of these

8. Which ordered pair (x, y) is a solution of the system
   $ax + by = 7ab$
   $3ax - 2by = 6ab$? **B**

   (A) $(3b, 4a)$ (B) $(4b, 3a)$
   (C) $(2b, 0)$ (D) All of these
   (E) None of these

9. Find the area of the triangle determined by the lines described by
   $\qquad x = -4$
   $\qquad y = \quad 0$
   $x + 3y = \quad 8$. **B**

   (A) 12   (B) 24   (C) 32
   (D) 48   (E) None of these

10. Circle I has a radius of 4 with center at $P(-3, 4)$. Circle II has a radius of 2 with center at $Q(2, 4)$. Circles I and II intersect in exactly **B**

    (A) one point   (B) two points
    (C) infinitely many points
    (D) no points   (E) None of these

14 PROGRESSIONS, SERIES, AND BINOMIAL EXPANSIONS

Blaise Pascal

Blaise Pascal was born at Clermont-Ferrand in Auvergne on June 19, 1623. Blaise showed phenomenal ability in mathematics at an early age. Even though his father, Etienne, was an able and noted mathematician, he wanted his son to study languages rather than mathematics. Therefore, he took away from Blaise all books on mathematics. Blaise secretly studied geometry on his own and he succeeded considerably before the endeavors were realized by his father.

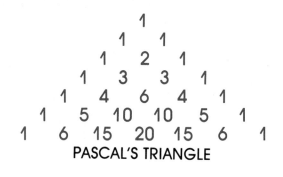

PASCAL'S TRIANGLE

Blaise Pascal is credited with many mathematical discoveries. At the age of nineteen, he invented a computing machine that served as a starting point in the development of the modern-day calculator. Blaise wrote extensively on the triangular arrangement of the coefficients of the powers of a binomial, $(a + b)^n$. (See page 382.) This arrangment is known today as Pascal's Triangle.

14.1 Arithmetic Progressions

OBJECTIVES ► **To write several consecutive terms of an arithmetic progression**
To find a specified term of a given arithmetic progression

$$12, 17, 22, 27, \ldots \qquad 2, -4, -10, -16, \ldots \qquad -2, -0.5, 1, 2.5$$

An ordered list of numbers formed according to some pattern is called a **progression** or a **sequence**. Three progressions are shown above. The numbers in each progression are called the **terms** of the progression.

In the first progression above, notice that the **common difference** between consecutive terms is 5.

$$17 - 12 = 5 \qquad 22 - 17 = 5 \qquad 27 - 22 = 5$$

A progression formed in this way is called an **arithmetic progression** (abbreviated as A.P.). Note: When "arithmetic" is used as an adjective as in "arithmetic progression," it is pronounced as air-ith-MEH-tik.

Definition:
Arithmetic
Progression

> An arithmetic progression is a progression in which the difference found by subtracting any term from the next term is constant.

In general, if $x_1, x_2, x_3, x_4, \ldots$ is an arithmetic progression (A.P.) with common difference d, then $d = x_2 - x_1 = x_3 - x_2 = x_4 - x_3 = \ldots$.

Example 1 **For each progression that is an A.P., find the common difference d. Give a reason for each answer.**

Progression	Answer	Reason
$5, 7, 10, 14, 19, \ldots$	Not an A.P.	$7 - 5 \neq 10 - 7$
$-6, -1, 4, 9, \ldots$	$d = 5$	$-1 - (-6) = 5; 4 - (-1) = 5;$ and so on
$2, -4, -10, -16, \ldots$	$d = -6$	$-4 - 2 = -6; -10 - (-4) = -6;$ and so on
$6, 12, 24, 48, \ldots$	Not an A.P.	$12 - 6 \neq 24 - 12$
$-2, -0.5, 1, 2.5, \ldots$	$d = 1.5$	$-0.5 - (-2) = 1.5; 1 - (-0.5) = 1.5;$ and so on
$3, 3 + 2\sqrt{5}, 3 + 4\sqrt{5}, \ldots$	$d = 2\sqrt{5}$	$(3 + 2\sqrt{5}) - 3 = 2\sqrt{5}; (3 + 4\sqrt{5}) - (3 + 2\sqrt{5}) = 2\sqrt{5};$ and so on

You can write several consecutive terms of an arithmetic progression by using the following procedure. First find the common difference d. Then add d to any term to get the next term.

Example 2 **Write the next three terms of the A.P.: 16, 4, −8, −20, ...**

$d = 4 - 16$, or -12. Add -12 to obtain consecutive terms.

Thus, the next three terms are $-32, -44,$ and -56.

Example 3 Write the first four terms of the A.P. whose first term a is 5 and common difference d is -3.

$$a = 5 \qquad 5 + (-3) = 2 \qquad 2 + (-3) = -1 \qquad -1 + (-3) = -4$$

Thus, the first four terms are 5, 2, -1, and -4.

The arithmetic progression 12, 17, 22, 27, . . . with common difference 5 can be written in a way that will help you find a specified term, such as the 81st term, of the progression.

12	17	22	27	. . .	412
↓	↓	↓	↓		↑
$12 + 0 \cdot 5$	$12 + 1 \cdot 5$	$12 + 2 \cdot 5$	$12 + 3 \cdot 5$	. . .	$12 + 80 \cdot 5$
1st	2nd	3rd	4th	. . .	81st

Notice that the 3rd term is $12 + (3 - 1) \cdot 5$ and that the 4th term is $12 + (4 - 1) \cdot 5$. Thus, the 81st term is $12 + (81 - 1) \cdot 5$, or $12 + 80 \cdot 5$. This leads to the following formula for the nth term of an arithmetic progression.

nth Term of an Arithmetic Progression

> The nth term of an arithmetic progression is given by the formula
> $$l = a + (n - 1)d, \qquad n \geq 1,$$
> where l is the nth term, a is the first term, and d is the common difference.

You can use this formula to find a specified term of an arithmetic progression (A.P.).

Example 4 Find the specified term of each A.P.

26th term of 8, 5.4, 2.8, 0.2, . . .   31st term of $3 - \sqrt{2}$, 1, $-1 + \sqrt{2}$, . . .

$d = 5.4 - 8 = -2.6$ $d = 1 - (3 - \sqrt{2}) = -2 + \sqrt{2}$
$a = 8$ $a = 3 - \sqrt{2}$
$n = 26$ $n = 31$
$l = a + (n - 1)d$ $l = a + (n - 1)d$
$\quad = 8 + (26 - 1)(-2.6)$ $\quad = (3 - \sqrt{2}) + (31 - 1)(-2 + \sqrt{2})$
$\quad = 8 + 25(-2.6)$ $\quad = (3 - \sqrt{2}) + 30(-2 + \sqrt{2})$
$\quad = 8 - 65$ $\quad = 3 - \sqrt{2} - 60 + 30\sqrt{2}$
$\quad = -57$ $\quad = -57 + 29\sqrt{2}$

Thus, the 26th term is -57.   **Thus,** the 31st term is $-57 + 29\sqrt{2}$.

Reading in Algebra

Match each arithmetic progression at the left with exactly one statement at the right.

1. 7, 5, 3, 1, . . . **B**
2. 4, 11, 18, 25, . . . **A**
3. 5, 6, 7, 8, . . . **E**
4. −1, 1, 3, 5, . . . **C**
5. 2, 4, 6, 8, . . . **D**

A 7 is the common difference of the A.P.
B 7 is the first term of the A.P.
C 7 is the next term of the A.P.
D 7 is the counting number corresponding to the term 14 of the A.P.
E 7 is the third term of the A.P.

Oral Exercises

For each progression that is an A.P., find the common difference d. **6. Not an A.P.**

1. 23, 35, 47, 59, . . . **12**
2. 36, 23, 10, −3, . . . **−13**
3. −10, −8, −6, −4, . . . **2**
4. 2, 4, 8, 16, . . . **Not an A.P.**
5. 4, 6.6, 9.2, 11.8, . . . **2.6**
6. 9.7, 7.4, 6.7, 5, . . .
7. 16, $15\frac{1}{3}$, $14\frac{2}{3}$, 14, . . . **$-\frac{2}{3}$**
8. $7\frac{1}{8}$, $8\frac{3}{4}$, $10\frac{3}{8}$, 12, . . . **$1\frac{5}{8}$**
9. −2, 4, −6, 8, . . . **Not an A.P.**

Written Exercises

4. 18, 25, 32, 39   5. 9, 3, −3, −9   6. −7, −10, −13, −16

19. Not an A.P.   20. Not an A.P.   21. $5\sqrt{2}, 6\sqrt{2}, 7\sqrt{2}$

Write the next three terms of each arithmetic progression.

Ⓐ 1. 22, 23.2, 24.4, 25.6, . . .
   26.8, 28, 29.2
2. 7, $6\frac{3}{4}$, $6\frac{1}{2}$, $6\frac{1}{4}$, . . . 6, $5\frac{3}{4}$, $5\frac{1}{2}$
3. $\frac{1}{4}$, $\frac{1}{3}$, $\frac{5}{12}$, $\frac{1}{2}$, . . . $\frac{7}{12}$, $\frac{2}{3}$, $\frac{3}{4}$

Write the first four terms of each A.P. whose first term and common difference are given.

4. $a = 18$ and $d = 7$
5. $a = 9$ and $d = -6$
6. $a = -7$ and $d = -3$
7. $a = \$5.00$ and $d = \$2.40$
8. $a = -6°C$ and $d = 4°C$
9. $a = 15$ kg and $d = -3.4$ kg

$5.00, $7.40, $9.80, $12.20   **−6°C, −2°C, 2°C, 6°C**   **15 kg, 11.6 kg, 8.2 kg, 4.8 kg**

Find the specified term of each arithmetic progression.

10. 21st term of 11, 15, 19, 23, . . . **91**
11. 36th term of 10, 4, −2, −8, . . . **−200**
12. 31st term of 8.6, 8.3, 8, 7.7, . . . **−0.4**
13. 46th term of −9, −7.6, −6.2, −4.8, . . . **54**
14. 81st term of 7, $7\frac{1}{2}$, 8, $8\frac{1}{2}$, . . . **47**
15. 26th term of $12\frac{4}{5}$, $11\frac{2}{5}$, 10, $8\frac{3}{5}$, . . . **$-22\frac{1}{5}$**

16. $3 + 3\sqrt{2}, 3 + 4\sqrt{2}, 3 + 5\sqrt{2}$ 17. $-1 + 3\sqrt{3}, -3 + 4\sqrt{3}, -5 + 5\sqrt{3}$ 18. $7 - 2i, 9 - 3i, 11 - 4i$

Ⓑ **For each progression that is an A.P., write the next three terms.**

16. 3, $3 + \sqrt{2}$, $3 + 2\sqrt{2}$, . . .
17. 5, $3 + \sqrt{3}$, $1 + 2\sqrt{3}$ . . .
18. $1 + i$, 3, $5 - i$ . . .
19. −2, $4 - \sqrt{2}$, $8 - \sqrt{2}$, . . .
20. $\sqrt{15}$, $\sqrt{17}$, $\sqrt{19}$, $\sqrt{21}$, . . .
21. $\sqrt{2}$, $\sqrt{8}$, $\sqrt{18}$, $\sqrt{32}$, . . .
22. $5x + 2$, $7x$, $9x - 2$, . . .
23. $8x - y$, $5x + 2y$, $2x + 5y$, . .
24. $x^2 + 1$, $x^3 + 1$, $x^4 + 1$, . . .

$11x - 4, 13x - 6, 15x - 8$ **$-x + 8y, -4x + 11y, -7x + 14y$**   **Not an A.P.**

Write the first four terms of each A.P. whose first term and common difference are given.

25. $a = -3$ and $d = 3 + \sqrt{6}$
26. $a = 4 + \sqrt{5}$ and $d = -2 + 3\sqrt{5}$
27. $a = x^2 - y$ and $d = x^2 + y$
   $4 + \sqrt{5}, 2 + 4\sqrt{5}, 7\sqrt{5}, -2 + 10\sqrt{5}$
25. **$-3, \sqrt{6}, 3 + 2\sqrt{6}, 6 + 3\sqrt{6}$**   27. **$x^2 - y, 2x^2, 3x^2 + y, 4x^2 + 2y$**

Find the 21st term of each arithmetic progression in Exercises 28–31.

28. 4, $4 + 2\sqrt{3}$, $4 + 4\sqrt{3}$, . . . **$4 + 40\sqrt{3}$**
29. $5 - \sqrt{2}$, $6 - 2\sqrt{2}$, $7 - 3\sqrt{2}$, . . . **$25 - 21\sqrt{2}$**
30. $4 + 3i$, 5, $6 - 3i$, . . . **$24 - 57i$**
31. $3x + 2y + 1$, $2x + 3y$, $x + 4y - 1$, . . .
   $-17x + 22y - 19$

ARITHMETIC PROGRESSIONS

32. Some boxes are stacked so that there are 3 in the top row, 5 in the second row, 7 in the third row, and so on. How many boxes are in the fifteenth row? **31**

33. A mechanic's starting salary is $12,500. He is guaranteed a minimum annual increase of $600. What minimum salary may he expect in his twelfth year? **$19,100**

34. Mrs. Prince deposited $200 in a bank on January 15. Then, each month she deposited $35 more than she had deposited the preceding month. What was her deposit on December 15? **$585**

35. A parachutist in free fall travels 5 m in the first second, 15 m during the second, 25 m during the third second. How far would the chutist travel in free fall during the eighth second? **75 m**

Example   If 76 is the *n*th term of −4, −2, 0, 2, . . ., find the value of *n*.

−4, −2, 0, 2, . . ., 76, . . .

$\leftarrow$ *n*th term

$l = a + (n - 1)d$
$76 = -4 + (n - 1) \cdot 2$ ◄ $d = -2 - (-4) = 2$
$80 = (n - 1) \cdot 2$
$40 = n - 1$ $n = 41$

Thus, 76 is the 41st term of the A.P.

Find the value of *n* in each exercise.

39. 21   41. 26

36. 62 is the *n*th term of −4, −1, 2, 5, ... **23**

37. 129 is the *n*th term of 5, 9, 13, 17, ... **32**

38. −54 is the *n*th term of 11, 6, 1, −4, ... **14**

39. −106 is the *n*th term of −26, −30, −34, ...

40. 7 is the *n*th term of 1, 1.2, 1.4, 1.6, ... **31**

41. 8 is the *n*th term of −2, −1.6, −1.2, −0.8, ...

Ⓒ **42.** Find the value of *y* so that $y + 3$, $4y + 1$, $8y - 3$ is an A.P. [HINT: $d = x_2 - x_1 = x_3 - x_2$ if x_1, x_2, x_3 is an A.P.] **y = 2**

43. Find two values of *c* such that $\frac{1}{c}$, 1, $\frac{10}{c + 3}$ is an A.P.   **c = 3 or c = −½**

44. Find the first term of the A.P. whose 16th term is 110 and common difference is 7. **5**

45. Find the 1st term of the A.P. whose 41st term is −124 and common difference is −3. **−4**

46. Find the first three terms of the A.P. whose 9th term is 26 and 20th term is 59.   **2, 5, 8**

47. Find the first three terms of the A.P. whose 48th term is −189 and 26th term is −79.   **46, 41, 36**

48. Prove that the progression formed by every odd-numbered term of an A.P. is also an A.P.

49. Prove: The progression formed by reversing the order in a finite A.P. is also an A.P.

For Ex. 48–49, see TE Answer Section.

CALCULATOR ACTIVITIES

Find the 93rd term of the A.P. where *a* = 62.34 and *d* = −1.25.

$l = a + (n - 1)d = 62.34 + (93 - 1)(-1.25) = \ominus 1.25 \otimes 92 \oplus 62.34 \ominus -52.66$

Find the *n*th term of each A.P. for the given values of *n*, *a*, and *d*.

1. $n = 119$, $a = -73$, $d = 6.75$ **723.5**

2. $n = 43$, $a = 72.58$, $d = -2.5$ **−32.42**

3. $n = 2,000$, $a = -8.6$, $d = -5.4$ **−10,803.2**

14.2 The Arithmetic Mean

OBJECTIVES ▶ **To find arithmetic means between two given terms of an arithmetic progression**
To find the arithmetic mean of two numbers

The terms between two given terms of an arithmetic progression are called **arithmetic means** between the given terms. For example, three arithmetic means between 2 and 18 in the progression below are 6, 10, and 14 since 2, 6, 10, 14, 18, . . . is an arithmetic progression.

$$2, \underline{6}, \underline{10}, \underline{14}, 18, . . .$$

As shown in the examples below, you can find any specified number of arithmetic means between two given numbers.

Example 1 Find the four arithmetic means between 24 and 20.

$$24, \underline{\quad}, \underline{\quad}, \underline{\quad}, \underline{\quad}, 20$$

When the four arithmetic means are found, an A.P. with six terms will be formed.

$$n = 6 \qquad a = 24 \qquad l = 20$$

Use $l = a + (n - 1)d$ to find d.

$$20 = 24 + (6 - 1)d \quad \blacktriangleleft \textit{Substitute for l, a, and n.}$$
$$-4 = 5d$$
$$-0.8 = d$$

Add -0.8 to each term.

$$24, \underline{23.2}, \underline{22.4}, \underline{21.6}, \underline{20.8}, 20$$

Thus, the four arithmetic means are 23.2, 22.4, 21.6, and 20.8.

Example 2 Find the one arithmetic mean between 5 and 17.

$$5, \underline{\quad}, 17$$

$$l = a + (n - 1)d$$
$$17 = 5 + (3 - 1)d \quad \blacktriangleleft \textit{Substitute 17 for l, 5 for a, and 3 for n.}$$
$$12 = 2d$$
$$6 = d$$

$$5, \underline{11}, 17$$

Thus, the one arithmetic mean is 11.

In Example 2, notice that the one arithmetic mean is the "average" of 5 and 17, since $(5 + 17) \div 2 = 11$. In this case, 11 is called **the arithmetic mean** of 5 and 17.

The *arithmetic mean* of the real numbers x and y is $\dfrac{x + y}{2}$.

In Exercise 32, you will prove that the statement above is true.

Example 3

The arithmetic mean of two numbers is 12. If the greater number is decreased by 5 times the smaller number, the result is 6. Find the two numbers.

*Represent
the data.*

Let x = the smaller number and y = the greater number.

*Write a system
of equations.*

(1) $\dfrac{x + y}{2} = 12 \rightarrow x + y = 24$ (2) $y - 5x = 6 \rightarrow y = 5x + 6$

*Solve the
system.*

$$x + (5x + 6) = 24$$
$$6x = 18$$
$$x = 3$$

$$y - 5x = 6$$
$$y - 5 \cdot 3 = 6$$
$$y = 21$$

Check.

Arithmetic mean	12
$\dfrac{3 + 21}{2}$	12
$\dfrac{24}{2}$, or 12	

$y - 5x$	6
$21 - 5 \cdot 3$	6
$21 - 15$	
6	

*Answer the
question.*

▶ **Thus,** the two numbers are 3 and 21.

Oral Exercises

For each progression that is an A.P., state the arithmetic means between the first term
and the last term.

1. 10, 7, 4 **7**
2. 1, 2, 4, 8 **not an A.P.**
3. 4, 1, −2, −5 **1, −2**
4. −4, −2, 2, 4 **Not an A. P.**
5. −7, −4, −1, 2, 5 **−4, −1, 2**
6. 3, 5, 7, 9, 11, 13 **5, 7, 9, 11**

Written Exercises

Find the indicated number of arithmetic means between each pair of numbers.

(A)
1. Two, between 12 and 33 **19, 26**
2. Three, between 30 and 2 **23, 16, 9**
3. Four, between −2 and 18 **2, 6, 10, 14**
4. Five, between 22 and −8 **17, 12, 7, 2, −3**
5. Three, between 6 and 8 **$6\frac{1}{2}$, 7, $7\frac{1}{2}$**
6. Four, between 15 and 7 **$13\frac{2}{5}$, $11\frac{4}{5}$, $10\frac{1}{5}$, $8\frac{3}{5}$**
7. Two, between 3.4 and 10.3 **5.7, 8**
8. Five, between 10.6 and −8.6 **7.4, 4.2, 1, −2.2, −5.4**

Find the arithmetic mean of each pair of numbers.

9. 26 and 72 **49**
10. 40 and −12 **14**
11. 2.1 and 3.5 **2.8**
12. 12.8 and 4.2 **8.5**

Solve each problem.

13. The arithmetic mean of two numbers is 15. Two less than the larger number is 3 times the smaller number. Find the two numbers.

7, 23

14. The arithmetic mean of two numbers is 25. One of the numbers increased by twice the other number is 79. Find the two numbers.

21, 29

(B) 15. A teacher's annual salary for ten consecutive years was in arithmetic progression from $12,200 to $19,400. Find the salary for each of the ten years. **$12,200, $13,000, $13,800, $14,600, $15,400, $16,200, $17,000, $17,800, $18,600, $19,400**

16. Eight different weights are used in a science laboratory to balance small masses. The weights are in arithmetic progression. Find each weight if the heaviest is 22 g and the lightest is 1 g. **1 g, 4 g, 7 g, 10 g, 13 g, 16 g, 19 g, 22 g**

17. If the arithmetic mean of two numbers is increased by one-fourth of the greater number, the sum is four times the smaller number. Find the two numbers if five times the smaller number is three more than the greater number. **42, 9**

18. The reciprocal of the arithmetic mean of two numbers is $\frac{4}{21}$ and the difference of the two numbers is the reciprocal of $\frac{2}{5}$. Find the two numbers.

18. $4, 6\frac{1}{2}$ 19. $7\sqrt{7}, 11\sqrt{7}$ 20. $7 + \sqrt{5}, 10 + 2\sqrt{5}, 13 + 3\sqrt{5}$ 21. $-2 - 2i, -4 + i, -6 + 4i, -8 + 7i$

Find the indicated number of arithmetic means between each pair of terms.

19. Two, between $3\sqrt{7}$ and $15\sqrt{7}$

20. Three, between 4 and $16 + 4\sqrt{5}$

21. Four, between $-5i$ and $-10 + 10i$

22. Two, between $1 + \sqrt{3}$ and $7 - 5\sqrt{3}$

23. Three, between $-8a + 9b$ and $4a - 3b$

24. Four, between $10x$ and $15y$.

22. $3 - \sqrt{3}, 5 - 3\sqrt{3}$ 23. $-5a + 6b, -2a + 3b, a$ 24. $8x + 3y, 6x + 6y, 4x + 9y, 2x + 12y$

For Exercises 25–30, find the arithmetic mean of each pair of terms.

25. $-6x$ and $14x$ **4x**

26. $15x - 3y + 2z$ and $9x + 15y - 18z$ **12x + 6y − 8z**

27. $3 + \sqrt{2}$ and $7 - 7\sqrt{2}$ **5 − 3√2**

28. $9\sqrt{21} - 5\sqrt{10}$ and $9\sqrt{21} + 5\sqrt{10}$ **9√21**

(C) 29. The complex number $a + bi$ and its conjugate **a**

30. $(x + y)^2$ and $(x - y)^2$ **x² + y²**

31. Find the two arithmetic means between x and y. Write each mean as a rational expression. $\frac{2x + y}{3}, \frac{x + 2y}{3}$

32. Prove: The arithmetic mean of x and y is $\frac{x + y}{2}$. $\left[\begin{array}{l}\text{Hint: Use the formula}\\ l = a + (n - 1)d.\end{array}\right]$

33. Prove: The arithmetic mean of any two consecutive odd integers is an even integer. [Hint: If x is an integer, then $2x - 1$ is an odd integer and $2x$ is an even integer.] **For Ex. 32–33, see TE Answer Section.**

Cumulative Review

1. Solve the formula $T = \frac{n}{2}(x + y)$ for y. Then find the value of y if $T = 750$, $n = 25$, and $x = 20$. $y = \frac{2T - nx}{n}$; **40**

2. Solve the formula $2T + nd = 2an + n^2d$ for d. Then find the value of d if $T = 210$, $n = 10$, and $a = 3$. $d = \frac{2(T - an)}{n(n - 1)}$; **4**

THE ARITHMETIC MEAN

14.3 Arithmetic Series and Σ-Notation

OBJECTIVES ▶ **To find the sum of the first *n* terms of an arithmetic series**
To write an arithmetic series using Σ-notation

If you take the arithmetic progression 10, 6, 2, −2, −6, . . . and write it as the indicated sum 10 + 6 + 2 − 2 − 6 − . . . , the result is an **arithmetic series**.

Definition:
Arithmetic
Series

> An *arithmetic series* is an indicated sum of the terms of an arithmetic progression.

Example 1 **Write each A.P. as an arithmetic series. Find the common difference *d* of the series.**

$$-7, 2, 11, 20, \ldots \qquad\qquad 8, 3, -2, -7, \ldots$$

The arithmetic series is
$-7 + 2 + 11 + 20 + \ldots.$
$d = 2 - (-7)$, or 9

The arithmetic series is
$8 + 3 - 2 - 7 - \ldots.$
$d = 3 - 8$, or -5

You can find the sum *S* of the first 20 terms of the arithmetic series $3 + 6 + 9 + 12 + \ldots$ as follows: Write the series in its given order and also in reverse order. Then add the two series.

$$
\begin{array}{rcl}
S = & 3 + 6 + 9 + \ldots + 54 + 57 + 60 \\
S = & 60 + 57 + 54 + \ldots + 9 + 6 + 3 \\
\hline
2S = & 63 + 63 + 63 + \ldots + 63 + 63 + 63
\end{array}
$$

$$2S = 20 \cdot 63$$
$$S = 630$$

The steps above suggest a method for obtaining a formula for the sum *S* of the first *n* terms of an arithmetic series. Let *l* represent the *n*th term.

$$
\begin{array}{rcl}
S = & a + (a + d) + (a + 2d) + \ldots + (l - 2d) + (l - d) + l \\
S = & l + (l - d) + (l - 2d) + \ldots + (a + 2d) + (a + d) + a \\
\hline
2S = & (a + l) + (a + l) + (a + l) + \ldots + (a + l) + (a + l) + (a + l)
\end{array}
$$

n binomials
$$2S = n(a + l)$$
$$S = \frac{n}{2}(a + l)$$

Sum of
n Terms of
Arithmetic
Series

> The sum *S* of the first *n* terms of an arithmetic series is given by the formula
> $$S = \frac{n}{2}(a + l),$$
> where *a* is the first term and *l* is the *n*th term.

Example 2 Find the sum of the arithmetic series in which the number of terms $n = 35$, the first term $a = 12$, and the last term $l = 114$.

$$S = \frac{n}{2}(a + l) = \frac{35}{2}(12 + 114)$$
$$= \frac{35}{2} \cdot 126$$
$$= 35 \cdot 63, \text{ or } 2{,}205$$

Thus, the sum of the arithmetic series is 2,205.

You can find the sum of the first 34 terms of the arithmetic series $24.5 + 21.5 + 18.5 + 15.5 + \ldots$ without finding the 34th term, or l. To do this, another sum formula is used. It is obtained by substitution, as shown below:

$$S = \frac{n}{2}[a + l] \text{ and } l = a + (n - 1)d$$

$$S = \frac{n}{2}[a + \underbrace{a + (n - 1)d}_{l}], \text{ or } S = \frac{n}{2}[2a + (n - 1)d]$$

Use this second sum formula when l, the last term, is not known but a, the first term, and d, the common difference, are easily determined for a given arithmetic series.

Example 3 Find the sum of the first 34 terms of the arithmetic series:
$24.5 + 21.5 + 18.5 + 15.5 + \ldots.$

$$n = 34 \qquad a = 24.5 \qquad d = -3$$
$$S = \frac{n}{2}[2a + (n - 1)d] = \frac{34}{2}[2(24.5) + 33(-3)]$$
$$= 17[49 - 99], \text{ or } -850$$

Thus, the sum of the first 34 terms is -850.

The indicated sum, $4 + 8 + 12 + 16 + 20$, can be written in a more compact form as $\sum\limits_{k=1}^{5} 4k$. The Greek letter Σ (read: sigma) is used as a **summation sign** and k is called the **index of summation**.

$$\underbrace{\sum_{k=1}^{5} 4k = \underbrace{4 \cdot 1 + 4 \cdot 2 + 4 \cdot 3 + 4 \cdot 4 + 4 \cdot 5}_{\text{Expanded Form}} = \underbrace{4 + 8 + 12 + 16 + 20}_{\text{Series Form}} = \underbrace{60}_{\text{Sum}}}$$

$\sum\limits_{k=1}^{5} 4k$ is read "the summation from 1 to 5 of $4k$." Notice that the five terms of the series are found by substituting 1, 2, 3, 4, and 5 for k in the general term, $4k$.

Example 4 Write the expanded form and the series form of $\displaystyle\sum_{j=3}^{6} (5j - 22)$. Find the sum of the series.

Substitute 3, 4, 5, and 6 for j in $(5j - 22)$.

$$\sum_{j=3}^{6} (5j - 22) = (5 \cdot 3 - 22) + (5 \cdot 4 - 22) + (5 \cdot 5 - 22) + (5 \cdot 6 - 22) \quad \blacktriangleleft \textit{Expanded form}$$

$$= -7 - 2 + 3 + 8 \quad \blacktriangleleft \textit{Series form}$$
$$= 2 \quad \blacktriangleleft \textit{Sum of the series}$$

Example 5 Write the expanded form and the series form of $\displaystyle\sum_{c=1}^{35} (90 - 2c)$. Find the sum of the series.

$$\sum_{c=1}^{35} (90 - 2c) = (90 - 2 \cdot 1) + (90 - 2 \cdot 2) + (90 - 2 \cdot 3) + \ldots + (90 - 2 \cdot 35) \quad \blacktriangleleft \textit{Expanded form}$$
$$= 88 + 86 + 84 + \ldots + 20 \quad \blacktriangleleft \textit{Series form}$$
$$= \frac{35}{2} (88 + 20) \quad \blacktriangleleft \textit{Use } S = \frac{n}{2} (a + l) \textit{ to find the sum.}$$
$$= 1{,}890 \quad \blacktriangleleft \textit{Sum of the series}$$

You can reverse the procedure above and write certain arithmetic series using Σ-notation. For example,

$$-2 - 4 - 6 - 8 - \ldots - 40 = -2 \cdot 1 - 2 \cdot 2 - 2 \cdot 3 - 2 \cdot 4 - \ldots - 2 \cdot 20 = \sum_{n=1}^{20} -2n$$

Notice that the common difference d is -2 and that n goes from 1 to 20.

Example 6 Write $10 + 13 + 16 + 19 + \ldots + 52$ using Σ-notation.

The series is arithmetic and the common difference is 3.
Write each term in the form $3k + t$ where

$$k = 1, 2, 3, 4, \ldots \qquad \text{and } t \text{ is a real number.}$$

Notice that the first term is 10 and that $10 = 3 \cdot 1 + 7$. So, $t = 7$.

$$\begin{array}{ccccccccc}
10 & + & 13 & + & 16 & + & 19 & + \ldots + & 52 \\
\downarrow & & \downarrow & & \downarrow & & \downarrow & & \downarrow \\
(3 \cdot 1 + 7) & + & (3 \cdot 2 + 7) & + & (3 \cdot 3 + 7) & + & (3 \cdot 4 + 7) & + \ldots + & (3 \cdot 15 + 7)
\end{array}$$

$$\sum_{k=1}^{15} (3k + 7)$$

Oral Exercises

State each A.P. as an arithmetic series.

1. $5, 9, 13, 17, \ldots$
$5 + 9 + 13 + 17 + \ldots$

2. $5, 1, -3, -7, \ldots$
$5 + 1 - 3 - 7 - \ldots$

3. $-2, -3, -4, -5, \ldots$
$-2 - 3 - 4 - 5 - \ldots$

4. $5 + 10 + 15 + \ldots + 50$　　　**5.** $-8 - 9 - 10 - 11 - 12$　　　**6.** $3 + 4 + 5 + 6 + 7 + 8$

Read each summation aloud. State the series form.　**7.** $12 + 11 + 10$　**8.** $\frac{1}{5} + \frac{2}{5} + \frac{3}{5} + \frac{4}{5}$

4. $\displaystyle\sum_{k=1}^{10} 5k$　　　**5.** $\displaystyle\sum_{j=8}^{12} -j$　　　**6.** $\displaystyle\sum_{c=1}^{6} (c + 2)$　　　**7.** $\displaystyle\sum_{n=5}^{7} (17 - n)$　　　**8.** $\displaystyle\sum_{p=1}^{4} \frac{p}{5}$

Find the common difference d of each arithmetic series.

9. $12 + 15 + 18 + 21 + \ldots$　　**10.** $3 + 1 - 1 - 3 - \ldots$　$d = -2$　**11.** $1 + 1.4 + 1.8 + 2.2 + \ldots$

$d = 3$

12. $\displaystyle\sum_{j=1}^{4} 5j$　$d = 5$　　**13.** $\displaystyle\sum_{k=1}^{3} (k + 2)$　$d = 1$　　**14.** $\displaystyle\sum_{c=1}^{3} -2c$　$d = -2$　　$d = 0.4$

21. $\displaystyle\sum_{k=4}^{8} 2k$　**22.** $\displaystyle\sum_{k=1}^{9} (4k + 11)$　**23.** $\displaystyle\sum_{k=1}^{12} (14 - 5k)$　**24.** $\displaystyle\sum_{j=1}^{13} (-4 - 3j)$

Written Exercises

Find the sum of each arithmetic series for the given data.

Ⓐ　**1.** $n = 20, a = 1, l = 154$　**1,550**　　　　　　　**2.** $n = 40, a = 2, l = -115$　**−2,260**

3. $n = 25, a = 16, l = 184$　**2,500**　　　　　　　**4.** $n = 45, a = 3, l = -50$　**−1,057$\frac{1}{2}$**

5. $n = 35, a = -5.2, l = 60$　**959**　　　　　　　**6.** $n = 30, a = -7, l = -60.2$　**−1,008**

7. $n = 30; 5 + 15 + 25 + 35 + \ldots$　**4,500**　　　**8.** $n = 40; 6 + 2 - 2 - 6 - \ldots$　**−2,880**

9. $n = 65; 7 + 7.2 + 7.4 + 7.6 + \ldots$　**871**　　**10.** $n = 45; -2 - 0.9 + 0.2 + 1.3 + \ldots$　**999**

11. $\displaystyle\sum_{k=1}^{6} 3k$　**63**　　　　**12.** $\displaystyle\sum_{j=1}^{5} -j$　**−15**　　　　**13.** $\displaystyle\sum_{c=1}^{50} (c + 1)$　**1,325**

14. $\displaystyle\sum_{j=5}^{8} (3j - 4)$　**62**　　　**15.** $\displaystyle\sum_{m=40}^{43} (8 - m)$　**−134**　　　**16.** $\displaystyle\sum_{k=1}^{25} (15 - 3k)$　**−600**

Write each arithmetic series using Σ-notation.

17. $6 + 12 + 18 + 24$　　　　　**18.** $-8 - 16 - 24 - 32 - \ldots - 80$　　**18.** $\displaystyle\sum_{j=1}^{10} -8j$

19. $7 + 8 + 9 + 10 + \ldots + 26$　　　**17.** $\displaystyle\sum_{k=1}^{4} 6k$　　**20.** $12 + 11 + 10 + 9 + \ldots - 5$

Ⓑ　**21.** $8 + 10 + 12 + 14 + 16$　　　**19.** $\displaystyle\sum_{k=7}^{26} k$　　　**22.** $15 + 19 + 23 + 27 + \ldots + 47$　**20.** $\displaystyle\sum_{j=1}^{18} (13 - j)$

23. $9 + 4 - 1 - 6 - \ldots - 46$　　　　　**24.** $-7 - 10 - 13 - 16 - \ldots - 43$

Find the sum of each arithmetic series for the given data.　**26.** $8(-44x + 20y) = -352x + 160y$

25. $n = 41, a = 2\sqrt{3}, l = 198\sqrt{3}$　**4,100$\sqrt{3}$**　　**26.** $n = 16, a = 3x - 10y, l = -47x + 30y$

27. $n = 26; 0.3 + 0.8 + 1.3 + 1.8 + \ldots$　**170.3**　　**28.** $n = 37; -1.3 - 0.1 + 1.1 + 2.3 + \ldots$　**751.1**

29. $\displaystyle\sum_{n=1}^{100} \frac{n}{4}$　**1,262.5**　　　　　**30.** $\displaystyle\sum_{n=1}^{30} \frac{n + 4}{3}$　**195**

31. Cartons are stacked in 20 rows with 2 in the top row, 5 in the 2nd row, 8 in the 3rd row, and so on. How many cartons are stacked? **610 cartons**

32. Gerry saved 1 dime the 1st day, 2 dimes the 2nd day, 3 on the 3rd day, and so on. How much money did she save in 30 days?　**$46.50**

Ⓒ　**33.** Prove: $\displaystyle\sum_{k=1}^{50} 10kx = 10x \cdot \sum_{k=1}^{50} k$.　　　**34.** Prove: $\displaystyle\sum_{j=1}^{20} (jx + jy) = \sum_{j=1}^{20} jx + \sum_{j=1}^{20} jy$.

35. Prove: $\displaystyle\sum_{c=1}^{30} (c + t) = 30t + \sum_{c=1}^{30} c$.　　　**36.** Solve $\displaystyle\sum_{k=4}^{7} (kx - 3) = 32$ for x.

37. Prove: $\displaystyle\sum_{n=1}^{k} (2n - 1) = k^2$. What does this say about adding odd integers?

38. Prove: $\displaystyle\sum_{n=1}^{k} 2n = k(k + 1)$. What does this say about adding even integers?

For Ex. 33–38, see TE Answer Section.

14.4 Geometric Progressions

OBJECTIVES ▶ **To write several consecutive terms of a geometric progression**
To find a specified term of a given geometric progression

Another type of progression (or sequence) is one such as

$$5, 10, 20, 40, \ldots$$

in which each consecutive term is found by multiplying the preceding term by a given number. Notice that in the progression 5, 10, 20, 40, . . . , the **common ratio** of consecutive terms is 2.

$$\frac{10}{5} = 2 \qquad \frac{20}{10} = 2 \qquad \frac{40}{20} = 2$$

A progression formed in this way is called a **geometric progression** (abbreviated as G.P.). Note: Pronounce "geometric" as gee-oh-MEH-trik.

Definition:
Geometric
Progression

> A *geometric progression* is a progression in which the ratio found by dividing any term by the preceding term is constant.

In general, if $x_1, x_2, x_3, x_4, \ldots$ is a geometric progression (G.P.) with common ratio $r \neq 0$, then $r = \dfrac{x_2}{x_1} = \dfrac{x_3}{x_2} = \dfrac{x_4}{x_3} = \ldots$.

Example 1

For each progression that is a G.P., find the common ratio r. Give a reason for each answer.

Progression	Answer	Reason
3, 6, 9, 12, . . .	Not a G.P.	$6 \div 3 \neq 9 \div 6$
$-2, -8, -32, -128, \ldots$	$r = 4$	$\dfrac{-8}{-2} = 4; \dfrac{-32}{-8} = 4$; and so on
$64, -16, 4, -1, \ldots$	$r = -\dfrac{1}{4}$	$\dfrac{-16}{64} = -\dfrac{1}{4}; \dfrac{4}{-16} = -\dfrac{1}{4}$; and so on
6, 0, 0, 0, . . .	Not a G.P.	$0 \div 6 \neq 0 \div 0$ ($0 \div 0$ is undefined)
7, 0.7, 0.07, 0.007, . . .	$r = 0.1$	$0.7 \div 7 = 0.1; 0.07 \div 0.7 = 0.1$; and so on
$5, 5\sqrt{2}, 10, 10\sqrt{2}, \ldots$	$r = \sqrt{2}$	$\dfrac{5\sqrt{2}}{5} = \sqrt{2}; \dfrac{10}{5\sqrt{2}} = \sqrt{2}$; and so on

You can write several consecutive terms of a G.P. as shown below.

Example 2

Write the next three terms of the G.P.: 128, -64, 32, -16, ...

$r = \dfrac{-64}{128}$, or $-\dfrac{1}{2}$. Multiply by $-\dfrac{1}{2}$ to obtain consecutive terms.

Thus, the next three terms are 8, -4, and 2.

Example 3 Write the first four terms of the G.P. whose first term a is 2 and common ratio r is -5.

$$a = -2 \qquad -2(-5) = 10 \qquad 10(-5) = -50 \qquad -50(-5) = 250$$

Thus, the first four terms are -2, 10, -50, and 250.

The geometric progression 5, 10, 20, 40, 80, . . . with common ratio 2 can be written in a way that will help you find a specified term, such as the 11th term, of the progression.

5	10	20	40	80	. . . 5,120
↓	↓	↓	↓	↓	↑
5	$5 \cdot 2^1$	$5 \cdot 2^2$	$5 \cdot 2^3$	$5 \cdot 2^4$	. . . $5 \cdot 2^{10}$
1st	2nd	3rd	4th	5th	. . . 11th

Notice that the 4th term is $5 \cdot 2^{4-1}$, or $5 \cdot 2^3$, and that the 5th term is $5 \cdot 2^{5-1}$, or $5 \cdot 2^4$. Thus, the 11th term is $5 \cdot 2^{11-1}$, or $5 \cdot 2^{10}$. This leads to the following formula for the nth term of a geometric progression.

nth Term of a Geometric Progression

The nth term of a geometric progression is given by the formula

$$l = a \cdot r^{n-1}, n \geq 1,$$

where l is the nth term, a is the first term, and r is the common ratio.

Example 4 Find the specified term of each geometric progression, given the first term a and the common ratio r.

5th term: $a = 12$ and $r = 0.1$

$$\begin{aligned} l = a \cdot r^{n-1} &= 12(0.1)^{5-1} \\ &= 12(0.1)^4 \\ &= 12(0.0001) \\ &= 0.0012 \end{aligned}$$

Thus, the 5th term is 0.0012.

7th term: $a = -8$ and $r = -\dfrac{1}{2}$

$$\begin{aligned} l = a \cdot r^{n-1} &= -8\left(-\frac{1}{2}\right)^{7-1} \\ &= -8 \cdot \frac{1}{64} = -\frac{1}{8} \end{aligned}$$

Thus, the 7th term is $-\dfrac{1}{8}$.

Example 5 Find the 10th term of the G.P.: $\dfrac{1}{2}$, -1, 2, -4, ...

$$r = -1 \div \frac{1}{2}, \text{ or } -2 \qquad a = \frac{1}{2} \qquad n = 10 \qquad l \text{ is the 10th term.}$$

$$l = a \cdot r^{n-1} = \frac{1}{2}(-2)^9 = \frac{1}{2}(-512) = -256$$

Thus, the 10th term is -256.

GEOMETRIC PROGRESSIONS

Reading in **Algebra**

Match each geometric progression at the left with exactly one statement at the right.

1. 0.003, 0.03, 0.3, . . . C
2. 5, 15, 45, . . . A
3. $3, 1, \frac{1}{3}, \ldots$ B
4. 48, 24, 12, . . . E
5. $x, x^3, x^5, \ldots$ D

A 3 is the common ratio of the G. P.
B 3 is the first term of the G. P.
C 3 is the next term of the G. P.
D 3 is the counting number for the term, x^5.
E 3 is the 5th term of the G. P.

Oral **Exercises**

For each progression that is a G. P., find the common ratio r.

1. 2, 8, 32, 128, . . . 4
2. 2, −6, 18, −54, . . . −3
3. 16, 8, 4, 2, . . . $\frac{1}{2}$
4. 5, 10, 15, 20, . . . Not a G.P.
5. −40, −20, −10, −5, . . . $\frac{1}{2}$
6. 3, −3, 3, −3, . . . −1
7. $-9, 3, -1, \frac{1}{3}, \ldots$ $-\frac{1}{3}$
8. 4, 0.4, 0.04, 0.004, . . . 0.1
9. $2\sqrt{3}, 6, 6\sqrt{3}, 18, \ldots \sqrt{3}$
10. $\frac{1}{8}, \frac{1}{4}, \frac{1}{2}, 1, \ldots$ 2
11. $3, 2, \frac{4}{3}, \frac{8}{9}, \ldots$ $\frac{2}{3}$
12. $5x, 10x^2, 20x^3, 40x^4, \ldots$ 2x

Written **Exercises**

Write the next three terms of each geometric progression.

(A) 1. 30, 60, 120, . . . **240, 480, 960** 2. −0.1, −0.2, −0.4, . . . ⏎
−0.8, −1.6, −3.2 3. $-\frac{1}{3}, 1, -3, \ldots$ **9, −27, 81**

Write the first four terms of each G. P. whose first term and common ratio are given.

4. $a = 20$ and $r = 2$ **20, 40, 80, 160** 5. $a = -\frac{1}{4}$ and $r = 4$ 6. $a = 0.25$ and $r = 4$
7. $a = 32$ and $r = \frac{1}{2}$ **32, 16, 8, 4** 8. $a = -8$ and $r = \frac{1}{4}$ 9. $a = 6$ and $r = 0.1$
10. $a = \frac{1}{8}$ and $r = -2$ 11. $a = 64$ and $r = -\frac{3}{8}$ 12. $a = -2$ and $r = -3$

5. $-\frac{1}{4}, -1, -4, -16$ 6. 0.25, 1, 4, 16 8. $-8, -2, -\frac{1}{2}, -\frac{1}{8}$ 9. 6, 0.6, 0.06, 0.006 10. $\frac{1}{8}, -\frac{1}{4}, \frac{1}{2}, -1$

Find the specified term of each geometric progression. 11. $64, -24, 9, -3\frac{3}{8}$ 12. $-2, 6, -18, 54$

13. 5th term: $a = -10, r = 3$
14. 6th term: $a = 20, r = -5$
15. 7th term: $a = 34, r = 10$
16. 7th term: $a = 900, r = 0.1$
17. 6th term: $a = -30, r = 0.2$
18. 5th term: $a = 72, r = -0.1$
19. 10th term: 4, 8, 16, . . .
20. 9th term: 10, −20, 40, . . .
21. 10th term: $-\frac{1}{4}, -\frac{1}{2}, -1, \ldots$
22. 11th term: −8, −4, −2, . . .
23. 12th term: −32, 16, −8, . . .
24. 11th term: 96, 48, 24, . . .
25. 8th term: 370, 37, 3.7, . . .
26. 9th term: 0.24, 2.4, 24, . . .
27. 7th term: 1, 0.2, 0.04, . . .

13. −810 14. −62,500 15. 34,000,000 16. 0.0009 17. −0.0096 18. 0.0072 19. 2048 20. 2560

(B) 28. 6th term: $a = -9, r = \frac{1}{3}$ $-\frac{1}{27}$ 29. 4th term: $a = 80, r = -\frac{1}{4}$ $-\frac{5}{4}$ 30. 5th term: $a = 25, r = \frac{2}{5}$ $\frac{16}{25}$
31. 8th term: $a = 6x, r = 2x$ **768x⁸** 32. 7th term: $a = 4y, r = 2y^2$ 33. 8th term: $a = 8xy, r = x^2y^3$
34. 7th term: $a = 10, r = \sqrt{3}$ **270** 35. 6th term: $a = -4, r = \sqrt{5}$ 36. 5th term: $a = \sqrt{2}, r = 3\sqrt{2}$

21. −128 22. $-\frac{1}{128}$ 23. $\frac{1}{64}$ 24. $\frac{3}{32}$ 25. 0.000037 26. 24,000,000 27. 0.000064 32. $256y^{13}$ 33. $8x^{15}y^{22}$

Write the next three terms of each geometric progression in Exercises 37–42. 35. $-100\sqrt{5}$ 36. $324\sqrt{2}$

37. $2x^2, 8x^5, 32x^8, \ldots$
38. $1, i, -1, -i, \ldots$
39. $3 + 2\sqrt{5}, 6 + 4\sqrt{5}, 12 + 8\sqrt{5}, \ldots$
40. $2 + \sqrt{6}, 6 + 2\sqrt{6}, 12 + 6\sqrt{6}, \ldots$
41. $-3x^3, 6x^5, -12x^7, \ldots$
42. $3i, -6, -12i, 24, \ldots$

37. $128x^{11}, 512x^{14}, 2048x^{17}$ 38. $1, i, -1$ 39. $24 + 16\sqrt{5}, 48 + 32\sqrt{5}, 96 + 64\sqrt{5}$
40. $36 + 12\sqrt{6}, 72 + 36\sqrt{6}, 216 + 72\sqrt{6}$ 41. $24x^9, -48x^{11}, 96x^{13}$ 42. $48i, -96, -192i$

43. A tennis ball, dropped from a height of 128 dm, rebounds on each bounce one-half the distance from which it fell. How high does it go on its 9th rebound? $\frac{1}{4}$ **dm, or 0.25 dm**

44. A tank contains 4,000 L of water. Each day, one-half of the water will be removed. How much water will be in the tank at the end of the eighth day? **15$\frac{5}{8}$ L, or 15.625 L**

45. A golf ball, dropped from a height of 81 m, rebounds on each bounce two-thirds of the distance from which it fell. How far does it fall on its 6th descent? **10$\frac{2}{3}$ m**

46. A tank contains 243 L of gasoline. Each time that a valve is opened, one-third of the gasoline is released. How much gas will be in the tank after the valve is operated 6 times? **21$\frac{1}{3}$ L**

47. Find the first term of the geometric progression whose 7th term is 512 and 8th term is 1,024. [Hint: Use the formula $l = ar^{n-1}$.] **8**

$a, \ldots, 256, 512, 1024, \ldots$
$1st \qquad\qquad 7th \;\; 8th$

48. Find the first term of the G.P. whose 9th term is $\frac{1}{64}$ and 10th term is $\frac{1}{128}$. **4**

49. What is the first term of a G.P., if its 8th and 9th terms are 6,250 and $-31,250$, respectively? $-\frac{2}{25}$

© **50.** Find two values of t so that $\frac{1}{3}, t - 1, 4t$ is a geometric sequence.

$\left[\text{Hint: } r = \dfrac{x_2}{x_1} = \dfrac{x_3}{x_2} \text{ if } x_1, x_2, x_3 \text{ is a geometric sequence.} \right]$ $t = 3 \text{ or } t = \frac{1}{3}$

8th term

51. Find two values of t so that $6t, t + 1,$ $\frac{3}{4}$ is a G.P. $t = 2 \text{ or } t = \frac{1}{2}$

52. Which term of $3, -6, 12, \ldots$ is -384?

53. Which term of $\frac{1}{8}, \frac{1}{4}, \frac{1}{2}, \ldots$ is 128?

11th term

CALCULATOR ACTIVITIES

Find the 7th term of the G.P. where $a = 12.5$ and $r = 3$.

$$l = a \cdot r^{n-1} = 12.5 \times 3^6$$
$$l = 12.5 \otimes 3 \otimes 3 \otimes 3 \otimes 3 \otimes 3 \otimes 3 \ominus 9112.5 \quad \blacktriangleleft \textit{ The 7th term}$$

Find the nth term of each G.P. for the given values of n, a, and r.

1. $n = 9, a = -7.2, r = 2$
-1843.2

2. $n = 6, a = 640, r = 4$
655, 360

3. $n = 8, a = 0.2, r = 0.5$
0.0015625

Cumulative Review

Solve each equation for n.

1. $2^n = 64$ $n = 6$ **2.** $3^n = \dfrac{1}{81}$ $n = -4$ **3.** $5^{3n+1} = 625$
$n = 1$

4. $8^n = 128$ $n = \frac{7}{3}$ **5.** $9^n = \dfrac{1}{27}$ $n = -\frac{3}{2}$

14.5 The Geometric Mean

OBJECTIVES ▶ **To find geometric means between two given terms of a geometric progression**
To find the geometric mean (mean proportional) of two numbers

The terms between two given terms of a geometric progression are called **geometric means** between the given terms. For example, four geometric means between 3 and 96 in the progression below are 6, 12, 24, and 48, since 3, 6, 12, 24, 48, 96, . . . is a geometric progression.

$$3, \underline{6}, \underline{12}, \underline{24}, \underline{48}, 96, \ldots$$

Example 1 Find three geometric means between -2 and -162.

$$-2, \underline{\hspace{1cm}}, \underline{\hspace{1cm}}, \underline{\hspace{1cm}}, -162$$

When the three geometric means are found, a G.P. with five terms will be formed.

$n = 5 \qquad a = -2 \qquad l = -162$

Use $\quad l = a \cdot r^{n-1}$ to find r.

$-162 = -2 \cdot r^{5-1}$ ◀ *Substitute for l, a, and n.*

$81 = r^4$

$r = \sqrt[4]{81} \quad$ or $\quad r = -\sqrt[4]{81}$

$r = 3 \qquad\qquad r = -3 \qquad$ ◀ *Two real numbers for r*

Multiply each term by either 3 or -3.

$-2, \underline{-6}, \underline{-18}, \underline{-54}, -162 \quad$ or $\quad -2, \underline{6}, \underline{-18}, \underline{54}, -162$

Thus, the means are $-6, -18, -54 \quad$ or $\quad 6, -18, 54$.

Example 2 Find two real geometric means between 9 and $-\dfrac{8}{3}$.

$$9, \underline{\hspace{1cm}}, \underline{\hspace{1cm}}, -\frac{8}{3}$$

$l = a \cdot r^{n-1}$

$-\dfrac{8}{3} = 9 \cdot r^3 \quad$ ◀ *Substitute $-\dfrac{8}{3}$ for l, 9 for a, and 4 for n.*

$-\dfrac{8}{27} = r^3$

$r = \sqrt[3]{-\dfrac{8}{27}} = -\dfrac{2}{3}$

Multiply each term by $-\dfrac{2}{3}$: $\qquad 9, \underline{-6}, \underline{4}, -\dfrac{8}{3}$.

Thus, the two real geometric means are -6 and 4.

A single geometric mean between two numbers is called **the geometric mean** or **mean proportional** of the two numbers.

Example 3 Find the geometric mean (mean proportional) of 5 and 10.

$$5, \underline{\hspace{1cm}}, 10$$

$l = ar^{n-1}$

$10 = 5 \cdot r^2$ ◀ *Substitute 10 for l, 5 for a, and 3 for n.*

$2 = r^2$

$r = \sqrt{2}$ or $r = -\sqrt{2}$

Multiply by either $\sqrt{2}$ or $-\sqrt{2}$.

$$5, \underline{5\sqrt{2}}, 10 \quad \text{or} \quad 5, \underline{-5\sqrt{2}}, 10$$

Thus, the geometric mean (mean proportional) is $5\sqrt{2}$ or $-5\sqrt{2}$.

In Example 3, the *positive* geometric mean of 5 and 10 is $\sqrt{5 \cdot 10}$, or $5\sqrt{2}$, and the *negative* geometric mean of 5 and 10 is $-\sqrt{5 \cdot 10}$, or $-5\sqrt{2}$. This suggests the following statement about the geometric mean of two nonzero real numbers x and y. You will prove this statement in Exercise 45.

The Geometric Mean

> The geometric mean (mean proportional) of the real numbers x and y ($xy > 0$) is $\sqrt{xy}$ or $-\sqrt{xy}$.

Some word problems that involve the geometric mean of two numbers can be solved by using a system of two equations as shown below.

Example 4 One number is 30 more than another number and the positive geometric mean of the two numbers is 8. Find the two numbers.

Let x and y represent the two numbers. Write a system of equations.

(1) $y = x + 30$ (2) $\sqrt{xy} = 8$

Solve the system by substitution.

$\sqrt{x(x + 30)} = 8$ ◀ *Substitute for y in equation (2).*

$(\sqrt{x^2 + 30x})^2 = 8^2$

$x^2 + 30x = 64$

$x^2 + 30x - 64 = 0$

$(x - 2)(x + 32) = 0$

$x = 2$ or $x = -32$

If $x = 2$, then $y = x + 30 = 32$. If $x = -32$, then $y = x + 30 = -2$. Check each pair of numbers in both equations, (1) and (2).

Thus, the numbers are 2 and 32 or -32 and -2.

When you are asked to find "*n* real geometric means" between a pair of given numbers, there are two sets of means if n is odd, as in Examples 1 and 3. If n is even, there is only one set of means, as in Example 2.

THE GEOMETRIC MEAN   **373**

Written **Exercises**

10. −32, −16, −8 or 32, −16, 8   12. 10, 50, 250 or −10, 50, −250

Find the indicated number of real geometric means between each pair of numbers.

(A)
1. Three, between 1 and 81 **3, 9, 27 or −3, 9, −27**
2. One positive, between 3 and 12 **6**
3. One negative, between 2 and 50 **−10**
4. Two, between 5 and 320 **20, 80**
5. Two, between −3 and 24 **6, −12**
6. Two, between −2 and −128 **−8, −32**
7. One positive, between −4 and −36 **12**
8. One negative, between −5 and −80 **−20**
9. Two, between 16 and −2 **−8, 4**
10. Three, between −64 and −4
11. Three, between −5 and −405
12. Three, between 2 and 1250
13. One positive, between 8 and $\frac{1}{2}$ **2**
14. One negative, between $\frac{2}{5}$ and 10 **−2**
15. Two, between 9 and $\frac{1}{3}$ **3, 1**
16. Two, between $\frac{3}{5}$ and 75 **3, 15**
17. Four, between 11 and 352 **22, 44, 88, 176**
18. Four, between 2 and 200,000
19. One positive, between 3 and 6 **3√2**
20. One negative, between 4 and 12 **−4√3**
21. One negative, between $5\sqrt{2}$ and $10\sqrt{2}$
22. One positive, between $3\sqrt{5}$ and $15\sqrt{5}$ **15**

11. 15, −45, 135 or −15, −45, −135   21. −10   18. 20, 200, 2,000, 20,000

23. One number is 4 times another number and the positive geometric mean of the two numbers is 6. Find the two numbers. **3, 12 or −3, −12**
24. Eight more than the positive geometric mean of two numbers is 20. Find the two numbers if one number is 9 times the other number. **4, 36 or −4, −36**
25. If one number is 6 more than another number and the positive geometric mean of the two numbers is 4, what are the two numbers? **2, 8 or −8, −2**
26. Find two numbers whose difference is 5 and whose positive geometric mean is 6. **9, 4 or −4, −9**

(B)
27. Seven different weights are used to balance small masses in a laboratory. These weights are in geometric progression. Find each weight if the lightest is 0.5 g and the median (middle) weight is 4 g. **0.5 g, 1 g, 2 g, 4 g, 8 g, 16 g, 32 g**
28. Crude oil is pumped from a tanker so that the amounts remaining at the end of successive hours are in G.P. At the end of 3 hours, 6,400 kiloliters (kL) remain in the tanker, and at the end of 6 hours, there are 2,700 kL. How much oil remains in the tanker at the end of 4 hours? **4,800 kL**

Find the indicated number of real geometric means between each pair of terms.

29. One positive, between 0.1 and 0.016 **0.04**
30. Two, between 0.2 and 0.0128 **0.08, 0.032**
31. Two, between 3 and $21\sqrt{7}$ **3√7, 21**
32. Two, between $3\sqrt{5}$ and 75 **15, 15√5**
33. Three, between $5x^3$ and $80x^{11}$
34. Five, between y^2 and $64y^{20}$ **below**
35. One positive, between $2i$ and $-18i$ **6**
36. One negative, between $-3i$ and $15i$ **−3√5**

33. $10x^5, 20x^7, 40x^9$ or $-10x^5, 20x^7, -40x^9$

Find the geometric mean of each two numbers. (Each exercise has two answers.)

(C)
37. i and $4i$ **±2i**
38. 3 and −27 **±9i**
39. −4 and 12 **±4i√3**
40. $5i$ and $8i$ **±2i√10**
41. $1 + i$ and $1 - i$ **±√2**
42. $3 - 4i$ and $3 + 4i$ **±5**
43. x^3 and y^3 **±xy√xy**
44. $\sqrt{x}$ and $\sqrt{y}$ **±⁴√xy**

34. $2y^5, 4y^8, 8y^{11}, 16y^{14}, 32y^{17}$ or $-2y^5, 4y^8, -8y^{11}, 16y^{14}, -32y^{17}$

Use the formula $l = a \cdot r^{n-1}$ to prove each statement.

45. The geometric mean of the real numbers x and $y (xy > 0)$ is $\sqrt{xy}$ or $-\sqrt{xy}$.
For Ex. 45–46, see TE Answer Section.

46. The geometric mean of the complex number $a + bi$ and its conjugate is a real number.

14.6 Geometric Series

OBJECTIVE ▶ **To find the sum of the first *n* terms of a geometric series**

If you take the geometric progression 2, 10, 50, 250, . . .
and write it as the indicated sum 2 + 10 + 50 + 250 + . . . ,
the result is a **geometric series.**

Definition:
Geometric
Series

> A *geometric series* is an indicated sum of the terms of a geometric
> progression.

Example 1 Write each G.P. as a geometric series. Find the common ratio *r* of the series.

$$-2, 8, -32, 128, \ldots \qquad\qquad -8, -2, -\frac{1}{2}, -\frac{1}{8}, \ldots$$

The geometric series is	The geometric series is
$-2 + 8 - 32 + 128 - \ldots$	$-8 - 2 - \frac{1}{2} - \frac{1}{8} - \ldots$
$r = \dfrac{8}{-2}$, or -4	$r = \dfrac{-2}{-8}$, or $\dfrac{1}{4}$

You can find the sum S of the terms of the geometric series $5 + 15 + 45 +$
$\ldots + 3.645$ with common ratio 3 in the following way:

(1) Write the series in the form $a + ar + ar^2 + ar^3 + \ldots + l$.
(2) Multiply each term by -3 to get a second series.
(3) Then add the two series.

$$S = 5 + 5 \cdot 3 + 5 \cdot 3^2 + 5 \cdot 3^3 + \ldots + 3{,}645$$
$$\underline{-3S = \quad - 5 \cdot 3 - 5 \cdot 3^2 - 5 \cdot 3^3 - \ldots - 3{,}645 - 3(3{,}645)}$$
$$-2S = 5 + \quad 0 \quad + 0 \quad + 0 \quad + \ldots + 0 \quad - 3(3{,}645)$$
$$S = \frac{5 - 3(3{,}645)}{-2}, \text{ or } 5{,}465$$

The steps above suggest a method for obtaining a formula for the sum S of the
terms of a finite geometric series with first term a, common ratio r, and last
term l.

$$S = a + ar + ar^2 + ar^3 + \ldots + l$$
$$\underline{-r \cdot S = \quad - ar - ar^2 - ar^3 - \ldots - l - rl}$$
$$S - rS = a + 0 \quad + 0 \quad + 0 \quad + \ldots + 0 - rl$$

$$S - rS = a - rl$$
$$(1 - r)S = a - rl$$
$$S = \frac{a - rl}{1 - r}$$

**Sum of
the Terms
of Finite
Geometric
Series**

The sum S of the terms of a finite geometric series is given by the formula
$$S = \frac{a - rl}{1 - r}, (r \neq 1)$$
where a is the first term, r is the common ratio, and l is the last term.

In this book, "the sum of a geometric series" will be used to mean "the sum of the terms of a geometric series."

Example 2 **Find the sum of the geometric series in which the first term $a = 3$, the common ratio $r = -5$, and the last term $l = 375$.**

$$S = \frac{a - rl}{1 - r} = \frac{3 - (-5)(375)}{1 - (-5)} = \frac{3 + 1875}{6} = 313$$

Thus, the sum of the geometric series is 313.

Example 3 **Find the sum of the geometric series: $8 - 4 + 2 - \ldots - \frac{1}{16}$.**

$$a = 8 \qquad r = \frac{-4}{8}, \text{ or } -\frac{1}{2} \qquad l = -\frac{1}{16}$$

$$S = \frac{8 - \left(-\frac{1}{2}\right)\left(-\frac{1}{16}\right)}{1 - \left(-\frac{1}{2}\right)} = \left(8 - \frac{1}{32}\right) \div \frac{3}{2} \qquad \blacktriangleleft \quad \begin{array}{l} \textit{Use the sum formula.} \\ \textit{Simplify.} \end{array}$$

$$= \frac{255}{32} \cdot \frac{2}{3}$$

$$= \frac{85}{16}, \text{ or } 5\frac{5}{16} \qquad \blacktriangleleft \quad \textit{Sum of the series}$$

You can find the sum of the first 9 terms of the geometric series $-\frac{1}{4} + \frac{1}{2} - 1 + 2 - \ldots$ without finding the 9th term, or l. To do this, another sum formula is used. This formula is obtained by substitution.

$$S = \frac{a - r \cdot l}{1 - r} \text{ and } l = a \cdot r^{n-1}$$

$$S = \frac{a - r(a \cdot r^{n-1})}{1 - r} = \frac{a - a \cdot r^1 \cdot r^{n-1}}{1 - r} = \frac{a - a \cdot r^n}{1 - r}, \text{ or } \frac{a(1 - r^n)}{1 - r}$$

Example 4 **Find the sum of the first 9 terms of the geometric series: $-\frac{1}{4} + \frac{1}{2} - 1 + 2 - \ldots$.**

$$S = \frac{a(1 - r^n)}{1 - r} = \frac{-\frac{1}{4}[1 - (-2)^9]}{1 - (-2)} = \frac{-\frac{1}{4}(1 + 512)}{3} = -\frac{1}{4} \cdot \frac{513}{3} = -\frac{1}{4} \cdot 171 = -42\frac{3}{4}$$

$\sum\limits_{k=3}^{6} 2k$ is the arithmetic series $2 \cdot 3 + 2 \cdot 4 + 2 \cdot 5 + 2 \cdot 6$, or

$6 + 8 + 10 + 12$, whose common difference is 2. In a similar way, $\sum\limits_{k=3}^{6} 2^k$ is

the geometric series $2^3 + 2^4 + 2^5 + 2^6$, or $8 + 16 + 32 + 64$, whose common ratio is 2.

Example 5 Write the expanded form and the series form of $\sum\limits_{j=1}^{5} 5(-3)^j$. Find the sum of the series.

Substitute 1, 2, 3, 4, and 5 for j in $5(-3)^j$.

$\sum\limits_{j=1}^{5} = 5(-3)^1 + 5(-3)^2 + 5(-3)^3 + 5(-3)^4 + 5(-3)^5$ ◀ *Expanded form*

$= -15 + 45 - 135 + 405 - 1215$ ◀ *Series form*

$= \dfrac{-15 - (-3)(-1215)}{1 - (-3)}$ ◀ *Use $S = \dfrac{a - rl}{1 - r}$ to find the sum.*

$= -915$ ◀ *Sum of the series*

Reading in Algebra

Determine whether each expression is (A) an arithmetic progression, (B) an arithmetic series, (C) a geometric progression, or (D) a geometric series.

1. $5 + 10 + 15 + 20 + \dots$ **B**　　2. $5, 15, 45, 135, \dots$ **C**　　3. $4 - 12 + 36 - 108 + \dots$ **D**

4. $4, -1, -6, -11, \dots$ **A**　　5. $\sum\limits_{k=1}^{6} 3k$ **B**　　6. $\sum\limits_{k=1}^{6} 3^k$ **D**

Oral Exercises

1. $4 + 12 + 36 + 108 + \dots$　　2. $3 - 1 + \dfrac{1}{3} - \dfrac{1}{9} + \dots$　　3. $-\dfrac{2}{5} - 2 - 10 - 50 - \dots$

State each G.P. as a geometric series.

1. $4, 12, 36, 108, \dots$　　2. $3, -1, \dfrac{1}{3}, -\dfrac{1}{9}, \dots$　　3. $-\dfrac{2}{5}, -2, -10, -50, \dots$

Find the common ratio r of each geometric series.

4. $-\dfrac{1}{9} + \dfrac{1}{3} - 1 + 3 - \dots$ **-3**　　5. $6 + 0.6 + 0.06 + 0.006 + \dots$ **0.1**　　6. $14 + 0.14 + 0.0014 + \dots$ **0.01**

7. $25 - 5 + 1 - \dfrac{1}{5} + \dots$ $-\dfrac{1}{5}$　　8. $\sum\limits_{j=3}^{6} (-2)^j$ **-2**　　9. $\sum\limits_{c=1}^{5} 4(5^c)$ **5**

Written Exercises

Find the sum of each geometric series for the given data.

Ⓐ 1. $a = 6, r = 10, l = 60{,}000$ **66,666**　　2. $a = -2, r = 3, l = -1{,}458$ **-2,186**

3. $a = -4, r = -2, l = -1{,}024$ **-684**　　4. $a = 256, r = -\dfrac{1}{2}, l = 4$ **172**

5. $16 + 8 + 4 + \dots + \dfrac{1}{8}$ $31\dfrac{7}{8}$

6. $\dfrac{1}{9} + \dfrac{1}{3} + 1 + \dots + 243$ $364\dfrac{4}{9}$

7. $0.3 + 3 + 30 + \ldots + 300{,}000$ **333,333.3**

8. $-1{,}024 - 512 - 256 - \ldots - \dfrac{1}{4}$ **$-2{,}047\dfrac{3}{4}$**

9. $0.2 + 0.4 + 0.8 + \ldots + 51.2$ **102.2**

10. $900 - 90 + 9 - \ldots + 0.0009$ **818.1819**

11. $n = 10;\ 5 + 10 + 20 + 40 + \ldots$ **5,115**

12. $n = 9;\ -3 - 6 - 12 - 24 - \ldots$ **$-1{,}533$**

13. $n = 8;\ 4 - 8 + 16 - 32 + \ldots$ **-340**

14. $n = 10;\ -\dfrac{1}{8} + \dfrac{1}{4} - \dfrac{1}{2} + 1 - \ldots$ **$42\dfrac{5}{8}$**

15. $n = 7;\ 0.06 + 0.6 + 6 + 60 + \ldots$ **66,666.66**

16. $n = 8;\ -1 + 10 - 100 + 1{,}000 - \ldots$ **9,090,909**

17. $a = 12,\ r = 3,\ n = 6$ **4,368**

18. $a = -4,\ r = -3,\ n = 5$ **-244**

19. $a = 20,\ r = 0.2,\ n = 6$ **24.9984**

20. $a = -300,\ r = 0.3,\ n = 5$ **-427.53**

21. $a = \dfrac{1}{5},\ r = 10,\ n = 7$ **222,222.2**

22. $a = \dfrac{3}{5},\ r = -10,\ n = 8$ **$-5{,}454{,}545.4$**

23. $\displaystyle\sum_{k=1}^{6} 2^k$ **126**

24. $\displaystyle\sum_{j=3}^{6} (-3)^j$ **540**

25. $\displaystyle\sum_{c=1}^{5} \left(\dfrac{1}{2}\right)^c$ **$\dfrac{31}{32}$**

26. $\displaystyle\sum_{k=4}^{7} (0.2)^{k-3}$ **.2496**

Ⓑ **27.** $\displaystyle\sum_{j=1}^{4} \dfrac{1}{2}(4^j)$ **170**

28. $\displaystyle\sum_{k=1}^{4} 6(-2)^{k-1}$ **-30**

29. $\displaystyle\sum_{c=1}^{5} -64\left(\dfrac{1}{4}\right)^{c-1}$ **$-85\dfrac{1}{4}$**

30. $\displaystyle\sum_{j=1}^{6} -27\left(-\dfrac{1}{3}\right)^{j-1}$ **$-20\dfrac{2}{9}$**

31. $n = 9;\ -32 + 16 - 8 + 4 - \ldots$ **$-21\dfrac{3}{8}$**

32. $n = 7;\ 125 + 25 + 5 + 1 + \ldots$ **$156\dfrac{31}{125}$**

33. $n = 7;\ \dfrac{2}{3} + 2 + 6 + 18 + \ldots$ **$728\dfrac{2}{3}$**

34. $n = 6;\ \dfrac{2}{5} + 2 + 10 + 50 + \ldots$ **$1{,}562\dfrac{2}{5}$**

35. $a = -243,\ r = \dfrac{1}{3},\ n = 6$ **-364**

36. $a = 64,\ r = -\dfrac{1}{4},\ n = 4$ **51**

37. $a = 2{,}500,\ r = -\dfrac{1}{5},\ n = 5$ **2,084**

38. $a = -128,\ r = -\dfrac{1}{4},\ n = 6$ **$-102\dfrac{3}{8}$**

39. $a = 5,\ r = 4,\ n = 6$ **6,825**

40. $a = -3,\ r = 5,\ n = 6$ **$-11{,}718$**

41. A golf ball, dropped from a height of **382 m** 128 m, rebounds on each bounce one-half the distance from which it fell. When the ball hits the ground the 8th time, how far has it traveled since it was first dropped?

42. A steel ball rebounds on each bounce two-thirds the distance from which it fell. If the ball is dropped from a height of 81 m, how far will it travel before it hits the ground the 6th time? **$362\dfrac{1}{3}$ m**

43. Smaller and smaller squares are formed consecutively as shown at the right. Find the sum of the perimeters of the first 8 squares so formed, if the width of the first square is 20 cm. **159.375 cm**

44. Find the sum of the areas of the first 5 squares formed, as shown at the right, if the first square is 20 cm wide. **532.8125 cm²**

For Ex. 45–46, see TE Answer Section.

Ⓒ **45.** Prove: $\displaystyle\sum_{k=1}^{4} ax^{k-1} = a + \left(a \cdot \sum_{k=1}^{3} x^k\right)$.

46. Solve $\displaystyle\sum_{k=3}^{5} (x^k + 3) = 9$ for x.

CALCULATOR ACTIVITIES

Find the sum of each geometric series for the given data.

(1) $3 + 15 + 75 + \ldots + 234{,}375$

(2) $n = 7:\ 2 - 6 + 18 - 54 + \ldots$

(1) $S = \dfrac{a - r \cdot l}{1 - r} = \dfrac{3 - 5 \times 234{,}375}{-4}$: $\ominus 5 \otimes 234375 \oplus 3 \oslash 4$ Answer: 292968

(2) $S = \dfrac{a(1 - r^n)}{1 - r} = \dfrac{2[1 - (-3)^7]}{1 - (-3)} = \dfrac{2(1 + 3^7)}{4} = $ $3 \otimes 3 \otimes 3 \otimes 3 \otimes 3 \otimes 3$ $\oplus 1 \otimes 2 \oslash 4 \ominus 1094$

14.7 Infinite Geometric Series

OBJECTIVES ▶ **To find the sum, if it exists, of an infinite geometric series**
To write a repeating decimal as an infinite geometric series or an infinite indicated sum

To write a repeating decimal in the form $\dfrac{x}{y}$ where x and y are integers

The geometric series, $2 + 1 + \dfrac{1}{2} + \dfrac{1}{4} + \dfrac{1}{8} + \ldots$, is an **infinite geometric series.**

The sum of the first 10 terms of the series is $3\dfrac{255}{256}$. This sum is found by

using the formula $S = \dfrac{a(1 - r^n)}{1 - r}$, where $S = \dfrac{2\left[1 - \left(\dfrac{1}{2}\right)^{10}\right]}{1 - \dfrac{1}{2}}$. The value of r^n

in this sum is $\left(\dfrac{1}{2}\right)^{10}$, or $\dfrac{1}{1024}$. Observe how rapidly $\left(\dfrac{1}{2}\right)^n$ approaches 0 as n increases by 5.

$$\left(\frac{1}{2}\right)^0 = 1 \qquad \left(\frac{1}{2}\right)^5 = \frac{1}{32} \qquad \left(\frac{1}{2}\right)^{10} = \frac{1}{1024} \qquad \left(\frac{1}{2}\right)^{15} = \frac{1}{32{,}768}$$

The sum formula $S = \dfrac{a(1 - r^n)}{1 - r}$ can be written as $S = \dfrac{a}{1 - r} \cdot (1 - r^n)$.

If $-1 < r < 1$ and n increases without limit, then

r^n approaches 0 as a limit and $\dfrac{a}{1 - r} \cdot (1 - r^n)$ approaches $\dfrac{a}{1 - r} \cdot (1 - 0)$, or

$\dfrac{a}{1 - r}$, as a limit. This limit, $\dfrac{a}{1 - r}$, is defined to be the sum of the infinite geometric series with first term a and common ratio r.

Sum of Infinite Geometric Series

> The sum S of the terms of an infinite geometric series is given by the formula
> $$S = \frac{a}{1 - r}, \qquad [-1 < r < 1,\ r \neq 0]$$
> where a is the first term and r is the common ratio.

In Example 1, you will show that the sum of the infinite geometric series,
$2 + 1 + \dfrac{1}{2} + \dfrac{1}{4} + \ldots$, is 4. This sum can be interpreted on a number line as
shown in the figure below, where 4 is the limit of the infinite progression
$2, 3, 3\dfrac{1}{2}, 3\dfrac{3}{4}, 3\dfrac{7}{8}, 3\dfrac{15}{16}, 3\dfrac{31}{32}, \ldots, 3\dfrac{255}{256}, \ldots$.

Example 1 **Find the sum, if it exists, of each infinite geometric series.**

$$2 + 1 + \frac{1}{2} + \frac{1}{4} + \dots \qquad 8 - 2 + \frac{1}{2} - \frac{1}{8} + \dots \qquad \frac{1}{4} + \frac{1}{2} + 1 + 2 + \dots$$

$r = \frac{1}{2}$

$S = \dfrac{a}{1 - r} = \dfrac{2}{1 - \frac{1}{2}}$

$ = 2 \div \frac{1}{2}$

$ = 4$

$r = -\frac{1}{4}$

$S = \dfrac{a}{1 - r} = \dfrac{8}{1 - \left(-\frac{1}{4}\right)}$

$ = 8 \div \frac{5}{4}$

$ = \dfrac{32}{5}, \text{ or } 6\frac{2}{5}$

$r = 2$

Since r is not between -1 and 1, the sum of the series does not exist.

The decimal 0.56 is a terminating decimal while 0.434343 . . . and $0.27\overline{7}$ are repeating decimals. Any repeating decimal can be written as an infinite geometric series or as the indicated sum of a terminating decimal and an infinite geometric series.

$$0.434343 \dots = 0.43 + 0.0043 + 0.000043 + \dots, \text{ an infinite geometric series}$$
$$\text{with } a = 0.43 \text{ and } r = 0.01$$

$$0.27\overline{7} = \underset{\uparrow}{0.2} + (\underset{\uparrow}{0.07} + 0.007 + 0.0007 + \dots), \text{ an infinite indicated sum}$$

terminating decimal   infinite geometric series with $a = 0.07$ and $r = 0.1$

After a repeating decimal is written in series form, the formula $S = \dfrac{a}{1 - r}$ can be used to write the decimal in the form $\dfrac{x}{y}$ where x and y are integers.

Example 2 **Write 0.434343 . . . in the form $\dfrac{x}{y}$ where x and y are integers.**

$0.434343 \dots = 0.43 + 0.0043 + 0.000043 + \dots$ ◀ *Infinite geometric series*

$a = 0.43 \qquad r = 0.01$

$$S = \dfrac{a}{1 - r} = \dfrac{0.43}{1 - 0.01} = \dfrac{0.43}{0.99} = \dfrac{43}{99}$$

Thus, $0.434343 \dots = \dfrac{43}{99}$.

Example 3 **Write $6.012\overline{12}$ in the form $\dfrac{x}{y}$ where x and y are integers.**

$6.012\overline{12} = 6.0 + (0.012 + 0.00012 + 0.0000012 + \dots)$ ◀ *Infinite indicated sum*

$a = 0.012 \qquad r = 0.01$

$$S = \dfrac{a}{1 - r} = \dfrac{0.012}{1 - 0.01} = \dfrac{0.012}{0.99} = \dfrac{2}{165} \qquad 6 + \dfrac{2}{165} = \dfrac{992}{165}$$

Thus, $6.012\overline{12} = \dfrac{992}{165}$.

Written Exercises _____

Find the sum, if it exists, of each infinite geometric series.

(A)
1. $\frac{1}{2} + 1 + 2 + 4 + \ldots$

2. $8 + 4 + 2 + 1 + \ldots$ **16**

3. $9 - 3 + 1 - \frac{1}{3} + \ldots$ **$6\frac{3}{4}$**

4. $9 + 6 + 4 + \frac{8}{3} + \ldots$ **27**

5. $\frac{1}{2} + \frac{1}{4} + \frac{1}{8} + \frac{1}{16} + \ldots$ **1**

6. $\frac{1}{4} - \frac{1}{8} + \frac{1}{16} - \frac{1}{32} + \ldots$ **$\frac{1}{6}$**

7. $1 - \frac{1}{3} + \frac{1}{9} - \frac{1}{27} + \ldots$ **$\frac{3}{4}$**

8. $2 + 0.2 + 0.02 + 0.002 + \ldots$

9. $70 + 7 + 0.7 + 0.07 + \ldots$

1. does not exist   8. $2\frac{2}{9}$, or 2.2$\overline{2}$ 9. $77\frac{7}{9}$, or 77.$\overline{7}$

Write each repeating decimal as an infinite geometric series or as an infinite indicated sum and then in the form $\frac{x}{y}$ where x and y are integers.

10. $0.55\overline{5} \ldots$ $\frac{5}{9}$

11. $0.7\overline{7}$ $\frac{7}{9}$

12. $3.33\overline{3} \ldots$ $\frac{10}{3}$

13. $22.2\overline{2}$ $\frac{200}{9}$

14. $0.04\overline{4}$ $\frac{2}{45}$

15. $4.66\overline{6} \ldots$ $\frac{14}{3}$

16. $7.54\overline{4}$ $\frac{679}{90}$

17. $6.25\overline{5} \ldots$ $\frac{563}{90}$

Solve each problem.

(B)
18. The midpoints of the sides of an equilateral triangle are connected to form a second triangle. This procedure is repeated on each resulting triangle. Find the sum of the perimeters of all triangles so formed, if one side of the first triangle measures 60 cm. **360 cm**

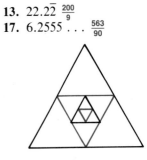

19. The midpoints of the sides of a square are joined to form a second square. This process is repeated on each resulting square. What is the sum of the areas of all squares so formed, if one side of the first square measures 8 m? **128 m²**

20. A golf ball, dropped from a height of 128 m, rebounds on each bounce one-half the distance from which it falls. How far will it travel before coming to rest? **384 m**

21. A steel ball was dropped from a height of 81 m and rebounded, on each bounce, two-thirds of the distance from which it fell. How far did it travel before coming to rest? **405 m**

Find the sum, if it exists, of each infinite geometric series.

22. $\frac{1}{5} + 1 + 5 + 25 + \ldots$

23. $-16 + 12 - 9 + \frac{27}{4} - \ldots$ **$-9\frac{1}{7}$**

24. $25 - 10 + 4 - \frac{8}{5} + \ldots$ **$17\frac{6}{7}$**

25. $8\sqrt{5} + 4\sqrt{5} + 2\sqrt{5} + \ldots$

26. $64\sqrt{7} + 48\sqrt{7} + 36\sqrt{7} + \ldots$

27. $\sqrt{48} + \sqrt{12} + \sqrt{3} + \ldots$ **$8\sqrt{3}$**

22. does not exist   25. $16\sqrt{5}$ 26. $256\sqrt{7}$

Use the formula $S = \dfrac{a}{1 - r}$ to write each repeating decimal in the form $\frac{x}{y}$ where x and y are integers.

28. $53.53\overline{53}$ $\frac{5300}{99}$

29. $67.47\overline{474}$ $\frac{6680}{99}$

30. $3.02\overline{929}$ $\frac{2999}{990}$

31. $17.17\overline{17}$ $\frac{1700}{99}$

32. $8.03\overline{232}$ $\frac{7952}{990}$

33. $63.53\overline{535}$ $\frac{6290}{99}$

For what values of x does each infinite geometric series have a sum? [Hint: $-1 < r < 1$, $r \neq 0$]

(C)
34. $(x - 1)^0 + (x - 1)^1 + (x - 1)^2 + \ldots$

$0 < x < 2$ and $x \neq 1$

35. $\frac{1}{x} + \frac{1}{x^3} + \frac{1}{x^5} + \ldots$

$x < -1$ or $x > 1$

36. $\frac{1}{x^2} + \frac{1}{x^3} + \frac{1}{x^4} + \ldots$

$x < -1$ or $x > 1$

14.8 Binomial Expansions

OBJECTIVES ▶ **To expand a positive integral power of a binomial**
To find a specified term of a binomial expansion

The first few consecutive whole number powers of $(a + b)$ reveal eight patterns that can be used to expand any integral power of a binomial.

$$(a + b)^0 = 1$$
$$(a + b)^1 = a + b$$
$$(a + b)^2 = a^2 + 2ab + b^2$$
$$(a + b)^3 = a^3 + 3a^2b + 3ab^2 + b^3$$
$$(a + b)^4 = a^4 + 4a^3b + 6a^2b^2 + 4ab^3 + b^4$$
$$(a + b)^5 = a^5 + 5a^4b + 10a^3b^2 + 10a^2b^3 + 5ab^4 + b^5$$

Notice in the expansion of $(a + b)^n$ that:

(1) The number of terms is always $n + 1$.
(2) The first term is a^n and the last term is b^n.
(3) The exponent of a decreases by 1, from one term to the next.
(4) The exponent of b increases by 1, from one term to the next.
(5) For each term, the sum of the exponents of a and b is n.
(6) The coefficients are symmetrical. (They read the same from left to right as right to left.)
(7) The second term is $n \cdot a^{n-1}b$.

There is a pattern among the coefficients of all the expansions that can be seen more easily if the coefficients are displayed alone.

This triangular display of the coefficients is called **Pascal's Triangle.** (See page 356.)

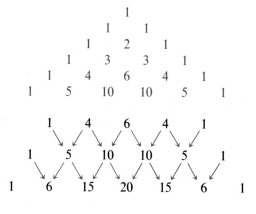

Pascal's triangle can be extended indefinitely, as shown at the right.

(8) Each new row of coefficients is formed by adding elements of the previous row. Each row begins and ends with 1.

The last row above shows that
$$(a + b)^6 = a^6 + 6a^5b + 15a^4b^2 + 20a^3b^3 + 15a^2b^4 + 6ab^5 + b^6.$$

Example 1 Expand $(5x + y)^4$. Simplify.

Use the form $(a + b)^4 = a^4 + 4a^3b + 6a^2b^2 + 4ab^3 + b^4$.

$$a = 5x \qquad b = y$$

$$
\begin{aligned}
(5x + y)^4 &= (5x)^4 + 4(5x)^3y + 6(5x)^2y^2 + 4(5x)y^3 + y^4 \\
&= 625x^4 + 500x^3y + 150x^2y + 20xy^3 + y^4
\end{aligned}
$$

Example 2 Expand $(x^2 - 2y)^5$. Simplify.

Rewrite $(x^2 - 2y)^5$ as $[x^2 + (-2y)]^5$.
Use the form $(a + b)^5 = a^5 + 5a^4b + 10a^3b^2 + 10a^2b^3 + 5ab^4 + b^5$.

$$a = x^2 \qquad b = -2y$$

$$
\begin{aligned}
[x^2 + (-2y)]^5 &= (x^2)^5 + 5(x^2)^4(-2y) + 10(x^2)^3(-2y)^2 + 10(x^2)^2(-2y)^3 + 5(x^2)(-2y)^4 + (-2y)^5 \\
&= x^{10} + 5x^8(-2y) + 10x^6(4y^2) + 10x^4(-8y^3) + 5x^2(16y^4) + (-32y^5) \\
&= x^{10} - 10x^8y + 40x^6y^2 - 80x^4y^3 + 80x^2y^4 - 32y^5
\end{aligned}
$$

Examples 1 and 2 suggest the following properties of the signs in a binomial expansion:
(1) In the expansion of $(a + b)^n$, $b > 0$, the signs will all be $+$.
(2) In the expansion of $(a - b)^n$, $b > 0$, the signs will alternate $+$ and $-$.

You can use Pascal's triangle to find a specified term of a binomial expansion. For example, the 4th term in the expansion of $(a + b)^5$ is $10a^2b^3$. Use the appropriate row in Pascal's triangle to find the coefficient of the 4th term. Then find the exponents for the a and b factors.

In the row for $(a + b)^5$, the 4th coefficient is 10.   1 5 10 [10] 5 1

The exponents of a decrease from 5 to 0.   5 4 3 ② 1 0

The sum of the exponents of a and b is 5.   0 1 2 ⟨3⟩ 4 5

Example 3 Find the 5th term in the expansion of $(2x - y^3)^6$. Simplify.

Coefficients ▶   1 6 15 20 [15] 6 1   6 5 4 3 ② 1 0 ◀ *Exponents*

0 1 2 3 ⟨4⟩ 5 6

$$15(2x)^2(-y^3)^4 = 15 \cdot 4x^2 \cdot y^{12} = 60x^2y^{12}$$

Thus, the 5th term is $60x^2y^{12}$.

You can write the terms of a binomial expansion without using Pascal's triangle. Notice that

$$
\begin{aligned}
(a + b)^6 &= a^6 + \frac{6}{1} \cdot a^5b^1 + \frac{6 \cdot 5}{1 \cdot 2} \cdot a^4b^2 + \frac{6 \cdot 5 \cdot 4}{1 \cdot 2 \cdot 3}a^3b^3 + \ldots + \frac{6 \cdot 5 \cdot 4 \cdot 3 \cdot 2 \cdot 1}{1 \cdot 2 \cdot 3 \cdot 4 \cdot 5 \cdot 6} \cdot b^6 \\
&= a^6 + 6a^5b \quad + 15a^4b^2 \quad + 20a^3b^3 \quad + \ldots + b^6.
\end{aligned}
$$

The Binomial Theorem	For each positive integer n, $(a + b)^n =$ $$a^n + \frac{n}{1} \cdot a^{n-1}b^1 + \frac{n(n-1)}{1 \cdot 2} \cdot a^{n-2}b^2 + \frac{n(n-1)(n-2)}{1 \cdot 2 \cdot 3} \cdot a^{n-3}b^3 + \ldots + b^n.$$

Example 4

Find the first five terms in the expansion of $(x + 2y)^{10}$. Simplify.

Use the Binomial Theorem with $n = 10$, $a = x$, and $b = 2y$.

$$(x + 2y)^{10} = x^{10} + \frac{10}{1} \cdot x^9(2y)^1 + \frac{10 \cdot 9}{1 \cdot 2} \cdot x^8(2y)^2 + \frac{10 \cdot 9 \cdot 8}{1 \cdot 2 \cdot 3} \cdot x^7(2y)^3 + \frac{10 \cdot 9 \cdot 8 \cdot 7}{1 \cdot 2 \cdot 3 \cdot 4} \cdot x^6(2y)^4 + \ldots$$
$$= x^{10} + 10 \cdot x^9 \cdot 2y + 45 \cdot x^8 \cdot 4y^2 + 120 \cdot x^7 \cdot 8y^3 + 210 \cdot x^6 \cdot 16y^4 + \ldots$$
$$= x^{10} + 20x^9y + 180x^8y^2 + 960x^7y^3 + 3360x^6y^4 + \ldots$$

Reading in Algebra

Supply the missing expressions in the following paragraph.

In the __expansion__ of $(a + b)^7$, there are __8__ terms, among which the first term is __a^7__ and the __last__ __term__ is b^7. The exponents of a __decrease__ from __7__ to 0, and the __exponents__ of b increase from 0 to __7__. The coefficients of the terms form the progression __1__, 7, 21, __35__, 35, __21__, __7__, __1__.

Written Exercises

For complete solutions, see TE Answer Section.

10. $270c^2d^3$ 11. $-20x^6y^3$ 12. $24x^2y^4$
13. $720x^9y^2$ 14. $135c^4d^2$ 15. $160x^9$

(A) **Expand each power of a binomial. Simplify.**
1. $(a + b)^8$
2. $(a - b)^9$
3. $(x + 2)^6$
4. $(2c - 3)^5$
5. $(x^2 + y)^8$
6. $(m^2 - 2n)^5$
7. $(2r + 5t)^4$
8. $(y - 0.2)^4$
9. $(2x + 0.1)^6$

Find the specified term of each expansion. Simplify.
(B) 10. 4th term of $(c + 3d)^5$
11. 4th term of $(x^2 - y)^6$
12. middle term of $(2x + y^2)^4$
13. 3rd term of $(2x^3 + 3y)^5$
14. 5th term of $(3c^2 - \sqrt{d})^6$
15. middle term of $(4x^2 + \frac{x}{2})^6$

Expand each power of a binomial. Simplify.
16. $(x^3 - 2y)^4$
17. $(2c^3 + 3d^2)^5$
18. $(x + \sqrt{2})^6$
19. $(2x - \sqrt{y})^4$
20. $(2r^2 + \frac{t}{2})^4$
21. $(\frac{1}{x} + \frac{1}{y})^5$

Find the first four terms of each expansion. Simplify.
22. $(x + y)^{12}$
23. $(x - 2y)^{11}$
24. $(x^2 + 3y^3)^{10}$
25. $(1 + 0.01)^7$
26. $(1 + 0.02)^8$
27. $(1 + 0.03)^6$

The Binomial Theorem is true for $(a + b)^q$, where q is a rational number. For each expansion, write the first four terms in simplest radical form.
(C) 28. $(x + 4)^{\frac{1}{2}}$
29. $(x + 9)^{\frac{2}{3}}$
30. $(x - 9)^{-\frac{1}{3}}$

Computer Activities

Fibonacci Numbers

The **Fibonacci sequence** is an ordered
list of numbers that is formed according
to a pattern that occurs quite often in
nature.

In biology the family tree of a drone
bee can be represented by a Fibonacci
sequence of real numbers. A given
drone bee has only one parent, the queen, but each queen has two parents, a
queen and a drone. This is shown in the diagram above and reflected in the
sequence below.

$$1, 1, 2, 3, 5, 8, 13, 21, 34, \ldots$$

Statement 60 in the program below defines the general term of a Fibonacci
sequence and the program prints out a sequence of 20 terms.

PROGRAM

```
 10 PRINT "FIBONACCI SEQUENCE"
 20 DIM S(20)
 30 LET S(1) = 1
 40 LET S(2) = 1
 50 FOR T = 1 TO 18
 60 LET S(T + 2) = S(T + 1) + S(T)
 70 NEXT T
 80 FOR X = 1 TO 20
 90 PRINT S(X)
100 NEXT X
110 END
```

Exercises

1. Type in the above program and run it. What are the first and last terms? **1; 6765**

2. Alter the program to run for 50 terms.
   20 DIM S(50), 50 FOR T = 1 TO 48, 80 FOR X = 1 TO 50

3. The <u>divine</u> <u>proportion</u> is found by determining successive ratios of the
   terms of the Fibonacci sequence: $1/1 = 1$ $2/1 = 2$ $3/2 = 1.5$
   $5/3 = 1.66$, and so on. Write a program to compute the divine proportion
   for the first 20 terms. **For Ex. 3, see TE Answer Section.**

ACTIVITY: FIBONACCI NUMBERS   **385**

Chapter Fourteen Review

Vocabulary
arithmetic means [14.2]
arithmetic progression [14.1]
arithmetic series [14.3]
binomial expansion [14.8]
geometric means [14.5]
geometric progression [14.4]
geometric series [14.6]
mean proportional [14.5]
progression [14.1]   sequence [14.1]

Write the first four terms of each A.P. [14.1]
1. $a = 14$ and $d = -8$ **14, 6, -2, -10**
2. $a = 3x - 4$ and $d = -x + 2$ **below**
3. Find the 36th term of the A.P.:
   $-7.2, -3.4, 0.4, 4.2, \ldots$ [14.1] **125.8**
4. Find the three arithmetic means between 12 and 22.8. [14.2] **14.7, 17.4, 20.1**
5. Find the arithmetic mean of -11.8 and 19.6. [14.2] **3.9**   **2. $3x - 4, 2x - 2, x, 2$**

Find the sum of each arithmetic series [14.3]
6. $n = 35, a = -15.4, l = 43.8$ **497**
7. $n = 26; 2.5 + 2.9 + 3.3 + 3.7 + \ldots$ **195**
8. $\displaystyle\sum_{k=1}^{14} -5k$ **-525**
9. $\displaystyle\sum_{j=3}^{6} (2j - 5)$ **16**

Write each arithmetic series using Σ-notation.
10. $-10 - 20 - 30 - 40 - 50$ **below** [14.3]
11. $18 + 22 + 26 + 30 + \cdots + 58$

Write the next three terms of each G.P. [14.4]
12. $-\frac{1}{3}, 1, -3, \ldots$ **9, -27, 81** [14.4]
13. $-4x, -8x^2, -16x^3, \ldots$ **$-32x^4, -64x^5, -128x^6$**

Find the specified term of each G.P. [14.4]
14. 10th term: $6, -12, 24, \ldots$ **-3,072**
15. 5th term: $a = -4, r = 3$ **-324**

Find the indicated number of real geometric means between each pair of numbers. [14.5]
16. One positive, between $\frac{1}{5}$ and 20 **2**
17. Three, between -3 and -48
18. Two, between $2\sqrt{6}$ and 72 **12, 12√6**

17. **-6, -12, -24, or 6, -12, 24**

Find the sum of each geometric series for the given data. [14.6]
19. $64 + 32 + 16 + \ldots + \frac{1}{4}$ **$127\frac{3}{4}$**
20. $a = 3, r = 5, l = 1,875$ **2,343**
21. $n = 8; 32 - 16 + 8 - 4 + \ldots$ **$21\frac{1}{4}$**
22. $a = -2, r = -4, n = 5$ **-410**
23. $\displaystyle\sum_{k=2}^{6} (-5)^{k-1}$ **-2,605**   24. $\displaystyle\sum_{j=1}^{4} 25\left(\frac{1}{5}\right)^j$ **$6\frac{6}{25}$**

Find the sum, if it exists, of each infinite geometric series. [14.7]
25. $\frac{1}{3} + 1 + 3 + 9 + \ldots$ **does not exist**
26. $64 - 16 + 4 - 1 + \ldots$ **51.2**
27. $16\sqrt{3} + 8\sqrt{3} + 4\sqrt{3} + 2\sqrt{3} + \ldots$ **32√3**

28. Use the formula $S = \dfrac{a}{1 - r}$ to write $\dfrac{8290}{99}$
    $83.73\overline{73}$ in the form $\dfrac{x}{y}$, where x and y are integers. [14.7]

For Ex. 29–31, see TE Answer Section.

Expand each power of a binomial. Simplify. [14.8]
29. $(x + 3y)^4$ 30. $(2x^3 - y)^5$ 31. $\left(\dfrac{1}{m} + \dfrac{1}{n}\right)^4$

32. Find the 5th term of $(3x^2 - \sqrt{5})^6$. Simplify. **$3,375x^4$**
33. Find the first four terms of $(x - 2y^2)^{10}$. Simplify. [14.8]
    $x^{10} - 20x^9y^2 + 180x^8y^4 - 960x^7y^6$

Solve each problem.
34. Mr. Edwards began a 30-day training program by jogging 440 m. Each day, he ran 50 m more than he did the preceding day. How far did Mr. Edwards jog on the 30th day? [14.1] **1,890 m**
35. The arithmetic mean of two numbers is 24. Six less than the larger number is 5 times the smaller number. Find the numbers. [14.2] **41, 7**   **12, 3 or -3, -12**
36. If one number is 9 less than another number and their positive geometric mean is 6, what are the two numbers? [14.5]

Chapter Fourteen Test

1. Write the first four terms of the A.P. whose first term is -2 and common difference is 1.5. **-2, -0.5, 1, 2.5**

2. Find the 31st term of the A.P.: 6.0, 6.4, 6.8, 7.2 . . . . **18**

3. Find the three arithmetic means between 18 and 29. **$20\frac{3}{4}$, $23\frac{1}{2}$, $26\frac{1}{4}$**

4. Find the arithmetic mean of -5.4 and 8.2. **1.4**

Find the sum of each arithmetic series.

5. $n = 26$; $7.6 + 7.2 + 6.8 + 6.4 + \ldots$ **67.6**

6. $\displaystyle\sum_{k=1}^{20} (2k + 3)$ **480**

8. $\displaystyle\sum_{k=3}^{7} (3k + 1)$

7. Cartons are stacked in 16 rows with 4 cartons in the top row, 7 in the second row, 10 in the next row, and so on. How many cartons are in the stack? **424**

8. Write the arithmetic series, $10 + 13 + 16 + 19 + 22$, using Σ-notation. **above**

9. Write the next three terms of the G.P.: $\frac{3}{4}$, $\frac{3}{2}$, 3, ... **6, 12, 24**

10. Find the 10th term of the G.P.: $\frac{1}{4}$, $\frac{1}{2}$, 1, 2, ... **128**

Find the indicated number of real geometric means between each pair of numbers.

11. Two between -4 and 108 **12, -36**

12. One positive, between $\frac{1}{6}$ and 24 **2**

Find the sum of each geometric series.

13. $a = 5$, $r = 4$, $l = 5{,}120$ **6,825**

14. $n = 6$; $100 - 50 + 25 - 12\frac{1}{2} + \ldots$ **$65\frac{5}{8}$**

15. $a = 5$, $r = -10$, $n = 4$ **$-4{,}545$**

16. $\displaystyle\sum_{j=1}^{4} 81\left(\frac{1}{3}\right)^{j}$ **40**

17. Find the sum of the infinite geometric series: $16 - 4 + 1 - \frac{1}{4} + \ldots$. **$12\frac{4}{5}$**

18. Write 7.2888 . . . as an infinite indicated sum and then in the form $\frac{x}{y}$, where x and y are integers. **$\frac{328}{45}$**

19. Expand $(3x - y^2)^4$. Simplify.

20. Find the 5th term of $(4x - \sqrt{2})^6$. Simplify.

21. Find the first four terms of $(x^2 + \frac{1}{2}y)^{10}$. Simplify. **$x^{20} + 5x^{18}y + 11\frac{1}{4}x^{16}y^2 + 15x^{14}y^3$**

19. **$81x^4 - 108x^3y^2 + 54x^2y^4 - 12xy^6 + y^8$**

Solve each problem.   20. **$960x^2$**

22. An object, shot upward at 200 m/s, travels 195 m during the 1st second, 185 m during the 2nd second, 175 m during the 3rd second, and so on. How far does it travel during the 14th second? **65 m**   12, 28

23. The arithmetic mean of two numbers is 20. Four less than one number is twice the other number. Find the two numbers.

24. Two more than the geometric mean of two numbers is 10. Find the two numbers if one number is 12 more than the other number. **-16, -4 or 4, 16**

Smaller and smaller squares are formed, one after the other, as shown at the right. The width of the first square is 32 m. Use this information in Ex. 25–26.

25. Find the sum of the perimeters of the first eight squares. **255 m**

26. Find the sum of the areas of all such squares. **$1{,}365\frac{1}{3}$ m^2**

★ 27. Find two values of c such that $\frac{2}{c}$, 4, $\frac{15}{c-2}$ is an A.P. **4; $\frac{1}{8}$**

★ 28. Find two values of x such that $x - 9$, 12, $4x$ is a G.P. **12; -3** $\pm 2\sqrt{5}$

★ 29. Find the geometric mean of $-2i$ and $10i$.

★ 30. For what values of x does the infinite geometric series $\frac{x}{2} - 2x^3 + 8x^5 - 32x^7 + \ldots$ have a sum? **$-\frac{1}{2} < x < \frac{1}{2}$ and $x \neq 0$**

College Prep Test

DIRECTIONS: In each item, you are to compare a quantity in Column 1 with a quantity in Column 2. Write the letter of the correct answer from these choices:

A The quantity in Column 1 is greater than the quantity in Column 2.
B The quantity in Column 2 is greater than the quantity in Column 1.
C The quantity in Column 1 is equal to the quantity in Column 2.
D The relationship cannot be determined from the given information.

Notes: Information centered over both columns refers to one or both of the quantities to be compared.
A symbol that appears in both columns has the same meaning in each column.
All variables represent real numbers.

SAMPLE ITEM AND ANSWER

Column 1	Column 2
$x = 2$ and $y = -2$	
The value of the next term of the A.P.: $x, 2x, 3x, 4x$	The value of the next term of the G.P.: y, y^2, y^3, y^4

The answer is A because $5x = 5 \cdot 2 = 10$, $y^5 = (-2)^5 = -32$, and $10 > -32$.

	Column 1		Column 2
1.	Arithmetic mean of $\frac{1}{2}$ and $\frac{1}{8}$	**C**	Arithmetic mean of $-\frac{1}{8}$ and $\frac{3}{4}$
2.	The next term in the G.P.: 9, 3, 1	**B**	The next term in the G.P.: $\frac{1}{16}, \frac{1}{8}, \frac{1}{4}$
3.	Next term in the sequence: 0, 1, 1, 2, 3, 5, 8, 13	**A**	Next term in the sequence: 75, 64, 53, 42, 31
4.	Sum of the series: $-20 - 15 - 10 - \ldots + 30$	**B**	Sum of the series: $-25 - 20 - 15 - \ldots + 35$

	Column 1		Column 2
5.	Arithmetic mean of 2 and 8	**A**	Geometric mean of 2 and 8
6.	$(x + 5)^3$	**D**	$(x + 5)^4$
7.	$\sum_{k=1}^{5} 2^{k-1}$	**C**	$\sum_{j=3}^{7} 2^{j-3}$
8.	The value of x if $x + 3, 2x, x - 7$ is an arithmetic progression	**A**	The value of n if $2n, n - 1, n + 1$ is an arithmetic progression
	$x > 0$ and $n > 0$		
9.	Value of x if 3, $3x, 12x$ is a G.P.	**B**	Value of n if $-2, -2n, -10n$ is a G.P.
10.	Coefficient of the 3rd term in the expansion of $(x + 2)^{12}$	**C**	Coefficient of the 3rd term in the expansion of $(y - 2)^{12}$

---

15 LOGARITHMIC AND EXPONENTIAL FUNCTIONS

Logarithms in Stamps

The discovery of logarithms in the 17th century preceded the discovery of exponents. Common (base-10) logarithms were created by John Napier, a Scottish mathematician, in 1614. At about the same time, Jobst Bürgi of Switzerland independently developed a similar system of logarithms.

A philatelist (stamp collector) who understands logarithms will be especially interested in a group of ten stamps issued by the government of Nicaragua in 1971. The last line on each stamp reads "LAS 10 FORMULAS MATEMATICAS QUE CAMBARON LA FAZ DE LA TIERRA," or "the 10 mathematical formulas that changed the face of the earth." Two of the ten stamps are shown below.

The formula on the second stamp is

$$e^{\ln N} = N.$$

This formula defines a **natural logarithm,** or **base-e logarithm.** In the system of natural logarithms, the base is the irrational number e where

$$e = 2 + \frac{1}{2} + \frac{1}{2 \times 3} + \frac{1}{2 \times 3 \times 4} + \ldots = 2.71828 \ldots.$$

Natural logarithms are used in theoretical mathematics. Many important formulas in calculus are written in their simplest forms using natural logarithms. The natural logarithm, $\log_e x$, is often written as $\ln x$.

PROJECT

From a table of natural logarithms, find ln 2, ln 6, and ln 10. How do these values compare with their corresponding common logarithms: log 2, log 6, log 10?

15.1 Common Logarithms and Antilogarithms

OBJECTIVES ▶ **To find the base-10 logarithm of a number between 1 and 10**
To find the base-10 antilogarithm of a number between 0 and 1

If y is an integral power of 10, such as 1,000, then y can be written as 10^x where x is an integer. $y = 1,000 = 10^3$
This exponential equation can then be rewritten as a **logarithmic equation**. The base-10 **logarithm (log)** of 1,000, or 10^3, is 3.

$$\log 1,000 = \log 10^3 = 3$$

Read "log 1,000" as "the log of 1,000." Think of log 1,000 as the exponent 3. This is the power to which 10 must be raised to yield 1,000.

The base-10 log y is written as $\log_{10} y$ or simply as $\log y$ where the base is understood to be 10. Log y is not defined if $y \leq 0$, since 0 or a negative number cannot be written as a power of 10.

Definition:
Base-10
Logarithm

> For each real number $y > 0$, if $y = 10^x$, then
> $\log y = \log 10^x = x.$

The equation $10^3 = 1,000$ can also be written as an **antilogarithmic equation**. The base-10 **antilogarithm (antilog)** of 3 is 10^3, or 1,000.

$$\text{antilog } 3 = 10^3 = 1,000$$

Read "antilog 3" as "the antilog of 3." Think of antilog 3 as the number obtained when 10 is raised to the third power, or 1,000.

Definition:
Base-10
Antilogarithm

> For each real number x, $antilog\ x = 10^x.$

Example 1 Find log 10,000 and antilog 5.

$$10,000 = 10^4 \qquad\qquad 10^5 = 100,000$$
$$\log 10,000 = \log 10^4 = 4 \qquad\qquad \text{antilog } 5 = 10^5 = 100,000$$

Thus, log 10,000 is 4 and antilog 5 is 100,000.

If y is a number between 1 and 10, then log y is a decimal between 0 and 1.

$$1 < y < 10$$
$$10^0 < y < 10^1$$
$$\log 10^0 < \log y < \log 10^1$$
$$0 < \log y < 1$$

Base-10 logarithms are called **common logarithms**. The tables on page 595 give the logarithms of numbers from 1 to 10.

The number 6.32 is between 1 and 10. You can find log 6.32, correct to the nearest 0.0001, in the table as follows.

Notice that 6.32 has three significant digits: 6, 3, and 2. To find log 6.32, locate the row labeled *63* and the column headed *2*. The row and the column intersect at 8007. This means that
$$6.32 = 10^{.8007} \text{ or } \log 6.32 = 0.8007,$$
correct to the nearest 0.0001. Notice that all decimal points are omitted in the table.

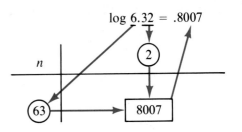

This table can also be used to find antilog 0.8007. Find 8007 in the table and reverse the steps above to find the row labeled *63* and the column headed *2*. This means that
$$10^{.8007} = 6.32 \text{ or antilog } 0.8007 = 6.32, \text{ correct to 3 significant digits.}$$

Example 2 Find log 5.46 and antilog 0.5391. Use the table on page 595.

$1 < 5.46 < 10$	Find 5391 in the table.
Row *54* and column 6 intersect at 7372.	5391 is in row *34* and column 6.
	$1 < 3.46 < 10$

Thus, log 5.46 = 0.7372 and antilog 0.5391 = 3.46.

For each real number $y > 0$ where y is not an integral power of 10, log y is an irrational number. However, in this chapter the equals sign (=) will be used to show logarithms correct to the nearest 0.0001 and to show antilogarithms correct to 3 significant digits.

Written Exercises

Find each logarithm or antilogarithm.

(A)
1. log 100,000 **5**
2. log 1 **0**
3. antilog 1 **10**
4. antilog 2 **100**
5. log 3.45 **0.5378**
6. antilog 0.2430 **1.75**
7. log 8.02 **0.9042**
8. antilog 0.3096 **2.04**
9. antilog 0.8142 **6.52**
10. log 7.60 **0.8808**
11. antilog 0.9943 **9.87**
12. log 4.69 **0.6712**

(B)
13. log 4.3 **0.6335**
14. antilog 0.3802 **2.40**
15. log 5 **0.6990**
16. antilog 0.9542 **9.00**
17. log 10^6 **6**
18. log $10^{.2253}$ **0.2253**
19. antilog 0 **1.00**
20. antilog (log 2.8) **2.8**

Solve each equation for x. [Hint: First, find each logarithm.]

21. $x^2 = \log 10^{5x-6}$ **2, 3**
22. $\dfrac{x+5}{\log 100} = \dfrac{\log 1{,}000}{x}$ **−6, 1**
23. $\dfrac{\log 10^{\frac{1}{x}}}{x} = \dfrac{1}{9}$ **3, −3**

Find the sum of each series for the given data.

(C)
24. $\displaystyle\sum_{k=1}^{5} \log (0.1)^{k-4}$ **5**
25. $\displaystyle\sum_{n=2}^{5} \log \sqrt[n]{10}$ $1\frac{17}{60}$
26. $5 \cdot \displaystyle\sum_{j=1}^{5} \text{antilog } (j-1)$
   55, 555

15.2 Characteristic and Mantissa

OBJECTIVES ▶ **To find the log of a number between 0 and 1 or greater than 10**
To find the antilog of a number greater than 1 or less than 0

In the previous lesson, you found logarithms of numbers that were either positive integral powers of 10 or were between 1 and 10. You can find the logarithm of a negative integral power of 10 by using the definition of the base-10 log y. For example, $0.01 = 10^{-2}$ and

$$\log 0.01 = \log 10^{-2} = -2.$$

You can find logarithms of numbers between 0 and 1 and logarithms of all real numbers greater than 10 by using scientific notation. Recall that a number is in scientific notation when it is written in the form $a \times 10^c$ where $1 \leq a < 10$ and c is an integer.

Scientific notation:	$54{,}600 = 5.46 \times 10^4$	$0.0546 = 5.46 \times 10^{-2}$
Log $5.46 = 0.7372$:	$54{,}600 = 10^{.7372} \times 10^4$	$0.0546 = 10^{.7372} \times 10^{-2}$
$10^m \cdot 10^n = 10^{m+n}$:	$54{,}600 = 10^{4 + .7372}$	$0.0546 = 10^{-2 + .7372}$

Log $54{,}600 = 4 + .7372$, or 4.7372, and $\log 0.0546 = -2 + .7372$, or $8.7372 - 10$. Notice that each of these logs has an *integer part* and a *decimal part*.

log $54{,}600 = 4.7372$,   or $4 + .7372$
log $0.0546 = 8.7372 - 10$,   or $-2 + .7372$

Characteristic, or integer part ——┘   └—— **Mantissa,** or decimal part

Notice that: (1) The mantissa of log 5.46, log 54,600, and log 0.0546 is the same, 0.7372.
(2) Log $0.0546 = -2 + .7372$. It is not written as -1.2628, or $-1 + (-.2628)$. A mantissa of a log is a positive number found in a table of logarithms.
(3) The characteristic of log 0.0546 is written as either -2 or $8 - 10$. A characteristic of a log is determined by the location of the decimal point.

Definition:
Characteristic
Mantissa

For each positive real number y, if $y = a \times 10^c$ where $1 \leq a < 10$ and c is an integer, then $\log y = c + \log a$. The variable c represents the *characteristic* and $\log a$ is the *mantissa* of $\log y$.

Example 1 Find log 2,940 and log 0.00294.

$2{,}940 = 2.94 \times 10^3$ $0.00294 = 2.94 \times 10^{-3}$
log $2.94 = 0.4683$ log $2.94 = 0.4683$

Thus, log $2{,}940 = 3.4683$, and $\log 0.00294 = -3 + 0.4683$, or $7.4683 - 10$.

You can find the antilog of a number greater than 1 or less than 0 by using the definition: antilog $x = 10^x$.

Example 2 Find antilog 4.9309 and antilog 6.9309 − 10.

	antilog (4 + .9309)		antilog (−4 + .9309)
$antilog\ x = 10^x$ ▶	$10^{4+.9309}$		$10^{-4+.9309}$
$10^{m+n} = 10^m \cdot 10^n$ ▶	$10^4 \cdot 10^{.9309}$		$10^{-4} \cdot 10^{.9309}$
$10^{.9309} = antilog\ 0.9309$ ▶	$10^4 \cdot 8.53$		$10^{-4} \cdot 8.53$
	85,300		0.000853

Thus, antilog 4.9309 = 85,300 and antilog 6.9309 − 10 = 0.000853.

Reading in Algebra

Using the equation, log 346 = 2.5391, identify each of the following.

2.5391 ⟩

1. The logarithm **2.5391**
2. The antilogarithm **346**
3. The value of x if $346 = 10^x$ **2.5391**
4. The mantissa **.5391**
5. The characteristic **2**
6. The value of y if $y = 10^{2.5391}$ **346**

Write the characteristic of each logarithm in two ways.

7. log 0.0023 = 7.3617 − 10 **−3, 7 − 10**
8. log 0.23 = −1 + .3617 **−1, 9 − 10**

Written Exercises

Find each logarithm or antilogarithm.

Ⓐ
1. log 0.001 **−3**
2. antilog −1 **0.1**
3. antilog 0 **1**
4. log 6,450 **3.8096**
5. antilog 1.8129 **65.0**
6. log 19,800 **4.2967**
7. antilog 2.5132 **326**
8. log 0.207 **9.3160 − 10**
9. antilog 7.5132 − 10 **0.00326**
10. log 0.00613 **7.7875 − 10**
11. antilog (−2 + .2227) **0.0167**
12. log 0.000502 **6.7007 − 10**
13. antilog 9.7987 − 10 **0.629**
14. log 0.0534 **8.7275 − 10**
15. antilog 4.9206 **83,300**

Ⓑ
16. log 32,600,000 **7.5132**
17. antilog 6.9345 − 10 **0.000860**
18. log 0.000000732 **3.8645 − 10**
19. log $10^{\frac{1}{2}}$ **$\frac{1}{2}$**
20. log $\sqrt[3]{10}$ **$\frac{1}{3}$**
21. log $\sqrt[3]{100}$ **$\frac{2}{3}$**

➤ A Challenge To You

1. Find log (antilog (log (antilog (log 123)))). **2.0899**
2. Find $\sum\limits_{k=1}^{6} \log 100^{k-3}$. **6**

Cumulative Review

Simplify and write each expression with positive exponents.

1. $x^7 y^{-4} z^{-2} \cdot x^{-5} y^6 z^{-3}$ **$\dfrac{x^2 y^2}{z^5}$**
2. $\dfrac{m^5 n^{-3} p^{-2}}{m^{-2} n^4 p^{-6}}$ **$\dfrac{m^7 p^4}{n^7}$**
3. $(5a^2 b^{-4})^3$ **$\dfrac{125 a^6}{b^{12}}$**
4. $\left(\dfrac{27 c^{12}}{d^{-6}}\right)^{\frac{2}{3}}$ **$9 c^8 d^4$**

15.3 Logs of Products and Quotients

OBJECTIVES ▶ **To find products and quotients using logarithms**
To solve a logarithmic equation containing a sum or difference of logarithms

Positive numbers can be multiplied or divided using logarithms and antilogarithms. To do this, two properties of the base-10 log function are needed. Each log property is based on an exponent property, since a logarithm is an exponent.

$$\log (100 \cdot 1{,}000) = \log (10^2 \cdot 10^3) = \log (10^{2+3}) = 2 + 3 = \log 100 + \log 1{,}000$$

$$\log \left(\frac{100{,}000}{1{,}000}\right) = \log \left(\frac{10^5}{10^3}\right) = \log (10^{5-3}) = 5 - 3 = \log 100{,}000 - \log 1{,}000$$

Log of a Product
Log of a Quotient

> For all positive real numbers a and b, $\log (a \cdot b) = \log a + \log b$ and
> $$\log \frac{a}{b} = \log a - \log b.$$

To find the logarithm of a product, add the logarithms of the factors.
To find the logarithm of a quotient, subtract the logarithm of the divisor from the logarithm of the dividend.

Example 1

Find 3.42 × 5,170 to three significant digits. Use logarithms.

$$\begin{aligned}
\log (3.42 \times 5{,}170) &= \log 3.42 + \log 5{,}170 \qquad \blacktriangleleft \; log \, (a \cdot b) = log \, a + log \, b \\
&= 0.5340 + 3.7135 \\
&= 4.2475 \qquad\qquad\quad \blacktriangleleft \; 0.2475 \; is \; between \; 0.2455 \; and \\
&\qquad\qquad\qquad\qquad\qquad\qquad 0.2480 \; in \; the \; table. \\
&\doteq 4.2480 \qquad\qquad\quad \blacktriangleleft \; Use \; 0.2480, \; the \; nearest \; mantissa.
\end{aligned}$$

antilog $4.2480 = 10^4 \times 1.77$

Thus, 3.42 × 5,170 = 17,700 to three significant digits.

Example 2

Find $\dfrac{61.7}{0.0913}$ to three significant digits. Use logarithms.

$$\log \left(\frac{61.7}{0.0913}\right) = \log 61.7 - \log 0.0913 = 1.7903 - (8.9605 - 10)$$

$$\begin{array}{r}
11.7903 - 10 \\
(-) \;\; 8.9605 - 10 \\
\hline
2.8298
\end{array}$$

◀ *Write the characteristic as 11 − 10.*

◀ *Use the nearest mantissa, 0.8299.*

antilog $(2 + .8299) = 10^2 \times 6.76$

Thus, $\dfrac{61.7}{0.0913} = 676$ to three significant digits.

Example 6 Solve $\frac{1}{2} \log y + \frac{1}{2} \log (y - 6) = \log 4$. Check.

$\log y^{\frac{1}{2}} + \log (y - 6)^{\frac{1}{2}} = \log 4$

$\log \sqrt{y} + \log \sqrt{y - 6} = \log 4$

$\log (\sqrt{y} \cdot \sqrt{y - 6}) = \log 4$

$\sqrt{y^2 - 6y} = 4$

$y^2 - 6y = 16$

$y^2 - 6y - 16 = 0$

$(y - 8)(y + 2) = 0$

$y = 8 \quad \text{or} \quad y = -2$

Check: $y = 8$	$\frac{1}{2} \log y + \frac{1}{2} \log (y - 6)$	$\log 4$
	$\frac{1}{2} \log 8 + \frac{1}{2} \log 2$	$\log 4$
	$\log \sqrt{8} + \log \sqrt{2}$	
	$\log (\sqrt{8} \cdot \sqrt{2})$	
	$\log \sqrt{16}$, or $\log 4$	

Check: $y = -2$ Log (-2) is undefined, so -2 is extraneous.

Thus, 8 is the solution.

Written Exercises

Find the value of each expression to three significant digits. Use logarithms.

Ⓐ 1. 49.4^3 **121,000** 2. 2.37^5 **74.7** 3. 0.0871^2 **0.00759**

4. 0.723^4 **0.273** 5. $\sqrt[4]{82.1}$ **3.01** 6. $\sqrt[3]{19,400}$ **26.9**

7. $\sqrt{0.00592}$ **0.0769** 8. $\sqrt[3]{0.0736}$ **0.419** 9. $(18.9 \times 4.04)^3$ **445,000**

10. $\sqrt{\dfrac{735}{3,420}}$ **0.464** 11. $\left(\dfrac{0.756}{1.83}\right)^4$ **0.0291** 12. $\sqrt[4]{0.263 \times 31.4}$ **1.70**

Solve each equation. Check.

13. $2 \log y = \log 4 + \log (y + 8)$ **8**

14. $3 \log a = \log a + \log (5a - 6)$ **2, 3**

15. $\frac{1}{2} \log a + \frac{1}{2} \log (a + 5) = \log 6$ **4**

16. $\frac{1}{3} \log y + \frac{1}{3} \log (y + 2) = \log 2$ **2**

Ⓑ 17. $2 \log (2y + 2) = \log 16 + 2 \log (y - 2)$ **5**

18. $2 \log (3a + 1) = \log 4 + 2 \log (2a - 1)$ **3**

19. $\frac{1}{2} \log (c + 1) + \frac{1}{2} \log (c - 4) = \log 6$ **8**

20. $\frac{1}{2} \log (y - 1) - \frac{1}{2} \log (2y - 1) = \log 2 - \log 3$ **5**

Find the value of each expression to three significant digits. Use logarithms.

21. $\sqrt{5.76^3}$ **13.8** 22. $\sqrt[3]{502^2}$ **63.2** 23. $\dfrac{\sqrt{37.6}}{\sqrt[3]{23.8}}$ **2.13**

24. $\dfrac{\sqrt{0.0462}}{1.73^3}$ **0.0415** 25. $\dfrac{\sqrt[3]{93.2}}{0.064 \times 27.3}$ **2.59** 26. $\sqrt{\dfrac{0.813^2}{283 \times 0.046}}$ **0.225**

27. Can logarithms be used to do a computation like $4.71 + 68.5 - 32.4$? **No**

28. List the kinds of computations that are convenient to do using logarithms.
products, quotients, powers, roots

Use the properties of logarithms to prove each statement.

Ⓒ 29. $\log \left(\dfrac{a^2}{bc}\right)^r = 2r \cdot \log a - r \cdot \log b - r \cdot \log c$

30. $\log \sqrt[n]{\dfrac{ab}{c}} = \dfrac{\log a + \log b - \log c}{n}$

For Ex. 29–30, see TE Answer Section.

LOGS OF POWERS AND RADICALS

Applications

Read → Plan → Solve → Interpret

If an investment is earning simple interest, the principal remains constant. If the investment is earning *compound interest* and it is compounded annually, the principal is increased each year by the amount of interest earned in the previous year.

If $500 is invested at a simple interest rate of 10% per year for 10 years, the total amounts at the end of the year for the years 0 through 10 form an arithmetic progression as shown below.

Year ▶	**0**	**1**	**2**	**3**	**4**	**5**	**6**	**7**	**8**	**9**	**10**
Amount ▶	$500,	$550,	$600,	$650,	$700,	$750,	$800,	$850,	$900,	$950,	$1,000

If the $500 earns compound interest at a rate of 10% per year, compounded annually for 10 years, the total amounts at the end of each year are as follows.

Year 0: $500
Year 1: $500 + $50 = $550
Year 2: $550 + $55 = $605
Year 3: $605 + $60.50 = $665.50
Year 4: $665.50 + $66.55 = $732.05

Year 5: $805.25
Year 6: $885.78
Year 7: $974.36
Year 8: $1,071.79
Year 9: $1,178.97
Year 10: $1,296.87

Notice that the difference between the earnings on the two investments at the end of ten years amounts to about $300. The bar graphs below illustrate the increasing differences year by year.

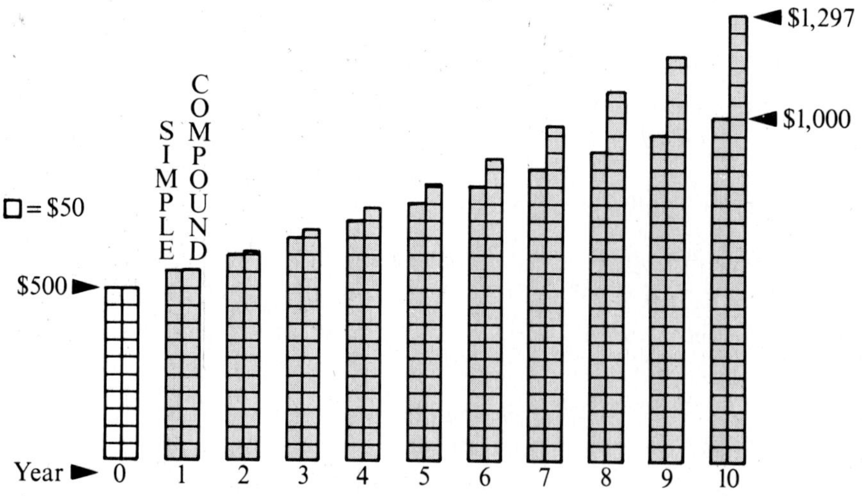

If the interest on an investment is compounded *semiannually*, then every 6 months the interest earned for a half year is added to the previous principal. This creates an even larger principal on which interest will be paid. Interest that is compounded *quarterly* is added to the previous principal every 3 months. In either case, the total earnings from the investment will be greater than that of an investment that is compounded annually.

Recall that the formula for *simple interest* is $i = prt$. The formula for compound interest is given below.

The formula for compound interest is

$$A = P\left(1 + \frac{r}{n}\right)^{nt}$$

Compound Interest Formula

where P is the principal invested,
r is the annual interest rate,
t is the number of years,
n is the number of times the interest is compounded in a year, and
A is the total amount in the account at the end of t years.

Example

A bond paying 8% interest, compounded semiannually, is bought for $3,000. How much will the bond be worth 10 years from now? Use logarithms.

$P = 3,000 \quad r = 0.08 \quad t = 10 \quad n = 2$

$A = P\left(1 + \frac{r}{n}\right)^{nt} = 3,000\left(1 + \frac{0.08}{2}\right)^{20} = 3,000(1.04)^{20}$

$\log A = \log 3,000 + 20 \cdot \log 1.04$
$\quad \doteq 3.4771 + 20(0.0170)$
$\quad = 3.8171$
$\quad A \doteq \text{antilog } 3.8171 = 10^3 \times 6.56 = 6,560$

Thus, the $3,000 bond will be worth $6,560 in 10 years.
(It will earn $3,560 in compound interest.)

Solve each problem.

1. How much would $3,000 earn in simple interest if it were invested at a simple interest rate of 8% per year for 10 years? Compare this earning with the earning in the Example. **$2,400**
2. How much will the bond in the Example be worth in 10 years if the interest is compounded quarterly? **$6,620**
3. How much will a $3,000 bond, paying 18% interest compounded every two months, be worth 10 years from now? **$17,600**
4. If the interest is compounded annually, how much will the bond in the Example be worth in 10 years? **$6,470**
5. Write the compound interest formula for the total amount where the interest is compounded annually. $A = P(1 + r)^t$

15.5 Logarithmic Expressions

OBJECTIVES ▶ To write a logarithmic expression in expanded form
To write a formula as a logarithmic equation in expanded form
To write an indicated sum of logarithmic terms as the log of one
expression

Many formulas found in areas of business and science involve products, quotients, powers, and radicals. Such formulas can be written as logarithmic equations in standard form. These logarithmic equations are often used to find the value of one of the variables in the formula.

Example 1 Write $\log \dfrac{2t^3}{mn}$ in expanded form.

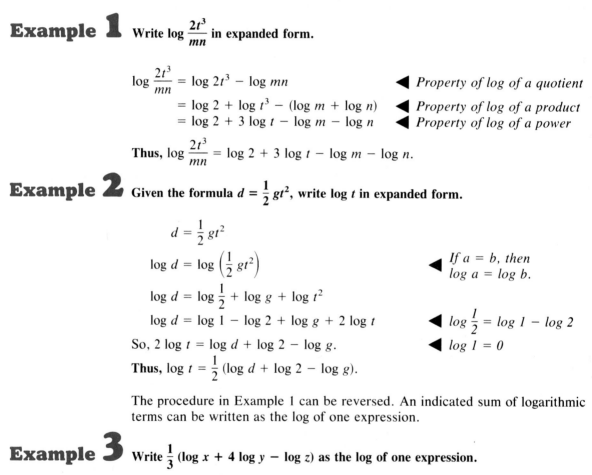

$\log \dfrac{2t^3}{mn} = \log 2t^3 - \log mn$ ◀ *Property of log of a quotient*

$= \log 2 + \log t^3 - (\log m + \log n)$ ◀ *Property of log of a product*
$= \log 2 + 3 \log t - \log m - \log n$ ◀ *Property of log of a power*

Thus, $\log \dfrac{2t^3}{mn} = \log 2 + 3 \log t - \log m - \log n.$

Example 2 Given the formula $d = \dfrac{1}{2} gt^2$, write $\log t$ in expanded form.

$d = \dfrac{1}{2} gt^2$

$\log d = \log \left(\dfrac{1}{2} gt^2 \right)$ ◀ *If a = b, then log a = log b.*

$\log d = \log \dfrac{1}{2} + \log g + \log t^2$

$\log d = \log 1 - \log 2 + \log g + 2 \log t$ ◀ *$\log \dfrac{1}{2} = \log 1 - \log 2$*

So, $2 \log t = \log d + \log 2 - \log g.$ ◀ *$\log 1 = 0$*

Thus, $\log t = \dfrac{1}{2} (\log d + \log 2 - \log g).$

The procedure in Example 1 can be reversed. An indicated sum of logarithmic terms can be written as the log of one expression.

Example 3 Write $\dfrac{1}{3} (\log x + 4 \log y - \log z)$ as the log of one expression.

$\dfrac{1}{3} (\log x + 4 \log y - \log z) = \dfrac{1}{3} (\log x + \log y^4 - \log z)$

$= \dfrac{1}{3} \cdot \log \dfrac{xy^4}{z} = \log \sqrt[3]{\dfrac{xy^4}{z}}$

Thus, $\dfrac{1}{3} (\log x + 4 \log y - \log z) = \log \sqrt[3]{\dfrac{xy^4}{z}}.$

Oral Exercises

Give each expression in expanded form.

1. $\log 5a$ **2.** $\log a^5$ **3.** $\log \frac{a}{3}$ **4.** $\log \sqrt[3]{a}$ **5.** $\log \frac{4}{a}$ **6.** $\log \sqrt{a}$

1. $\log 5 + \log a$ **2.** $5 \log a$ **3.** $\log a - \log 3$ **4.** $\frac{1}{3} \log a$ **5.** $\log 4 - \log a$ **6.** $\frac{1}{2} \log a$

State each expression as the log of one expression.

7. $\log 7 - \log b$ $\log \frac{7}{b}$ **8.** $4 \log b$ $\log b^4$ **9.** $\log 9 + \log b$ $\log 9b$ **10.** $\frac{1}{4} \log b$ $\log \sqrt[4]{b}$

Written Exercises For complete solutions, see TE Answer Section.

Write each logarithmic expression in expanded form.

Ⓐ
1. $\log 6lw$ **2.** $\log m^2 n$ **3.** $\log 3t^3 v^2$

4. $\log \frac{8f}{g}$ **5.** $\log \frac{v^2}{2h}$ **6.** $\log \frac{5d}{t^2}$

7. $\log \left(\frac{mn}{p}\right)^3$ **8.** $\log (t^2 v)^4$ **9.** $\log \left(\frac{a^2}{bc^4}\right)^3$

10. $\log \sqrt{2gh}$ **11.** $\log \sqrt[3]{\pi d^2}$ **12.** $\log \sqrt[4]{\frac{5d}{g^3}}$

For each formula, write the indicated log in expanded form.

13. $L = 2\pi rh$: $\log L$ **14.** $A = \pi r^2$: $\log A$ **15.** $A = \frac{1}{2} bh$: $\log A$

16. $i = prt$: $\log t$ **17.** $V = \frac{1}{3} Bh$: $\log B$ **18.** $d = \frac{1}{2} gt^2$: $\log g$

19. $v = \sqrt{2gh}$: $\log v$ **20.** $V = e^3$: $\log e$ **21.** $E = mc^2$: $\log c$

Write each expression as the log of one expression.

22. $\log 6 + \log 2x + \log 3y$ $\log 36xy$ **23.** $\log 5x + \log 4x - \log 3y - \log y$ $\log \frac{20x^2}{3y^2}$

24. $\log 4 + 2 \log t + 3 \log v$ $\log 4t^2 v^3$ **25.** $2 \log a + 4 \log b - \log c - 3 \log d$ $\log \frac{a^2 b^4}{cd^3}$

Ⓑ
26. $\log 7 + \frac{1}{2} \log x - \log y$ $\log \frac{7\sqrt{x}}{y}$ **27.** $\frac{1}{3} \log 2a + \frac{1}{3} \log 5b - 2 \log a - \log b$ $\log \frac{\sqrt[3]{10ab}}{a^2 b}$

28. $3(\log m + 2 \log n - \log p)$ $\log \left(\frac{mn^2}{p}\right)^3$ **29.** $\frac{1}{4} (\log 3 + 3 \log x - \log 2 - \log 5y)$ $\log \sqrt[4]{\frac{3x^3}{10y}}$

For each formula, write the indicated log in expanded form.

30. $A = P(1.09)^{12}$: $\log A$ **31.** $V = \frac{4}{3} \pi r^3$: $\log V$

32. $A = 4\pi r^2$: $\log r$ **33.** $V = \frac{1}{3} \pi r^2 h$: $\log r$

34. If a sphere of radius r has a volume V, then $V = \frac{4}{3} \pi r^3$. Find the radius of the sphere where $V = 924$ cm^3 and $\pi = 3.14$. Use logarithms. **6.04 cm**

35. The time T for one period of a simple pendulum is given by the formula $T = 2\pi \sqrt{\frac{l}{g}}$ where l is the length of the pendulum and g is the acceleration due to gravity. Find l if $T = 4.5$ seconds, $g = 98$ meters per second per second, and $\pi = 3.14$. Use logarithms. **50.3 m**

Ⓒ
36. Prove: $\log \sqrt[3]{y^2} - \log \sqrt[4]{y^3} + 4 \log \sqrt[3]{y} - 5 \log \sqrt[4]{y} = 0$

37. Prove: $\frac{2}{5} \log 3 - \frac{1}{5} \log 2 - \frac{2}{5} \log 4 + \frac{1}{5} \log 27 = \log 3 - \log 2$

LOGARITHMIC EXPRESSIONS

15.6 Base-*n* Logarithms and Antilogarithms

OBJECTIVES ▶ To find the base-*n* logarithm of a positive number
To find the base-*n* antilogarithm of a real number
To solve a base-*n* logarithmic equation for *n*

You have been studying and using the base-10 log and antilog functions which are denoted by $\log_{10}$ and antilog_{10}, or log and antilog, respectively.

Any positive number $n \neq 1$ may be used as the base of a logarithmic function. Some base-5 logs ($\log_5$) and base-5 antilogs (antilog_5) are given below along with the corresponding powers of 5. Read "$\log_5 y$" as "the base-5 log of y" and read "$\text{antilog}_5 x$" as "the base-5 antilog of x."

Powers of 5	Base-5 logs	Base-5 antilogs
$125 = 5^3$	$\log_5 125 = 3$	$\text{antilog}_5 3 = 5^3 = 125$
$1 = 5^0$	$\log_5 1 = 0$	$\text{antilog}_5 0 = 5^0 = 1$
$\dfrac{1}{25} = 5^{-2}$	$\log_5 \dfrac{1}{25} = -2$	$\text{antilog}_5 -2 = 5^{-2} = \dfrac{1}{25}$
$\sqrt{5} = 5^{\frac{1}{2}}$	$\log_5 \sqrt{5} = \dfrac{1}{2}$	$\text{antilog}_5 \dfrac{1}{2} = 5^{\frac{1}{2}} = \sqrt{5}$

Think of $\log_5 125$ as the exponent 3. This is the power to which 5 must be raised to yield 125. Think of $\text{antilog}_5 3$ as 5^3, or 125.

Definition:
Base-*n* Logarithm
Base-*n* Antilogarithm

For each positive number y and each positive number $n \neq 1$, if $y = n^x$, then $\log_n y = \log_n n^x = x$.
For each real number x and each positive number $n \neq 1$, $\text{antilog}_n x = n^x$.

Example 1 Find $\log_2 8$ and $\log_2 \dfrac{1}{16}$.

$$8 = 2^3$$
$$\log_2 8 = \log_2 2^3 = 3$$

$$\frac{1}{16} = \frac{1}{2^4} = 2^{-4}$$
$$\log_2 \frac{1}{16} = \log_2 2^{-4} = -4$$

Thus, $\log_2 8 = 3$ and $\log_2 \dfrac{1}{16} = -4$.

Example 2 Find $\log_2 \sqrt[4]{2}$ and $\log_2 \sqrt[5]{8}$.

$$\sqrt[4]{2} = 2^{\frac{1}{4}}$$
$$\log_2 \sqrt[4]{2} = \log_2 2^{\frac{1}{4}} = \frac{1}{4}$$

$$\sqrt[5]{8} = \sqrt[5]{2^3} = 2^{\frac{3}{5}}$$
$$\log_2 \sqrt[5]{8} = \log_2 2^{\frac{3}{5}} = \frac{3}{5}$$

Thus, $\log_2 \sqrt[4]{2} = \dfrac{1}{4}$ and $\log_2 \sqrt[5]{8} = \dfrac{3}{5}$.

In the next example, a base-2 antilog and a base-3 antilog are computed.

Example 3 Find antilog$_2$ 7 and antilog$_3$ −4.

$$\text{antilog}_2 7 = 2^7 \quad \blacktriangleleft \quad antilog_n\ x = n^x \qquad \text{antilog}_3 -4 = 3^{-4}$$
$$= 128 \qquad\qquad\qquad\qquad\qquad = \frac{1}{3^4},\ \text{or}\ \frac{1}{81}$$

Thus, antilog$_2$ 7 = 128 and antilog$_3$ −4 = $\frac{1}{81}$.

You can solve a base-n logarithmic equation for n. Begin by rewriting a logarithmic equation of the form $\log_n y = x$ in the exponential form $y = n^x$.

Example 4 Solve each logarithmic equation for n.

$$\log_n 243 = 5 \quad \blacktriangleleft \quad Logarithmic\ form \qquad \log_n \frac{1}{25} = -2$$
$$243 = n^5 \quad \blacktriangleleft \quad Exponential\ form \qquad \frac{1}{25} = n^{-2}$$
$$3^5 = n^5 \qquad\qquad\qquad\qquad 5^{-2} = n^{-2}$$
$$3 = n \qquad\qquad\qquad\qquad\qquad 5 = n$$

Written Exercises

Find each logarithm or antilogarithm.

Ⓐ
1. $\log_7 49$ **2**
2. $\log_4 64$ **3**
3. $\log_3 81$ **4**
4. $\log_6 1$ **0**

5. $\log_3 3$ **1**
6. $\log_{12} 1$ **0**
7. $\log_2 \frac{1}{2}$ **−1**
8. $\log_4 \frac{1}{16}$ **−2**

9. $\log_3 \frac{1}{81}$ **−4**
10. $\log_2 \sqrt[3]{2}$ $\frac{1}{3}$
11. $\log_3 \sqrt[5]{3}$ $\frac{1}{5}$
12. $\log_6 \sqrt{6}$ $\frac{1}{2}$

13. antilog$_2$ 8 **256**
14. antilog$_3$ 5 **243**
15. antilog$_5$ 3 **125**
16. antilog$_{\frac{1}{2}}$ 5 $\frac{1}{32}$

17. antilog$_3$ −1 $\frac{1}{3}$
18. antilog$_6$ −2 $\frac{1}{36}$
19. antilog$_2$ −5 $\frac{1}{32}$
20. antilog$_8$ $\frac{2}{3}$ **4**

Solve each equation for n.

21. $\log_n 81 = 4$ **3**
22. $\log_n 32 = 5$ **2**
23. $\log_n 6 = 1$ **6**

Ⓑ
24. $\log_n \frac{1}{9} = -2$ **3**
25. $\log_n \frac{1}{125} = -3$ **5**
26. $\log_n \frac{1}{64} = -6$ **2**

Find each logarithm or antilogarithm.

27. $\log_2 \sqrt[5]{16}$ $\frac{4}{5}$
28. $\log_3 \sqrt[4]{27}$ $\frac{3}{4}$
29. $\log_5 \sqrt{125}$ $\frac{3}{2}$
30. antilog$_{\frac{2}{3}}$ −4 $\frac{81}{16}$

31. $\log_{\frac{1}{2}} \frac{1}{16}$ **4**
32. $\log_{\frac{3}{5}} \frac{27}{125}$ **3**
33. $\log_{\frac{3}{4}} \frac{16}{9}$ **−2**
34. antilog$_{\frac{16}{25}}$ 2 $\frac{64}{125}$

The properties of base-10 logs extend to base-n logs. Solve each equation for y.

35. $\log_4 3 + \log_4 (y - 2) = \log_4 2 + \log_4 y$ **6**
36. $\log_3 (y + 2) + \log_3 (y + 10) = 2 \log_3 (y + 4)$ **−1**

37. $\log_2 (2y - 5) - \log_2 2 = \log_2 (y + 5) - \log_2 4$ **5**
38. $\frac{1}{2} \log_5 2y + \frac{1}{2} \log_5 3 = \log_5 12$ **24**

Ⓒ
39. $\log_2 (y + 4) + \log_2 y = 5$ **4**
40. $\log_4 (3y + 1) + \log_4 (y - 1) = 3$ **5**

41. $\log_5 (y^2 + 2y + 5) - \log_5 (y - 5) = 2$ **10, 13**
42. $2 \log_3 (y - 2) - \log_3 (y - 4) = 2$ **5, 8**

15.7 Exponential Equations

▶ **To solve an exponential equation using base-10 logarithms**
To find the base-*n* log of a positive number, using a table of base-10 logarithms

An equation like $3^x = 17$ is called an **exponential equation** since the variable appears in the exponent. You can locate x between consecutive integers by knowing some powers of 3.

$$3^{-1} = \frac{1}{3} \quad 3^0 = 1 \quad 3^1 = 3 \quad 3^2 = 9 \quad 3^3 = 27$$

Since $9 < 17 < 27$, then $3^2 < 3^x < 3^3$. Thus, it follows that $2 < x < 3$. You can find x to three significant digits by using base-10 logs as shown below.

Example 1 Solve $3^x = 17$ for x to three significant digits.

$$3^x = 17$$
$$\log 3^x = \log 17 \quad ◀ \quad \textit{If } a = b, \textit{ then } \log a = \log b$$
$$x \cdot \log 3 = \log 17 \quad ◀ \quad \log a^r = r \cdot \log a$$
$$x = \frac{\log 17}{\log 3} \quad ◀ \quad \textit{Divide each side by } \log 3.$$
$$= \frac{1.2304}{0.4771}$$
$$= 2.579$$

Thus, $x = 2.58$ to three significant digits.

Example 2 Solve $4^{2x-1} = 7.65$ for x to three significant digits.

$$4^{2x-1} = 7.65$$
$$\log 4^{2x-1} = \log 7.65$$
$$(2x - 1)\log 4 = \log 7.65$$
$$2x - 1 = \frac{\log 7.65}{\log 4}$$
$$2x - 1 = \frac{0.8837}{0.6021}$$
$$2x - 1 = 1.468$$
$$2x = 2.468$$
$$x = 1.234$$

Thus, $x = 1.23$ to three significant digits.

You can estimate the value of x in the equation $4^{2x-1} = 7.65$ (Example 2).

$$4^1 = 4 \qquad 4^2 = 16 \qquad 4 < 7.65 < 16$$

So, $4^1 < 4^{2x-1} < 4^2 \rightarrow 1 < 2x - 1 < 2 \rightarrow 2 < 2x < 3 \rightarrow 1 < x < 1.5$.

In Example 2, the value of x was found to be 1.23. Notice that this agrees with your estimate that the value of x should be greater than 1 and less than 1.5.

A base-10 log such as log 4 is found in the table on page 595. A base-n log such as $\log_3 4$ can be found to three significant digits by solving an exponential equation using base-10 logs as shown in Example 3.

Example 3 Find $\log_3 4$ to three significant digits.

$$
\begin{aligned}
\text{Let} \quad \log_3 4 &= x. \qquad \blacktriangleleft \text{ Base-3 log} \\
3^x &= 4 \qquad \blacktriangleleft \text{ Change the equation to exponential form.} \\
\log 3^x &= \log 4 \qquad \blacktriangleleft \text{ Base-10 logs} \\
x \cdot \log 3 &= \log 4 \\
x &= \frac{\log 4}{\log 3} \\
&= \frac{0.6021}{0.4771} \\
&= 1.262
\end{aligned}
$$

Thus, $\log_3 4 = 1.26$ to three significant digits.

Reading in Algebra

For each equation, locate x between consecutive integers.

1. $5^x = 75$ $2 < x < 3$ 2. $3^x = 75$ $3 < x < 4$ 3. $2^x = 25$ $4 < x < 5$ 4. $4^x = 2$ $0 < x < 1$

Written Exercises

Solve each equation for x to three significant digits.

(A) 1. $4^x = 25$ **2.32**   2. $4^{2x} = 25$ **1.16**   3. $4^{x-1} = 25$ **3.32**
4. $9^x = 6$ **0.816**   5. $7^{x+1} = 56$ **1.07**   6. $8^{3x} = 72$ **0.686**

Find each logarithm to three significant digits.

7. $\log_2 6$ **2.59**   8. $\log_6 2$ **0.387**   9. $\log_5 14$ **1.64**
(B) 10. $\log_3 8.64$ **1.96**   11. $\log_2 \sqrt[3]{7}$ **0.936**   12. $\log_{2.72} 96.4$ **4.57**

Solve each equation for x to three significant digits.

13. $9^{2x+1} = 62.4$ **0.441**   14. $7^{3x-2} = 834$ **1.82**   15. $4 = 9^{2x-3}$ **1.82**
16. $6 = 15^{1-x}$ **0.338**   17. $1.76^x = 23.4$ **5.58**   18. $8 = 3 \cdot 5^x$ **0.609**
(C) 19. $3^x = 4 \cdot 2^x$ **3.42**   20. $2 \cdot 5^{x+1} = 5 \cdot 2^{x+2}$ **0.756**   21. $2^{6x-3} = 4 \cdot 2^{4x}$ **2.50**

Prove that each statement is true. Each variable represents a positive number $\neq 1$.

22. $\log_a y = \dfrac{\log y}{\log a}$ 23. $\log_a y = \dfrac{\log_b y}{\log_b a}$ 24. $\log_a y = \dfrac{1}{\log_y a}$

For Ex. 22–24, see TE Answer Section.

EXPONENTIAL EQUATIONS

Applications

Exponential equations and functions can be applied to measure the amount of growth or decay of certain materials. An example of an application of this type is the growth of bacteria.

Bacteria are one-celled organisms. One *bacterium* of a common type measures 0.0001 cm across. One thousand such bacteria would just about cover the period at the end of this sentence.

Some bacteria reproduce by splitting themselves into two new bacteria at the end of a growth period. This process of splitting is called *simple fission*. Under optimum conditions, bacteria reproduce very rapidly. One bacterium can grow and split into two new bacteria in less than thirty minutes.

If simple fission takes place once each hour, how many bacteria will be present at the end of a 24-hour period if you start with one bacterium?

Elapsed time in hours ▶	0	1	2	3	4	5	6 ⋯	10 ⋯	15 ⋯	20 ⋯	24
Number of bacteria ▶	1	2	4	8	16	32	64 ⋯	1,024 ⋯	32,768 ⋯	1,048,576 ⋯	16,777,216

Thus, there will be more than 16 million, or 1.6×10^7, bacteria at the end of 24 hours.

Suppose there are 400 bacteria at the start of an experiment and simple fission takes place every 20 minutes, or 3 times in each hour. How many bacteria will be present at the end of 6 hours?

Elapsed time in k periods, 20 minutes per period ▶	0	1	2	3	4	⋯	k	⋯	18
	400	800	1,600	3,200	6,400		↓		104,857,600
Number of bacteria, N ▶	400	$400 \cdot 2$	$400 \cdot 2^2$	$400 \cdot 2^3$	$400 \cdot 2^4$ ⋯		$400 \cdot 2^k$	⋯	$400 \cdot 2^{18}$

Since there are 3×6, or 18, twenty-minute periods in 6 hours, the number, N, of bacteria at the end of 6 hours is $400 \cdot 2^{18}$, or more than 104 million.

In general,
$$N = N_0 \cdot 2^k$$

where N is the number of bacteria present at the end of k periods of simple fission, and N_0 is the number of bacteria at the start.

Example

To three significant digits, find the number of bacteria produced from 500 bacteria at the end of 4 hours if simple fission occurs every 12 minutes. Use logarithms.

There are 5×4, or 20, twelve-minute periods in 4 hours.

$$N = N_0 \cdot 2^k = 500 \cdot 2^{20}$$
$$\log N = \log (500 \cdot 2^{20})$$
$$= \log 500 + \log 2^{20}$$
$$= \log 500 + 20 \log 2$$
$$= 2.6990 + 20(0.3010)$$
$$= 8.7190$$
antilog $8.7190 = 10^8 \times 5.24$
Thus, $N \doteq 5.24 \times 10^8$, or 524,000,000 bacteria.

Solve each problem.

Find N to three significant digits for the given data. Use logarithms and the formula $N = N_0 \cdot 2^k$.

1. $N_0 = 750$ and simple fission occurs every 15 minutes for 3 hours.

   3,070,000

2. $N_0 = 3,000$ and simple fission occurs every 90 minutes for 18 hours.

   12,300,000

3. $N_0 = 25,000$ and simple fission occurs every 30 minutes for 24 hours.

   7.01×10^{18}

15.8 Graphs of Exponential and Logarithmic Functions

OBJECTIVES ▶ **To draw the graph of an exponential function**
To draw the graph of a logarithmic function
To read and interpret the graphs of exponential and logarithmic functions

The exponential equation $y = 2^x$ defines the base-2 **exponential function.**
A graph of this function is drawn using the table of ordered pairs below.

x	-3	-2	-1	0	1	2	3	4
$y = 2^x$	$\frac{1}{8}$	$\frac{1}{4}$	$\frac{1}{2}$	1	2	4	8	16

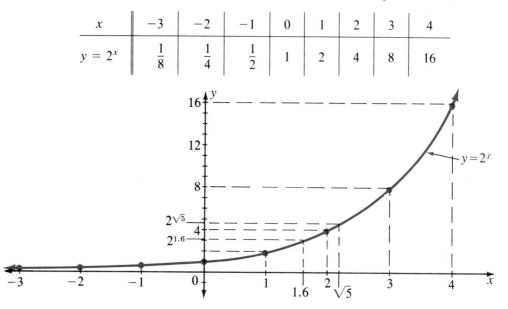

The ordered pairs of the table are plotted at the 8 points shown by the dots.
Notice that different scales are used along the x and y axes of the graph.

To draw the graph of the function defined by $y = 2^x$, integers were used as
the values for x. However, any rational or irrational number could be used.

Let $x = 1.6$. Then $2^{1.6}$ can be found
to three significant digits with logs.
$$\log 2^{1.6} = 1.6 \cdot \log 2$$
$$= 0.4816$$
antilog $0.4816 = 3.03$
So, $2^{1.6} = 3.03$.

Let $x = \sqrt{5} \doteq 2.236$. Then $2^{\sqrt{5}}$ can
be approximated with logs.
$$\log 2^{2.236} = 2.236 \cdot \log 2$$
$$= 0.6730$$
antilog $0.6730 = 4.71$
So, $2^{\sqrt{5}} \doteq 4.71$.

From the graph, you can list the following properties of the function defined by
$y = 2^x$:
    (1) The domain is {all real numbers}.
    (2) The range is $\{y \mid y > 0\}$.
    (3) The ordered pair $(0, 1)$ belongs to the function. That is, $2^0 = 1$.
    (4) The function is *constantly increasing*. If $x_2 > x_1$, then $y_2 > y_1$.

410

Example 1 Graph the exponential function defined by the equation $y = \left(\frac{1}{2}\right)^x$. List four properties of the function.

Make a table of ordered pairs. Notice that $y = \left(\frac{1}{2}\right)^x = \frac{1}{2^x} = 2^{-x}$.

x	-3	-2	-1	0	1	2	3
$y = \left(\frac{1}{2}\right)^x = 2^{-x}$	8	4	2	1	$\frac{1}{2}$	$\frac{1}{4}$	$\frac{1}{8}$

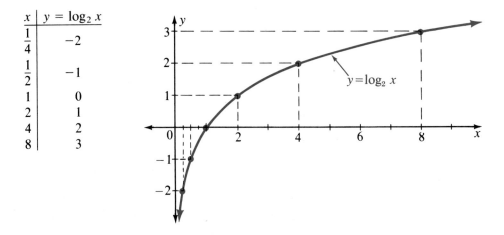

Properties: (1) The domain is {all real numbers}.
(2) The range is $\{y \mid y > 0\}$.
(3) The ordered pair $(0, 1)$ belongs to the function.
(4) The function is *constantly decreasing*. If $x_2 > x_1$, then $y_2 < y_1$.

Notice that the graph of $y = \left(\frac{1}{2}\right)^x = 2^{-x}$ is symmetric to the graph of $y = 2^x$ (page 410) with respect to the y-axis.

The base-2 **logarithmic function** is defined by the equation $y = \log_2 x$. A graph of this function is shown below.

x	$y = \log_2 x$
$\frac{1}{4}$	-2
$\frac{1}{2}$	-1
1	0
2	1
4	2
8	3

The preceding graph shows the following properties of the function defined by $y = \log_2 x$:

    (1) The domain is $\{x | x > 0\}$.
    (2) The range is {all real numbers}.
    (3) The ordered pair $(1, 0)$ belongs to the function.
    (4) The function is constantly increasing. If $x_2 > x_1$, then $y_2 > y_1$.

As shown below, the graph of $y = \log_2 x$ is symmetric to the graph of $y = 2^x$ with respect to the line described by $y = x$. This suggests that these two functions are a pair of *inverse functions*.

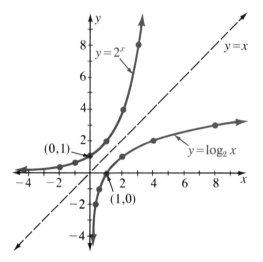

Recall that you can write an equation of the inverse of a function by interchanging the variables in an equation of the function.

The inverse of $y = 2^x$ is $x = 2^y$. If $x = 2^y$, then $y = \log_2 x$.

Therefore, the base-2 exponential function and the base-2 logarithmic function are a pair of inverse functions.

Inverse of log$_n$ Function

> For each positive number $n \neq 1$, the inverse of the $\log_n$ function is the base-n exponential function.

The graph of the base-$\frac{1}{2}$ log function, defined by $y = \log_{\frac{1}{2}} x$, is drawn in Example 2 on page 413. Notice that

(1) The graph of $y = \log_{\frac{1}{2}} x$ is symmetric to the graph of $y = \log_2 x$ with respect to the x-axis.

(2) The graph of $y = \log_{\frac{1}{2}} x$ is symmetric to the graph of $y = \left(\frac{1}{2}\right)^x$ with respect to the line described by $y = x$. This shows that the base-$\frac{1}{2}$ log function and the base-$\frac{1}{2}$ exponential function are a pair of inverse functions.

Example 2 Graph the logarithmic function defined by the equation $y = \log_{\frac{1}{2}} x$. List four properties of the function.

Make a table of ordered pairs. Notice that $y = \log_{\frac{1}{2}} x$ is equivalent to

$$x = \left(\frac{1}{2}\right)^y, \text{ or } x = 2^{-y}.$$

x	$\frac{1}{8}$	$\frac{1}{4}$	$\frac{1}{2}$	1	2	4	8
$y = \log_{\frac{1}{2}} x$, or $x = 2^{-y}$	3	2	1	0	-1	-2	-3

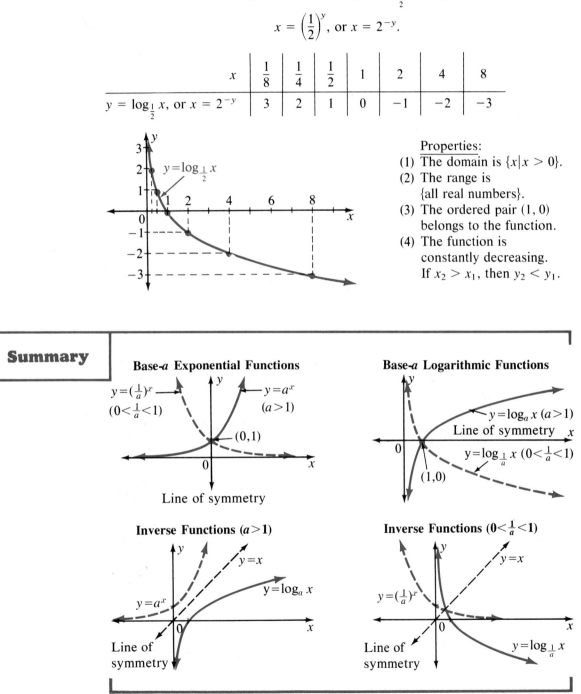

Properties:
(1) The domain is $\{x \mid x > 0\}$.
(2) The range is {all real numbers}.
(3) The ordered pair $(1, 0)$ belongs to the function.
(4) The function is constantly decreasing. If $x_2 > x_1$, then $y_2 < y_1$.

Summary

Base-a Exponential Functions

$y = \left(\frac{1}{a}\right)^x$ $(0 < \frac{1}{a} < 1)$

$y = a^x$ $(a > 1)$

$(0, 1)$

Line of symmetry

Base-a Logarithmic Functions

$y = \log_a x$ $(a > 1)$

Line of symmetry

$y = \log_{\frac{1}{a}} x$ $(0 < \frac{1}{a} < 1)$

$(1, 0)$

Inverse Functions $(a > 1)$

$y = x$

$y = \log_a x$

$y = a^x$

Line of symmetry

Inverse Functions $(0 < \frac{1}{a} < 1)$

$y = x$

$y = \left(\frac{1}{a}\right)^x$

$y = \log_{\frac{1}{a}} x$

Line of symmetry

Reading in Algebra

The equations of two functions are given. Determine whether the graphs of the functions are symmetric with respect to the x-axis, the y-axis, or to the line described by $y = x$. Are the two functions inverses of each other?

1. $y = \log_6 x$, $y = \log_{\frac{1}{6}} x$ x-axis; not inverses

2. $y = \log_6 x$, $y = 6^x$ line y = x; inverses

3. $y = 6^x$, $y = \left(\frac{1}{6}\right)^x$ y-axis; not inverses

4. $y = \log_{\frac{1}{6}} x$, $y = \left(\frac{1}{6}\right)^x$ line y = x; inverses

Written Exercises

For Ex. 1–14, see TE Answer Section.

Graph the function defined by each equation. List four properties of the function.

Ⓐ **1.** $y = 3^x$

2. $y = \left(\frac{1}{3}\right)^x$

3. $y = \log_3 x$

4. $y = \log_{\frac{1}{3}} x$

5. $y = 10^x$

6. $y = \log x$

Graph each pair of functions in the same coordinate plane.

7. The base-4 log function and the base-4 exponential function

8. The base-$\frac{1}{5}$ exponential function and the base-$\frac{1}{5}$ log function

Graph the function defined by each equation. List four properties of the function.

9. $y = 3 \cdot 2^x$

10. $y = 2\left(\frac{1}{3}\right)^x$

Ⓑ **11.** $y = 5 \cdot \log_2 x$

12. $y = 3 \cdot \log_3 x$

13. $y = 3^x + 2$

14. $y = \left(\frac{1}{2}\right)^x - 4$

For the function defined by each equation, write an equation of the inverse function.

15. $y = 5^x$ $y = \log_5 x$

16. $y = \log_{\frac{1}{3}} x$ $y = \left(\frac{1}{3}\right)^x$

17. $y = \log_8 x$ $y = 8^x$

18. $y = \left(\frac{1}{4}\right)^x$ $y = \log_{\frac{1}{4}} x$

For each function, write an equation of another function so that their graphs are symmetric with respect to the x-axis.

19. $y = \log_5 x$ $y = \log_{\frac{1}{5}} x$

20. $y = \log_{\frac{1}{4}} x$ $y = \log_4 x$

For each function, write an equation of another function so that their graphs are symmetric with respect to the y-axis.

21. $y = 4^x$ $y = \left(\frac{1}{4}\right)^x$

22. $y = \left(\frac{1}{7}\right)^x$ $y = 7^x$

Ⓒ **23.** Prove: The functions described by $f(x) = \log_5 x$ and $g(x) = 5^x$ are inverse functions.

24. Prove: The base-n log function and the base-n exponential function are a pair of inverse functions, for each $n > 0$ and $n \neq 1$.

25. Graph the function defined by $y = 2^{x-3}$.

26. Graph the function defined by $y = \log_2(x - 2)$.

For Ex. 23–26, see TE Answer Section.

Cumulative Review

1. Solve $\frac{y}{10} = \frac{7}{11}$. $6\frac{4}{11}$

2. Solve $\frac{9}{10} = \frac{x}{12}$. $10\frac{4}{5}$

3. Solve $\frac{y}{10} = \frac{11}{25}$. $4\frac{2}{5}$

15.9 Linear Interpolation

OBJECTIVES ▶ **To approximate logarithms and antilogarithms using linear interpolation**
To find products and quotients using logarithms and linear interpolation

At a constant speed, an automobile traveled 48 km in 30 minutes and 64 km in 40 minutes. The distance traveled in 33 minutes can be found by solving a proportion that expresses the relationship between time and distance.

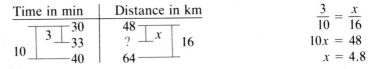

$$\frac{3}{10} = \frac{x}{16}$$
$$10x = 48$$
$$x = 4.8$$

Thus, the car traveled 48 + 4.8 km, or 52.8 km, in 33 minutes.

The procedure used above is called **linear interpolation.** As shown in the graph at the right, the point whose coordinates are (33, 52.8) was found between the points with coordinates (30, 48) and (40, 64). The term "linear" interpolation is used since $\frac{t}{10} = \frac{d}{16}$, or $d = \frac{8}{5}t$, is an equation of a linear function.

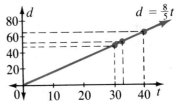

The graph of the function defined by $y = \log x$ is not a line, but over a short interval, the graph is very "close to" a horizontal segment. Thus, linear interpolation can be used to approximate the logarithm of a number, such as log 35.26, that cannot be found directly in a table of common logarithms.

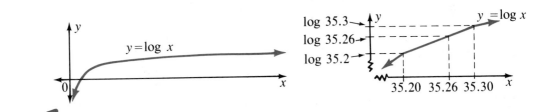

Example 1 Find log 35.26 to four decimal places. Use linear interpolation.

35.20 < 35.26 < 35.30

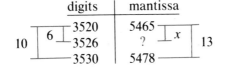

The mantissas for log 35.20 and log 35.30 are in the table.

$$\frac{6}{10} = \frac{x}{13}$$ ◀ *Write a proportion.*
$$10x = 78$$
$$x = 7.8, \text{ or } 8$$

So, 5465 + 8 = 5473.

Thus, log 35.26 = 1 + 0.5473 = 1.5473.

Linear interpolation can also be used to find an antilogarithm that cannot be found directly in the table. For example, antilog $(8.4239 - 10)$ can be found to four significant digits as shown in Example 2.

Example 2

Find antilog $(8.4239 - 10)$ to four significant digits. Use linear interpolation.

In the table, the nearest mantissas to 4239 are 4232 and 4249.

$$4232 < 4239 < 4249$$
$$\text{antilog } .4232 = 2.650 \qquad \text{antilog } .4249 = 2.660$$

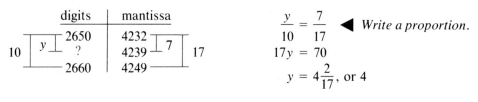

$$\frac{y}{10} = \frac{7}{17} \qquad \blacktriangleleft \textit{Write a proportion.}$$
$$17y = 70$$
$$y = 4\frac{2}{17}, \text{ or } 4$$

So, $2650 + 4 = 2654$.

Thus, antilog $(8.4239 - 10) = 10^{-2} \times 2.654$, or 0.02654.

When using logs to find a product, quotient, power, or root, you may have to use linear interpolation.

Example 3

Find 589.3×0.04716 to four significant digits. Use logarithms and linear interpolation.

digits	mantissa
5890	7701
5893	(7703)
5900	7709

$\dfrac{3}{10} = \dfrac{x}{8}$

$x = 2.4$

$\doteq 2$

digits	mantissa
4710	6730
4716	(6735)
4720	6739

$\dfrac{6}{10} = \dfrac{x}{9}$

$x = 5.4$

$\doteq 5$

$$\log 589.3 = 2.7703 \qquad \log 0.04716 = 8.6735 - 10$$

$$\log (589.3 \times 0.04716) = \log 589.3 + \log 0.04716 \qquad \blacktriangleleft \log (a \cdot b) = \log a + \log b$$
$$= 2.7703 + (8.6735 - 10)$$
$$= 1.4438$$
$$\text{antilog } 1.4438 = 27.79 \qquad \blacktriangleleft \textit{Interpolated to four significant digits}$$

Thus, $589.3 \times 0.04716 = 27.79$.

Reading in Algebra

If linear "inter-polating" is finding the coordinates of a point on a line that is between two given points of the line whose coordinates are known, what is meant by linear "extra-polating?"
Finding the coordinates of a point on a line that is not *between* two given points of the line.

Written **Exercises**

Find each logarithm to four decimal places. Use linear interpolation.

(A) **1.** log 19.22 **1.2838**   **2.** log 354.5 **2.5496**   **3.** log 0.7347 **9.8661 − 10**   **4.** log 0.002073
7.3166 − 10

Find each antilogarithm to four significant digits. Use linear interpolation.

5. antilog 0.4189   **6.** antilog 3.3394 **2,185**   **7.** antilog(−1 + .2681)   **8.** antilog(8.5152 − 10)
2.624   **0.1854**   **0.03275**

Find each value to four significant digits. Use logarithms and linear interpolation.

9. 37.45 × 4.530   **10.** $\dfrac{89.27}{3.620}$ **24.67**   **11.** 0.2744 × 34.60   **12.** $\dfrac{0.09438}{2.530}$ **0.03731**
169.7   **9.495**

(B) **13.** 6.202 × 5463   **14.** 2.403^4 **33.33**   **15.** 0.06814 × 7.126   **16.** $\sqrt[3]{52.35}$ **3.741**

17. $\dfrac{276.6}{54.21}$ **5.103**   **18.** $\sqrt[3]{0.04823 \times 73.60}$ **19.** $\left(\dfrac{0.7841}{1.920}\right)^3$ **0.06813**   **20.** $\sqrt{7.074^3}$ **18.81**
13. 33,880   **1.526**   **15. 0.4857**

Solve each problem.

(C) **21.** If f is a linear function for which $f(4) = 6.2$ and $f(7) = 12.8$, use linear interpolation to find $f(6)$. **10.6**

22. Given a linear function g for which $g(18) = -12$ and $g(32) = 44$, use linear interpolation to determine the value of a so that $g(a) = 18$. **25.5**

23. If j is a linear function such that $j(2.8) = 8.6$ and $j(9.6) = 29$, use linear extrapolation to find $j(14)$. **42.2**

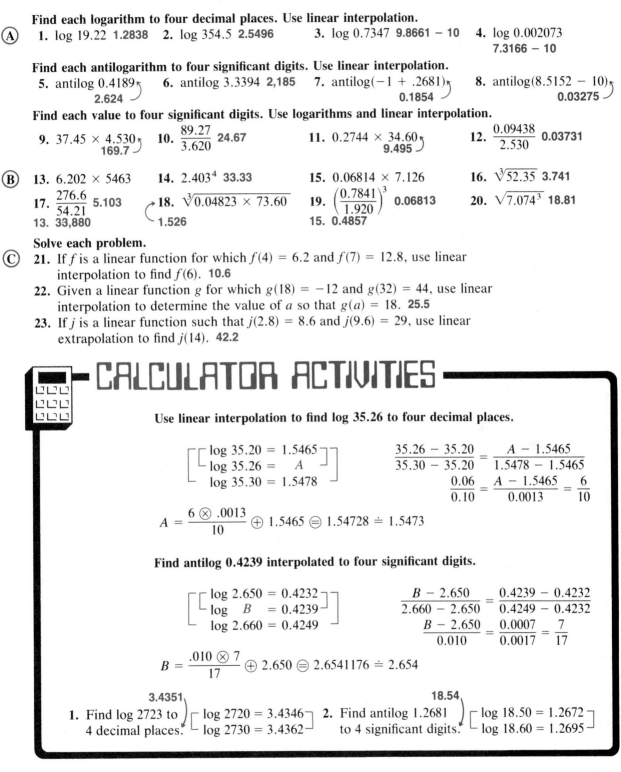

CALCULATOR ACTIVITIES

Use linear interpolation to find log 35.26 to four decimal places.

$$\begin{bmatrix} \begin{bmatrix} \log 35.20 = 1.5465 \\ \log 35.26 = A \end{bmatrix} \\ \log 35.30 = 1.5478 \end{bmatrix}$$

$$\frac{35.26 - 35.20}{35.30 - 35.20} = \frac{A - 1.5465}{1.5478 - 1.5465}$$

$$\frac{0.06}{0.10} = \frac{A - 1.5465}{0.0013} = \frac{6}{10}$$

$$A = \frac{6 \otimes .0013}{10} \oplus 1.5465 \ominus 1.54728 \doteq 1.5473$$

Find antilog 0.4239 interpolated to four significant digits.

$$\begin{bmatrix} \begin{bmatrix} \log 2.650 = 0.4232 \\ \log\ B\ = 0.4239 \end{bmatrix} \\ \log 2.660 = 0.4249 \end{bmatrix}$$

$$\frac{B - 2.650}{2.660 - 2.650} = \frac{0.4239 - 0.4232}{0.4249 - 0.4232}$$

$$\frac{B - 2.650}{0.010} = \frac{0.0007}{0.0017} = \frac{7}{17}$$

$$B = \frac{.010 \otimes 7}{17} \oplus 2.650 \ominus 2.6541176 \doteq 2.654$$

1. Find log 2723 to **3.4351** $\begin{bmatrix} \log 2720 = 3.4346 \\ \log 2730 = 3.4362 \end{bmatrix}$ **2.** Find antilog 1.2681 **18.54** $\begin{bmatrix} \log 18.50 = 1.2672 \\ \log 18.60 = 1.2695 \end{bmatrix}$
4 decimal places.   to 4 significant digits.

Applications

Given two (or more) points that are on a straight line, write an equation of the line. The process is reviewed below.

Example

Write an equation of the line that passes through the points described by the table.

x	3	5	7
y	1.85	4.35	6.85

The three points are plotted on *rectangular coordinate* graph paper and appear to lie on a straight line. Use the equation form

$$y - y_1 = m(x - x_1)$$

where $m = \dfrac{4.35 - 1.85}{5 - 3} = \dfrac{2.50}{2} = 1.25.$

$$y - 1.85 = 1.25(x - 3)$$

Thus, $y = 1.25x - 1.90$ is the equation of the line that passes through the points in the table.

Use the equation obtained in the example above to predict values of y for each value of x.

1. $x = 4$ **3.1**   2. $x = 6.5$ **6.225**   3. $x = 9$ **9.35**

The process in the example above is called *curve fitting*. In this case, the curve is a straight line. You can write an equation of a curve that passes through some given points belonging to an exponential function that is described by an equation of the form:

$$y = a \cdot b^x.$$

Example 2

At the end of x hours, the number y of bacteria in a culture is given in the table. Fit an exponential curve to the data.

x	0	1	2	3
y	100	145	210	305

The 4 points are plotted on *semilogarithmic* graph paper where an exponential curve becomes a straight line.

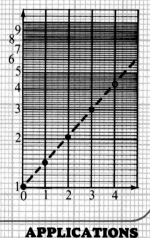

$$y = a \cdot b^x$$

If $x = 0$ and $y = 100$ ▶ $100 = a \cdot b^0$ So, $a = 100$ since $b^0 = 1$.

If $x = 0$ and $y = 145$ ▶ $145 = 100 \cdot b^1$ So, $b = 145 \div 100$, or 1.45.

Thus, $y = 100(1.45)^x$ is the desired equation.

Use the equation obtained in the example to predict the number of bacteria present after:

4. 4 hours. **442**   5. 24 hours. **747,500**

Computer Activities

Interpolating

Numerical tables found in a textbook are very helpful but often are incomplete. One reason for this is the limited amount of space in the book. The computer can be a useful tool for filling in the missing table values accurately and quickly. You can use the program below to find values by interpolation when working with common logarithms.

PROGRAM

```
 10  PRINT "PROGRAM INTERPOLATES"
 20  PRINT "ENTER THE LOGS BETWEEN WHICH THE LOG YOU"
 30  PRINT "WANT ARE FOUND. ENTER SMALLER FIRST"
 40  INPUT X, Y
 50  PRINT "ENTER LOG FOR WHICH YOU WANT MANTISSA"
 60  INPUT V
 70  PRINT "ENTER AS .XXXX THE MANTISSA OF"; X
 80  INPUT X1
 90  PRINT "ENTER AS .XXXX THE MANTISSA OF"; Y
100  INPUT Y1
110  LET V1 = ((V - X) * (Y1 - X1))/(Y - X)
120  LET V1 = V1 + X1
130  PRINT "MANTISSA OF"; V; "IS"; V1
140  END
```

Exercises

Type in the above program and run it to find mantissas for the following logs. Use a log table to find the mantissas for INPUT statements 70 and 90.

1. Log 45.36 ($x = 4530$, $y = 4540$, $v = 4536$) **.6567**

2. Log 70.58 ($x = 7050$, $y = 7060$, $v = 7058$) **.84868**

3. Log 0.0498 ($x = 4980$, $y = 4990$, $v = 4980$) **.6972**

4. Log 2.521 ($x = 2520$, $y = 2530$, $v = 2521$) **.40157**

5. Alter the above program to print out a table of logs for a range of values from 10 to 15 with increments of 0.01 (i.e., 10.00, 10.01, 10.02, 10.03, . . . , 14.99, 15.00).

6. Write a program to interpolate antilogs.
   For Ex. 5–6, see TE Answer Section.

ACTIVITY: INTERPOLATING

Chapter Fifteen Review

Vocabulary

base-n antilogarithm [15.6]
base-n logarithm [15.6]
base-10 antilogarithm [15.1]
base-10 logarithm [15.1]
characteristic [15.2]
common logarithms [15.1]
exponential equation [15.7]
exponential function [15.8]
inverse of $\log_n$ function [15.8]
linear interpolation [15.9]
logarithmic equation [15.3]
logarithmic function [15.8]
mantissa [15.2]

Find each logarithm or antilogarithm.

1. log 8.24
2. antilog 0.6484 [15.1]
3. log 30,400
4. log 0.00346 [15.2]
5. antilog 2.7619 **below**
6. antilog $(8.2227 - 10)$
7. $\log_2 64$ **6**
8. $\log_5 \sqrt[3]{5}$ $\frac{1}{3}$
9. $\log_2 \sqrt[5]{16}$ [15.6]
10. $\log_5 \frac{1}{125}$ **−3**
11. $\log_{\frac{1}{3}} 27$ **3**
12. $\log_{\frac{2}{5}} \frac{25}{4}$ **−2**
13. $\text{antilog}_2 7$ **128**
14. $\text{antilog}_4 -3$ $\frac{1}{64}$

1. 0.9159 2. 4.45 3. 4.4829 4. 7.5391 − 10

Find the value of each expression to three significant digits. Use logarithms.

15. $0.371 \times 5{,}480 \times 0.024$ **48.8** [15.3]
16. $\frac{0.0076}{0.842}$ **0.00903**
17. $\frac{8250}{6.12 \times 40.7}$ **33.1**
18. 26.3^3 **18,200**
19. $\sqrt[3]{0.0436}$ [15.4]
20. $\sqrt{3.27^3}$ **5.91**
21. $\left(\frac{2.75}{0.372}\right)^4$ **0.352** **2,990**

Solve each equation. Check.

22. $\log (4y + 3) - \log 9 = \log (y - 3)$ **6** [15.3]
23. $\frac{1}{2} \log y + \frac{1}{2} \log (2y + 4) = \log 4$ **2** [15.4]
★24. Find the sum of the series:
$3 \cdot \sum_{k=2}^{6} \log (0.1)^{k-5}$. **15** [15.1]

25. Write $\log \sqrt[3]{\frac{3v^2}{4k}}$ in expanded form. [15.5]
26. Given the formula $V = \frac{1}{3} \pi r^2 h$, write $\log h$ in expanded form. [15.5]
27. Write $3(\log x + 2 \log y - 3 \log z)$ as the log of one expression. [15.5]
For Ex. 25–27, see TE Answer Section.

Solve each equation for n. [15.6]

28. $\log_n 125 = 3$ **5**
29. $\log_n \frac{1}{81} = -4$ **3**
★30. Solve $\log_2 (y - 3) + \log_2 (2y + 2) = 6$ for y. **7** [15.6]
31. Solve $5^{2x-3} = 17$ for x to three significant digits. **2.38** [15.7]
32. Find $\log_3 54.2$ to three significant digits. **3.63** [15.7]

Graph the function defined by each equation. List four properties of the function. [15.8]

33. $y = \left(\frac{1}{6}\right)^x$
34. $y = \log_6 x$
For Ex. 33–34, see TE Answer Section.

35. Find log 59.32 to four decimal places. Use linear interpolation. **1.7732** [15.9]
36. Find antilog $(8.3394 - 10)$ to four significant digits. Use linear interpolation. [15.9]
37. Find the value of $\left(\frac{603.5}{28.40}\right)^2$ to four **0.02185** significant digits. Use logarithms and linear interpolation. **451.7** [15.9]
★38. Given a linear function g for which $g(-10) = 12.4$ and $g(14) = -3.6$, use linear interpolation to find $g(2.3)$. **4.2** [15.9]
For Ex. 39–41, see TE Answer Section.

Prove that each statement is true.

★39. $\frac{2}{5} \log 4 - \frac{1}{5} \log 2 = \frac{1}{5} \log 8$ [15.5]
★40. $\log_n 69 = \frac{\log 69}{\log n}$ for each positive number $n \neq 1$. [15.7]
★41. The two functions defined by $y = \log_4 x$ and by $y = 4^x$ are a pair of inverse functions. [15.8]

5. 578 6. 0.0167

Chapter Fifteen Test

Find each logarithm or antilogarithm.

1. log 0.00374 **7.5729 − 10**

2. $\log_5 125$ **3**

3. antilog 1.7818 **60.5**

4. $\text{antilog}_5 -2$ $\frac{1}{25}$

5. $\log_3 \sqrt[4]{27}$ $\frac{3}{4}$

6. $\log_{\frac{3}{5}} \frac{9}{25}$ **2**

Find the value of each expression to three significant digits. Use logarithms.

7. $\dfrac{0.048 \times 730}{863}$ **0.0406**

8. $\sqrt[3]{\dfrac{5.91}{21.7}}$ **0.648**

9. $(6.32 \times 0.037)^2$ **0.0547**

10. Solve $\log (y + 1) - \log 8 = \log (y - 3) - \log 6$. **15**

11. Write $\log \dfrac{5x^3 \sqrt{y}}{2a^2 b}$ in expanded form. **below**

12. Given the formula $V = \dfrac{4}{3} \pi r^3$, write $\log r$ in expanded form. **below**

13. Write $\dfrac{1}{3} (\log m + 2 \log n - \log p - \log t)$ as the log of one expression. **below**

14. Solve $\log_n 64 = 3$ for n. **4**

15. Solve $3^{x-1} = 42$ for x to three significant digits. **4.40** **2.39**

16. Find $\log_6 72.4$ to three significant digits.

17. Find antilog $(9.6800 - 10)$ to four significant digits. Use linear interpolation. **0.4787**

18. Find the value of 4.324×71.30 to four significant digits. Use logarithms and linear interpolation. **308.3**

Graph the function defined by each equation. List four properties of the function.

19. $y = \left(\dfrac{1}{4}\right)^x$

20. $y = \log_5 x$

For Ex. 19–20, see TE Answer Section.

★ 21. Solve $\log_2 (y + 1) + \log_2 (3y - 1) = 5$. **3**

★ 22. Find the sum of the series:
$$\sum_{j=1}^{4} \text{antilog} (3 - j).$$ **111.1**

★ 23. Given a linear function f such that $f(2.8) = 4.1$ and $f(9.2) = 8.9$, use linear interpolation to find $f(6.4)$. **6.8**

Prove that each statement is true.

★ 24. $2 \log xy - \log xy^4 = \log x - 2 \log y$.

★ 25. $\dfrac{3}{4} \log 9 - \dfrac{1}{2} \log 3 = \dfrac{1}{3} \log 27$

★ 26. $\log_8 59 = \dfrac{\log 59}{\log 8}$

★ 27. The two functions defined by $y = \log_6 x$ and by $y = 6^x$ are a pair of inverse functions.

For Ex. 24–27, see TE Answer Section.

11. $\log 5 + 3 \log x + \dfrac{1}{2} \log y - \log 2 - 2 \log a - \log b$

12. $\log r = \dfrac{1}{3} (\log V - \log 4 + \log 3 - \log \pi)$

13. $\log \sqrt[3]{\dfrac{mn^2}{pt}}$

College Prep Test

DIRECTIONS: Choose the *one* best answer to each question or problem.

1. If $x^2 = \log 10^{16}$ and $x > 0$, then $x =$ **B**

   (A) 2   (B) 4   (C) 8   (D) 10   (E) 16

2. $\log \dfrac{1}{xy} =$ **D**

   (A) $\log x + \log y$ (B) $\log x - \log y$
   (C) $1 - \log x - \log y$ (D) $-\log x - \log y$
   (E) None of these

3. If $\log 3x + \log 4x = \log 24$, then **C**

   (A) $x = \dfrac{24}{7}$ (B) $x = 2$
   (C) $x^2 = 2$ (D) $x^2 = 12$
   (E) None of these

4. $\log \sqrt[3]{ab^2} =$ **A**

   (A) $\dfrac{\log a + \log b + \log b}{3}$

   (B) $\dfrac{2}{3}(\log a + \log b)$

   (C) $\dfrac{1}{3}(2 \log a + \log b)$

   (D) $3\left(\log a + \dfrac{1}{2} \log b\right)$

   (E) None of these

5. $4\left(\log a + 2 \log b - \dfrac{1}{2} \log c\right) =$ **D**

   (A) $\log \left(\dfrac{ab}{c}\right)^4$ (B) $\log \dfrac{4ab^2}{\sqrt{c}}$

   (C) $\log \dfrac{ab^8}{\sqrt{c}}$ (D) $\log \dfrac{a^4 b^8}{c^2}$

   (E) None of these

6. If $2^{x+1} = 50$, then **B**

   (A) $x = 24$ (B) $4 < x < 5$
   (C) $5 < x < 6$ (D $6 < x < 7$
   (E) None of these

7. If $a = \log_b c$, then **A**

   (A) $b^a = c$ (B) $b^c = a$
   (C) $a^b = c$ (D) $a^c = b$
   (E) None of these

8. If $y = 10^{7.6543 - 10}$, then the characteristic of $\log y$ is **D**

   (A) $7.6543 - 10$ (B) $.6543$
   (C) antilog $.6543$ (D) -3
   (E) None of these

9. Find the false statement among (A), (B), and (C), if any. **E**

   (A) $\log_2 8 = \log_4 64$
   (B) $\log_5 1 = \log_6 1$
   (C) antilog$_2$ 4 = antilog$_4$ 2
   (D) All three are false.
   (E) All three are true.

10. If $\log_2 y = x$, then **B**

   (A) $y < x$ (B) $y > x$
   (C) $y = x$ (D) $y = 2x$
   (E) None of these

11. Find the false statement, if any. **C**

   (A) $\log_{10} 100 = \log_{100} 10,000$
   (B) If $y = \log_{\frac{1}{3}} x$, then $x = 3^{-y}$.
   (C) $\log (x^2 + y^2) = 2 \log x + 2 \log y$
   (D) $\log (x^2 - 4) = \log (x + 2) + \log (x - 2)$
   (E) None of these

16 PERMUTATIONS, COMBINATIONS, AND PROBABILITY
Probability and the Normal Curve

If you buy a light bulb, what is the probability that it will burn longer than its average life expectancy? Two types of information are needed to make such predictions. You must know both the average life expectancy as well as how the life expectancy varies from one bulb to another. The measure of variation usually used is called *standard deviation.*

A measure, such as a measure of life expectancy of a product, is normally distributed. If many such measures are plotted, they form a **normal (bell-shaped) curve.** The normal curve reflects the mean and the variation for a given measure. For a measure that is normally distributed, approximately 68.2% of the cases will fall between ±1 standard deviations (±1 σ) of the mean, 95.4% will fall between ±2 σ of the mean, and 99.8% between ±3 σ of the mean.

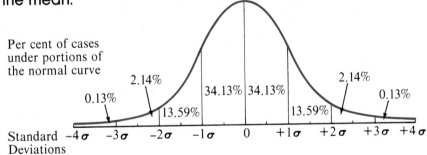

Per cent of cases under portions of the normal curve

0.13%   2.14%   13.59%   34.13%   34.13%   13.59%   2.14%   0.13%

Standard Deviations -4σ -3σ -2σ -1σ 0 $+1\sigma$ $+2\sigma$ $+3\sigma$ $+4\sigma$

PROJECT

The life expectancy of a certain automobile tire closely approximates the normal curve. The estimated average life is 35,000 miles, with one standard deviation of 4,000 miles.
(1) If you purchase a tire, what is the probability that it will last between 31,000 and 39,000 miles? more than 31,000 miles?
(2) A rental company buys 40,000 tires. Find the total number of tires expected to last between 27,000 and 43,000 miles. Find the total number expected to last less than 27,000 miles. **(1) 0.683; 0.864   (2) 38,176; 908**

16.1 Fundamental Counting Principle

OBJECTIVE ▶ **To find the number of possible arrangements of objects by using the Fundamental Counting Principle**

A truck driver must drive from Miami to Orlando and then continue on to Lake City. There are 4 different routes that he can take from Miami to Orlando and 3 different routes from Orlando to Lake City.

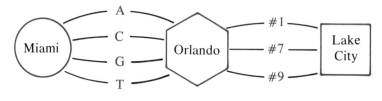

One Miami-Orlando-Lake City route is *first* to take A and *then* take #1, or simply $A1$. All of the possible routes are listed below.

$A1$ $A7$ $A9$ $C1$ $C7$ $C9$ $G1$ $G7$ $G9$ $T1$ $T7$ $T9$

Notice that each route is identified by a letter and then a digit, in that order. By counting, you can find that there are 12 possible Miami-Orlando-Lake City routes. The number of possible routes can also be found without listing any of the routes.

The driver had to make 2 decisions. Mark 2 places.   ___ ___
First decision: Choose a Miami-Orlando route.
                   There are 4 choices: A, C, G, or T.   4   ___
Second decision: Choose an Orlando-Lake City route.
                   There are 3 choices: 1, 7, or 9.   ___   3

$$\underset{\left(\substack{\text{number of} \\ \text{letter-choices}}\right)}{\underline{4}} \times \underset{\left(\substack{\text{number of} \\ \text{digit-choices}}\right)}{\underline{3}} = 12$$

$\left(\substack{\text{number of} \\ \text{letter-choices}}\right) \times \left(\substack{\text{number of} \\ \text{digit-choices}}\right) = \text{number of possible routes}$

This suggests a principle for finding the number of possible arrangements of objects without listing all of the arrangements.

Fundamental Counting Principle

> If one choice can be made in a ways and a second choice can be made in b ways, then the choices *in order* can be made in $a \times b$ different ways.

This Fundamental Counting Principle can be extended to three or more choices made *in order*. If the truck driver above had to make a round trip, Miami-Orlando-Lake City-Orlando-Miami, there would be 144 possible routes. One such route is $C79T$. The driver would have to make 4 decisions. The number of choices for each decision is shown below:

$$\underline{4} \times \underline{3} \times \underline{3} \times \underline{4} = 144$$

The Fundamental Counting Principle is used to find the number of possible arrangements of *n* objects taken *r* at a time. In Example 1, 6 digits are available and they are taken 3 at a time to form three-digit numbers.

Example 1 How many three-digit numbers can be formed from the 6 digits, 1, 2, 6, 7, 8, 9, if no digit may be repeated in a number?

There are three decisions to make. Choose (1) a 100s digit, then (2) a 10s digit, and then (3) a 1s digit.

$$\underline{\quad}\ \underline{\quad}\ \underline{\quad}$$
(100s) (10s) (1s)

1 2 6 ⑦ 8 9 ▶ There are 6 choices for a 100s digit. $\underline{6}\ \underline{\quad}\ \underline{\quad}$

1 ② 6   8 9 ▶ This leaves 5 choices for a 10s digit. $\underline{\quad}\ \underline{5}\ \underline{\quad}$

1   6   ⑧ 9 ▶ Four choices remain for a 1s digit. $\underline{\quad}\ \underline{\quad}\ \underline{4}$

Use the Fundamental Counting Principle. $\underline{6}\ \times\ \underline{5}\ \times\ \underline{4}$

Thus, 120 three-digit numbers can be formed.

Six of the 120 three-digit numbers from Example 1 are listed below.

267   276   627   672   726   762

Each of these numbers is a **permutation** of the digits 2, 6, and 7.

Definition: Permutation

> A *permutation* is an arrangement of objects in a definite order.

In Example 1, it was specified that a digit should not be repeated in a number. If such repetition is allowed, more than 120 three-digit numbers are possible. Four of these numbers, with a repeated digit, are shown below.

222   227   272   722

Example 2 How many three-digit numbers can be formed from the digits 2, 4, 6, 8, 9, if a digit may be repeated in a number?

$$\underline{5}\ \times\ \underline{5}\ \times\ \underline{5}\ = 125$$

Thus, 125 three-digit numbers can be formed.

FUNDAMENTAL COUNTING PRINCIPLE   **425**

The Fundamental Counting Principle can be used to find the number of permutations of objects other than digits and letters.

Example 3

A manufacturer makes sweaters in 6 different colors. Each sweater is available with choices of 3 fabrics, 4 kinds of collars, and with or without buttons. How many different types of sweaters does the manufacturer make?

There are 4 decisions to be made.

$$\underset{\text{color}}{6} \times \underset{\text{fabric}}{3} \times \underset{\text{collar}}{4} \times \underset{\text{buttons}}{2} = 144$$

Thus, 144 types of sweaters are made by the manufacturer.

The number of permutations of n distinct objects taken n at a time forms a pattern. This is shown in the next example.

Example 4

Find the number of possible batting orders (permutations) for the nine starting players on a baseball team.

The coach has to make 9 decisions.

$$\underset{\substack{\text{Leadoff}\\\text{batter}}}{9} \times \underset{\substack{\text{Second}\\\text{batter}}}{8} \times \underset{\substack{\text{Third}\\\text{batter}}}{7} \times \underset{\substack{\text{Cleanup}\\\text{batter}}}{6} \times \underset{\substack{\text{No.}\\5}}{5} \times \underset{\substack{\text{No.}\\6}}{4} \times \underset{\substack{\text{No.}\\7}}{3} \times \underset{\substack{\text{No.}\\8}}{2} \times \underset{\substack{\text{No.}\\9}}{1} = 362{,}880$$

Thus, a baseball coach can select his batting order from among 362,880 possible orders.

In Example 4, the number of permutations, $9 \times 8 \times 7 \times \ldots \times 3 \times 2 \times 1$, can be written as 9! The expression 9! is read "9 factorial." The value of $n!$ increases rapidly as n increases.

$4! = 4 \times 3 \times 2 \times 1 = 24 \qquad 8! = 8 \times 7 \times 6 \times 5 \times 4 \times 3 \times 2 \times 1 = 40{,}320$
$10! = 10 \times 9 \times 8 \times \ldots \times 3 \times 2 \times 1 = 3{,}628{,}800$

Definition:
n!

> For each positive integer n,
> $$n! = 1 \cdot 2 \cdot 3 \ldots n.$$

You should notice that the number of arrangements (permutations) of n objects taken n at a time is always $n!$ for each positive integer n.

Oral Exercises

State each of the following expressions in factored form.

1. 6!   2. 2! 2×1 3. 9!   4. 21!

$6 \times 5 \times 4 \times 3 \times 2 \times 1$

$9 \times 8 \times 7 \times 6 \times 5 \times 4 \times 3 \times 2 \times 1$ $21 \times 20 \times 19 \ldots 3 \times 2 \times 1$

Written Exercises

Ⓐ 1. How many four-digit numbers can be formed from the digits 1, 3, 5, 7, and 9, if no digit may be repeated in a number? **120**

2. If a digit may be repeated in a number, how many 4-digit numbers can be formed from the digits 2, 4, 6, 8, and 9? **625**

3. In how many ways can 6 different books be placed side by side on a shelf? **720**

4. Find the number of different ways that 8 waiters can be assigned to 8 tables if each waiter services one table. **40,320**

5. Find the number of 3-letter permutations of the letters in the word CAR if no letter is repeated in an arrangement. **6**

6. How many 4-letter "words" can be made from the letters in WEST if no letter is repeated in a "word"? **24**

7. How many different signals can be shown by arranging 3 flags in a row if 7 different flags are available? **210**

8. If a signal consists of 5 flags arranged in a row, how many signals can be made from 9 different flags? **15,120**

9. Find the number of different automobile license-plate numbers that can be formed using a letter followed by five digits. **2,600,000**

10. Find the number of 7-digit phone numbers that can be formed if the first digit of a telephone number cannot be zero. **9,000,000**

A sports stadium has eleven gates with six on the north side and five on the south side. Solve Exercises 11–14 using this information.

Ⓑ 11. In how many ways can a person enter the stadium through a north gate and later leave the stadium through a south gate? **30**

12. Find the number of ways that you can enter the stadium through a south gate and then exit through a north gate. **30**

13. Find the number of ways that you can enter from the north side and then exit from the north side. **36**

14. In how many different ways can a person enter and then leave the stadium? **121**

15. A company makes trucks in 6 different sizes. Each size comes with a choice of 5 exterior colors, a choice of 3 interior colors, with or without a CB radio, and with or without an extra horn. How many different types of trucks does the company make? **360**

16. A school cafeteria offers each student 2 choices of meat, 4 choices of vegetable, 3 choices of drink, and 6 choices of fruit. How many different four-item lunch trays are available? **144**

17. Find the number of 3-letter permutations of the letters in STUDY if a letter may be repeated in a permutation. **125**

18. How many 5-letter code words can be formed from the letters in MONETARY if no letter is repeated in a code word? **6,720**

19. How many different auto license-plate numbers can be formed by 3 different letters followed by 3 digits? **15,600,000**

20. In how many different ways can 6 multiple-choice questions be answered if each question has 5 choices for the answer? **15,625**

FUNDAMENTAL COUNTING PRINCIPLE

16.2 Conditional Permutations

OBJECTIVE ▶ **To find the number of permutations of objects when conditions are attached to the arrangement**

Problems involving permutations may have specific conditions attached to the arrangement of the objects. Some examples follow:
(1) The numbers are <u>odd</u> numbers.
(2) The numbers contain <u>one</u> <u>or</u> <u>more</u> digits.
(3) The words <u>end</u> with the letter *t*.
(4) The numbers are <u>less than</u> 600.

Example 1 **How many permutations of all the letters in the word *MONEY* end with either the letter *E* or the letter *Y*?**

The first decision is to choose the 5th letter, which must be *E* or *Y*.

$$\underline{\ 4\ } \times \underline{\ 3\ } \times \underline{\ 2\ } \times \underline{\ 1\ } \times \underline{\ 2\ } = 48$$

⎣— Two choices: *E* or *Y*

Thus, 48 permutations of *M, O, N, E, Y* end with *E* or *Y*.

From the digits 7, 8, 9, you can form 10 *odd* numbers containing *one or more* digits if no digit may be repeated in a number. Since the numbers are odd, there are two choices for the units digit, 7 or 9. In this case, the numbers may contain one, two, or three digits.

One-digit numbers:	7	9		
Two-digit numbers:	79	87	89	97
Three-digit numbers:	789	879	897	987

Notice that there are 2 one-digit numbers, 4 two-digit numbers, 4 three-digit numbers and that $2 + 4 + 4 = 10$. This suggests that an "or" decision, like <u>one</u> <u>or</u> <u>more</u> digits, involves <u>addition</u>.

Example 2 **How many even numbers containing one or more digits can be formed from 2, 3, 4, 5, 6 if no digit may be repeated in a number?**

There are 3 choices for a units digit: 2, 4, or 6. ▶

$$3 = 3$$
$$4 \times 3 = 12$$
$$4 \times 3 \times 3 = 36$$
$$4 \times 3 \times 2 \times 3 = 72$$
$$4 \times 3 \times 2 \times 1 \times 3 = 72$$

$$3 + 12 + 36 + 72 + 72 = 195$$

Thus, there are 195 such even numbers.

In some situations, the total number of permutations is the *product* of two or more numbers of permutations. For example, there are 12 permutations of A, B, X, Y, Z with A, B to the left "and" X, Y, Z to the right.

| *ABXYZ* | *ABXZY* | *ABYXZ* | *ABYZX* | *ABZXY* | *ABZYX* |
| *BAXYZ* | *BAXZY* | *BAYXZ* | *BAYZX* | *BAZXY* | *BAZYX* |

Notice that (1) A, B can be arranged in 2!, or 2 ways;
(2) X, Y, Z can be arranged in 3!, or 6 ways; and
(3) A, B, X, Y, Z can be arranged in 2! × 3!, or 12 ways.

An "and" decision involves multiplication.

Example 3

Four different algebra books and three different geometry books are to be displayed on a shelf with the algebra books together and to the left of the geometry books. How many such arrangements are possible?

Algebra books (left)				Geometry books (right)		
4	× 3	× 2	× 1	× 3	× 2	× 1 = 144
ALG	ALG	ALG	ALG	GEOM	GEOM	GEOM
I	II	III	IV	I	II	III

Thus, there are 4! × 3!, or 144, possible arrangements.

Written Exercises

Solve each problem.

(A)

1. How many even five-digit numbers can be formed from the digits 2, 3, 4, 5, 6, if no digit may be repeated in a number? **72**

2. How many odd three-digit numbers can be formed from the digits 1, 2, 3, 4, 5, if a digit may be repeated in a number? **75**

3. Find the number of four-digit numbers that can be formed from the digits 0, 2, 4, 5, 6, 9, if a digit may be repeated in a number. (Consider 0495 as a three-digit number.) **1,080**

4. Find the number of three-digit numbers less than 500 that can be formed from the digits 0, 2, 4, 6, 8, if no digit may be repeated in a number. **24**

   6. **4,320**

5. How many permutations of all the letters in the word JUNIOR begin with *N*? **120**

6. How many permutations of all the letters in the word NUMBERS do not end with *N*?

7. Six different biology books and four different chemistry books are to be placed on a shelf with the chemistry books together and to the left of the biology books. How many such arrangements are possible? **17,280**

8. A grocery store displays five brands of ground coffee and four brands of instant coffee on a shelf in a row. How many different displays of the nine brands are possible if all of the ground coffees must be shown to the right of the instant coffees? **2,880**

CONDITIONAL PERMUTATIONS

9. How many three-digit or five-digit numbers can be formed from 1, 3, 5, 7, 9, if a digit may be repeated in a number? **3,250**

10. Find the number of two-digit, three-digit, or four-digit numbers that may be formed from 0, 2, 4, 6, if repetition of digits is not allowed. (Consider 024 and 24 as the same number.) **45**

Ⓑ 11. How many numbers of one or more digits can be formed from the digits 6, 7, 8, 9, if no digit is repeated in a number? **64**

12. How many numbers of one or more digits can be formed from the digits 1, 2, 3, if the numbers are less than 400 and repetition of digits is allowed? **39**

13. Find the number of permutations of *a, e, i, o, u, y* that end with *a*, or *i*, or *y*. **360**

14. How many permutations of the letters in *UNTIL* begin with the prefix *UN-*? **6**

15. Five novels and six short stories are to be displayed. In how many ways can this be done if the novels are kept together and the short stories are kept together on a shelf? (Note: The novels can be at the left *or* the right.) **172,800**

16. A 3-volume dictionary, a 4-volume atlas, and a 6-volume collection of plays are placed on a shelf. In how many ways can this be done if volumes of the same type are kept together? **622,080**

17. How many even numbers of one or more digits can be formed from 2, 4, 6, 7, 8, 9, if repetition of digits is not allowed in a number? **1,304**

18. Find the number of odd numbers less than 1,000 that can be formed from the digits 1, 2, 3, 4, 5, 6, 7, if repetition of digits is allowed. **228**

Ⓒ 19. In how many ways can a family of five stand together in line for tickets if the twins, Mary and Mark, are not to be separated? **48**

20. In how many ways can 6 students be seated in a row of 6 chairs if two of them are a brother and sister who do not want to sit together? **480**

21. A secretary typed 3 letters and then addressed 3 envelopes for the letters. The letters were placed in the envelopes at random with one letter per envelope. In how many different ways could this be done? **6**

22. How many even numbers of one or more digits can be formed from 0, 1, 2, 3, 4, if no digit may be repeated in a number? Note: Do not count a number like 034. [Hint: First, count the numbers ending with 0.] **163**

➔ A Challenge To You

In how many ways can a tennis game of mixed doubles be arranged from a group of 6 males and 4 females? **180**

16.3 Distinguishable Permutations

OBJECTIVES ▶ **To find the quotient of numbers given in factorial notation**
To find the number of distinguishable permutations when some of the objects in an arrangement are alike

Some permutation problems lead to expressions like $\dfrac{8!}{4! \times 3!}$. To find the value of such an expression, begin by dividing out common factors of the numerator and denominator.

Example 1 Find the value of $\dfrac{8!}{4! \times 3!}$.

One Method
$$\frac{8 \times 7 \times 6 \times 5 \times (4 \times 3 \times 2 \times 1)}{(4 \times 3 \times 2 \times 1) \times 3 \times 2 \times 1}$$
$$\frac{8 \times 7 \times \cancel{6} \times 5}{\cancel{3 \times 2 \times 1}}$$
280

Short Method
$$\frac{8 \times 7 \times \cancel{6} \times 5 \times \cancel{(4!)}}{\cancel{(4!)} \times 3 \times 2 \times 1}$$
280

The letters in the word *Pop* are distinguishable since one of the two *p*'s is a capital letter. There are 3!, or 6, **distinguishable permutations** of *P, o, p*.

Pop   *Ppo*   *oPp*   *opP*   *poP*   *pPo*

In the word *pop*, the two *p*'s are alike and can be permuted in 2! ways. The number of distinguishable permutations of *p, o, p* is $\dfrac{3!}{2!}$, or 3.

pop   *ppo*   *opp*

The number of distinguishable permutations of the 5 letters in *daddy* is $\dfrac{5!}{3!}$ since the three *d*'s are alike and can be permuted in 3! ways. This suggests the following rule.

Number of Distinguishable Permutations

> Given *n* objects in which *a* of them are alike, the number of distinguishable permutations of the *n* objects is $\dfrac{n!}{a!}$.

You can extend this rule to find the number of distinguishable permutations of *n* objects in which more than one group of the objects are alike. For example, the word *pepper* contains three *p*'s which are alike and two *e*'s which are alike. The three *p*'s can be permuted in 3! ways, the two *e*'s can be permuted in 2! ways, and the number of distinguishable permutations of the 6 letters

p, e, p, p, e, r is $\dfrac{6!}{3! \times 2!}$, or 60.

DISTINGUISHABLE PERMUTATIONS **431**

Example 2 How many distinguishable six-digit numbers can be formed from the digits of 747457?

The 7's can be permuted in 3! ways and the 4's can be permuted in 2! ways.

$$\frac{6!}{3! \times 2!} = \frac{6 \times 5 \times 4 \times (3!)}{(3!) \times 2 \times 1} = 6 \times 5 \times 2 = 60$$

Thus, 60 such numbers can be formed.

Example 3 How many distinguishable signals can be formed by displaying eleven flags if 3 of the flags are red, 5 are green, 2 are yellow, and 1 is white?

$$\frac{11!}{3! \times 5! \times 2!} = \frac{11 \times 10 \times 9 \times \overset{4}{8} \times 7 \times \overset{1}{6} \times \overset{1}{5!}}{(3 \times 2 \times 1) \times (2 \times 1) \times 5!} = 27{,}720$$

Thus, 27,720 signals can be formed.

Written Exercises

Find the value of each expression.

(A) 1. $\frac{7!}{3!}$ **840** 2. $\frac{10!}{7!}$ **720** 3. $\frac{12!}{8! \times 4!}$ **495** 4. $\frac{10!}{2! \times 6! \times 3!}$ **420** 5. $\frac{12!}{2! \times 3! \times 8!}$ **990**

How many distinguishable eight-digit numbers can be formed from the digits of each number?

6. 33553533 **56**   7. 24227242 **168**   8. 19116136 **840**   9. 88775599 **2,520**

Find the number of distinguishable permutations of all the letters in each word.

10. *root* **12**   11. *tepee* **20**   12. *puppet* **120**   13. *scissors* **1,680**

(B) 14. *divided* **420**   15. *murmur* **90**   16. *nonsense* **1,680**   17. *Tennessee* **3,780**

18. How many distinguishable signals can be formed by displaying 9 flags if 3 of the flags are blue, 2 are orange, and 4 are black? **1,260**

19. In how many distinguishable ways can 4 nickels, 3 dimes, 2 quarters, and 1 penny be distributed to 10 children if each child is to receive one coin? **12,600**

CALCULATOR ACTIVITIES

Find the value of each expression.

1. $2 \times (4! \times 9!)$ **17,418,240**   2. $6! \times 5! \times 4! \times 3!$ **12,441,600**   3. $(8! \times 5!) \div 630$ **7,680**

A Challenge To You

In how many distinguishable ways can $1.14 in pennies, nickels, dimes, quarters, and half-dollars be distributed among 12 children if each child is to receive one coin? **166,320**

16.4 Circular Permutations

OBJECTIVE ▶ **To find the number of possible permutations of objects in a circle**

Three objects may be arranged in a line in 3!, or 6, ways. Any one of the objects may be placed in the first position.

$$ABC \quad ACB \quad BAC \quad BCA \quad CAB \quad CBA$$

In a **circular permutation** of objects, there is no first position. Only the positions of the objects relative to one another are considered. In the figures below, Al, Betty, and Carl are seated in a circular arrangement with each person facing the center of the circle.

In each of the first three figures, Al has Betty to his left and Carl to his right. This is *one circular permutation* of Al, Betty, and Carl.

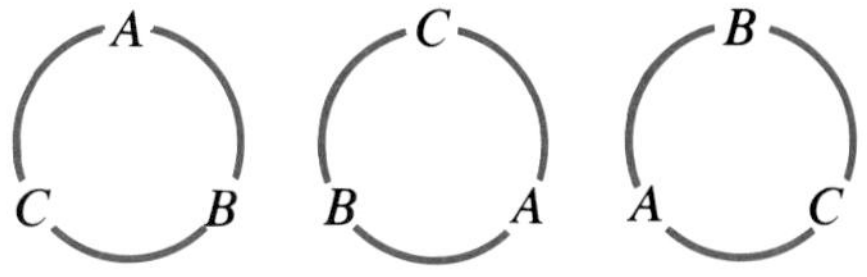

The remaining three figures each show Al with Betty to his right and Carl to his left. Again, these count as only one circular permutation of the three people.

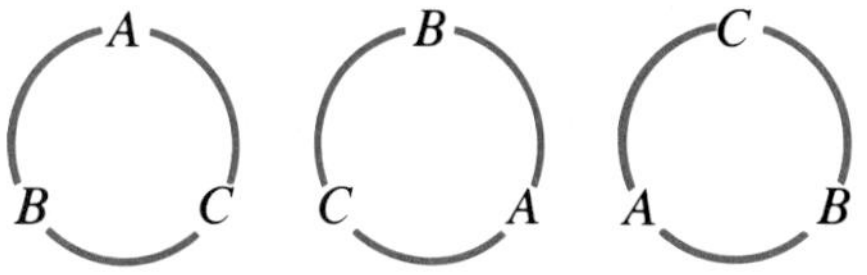

Thus, there are 2!, or 2, circular permutations of the 3 people.

To find the circular permutations of n distinct objects, begin by placing one object on the circle. Then arrange the remaining $(n - 1)$ objects in $(n - 1)!$ ways relative to the first object.

Number of Circular Permutations

> The number of circular permutations of n distinct objects is $(n - 1)!$

Example

A married couple invites 3 other couples to an anniversary dinner. In how many different ways can all of the 8 people be seated around a circular table?

$$(n - 1)! = (8 - 1)! = 7! = 5,040$$

Thus, there are 5,040 different ways to seat the 8 people.

Oral Exercises

Tell whether each arrangement is <u>linear</u>, <u>circular</u>, or <u>either</u> of these.
1. Digits in a 5-digit number **linear**
2. Keys on a key ring **circular**
3. Football players in a huddle **circular**
4. Letters in your last name **linear**
5. Books on a table **either**
6. Charms on a bracelet **circular**
7. Flags in a signal **linear**
8. Trees in a park **either**

Reading in Algebra _____

Tell which number of permutations is the greater for each pair below.
1. (a) 5 people in a line
   (b) 5 people in a circle **a**
2. (a) all the letters in *HOBO*
   (b) all the letters in *HOPE* **b**
3. (a) 6 people in a circle
   (b) all the letters in *GEESE* **a**
4. (a) all the digits in 52,466
   (b) all the digits in 63,777 **a**

Written **Exercises** _____

Solve each problem.

(A) 1. In how many different ways can seven children be seated around a circular table at a birthday party? **720**

2. The president of a company and his seven vice-presidents are to be seated around a circular conference table. In how many ways can this be done? **5,040**

3. A football team of eleven players forms a circular huddle before each play. In how many different ways can the players be arranged? **3,628,800**

4. Find the number of different ways that a gardener may plant a dozen different bushes around a circular flower bed. **39,916,800**

(B) 5. A husband and wife invite four other couples to dinner. In how many ways can they all be seated around the circular dining table? **362,880**

6. A woman and her daughter each invite three friends to lunch. Find the number of ways that all of them can be seated around one circular table. **5,040**

7. Four teachers and four students are seated in a circular discussion group. Find the number of ways this can be done if teachers and students must be seated alternately. **144**

8. In how many different ways can five girls and five boys be seated around a circular table if no two girls may be seated next to each other? **2,880**

Example   In how many different ways can 3 keys be arranged on a ring?

A key ring has a front view and a rear view, but the two views are considered to be one arrangement.

The 3 keys can be arranged in $\dfrac{(3-1)!}{2}$ ways.

Thus, the 3 keys can be arranged in only 1 way.

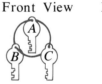
Front View   Rear View

(C) 9. In how many ways can 4 keys be arranged on a ring? **3**

10. Find the number of ways that 7 charms can be arranged on a bracelet. **360**

Use the definition of $n!$ to simplify each expression.

11. $\dfrac{n!}{(n-3)!}$ $\;n(n-1)(n-2)$

12. $\dfrac{(n+2)!}{n!}$ $\;(n+2)(n+1)$

13. $\dfrac{(n-4)!}{(n-6)!}$ $\;(n-4)(n-5)$

14. $\dfrac{(n+2)!}{(n-1)!}$ $\;(n+2)(n+1)(n)$

15. $(n+1) \cdot n \cdot (n-1)!$ $\;(n+1)!$

16. $(n-3)(n-4)(n-5)!$ $\;(n-3)!$

16.5 Combinations

OBJECTIVES ▶ **To find the number of possible selections of *n* objects taken *r* at a time without regard to order**

To find the value of $\binom{n}{r}$ for nonnegative integers *n* and *r* where $n \geq r$

In a permutation, the order of the objects is important. Another type of problem involves selecting objects where the order in which they are selected or arranged does not matter. A selection of this type is called a **combination** of the objects. Some examples are listed below.

Committee: The Al-Betty-Carl committee is the same as the Carl-Al-Betty committee.

Vertices of a triangle: $\triangle DEF$ is the same as $\triangle EFD$, which is the same as $\triangle FDE$.

Value of 3 coins: A dime, a nickel, and a penny have the same total value as a nickel, a penny, and a dime.

Definition: Combination

> A *combination* is a selection of objects without regard to order.

Notice that there are 6 permutations of the letters *a*, *b*, *c* but only 1 combination of them. In a combination, the order of the letters does not matter.

Example 1   **List all of the three-letter combinations that can be formed from the 5 letters *a*, *b*, *c*, *d*, *e*. Find the number of combinations.**

a-b-c	*a-c-d*	*a-d-e*	*b-c-d*	*b-d-e*	*c-d-e*
a-b-d	*a-c-e*		*b-c-e*		
a-b-e					

Thus, 10 three-letter combinations can be formed.

Example 1 shows that there are ten combinations of 5 things taken 3 at a time. $\binom{5}{3}$ is the symbol for "the number of combinations of 5 things taken 3 at a time." The value of $\binom{5}{3}$ is found in the following way.

$$\binom{5}{3} = \frac{5!}{3!(5-3)!} = \frac{5!}{3! \times 2!} = \frac{5 \times 4 \times 3\!\!\!/}{3\!\!\!/ \times 2 \times 1} = 10$$

Number of Combinations

$\binom{n}{r}$ is the number of combinations of n things taken r at a time.

$$\binom{n}{r} = \frac{n!}{r!(n-r)!}$$

You can use the above formula to evaluate $\binom{n}{r}$ for nonnegative integers n and r where $n > r$.

Example 2 Find the value of $\binom{7}{4}$.

$$\binom{7}{4} = \frac{7!}{4!(7-4)!} = \frac{7!}{4! \times 3!} = \frac{7 \times \cancel{6} \times 5 \times \cancel{4}!}{\cancel{4}! \times \cancel{3} \times \cancel{2} \times 1} = 35$$

Example 3 How many different 4-member committees can be formed if 10 people are available for appointment to a committee?

$$\binom{10}{4} = \frac{10!}{4! \times 6!} = \frac{10 \times 9 \times 8 \times 7 \times 6!}{4 \times 3 \times 2 \times 1 \times 6!} = 210$$

Thus, 210 committees can be formed.

Example 4 Seven points, *A* through *G*, are located on a circle. How many triangles are determined by the 7 points?

A triangle is determined by any 3 points that are not on the same line.

$$\binom{7}{3} = \frac{7!}{3! \times 4!} = \frac{7 \times 6 \times 5 \times 4!}{3 \times 2 \times 1 \times 4!} = 35$$

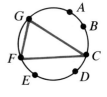

Thus, 35 triangles are determined.

Notice what happens when the formula for $\binom{n}{r}$ is used to find the number of combinations of 5 things taken 5 at a time:

$$\binom{5}{5} = \frac{5!}{5! \times 0!} = \frac{1}{0!}$$

Without a definition of 0! you cannot evaluate the expression $\frac{1}{0!}$. However, you know there can be only 1 combination of 5 things taken 5 at a time. This suggests that $\frac{1}{0!} = 1$, or that $0! = 1$. With this definition of 0!, the formula for $\binom{n}{r}$ can be used with any nonnegative integers n and r where $n \geq r$.

Reading in Algebra

Tell whether each collection of objects is a <u>permutation</u> or a <u>combination</u> of the objects in the collection.

1. A four-digit number **permutation**
2. A four-letter name of a rectangle **combination**
3. A five-person committee **combination**
4. A six-flag signal **permutation**
5. A five-letter code word **permutation**
6. A six-card hand in a card game **combination**
7. A two-letter name of a line **combination**
8. A three-digit even number **permutation**

Written Exercises

(A)
1. List all of the different amounts of money that can be determined by selecting three coins from 1 penny, 1 nickel, 1 dime, and 1 quarter. **16¢, 31¢, 36¢, 40¢**

2. List one 2-letter name for each line determined by the points A, B, C, and D which are located on a circle. $\overrightarrow{AB}, \overrightarrow{AC}, \overrightarrow{AD}, \overrightarrow{BC}, \overrightarrow{BD}, \overrightarrow{CD}$

Find the value of each expression.

3. $\binom{7}{2}$ **21**
4. $\binom{10}{6}$ **210**
5. $\binom{18}{3}$ **816**
6. $\binom{6}{6}$ **1**
7. $\binom{63}{1}$ **63**
8. $\binom{8}{0}$ **1**

9. How many 4-letter combinations can be formed from the first half of our alphabet? **715**

10. How many different 5-member committees can be formed if 20 people are available for membership? **15,504**

11. Find the number of lines determined by 10 points, A through J, on a circle. **45**

12. Find the number of triangles determined by 15 points, A through O, on a circle. **455**

(B)
13. An algebra student must solve 7 out of 10 word problems. In how many different ways can the 7 problems be selected? **120**

14. In how many different ways can a team of 33 football players choose three captains for its first game of the season? **5,456**

15. During the baseball season, an 8-school athletic conference requires that each school play 3 games with each of the other schools. Find the total number of baseball games played. **84**

16. There are 5 pellets lettered A, B, C, D, E which weigh 1 g, 2 g, 4 g, 8 g, 16 g, respectively. How many different masses can be measured by using one or more of the 5 weights on a balance scale? **31**

17. How many different amounts of money can be determined by selecting one or more coins from 1 penny, 1 nickel, 1 dime, 1 quarter, 1 half dollar, and 1 silver dollar? **63**

18. Find the number of inscribed hexagons determined by 18 points on a circle. **18,564**

(C)
19. Solve $\binom{n}{2} = \binom{20}{18}$. **20**

20. Solve $\binom{n}{6} = \binom{n}{4}$. **10**

21. Prove that $\binom{n}{r} = \binom{n}{n-r}$ and $\binom{n}{r} + \binom{n}{r+1} = \binom{n+1}{r+1}$. **For Ex. 21, see TE Answer Section.**

A Challenge To You

Find the number of different 5-card hands that may be drawn from a deck of 52 cards. **2,598,960**

16.6 Probability: Simple Event

OBJECTIVE ▶ **To determine the probability of a simple event**

When a "fair" coin is tossed it seems reasonable to expect that the coin is just as likely to come up heads (*H*) as tails (*T*). These two outcomes, heads and tails, have equal chances of occurring. In everyday language, we say the coin has 1 chance in 2 of coming up heads and 1 chance in 2 of coming up tails. In mathematical language, we say the **probability** of obtaining a head in one flip of a coin is $\frac{1}{2}$. In symbols, $P(\text{head}) = \frac{1}{2}$.

One way of obtaining the probability of a simple event occurring is to determine the number of ways the event can occur, called *favorable outcomes*, and then divide by the *total number of all possible outcomes*.

Probability of Simple Event

The probability of a simple event is given by the formula:
$$P(\text{simple event}) = \frac{\text{Number of favorable outcomes}}{\text{Total number of all possible outcomes}}.$$

Example 1  **What is the probability that in a throw of a die (plural: dice) a face with 4 dots will appear?**

$$P(\text{simple event}) = \frac{\text{Number of favorable outcomes}}{\text{Total number of all possible outcomes}}$$

One face of a die contains 4 dots. There is only 1 favorable outcome. There are 6 faces on a die. There are 6 possible outcomes.

Thus, $P(\text{a face with 4 dots}) = \frac{1}{6}$.

Example 2 **What is the probability that in a throw of a die a face with an even number of dots will appear?**

Three faces of a die contain even numbers: 2, 4, 6.
There are 6 faces on a die.

The number of favorable outcomes is 3 and the number of possible outcomes is 6.

Thus, $P(\text{even number of dots}) = \frac{3}{6}$, or $\frac{1}{2}$.

Example 3

A bag contains 5 red balls and 4 black balls. One ball is drawn from the bag. What is the probability that the ball is red? What is the probability that it is black?

There are 5 + 4, or 9 possible outcomes.
When looking for a red ball, there are 5 favorable outcomes.
When looking for a black ball, there are 4 favorable outcomes.

Thus, $P(\text{red ball}) = \dfrac{5}{9}$, and $P(\text{black ball}) = \dfrac{4}{9}$.

There are times when an event is certain to happen and times when it is impossible for an event to happen.

Probability of 1 and 0

> The probability of an event that is certain to happen is 1.
> The probability of an event that cannot happen is 0.

As shown below, the probability of a simple event E occurring is greater than or equal to 0 and less than or equal to 1:
$$0 \le P(E) \le 1.$$

Example 4

A bag contains 15 red balls. One ball is drawn from the bag. What is the probability that the ball is red? What is the probability that the ball is black?

There are 15 possible outcomes.
When looking for a red ball, there are 15 favorable outcomes.
When looking for a black ball, there are 0 favorable outcomes.

Thus, $P(\text{red ball}) = \dfrac{15}{15}$, or 1, and $P(\text{black ball}) = \dfrac{0}{15}$, or 0.

Example 5

A deck of cards contains 52 cards, 13 cards of each suit. One card is drawn. What is the probability that the card is an ace? That it is the ace of hearts? That it is not an ace?

There are 52 possible outcomes.
When looking for an ace, there are 4 favorable outcomes.
When looking for the ace of hearts, there is 1 favorable outcome.
When looking for a card that is not an ace, there are 48 favorable outcomes.

Thus, $P(\text{ace}) = \dfrac{4}{52}$, or $\dfrac{1}{13}$; $P(\text{ace of hearts}) = \dfrac{1}{52}$; and $P(\text{not an ace}) = \dfrac{48}{52}$, or $\dfrac{12}{13}$.

Written Exercises _____

(A) **1.** What is the probability that in a throw of a die, the 6 will appear? the 3 will appear? an odd number will appear? $\frac{1}{6}, \frac{1}{6}, \frac{1}{2}$

2. What is the probability that in a throw of a die, the 1 will appear? a prime number will appear? a number divisible by 2 will appear? $\frac{1}{6}, \frac{1}{2}, \frac{1}{2}$

3. A bag contains 8 white balls and 6 blue balls. A ball is drawn from the bag. What is the probability that the ball is white? that it is blue? $\frac{4}{7}, \frac{3}{7}$

4. A bag contains 12 red balls and 18 black balls. A ball is drawn from the bag. What is the probability that the ball is red? that it is black? $\frac{2}{5}, \frac{3}{5}$

5. A deck of cards contains 52 cards, 13 cards of each suit. One card is drawn. What is the probability that the card is a jack? that it is the jack of clubs? that it is not a jack? $\frac{1}{13}, \frac{1}{52}, \frac{12}{13}$

6. A deck of cards contains 52 cards, 13 cards of each suit. One card is drawn. What is the probability that the card is a ten? that it is the ten of spades? that it is not a ten? $\frac{1}{13}, \frac{1}{52}, \frac{12}{13}$

7. A bag contains 4 red, 3 white, and 5 blue balls. A ball is drawn from the bag. What is the probability that the ball is red? that it is white? that it is blue? that it is not red? that it is not blue? $\frac{1}{3}, \frac{1}{4}, \frac{5}{12}, \frac{2}{3}, \frac{7}{12}$

8. A deck of cards contains 52 cards, 13 cards of each suit. There are 2 black suits (spades and clubs) and 2 red suits (hearts and diamonds). One card is drawn. What is the probability that the card is red? that it is black? that it is a red ace? that it is a black 7? $\frac{1}{2}$ $\frac{1}{2}$ $\frac{1}{26}$ $\frac{1}{26}$

(B) **9.** A die is rolled 100 times. About how many times should it stop on 4? About how many times should an even number appear? About how many times should a number less than 3 appear? [Hint: First determine the probability of each event.] **16, 50, 33**

10. A die is rolled 6,000 times. About how many times should it not stop on 6? About how many times should it stop on 5? About how many times should a number greater than 2 appear? **5,000; 1,000; 4,000**

11. The probability that it will rain on any given day in December in the town of Los Altos is $\frac{8}{10}$. About how many days will it not rain in December? **6**

12. The probability of producing a defective part by a given machine is $\frac{1}{900}$. If 36,000 parts are produced in one day, about how many of the parts will be defective? **40**

The *odds* that a simple event E will occur are $\dfrac{P(E)}{P(\overline{E})}$ where $P(\overline{E})$ is the probability of E not occurring.

(C) **13.** A bag contains 16 red balls and 32 white balls. A ball is drawn from the bag. What are the odds that the ball is red? $\frac{1}{2}$, **or 1 to 2**

14. If the probability that it will snow on a given day is $\frac{2}{5}$, what is the probability that it will not snow? What are the odds that it will snow? that it will not snow? $\frac{3}{5}$, **2 to 3, 3 to 2**

440

16.7 Probability: Compound Events

OBJECTIVE ▶ **To determine the probability of an event using a sample space**

In the previous lesson, you learned how to find the probability of a simple event by determining the number of favorable outcomes and the number of all possible outcomes. In some situations, it is not easy to identify these number of outcomes. Making a list of all possible outcomes may be helpful. Such a listing is called a **sample space.**

A sample space showing all possible outcomes of rolling two dice, a red one and a white one, is shown below. In each ordered pair (r, w), the number rolled on the red die is listed first and the number rolled on the white die is listed second.

		White die					
		1	2	3	4	5	6
	1	(1, 1)	(1, 2)	(1, 3)	(1, 4)	(1, 5)	(1, 6)
Red	2	(2, 1)	(2, 2)	(2, 3)	(2, 4)	(2, 5)	(2, 6)
die	3	(3, 1)	(3, 2)	(3, 3)	(3, 4)	(3, 5)	(3, 6)
	4	(4, 1)	(4, 2)	(4, 3)	(4, 4)	(4, 5)	(4, 6)
	5	(5, 1)	(5, 2)	(5, 3)	(5, 4)	(5, 5)	(5, 6)
	6	(6, 1)	(6, 2)	(6, 3)	(6, 4)	(6, 5)	(6, 6)

Example 1 In a throw of two dice, a red one and a white one, what is the probability of obtaining a sum of 7? a sum of 2?

As shown in the sample space, there are 36 possible sums. For a sum of 7, there are 6 favorable outcomes: (6, 1), (5, 2), (4, 3), (3, 4), (2, 5), and (1, 6). For a sum of 2, there is 1 favorable outcome: (1, 1).

Thus, $P(\text{sum of } 7) = \frac{6}{36}$, or $\frac{1}{6}$, and $P(\text{sum of } 2) = \frac{1}{36}$.

Example 2 In a throw of two dice, a red one and a white one, what is the probability of obtaining a 2 or less on the red die?

There are 36 possible outcomes.
Two or less on the red die can occur in 12 ways, so there are 12 favorable outcomes.

Thus, $P(\text{2 or less on red die}) = \frac{12}{36}$, or $\frac{1}{3}$.

If two events can both occur at the same time, they are called **inclusive events.** If they cannot both occur at the same time, they are called **mutually exclusive events.**

Example 3 In a throw of two dice, a red one and a white one, find $P(r \leq 2 \text{ or } w \leq 3)$.

There are 36 possible outcomes.
There are 12 ways to get $r \leq 2$ and 18 ways to get $w \leq 3$, but 6 ordered pairs are common to both sets and cannot be counted twice.

For $r \leq 2$ or $w \leq 3$, there are $12 + 18 - 6$, or 24, favorable outcomes.

	1	2	3	4	5	6
1	(1, 1)	(1, 2)	(1, 3)	(1, 4)	(1, 5)	(1, 6)
2	(2, 1)	(2, 2)	(2, 3)	(2, 4)	(2, 5)	(2, 6)
r 3	(3, 1)	(3, 2)	(3, 3)			
4	(4, 1)	(4, 2)	(4, 3)			
5	(5, 1)	(5, 2)	(5, 3)			
6	(6, 1)	(6, 2)	(6, 3)			

(column header labelled w)

Thus, $P(r \leq 2 \text{ or } w \leq 3) = \dfrac{24}{36}$, or $\dfrac{2}{3}$.

In Example 3, notice that

$P(r \leq 2) = \dfrac{12}{36}$, or $\dfrac{1}{3}$, $\qquad P(w \leq 3) = \dfrac{18}{36}$, or $\dfrac{1}{2}$, $\qquad P(r \leq 2 \text{ and } w \leq 3) =$ $\dfrac{6}{36}$, or $\dfrac{1}{6}$ and that $\dfrac{1}{3} + \dfrac{1}{2} - \dfrac{1}{6} = \dfrac{2}{3}$, which is equal to $P(r \leq 2 \text{ or } w \leq 3)$.

This leads to the following statement about the probability of two events A or B occurring.

Probability of A or B

If A and B are inclusive events, then
$$P(A \text{ or } B) = P(A) + P(B) - P(A \text{ and } B).$$
If A and B are mutually exclusive events, then
$$P(A \text{ or } B) = P(A) + P(B).$$

Example 4 In a throw of 2 dice, what is the probability of obtaining either a sum of 7 or 11?

The sum 7 occurs 6 ways: (6, 1), (5, 2), (4, 3), (3, 4), (2, 5), (1, 6).
The sum 11 occurs 2 ways: (5, 6), (6, 5).
Both sums cannot occur at the same time.

The events are mutually exclusive. Use $P(A \text{ or } B) = P(A) + P(B)$.

$P(\text{sum of 7 or sum of 11}) = \dfrac{6}{36} + \dfrac{2}{36} = \dfrac{8}{36}$, or $\dfrac{2}{9}$.

Thus, $P(\text{sum of 7 or sum of 11}) = \dfrac{2}{9}$.

Recall that when the word "and" is used to connect two statements, the conditions of both statements must be met simultaneously if the compound statement is to be true. If you wish to find $P(A$ and $B)$, then you are interested in those ways in which event A and event B can both occur at the same time.

Example 5 In a throw of two dice, a red one and a white one, find $P(r \leq 3$ and $w \leq 2)$.

There are 36 possible outcomes.
There are 18 ways to get $r \leq 3$ and 12 ways to get $w \leq 2$, but only 6 ways to get both.

Six ordered pairs occur in both sets of ordered pairs.

Thus, $P(r \leq 3$ and $w \leq 2) = \dfrac{6}{36}$, or $\dfrac{1}{6}$.

		w				
	1	2	3	4	5	6
1	(1, 1)	(1, 2)	(1, 3)	(1, 4)	(1, 5)	(1, 6)
2	(2, 1)	(2, 2)	(2, 3)	(2, 4)	(2, 5)	(2, 6)
r 3	(3, 1)	(3, 2)	(3, 3)	(3, 4)	(3, 5)	(3, 6)
4	(4, 1)	(4, 2)				
5	(5, 1)	(5, 2)				
6	(6, 1)	(6, 2)				

In Example 5, the outcome of throwing the red die does not affect the outcome of throwing the white die. Events of this type in which neither event depends upon the other are called **independent events.**

Notice that $P(r \leq 3) = \dfrac{18}{36}$, or $\dfrac{1}{2}$, $P(w \leq 2) = \dfrac{12}{36}$, or $\dfrac{1}{3}$, and that $\dfrac{1}{2} \cdot \dfrac{1}{3} = \dfrac{1}{6}$, which is equal to $P(r \leq 3$ and $w \leq 2)$. This leads to the following statement about the probability of two events A and B occurring.

Probability of A and B

> If A and B are independent events, then
> $$P(A \text{ and } B) = P(A) \cdot P(B).$$

In the next example, the outcome of throwing each die is affected by the outcome of throwing the other. Events of this type in which one event depends upon the other are called **dependent events.** The sample space for dependent events is usually a reduced sample space of the original space.

Example 6 Find $P(r = 2$, given that $r + w \leq 5)$.

There are 10 ways to get $r + w \leq 5$ and so there are 10 possible outcomes. The 10 ordered pairs make up the reduced sample space.

There are 3 ways to get $r = 2$, so there are 3 favorable outcomes.

Thus, $P(r = 2$, given that $r + w \leq 5) = \dfrac{3}{10}$.

		w				
	1	2	3	4	5	6
1	(1, 1)	(1, 2)	(1, 3)	(1, 4)	(1, 5)	(1, 6)
2	(2, 1)	(2, 2)	(2, 3)	(2, 4)	(2, 5)	(2, 6)
r 3	(3, 1)	(3, 2)	(3, 3)	(3, 4)	(3, 5)	(3, 6)
4	(4, 1)	(4, 2)	(4, 3)	(4, 4)	(4, 5)	(4, 6)
5	(5, 1)	(5, 2)	(5, 3)	(5, 4)	(5, 5)	(5, 6)
6	(6, 1)	(6, 2)	(6, 3)	(6, 4)	(6, 5)	(6, 6)

PROBABILITY: COMPOUND EVENTS

Probability of A, given B	If A and B are dependent events, $P(A \text{ given } B) = \dfrac{P(A \text{ and } B)}{P(B)}$.

Written Exercises

4. $\frac{5}{36}$ **5.** $\frac{1}{18}$ **6.** $\frac{1}{36}$

7. $\frac{1}{6}$ **8.** $\frac{7}{12}$ **9.** $\frac{1}{36}$

For the following exercises, use the sample space showing all possible outcomes of rolling 2 dice, a red one, r, and a white one, w. Find each indicated probability.

(A)   **1.** $P(r = 4)$ $\frac{1}{6}$ **2.** $P(r \leq 3)$ $\frac{1}{2}$ **3.** $P(w \geq 5)$ $\frac{1}{3}$ **4.** $P(r + w = 8)$ **5.** $P(r + w = 11)$

6. $P(r + w = 2)$ **7.** $P(r + w \geq 10)$ **8.** $P(r + w \leq 7)$ **9.** $P(r + w < 3)$ **10.** $P(r + w \leq 1)$ 0

11. $P(r \leq 3 \text{ or } w = 2)$ $\frac{7}{12}$ **12.** $P(r \geq 5 \text{ or } w \geq 5)$ $\frac{5}{9}$ **13.** $P(r \leq 2 \text{ or } w \leq 5)$ $\frac{8}{9}$

14. $P(r \leq 4 \text{ or } w \geq 4)$ $\frac{5}{6}$ **15.** $P(\text{sum of 6 or sum of 10})$ $\frac{2}{9}$ **16.** $P(\text{sum of 2 or sum of 12})$ $\frac{1}{18}$

17. $P(\text{sum of 7 or sum of 11})$ $\frac{2}{9}$ **18.** $P(\text{sum of 11 or sum of 12})$ $\frac{1}{12}$ **19.** $P(r = 2 \text{ and } w \geq 5)$ $\frac{1}{18}$

20. $P(r \geq 4 \text{ and } w = 4)$ $\frac{1}{12}$ **21.** $P(r \geq 5 \text{ and } w \leq 2)$ $\frac{1}{9}$ **22.** $P(r \leq 2 \text{ and } w \leq 4)$ $\frac{2}{9}$

23. $P(r + w = 7, \text{ given that } r = 4)$ $\frac{1}{6}$ **24.** $P(r = 5, \text{ given that } r + w = 9)$ $\frac{1}{4}$

25. $P(w = 4, \text{ given that } r + w = 6)$ $\frac{1}{5}$ **26.** $P(r + w = 9, \text{ given that } w = 6)$ $\frac{1}{6}$

Example

A family has 3 children. Find the probability that all 3 are girls. That the first 2 are boys and the third is a girl.

Construct a sample space. List all possibilities.

1st child	2nd child	3rd child		all possibilities

	Girl or Boy	G G G ←
		G G B
		G B G
		G B B
		B G G
		B G B
		B B G ←
		B B B

Thus, $P(G, G, G) = \dfrac{1}{8}$ and $P(B, B, G) = \dfrac{1}{8}$.

Using the sample space above, find each of the following probabilities.

(B)   **27.** $P(3 \text{ boys})$ $\frac{1}{8}$ **28.** $P(2 \text{ girls and a boy})$ $\frac{3}{8}$ **29.** $P(2 \text{ boys and a girl})$ $\frac{3}{8}$

30. $P(\text{1st is a girl, 2nd is a boy, 3rd is a boy})$ $\frac{1}{8}$ **31.** $P(\text{1st is a boy, 2nd is a girl, 3rd is a boy})$ $\frac{1}{8}$

A family has 4 children. Find each indicated probability.

(C)   **32.** Find $P(4 \text{ boys})$ $\frac{1}{16}$ **33.** $P(3 \text{ girls and a boy})$ $\frac{1}{4}$ **34.** $P(2 \text{ girls and 2 boys})$ $\frac{3}{8}$

In a given town, there are 1,000 families, and each family has 4 children. Answer each question.

35. Approximately how many families have exactly 3 girls? exactly 3 boys? **250; 250**

36. Approximately how many families had 2 boys first and then 2 girls? **62**

16.8 Probability and Arrangements

OBJECTIVE ▶ To determine the probability of an event using the Fundamental Counting Principle, permutations, and combinations

The Fundamental Counting Principle as well as permutations and combinations can often be used to determine the probability of a given event.

Example 1 A matching test is given. There are 5 statements in the left column and 6 possible answers in the right column. If an answer can be used only once, what is the probability that a student can guess all the answers correctly?

$$P(\text{simple event}) = \frac{\text{Number of favorable outcomes}}{\text{Total number of all possible outcomes}}$$

There is 1 way all answers can be guessed correctly, so there is 1 favorable outcome. The total number of all possible outcomes is the number of 5-answer permutations that can be formed from the 6 answers.

Thus, $P\left(\begin{matrix}\text{guessing all answers using}\\\text{each answer only once}\end{matrix}\right) = \dfrac{1}{6 \times 5 \times 4 \times 3 \times 2} = \dfrac{1}{720}$.

In Example 1, to find the probability of guessing all the answers correctly if each answer can be used at least once, the Fundamental Counting Principle can be applied. The five answer choices in order can be made in $6 \times 6 \times 6 \times 6 \times 6$, or 7,776 different ways. So, $P\left(\begin{matrix}\text{guessing all answers using}\\\text{each answer at least once}\end{matrix}\right) = \dfrac{1}{7,776}$.

The next two examples show you how to determine the probability of an event using combinations.

Example 2 A deck of cards contains 52 cards, 13 cards of each suit. Five cards are drawn. What is the probability that all 5 cards are spades?

There are $\dbinom{13}{5}$ ways to draw 5 spades from 13 cards.

$$\dbinom{n}{r} = \dfrac{n!}{r!(n-r)!} \blacktriangleright \quad \dbinom{13}{5} = \dfrac{13!}{5!8!} = 1{,}287.$$

There are $\dbinom{52}{5}$ ways to draw 5 spades from a deck of 52 cards.

$$\dbinom{52}{5} = \dfrac{52!}{5!47!} = 2{,}598{,}960.$$

Thus, $P\left(\begin{matrix}\text{5-card hand}\\\text{of all spades}\end{matrix}\right) = \dfrac{1{,}287}{2{,}598{,}960}$, or $\dfrac{33}{66{,}640}$.

Example 3 A mathematics class of 25 students consists of 15 girls and 10 boys. A committee of 6 to represent the class is chosen at random. What is the probability that all 6 committee members are girls? that all 6 committee members are boys? that exactly 2 committee members are boys?

There are $\binom{15}{6}$ ways to choose 6 girls from a group of 15 girls.

$$\binom{15}{6} = \frac{15!}{6!9!} = \frac{15 \cdot 14 \cdot 13 \cdot 12 \cdot 11 \cdot 10 \cdot 9!}{6 \cdot 5 \cdot 4 \cdot 3 \cdot 2 \cdot 1 \cdot 9!} = 5{,}005$$

There are $\binom{10}{6}$ ways to choose 6 boys from a group of 10 boys.

$$\binom{10}{6} = \frac{10!}{6!4!}, \text{ or } 210.$$

To choose exactly 2 boys means that 4 committee members are girls. So, 2 boys and 4 girls are chosen. By the Fundamental Counting Principle, there are $\binom{10}{2}\binom{15}{4}$ ways to choose exactly 2 boys from a group of 10 boys and 4 girls from a group of 15 girls.

$$\binom{10}{2}\binom{15}{4} = \frac{10!}{2!8!} \times \frac{15!}{4!11!} = \frac{10 \cdot 9 \cdot 8!}{2 \cdot 1 \cdot 8!} \times \frac{15 \cdot 14 \cdot 13 \cdot 12 \cdot 11!}{4 \cdot 3 \cdot 2 \cdot 1 \cdot 11!}$$
$$= 45 \times 1{,}365, \text{ or } 61{,}425.$$

There are $\binom{25}{6}$ ways to choose a committee of 6 students from a group of 25 students.

$$\binom{25}{6} = \frac{25!}{6!19!} = \frac{25 \cdot 24 \cdot 23 \cdot 22 \cdot 21 \cdot 20 \cdot 19!}{6 \cdot 5 \cdot 4 \cdot 3 \cdot 2 \cdot 1 \cdot 19!} = 177{,}100$$

Thus, $P\left(\begin{matrix}\text{committee of}\\ \text{6 girls}\end{matrix}\right) = \frac{5{,}005}{177{,}100}, \text{ or } \frac{143}{5{,}060}.$

$P\left(\begin{matrix}\text{committee of}\\ \text{6 boys}\end{matrix}\right) = \frac{210}{177{,}100}, \text{ or } \frac{3}{2{,}530}.$

$P\left(\begin{matrix}\text{committee with}\\ \text{exactly 2 boys}\end{matrix}\right) = \frac{61{,}425}{177{,}100}, \text{ or } \frac{2{,}457}{7{,}084}.$

Written Exercises

Ⓐ 1. An envelope contains three slips of paper with each of the numerals 1, 2, and 3 printed on exactly one slip. If one slip of paper is drawn at a time, without replacement, what is the probability that the three-digit number 231 is drawn in that order? $\frac{1}{6}$

2. A bag contains one red, one white, and one blue cube. Each cube is drawn at random exactly once. What is the probability that the order of the cubes drawn is red, blue, and white? $\frac{1}{6}$

3. A deck of cards contains 52 cards, 13 cards of each suit. Six cards are drawn. What is the probability that all 6 cards are hearts? $\frac{33}{391,510}$

4. A deck of cards contains 52 cards, 13 cards of each suit. Five cards are to be drawn. What is the probability that two of the cards are diamonds? $\frac{9,139}{33,320}$

From a group of 5 boys and 3 girls, three violin students are to be selected at random to represent their school in a regional orchestra. Determine each probability.

(B) 5. The probability that all 3 students selected are girls $\frac{1}{56}$

6. The probability that all 3 students selected are boys $\frac{5}{28}$

7. The probability that exactly 1 student selected is a boy $\frac{15}{56}$

8. The probability that exactly 1 student selected is a girl $\frac{15}{28}$

9. The probability that 2 students selected are boys and 1 a girl $\frac{15}{28}$

10. The probability that 1 student selected is a boy and 2 are girls $\frac{15}{56}$

11. A box contains 6 red, 5 white, and 7 black marbles. What is the probability of drawing a black marble, then a red one, if the 1st marble is replaced before drawing the 2nd? $\frac{7}{54}$

12. A box contains 4 red, 8 white, and 10 black marbles. What is the probability of drawing a red marble, then a white marble, then a black marble, if each marble is not replaced before the next draw? $\frac{8}{231}$

(C) 13. A card is drawn from a deck of 52 cards. What is the probability that the card will be an ace, or red queen, or a ten of hearts? $\frac{7}{52}$

14. A card is drawn from a deck of 52 cards. What is the probability that the card will be an ace, king, or queen? $\frac{3}{13}$

15. A box contains 8 red marbles and 10 black marbles. Two marbles are drawn at random without replacement. What is the probability that both are the same color? that one will be red and one black? that both will be red? that both will be black? $\frac{73}{153}, \frac{80}{153}, \frac{28}{153}, \frac{5}{17}$

16. A box contains 4 red, 6 white, and 8 blue marbles. What is the probability of drawing a white marble, and then a red one, if the 1st marble is replaced before drawing the 2nd? if the 1st marble is not replaced before drawing the 2nd? $\frac{2}{27}, \frac{4}{51}$

CALCULATOR ACTIVITIES

Determine $\binom{10}{6}$ using a calculator.

$$\binom{10}{6} = \frac{10!}{6! \cdot 4!} = \frac{10 \cdot 9 \cdot 8 \cdot 7 \cdot \cancel{6}!}{\cancel{6}! \cdot 4 \cdot 3 \cdot 2 \cdot 1}$$

$$10 \otimes 9 \otimes 8 \otimes 7 \oslash 4 \oslash 3 \oslash 2 \oslash 1 \ominus 210$$

PROBABILITY AND ARRANGEMENTS

Chapter Sixteen Review

Vocabulary

circular permutation [16.4]
combination [16.5]
dependent events [16.7]
inclusive events [16.7]
independent events [16.7]
mutually exclusive events [16.7]
$n!$ [16.1]   permutation [16.1]
probability [16.6]   sample space [16.7]

Find the value of each expression.

1. $\dfrac{12!}{3! \times 8!}$ [16.3] **1,980**

2. $\dbinom{100}{3}$ [16.5] **161,700**

3. $\dbinom{9}{0}$ [16.5] **1**

4. How many four-digit numbers can be formed from the digits 4, 5, 6, 7, 8, 9, if (a) no digit may be repeated in a number and (b) a digit may be repeated in a number? [16.1] **360, 1,296**

5. How many odd four-digit numbers can be formed from the digits 4, 5, 6, 7, 8, 9, if no digit may be repeated in a number? [16.2]

6. How many even numbers of one or more digits can be formed from the digits 4, 5, 6, 7, 8, if no digit may be repeated in a number? [16.2] **195**

5. **180**

7. How many distinguishable six-digit numbers can be formed from the digits of 789778? [16.3] **60**

8. How many different auto license-plate numbers can be formed by 3 different letters followed by 4 digits? [16.1] **156,000,000**

9. Find the number of 7-letter permutations of all the letters in the word COMBINE. [16.1] **5,040**

10. Tom and Mary invite three other couples to a cookout. In how many ways can they all be seated around the fire? [16.4] **5,040**

★ 11. In how many ways can 6 keys be arranged on a ring? [16.4] **60**

12. How many different 6-member committees can be formed if 9 people are available for appointment to a committee? [16.5] **84**

13. A company makes sweaters in 7 colors. Each color is available with 5 choices of fabric and either with or without sleeves. How many different types of sweaters does the company make? [16.1] **70**

14. How many tennis games are played by 8 people if each person plays each of the others one game? [16.5] **28**

15. Three brands of canned soup and 4 brands of dried soup are to be displayed on a shelf with the dried soups together and to the right of the canned soups. How many displays are possible? [16.2] **144**

★ 16. In how many different ways can a family of seven be photographed in a line if the father and mother are not to be separated? [16.2] **1,440**

17. A deck of cards contains 52 cards, 13 cards of each suit. One card is drawn. What is the probability that the card is a king? that it is not a king? [16.6] $\frac{1}{13}, \frac{12}{13}$

18. A die is rolled 600 times. About how many times should it stop on 2? About how many times should an even number appear? [16.6] **100, 300**

For Exercises 19–21, use the sample space showing all possible outcomes of rolling 2 dice, a red one, r, and a white one, w. Find each indicated probability. [16.7]

19. $P(w \leq 4)$ $\frac{2}{3}$ 20. $P(r + w = 7)$ $\frac{1}{6}$

21. $P(r + w = 6$, given that $r = 3)$ $\frac{1}{6}$

★ 22. A family has 4 children. Find $P(3$ boys and a girl). [16.7] $\frac{1}{4}$

23. A box contains 12 red, 8 white, and 10 blue cubes. What is the probability of drawing a blue cube, then a red one, if the first cube is replaced before drawing the second? If the first cube is not replaced before drawing the second? [16.8] $\frac{2}{15}, \frac{4}{29}$

Chapter Sixteen Test

Find the value of each expression.

1. $\dfrac{12!}{9! \times 2!}$ **660** 2. $\dbinom{12}{8}$ **495** 3. $\dbinom{20}{20}$ **1**

4. How many three-digit numbers can be formed from the digits 2, 3, 4, 5, 6, 7, if no digit may be repeated in a number? **120**

5. A state uses 2 different letters followed by 5 digits on its auto license-plates. How many different license-plate numbers are possible in that state? **65,000,000**

6. How many distinguishable six-digit numbers can be formed from 335533? **15**

7. Find the number of 6-letter permutations of all the letters in EUCLID that end with either the letter E or the letter D. **240**

8. In how many ways can 6 bushes, all of different types, be planted around a statue? **120**

9. How many different 12-member juries can be selected from 15 qualified people? **455**

10. Find the number of distinguishable permutations of all the letters in the word BANANA. **60**

11. An amusement park has 9 gates with 5 on the north side and 4 on the south side. In how many different ways can you enter through a south gate and later exit through a north gate? **20**

12. Aluminum chips A, B, C, and D weigh 1 g, 5 g, 10 g, and 20 g, respectively. How many different masses can be measured by using one or more of the 4 weights on a balance scale? **15**

13. A box contains 15 green marbles, 12 orange marbles, and 23 purple marbles. A marble is drawn from the box. What is the probability that the marble is green? that it is not green? $\frac{3}{10}, \frac{7}{10}$

14. A deck of cards contains 52 cards, 13 cards of each suit. One card is drawn. What is the probability that the card is an ace? that it is the ace of spades? $\frac{1}{13}, \frac{1}{52}$

15. An 8-sided die is rolled 400 times. About how many times should it stop on 7? About how many times should an odd number appear? **50, 200**

For Exercises 16–18, use the sample space showing all possible outcomes of rolling 2 dice, a blue one, *b*, and a red one, *r*. Find each indicated probability.

16. $P(b = 2)$ $\frac{1}{6}$ 17. $P(b \geq 4 \text{ or } r \leq 2)$ $\frac{2}{3}$
18. $P(b \geq 2 \text{ and } r \leq 2)$ $\frac{5}{18}$

19. A bag contains 22 orange and 18 green balls. What is the probability of drawing a green ball, then an orange one, if the first ball is replaced before drawing the second? if the first ball is not replaced before drawing the second? $\frac{99}{400}, \frac{33}{130}$

★20. In how many ways can 6 cheerleaders be arranged in a line if 3 of them do not want to be separated? **144**

★21. In how many ways can 5 charms be arranged on a bracelet? **12**

★22. Solve $\dbinom{n}{4} = \dbinom{n}{1}$ for *n*. **5**

★23. A family has 4 children. Find $P(4 \text{ boys})$. $\frac{1}{16}$

Computer Activities

A Fair Game?

Video and electronic games are very popular. Sometimes you win and sometimes "the machine" beats you. A simple game based on the random selection of numbers is the *GUESS* game, which is presented by the computer program below.

In the game, the computer randomly selects a number from 1 to 100 and you are given a certain number of tries to guess the number. The probability that you will beat the computer on your first try is 0.01 [The *RND(X)* function specified by statement 30 generates numbers between 0 and 1.]

PROGRAM

```
10 PRINT "GENERATE RANDOM NUMBERS FROM 1 TO 100"
20 PRINT "PLAYER GETS 5 GUESSES"
25 RANDOMIZE
30 LET N = INT((100) * RND(0) + 1)
40 LET C = 0
50 PRINT "ENTER GUESS"
60 INPUT G
70 IF G = N, THEN 140
80 LET C = C + 1
90 IF C = 5, THEN 120
100 PRINT "WRONG, TRY AGAIN"
110 GO TO 50
120 PRINT "WRONG 5 TIMES, YOU LOSE, ANSWER IS"; N
130 GO TO 150
140 PRINT "CORRECT, YOU BEAT ME"
150 END
```

Exercises

1. Type in the program and run it several times. (Check your computer instructions to see if statement 25 is needed.) How does statement 30 work?

Numbers between 0 and 1 are selected randomly and multiplied by 100.

2. Alter the program to tell you if your guess is high or low.

72 IF G > N THEN 78   74 PRINT "WRONG, TOO LOW" 76 GO TO 80   78 PRINT "WRONG, TOO HIGH"

3. Write a program to play a card game with cards dealt randomly. The computer wins a point if its card is higher than yours. You win the point otherwise. Play for 52 draws, and print the total score and name of winner at the end.

For Ex. 3, see TE Answer Section.

College Prep Test

DIRECTIONS: In each item, you are to compare a quantity in Column 1 with a quantity in Column 2. Write the letter of the correct answer from these choices:

A The quantity in Column 1 is greater than the quantity in Column 2
B The quantity in Column 2 is greater than the quantity in Column 1
C The quantity in Column 1 is equal to the quantity in Column 2
D The relationship cannot be determined from the given information

Information centered over both columns refers to one or both of the quantities to be compared.

SAMPLE ITEMS AND ANSWERS

Column 1	Column 2
S1. $3! + 2!$	$3! \cdot 2!$

The answer is B: $3! + 2! = 6 + 2 = 8$, $3! \cdot 2! = 6 \cdot 2 = 12$, and $12 > 8$.

n and r are positive integers and $n > r$.

Column 1	Column 2
S2. $\binom{n}{r-1}$	$\binom{n-1}{r}$

The answer is D: If $n = 3$ and $r = 1$, then $\binom{n}{r-1} < \binom{n-1}{r}$, since $\binom{3}{0} < \binom{2}{1}$.

If $n = 3$ and $r = 2$, then $\binom{n}{r-1} > \binom{n-1}{r}$, since $\binom{3}{1} > \binom{2}{2}$, or $3 > 1$.

	Column 1	Column 2	
1.	$(5 - 5)!$	$5! - 5!$	A
2.	$\binom{8}{3}$	$\binom{8}{5}$	C
3.	$\binom{48}{2}$	$\binom{49}{3}$	B

	Column 1	Column 2	
4.	$\binom{20}{0}$	$\binom{40}{40}$	C
5.	$\dfrac{46! \times 29!}{15!}$	$\dfrac{47! \times 28!}{16!}$	A
6.	$\binom{6}{0} + \binom{6}{1} + \binom{6}{2}$	$\binom{6}{6} + \binom{6}{5} + \binom{6}{4}$	C

n and r are positive integers and $n > r$.

	Column 1	Column 2	
7.	$\binom{n}{r}$	$\binom{n+1}{r+1}$	B
8.	$\binom{n}{r}$	$\binom{n}{r+1}$	D
9.	$\binom{n}{r-1} + \binom{n}{r}$	$\binom{n+1}{r+1}$	D

$$\begin{matrix} & B\bullet & \bullet C & \\ A\bullet & & & \bullet D \\ & F\bullet & \bullet E & \end{matrix}$$

	Column 1	Column 2	
10.	Number of triangles determined by the points	Number of lines determined by the points	A
11.	Number of quadrilaterals determined	Number of polygons determined	B

Cumulative Review (Chapters 1–16)

DIRECTIONS: Choose the *one* best answer to each question or problem. (Exercises 1–15)

1. Find the solution set of $|x - 3| < 2$. **D**
   (A) $\{x|-1 < x < -5\}$ (B) $\{x|x < 3\}$
   (C) $\{x|x < 2\}$ (D) $\{x|1 < x < 5\}$

2. Solve $3^{3x-2} = 81$ for x. **D**
   (A) $\frac{5}{3}$ (B) -2 (C) 9 (D) 2

3. Evaluate $-2xy + 3x^2y - y^2$ if $x = -2$ and $y = 3$. **C**
   (A) -33 (B) 15 (C) 39 (D) 57

4. Factor $6x^3 + 4x^2 - 2x$ completely. **C**
   (A) $2x(3x^2 + 2x - 1)$
   (B) $x(3x - 1)(2x + 2)$
   (C) $2x(3x - 1)(x + 1)$
   (D) $2x(3x + 1)(x - 1)$

5. Subtract: $\dfrac{1}{n - 2} - \dfrac{3}{n^2 - 4}$. **B**
   (A) $\dfrac{-2}{n + 2}$ (B) $\dfrac{n - 1}{(n - 2)(n + 2)}$
   (C) $\dfrac{n + 5}{n - 2}$ (D) $\dfrac{-2}{(n - 2)(n + 2)}$

6. Solve $\dfrac{2a}{x - b} = \dfrac{-c}{x + b}$ for x. **B**
   (A) $\dfrac{c - 2ab}{2ac}$ (B) $\dfrac{bc - 2ab}{2a + c}$
   (C) $\dfrac{2ab - bc}{c + 2a}$ (D) $\dfrac{2ab - bc}{2ac}$

7. Simplify $\dfrac{x^{\frac{2}{3}}y^{-\frac{1}{4}}}{x^{-\frac{1}{3}}y^{-\frac{7}{4}}}$. **C**
   (A) $x^{\frac{1}{3}}y^{\frac{3}{2}}$ (B) $x^{\frac{1}{3}}y^2$
   (C) $xy^{\frac{3}{2}}$ (D) xy^2

8. Compute the discriminant and determine the nature of the solutions of $3x^2 - 7x + 6 = 0$. **D**
   (A) real and irrational (B) real and equal
   (C) real and rational (D) imaginary

9. Write an equation, in standard form, of the line that passes through $P(2, -1)$ and that is parallel to the line described by $2x - 7y = 12$. **B**
   (A) $7x + 2y = 12$ (B) $2x - 7y = 11$
   (C) $2x - 7y = -11$ (D) $7x - 2y = 16$

10. Multiply, if possible. **B**
    $$\begin{bmatrix} 3 & 1 & -2 \\ -1 & 2 & 1 \end{bmatrix} \cdot \begin{bmatrix} 1 & -1 & 2 \\ 3 & 1 & -2 \\ -4 & 2 & -3 \end{bmatrix}$$
    (A) $\begin{bmatrix} 15 & -1 & 1 \end{bmatrix}$ (B) $\begin{bmatrix} 14 & -6 & 10 \\ 1 & 5 & -9 \end{bmatrix}$
    (C) $\begin{bmatrix} 3 & -1 & -4 \\ 9 & 1 & -4 \\ 4 & 4 & 3 \end{bmatrix}$ (D) Not possible

11. A function f is defined by $y = -\frac{1}{2}x - 4$. Find an equation of f^{-1}. **A**
    (A) $y = -2x - 8$ (B) $y = 2x + 4$
    (C) $y = 2x + 8$ (D) $y = \frac{1}{2}x + 4$

12. Write an equation, in standard form, of an ellipse whose center is at the origin and whose x-intercepts are ± 6 and whose y-intercepts are ± 4. **A**
    (A) $\dfrac{x^2}{36} + \dfrac{y^2}{16} = 1$ (B) $\dfrac{x^2}{16} + \dfrac{y^2}{36} = 1$
    (C) $\dfrac{x^2}{36} - \dfrac{y^2}{16} = 1$ (D) $\dfrac{x^2}{16} - \dfrac{y^2}{36} = 1$

13. Find log 893.7 to four decimal places. Use linear interpolation. **C**
    (A) 2.9511 (B) $8.9511 - 10$
    (C) 2.9512 (D) $8.9512 - 10$

14. Find the value of $\binom{14}{12}$. **C**
    (A) 182 (B) $\dfrac{91}{6}$ (C) 91 (D) $\dfrac{91}{3}$

15. A deck of cards contains 52 cards, 13 cards of each suit. One card is drawn. What is the probability that the card is a red ace? **A**
    (A) $\dfrac{1}{26}$ (B) $\dfrac{2}{13}$ (C) $\dfrac{1}{13}$ (D) $\dfrac{1}{52}$

16. Solve $3x - 3(2x - 1) = -(x + 15)$. **9**

17. Simplify $\dfrac{12a^5b^{-6}}{-2a^{-3}b^{-7}}$ and write with positive exponents. **$-6a^8b$**

18. Factor $25a^2 - 100$ completely.
$25(a - 2)(a + 2)$

19. The height of a triangle is 12 cm more than 4 times the length of its base. Find the length of the base and the height of the triangle if its area is 20 cm². **base: 2 cm; height: 20 cm**

20. Alberta can pick the apples in 8 days and Elias can pick them in 12 days. How long would it take them to pick the apples if they work together? **$4\frac{4}{5}$ days**

21. Simplify: $\sqrt[3]{16a^5} + \sqrt[3]{54a^5}$. **$5a\sqrt[3]{2a^2}$**

22. Find the value of $81^{\frac{3}{4}}$. **27**

23. Write $3x^{\frac{2}{3}}$ in radical form. **$3\sqrt[3]{x^2}$**

24. Solve $x^2 - 8x = 5$ by completing the square. **$4 \pm \sqrt{21}$**

25. Simplify $-4 \div (3i)$ by rationalizing the denominator. **$\frac{4i}{3}$**

26. For what value(s) of k will $3x^2 + 6x - (3k - 2) = 0$ have exactly one solution? **$-\frac{1}{3}$**

27. Draw the graph of $-2x - 3y = 6$.
For Ex. 27, see TE Answer Section.

28. Find the slope and y-intercept of the line described by $y - 3(2 - x) = 6$.
$m = -3, b = 12$

29. Find the distance between $P(-3, -5)$ and $Q(5, -6)$. **$\sqrt{65}$**

30. Determine the coordinates of M, the midpoint of $\overline{AB}$, given $A(3, -1)$ and $B(7, 9)$. **(5, 4)**

31. Solve the system: $-3x + 2y + z = 8$
$x - 3y + 2z = -5$.
$-x + y - 3z = 0$
(−1, 2, 1)

32. Let $f(x) = 2x^2 - 1$. Find $f(-3)$. **17**

33. If $f(x) = \dfrac{2x}{x^2 + 2x - 15}$, determine the domain of f.
{all real numbers except −5 and 3}

34. Draw the graph of $y = -x^2 - 6x + 2$.
For Ex. 34, see TE Answer Section.

35. Find an equation of a circle whose center is at $C(-3, 2)$ and which passes through the point $P(1, -7)$. **$(x + 3)^2 + (y - 2)^2 = 97$**

36. Solve the system $x^2 + y^2 \le 36$ graphically.
$\dfrac{x^2}{9} + \dfrac{y^2}{4} \ge 1$
For Ex. 36, see TE Answer Section.

37. Find the sum, if it exists, of the infinite geometric series
$1 + \dfrac{1}{3} + \dfrac{1}{9} + \ldots$ **$1\frac{1}{2}$**

38. Find the 5th term in the expansion of $(2x - 3y)^7$. Simplify. **$22{,}680x^3y^4$**

39. Find $(0.0035 \times 54.7)^4$ to three significant digits. Use logarithms. **0.00134**

40. How many even numbers containing one or more digits can be formed from the digits 1, 2, 3, 4 if no digit may be repeated in a number? **32**

17 TRIGONOMETRIC FUNCTIONS

Sonya Kovalevsky

Sonya Kovalevsky was born in Moscow, Russia, on January 15, 1850. Her maiden name was Sonya Korvin-Krukovsky. She began the study of mathematics at age 15. Two years later she was studying calculus at the naval school in St. Petersburg.

In order to leave Russia, Sonya followed the practice of many other Russian girls. At age 18, a token marriage was arranged to Vladimir Kovalevsky; she then left Russia and moved to Germany. A year later she was studying elliptic functions at the University of Heidelberg in Germany.

At age 20, Sonya decided to learn from Karl Weierstrass, the master teacher and famous mathematician. (See page 337.) Karl agreed to tutor her privately twice a week, since the university senate would not allow a woman to attend classroom lectures. In 1874, Sonya was awarded a PhD degree, *in absentia*, from the University of Gottingham and returned to Russia to continue her research. In 1884, she became a professor of mathematics at Stockholm University in Sweden, and in 1889 the university named her a professor for life.

Sonya's mathematical study was mainly connected with the theory of differential equations, a theory to which she made many valuable contributions. She also established a reputation as a leader in the struggle for equal rights for women, especially in the area of higher education.

17.1 Angles of Rotation

OBJECTIVES ▶ **To sketch an angle of rotation associated with a directed degree measure**
To determine a reference angle and reference triangle for any angle

An **angle of rotation** is formed by rotating a ray about its end point, or vertex. Each angle formed is composed of two rays, the initial ray or side and terminal ray or side. A ray can be rotated in either a counterclockwise or clockwise direction and the terminal ray can lie in any quadrant or on any axis. Angles formed by a *counterclockwise* rotation have a *positive measure*. The figure at the right illustrates a counterclockwise rotation of a ray forming an angle with a positive measure of 150°.

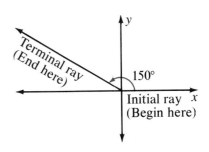

Example 1 Sketch angles of rotation with measures of 90°, 225°, and 330°.

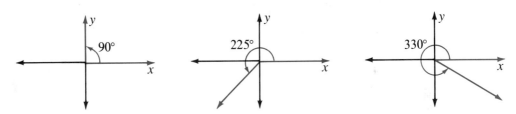

Angles formed by a *clockwise rotation* of a ray have *negative measures*. The figure at the right illustrates a clockwise rotation of a ray forming an angle with a measure of −45°.

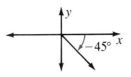

Example 2 Sketch angles of rotation with measures of −120°, −210°, and −315°.

Rays may be rotated through more than one revolution forming angles that measure more than 360°. The position of the terminal side of an angle determines the quadrant of the angle. Angles with terminal sides on an axis are called **quadrantal angles**. Angles with the same terminal sides are called **coterminal angles**.

Example 3 Sketch angles of rotation with measures of 270°, −570°, and 420°. Determine the quadrant of each angle or identify as a quadrantal angle.

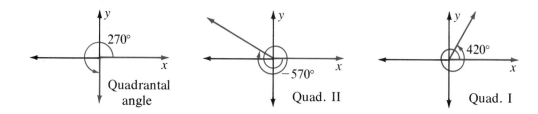

Each angle of rotation whose terminal side is not on an axis has a reference angle. A **reference angle** is the positive acute angle formed between the terminal side and the *x*-axis. The next example illustrates this idea.

Example 4 Sketch angles of rotation with measures of 135°, −120°, and 330°. Identify the reference angle and determine the quadrant of the angle of rotation.

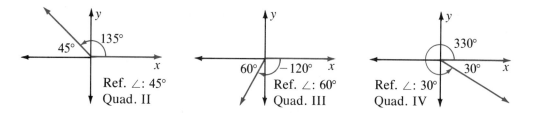

The triangle formed by drawing a perpendicular from a point on the terminal side to the *x*-axis is called a **reference triangle**. A *reference triangle* always includes the reference angle.

Example 5 Sketch angles of rotation with measures of 60°, 200°, and −310°. Identify the reference triangle and reference angle.

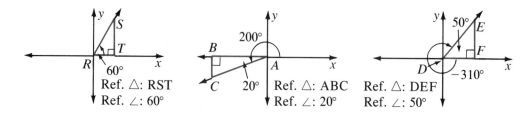

Reading in Algebra

Each item at the left can be described by one or more items at the right. Determine all items at the right that can be used to describe each item at the left. Justify.

1. 120° **B, C, F**   A. Clockwise rotation   F. Quad. II
2. −300° **A, C, E**   B. Counterclockwise rotation   G. Quad. III
3. 210° **B, D, G**   C. Ref. ∠: 60°   H. Quad. IV
4. −30° **A, D, H**   D. Ref. ∠: 30°   I. Quadrantal ∠
5. 270° **B, I**   E. Quad. I

Oral Exercises

Determine the quadrant of each angle of rotation, and state the measure of the reference angle.

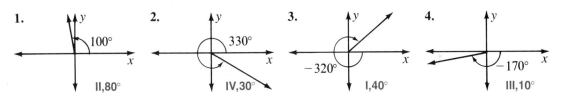

1. 100°   II, 80°
2. 330°   IV, 30°
3. −320°   I, 40°
4. −170°   III, 10°

Written Exercises

(A) Sketch angles of rotation with the given measures. Determine the quadrant of each angle of rotation or identify as a quadrantal angle (Quad. ∠).

1. 30° **I**	2. 300° **IV**	3. 210° **III**	4. 135° **II**	5. −30° **IV**	6. −150° **III**
7. −360°	8. −225° **II**	9. −90°	10. 225° **III**	11. 330° **IV**	12. 10° **I**
13. 515° **II**	14. −190° **II**	15. 400° **I**	16. −650° **I**	17. 100° **II**	18. 720°
Quad. ∠		**Quad. ∠**			**Quad. ∠**

Sketch angles of rotation with the given measures. Determine the quadrant of each angle of rotation. Identify the reference triangle.

19. 75° **I**	20. 160° **II**	21. 225° **III**	22. 330° **IV**	23. −40° **IV**	24. −195° **II**
25. −245° **II**	26. −300° **I**	27. 495° **II**	28. −780° **IV**	29. −510° **III**	30. −360°
					Quad. ∠

Sketch angles of rotation with the given measures. Identify the reference triangle and reference angle of each nonquadrantal angle.

31. −50° **50°**	32. 150° **30°**	33. −135° **45°**	34. −225° **45°**	35. 315° **45°**	36. 210° **30°**
37. −405° **45°**	38. −315° **45°**	39. 780° **60°**	40. 510° **30°**	41. −90°	42. 350° **10°**
				Quad. ∠	

(B) State two more measures, one positive and one negative, for angles of rotation that have the same terminal side as the one shown. **Answers may vary.**

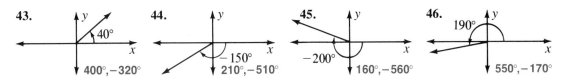

43. 40°   400°, −320°
44. −150°   210°, −510°
45. −200°   160°, −560°
46. 190°   550°, −170°

17.2 Special Right Triangles

OBJECTIVES ▶ To find lengths of sides in a 30°–60° or 45°–45° right triangle
To find points on a circle using 30°–60° or 45°–45° right triangles

Recall that in an equilateral △, an altitude bisects both the base and the vertex angle from which it is drawn. You can see that in equilateral △ABC, altitude $\overline{AD}$ bisects ∠A and base $\overline{BC}$. You can also see that in rt. △ABD, the leg opposite the 30° angle, $\overline{BD}$, has $\frac{1}{2}$ the measure of hypotenuse $\overline{AB}$.

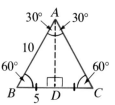

To find AD use the Pythagorean theorem.
$$(AB)^2 = (BD)^2 + (AD)^2$$
$$10^2 = 5^2 + (AD)^2$$
$$100 = 25 + (AD)^2$$
$$(AD)^2 = 75$$
$$(AD) = \sqrt{75}, \text{ or } 5\sqrt{3}$$

30°–60° Right Triangle Rule

In a 30°–60° right △:
1. the leg opposite the 30° angle has $\frac{1}{2}$ the measure of the hypotenuse
2. the leg opposite the 60° angle has $\frac{1}{2}$ the measure of the hypotenuse times $\sqrt{3}$

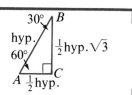

Example 1 In right △RST, RS = 8. Find ST and RT.

$\overline{ST}$ is opposite the 30° angle. $\overline{RT}$ is opposite the 60° angle.

$$ST = \tfrac{1}{2}(RS) \qquad RT = \tfrac{1}{2}(RS)\sqrt{3}$$
$$= \tfrac{1}{2}(8) \qquad\quad = \tfrac{1}{2}(8)\sqrt{3}$$
$$= 4 \qquad\qquad\quad = 4\sqrt{3}$$

Thus, $ST = 4$ and $RT = 4\sqrt{3}$.

Example 2 In right △XYZ, XZ = 5. Find XY and YZ.

$\overline{XZ}$ is opposite the 30° angle. $\overline{YZ}$ is opposite the 60° angle.

$$XZ = \tfrac{1}{2}(XY) \qquad YZ = \tfrac{1}{2}(XY)\sqrt{3}$$
$$5 = \tfrac{1}{2}XY \qquad\quad = \tfrac{1}{2}(10)\sqrt{3}$$
$$10 = XY \qquad\qquad = 5\sqrt{3}$$

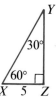

Thus, $XY = 10$ and $YZ = 5\sqrt{3}$.

Example 3

In right $\triangle ABC$, $BC = 6$.
Find AB and AC.

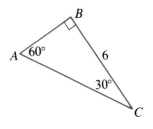

$\overline{AB}$ is opposite the 30° angle.
$\overline{BC}$ is opposite the 60° angle.

$BC = \frac{1}{2}(AC)\sqrt{3}$ | $AB = \frac{1}{2}(AC)$

$6 = \frac{1}{2}(AC)\sqrt{3}$ | $= \frac{1}{2}(4\sqrt{3})$

$12 = (AC)\sqrt{3}$ | $= 2\sqrt{3}$

$AC = \dfrac{12}{\sqrt{3}}$, or $4\sqrt{3}$

Thus, $AC = 4\sqrt{3}$ and $AB = 2\sqrt{3}$.

Recall that if two angles of a triangle have the same measure, the triangle is **isosceles** and the sides opposite the two angles have the same measure.
$\triangle ABC$ is an isosceles right triangle and
$AC = BC$. To find AC or BC, use the Pythagorean theorem.

$(AC)^2 + (BC)^2 = (AB)^2$
$(AC)^2 + (AC)^2 = (AB)^2$
$\qquad\quad 2(AC)^2 = 8^2$
$\qquad\quad\ (AC)^2 = 32$
$\qquad AC = BC = \sqrt{32}$, or $4\sqrt{2}$

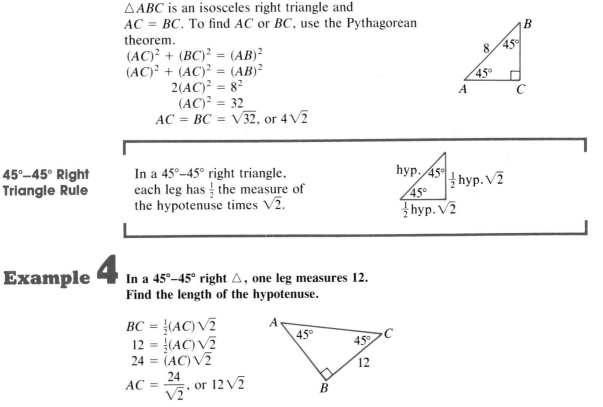

45°–45° Right Triangle Rule

In a 45°–45° right triangle, each leg has $\frac{1}{2}$ the measure of the hypotenuse times $\sqrt{2}$.

Example 4

In a 45°–45° right $\triangle$, one leg measures 12.
Find the length of the hypotenuse.

$BC = \frac{1}{2}(AC)\sqrt{2}$
$12 = \frac{1}{2}(AC)\sqrt{2}$
$24 = (AC)\sqrt{2}$
$AC = \dfrac{24}{\sqrt{2}}$, or $12\sqrt{2}$

Thus, the length of the hypotenuse is $12\sqrt{2}$.

SPECIAL RIGHT TRIANGLES

You have learned that each nonquadrantal angle of rotation has a corresponding reference angle and reference triangle. There is also a circle that is associated with an angle of rotation. The examples that follow illustrate the use of a circle with reference triangles and special triangles.

Example 5 **For a circle with radius of 8 units and a reference triangle of 30°–60°–90° as shown, find the point (x, y).**

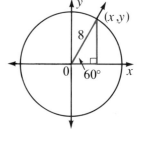

y is opposite the 60° angle.
x is opposite the 30° angle.

$$|y| = \tfrac{1}{2}(8)\sqrt{3} \qquad |x| = \tfrac{1}{2}(8)$$
$$|y| = 4\sqrt{3} \qquad\quad |x| = 4$$
$$y = 4\sqrt{3} \qquad\qquad x = 4$$

◀ *In Quad. I, $x > 0, y > 0$.*

Thus, the point (x, y) is $(4, 4\sqrt{3})$.

Example 6 **For the following circle, determine the radius r and the point (x, y) if $y = 3$.**

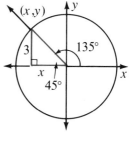

y is opposite a 45° angle.
x is opposite a 45° angle.

$$y = \tfrac{1}{2}r\sqrt{2} \qquad\quad |x| = |y|$$
$$3 = \tfrac{1}{2}r\sqrt{2} \qquad\quad |x| = 3$$
$$6 = r\sqrt{2} \qquad\qquad x = -3$$
$$r = \frac{6}{\sqrt{2}}, \text{ or } 3\sqrt{2}$$

◀ *In Quad. II, $x < 0, y > 0$.*

Thus, $r = 3\sqrt{2}$ and the point (x, y) is $(-3, 3)$.

Oral **Exercises** _____

State the length of the indicated side.

1.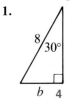

2.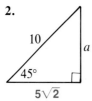

3.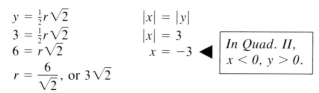

4.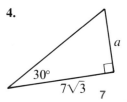

Written Exercises _____

(A) Determine the lengths of the indicated sides. Rationalize all denominators.

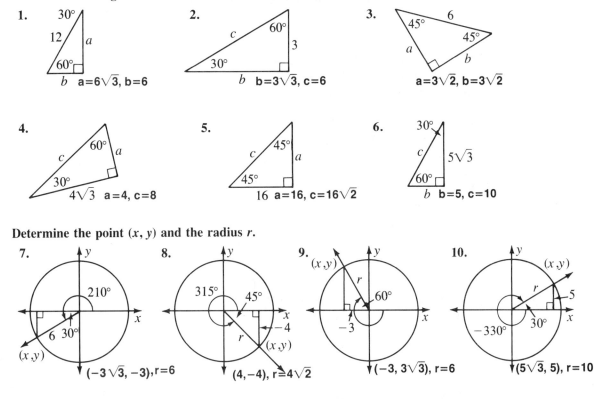

1.   30°
     12 / a
     60°
     b   a=6√3, b=6

2.   c / 60°
     3
     30°
     b   b=3√3, c=6

3.   45°   6
     a   45°
     b
     a=3√2, b=3√2

4.   60° / a
     c
     30°
     4√3   a=4, c=8

5.   45° / a
     c
     45°
     16   a=16, c=16√2

6.   30°
     c   5√3
     60°
     b   b=5, c=10

Determine the point (x, y) and the radius r.

7.   210°
     6   30°
     (x,y)
     $(-3\sqrt{3}, -3)$, r=6

8.   315°   45°
     −4
     r (x,y)
     $(4,-4)$, r=4√2

9. (x,y) r
     60°
     −3
     $(-3, 3\sqrt{3})$, r=6

10. (x,y)
     r   5
     −330°   30°
     $(5\sqrt{3}, 5)$, r=10

(B) Complete the chart.

17. 45°, 3√2   18. 30°, 2   19. 60°, 8   20. 45°, 5√2   21. 30°, 4
22. 60°, 8   23. 60°, 10   24. 45°, 7√2   25. 30°, 8   26. 60°, 6

	Length of hypotenuse	Length of leg opposite 30° ∠	Length of leg opposite 60° ∠
11.	16	a 8	b 8√3
12.	c 18	9	b 9√3
13.	c 4√3	a 2√3	6

	Length of hypotenuse	Length of leg opposite 45° ∠	Length of leg opposite other 45° ∠
14.	c 3√2	3	b 3
15.	c 12√2	a 12	12
16.	14	a 7√2	b 7√2

(C) Find the reference angle if its terminal side intersects a circle at the given point and the center of the circle is at the origin. Determine the radius of the circle.

17. $(-3, 3)$ 18. $(-\sqrt{3}, -1)$ 19. $(4, -4\sqrt{3})$ 20. $(5, -5)$ 21. $(-2\sqrt{3}, -2)$
22. $(4, 4\sqrt{3})$ 23. $(-5, 5\sqrt{3})$ 24. $(-7, -7)$ 25. $(4\sqrt{3}, 4)$ 26. $(3, -3\sqrt{3})$
27. $(-a, a)$ 28. $(m, m\sqrt{3})$ 29. $(-r, r\sqrt{3})$ 30. $(n\sqrt{3}, -n)$ 31. $(-r, -r)$
    45°, a√2   60°, 2m   60°, 2r   30°, 2n   45°, r√2

32. Prove the 45°–45° right triangle rule.   **33.** Prove the 30°–60° right triangle rule.

For Ex. 32–33, see TE Answer Section.

SPECIAL RIGHT TRIANGLES

17.3 Sine and Cosine Functions

OBJECTIVES ▶ **To find the sine and cosine of degree measures of 0°, 30°, 45°, 60°, 90° and their multiples**
To determine if the sine or cosine is positive or negative for a given degree measure
To find the measure of an angle whose sine or cosine is given

Examine the four reference triangles (one in each quadrant) shown in the figures below.

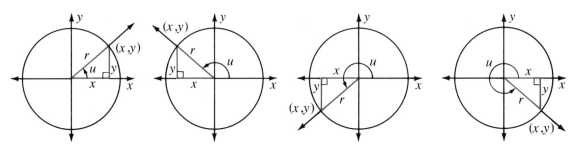

The ratios $\dfrac{y}{r}$ and $\dfrac{x}{r}$ in each of the figures determine trigonometric functions that are defined in terms of u as follows.

Definition:
Sine (sin) and
Cosine (cos)
Functions

> For any angle of rotation u, the sine of u is $\dfrac{y}{r}\left(\sin u = \dfrac{y}{r}\right)$ and the cosine of u is $\dfrac{x}{r}\left(\cos u = \dfrac{x}{r}\right)$.

Example 1 Find sin 30°, cos 30°, sin 150°, and cos 150°.

For each angle, sketch a circle with any radius (a radius of 2 is convenient) to show the angle of rotation and reference triangle.

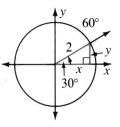

$$|y| = \tfrac{1}{2}r$$
$$= \tfrac{1}{2}(2) = 1$$

$$|x| = \tfrac{1}{2}(r)\sqrt{3}$$
$$= \tfrac{1}{2}(2)\sqrt{3} = \sqrt{3}$$

So, $y = 1$, $x = \sqrt{3}$,
$\dfrac{y}{r} = \dfrac{1}{2}$ and $\dfrac{x}{r} = \dfrac{\sqrt{3}}{2}$.

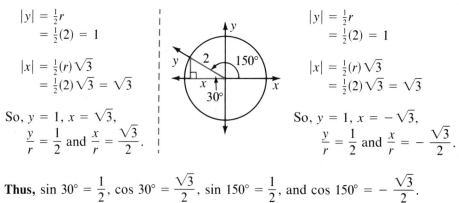

$$|y| = \tfrac{1}{2}r$$
$$= \tfrac{1}{2}(2) = 1$$

$$|x| = \tfrac{1}{2}(r)\sqrt{3}$$
$$= \tfrac{1}{2}(2)\sqrt{3} = \sqrt{3}$$

So, $y = 1$, $x = -\sqrt{3}$,
$\dfrac{y}{r} = \dfrac{1}{2}$ and $\dfrac{x}{r} = -\dfrac{\sqrt{3}}{2}$.

Thus, $\sin 30° = \dfrac{1}{2}$, $\cos 30° = \dfrac{\sqrt{3}}{2}$, $\sin 150° = \dfrac{1}{2}$, and $\cos 150° = -\dfrac{\sqrt{3}}{2}$.

Example 2

Find sin 225°, cos 225°, sin 315°, and cos 315°.

For each angle, sketch a circle with a radius of 2. Show the angle of rotation and reference triangle.

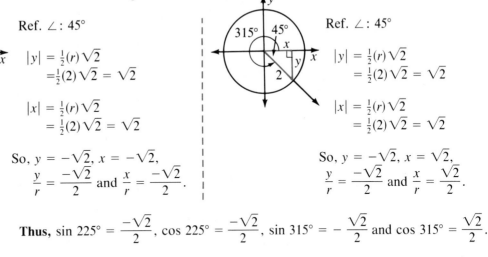

Ref. $\angle$: 45°

$|y| = \frac{1}{2}(r)\sqrt{2}$
$= \frac{1}{2}(2)\sqrt{2} = \sqrt{2}$

$|x| = \frac{1}{2}(r)\sqrt{2}$
$= \frac{1}{2}(2)\sqrt{2} = \sqrt{2}$

So, $y = -\sqrt{2}$, $x = -\sqrt{2}$,
$\frac{y}{r} = \frac{-\sqrt{2}}{2}$ and $\frac{x}{r} = \frac{-\sqrt{2}}{2}$.

Ref. $\angle$: 45°

$|y| = \frac{1}{2}(r)\sqrt{2}$
$= \frac{1}{2}(2)\sqrt{2} = \sqrt{2}$

$|x| = \frac{1}{2}(r)\sqrt{2}$
$= \frac{1}{2}(2)\sqrt{2} = \sqrt{2}$

So, $y = -\sqrt{2}$, $x = \sqrt{2}$,
$\frac{y}{r} = \frac{-\sqrt{2}}{2}$ and $\frac{x}{r} = \frac{\sqrt{2}}{2}$.

Thus, $\sin 225° = \frac{-\sqrt{2}}{2}$, $\cos 225° = \frac{-\sqrt{2}}{2}$, $\sin 315° = -\frac{\sqrt{2}}{2}$ and $\cos 315° = \frac{\sqrt{2}}{2}$.

Examples 1 and 2 suggest that the sine is positive $(+)$ in the first and second quadrants and negative $(-)$ in the third and fourth quadrants. They also suggest that the cosine is positive in the first and fourth quadrants and negative in the second and third quadrants.

	1st Quad.	2nd Quad.	3rd Quad.	4th Quad.
Sine	+	+	−	−
Cosine	+	−	−	+

The next example shows how to express the sine and cosine of any angle as a function of an acute angle.

Example 3

Write each in terms of the same trigonometric function of an acute angle: sin 240° and cos 315°.

For each angle, sketch a circle. Show the reference triangle.

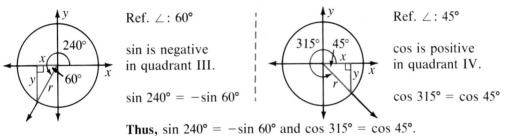

Ref. $\angle$: 60°

sin is negative
in quadrant III.

$\sin 240° = -\sin 60°$

Ref. $\angle$: 45°

cos is positive
in quadrant IV.

$\cos 315° = \cos 45°$

Thus, $\sin 240° = -\sin 60°$ and $\cos 315° = \cos 45°$.

Recall that angles whose terminal sides are on an axis are called *quadrantal* angles. The quadrantal angles 0°, 90°, 180°, and 270° are shown below. Their sines and cosines are summarized in the table.

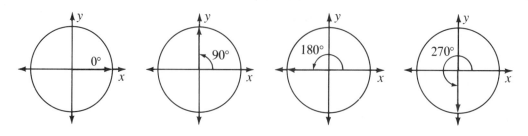

	0°	90°	180°	270°
sine: $\frac{y}{r}$	0	1	0	−1
cosine: $\frac{x}{r}$	1	0	−1	0

The following example illustrates how to solve an equation involving sin u or cos u.

Example 4 Find two values of u between 0° and 360° for which $\sin u = -\dfrac{\sqrt{2}}{2}$.

First, determine the quadrant of the angle: sine is negative in the 3rd and 4th quadrants.

Second, determine the reference angle: $\sin 45° = \dfrac{\sqrt{2}}{2}$.

Finally, determine the angle of rotation.

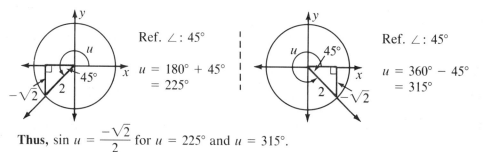

Ref. ∠: 45°

$u = 180° + 45°$
$\quad = 225°$

Ref. ∠: 45°

$u = 360° - 45°$
$\quad = 315°$

Thus, $\sin u = \dfrac{-\sqrt{2}}{2}$ for $u = 225°$ and $u = 315°$.

Summary	To find the measure of an angle whose sine or cosine is given: 1. Determine the quadrant from the sign (+ or −). 2. Determine the reference angle. 3. Use the reference angle to find the angle of rotation.

Reading in Algebra

Which value in each group is different from the others?

1. a) $\sin 45°$ b) $\sin 135°$ c) $\dfrac{\sqrt{2}}{2}$ d) $-\dfrac{\sqrt{2}}{2}$ **d**

2. a) $\cos 300°$ b) $\cos 60°$ c) $\cos 120°$ d) $\dfrac{\sqrt{3}}{2}$ **c**

3. a) $\sin 150°$ b) $\sin 210°$ c) $\sin 330°$ d) $-\dfrac{1}{2}$ **a**

4. a) $\dfrac{1}{2}$ b) $-\dfrac{1}{2}$ c) $\cos 120°$ d) $\cos 240°$ **a**

5. a) $\sin 0°$ b) 0 c) $\sin 180°$ d) 1 **d**

Written Exercises

For Ex. 1–36, see TE Answer Section.

(A) **Find each of the following. Rationalize any radical denominator.**

1. $\sin 60°$	**2.** $\cos 60°$	**3.** $\sin 45°$	**4.** $\cos 45°$	**5.** $\sin 30°$	**6.** $\cos 30°$
7. $\cos 270°$	**8.** $\cos 360°$	**9.** $\sin 180°$	**10.** $\cos 90°$	**11.** $\sin 0°$	**12.** $\sin 270°$
13. $\sin 135°$	**14.** $\cos 210°$	**15.** $\cos 150°$	**16.** $\sin 150°$	**17.** $\cos 180°$	**18.** $\cos 225°$
19. $\sin 315°$	**20.** $\sin 120°$	**21.** $\cos 330°$	**22.** $\sin 330°$	**23.** $\sin 390°$	**24.** $\cos 480°$

Write each in terms of the same trigonometric function of an acute angle.

25. $\cos 135°$	**26.** $\sin 330°$	**27.** $\cos 210°$	**28.** $\sin 225°$	**29.** $\sin 135°$	**30.** $\sin 300°$
31. $\sin 150°$	**32.** $\sin 210°$	**33.** $\sin 315°$	**34.** $\cos 300°$	**35.** $\cos 150°$	**36.** $\cos 330°$

(B) **Find two values of u between 0° and 360° for which each is true.**

37. $\sin u = \dfrac{\sqrt{2}}{2}$ **45°, 135°** **38.** $\cos u = \dfrac{1}{2}$ **60°, 300°** **39.** $\sin u = \dfrac{1}{2}$ **30°, 150°** **40.** $\cos u = 0$ **90°, 270°**

41. $\cos u = -\dfrac{\sqrt{2}}{2}$ **135°, 225°** **42.** $\sin u = \dfrac{\sqrt{3}}{2}$ **60°, 120°** **43.** $\cos u = -\dfrac{\sqrt{3}}{2}$ **150°, 210°** **44.** $\sin u = -\dfrac{\sqrt{3}}{2}$ **240°, 300°**

In which quadrants is each of the following true?

45. $\cos u < 0$ **II, III** **46.** $\sin u > 0$ **I, II** **47.** $\sin u < 0$ **III, IV** **48.** $\cos u > 0$ **I, IV**

(C) **Find two values of u between 0° and 720° for which each is true.**

49. $\cos u = -\dfrac{1}{2}$ and $\sin u > 0$ **120°, 480°** **50.** $\sin u = \dfrac{1}{2}$ and $\cos u > 0$ **30°, 390°**

51. $\cos u = \dfrac{\sqrt{3}}{2}$ and $\sin u < 0$ **330°, 690°** **52.** $\sin u = -\dfrac{\sqrt{2}}{2}$ and $\cos u < 0$ **225°, 585°**

53. $\sin u = -\dfrac{\sqrt{3}}{2}$ and $\cos u > 0$ **300°, 660°** **54.** $\cos u = -\dfrac{\sqrt{2}}{2}$ and $\sin u < 0$ **225°, 585°**

Cumulative Review

Complete the chart.

	0°	90°	180°	270°	360°
sin	0	1	0	−1	0
cos	1	0	−1	0	1

SINE AND COSINE FUNCTIONS

17.4 Tangent and Cotangent Functions

OBJECTIVES ▶ To find the tangent and cotangent of degree measures 0°, 30°, 45°, 60°, 90°, and their multiples

To determine if the tangent or cotangent is positive or negative for a given degree measure

To find the measure of an angle whose tangent or cotangent is given

To find tangents and cotangents using trigonometric relationships

Recall that for any given angle of rotation, u, the two ratios $\frac{y}{r}$ and $\frac{x}{r}$ were defined as sin u and cos u, respectively. Using a reference triangle, the ratios $\frac{y}{x}$ and $\frac{x}{y}$ determine the trigonometric functions tangent and cotangent.

**Definition:
Tangent (tan)
and Cotangent
(cot) Functions**

For any angle of rotation u:

The tangent of u is $\frac{y}{x}$ $\left(\tan u = \frac{y}{x}\right)$, and the cotangent of u is $\frac{x}{y}$ $\left(\cot u = \frac{x}{y}\right)$.
$(x \neq 0, y \neq 0)$

Example 1 Find tan 45°, cot 45°, tan 135°, and cot 135°.

For each angle, sketch a circle with radius 2. Show the angle of rotation and reference triangle.

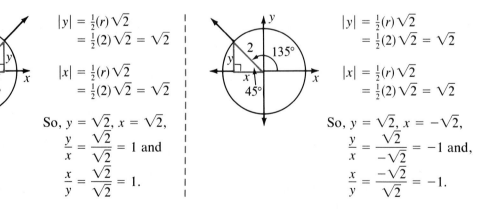

$|y| = \frac{1}{2}(r)\sqrt{2}$
$\quad = \frac{1}{2}(2)\sqrt{2} = \sqrt{2}$

$|x| = \frac{1}{2}(r)\sqrt{2}$
$\quad = \frac{1}{2}(2)\sqrt{2} = \sqrt{2}$

So, $y = \sqrt{2}$, $x = \sqrt{2}$,
$\frac{y}{x} = \frac{\sqrt{2}}{\sqrt{2}} = 1$ and
$\frac{x}{y} = \frac{\sqrt{2}}{\sqrt{2}} = 1.$

$|y| = \frac{1}{2}(r)\sqrt{2}$
$\quad = \frac{1}{2}(2)\sqrt{2} = \sqrt{2}$

$|x| = \frac{1}{2}(r)\sqrt{2}$
$\quad = \frac{1}{2}(2)\sqrt{2} = \sqrt{2}$

So, $y = \sqrt{2}$, $x = -\sqrt{2}$,
$\frac{y}{x} = \frac{\sqrt{2}}{-\sqrt{2}} = -1$ and,
$\frac{x}{y} = \frac{-\sqrt{2}}{\sqrt{2}} = -1.$

Thus, tan 45° = 1, cot 45° = 1, tan 135° = −1 and cot 135° = −1.

Example 2 Find tan 210°, cot 210°, tan 300°, and cot 300°.

For each angle, sketch a circle with a radius of 2. Show the angle of rotation and reference angle.

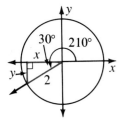

$$|y| = \tfrac{1}{2}(r)$$
$$= \tfrac{1}{2}(2) = 1$$

$$|x| = \tfrac{1}{2}(r)\sqrt{3}$$
$$= \tfrac{1}{2}(2)\sqrt{3} = \sqrt{3}$$

So, $y = -1$, $x = -\sqrt{3}$
$$\frac{y}{x} = \frac{-1}{-\sqrt{3}} = \frac{\sqrt{3}}{3} \text{ and}$$
$$\frac{x}{y} = \frac{-\sqrt{3}}{-1} = \sqrt{3}.$$

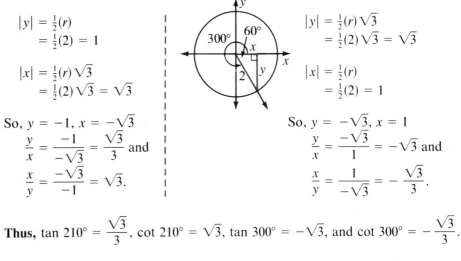

$$|y| = \tfrac{1}{2}(r)\sqrt{3}$$
$$= \tfrac{1}{2}(2)\sqrt{3} = \sqrt{3}$$

$$|x| = \tfrac{1}{2}(r)$$
$$= \tfrac{1}{2}(2) = 1$$

So, $y = -\sqrt{3}$, $x = 1$
$$\frac{y}{x} = \frac{-\sqrt{3}}{1} = -\sqrt{3} \text{ and}$$
$$\frac{x}{y} = \frac{1}{-\sqrt{3}} = -\frac{\sqrt{3}}{3}.$$

Thus, $\tan 210° = \dfrac{\sqrt{3}}{3}$, $\cot 210° = \sqrt{3}$, $\tan 300° = -\sqrt{3}$, and $\cot 300° = -\dfrac{\sqrt{3}}{3}$.

Examples 1 and 2 suggest that the tangent and cotangent are positive (+) in the first and third quadrants and negative (−) in the second and fourth quadrants.

	1st Quad.	2nd Quad.	3rd Quad.	4th Quad.
tangent	+	−	+	−
cotangent	+	−	+	−

The next example shows how to express the tan or cot of any angle as a function of an acute angle.

Example 3 Write each in terms of the same trigonometric function of an acute angle: tan 240° and cot 330°.

For each angle, sketch a circle. Show the reference triangle.

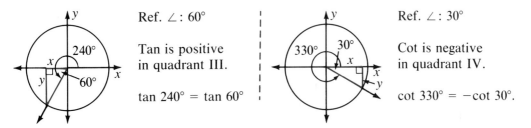

Ref. ∠: 60°

Tan is positive in quadrant III.

tan 240° = tan 60°

Ref. ∠: 30°

Cot is negative in quadrant IV.

cot 330° = −cot 30°

Thus, tan 240° = tan 60° and cot 330° = −cot 30°.

TANGENT AND COTANGENT FUNCTIONS

Example 4 Find the tan and cot of the quadrantal angles 0°, 90°, 180°, and 270°.

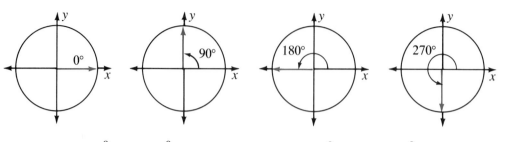

$$x = r, y = 0 \qquad x = 0, y = r \qquad x = -r, y = 0 \qquad x = 0, y = -r$$

$$\tan 0° = \frac{y}{x} = \frac{0}{r} \quad \tan 90° = \frac{y}{x} = \frac{r}{0} \quad \tan 180° = \frac{y}{x} = \frac{0}{-r} \quad \tan 270° = \frac{y}{x} = \frac{-r}{0}$$

$$\cot 0° = \frac{x}{y} = \frac{r}{0} \quad \cot 90° = \frac{x}{y} = \frac{0}{r} \quad \cot 180° = \frac{x}{y} = \frac{-r}{0} \quad \cot 270° = \frac{x}{y} = \frac{0}{-r}$$

Thus, the tan and cot of 0°, 90°, 180°, and 270° are summarized in the table below.

	0°	90°	180°	270°
tangent	0	undefined	0	undefined
cotangent	undefined	0	undefined	0

Notice that $\tan u \cdot \cot u = \frac{y}{x} \cdot \frac{x}{y} = 1$. Since their product is 1, $\tan u$ and $\cot u$ are called *reciprocal* functions. That is, $\tan u = \frac{1}{\cot u}$ or $\cot u = \frac{1}{\tan u}$, for any *nonquadrantal* angle of rotation u.

Example 5 If $\tan x = -\frac{5}{3}$, find $\cot x$.

The reciprocal of $-\frac{5}{3}$ is $-\frac{3}{5}$.   **Thus,** $\cot x = -\frac{3}{5}$.

Example 6 Find two values of u between 0° and 360° for which $\tan u = \frac{-\sqrt{3}}{3}$.

Use the three steps in the summary on page 464.

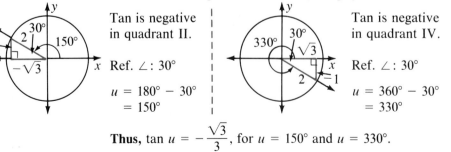

Tan is negative in quadrant II.

Ref. $\angle$: 30°

$u = 180° - 30°$
$\quad = 150°$

Tan is negative in quadrant IV.

Ref. $\angle$: 30°

$u = 360° - 30°$
$\quad = 330°$

Thus, $\tan u = -\frac{\sqrt{3}}{3}$, for $u = 150°$ and $u = 330°$.

Notice that $\dfrac{\sin u}{\cos u} = \dfrac{\frac{y}{r}}{\frac{x}{r}} = \dfrac{y}{r} \cdot \dfrac{r}{x} = \dfrac{y}{x} = \tan u$. So, $\tan u = \dfrac{\sin u}{\cos u}$.

Similarly, $\cot u = \dfrac{\cos u}{\sin u}$.

Quotient Identities

$$\tan u = \frac{\sin u}{\cos u} \qquad \cot u = \frac{\cos u}{\sin u}$$

Example 7 If $\sin w = \dfrac{3}{5}$ and $\cos w = \dfrac{4}{5}$, find $\tan w$ and $\cot w$.

$$\tan w = \frac{\sin w}{\cos w} = \frac{\frac{3}{5}}{\frac{4}{5}} = \frac{3}{4} \qquad \cot w = \frac{\cos w}{\sin w} = \frac{\frac{4}{5}}{\frac{3}{5}} = \frac{4}{3}$$

Written Exercises

(A) Find each of the following. Rationalize all radical denominators.

1. $\tan 45°$ 1
2. $\cot 45°$ 1
3. $\tan 60°$ $\sqrt{3}$
4. $\cot 60°$ $\frac{\sqrt{3}}{3}$
5. $\tan 30°$ $\frac{\sqrt{3}}{3}$
6. $\cot 30°$ $\sqrt{3}$
7. $\tan 90°$
8. $\cot 90°$ 0
9. $\cot 315°$ -1
10. $\tan 330°$ $\frac{-\sqrt{3}}{3}$
11. $\cot 180°$
12. $\tan 180°$ 0
13. $\tan 135°$ -1
14. $\cot 150°$
15. $\cot 300°$
16. $\cot 225°$ 1
17. $\tan 210°$ $\frac{\sqrt{3}}{3}$
18. $\cot 240°$
19. $\cot 450°$ 0
20. $\tan 120°$
21. $\tan 390°$ $\frac{\sqrt{3}}{3}$
22. $\tan 150°$ $\frac{-\sqrt{3}}{3}$
23. $\cot 360°$
24. $\tan 405°$ 1

7. undefined   14. $-\sqrt{3}$ 20. $-\sqrt{3}$ 23. undefined   11. undefined

Write each of the following in terms of the same trigonometric function of an acute angle. For Ex. 25–36, see TE Answer Section.   15. $\frac{-\sqrt{3}}{3}$ 18. $\frac{\sqrt{3}}{3}$

25. $\cot 110°$
26. $\tan 310°$
27. $\cot 230°$
28. $\tan 210°$
29. $\tan 340°$
30. $\cot 95°$
31. $\tan 250°$
32. $\cot 120°$
33. $\tan 150°$
34. $\cot 300°$
35. $\cot 250°$
36. $\tan 100°$

37. If $\cot w = -\dfrac{4}{3}$, find $\tan w$. $\dfrac{-3}{4}$

38. If $\tan u = \dfrac{5}{4}$, find $\cot u$. $\dfrac{4}{5}$

39. If $\tan v = -\dfrac{17}{8}$, find $\cot v$. $\dfrac{-8}{17}$

40. If $\cot u = \dfrac{12}{5}$, find $\tan u$. $\dfrac{5}{12}$

41. If $\sin m = \dfrac{4}{5}$ and $\cos m = -\dfrac{3}{5}$, find $\tan m$ and $\cot m$. $\dfrac{-4}{3}$, $-\dfrac{3}{4}$

42. If $\cos w = -\dfrac{12}{13}$ and $\sin w = -\dfrac{5}{13}$, find $\tan w$ and $\cot w$. $\dfrac{5}{12}$, $\dfrac{12}{5}$

43. If $\cos w = \dfrac{4\sqrt{41}}{41}$ and $\sin w = \dfrac{15\sqrt{41}}{41}$, find $\tan w$ and $\cot w$. $\dfrac{15}{4}$, $\dfrac{4}{15}$

44. 60°, 240°   45. 150°, 330°   46. 135°, 315°   47. 45°, 225°

(B) Find two values of u between 0° and 360° for which each is true.

44. $\tan u = \sqrt{3}$
45. $\cot u = -\sqrt{3}$
46. $\tan u = -1$
47. $\cot u = 1$
48. $\cot u = -\dfrac{\sqrt{3}}{3}$ 120°, 300°
49. $\tan u = -\dfrac{\sqrt{3}}{3}$ 150°, 330°
50. $\cot u = -1$ 135°, 315°
51. $\tan u = 1$ 45°, 225°

(C) Find two values of u between 0° and 720° for which each is true.

52. $\cot u = -\sqrt{3}$ and $\cos u < 0$ 150°, 510°
53. $\tan u = -\sqrt{3}$ and $\sin u > 0$ 120°, 480°
54. $\tan u = \dfrac{\sqrt{3}}{3}$ and $\sin u < 0$ 210°, 570°
55. $\cot u = -\dfrac{\sqrt{3}}{3}$ and $\cos u > 0$ 300°, 660°

TANGENT AND COTANGENT FUNCTIONS

17.5 Secant and Cosecant Functions

OBJECTIVES ▶ To find the secant and cosecant of degree measures of 30°, 45°, 60°, 90°, and their multiples
To determine if the secant or cosecant is positive or negative for a given degree measure
To find the measure of an angle whose secant or cosecant is given
To find secants and cosecants using trigonometric relationships

Thus far, four trigonometric functions have been defined for any angle of rotation u. Using a reference triangle, the ratios $\frac{r}{x}$ and $\frac{r}{y}$ determine the trigonometric functions **secant** and **cosecant**. Notice that these functions are the reciprocals of the cosine and sine functions, respectively.

Definition:
Secant (sec) and Cosecant (csc) Functions

For any angle of rotation u, the secant of u is $\frac{r}{x}$ $\left(\sec u = \frac{r}{x} \right)$, and the

cosecant of u is $\frac{r}{y}$ $\left(\csc u = \frac{r}{y} \right)$. $(x \neq 0, y \neq 0)$

Also, $\sec u = \frac{1}{\cos u}$ or $\cos u = \frac{1}{\sec u}$ and $\csc u = \frac{1}{\sin u}$ or $\sin u = \frac{1}{\csc u}$.

Example 1 Find sec 120° and csc 120°.

First Method
Use Ref. △: 30–60 rt. △.
$|y| = \frac{1}{2} (2) \sqrt{3} = \sqrt{3}$

$|x| = \frac{1}{2} (2) = 1$

So, $y = \sqrt{3}$, $x = -1$,
$\frac{r}{x} = \frac{2}{-1} = -2$ and
$\frac{r}{y} = \frac{2}{\sqrt{3}} = \frac{2\sqrt{3}}{3}$.

Thus, sec 120° $= -2$ and csc 120° $= \frac{2\sqrt{3}}{3}$.

Second Method
Use reciprocal functions.

$\sec u = \frac{1}{\cos u}$ $\qquad \csc u = \frac{1}{\sin u}$

$\cos 120° = -\frac{1}{2}$ $\qquad \sin 120° = \frac{\sqrt{3}}{2}$

$\sec 120° = \frac{1}{-\frac{1}{2}}$ $\qquad \csc 120° = \frac{1}{\frac{\sqrt{3}}{2}}$

$\sec 120° = -2$ $\qquad \csc 120° = \frac{2}{\sqrt{3}}$ or

$\qquad\qquad\qquad\qquad\qquad \frac{2\sqrt{3}}{3}$

The sine, and therefore its reciprocal cosecant, are positive in the first and second quadrants. The cosine, and therefore its reciprocal secant, are positive in the first and fourth quadrants.

	1st Quad.	2nd Quad.	3rd Quad.	4th Quad.
secant	+	−	−	+
cosecant	+	+	−	−

The next example shows how to express the secant or cosecant of any angle as a function of an acute angle.

Example 2 Write sec 135° and csc 240° as the same trigonometric function of an acute angle.

For each angle, sketch a circle. Show the reference triangle.

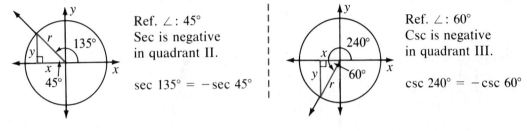

Ref. ∠: 45°
Sec is negative
in quadrant II.

sec 135° = − sec 45°

Ref. ∠: 60°
Csc is negative
in quadrant III.

csc 240° = − csc 60°

Thus, sec 135° = − sec 45° and csc 240° = − csc 60°.

Since the sec and csc are reciprocals of the cos and sin respectively, the following table can be constructed.

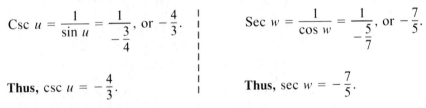

	0°	90°	180°	270°
sec	1	undefined	−1	undefined
csc	undefined	1	undefined	−1

Example 3 If $\sin u = -\frac{3}{4}$, find csc u. If $\cos w = -\frac{5}{7}$, find sec w.

$$\text{Csc } u = \frac{1}{\sin u} = \frac{1}{-\frac{3}{4}}, \text{ or } -\frac{4}{3}.$$

$$\text{Sec } w = \frac{1}{\cos w} = \frac{1}{-\frac{5}{7}}, \text{ or } -\frac{7}{5}.$$

Thus, csc $u = -\frac{4}{3}$.

Thus, sec $w = -\frac{7}{5}$.

Example 4 Find two values of u between 0° and 360° for which sec $u = -\sqrt{2}$.

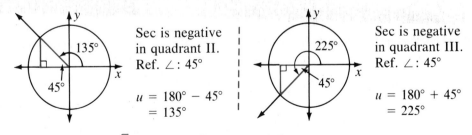

Sec is negative
in quadrant II.
Ref. ∠: 45°

$u = 180° − 45°$
$= 135°$

Sec is negative
in quadrant III.
Ref. ∠: 45°

$u = 180° + 45°$
$= 225°$

Thus, sec $u = -\sqrt{2}$ for $u = 135°$ and $u = 225°$.

SECANT AND COSECANT FUNCTIONS

Oral Exercises

State whether each of the following is positive or negative.

1. sec 45° +   **2.** csc 135° +   **3.** sec 120° −   **4.** csc 300° −   **5.** sec 330° +   **6.** sec 225° −
7. csc 225° −   **8.** sec 150° −   **9.** csc 240° −   **10.** sec 315° +   **11.** csc 120° +   **12.** csc 330° −

Written Exercises

(A) Find each of the following. Rationalize any radical denominator.

1. csc 45° $\sqrt{2}$ **2.** sec 45° $\sqrt{2}$ **3.** sec 60° 2   **4.** csc 60° $\frac{2\sqrt{3}}{3}$ **5.** sec 30° $\frac{2\sqrt{3}}{3}$ **6.** csc 30° 2
7. csc 210° −2   **8.** sec 240° −2   **9.** csc 225°   **10.** sec 225°   **11.** csc 150° 2   **12.** sec 150° $\frac{-2\sqrt{3}}{3}$
13. sec 300° 2   **14.** csc 300°   **15.** sec 315° $\sqrt{2}$ **16.** csc 315°   **17.** sec 330°   **18.** csc 330° −2
9. −$\sqrt{2}$ **10.** −$\sqrt{2}$ **14.** $\frac{-2\sqrt{3}}{3}$ **16.** −$\sqrt{2}$ **17.** $\frac{2\sqrt{3}}{3}$

Write each of the following in terms of the same trigonometric function of an
acute angle. **For Ex. 19–30, see TE Answer Section.**

19. sec 120°   **20.** csc 150°   **21.** csc 300°   **22.** sec 210°   **23.** sec 240°   **24.** csc 315°
25. csc 120°   **26.** csc 210°   **27.** sec 190°   **28.** sec 340°   **29.** csc 170°   **30.** csc 215°

31. If $\sin u = -\frac{1}{2}$, find csc u. −2   **32.** If $\cos u = -\frac{1}{3}$, find sec u. −3

33. If $\cos u = \frac{2}{3}$, find sec u. $\frac{3}{2}$ **34.** If $\sin u = \frac{4}{5}$, find csc u. $\frac{5}{4}$

35. If $\sin u = -\frac{5}{6}$, find csc u. $\frac{-6}{5}$ **36.** If $\cos u = -\frac{3}{7}$, find sec u. $\frac{-7}{3}$

(B) Find all values of u between and including 0° and 360° for which each is true.

37. sec $u = -1$ 180°   **38.** csc $u = -1$ 270°   **39.** csc $u = -\sqrt{2}$ **40.** sec $u = -2$
41. csc $u = \frac{2\sqrt{3}}{3}$ 60°, 120°   **42.** sec $u = \frac{-2\sqrt{3}}{3}$ 150°, 210°   **43.** sec $u = 2$ **44.** csc $u = 1$ 90°
39. 225°, 315°   **40.** 120°, 240°   **43.** 60°, 300°

(C) Find all values of u between 0° and 720° for which each is true.

45. sec $u = -1$ and $\sin u = 0$ 180°, 540°   **46.** sec $u = 2$ and $\cos u > 0$ 60°, 300°, 420°, 660°
47. csc $u = \frac{-2\sqrt{3}}{3}$ and $\tan u > 0$ 240°, 600°   **48.** csc $u = -2$ and $\cot u < 0$ 330°, 690°

A Challenge To You

A triangle has two angles with measure 30° and 45°. The side opposite the 30° angle has
length 12. Find the length of the side opposite the 45° angle. $12\sqrt{2}$

Cumulative Review

Solve each of the following using the quadratic formula.

1. $x^2 - 9x + 3 = 0$ $\frac{9 \pm \sqrt{69}}{2}$ **2.** $3x^2 + 5x - 4 = 0$ $\frac{-5 \pm \sqrt{73}}{6}$ **3.** $-2x^2 - 3x + 7 = 0$ $\frac{-3 \pm \sqrt{65}}{4}$

17.6 Functions of Negative Angles

OBJECTIVES ▶ **To find the sine, cosine, tangent, cotangent, secant, and cosecant of angles of negative measure**

The figure below illustrates two angles of rotation, u and $(-u)$, where $P(-a, b)$ is a point on the terminal side of angle u and $Q(-a, -b)$ is a point on the terminal side of the angle $(-u)$. The two reference triangles formed are congruent. Using the definitions of sin, cos, and tan of an angle, it follows that

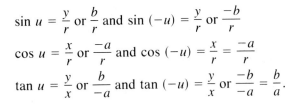

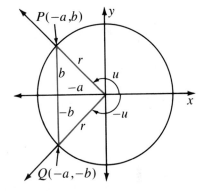

$$\sin u = \frac{y}{r} \text{ or } \frac{b}{r} \text{ and } \sin (-u) = \frac{y}{r} \text{ or } \frac{-b}{r}$$

$$\cos u = \frac{x}{r} \text{ or } \frac{-a}{r} \text{ and } \cos (-u) = \frac{x}{r} = \frac{-a}{r}$$

$$\tan u = \frac{y}{x} \text{ or } \frac{b}{-a} \text{ and } \tan (-u) = \frac{y}{x} \text{ or } \frac{-b}{-a} = \frac{b}{a}.$$

Since the cosecant, secant, and cotangent are reciprocal functions of the sine, cosine, and tangent, respectively, the following definitions are suggested.

Trigonometric Functions of Angles of Negative Measure

For any angles of rotation u and $(-u)$,

$\sin (-u) = -\sin u$	$\csc (-u) = -\csc u$
$\cos (-u) = \cos u$	$\sec (-u) = \sec u$
$\tan (-u) = -\tan u$	$\cot (-u) = -\cot u.$

Example 1 Find sin (−45°), cos (−45°), and tan (−45°).

Ref. ∠: 45°

$\sin 45° = \dfrac{\sqrt{2}}{2}$

$\cos 45° = \dfrac{\sqrt{2}}{2}$

$\tan 45° = 1$

$\sin (-45°) = -\sin 45°$
$= -\dfrac{\sqrt{2}}{2}$

$\cos (-45°) = \cos 45°$
$= \dfrac{\sqrt{2}}{2}$

$\tan (-45°) = -\tan 45°$
$= -1$

Example 2 Find cot (−330°), sec (−330°), and csc (−330°).

Ref. ∠: 30°

$\cot 30° = \sqrt{3}$

$\sec 30° = \dfrac{2\sqrt{3}}{3}$

$\csc 30° = 2$

$\cot (-330°) = -\cot 330°$
$= -(-\cot 30°)$
$= \sqrt{3}$

$\sec (-330°) = \sec 330°$
$= \sec 30°$
$= \dfrac{2\sqrt{3}}{3}$

$\csc (-330°) = -\csc 330°$
$= -(-\csc 30°)$
$= 2$

Example 3

Express sin (−315°) and cos (−315°) as functions of a positive acute angle.

$$\sin(-315°) = -\sin 315°$$
$$= -(-\sin 45°)$$
$$= \sin 45°$$

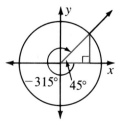

$$\cos(-315°) = \cos 315°$$
$$= \cos 45°$$

Example 4

Express sec (−190°), tan (−300°), and csc (−210°) as functions of a positive acute angle.

$$\sec(-190°) = \sec 190° \qquad \tan(-300°) = -\tan 300° \qquad \csc(-210°) = -\csc 210°$$
$$= -\sec 10° \qquad\qquad\qquad = \tan 60° \qquad\qquad\qquad = -(-\csc 30°)$$
$$\qquad\qquad\qquad\qquad\qquad\qquad\qquad\qquad\qquad\qquad\qquad\qquad = \csc 30°$$

Written Exercises

(A) Find each of the following. Rationalize any radical denominator.   2. $\frac{\sqrt{3}}{2}$ 3. $\frac{-\sqrt{3}}{3}$ 7. $\frac{-\sqrt{3}}{2}$

1. sin (−30°) $-\frac{1}{2}$ **2.** cos (−30°)   **3.** tan (−30°)   **4.** cot (−30°) $-\sqrt{3}$ **5.** sec (−30°) $\frac{2\sqrt{3}}{3}$
6. csc (−45°) $-\sqrt{2}$ **7.** sin (−60°)   **8.** cos (−60°) $\frac{1}{2}$ **9.** sec (−60°) 2   **10.** csc (−60°) $\frac{-2\sqrt{3}}{3}$
11. cos (−150°)   **12.** tan (−150°)   **13.** sin (−150°) $-\frac{1}{2}$ **14.** csc (−150°) −2 **15.** cot (−150°) $\sqrt{3}$
16. sec (−210°)   **17.** csc (−210°) 2   **18.** tan (−210°)   **19.** sin (−210°) $\frac{1}{2}$ **20.** cos (−210°) $\frac{-\sqrt{3}}{2}$
21. cos (−315°)   **22.** sin (−315°)   **23.** cot (−315°) 1   **24.** tan (−315°) 1   **25.** sec (−315°) $\sqrt{2}$

26. −cot 15°   27. −tan 10°   28. cos 80°   29. cot 85°   30. sin 80°   31. −sin 80°   32. −csc 15°

Express as a function of a positive acute angle.   33. sec 18°   34. csc 10°   35. cos 35°

26. cot (−15°)   **27.** tan (−190°)   **28.** cos (−280°)   **29.** cot (−95°)   **30.** sin (−260°)
(B) **31.** sin (−100°)   **32.** csc (−15°)   **33.** sec (−18°)   **34.** csc (−190°)   **35.** cos (−35°)
36. sec (−310°)   **37.** cos (−350°)   **38.** tan (−100°)   **39.** sin (−350°)   **40.** tan (−390°)
41. csc (−195° 35′) csc 15° 35′   **42.** sin (−18° 20′) −sin 18° 20′   **43.** cos (−300° 45′) cos 59° 15′

36. sec 50°   37. cos 10°   38. tan 80°   39. sin 10°   40. −tan 30°

(C) For any angle of rotation u with negative measure show the following.   11. $\frac{-\sqrt{3}}{2}$ 12. $\frac{\sqrt{3}}{3}$ 16. $\frac{-2\sqrt{3}}{3}$
44. tan (−u) = −tan u **45.** cot (−u) = −cot u
46. sec (−u) = sec u **47.** csc (−u) = −csc u 18. $\frac{-\sqrt{3}}{3}$ 21. $\frac{\sqrt{2}}{2}$ 22. $\frac{\sqrt{2}}{2}$
For Ex. 44–47, see TE Answer Section.

Cumulative Review

Solve each of the following by factoring.

1. $3x^2 - x = 0$ $0, \frac{1}{3}$ **2.** $9x^2 - 1 = 0$ $-\frac{1}{3}, \frac{1}{3}$ **3.** $6x^2 + 7x + 2 = 0$ $-\frac{1}{2}, -\frac{2}{3}$

17.7 Values of Trigonometric Functions

OBJECTIVE ▶ **To find the other five trigonometric functions of an angle of rotation u, given one of the six functions and the quadrant of the terminal side of u**

To find the value of five trigonometric functions of any angle of rotation u, given the value of one of them and the quadrant of the terminal side, do the following.
1. State two of the values of x, y, and r, using the definition of the given trigonometric function.
2. Find the remaining value of x, y, or r, using the Pythagorean theorem and the reference triangle.
3. Write the ratios for the other five trigonometric functions using x, y, and r.

Example 1 Find the value of each of the other five trigonometric functions of u if $\sin u = \dfrac{4}{5}$ and the terminal side is in the 2nd quadrant.

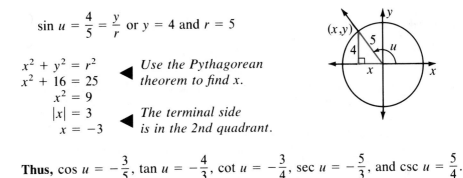

$$\sin u = \frac{4}{5} = \frac{y}{r} \text{ or } y = 4 \text{ and } r = 5$$

$x^2 + y^2 = r^2$
$x^2 + 16 = 25$ ◀ *Use the Pythagorean theorem to find x.*
$x^2 = 9$
$|x| = 3$ ◀ *The terminal side is in the 2nd quadrant.*
$x = -3$

Thus, $\cos u = -\dfrac{3}{5}$, $\tan u = -\dfrac{4}{3}$, $\cot u = -\dfrac{3}{4}$, $\sec u = -\dfrac{5}{3}$, and $\csc u = \dfrac{5}{4}$.

Example 2 Find the value of each of the other five trigonometric functions of u if $\tan u = -\dfrac{5}{12}$ and $\cos u < 0$.

Both the tan and cos are negative in the 2nd quadrant, so the terminal side lies in the 2nd quadrant.

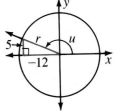

$$\tan u = -\frac{5}{12} = \frac{y}{x} \text{ or } y = 5 \text{ and } x = -12$$

$x^2 + y^2 = r^2$
$144 + 25 = r^2$ ◀ *Use the Pythagorean theorem.*
$r^2 = 169 \text{ or } r = 13$

Thus, $\sin u = \dfrac{5}{13}$, $\cos u = -\dfrac{12}{13}$, $\cot u = -\dfrac{12}{5}$, $\sec u = -\dfrac{13}{12}$, and $\csc u = \dfrac{13}{5}$.

Oral Exercises

For each of the following, tell in which quadrant(s) the terminal side of the angle may lie.

1. $\sin u = \dfrac{4}{5}$ **2.** $\sin u = -\dfrac{3}{4}$ **3.** $\cos u = -\dfrac{5}{7}$ **4.** $\cos u = \dfrac{7}{8}$ **5.** $\tan u = -\dfrac{3}{4}$

6. $\tan u = \dfrac{\sqrt{5}}{3}$ **7.** $\cot u = -\dfrac{5}{12}$ **8.** $\cot u = \dfrac{12}{5}$ **9.** $\sec u = \dfrac{13}{5}$ **10.** $\sec u = -\dfrac{13}{12}$

11. $\sin u > 0$ and $\tan u < 0$ II   **12.** $\sin u < 0$ and $\cos u < 0$ III

Written Exercises

For Ex. 1–30, see TE Answer section.

(A) Find the value of each of the other five trigonometric functions of u.

1. $\tan u = -\dfrac{12}{5}$ in 2nd quad.   **2.** $\sin u = \dfrac{12}{13}$ in 2nd quad.   **3.** $\cos u = -\dfrac{5}{13}$ in 3rd quad.

4. $\sin u = -\dfrac{3}{5}$ in 4th quad.   **5.** $\cot u = -\dfrac{3}{4}$ in 4th quad.   **6.** $\sec u = -\dfrac{13}{5}$ in 2nd quad.

7. $\cos u = -\dfrac{12}{13}$ in 2nd quad.   **8.** $\csc u = \dfrac{13}{5}$ in 1st quad.   **9.** $\tan u = \dfrac{4}{3}$ in 3rd quad.

10. $\sec u = \dfrac{13}{12}$ in 4th quad.   **11.** $\tan u = -1$ in 2nd quad.   **12.** $\cot u = -\sqrt{3}$ in 4th quad.

(B) **13.** $\sin u = \dfrac{5}{13}$ and $\sec u > 0$ **14.** $\cos u = -\dfrac{3}{5}$ and $\tan u < 0$

15. $\cot u = 1$ and $\cos u > 0$ **16.** $\tan u = -\dfrac{3}{4}$ and $\sin u > 0$

17. $\tan u = \dfrac{\sqrt{3}}{3}$ and $\cos u > 0$ **18.** $\cos u = \dfrac{\sqrt{2}}{2}$ and $\csc u < 0$

19. $\sec u = -\dfrac{2\sqrt{3}}{3}$ and $\sin u > 0$ **20.** $\csc u = -\sqrt{2}$ and $\tan u < 0$

(C) Find the value(s) of each of the other trigonometric functions of u.

21. $\sin u = \dfrac{\sqrt{3}}{2}$ and $\tan u = -\sqrt{3}$ **22.** $\cos u = -\dfrac{1}{2}$ and $\cot u = \dfrac{\sqrt{3}}{3}$

23. $\cos u = \dfrac{\sqrt{2}}{2}$ and $\sin u = -\dfrac{\sqrt{2}}{2}$ **24.** $\tan u = -1$ and $\sec u = -\sqrt{2}$

25. $\sec u = -\dfrac{13}{5}$ and $\tan u = \dfrac{12}{5}$ **26.** $\csc u = \dfrac{13}{12}$ and $\sin u = \dfrac{12}{13}$

27. $\tan u = -\dfrac{5}{4}$ and $\cos u = \dfrac{4\sqrt{41}}{41}$ **28.** $\cot u = -\sqrt{3}$ and $\cos u = -\dfrac{\sqrt{3}}{2}$

29. $\sin u = -\dfrac{7}{25}$ and $\csc u = -\dfrac{25}{7}$ **30.** $\sec u = -\dfrac{5}{4}$ and $\tan u = -\dfrac{3}{4}$

Cumulative Review

Graph each of the following. Find the domain and the range. Determine the coordinates of the vertex and an equation of the axis of symmetry.

1. $y = x^2$
D = {all real numbers};
R = $\{y|y \geq 0\}$; (0, 0); $x = 0$

2. $y = -x^2$
D = {all real numbers};
R = $\{y|y \leq 0\}$; (0, 0); $x = 0$

3. $y = x^2 - 2x - 8$
D = {all real numbers};
R = $\{y|y \geq -9\}$; (1, −9); $x = 1$

17.8 Using Trigonometric Tables

OBJECTIVES ▶ To determine the sin, cos, tan, and cot of any angle *u* reading a trigonometric table
To rewrite trigonometric functions using cofunctions
To find angle *u* by reading a trigonometric table when the sin *u*, cos *u*, tan *u*, or cot *u* is given

You have been finding trigonometric functions of angles with special measures like 30°, 45°, 60° and their multiples. You will now learn how to find trigonometric functions of angles with any measure by using a table. In the table, angle measure is given in multiples of 10 minutes. One degree equals sixty minutes ($1° = 60'$).

Example 1 Find sin 23° 30′ and cot 24° 50′ using the portion of a trigonometric table shown below.

The functions at the *top* of the table must be used with degree measure in the left-hand column, (0° to 45°).

x	sin x	cos x	tan x	cot x	sec x	csc x	
30′	.3827	.9239	.4142	2.4142	1.0824	2.6131	30′
40′	.3854	.9228	.4176	2.3945	1.0837	2.5949	20′
50′	.3881	.9216	.4210	2.3750	1.0850	2.5770	10′
23° 0′	.3907	.9205	.4245	2.3559	1.0864	2.5593	67° 0′
10′	.3934	.9194	.4279	2.3369	1.0877	2.5419	50′
20′	.3961	.9182	.4314	2.3183	1.0891	2.5247	40′
23° 30′ → 30′	.3987	.9171	.4348	2.2998	1.0904	2.5078	30′
40′	.4014	.9159	.4383	2.2817	1.0918	2.4912	20′
50′	.4041	.9147	.4417	2.2637	1.0932	2.4748	10′
24° 0′	.4067	.9135	.4452	2.2460	1.0946	2.4586	66° 0′
10′	.4094	.9124	.4487	2.2286	1.0961	2.4426	50′
20′	.4120	.9112	.4522	2.2113	1.0975	2.4269	40′
30′	.4147	.9100	.4557	2.1943	1.0990	2.4114	30′
40′	.4173	.9088	.4592	2.1775	1.1004	2.3961	20′
24° 50′ → 50′	.4200	.9075	.4628	2.1609	1.1019	2.3811	10′
25° 0′	.4226	.9063	.4663	2.1445	1.1034	2.3662	65° 0′
10′	.4253	.9051	.4699	2.1283	1.1049	2.3515	50′

Thus, sin 23° 30′ = .3987 and cot 24° 50′ = 2.1609.

Example 2 Find cos 45° 10′ and tan 46° 40′.

The functions at the *bottom* of the table must be used with degree measure in the right-hand column, (45° to 90°).

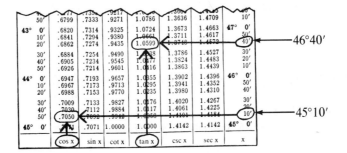

50′	.6799	.7333	.9271	1.0786	1.3636	1.4709	10′
43° 0′	.6820	.7314	.9325	1.0724	1.3673	1.4663	47° 0′
10′	.6841	.7294	.9380	1.0661	1.3711	1.4617	50′
20′	.6862	.7274	.9435	1.0599	1.3748	1.4572	40′ ← 46° 40′
30′	.6884	.7254	.9490	1.0538	1.3786	1.4527	30′
40′	.6905	.7234	.9545	1.0477	1.3824	1.4483	20′
50′	.6926	.7214	.9601	1.0416	1.3863	1.4439	10′
44° 0′	.6947	.7193	.9657	1.0355	1.3902	1.4396	46° 0′
10′	.6967	.7173	.9713	1.0295	1.3941	1.4352	50′
20′	.6988	.7153	.9770	1.0235	1.3980	1.4310	40′
30′	.7009	.7133	.9827	1.0176	1.4020	1.4267	30′
40′	.7030	.7112	.9884	1.0117	1.4061	1.4225	20′
50′	.7050	.7092	.9942	1.0058	1.4101	1.4184	10′ ← 45° 10′
45° 0′	.7071	.7071	1.0000	1.0000	1.4142	1.4142	45° 0′
	cos x	sin x	cot x	tan x	csc x	sec x	x

Thus, cos 45° 10′ = .7050 and tan 46° 40′ = 1.0599.

Since the trigonometric tables only show measures of acute angles, functions of larger angles must be written as functions of acute angles.

Example 3   Find sin 143° 20′ and cos 250° 40′.

Write each as the same trigonometric function of an acute angle. Sketch the angle of rotation and reference triangle.

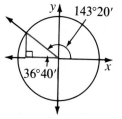

$$\begin{array}{r} 179°\,60' \\ -\;143°\,20' \\ \hline 36°\,40' \end{array}$$

sin 143° 20′ = sin 36° 40′
= .5972

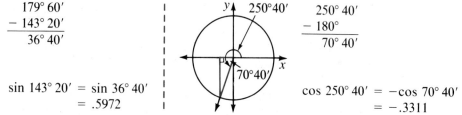

$$\begin{array}{r} 250°\,40' \\ -\;180° \\ \hline 70°\,40' \end{array}$$

cos 250° 40′ = −cos 70° 40′
= −.3311

Thus, sin 143° 20′ = .5972, and cos 250° 40′ = −.3311.

Example 4   Find the value of each pair from the table.

sin 70° and cos 20°
.9397

tan 33° 40′ and cot 56° 20′
.6661

Thus, sin 70° = cos 20° = .9397, and tan 33° 40′ = cot 56° 20′ = .6661.

Recall that two angles are complementary if the sum of their measures is 90°. The sine and *co*sine functions are called *complementary functions, or cofunctions.* Other examples of cofunctions are tangent and *co*tangent as well as secant and *co*secant. Example 4 suggests the following relationships concerning cofunctions.

Cofunction Relationships

sin u = cos (90° − u) and cos u = sin (90 − u)
tan u = cot (90° − u) and cot u = tan (90 − u)
sec u = csc (90° − u) and csc u = sec (90 − u)

Example 5   Express each function in terms of its cofunction.

         cos 63°   sec 13° 40′   cot 38° 10′

Use the cofunction and the complement.

     cos 63°   sec 13° 40′   cot 38° 10′
       ↓   ↓   ↓
     sin 27°   csc 76° 20′   tan 51° 50′

Example 6 Express each as a function of an angle measure less than 45°. Use cofunctions.

sin 100°   tan 290°

| sin 100° = sin 80° | tan 290° = −tan 70° |
| = cos 10° | = −cot 20° |

$sin (90° − u) = cos\ u$ ▶   ◀ $tan (90° − u) = cot\ u$

Thus, sin 100° = cos 10° and tan 290° = −cot 20°.

You can find u if sin u, cos u, tan u, or cot u is given.

Example 7

| sin u = .5200 | cos u = .8465 | tan u = 1.7205 |
| Find u if u < 90°. | Find u if u < 90°. | Find u if u < 90°. |

Look in the table to find the value, then find the corresponding angle u.

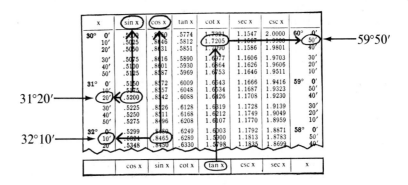

31°20'—   59°50'

32°10'—

Thus, if sin u = .5200, u = 31° 20'; if cos u = .8465, u = 32° 10'; and if tan u = 1.7205, u = 59° 50'.

The next example illustrates how to solve a trigonometric equation using a table of values.

Example 8 Find all values of u, 0° < u < 360°, for which tan u = −.6168.

Read the table in Example 7. The measure of the ref. ∠ is 31° 40'.

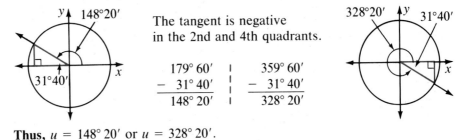

The tangent is negative
in the 2nd and 4th quadrants.

179° 60'		359° 60'
− 31° 40'		− 31° 40'
148° 20'		328° 20'

Thus, u = 148° 20' or u = 328° 20'.

Written **Exercises**

Ⓐ Use the table to find each of the following.

1. sin 24°   **2.** tan 78°   **3.** cos 23°   **4.** cot 43°   **5.** tan 47° 40′
6. sin 70° 30′   **7.** cot 23° 20′   **8.** cos 43° 30′   **9.** sin 60° 40′   **10.** tan 82° 50′
11. tan 39° 50′   **12.** sin 42° 30′   **13.** tan 52° 50′   **14.** cos 73° 40′   **15.** cot 50° 10′
16. cos 152°   **17.** cos 138°   **18.** sin 340°   **19.** cot 155°   **20.** sin 260°
21. cot 190° 40′ **22.** tan 340° 50′ **23.** cot 140° 10′ **24.** tan 100° 40′ **25.** cos 350° 30′

Use the table to find u, $u < 90°$.

26. sin u = .9293 **68° 20′**   **27.** cos u = .9652 **15° 10′**   **28.** tan u = .5930 **30° 40′**
29. cot u = .3607 **70° 10′**   **30.** tan u = .7954 **38° 30′**   **31.** sin u = .7373 **47° 30′**
32. cos u = .7333 **42° 50′**   **33.** sin u = .3773 **22° 10′**   **34.** cot u = 6.3138 **9°**
35. tan u = 3.8667 **75° 30′**   **36.** cot u = .3249 **72°**   **37.** cos u = .2363 **76° 20′**

Express each in terms of its cofunction.

38. sin 35°   **39.** cos 25°   **40.** tan 68°   **41.** cot 10°   **42.** sin 48°
43. cos 50° 10′ ⟋ **44.** tan 40° 40′ ⟋ **45.** cot 55° 20′ ⟋ **46.** sin 17° 40′ ⟋   **47.** cos 34° 30′ ⟋
   sin 39° 50′ ⟌   cot 49° 20′ ⟌   tan 34° 40′ ⟌   cos 72° 20′ ⟌   sin 55° 30′ ⟌

Ⓑ Find all values of u, $0° < u < 360°$, for which each is true. For Ex. 48–88, see TE Answer Section.
48. cos u = .9636   **49.** tan u = −2.7725   **50.** cot u = 1.2723
51. cot u = −.2648   **52.** cos u = −.4874   **53.** sin u = −.9283
54. sin u = .8124   **55.** sin u = .1650   **56.** cos u = .7808

Express as a function of an angle measure less than 45°.
57. tan 120°   **58.** cot 200°   **59.** sin 316°   **60.** cos 110°   **61.** sin 224°
62. sin 324° 20′ **63.** cos 125° 10′ **64.** tan 212° 40′ **65.** cot 331° 50′ **66.** tan 134° 40′

Ⓒ **Express each as a reciprocal function of an acute angle.**
67. cos 112°   **68.** sin 140° 10′   **69.** sin 176° 40′   **70.** tan 190° 40′
71. tan 304° 20′   **72.** cot 123° 40′   **73.** cos 340° 30′   **74.** cot 129° 20′

Find each of the following.
75. sec 35° 20′   **76.** csc 150° 20′   **77.** csc 50° 40′   **78.** sec 190° 40′

Find u if $u < 90°$.
79. sec u = 1.0003   **80.** csc u = 1.0712   **81.** csc u = 1.9801   **82.** sec u = 2.1657

Find all values of u, $0° < u < 360°$, for which each is true.
83. sec u = 1.1969   **84.** csc u = −6.8998   **85.** sec u = −1.2015
86. csc u = 1.6123   **87.** sec u = 2.7904   **88.** csc u = −2.5770

Cumulative **Review**

Find using logarithms.

1. $\dfrac{45\sqrt{13.5}}{\sqrt[3]{38}}$ **49.2**

2. $\dfrac{98^3\sqrt{48.7}}{24(105)}$ **2,606**

3. $\dfrac{86.45(425.6)^3}{.00735}$ **907,000,000,000**

17.9 Linear Trigonometric Equations

OBJECTIVE ▶ To solve linear trigonometric equations

You have learned how to determine all values of u, $0° \le u \le 360°$, that make equations like $\sin u = -\frac{1}{2}$ true. For $\sin u = -\frac{1}{2}$, the reference angle is 30°. The sin is negative in the 3rd and 4th quadrants. So, $u = 180° + 30°$ or 210° and $360° - 30°$ or 330°.

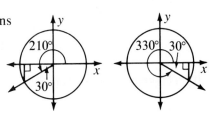

Example 1 Determine the values of u between 0° and 360° to the nearest ten minutes that make the equation $3 \sin u - 1 = 0$ true.

Solve for $\sin u$, write in decimal form, and determine the reference angle.

$$3 \sin u - 1 = 0$$
$$3 \sin u = 1$$
$$\sin u = \frac{1}{3}, \text{ or } .3333$$ ◀ *Use the trigonometric table to find closest value.*
$$\text{Ref. } \angle : 19° \, 30'$$

$u = 19° \, 30'$ $u = 180° - 19° \, 30'$ ◀ *Sin is positive in the 1st and*
                        $= 160° \, 30'$ *2nd quadrants.*

Thus, $u = 19° \, 30'$ or $u = 160° \, 30'$.

Example 2 Determine the values of θ between 0° and 360° to the nearest ten minutes that make the equations true.

$5 \tan \theta - 3 = -7$ $-3 \cos \theta - 4 = 5 \cos \theta + 2$

Solve for the trigonometric function. Determine the reference angle.

$5 \tan \theta - 3 = -7$	$-3 \cos \theta - 4 = 5 \cos \theta + 2$
$5 \tan \theta = -4$	$-6 = 8 \cos \theta$
$\tan \theta = -\frac{4}{5}, \text{ or } -.8000$	$\cos \theta = -\frac{6}{8}, \text{ or } -.7500$
Ref. $\angle : 38° \, 40'$	Ref. $\angle : 41° \, 20'$
$\theta = 180° - 38° \, 40'$	$\theta = 180° - 41° \, 20'$
$= 141° \, 20'$ (2nd quad.)	$= 138° \, 40'$
$\theta = 360° - 38° \, 40'$	$\theta = 180° + 41° \, 20'$
$= 321° \, 20'$ (4th quad.)	$= 221° \, 20'$
Thus, $\theta = 141° \, 20'$ or $321° \, 20'$.	**Thus, $\theta = 138° \, 40'$ or $221° \, 20'$.**

Example 3 Determine the values of *t* between 0° and 360° that make the equation
4 sin *t* − 3 = 2 sin *t* + 5 true.

$$4 \sin t - 3 = 2 \sin t + 5$$
$$2 \sin t = 8$$
$$\sin t = 4$$

Thus, there are no solutions, since $-1 \le \sin t \le 1$.

Written Exercises

(A) Determine the values of θ between 0° and 360° to the nearest ten minutes that make
each equation true.

1. 2 sin θ = 1 **30°, 150°**
2. 2 cos θ − √3 = 0 **30°, 330°**
3. 3 sin θ − 3 = 0 **90°**
4. 2 cos θ = −√3 **150°, 210°**
5. 3 sin θ + 2 = −1 **270°**
6. 6 cos θ − 2 = 0
7. cot θ = −1 **135°, 315°**
8. 3 tan θ − 1 = 0
9. √2 cos θ + 1 = 0 **135°, 225°**
10. 2 sin θ + 1 = 0 **210°, 330°**
11. 4 cos θ = 6 **none**
12. 3 tan θ = −√3 **150°, 330°**
13. 6 cos θ − 3 = 4 cos θ − 2
14. 5 sin θ + 3 = 2 sin θ **270°**
15. 7 tan θ − 1 = 2 tan θ + 4
16. −5 sin θ − 6 = 5 sin θ − 2
17. −8 tan θ − 12 = 6 tan θ − 1
18. 3 cos θ − 4 = 5 cos θ − 5

13. 60°, 300°   15. 45°, 225°   16. 203° 30′, 336° 30′   17. 141° 50′, 321° 50′   18. 60°, 300°

(B) Determine the values of θ between 0° and 720° to the nearest ten minutes that make
each equation true. For Ex. 19–36, see TE Answer Section. 6. 70° 30′, 289° 30′   8. 18° 30′, 198° 30′

19. 2 cos θ + √3 = 0
20. tan θ + 1 = 0
21. −cot θ = −√3
22. 5 sin θ − 8 = 3 sin θ − 9
23. −3 cos θ − 5 = −6 cos θ
24. −8 sin θ + 6 = −9 sin θ + 7
25. √3 tan θ − 2 = 1
26. 3 sin θ − 1 = −2 sin θ + 3
27. −4 cot θ − 7 = cot θ

(C) 28. 3 sec θ + 8 = 0
29. √3 csc θ = 5√3
30. −sec θ − 12 = 4 sec θ
31. −4 csc θ = 4
32. −2 sec θ + 8.4 = 0
33. −3 sec θ + 1 = 0
34. $\dfrac{\sec \theta}{4} - 3 = \dfrac{5 \sec \theta}{6}$
35. $\dfrac{1}{3} \csc \theta - \dfrac{3}{5} = 1$
36. $\dfrac{\csc \theta - 6}{3} = \dfrac{3}{4} \csc \theta + 1$

Determine the values of θ between 0° and 360° that make each equation true.

37. cos θ = sin θ **45°, 225°**
38. −sin θ = cos θ **135°, 315°**
39. tan θ = cot θ
40. sin θ = csc θ **90°, 270°**
41. cos θ = sec θ **0°, 180°**
42. −sec θ = cos θ **none**

39. 45°, 135°, 225°, 315°

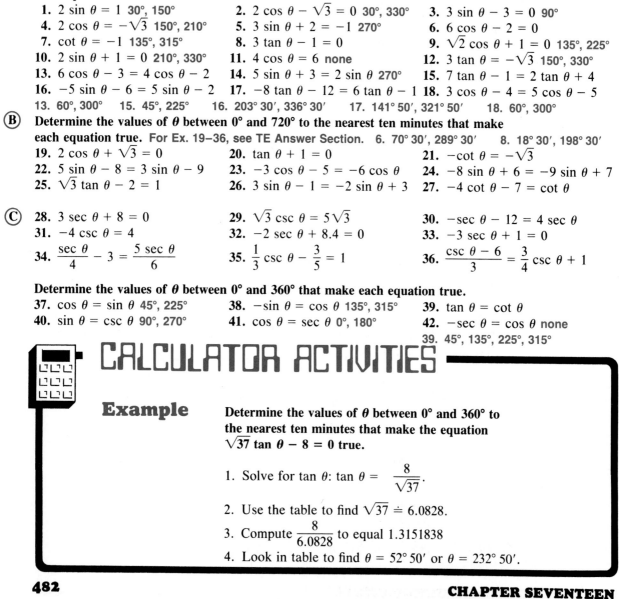

CALCULATOR ACTIVITIES

Example Determine the values of θ between 0° and 360° to
the nearest ten minutes that make the equation
√37 tan θ − 8 = 0 true.

1. Solve for tan θ: tan θ = $\dfrac{8}{\sqrt{37}}$.

2. Use the table to find √37 ≐ 6.0828.

3. Compute $\dfrac{8}{6.0828}$ to equal 1.3151838

4. Look in table to find θ = 52° 50′ or θ = 232° 50′.

17.10 Interpolation with Trigonometry

OBJECTIVES ▶ To use interpolation to determine functions of an angle measured to the nearest minute

To solve an equation of the form $a \tan \theta = b$, θ to the nearest minute

You have learned how to use a table to find trigonometric values for any angle measure in multiples of 10 minutes. You will now learn how to find trigonometric values for any degree and minute measure. The process of finding values for measures not in the tables is called **interpolation**.

Example 1 Find sin 36° 33′.

Look in the table for known values: 36° 33′ lies between the values 36° 30′ and 36° 40′. Make a table.

$$10 \begin{bmatrix} 3 \begin{bmatrix} \text{36° 30′} \\ \text{36° 33′} \\ \text{36° 40′} \end{bmatrix} & \begin{matrix} .5948 \\ .5972 \end{matrix} \Big] n \Big] .0024 \end{bmatrix}$$

measure	sine

Write a proportion and solve it.

$$\frac{n}{.0024} = \frac{3}{10}$$

$$10n = .0072$$

$$n = .00072, \text{ or } n \doteq .0007$$

Add. ▶ $.5948 + .0007 = .5955$ **Thus, sin 36° 33′ = .5955.**

Example 2 Find cos 311° 33′.

The reference ∠ is 48° 27′.
Look in the table for known values: 48° 27′ lies between the values of 48° 20′ and 48° 30′. Make a table.

measure	cosine

$$10 \begin{bmatrix} 7 \begin{bmatrix} \text{48° 20′} \\ \text{48° 27′} \\ \text{48° 30′} \end{bmatrix} & \begin{matrix} .6648 \\ .6626 \end{matrix} \Big] n \Big] -.0022 \end{bmatrix}$$

Write a proportion and solve it.

$$\frac{n}{-.0022} = \frac{7}{10}$$

$$10n = -.0154$$

$$n = .00154, \text{ or } n \doteq -.0015$$

Add. ▶ $.6648 + (-.0015) = .6633$ **Thus, cos 311° 33′ = .6633.**

The next example illustrates how to find u, if a trigonometric function of u is given.

Example 3

If tan u = .3463 ($0° < u < 90°$), find u to the nearest minute.

Look in the table for known values: .3463 lies between .3443 and .3476.

measure	tangent
19° 0'	.3443
19° 10'	.3463
	.3476

$$10\left[n\left[\begin{array}{c}19°\,0'\\19°\,10'\end{array}\right.\right.$$

$$\left.\left.\begin{array}{c}.3443\\.3463\\.3476\end{array}\right].0020\right].0033$$

Write a proportion and solve it.

$$\frac{n}{10} = \frac{.0020}{.0033} = \frac{20}{33}$$
$$33n = 200$$
$$n = \frac{200}{33}, \text{ or } n \doteq 6$$

Add. ▶ $19° 0' + 6' = 19° 6'$ **Thus, $u = 19° 6'$.**

Example 4

Find all values of $\theta(0° < \theta < 360°)$ to the nearest minute that make the equation $-4 \tan \theta - 3 = -7 \tan \theta + 5$ true.

Solve for tan θ. Determine the reference angle.
$$-4 \tan \theta - 3 = -7 \tan \theta + 5$$
$$3 \tan \theta = 8$$
$$\tan \theta = \frac{8}{3}, \text{ or } 2.6667$$

Use 2.6667 to find the reference angle.

measure	tangent
69° 20'	2.6511
69° 30'	2.6667
	2.6746

$$10\left[n\left[\begin{array}{c}69°\,20'\\69°\,30'\end{array}\right.\right.$$

$$\left.\left.\begin{array}{c}2.6511\\2.6667\\2.6746\end{array}\right].0156\right].0235$$

Write a proportion and solve.

$$\frac{n}{10} = \frac{.0156}{.0235} = \frac{156}{235}$$
$$235n = 1560$$
$$n = \frac{1560}{235} \doteq 6$$

Add. ▶ $69° 20' + 6' = 69° 26'$

*Tan is positive
in the 1st and 3rd
quadrants.* ▶ $\theta = 69° 26'$
$$\theta = 180° + 69° 26' = 249° 26'$$

Written Exercises

(A) Find each of the following.
1. sin 43° 15′ **.6852**
2. cos 18° 32′ **.9481**
3. tan 12° 57′ **.2300**
4. cot 62° 38′ **.5176**
5. cos 72° 18′ **.3040**
6. tan 55° 8′ **1.4352**
7. cos 33° 42′ **.8320**
8. cos 87° 53′ **.03694**
9. tan 31° 43′ **.6180**
10. cot 12° 24′ **4.5484**
11. sin 73° 47′ **.9602**
12. sin 16° 18′ **.2806**

Find u (0° < u < 90°) to the nearest minute.
13. cos u = .9753 **12° 46′**
14. tan u = .1573 **8° 56′**
15. sin u = .2875 **16° 43′**
16. sin u = .9264 **67° 53′**
17. cos u = .9214 **22° 52′**
18. cot u = 3.5352 **15° 48′**
19. cot u = .3567 **70° 22′**
20. sin u = .7954 **52° 42′**
21. cos u = .4535 **63° 2′**

Find all values of θ (0° < θ < 360°) to the nearest minute. **23. 30°, 150°   24. 38° 56′, 321° 4′**
22. 2 cos θ + 1 = 0 **120°, 240°**
23. 5 sin θ − 2 = 3 sin θ − 1
24. 6 cos θ − 4 = 3 − 3 cos θ
25. −3 tan θ + 5 = 4 + 3 tan θ **9° 28′, 189° 28′**
26. −2 cot θ + 8 = −5 cot θ **159° 27′, 339° 27′**
27. −7 sin θ + 5 = 7 − sin θ **199° 28′, 340° 32′**

(B) Find each of the following.
28. cos 124° 43′ **−.5695**
29. sin 312° 24′ **−.7384**
30. tan 86° 57′ **18.7793**
31. cot 204° 36′ **2.1842**
32. sin 197° 22′ **−.2985**
33. cot 342° 53′ **−3.2472**
34. cos 349° 45′ **.9840**
35. tan 224° 27′ **.9810**
36. sec 134° 38′ **−1.4233**
37. csc 248° 17′ **−1.0764**
38. csc 153° 54′ **2.2731**
39. sec 354° 48′ **1.0042**
40. **23° 08′, 203° 08′**
41. **156° 35′, 203° 25′**
42. **34° 19′, 214° 19′**

Find u (0° < u < 360°) to the nearest minute.
40. tan u = .4272
41. cos u = −.9177
42. cot u = 1.4650
43. sin u = .5987   **36° 47′, 143° 13′**
44. sin u = −.8221   **235° 18′, 304° 42′**
45. cos u = −.0650   **93° 44′, 266° 16′**

(C) Find all values of θ (0° ≤ θ < 360°).
46. $\dfrac{\sin \theta}{\cos \theta} = -1$ **135°, 315°**
47. $\dfrac{\cos \theta}{\sin \theta} = -\dfrac{\sqrt{3}}{3}$ **120°, 300°**
48. cot $\theta \cdot$ sin $\theta = \dfrac{\sqrt{3}}{2}$ **30°, 330°**
49. sin θ sec θ = −3.2658 **107° 2′, 287° 2′**
50. csc θ cos θ = −2.4536 **157° 50′, 337° 50′**
51. $\dfrac{\cot \theta \cdot \tan \theta}{\sec \theta} = -.7654$ **139° 57′, 220° 3′**
52. tan $\theta \cdot$ csc $\theta \cdot$ (cos $\theta)^2$ = −.3857

52. 112° 41′, 247° 19′

Cumulative Review

Simplify.

1. $\dfrac{1 - \dfrac{1}{3}}{4 + \dfrac{3}{5}}$ **$\dfrac{10}{69}$**

2. $\dfrac{\dfrac{2}{3} - \dfrac{4}{5}}{\dfrac{5}{2} + \dfrac{7}{9}}$ **$\dfrac{-12}{295}$**

3. 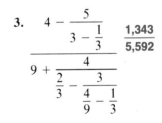 **$\dfrac{1,343}{5,592}$**

17.11 Trigonometry of a Right Triangle

OBJECTIVES ▶ To find trigonometric functions of acute angles in a right triangle
To simplify trigonometric expressions involving special angles

Remember that for any angle of rotation there is an associated reference right triangle with six trigonometric ratios. You will now learn about trigonometry of right triangles. The following diagrams will help make comparisons.

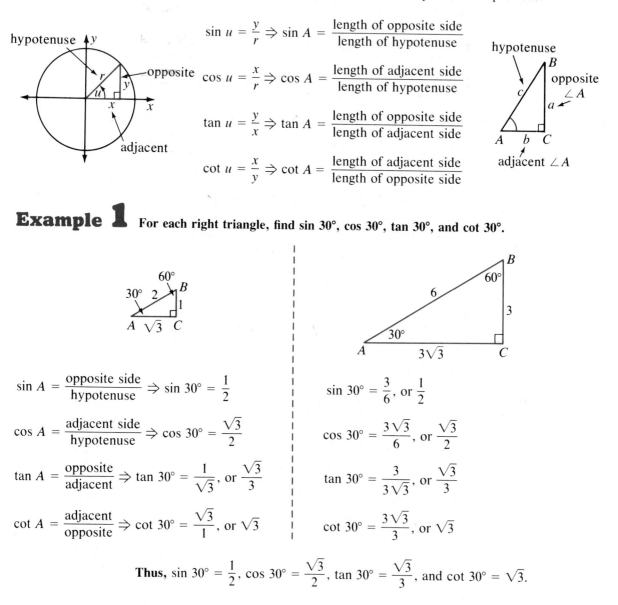

$$\sin u = \frac{y}{r} \Rightarrow \sin A = \frac{\text{length of opposite side}}{\text{length of hypotenuse}}$$

$$\cos u = \frac{x}{r} \Rightarrow \cos A = \frac{\text{length of adjacent side}}{\text{length of hypotenuse}}$$

$$\tan u = \frac{y}{x} \Rightarrow \tan A = \frac{\text{length of opposite side}}{\text{length of adjacent side}}$$

$$\cot u = \frac{x}{y} \Rightarrow \cot A = \frac{\text{length of adjacent side}}{\text{length of opposite side}}$$

Example 1 For each right triangle, find sin 30°, cos 30°, tan 30°, and cot 30°.

$$\sin A = \frac{\text{opposite side}}{\text{hypotenuse}} \Rightarrow \sin 30° = \frac{1}{2}$$

$$\cos A = \frac{\text{adjacent side}}{\text{hypotenuse}} \Rightarrow \cos 30° = \frac{\sqrt{3}}{2}$$

$$\tan A = \frac{\text{opposite}}{\text{adjacent}} \Rightarrow \tan 30° = \frac{1}{\sqrt{3}}, \text{ or } \frac{\sqrt{3}}{3}$$

$$\cot A = \frac{\text{adjacent}}{\text{opposite}} \Rightarrow \cot 30° = \frac{\sqrt{3}}{1}, \text{ or } \sqrt{3}$$

$$\sin 30° = \frac{3}{6}, \text{ or } \frac{1}{2}$$

$$\cos 30° = \frac{3\sqrt{3}}{6}, \text{ or } \frac{\sqrt{3}}{2}$$

$$\tan 30° = \frac{3}{3\sqrt{3}}, \text{ or } \frac{\sqrt{3}}{3}$$

$$\cot 30° = \frac{3\sqrt{3}}{3}, \text{ or } \sqrt{3}$$

Thus, $\sin 30° = \frac{1}{2}$, $\cos 30° = \frac{\sqrt{3}}{2}$, $\tan 30° = \frac{\sqrt{3}}{3}$, and $\cot 30° = \sqrt{3}$.

CHAPTER SEVENTEEN

Example 2 For the given triangle, find sin 60°, cos 60°, tan 60°, and cot 60°.

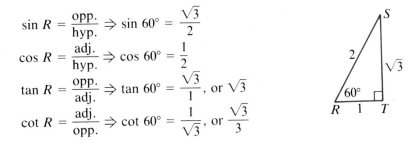

$$\sin R = \frac{\text{opp.}}{\text{hyp.}} \Rightarrow \sin 60° = \frac{\sqrt{3}}{2}$$

$$\cos R = \frac{\text{adj.}}{\text{hyp.}} \Rightarrow \cos 60° = \frac{1}{2}$$

$$\tan R = \frac{\text{opp.}}{\text{adj.}} \Rightarrow \tan 60° = \frac{\sqrt{3}}{1}, \text{ or } \sqrt{3}$$

$$\cot R = \frac{\text{adj.}}{\text{opp.}} \Rightarrow \cot 60° = \frac{1}{\sqrt{3}}, \text{ or } \frac{\sqrt{3}}{3}$$

Thus, $\sin 60° = \dfrac{\sqrt{3}}{2}$, $\cos 60° = \dfrac{1}{2}$, $\tan 60° = \sqrt{3}$, and $\cot 60° = \dfrac{\sqrt{3}}{3}$.

From Examples 1 and 2, notice the following cofunction relationship discussed on page 478.

$$\sin 30° = \cos 60° \qquad\qquad \tan 30° = \cot 60°$$
$$\sin 60° = \cos 30° \qquad\qquad \tan 60° = \cot 30°$$

Example 3 Find u ($0° < u < 90°$) if $\cos 20° = \sin u$, and find u if $\tan 50° = \cot u$.

$$\cos A = \sin (90° - A) \qquad\qquad \tan A = \cot (90° - A)$$
$$\cos 20° = \sin (90° - 20°) \qquad\qquad \tan 50° = \cot (90° - 50°)$$
$$= \sin 70° \qquad\qquad\qquad\qquad = \cot 40°$$

Thus, $u = 70°$.   **Thus,** $u = 40°$.

The next example illustrates how to simplify trigonometric expressions.

Example 4 Evaluate and simplify $\dfrac{\cos 30° + \tan 45°}{\sin 30°}$.

Evaluate each trigonometric function, substitute, and simplify.

$$\frac{\cos 30° + \tan 45°}{\sin 30°} = \frac{\dfrac{\sqrt{3}}{2} + 1}{\dfrac{1}{2}} \qquad \blacktriangleleft \quad \cos 30° = \frac{\sqrt{3}}{2}, \ \tan 45° = 1$$

$$\sin 30° = \frac{1}{2}$$

$$= \frac{\dfrac{\sqrt{3}}{2} + 1}{\dfrac{1}{2}} \cdot \frac{2}{2}, \text{ or } \frac{\sqrt{3} + 2}{1}$$

Thus, the value of the expression $\dfrac{\cos 30° + \tan 45°}{\sin 30°}$ is $\sqrt{3} + 2$.

TRIGONOMETRY OF A RIGHT TRIANGLE

Oral **Exercises**

For each triangle, state the measure of the side adjacent to and the side opposite the indicated angle.

1. $\angle A$ **2.** $\angle B$ **3.** $\angle H$ **4.** $\angle I$ **5.** $\angle D$ **6.** $\angle E$

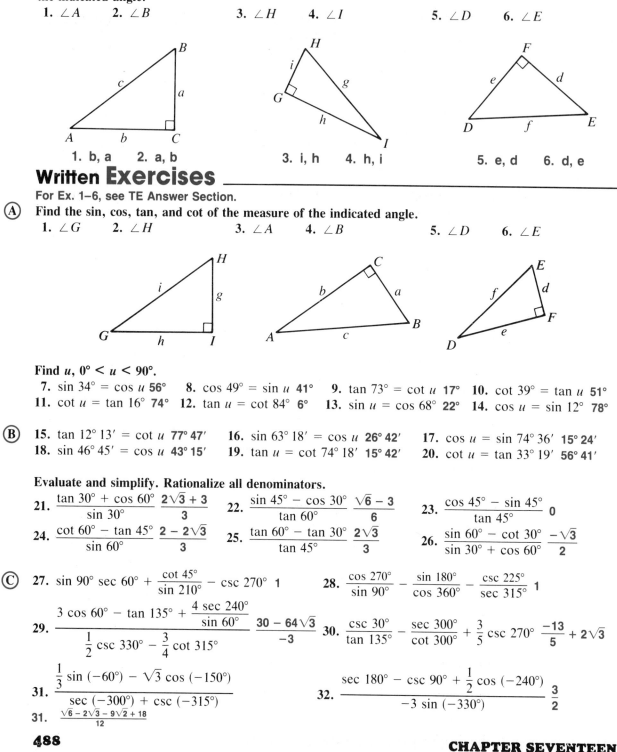

1. b, a 2. a, b **3. i, h 4. h, i** **5. e, d 6. d, e**

Written **Exercises**

For Ex. 1–6, see TE Answer Section.

Ⓐ Find the sin, cos, tan, and cot of the measure of the indicated angle.

1. $\angle G$ **2.** $\angle H$ **3.** $\angle A$ **4.** $\angle B$ **5.** $\angle D$ **6.** $\angle E$

Find u, $0° < u < 90°$.

7. $\sin 34° = \cos u$ **56°** **8.** $\cos 49° = \sin u$ **41°** **9.** $\tan 73° = \cot u$ **17°** **10.** $\cot 39° = \tan u$ **51°**

11. $\cot u = \tan 16°$ **74°** **12.** $\tan u = \cot 84°$ **6°** **13.** $\sin u = \cos 68°$ **22°** **14.** $\cos u = \sin 12°$ **78°**

Ⓑ **15.** $\tan 12° 13' = \cot u$ **77° 47′** **16.** $\sin 63° 18' = \cos u$ **26° 42′** **17.** $\cos u = \sin 74° 36'$ **15° 24′**

18. $\sin 46° 45' = \cos u$ **43° 15′** **19.** $\tan u = \cot 74° 18'$ **15° 42′** **20.** $\cot u = \tan 33° 19'$ **56° 41′**

Evaluate and simplify. Rationalize all denominators.

21. $\dfrac{\tan 30° + \cos 60°}{\sin 30°}$ $\dfrac{2\sqrt{3}+3}{3}$ **22.** $\dfrac{\sin 45° - \cos 30°}{\tan 60°}$ $\dfrac{\sqrt{6}-3}{6}$ **23.** $\dfrac{\cos 45° - \sin 45°}{\tan 45°}$ **0**

24. $\dfrac{\cot 60° - \tan 45°}{\sin 60°}$ $\dfrac{2-2\sqrt{3}}{3}$ **25.** $\dfrac{\tan 60° - \tan 30°}{\tan 45°}$ $\dfrac{2\sqrt{3}}{3}$ **26.** $\dfrac{\sin 60° - \cot 30°}{\sin 30° + \cos 60°}$ $\dfrac{-\sqrt{3}}{2}$

Ⓒ **27.** $\sin 90° \sec 60° + \dfrac{\cot 45°}{\sin 210°} - \csc 270°$ **1** **28.** $\dfrac{\cos 270°}{\sin 90°} - \dfrac{\sin 180°}{\cos 360°} - \dfrac{\csc 225°}{\sec 315°}$ **1**

29. $\dfrac{3\cos 60° - \tan 135° + \dfrac{4\sec 240°}{\sin 60°}}{\dfrac{1}{2}\csc 330° - \dfrac{3}{4}\cot 315°}$ $\dfrac{30 - 64\sqrt{3}}{-3}$ **30.** $\dfrac{\csc 30°}{\tan 135°} - \dfrac{\sec 300°}{\cot 300°} + \dfrac{3}{5}\csc 270°$ $\dfrac{-13}{5} + 2\sqrt{3}$

31. $\dfrac{\dfrac{1}{3}\sin(-60°) - \sqrt{3}\cos(-150°)}{\sec(-300°) + \csc(-315°)}$ **32.** $\dfrac{\sec 180° - \csc 90° + \dfrac{1}{2}\cos(-240°)}{-3\sin(-330°)}$ $\dfrac{3}{2}$

31. $\dfrac{\sqrt{6} - 2\sqrt{3} - 9\sqrt{2} + 18}{12}$

17.12 Using Trigonometry of a Right Triangle

OBJECTIVES ▶ **To find the length of a side of a right triangle given the length of one side and the measure of an acute angle**
To find the measure of an acute angle of a right triangle given the lengths of two sides
To apply right triangle trigonometry

Right triangle trigonometry is often used to find the length of one side or the measure of an acute angle of a right triangle. To do this, use a function which relates that which is given and that which is to be determined. Sometimes one function is more convenient to use than another.

Example 1 **In right triangle ABC, $\angle A$ measures 43°, $c = 4.3$ m and m$\angle C = 90°$. Find a to the nearest meter.**

The *trigonometric* function that relates $\angle A$, a, and c is the sin function.

$$\sin A = \frac{\text{opp.}}{\text{hyp.}} \Rightarrow \sin 43° = \frac{a}{4.3}$$

Solve: $a = 4.3 \, (\sin 43°)$
$\doteq 4.3 \, (.6820)$, or 2.9326

Thus, $a = 3m$ to the nearest meter.

Example 2 **Find to the nearest degree the measure of each acute angle in right triangle ABC, if $b = 5$ and $c = 13$. Angle C is a right angle.**

Draw and label the diagram.
Cos A relates $\angle A$, b, and c.

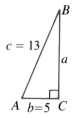

$$\cos A = \frac{\text{adj.}}{\text{hyp.}} \Rightarrow \cos A = \frac{5}{13}, \text{ or } .3846$$
$$A \doteq 67°$$

$\angle A$ and $\angle B$ are complementary.
$$A + B = 90°$$
$$67° + B = 90$$
$$B \doteq 23°$$

Thus, $\angle A$ measures 67° and $\angle B$ measures 23°.

In Examples 3 and 4 below, the angle of elevation or angle of depression is the angle between the horizontal and the line of sight. The angle of elevation equals the angle of depression.

Example 3

What is the length of a shadow cast by a 10-meter pole when the angle of elevation of the sun is 54°?

Draw and label the diagram.
The tan A or cot A relate $\angle A$, a, and b.

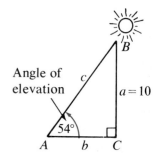

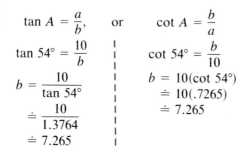

$$\tan A = \frac{a}{b}, \quad \text{or} \quad \cot A = \frac{b}{a}$$

$$\tan 54° = \frac{10}{b} \qquad\qquad \cot 54° = \frac{b}{10}$$

$$b = \frac{10}{\tan 54°} \qquad\qquad b = 10(\cot 54°)$$

$$\doteq \frac{10}{1.3764} \qquad\qquad \doteq 10(.7265)$$

$$\doteq 7.265 \qquad\qquad\qquad \doteq 7.265$$

Angle of elevation

c

$a = 10$

54°

A   b   C

Thus, the length of the shadow is approximately 7 m.

Example 4

A pilot flying at an altitude of 1200 m observes that the angle of depression of an airport is 43°. Find to the nearest meter the distance to the airport from the point on the ground directly below the plane.

Draw and label the diagram.
The tan A or cot A relate $\angle A$, a, and b.
Use cot A since the unknown will be in the numerator.

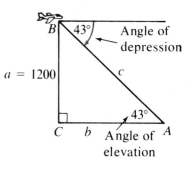

Angle of depression

$a = 1200$ c

b Angle of elevation

$$\cot A = \frac{b}{a}$$

$$\cot 43° = \frac{b}{1200}$$

$$b = 1200(\cot 43°)$$

$$\doteq 1200(1.0724)$$

$$\doteq 1286.88$$

Thus, the distance from C to A is 1287 m, to the nearest meter.

Oral Exercises

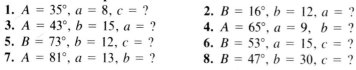

For Ex. 1–8, see TE Answer Section.
In right triangle ABC, which trigonometric function(s) relates the given parts with the unknown parts?

1. $A = 35°$, $a = 8$, $c = ?$
2. $B = 16°$, $b = 12$, $a = ?$
3. $A = 43°$, $b = 15$, $a = ?$
4. $A = 65°$, $a = 9$, $b = ?$
5. $B = 73°$, $b = 12$, $c = ?$
6. $B = 53°$, $a = 15$, $c = ?$
7. $A = 81°$, $a = 13$, $b = ?$
8. $B = 47°$, $b = 30$, $c = ?$

CHAPTER SEVENTEEN

Written Exercises _____

1. $b = 8, c = 11$ 2. $a = 11, b = 15$ 3. $a = 24, c = 29$ 4. $a = 13, b = 7$ 5. $b = 61, c = 62$

(A) Find the measure of each of the other two sides of right triangle ABC, with
$m \angle C = 90$, to the nearest whole number. 6. $b = 29, c = 48$ 7. $a = 30, c = 31$ 8. $a = 10, c = 39$

1. $m \angle B = 46$, $a = 7.3$ 2. $m \angle A = 36°$, $c = 18.3$ 3. $m \angle B = 34°$, $b = 16.3$
4. $m \angle A = 63°$, $c = 15.1$ 5. $m \angle B = 78°$, $a = 12.9$ 6. $m \angle A = 53°$, $a = 38.7$
7. $m \angle B = 18$, $b = 9.6$ 8. $m \angle A = 15°$, $b = 37.3$ 9. $m \angle B = 82°$, $c = 46.5$

$a = 6, b = 46$

Find the measure of each acute angle of right triangle ABC, with $m \angle C = 90$, to
the nearest degree. 10. $m \angle A = 55, m \angle B = 35$ 11. $m \angle A = 37, m \angle B = 53$ 12. $m \angle A = 44, m \angle B = 46$
10. $c = 8.6$ $b = 4.9$ 11. $b = 12.7$ $a = 9.7$ 12. $b = 14.6$ $c = 20.3$
13. $a = 9.1$ $c = 12.3$ 14. $c = 18.6$ $a = 14.1$ 15. $a = 15.1$ $b = 7.6$
13. $m \angle A = 48, m \angle B = 42$ 14. $m \angle A = 49, m \angle B = 41$ 15. $m \angle A = 63, m \angle B = 27$

16. A ladder leans against a building. The top
    of the ladder reaches a point on the
    building that is 9 m above the ground. The
    foot of the ladder is 4 m from the building.
    Find to the nearest degree the measure of the
    angle that the ladder makes with the level
    ground. **66**

17. From the top of a lighthouse 48 m high, the
    angle of depression of a boat at sea
    measures 23° 30′. Find, to the nearest m,
    the distance from the boat to the foot of
    the lighthouse. **110 m**

18. From an airplane 925 m above sea level,
    the angle of depression of a ship measures
    42° 20′. Find to the nearest meter the
    distance to the ship from the point at sea
    directly below the plane. **1,015 m**

19. At a point on the ground 8 m from the foot
    of a cliff, the angle of elevation of the top
    of the cliff measures 38° 40′. Find the
    height of the cliff to the nearest meter. **6 m**

(B) Find the measure of each of the other two sides to the nearest tenth and the
measure of each acute angle of right triangle ABC, with $m \angle C = 90$, to the
nearest minute. **For Ex. 20–28, see TE Answer Section.**

20. $A = 13° 23′$, $a = 9.6$ 21. $B = 49° 18′$, $c = 13.3$ 22. $A = 63° 38′$, $b = 9.1$
23. $B = 74° 46′$, $b = 12.3$ 24. $A = 11° 12′$, $b = 7.8$ 25. $B = 16° 56′$, $c = 11.8$
26. $A = 33° 11′$, $c = 16.5$ 27. $B = 73° 33′$, $a = 6.3$ 28. $A = 38° 37′$, $a = 12.5$

(C) Determine BC to the nearest tenth.
29. $m \angle \theta = 60°$, $m \angle A = 45°$, $AD = 12$ **28.4**
30. $m \angle \theta = 45°$, $m \angle A = 30$, $AD = 10$ **13.6**
31. $m \angle \theta = 60°$, $m \angle A = 30°$, $AD = 16$ **13.9**
32. $m \angle \theta = 49° 18′$, $m \angle A = 32° 16′$, $AD = 14.3$ **19.7**
33. $m \angle \theta = 74° 48′$, $m \angle A = 48° 35′$, $AD = 28.6$ **46.8**

34. From point B on the ground, the angle of elevation of a kite measures
    46° 18′. The kite is attached to a rope 86 m long. Find to the nearest meter
    the height of the kite. **62 m**

35. From an airplane flying 1250 m above sea level, the angles of depression of
    two ships due west measure 33° 10′ and 20° 40′. Find the distance between
    the ships to the nearest meter. **1,401 m**

USING TRIGONOMETRY OF A RIGHT TRIANGLE   **491**

Chapter Seventeen Review

Vocabulary
angle of rotation [17.1]   sec, csc [17.5]
cofunction [17.8, 17.11]   sin, cos [17.3]
quadrantral angle [17.3]   tan, cot [17.4]

Sketch angles of rotation with the given measures. Determine the quadrant of each nonquadrantle angle. Identify the reference angle and reference triangle. [17.1]
1. 45°   **2.** −150°   **3.** 225°   **4.** −240°
5. −330°   **6.** 450°   **7.** 780°   **8.** −420°
9. −100°   **10.** −270°   **11.** 400°   **12.** −720°
For Ex. 1–12, see TE Answer Section.

★**Find the reference angle if its terminal side intersects a circle at the following points and the center of the circle is at the origin. Determine the radius of the circle.** [17.2]
13. (2, 2) **45°, 2√2**   **14.** (−√3, 1) **30°, 2**
15. (a, a√3) **60°, 2a**   **16.** (a, −a) **45°, a√2**

Find each of the following. Rationalize any radical denominator. [17.3–17.6]
17. cos 60°   **18.** tan (−30°)   **19.** sec 150°
20. sin (−480°)   **21.** sin 0°   **22.** sec 90°
23. cot 360°   **24.** cos (−270°)
For Ex. 17–24, see TE Answer Section.

Write each of the following in terms of the same trigonometric function of an acute angle. [17.3, 17.6]
25. sin 130° **sin 50°**   **26.** cot 150° **−cot 30°**
27. cos (−160°)   **28.** tan (−220°)
27. −cos 20°   **28.** −tan 40°

In which quadrants is each of the following true?
29. sin < 0 **30.** cos > 0 **31.** tan < 0 **32.** sec > 0
29. III, IV **30.** I, IV **31.** II, IV **32.** I, IV [17.3–17.4]

Find two values of u between 0° and 360° for which each is true. [17.3]
33. 120°, 240°
33. cos u = −$\frac{1}{2}$ **34.** sin u = −$\frac{\sqrt{2}}{2}$
    34. 225°, 315°
35. cot u = $\frac{-\sqrt{3}}{3}$ **35.** 120°, 300°

For Ex. 36–38, see TE Answer Section.
Find the value of each of the other trigonometric functions of u. [17.7]
36. tan u = $\frac{5}{12}$ and sin u > 0
37. cos u = −$\frac{3}{5}$ and cot u < 0
38. sin u = $\frac{7}{25}$ and sec u = −$\frac{25}{24}$
39. .6157 **40.** 2.0965 **41.** −.7314

Use the trig. table to find each of the following.
39. sin 38°   **40.** tan 64° 30′   **41.** cos 223°
42. cos 34° 17′ **.8263**   **43.** cot 115° 36′ **−.4792**
44. cos 215° 33′ **−.8136** **45.** sin (−196° 54′) **.2907**
46. tan (−338° 28′)   **47.** cot (−134° 42′)
    .3946   .9896

Find u, u < 90°. [17.8, 17.10]
48. cos u = .7790   **49.** sin u = .9717
50. sin 73° = cos u **17°** **51.** cot u = tan 22° **68°**
48. 38° 50′ **49.** 76° 20′

Find all values of θ, 0° < θ < 360°. [17.10]
52. tan θ = −2.8258   **53.** cot θ = 6.9600
54. cos θ = −.7796   **55.** sin θ = .4562
52. 109° 29′. 289° 29′ **54.** 141° 13′, 218° 47′

Express in terms of the cofunction. [17.8]
56. sin 48° 25′   **57.** tan 64° 42′ **cot 25° 18′**
53. 8° 11′, 188° 11′ **55.** 27° 9′, 152° 51′ **56.** cos 41° 35′

Express as a function of an angle measure less than 45°. [17.8]
58. cos 320° **cos 40°**   **59.** cot 105° 30′
                −tan 15° 30′

Determine the values of θ between 0° and 360° that make each equation true. [17.9]
60. sin θ = −$\frac{1}{2}$ **61.** 2 cos θ − 1 = 5 cos θ + 1
62. 5 tan θ − 8 = −3 tan θ − 5 **60.** 210°, 330°
61. 131° 49′, 228° 11′ **62.** 20° 33′, 200° 33′

Evaluate and simplify. [17.11]
63. $\dfrac{\cos 45° - 3 \sin 60°}{\sec 120°}$ $\dfrac{\sqrt{2} - 3\sqrt{3}}{-4}$
64. $\dfrac{\sin 45° + \cot 45°}{\cos (-120°)}$ $-\sqrt{2} - 2$
★**65.** $\dfrac{\csc 90° + 3 \tan (-135°) - \sin 60°}{4 \cos (-315°)}$ $\dfrac{8\sqrt{2} - \sqrt{6}}{8}$

Find the measure of each of the other two sides of right triangle ABC, with m∠C = 90°, to the nearest whole number. [17.12]
66. m∠A = 46°, b = 9.2 **a = 10, c = 13**
67. m∠B = 12° 18′, a = 12.3 **b = 3, c = 13**

Chapter Seventeen Test

Sketch angles of rotation with the given measures. Determine the quadrant of each angle of rotation. Identify the reference angle and reference triangle.

1. 110°   2. −130°   3. 250°   4. −340°

For Ex. 1–4, see TE Answer Section.

Determine the lengths of the indicated sides. Rationalize all denominators.

5.

x = 6
y = 3√3

6.

a = 8√2
b = 8√2

Determine the point (x, y) and the radius r.

7.

(5, 5√3)
r = 10

8.

(−5, 5)
r = 5√2

Find each of the following. Rationalize any radical denominator.

9. cos (−60°) $\frac{1}{2}$ 10. cos 180°   11. sin 420° $\frac{\sqrt{3}}{2}$
12. tan 135° −1   13. sec 180°   14. csc 420°

10. −1   13. −1   14. $\frac{2\sqrt{3}}{3}$

Write each of the following in terms of the same trigonometric function of an acute angle.

15. tan 340°   16. cos 100°   17. sin 310°

15. −tan 20°   16. −cos 80°   17. −sin 50°

In which quadrants is each of the following true?

18. sin > 0   19. cos < 0   20. tan < 0
21. cos θ < 0 and sin θ > 0 II

18. I and II   19. II and III   20. II and IV

Find two values of u between 0° and 360° for which each is true.

22. cos u = −$\frac{\sqrt{3}}{2}$
   150°, 210°

23. sin u = $\frac{1}{2}$ 30°, 150°

Find the values of each of the other five trigonometric functions of u.

24. sin u = −$\frac{5}{13}$ and tan u < 0   For Ex. 24–25,
25. cos u = −$\frac{3}{5}$ and sin u > 0   see TE Answer Section.

Use the trig. table to find each of the following.

26. cos 37° .7986   27. sin 215° 40′ −.5831
28. tan (−139° 46′)   29. cos 326° 10′ .8307
   .8461

Find u, u < 90°.

30. sin u = .5664   31. cos u = .2464
32. sin 65° = cos u 30. 34° 30′ 31. 75° 44′
32. 25°

Find all values of θ, 0° < θ < 360°.

33. tan θ = −.6778   34. cos θ = −.4083
33. 145° 52′, 325° 52′   34. 114° 6′, 245° 54′

Express in terms of the cofunction.

35. sin 34° cos 56°   36. tan 75° 26′
   cot 14° 34′

Express as a function of an angle measure less than 45°.

37. sin 110° cos 20°   38. cos 305° 10′
   sin 35° 10′

Determine the values of θ between 0° and 360° that make each equation true.

39. 3 cos θ − 1 = −2 cos θ 78° 28′, 281° 32′
40. −5 sin θ − 3 = 2 sin θ 205° 23′, 334° 37′

Evaluate and simplify.

41. $\frac{\cos 60° − \sin 60°}{\cot 45°}$ $\frac{1 − \sqrt{3}}{2}$

Find the measure of each of the other two sides of right triangle ABC, with m∠C = 90, to the nearest whole number.

42. m∠A = 47°, b = 4.7 a = 5, c = 7
43. m∠B = 74° 25′, a = 10.3 b = 37, c = 38

44. At a point on the ground 23 m from the foot of a building, the angle of elevation of the top of the building is 48° 37′. Find to the nearest meter the height of the building. 26 m

Computer Activities

Boating

In rigging masts on a boat, support wires are necessary. The length of a wire can be found by knowing the height of the mast and the angle at which the wire is fastened to the boat.
You can solve this problem by using the sine function.

$$\sin A = \frac{H}{L}$$

PROGRAM

```
10 PRINT "PROGRAM FINDS LENGTH OF WIRE"
20 PRINT "ENTER HEIGHT OF MAST"
30 INPUT H
40 PRINT "ENTER MEASURE OF ANGLE A IN DEGREES"
50 INPUT A
60 REM MEASURE IN DEGREES CHANGED TO RADIANS
70 LET R = A * (3.14159/180)
80 LET L = H/SIN (R)
90 PRINT "LENGTH OF WIRE IS"; L
100 END
```

Exercises

Type in the above program and run it for the following values:

1. $H = 40$ m $\angle A = 71°$ **42.30484**

2. $H = 20$ m $\angle A = 43°$ **29.32559**

3. $H = 35$ m $\angle A = 24°$ **86.05086**

4. Alter the program to find the length of wire, given the distance B from the mast to the point where the wire joins the boat, and $\angle A$.
   For Ex. 4, see TE Answer Section.

5. Angles formed by a counterclockwise or clockwise rotation of a ray may be more than 360°. The position of the terminal side of the ray determines whether an angle is quadrantal or not. Write a program to find if an angle is quadrantal. If not, find the quadrant in which the angle ends.

   a) 225° **3**   b) 330° **4**   c) 405° **1**   d) 180° **quadrantal**   e) −315° **1**   f) −210° **2**

494

College Prep Test

Directions: Choose the one best answer to each question or problem.

1. The lengths of the three sides of a triangle are 5, 12, and 13. A circle passes through the vertices of the triangle. Which is the length of the radius of the circle? **A**

   (A) $\frac{13}{2}$ (B) 4   (C) 5

   (D) 6   (E) None of these

2.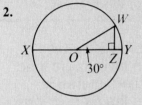

   $\overline{OW}$ is a radius of the circle with center O. If $OW = 12$, which is the value of WZ? **C**

   (A) $6\sqrt{2}$ (B) 4   (C) 6
   (D) $6\sqrt{3}$ (E) None of these

3.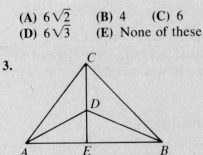

   ABC is a triangle with altitude $\overline{CE}$. $CD = 6$ and $AB = 18$. Which is the area of $ADBC$? **B**

   (A) 108   (B) 54   (C) 90
   (D) $\frac{189}{2}$ (E) None of these

4. The average of five numbers is 5.1. Four of the numbers are 4.2, 5.7, 4.9 and 5.4. Which is the fifth number? **D**
   (A) 5.06   (B) 5.14   (C) 5.1
   (D) 5.3   (E) None of these

5. A wheel rotates m times each minute. How many degrees does it rotate in t seconds? **B**

   (A) $\frac{360\,m}{t}$ (B) $6\,mt$ (C) $\frac{60\,t}{m}$

   (D) $\frac{60\,m}{t}$ (E) $\frac{360\,t}{m}$

Directions: In each question you are to *compare* a Quantity I and a Quantity II. Choose your answer in the following way. Choose:
(A) if Quantity I is greater than II,
(B) if Quantity II is greater than I,
(C) if Quantity I = Quantity II,
(D) if the relationship cannot be determined.

6.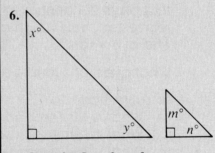

   Quantity I $x° + y°$
   Quantity II $m° + n°$ **C**

7.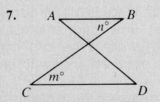

   $\overline{AB}$ is parallel to $\overline{CD}$ **C**

   Quantity I m Quantity II n

8. Quantity I   area of circle with diameter length $\frac{2\sqrt{\pi}}{\pi}$

   Quantity II   area of a square whose side is 1. **C**

18 TRIGONOMETRIC GRAPHS AND IDENTITIES

Read The Problem Carefully

PROBLEM: Ms Fernandez's starting salary as an air traffic controller is $22,000. She is 47 years of age and plans to retire after 15 years. It is estimated that her average yearly wage increase will be 8% per year. Her annual retirement income is computed by taking 30% of her final 3-year average salary. What is Ms Fernandez's monthly retirement income?

Ms Fernandez plans to invest 10% of her net annual salary (deduct 30% of her gross annual salary) in an investment fund that pays 9% annual interest. If the accumulated interest is reinvested, how much money will she have in the fund at the end of 6 years?

What questions must be answered?

To solve part 1:
(a) What is Ms Fernandez's yearly salary after her raise?
(b) What is her yearly salary for her last 3 years of employment?
(c) What is her average salary for the last 3 years?

To solve part 2:
(d) What is Ms Fernandez's net annual salary?
(e) How much interest will be reinvested each year?
(f)   What is the total amount of money, both principal and interest, that will be invested each year?

PROJECT

Represent the data in a table and solve the problem. (Hint: To calculate yearly salary, multiply the preceding salary by 1.08.)

	1	2	3	4 … 15
Salary	$22,000	$23,760	$25,660.80	
Principal		$1,540.00	$3,341.80	
Interest		138.60	300.76	
Total		$1,678.60	$3,642.56	

18.1 Graphing $y = \sin x$ and $y = \cos x$

OBJECTIVES ▶ To graph $y = \sin x$ and $y = \cos x$
To determine the amplitude and the period of the sine and the cosine functions
To determine the quadrants in which the sin and cos functions increase or decrease

To graph the function $y = \sin x$, make a table of values by choosing special degree measures for x and finding corresponding values for y. The graph of $y = \sin x$ for $-360° \leq x \leq 360°$ is shown below.

x	$-360°$	$-270°$	$-180°$	$-90°$	$0°$	$90°$	$180°$	$270°$	$360°$
$\sin x$	0	1	0	-1	0	1	0	-1	0

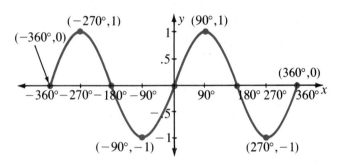

Note that the maximum value of the function is 1 and that this occurs when $x = 90°$ and when $x = -270°$. The amplitude of a trig function is its maximum value. The amplitude of the sine function is 1.

A *periodic function* is one that repeats itself. Note that the sine function is a periodic function with a period of 360°.

Example 1 Graph $y = \cos x$ for $-360° \leq x \leq 360°$ and determine its amplitude and period.

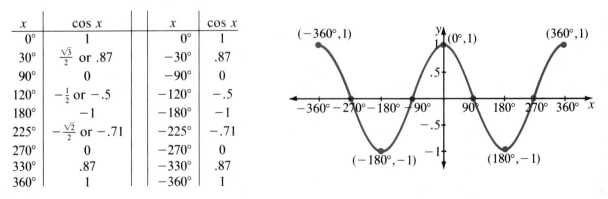

x	$\cos x$		x	$\cos x$
$0°$	1		$0°$	1
$30°$	$\frac{\sqrt{3}}{2}$ or .87		$-30°$	.87
$90°$	0		$-90°$	0
$120°$	$-\frac{1}{2}$ or $-.5$		$-120°$	$-.5$
$180°$	-1		$-180°$	-1
$225°$	$-\frac{\sqrt{2}}{2}$ or $-.71$		$-225°$	$-.71$
$270°$	0		$-270°$	0
$330°$	.87		$-330°$	.87
$360°$	1		$-360°$	1

Thus, the amplitude of the cosine function is 1 and the period is 360°.

By looking at the graphs of $y = \sin x$ and $y = \cos x$, you can find where the sine increases or decreases and where the cosine increases or decreases.

1st quadrant	2nd quadrant	3rd quadrant	4th quadrant
$0° < x < 90°$	$90° < x < 180°$	$180° < x < 270°$	$270° < x < 360°$
sin increases	sin decreases	sin decreases	sin increases
cos decreases	cos decreases	cos increases	cos increases

You have learned that the values of a trig function can be found in a table. The values can also be estimated from a graph. The next example illustrates this.

Example 2 Graph $y = \cos x$ for $0° \leq x \leq 90°$. Estimate $\cos 45°$ to the nearest tenth.

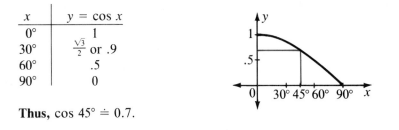

x	$y = \cos x$
$0°$	1
$30°$	$\frac{\sqrt{3}}{2}$ or $.9$
$60°$	$.5$
$90°$	0

Thus, $\cos 45° \doteq 0.7$.

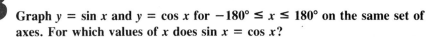

The next example illustrates how to solve a system of two trigonometric equations graphically.

Example 3 Graph $y = \sin x$ and $y = \cos x$ for $-180° \leq x \leq 180°$ on the same set of axes. For which values of x does $\sin x = \cos x$?

x	$y = \sin x$	$y = \cos x$
$-30°$	$-.5$	$.9$
$-90°$	-1	0
$-120°$	$-.9$	$-.5$
$-180°$	0	-1
$0°$	0	1
$30°$	$.5$	$.9$
$90°$	1	0
$120°$	$.9$	$-.5$
$180°$	0	-1

Thus, for $x = -135°$ or $x = 45°$, $\sin x = \cos x$.

Written Exercises

(A) Complete the chart.

	$y = \sin x$	$y = \cos x$
1. Amplitude	1	1
2. Period	360°	360°
3. Maximum value	1	1
4. Minimum value	−1	−1
5. Quadrants where function increases	I & IV	III & IV
6. Quadrants where function decreases	II & III	I & II

Sketch $y = \sin x$ for $0° \leq x \leq 180°$. Estimate each of the following.

7. $\sin 20°$ **0.35**   8. $\sin 65°$ **0.9**   9. $\sin 75°$ **0.97**   10. $\sin 140°$ **0.65**   11. $\sin 160°$ **0.34**

Sketch $y = \cos x$ for $0° \leq x \leq 180°$. Estimate each of the following.

12. $\cos 40°$ **0.75**   13. $\cos 70°$ **0.34**   14. $\cos 100°$ **−0.2**   15. $\cos 130°$ **−0.64**   16. $\cos 170°$ **−0.98**

(B) 17. Sketch $y = \sin x$ and $y = \cos x$ for $0° \leq x \leq 360°$ on the same set of axes. For which values of x is $\sin x = \cos x$? **45°, 225°**

18. Sketch $y = \sin x$ and $y = \cos x$ for $-360° \leq x \leq 180°$ on the same set of axes. For which values of x is $\sin x = \cos x$? **−135°, −315°, 45°**

19. Sketch $y = \sin x$ and $y = \cos x$ for $-180° \leq x \leq 360°$ on the same set of axes. For which values of x is $\sin x = \cos x$? **−135°, 45°, 225°**

20. Sketch $y = \sin x$ and $y = \cos x$ for $-360° \leq x \leq 0°$ on the same set of axes. For which values of x is $\sin x = \cos x$? **−315°, −135°**

(C) Sketch the graph for $0° \leq x \leq 360°$. For Ex. 21–28, see TE Answer Section.

21. $y = -\cos x$ 22. $y = \sin(-x)$ 23. $y = -\sin x$ 24. $y = \cos(-x)$

25. $y = \sec x$ 26. $y = -\sec x$ 27. $y = \csc x$ 28. $y = \csc(-x)$

29. Sketch $y = \sin(-x)$ and $y = \cos(-x)$ for $-180° \leq x \leq 180°$ on the same set of axes. For which values of x is $\sin(-x) = \cos(-x)$? **−45°, 135°**

30. Sketch $y = -\sin x$ and $y = -\cos x$ for $-180° \leq x \leq 180°$ on the same set of axes. For which values of x is $-\sin x = -\cos x$? **−135°, 45°**

A Challenge To You

In right triangle PRQ, the hypotenuse $\overline{QR}$ measures 20 cm and leg $\overline{PQ}$ measures 10 cm. Points S and T are on $\overline{QR}$ such that $\overline{SP}$ and $\overline{TP}$ trisect angle P. Find the length of $\overline{SP}$. **$5\sqrt{3}$ cm**

Cumulative Review

Find the distance between the given points. Answers should be in simplified radical form.

1. $A(3, -2)$, $B(-6, 1)$ $3\sqrt{10}$ 2. $A(-7, 8)$, $B(7, -3)$ $\sqrt{317}$ 3. $A(12, -8)$, $B(4, -6)$ $2\sqrt{17}$

18.2 Determining Amplitude

OBJECTIVE ▶ **To determine the amplitude of the sine and cosine functions**

You have learned that the amplitude for $y = \sin x$ and $y = \cos x$ is their maximum value, 1. You will now learn how multiplying $\sin x$ or $\cos x$ by a constant changes its amplitude.

Example 1 Sketch $y = 2 \sin x$ and $y = \sin x$ for $-180° \le x \le 360°$ on the same set of axes. Determine the period and amplitude for each function.

Make a table of values. Multiply $\sin x$ values by 2.

x	$y = \sin x$	$y = 2 \sin x$
0°	0	0
90°	1	2
180°	0	0
270°	−1	−2
360°	0	0
−90°	−1	−2
−180°	0	0

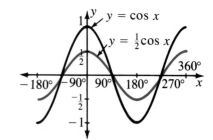

Thus, amplitude for $y = \sin x$ is 1.   Period for $y = \sin x$ is 360°.
  Amplitude for $y = 2 \sin x$ is 2.   Period for $y = 2 \sin x$ is 360°.

Example 2 Sketch $y = \frac{1}{2} \cos x$ and $y = \cos x$ for $-180° \le x \le 360°$ on the same set of axes. Determine the period and amplitude for each function.

Make a table of values. Multiply $\cos x$ values by $\frac{1}{2}$.

x	$y = \cos x$	$y = \frac{1}{2} \cos x$
0°	1	$\frac{1}{2}$
90°	0	0
180°	−1	$-\frac{1}{2}$
270°	0	0
360°	1	$\frac{1}{2}$
−90°	0	0
−180°	−1	$-\frac{1}{2}$

Thus, amplitude for $y = \cos x$ is 1.   Period for $y = \cos x$ is 360°.
  Amplitude for $y = \frac{1}{2} \cos x$ is $\frac{1}{2}$.   Period for $y = \frac{1}{2} \cos x$ is 360°.

Example 3 Sketch $y = 3 \cos x$ and $y = \frac{1}{2} \cos x$ for $-180° \le x \le 360°$ on the same set of axes. Determine the period and amplitude for each function.

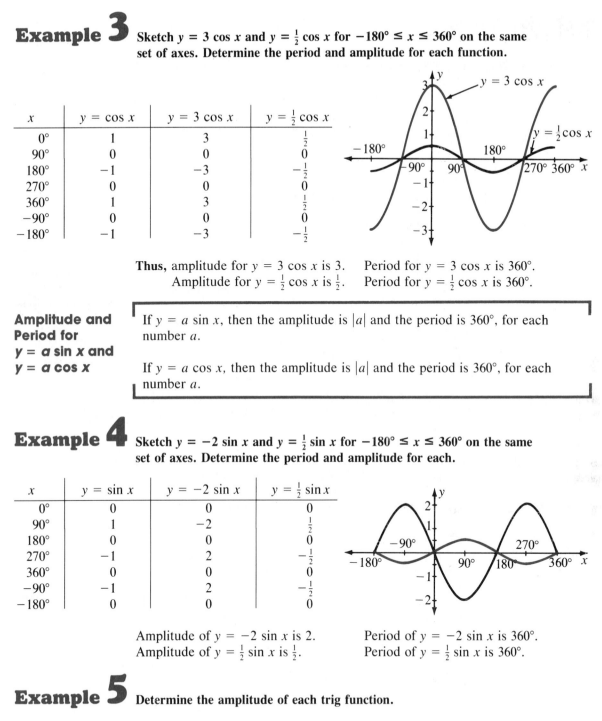

x	$y = \cos x$	$y = 3 \cos x$	$y = \frac{1}{2} \cos x$
0°	1	3	$\frac{1}{2}$
90°	0	0	0
180°	-1	-3	$-\frac{1}{2}$
270°	0	0	0
360°	1	3	$\frac{1}{2}$
$-90°$	0	0	0
$-180°$	-1	-3	$-\frac{1}{2}$

Thus, amplitude for $y = 3 \cos x$ is 3. Period for $y = 3 \cos x$ is 360°.
Amplitude for $y = \frac{1}{2} \cos x$ is $\frac{1}{2}$. Period for $y = \frac{1}{2} \cos x$ is 360°.

Amplitude and Period for $y = a \sin x$ and $y = a \cos x$

If $y = a \sin x$, then the amplitude is $|a|$ and the period is 360°, for each number a.

If $y = a \cos x$, then the amplitude is $|a|$ and the period is 360°, for each number a.

Example 4 Sketch $y = -2 \sin x$ and $y = \frac{1}{2} \sin x$ for $-180° \le x \le 360°$ on the same set of axes. Determine the period and amplitude for each.

x	$y = \sin x$	$y = -2 \sin x$	$y = \frac{1}{2} \sin x$
0°	0	0	0
90°	1	-2	$\frac{1}{2}$
180°	0	0	0
270°	-1	2	$-\frac{1}{2}$
360°	0	0	0
$-90°$	-1	2	$-\frac{1}{2}$
$-180°$	0	0	0

Amplitude of $y = -2 \sin x$ is 2.   Period of $y = -2 \sin x$ is 360°.
Amplitude of $y = \frac{1}{2} \sin x$ is $\frac{1}{2}$.   Period of $y = \frac{1}{2} \sin x$ is 360°.

Example 5 Determine the amplitude of each trig function.

$y = 12 \sin x$ $\qquad$ $y = -6 \cos x$ $\qquad$ $y = -\frac{7}{2} \cos x$
$\downarrow$ $\qquad\qquad$ $\downarrow$ $\qquad\qquad\quad$ $\downarrow$
Amplitude: 12 $\qquad$ Amplitude: 6 $\qquad$ Amplitude: $\frac{7}{2}$

Oral Exercises

Determine the amplitude of each trig function.

1. $y = 5 \cos x$ **5**
2. $y = -2 \sin x$ **2**
3. $y = \frac{1}{3} \sin x$ **$\frac{1}{3}$**
4. $y = \frac{1}{5} \cos x$ **$\frac{1}{5}$**
5. $y = 15 \sin x$ **15**
6. $y = 12 \cos x$ **12**
7. $y = -\frac{4}{5} \cos x$ **$\frac{4}{5}$**
8. $y = -\frac{2}{3} \sin x$ **$\frac{2}{3}$**

Written Exercises

Ⓐ **Sketch the graph for $0° \leq x \leq 360°$. Determine the period and amplitude.**

1. $y = 3 \cos x$ **360°, 3**
2. $y = 2 \sin x$ **360°, 2**
3. $y = \frac{1}{2} \sin x$ **360°, $\frac{1}{2}$**
4. $y = \frac{1}{3} \sin x$ **360°, $\frac{1}{3}$**
5. $y = 4 \sin x$ **360°, 4**
6. $y = 5 \cos x$ **360°, 5**
7. $y = \frac{3}{4} \sin x$ **360°, $\frac{3}{4}$**
8. $y = \frac{4}{5} \cos x$ **360°, $\frac{4}{5}$**

9. Sketch $y = 2 \cos x$ and $y = \frac{1}{2} \cos x$ for $-360° \leq x \leq 360°$ on the same set of axes. Determine the period and the amplitude for each. **360°, 2; 360°, $\frac{1}{2}$**

10. Sketch $y = 3 \sin x$ and $y = \frac{1}{2} \sin x$ for $-360° \leq x \leq 360°$ on the same set of axes. Determine the period and the amplitude for each. **360°, 3; 360°, $\frac{1}{2}$**

Ⓑ **Sketch the graph for $-360° \leq x \leq 360°$. Determine the period and amplitude.**

11. $y = -\frac{1}{2} \cos x$ **360°, $\frac{1}{2}$**
12. $y = -2 \sin x$ **360°, 2**
13. $y = -\frac{1}{3} \sin x$ **360°, $\frac{1}{3}$**
14. $y = -3 \cos x$ **360°, 3**
15. $y = -3 \sin x$ **360°, 3**
16. $y = -4 \cos x$ **360°, 4**
17. $y = -\frac{2}{5} \cos x$ **360°, $\frac{2}{5}$**
18. $y = -\frac{1}{2} \sin x$ **360°, $\frac{1}{2}$**

19. Sketch $y = -\frac{1}{2} \sin x$ and $y = 2 \cos (-x)$ for $0° \leq x \leq 360°$ on the same set of axes. For how many values of x does $-\frac{1}{2} \sin x = 2 \cos (-x)$? **2**

20. Sketch $y = -2 \cos x$ and $y = 2 \sin x$ for $0° \leq x \leq 360°$ on the same set of axes. For how many values of x does $-2 \cos x = 2 \sin x$? **2**

Ⓒ **Sketch the graph for $-360° \leq x \leq 360°$. Determine the period and amplitude.**

21. $y = 2 \csc x$ **360°, none**
22. $y = -\frac{1}{2} \csc x$ **360°, none**
23. $y = \frac{1}{2} \sec x$ **360°, none**
24. $y = -2 \sec x$ **360°, none**

25. Sketch $y = -2 \sin x$ and $y = -\frac{1}{2} \sin x$ for $0° \leq x \leq 360°$ on the same set of axes. Estimate the values of x for which $-2 \sin x = -\frac{1}{2} \sin x$. **0°, 180°, 360°**

26. Sketch $y = -\frac{1}{2} \cos x$ and $y = -2 \cos x$ for $0° \leq x \leq 360°$ on the same set of axes. Estimate the values of x for which $-\frac{1}{2} \cos x = -2 \cos x$. **90°, 270°**

27. Sketch $y = -3 \cos x$ and $y = -2 \sin x$ for $-360° \leq x \leq 360°$ on the same set of axes. Estimate the values of x for which $-3 \cos x = -2 \sin x$. **56°, 236°, −124°, −304°**

28. Sketch $y = -2 \cos x$ and $y = \frac{1}{2} \sin x$ for $-360° \leq x \leq 360°$ on the same set of axes. Estimate the values of x for which $-2 \cos x = \frac{1}{2} \sin x$. **104°, 284°, −76°, −256°**

29. Sketch $y = \frac{1}{2} \sec x$ and $y = 2 \cos x$ for $0° \leq x \leq 360°$ on the same set of axes. Estimate the values of x for which $\frac{1}{2} \sec x = 2 \cos x$. **60°, 120°, 240°, 300°**

30. Sketch $y = \frac{1}{3} \csc x$ and $y = 2 \cos x$ for $0° \leq x \leq 360°$ on the same set of axes. Estimate the values of x for which $\frac{1}{3} \csc x = 2 \cos x$. **10°, 190°, 57°, 237°**

18.3 Determining Period

OBJECTIVE ▶ **To determine the period for $y = \sin bx$ and $y = \cos bx$**

You have learned that the period for $y = \sin x$ and $y = \cos x$ is 360°. You will now learn how multiplying the measure of an angle by a constant changes the period.

Example 1 Sketch $y = \cos 2x$ and $y = \cos x$ for $0° \le x \le 360°$ on the same set of axes. Determine the period and amplitude of each function.

x	$2x$	$y = \cos 2x$
0°	0°	1
30°	60°	$\frac{1}{2}$
45°	90°	0
90°	180°	-1
135°	270°	0
180°	360°	1
225°	450°	0
270°	540°	-1
315°	630°	0
360°	720°	1

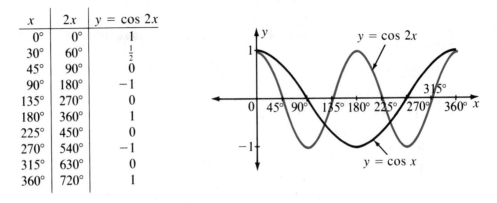

The graph of $y = \cos 2x$ completes 2 cycles from 0° to 360°. It completes one cycle every 180°. Note: $\frac{360°}{2} = 180°$.

Thus, period for $y = \cos x$ is 360°. Amplitude for $y = \cos x$ is 1.
Period for $y = \cos 2x$ is 180°. Amplitude for $y = \cos 2x$ is 1.

Example 2 Sketch $y = \sin \frac{1}{2} x$ and $y = \sin x$ for $0° \le x \le 720°$ on the same set of axes. Determine the period and amplitude of each function.

x	$\frac{1}{2} x$	$y = \sin \frac{1}{2} x$
0°	0°	0
60°	30°	$\frac{1}{2}$
90°	45°	$\frac{\sqrt{2}}{2}$
180°	90°	1
360°	180°	0
540°	270°	-1
720°	360°	0

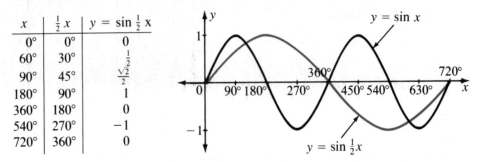

The graph of $y = \sin \frac{1}{2} x$ completes $\frac{1}{2}$ cycle from 0° to 360°. It completes one cycle every 720°. Note: $\dfrac{360°}{\frac{1}{2}} = 720°$.

Thus, period for $y = \sin x$ is 360°. Amplitude for $y = \sin x$ is 1.
Period for $y = \sin \frac{1}{2} x$ is 720°. Amplitude for $y = \sin \frac{1}{2} x$ is 1.

Example 3

Sketch $y = \sin 3x$ and $y = \sin x$ for $0° \le x \le 360°$ on the same set of axes. Determine the period and amplitude for each function.

x	$3x$	$y = \sin 3x$
0°	0°	0
30°	90°	1
60°	180°	0
90°	270°	−1
120°	360°	0
150°	450°	1
180°	540°	0
210°	630°	−1
240°	720°	0
270°	810°	1
300°	900°	0
330°	990°	−1
360°	1080°	0

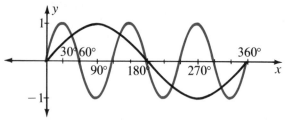

Notice that $y = \sin 3x$ completes 3 cycles from 0° to 360°. It completes one cycle every 120°.

Note: $\dfrac{360°}{3} = 120°$.

Thus, period for $y = \sin 3x$ is 120°. Amplitude for $y = \sin 3x = 1$. Period for $y = \sin x$ is 360°. Amplitude for $y = \sin x = 1$.

Period and Amplitude for $y = \sin bx$ and $y = \cos bx$

If $y = \sin bx$, then the period is $\dfrac{360°}{|b|}$ and the amplitude is 1, for each *real* number $b\,(b \ne 0)$. If $y = \cos bx$, then the period is $\dfrac{360°}{|b|}$ and the amplitude is 1, for each *real* number $b\,(b \ne 0)$. Each function completes $|b|$ cycles in 360°.

Example 4

Sketch $y = \sin\left(-\frac{1}{2}x\right)$ and $y = \sin\frac{1}{2}x$ for $0° \le x \le 720°$ on the same set of axes. Determine the period and amplitude for each function.

x	$-\frac{1}{2}x$	$y = \sin\left(-\frac{1}{2}x\right)$
0°	0°	0
180°	−90°	−1
360°	−180°	0
540°	−270°	1
720°	−360°	0

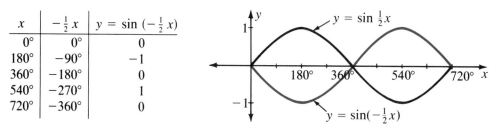

Since $\sin(-u) = -\sin u$, $\sin\left(-\frac{1}{2}x\right) = -\sin\frac{1}{2}x$. Therefore, the graph of $y = \sin\left(-\frac{1}{2}x\right)$ is symmetric to the graph of $y = \sin\frac{1}{2}x$. The x-axis is the axis of symmetry. Note: $\dfrac{360°}{\frac{1}{2}} = 720°$.

Thus, period for $y = \sin\frac{1}{2}x$ and $\sin\left(-\frac{1}{2}x\right)$ is 720°. Amplitude for $y = \sin\frac{1}{2}x$ and $\sin\left(-\frac{1}{2}x\right)$ is 1.

Example 5 Determine the period of each trig function.

$$y = \sin 6x$$
$$\text{Period: } \frac{360°}{|6|} = 60°$$

$$y = \cos\left(-\tfrac{1}{3}x\right)$$
$$\text{Period: } \frac{360°}{\left|-\tfrac{1}{3}\right|} = 1080°$$

$$y = \sin \tfrac{2}{3}x$$
$$\text{Period: } \frac{360°}{\left|\tfrac{2}{3}\right|} = 540°$$

Oral Exercises _____

Determine the period of each trig function.

1. $y = \sin x$ **360°**
2. $y = \cos x$ **360°**
3. $y = \sin \tfrac{1}{2}x$ **720°**
4. $y = \cos \tfrac{1}{2}x$ **720°**
5. $y = \cos 2x$ **180°**
6. $y = \sin \tfrac{1}{3}x$ **1,080°**
7. $y = \cos 9x$ **40°**
8. $y = \sin 12x$ **30°**

Written Exercises _____

Ⓐ Sketch the graph for $0° \leq x \leq 360°$. Determine the period and amplitude.

1. $y = \cos 2x$ **180°, 1**
2. $y = \cos \tfrac{1}{2}x$ **720°, 1**
3. $y = \sin 2x$ **180°, 1**
4. $y = \sin \tfrac{1}{2}x$ **720°, 1**
5. $y = \sin \tfrac{1}{3}x$ **1080°, 1**
6. $y = \sin 3x$ **120°, 1**
7. $y = \cos \tfrac{1}{3}x$ **1080°, 1**
8. $y = \cos 3x$ **120°, 1**
9. $y = \cos 4x$ **90°, 1**
10. $y = \sin \tfrac{1}{4}x$ **1440°, 1**
11. $y = \cos \tfrac{1}{4}x$ **1440°, 1**
12. $y = \sin 4x$ **90°, 1**

Ⓑ 13. $y = \sin(-2x)$ **180°, 1** 14. $y = \cos(-2x)$
15. $y = \cos\left(-\tfrac{1}{2}x\right)$
16. $y = \sin\left(-\tfrac{1}{3}x\right)$ **1080°, 1**
17. $y = \cos\left(-\tfrac{3}{2}x\right)$
18. $y = \sin\left(-\tfrac{5}{4}x\right)$ **288°, 1** 19. $y = \sin(-3x)$ **120°, 1** 20. $y = \cos(-3x)$ **120°, 1**
14. **180°, 1** 15. **720°, 1** 17. **240°, 1**

21. Sketch $y = \cos 2x$ and $y = \sin 2x$ for   **4**
   $0° \leq x \leq 360°$ on the same set of axes. For
   how many values of x does $\cos 2x = \sin 2x$?

22. Sketch $y = \sin \tfrac{1}{2}x$ and $y = \cos \tfrac{1}{2}x$ for   **1**
   $0° \leq x \leq 360°$ on the same set of axes. For
   how many values of x does $\sin \tfrac{1}{2}x = \cos \tfrac{1}{2}x$?

For Exercises 25–26, see TE Answer Section.

Ⓒ Sketch the graph for $0° \leq x \leq 360°$. Determine the period and amplitude.

23. $y = \sec 2x$ **180°, none** 24. $y = \csc 3x$ **120°, none** 25. $y = \sec \tfrac{1}{2}x$
26. $y = \csc(-x)$

27. Sketch the graph of $y = \sec(-2x)$ and $y = \cos(-2x)$ in the interval 0° to
   360° on the same set of axes. For how many values of x does $\sec(-2x) = \cos(-2x)$? **5**

➔ A Challenge To You ══════════

Solve for all real values of x and y such that:
$2 \cdot 3^x = 81y$ and $2^x = 8y$. **x = 4, y = 2**

Cumulative Review _____

1. The height of a triangle is twice the length
   of its base. The area is 144 cm². Find the
   length of the base and the height.
   12 cm, 24 cm

2. The height of a triangle is 5 dm less than
   the length of its base. The area is 12 dm².
   Find the length of the base and the height.
   8 dm, 3 dm

DETERMINING PERIOD

18.4 Change of Period and Amplitude

OBJECTIVES ▶ To sketch the functions defined by $y = a \sin bx$ and $y = a \cos bx$
To solve a system of two trigonometric equations graphically

Recall that for the function defined by $y = 3 \sin x$, the amplitude is 3 and the period is 360°. In general, the amplitude for $y = a \sin x$ and $y = a \cos x$ is $|a|$. Also recall that for the function defined by $y = \cos \frac{1}{2}x$, the amplitude is 1 and the period is $\frac{360°}{\frac{1}{2}}$, or 720°. In general, the period of $y = \sin bx$ and $y = \cos bx$ is $\frac{360°}{|b|}$.

Example 1 Sketch $y = \frac{1}{2} \cos 3x$ for $0° \le x \le 360°$.

Period of $y = \frac{1}{2} \cos 3x$ is $\frac{360°}{3}$, or 120°. Amplitude of $y = \frac{1}{2} \cos 3x$ is $\frac{1}{2}$.

x	$3x$	$\cos 3x$	$y = \frac{1}{2}\cos 3x$
0°	0°	1	$\frac{1}{2}$
30°	90°	0	0
60°	180°	−1	$-\frac{1}{2}$
90°	270°	0	0
120°	360°	1	$\frac{1}{2}$
150°	450°	0	0
180°	540°	−1	$-\frac{1}{2}$
210°	630°	0	0
240°	720°	1	$\frac{1}{2}$
270°	810°	0	0
300°	900°	−1	$-\frac{1}{2}$
330°	990°	0	0
360°	1080°	1	$\frac{1}{2}$

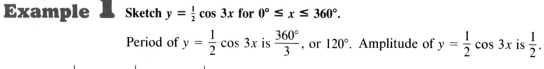

Example 2 Sketch $y = 3 \sin \frac{1}{2}x$ for $0° \le x \le 720°$.

Period of $y = 3 \sin \frac{1}{2}x$ is $\frac{360°}{\frac{1}{2}}$, or 720°.

Amplitude of $y = 3 \sin \frac{1}{2}x$ is 3.

x	$\frac{1}{2}x$	$\sin \frac{1}{2}x$	$y = 3 \sin \frac{1}{2}x$
0°	0°	0	0
180°	90°	1	3
360°	180°	0	0
540°	270°	−1	−3
720°	360°	0	0

As you have learned, a system of algebraic equations may have some common solutions or no common solution. You will now study systems of two trigonometric equations. You will learn that there also may be no common solutions or many solutions. Usually, the number of points of intersection depends on the interval in which the functions are to be graphed.

Example 3 Sketch $y = 3 \sin x$ and $y = 2 \cos \frac{1}{2}x$ for $0° \leq x \leq 720°$. For how many values of x does $3 \sin x = 2 \cos \frac{1}{2}x$?

x	$3 \sin x$	$2 \cos \frac{1}{2}x$
0°	0	2
90°	3	$2(\frac{\sqrt{2}}{2})$, or 1.4
180°	0	0
270°	−3	$2(-\frac{\sqrt{2}}{2})$, or −1.4
360°	0	−2
450°	3	$2(-\frac{\sqrt{2}}{2})$, or −1.4
540°	0	0
630°	−3	$2(\frac{\sqrt{2}}{2})$, or 1.4
720°	0	2

Thus, $3 \sin x = 2 \cos \frac{1}{2}x$ for 4 values of x for $0° \leq x \leq 720°$.

Example 4 Sketch $y = -\sin 2x$ and $y = 3 \cos x$ for $-90° \leq x \leq 360°$. For how many values of x does $- \sin 2x = 3 \cos x$?

x	$-\sin 2x$	$3 \cos 2x$
0°	0	3
45°	−1	0
90°	0	−3
135°	1	0
180°	0	3
225°	−1	0
270°	0	−3
315°	1	0
360°	0	3
−45°	1	0
−90°	0	−3

Thus, $-\sin 2x = 3 \cos x$ for 5 values of x for $-90° \leq x \leq 360°$.

Reading in Algebra

Each choice is related to the period or amplitude. Which one or ones don't belong? Defend your choices.

1. $y = 3 \sin 2x$ **c, d**   **a.** 3   **b.** 180°   **c.** 720°   **d.** −3
2. $y = \frac{1}{2} \cos (3x)$ **b, d**   **a.** 120°   **b.** 1080°   **c.** $\frac{1}{2}$ **d.** 180°
3. $y = -2 \sin \frac{1}{2}x$ **a, d**   **a.** 180°   **b.** 720°   **c.** 2   **d.** −2

Written Exercises

(A) Determine the period and amplitude for each of the following.

1. $y = -2 \cos \frac{1}{2}x$ **720°, 2** 2. $y = 3 \sin (-2x)$ **180°, 33.** $y = \frac{1}{2} \sin 2x$ **180°, $\frac{1}{2}$**   4. $y = \frac{1}{4} \cos 4x$ **90°, $\frac{1}{4}$**
5. $y = \frac{1}{3} \sin 9x$ **40°, $\frac{1}{3}$**   6. $y = -3 \cos \frac{1}{3}x$ **1080°, 37.** $y = -2 \sin \frac{1}{2}x$ **720°, 2** 8. $y = 12 \cos \frac{1}{12}x$
4, 320°, 12

Sketch the graph for $0° \leq x \leq 360°$. Determine the period and amplitude.

9. $y = \frac{1}{3} \cos 3x$ **120°, $\frac{1}{3}$** 10. $y = 2 \sin 2x$ **180°, 2**   11. $y = 2 \cos 3x$ **120°, 2** 12. $y = \frac{1}{2} \sin 4x$ **90°, $\frac{1}{2}$**
13. $y = 3 \sin \frac{1}{3}x$ **1080°, 3** 14. $y = \frac{1}{2} \cos 2x$ **180°, $\frac{1}{2}$** 15. $y = 3 \sin 2x$ **180°, 3** 16. $y = 3 \cos \frac{1}{2}x$ **720°, 3**

(B) 17. $y = -2 \sin \frac{1}{2}x$ **720°, 2**   18. $y = -2 \cos \frac{1}{2}x$ **720°, 2**   19. $y = -2 \sin (-\frac{1}{2}x)$ **720°, 2**
20. $y = -\frac{1}{2} \cos 2x$ **180°, $\frac{1}{2}$**   21. $y = -\frac{1}{2} \cos (-2x)$ **180°, $\frac{1}{2}$**   22. $y = -\frac{1}{2} \sin 2x$ **180°, $\frac{1}{2}$**

23. Sketch $y = \cos \frac{1}{2}x$ and $y = 3 \cos x$ for $0° \leq x \leq 360°$ on the same set of axes. For how many values of x does $\cos \frac{1}{2}x = 3 \cos x$? **2**

24. Sketch $y = \cos 2x$ and $y = \frac{1}{2} \sin x$ for $0° \leq x \leq 360°$ on the same set of axes. For how many values of x does $\cos 2x = \frac{1}{2} \sin x$? **4**

25. Sketch $y = -2 \cos x$ and $y = \sin (-\frac{1}{2}x)$ in the interval $-360°$ to $360°$ on the same set of axes. For how many values of x does $-2 \cos x = \sin (-\frac{1}{2}x)$? **4**

26. Sketch $y = \sin (-2x)$ and $y = -\frac{1}{2} \cos x$ in the interval $0°$ to $360°$ on the same set of axes. For how many values of x does $\sin (-2x) = -\frac{1}{2} \cos x$? **4**

(C) Sketch the graph for $0° \leq x \leq 360°$. Determine the period and amplitude.

27. $y = \frac{1}{2} \sec 2x$ **180°, none**   28. $y = 2 \csc 3x$ **120°, none**   29. $y = -2 \sec 3x$ **120°, none**
30. $y = 2 \sec (-2x)$ **180°, none**   31. $y = 2 \sec 2x$ **180°, none**   32. $y = -2 \csc (-\frac{1}{2}x)$ **720°, none**

33. Sketch the graph of $y = -2 \sin (-\frac{1}{2}x)$ and $y = -\frac{1}{2} \cos (-2x)$ in the interval $0°$ to $360°$ on the same set of axes. For how many values of x does $-2 \sin (-\frac{1}{2}x) = -\frac{1}{2} \cos (-2x)$? **0**

34. Sketch the graph of $y = 2 \sec 2x$ and $y = \frac{1}{2} \sec \frac{1}{2}x$ for $0° \leq x \leq 360°$ on the same set of axes. For how many values of x does $2 \sec 2x = \frac{1}{2} \sec \frac{1}{2}x$? **1**

Cumulative Review

Express each as the same function of a positive acute angle.

1. $\sin (-68°)$ **−sin 68°**   2. $\cos 130° 40'$ **−cos 49° 20'**   3. $\sin 305° 18'$ **−sin 54° 42'**

18.5 Graphing $y = \tan x$ and $y = \cot x$

OBJECTIVES ▶ To graph $y = \tan x$ and $y = \cot x$
To determine the amplitude and period for $y = \tan bx$ and $y = \cot bx$
To determine the quadrants in which the tan increases or decreases
and in which the cot increases or decreases

To graph the function $y = \tan x$, make a table of values. After graphing, observe where the function is increasing. Also observe the period and amplitude. The graph of $y = \tan x$ for $0° \le x \le 360°$ is shown below.

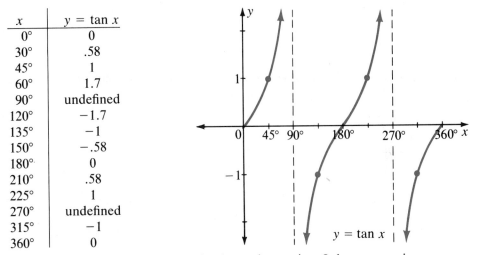

x	$y = \tan x$
0°	0
30°	.58
45°	1
60°	1.7
90°	undefined
120°	−1.7
135°	−1
150°	−.58
180°	0
210°	.58
225°	1
270°	undefined
315°	−1
360°	0

Notice that the tangent function is always increasing. It has no maximum or minimum value, hence it has no amplitude, and a period of 180°.

Example 1 Graph $y = \tan 2x$ for $0° \le x \le 180°$.

x	$2x$	$\tan 2x$
0°	0°	0
22.5°	45°	1
45°	90°	undefined
67.5°	135°	−1
90°	180°	0
112.5°	225°	1
135°	270°	undefined
157.5°	315°	−1
180°	360°	0

The graph of $y = \tan 2x$ completes 2 cycles from 0° to 180°. It completes one cycle every 90°. Note: $\dfrac{180°}{2} = 90°$.

Period for $y = \tan x$ is 180°. Period for $y = \tan 2x$ is 90°.

The function $y = \tan x$ has no amplitude.
The period of $y = \tan x$ is 180°.

If $y = \tan bx$, then the period is $\dfrac{180°}{|b|}$ for each *real* number $b(b \neq 0)$.

Example 2 Sketch $y = \cot x$ for $-180° \leq x \leq 360°$.

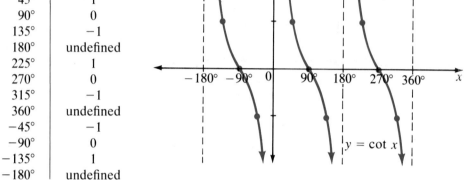

x	$y = \cot x$
0°	undefined
45°	1
90°	0
135°	-1
180°	undefined
225°	1
270°	0
315°	-1
360°	undefined
$-45°$	-1
$-90°$	0
$-135°$	1
$-180°$	undefined

Notice that the cotangent function is always decreasing. It has no maximum or minimum value, hence it has no amplitude. Also notice that the graph repeats itself every 180°.

Example 3 Sketch $y = 2 \cot \frac{1}{2}x$ for $-180° \leq x \leq 360°$.

x	$\frac{1}{2}x$	$\cot \frac{1}{2}x$	$y = 2\cot\frac{1}{2}x$
0°	0°	undefined	undefined
90°	45°	1	2
180°	90°	0	0
270°	135°	-1	-2
360°	180°	undefined	undefined
450°	225°	1	2
540°	270°	0	0
630°	315°	-1	-2
720°	360°	undefined	undefined
$-90°$	$-45°$	-1	-2
$-180°$	$-90°$	0	0

The function $y = \cot x$ has no amplitude.
The period for $y = \cot x$ is 180°.

If $y = \cot bx$, then the period is $\dfrac{180°}{|b|}$ for each real number $b(b \neq 0)$.

Written Exercises

Ⓐ Complete the chart.

	$y = \tan x$	$y = \cot x$
1. Amplitude	None	None
2. Period	180°	180°
3. Maximum value	None	None
4. Minimum value	None	None
5. Quadrants where function increases	I, II, III, IV	None
6. Quadrants where function decreases	None	I, II, III, IV
7. Values for $-180° \le x \le 360°$ where the function is undefined	−90°, 90°, 270°	−180°, 0°, 180°, 360°

Determine the period for each of the following.

8. $y = 2 \tan 3x$ **60°**
9. $y = 4 \cot \frac{1}{2}x$ **360°**
10. $y = -2 \tan 3x$ **60°**
11. $y = -\frac{1}{2} \cot 3x$ **60°**

12. $y = \frac{1}{2} \tan \frac{1}{2}x$ **360°**
13. $y = -\frac{1}{2} \cot 2x$ **90°**
14. $y = 3 \tan \frac{1}{3}x$ **540°**
15. $y = -6 \cot \frac{1}{3}x$ **540°**

16. $y = -6 \cot (-2x)$ **90°**
17. $y = -\frac{1}{2} \tan (-\frac{1}{2}x)$ **360°**
18. $y = -\frac{1}{4} \cot (-\frac{1}{3}x)$ **540°**

Sketch the graph in the interval $-90° \le x \le 360°$. Determine the period.

19. $y = \tan \frac{1}{2}x$ **360°**
20. $y = \cot 2x$ **90°**
21. $y = \tan 3x$ **60°**
22. $y = \cot \frac{1}{2}x$ **360°**

23. $y = 2 \cot 2x$ **90°**
24. $y = \frac{1}{2} \tan 2x$ **90°**
25. $y = 2 \tan \frac{1}{2}x$ **360°**
26. $y = 4 \cot 3x$ **60°**

Ⓑ **27.** $y = -2 \tan (-2x)$ **90°**
28. $y = -\frac{1}{2} \cot (-2x)$ **90°**
29. $y = -3 \tan (-\frac{1}{2}x)$ **360°**

30. $y = -\frac{1}{2} \cot (3x)$ **60°**
31. $y = 6 \tan (-\frac{1}{3}x)$ **540°**
32. $y = -\cot (-\frac{1}{2}x)$ **360°**

33. Sketch $y = \cot \frac{1}{2}x$ and $y = \tan 2x$ for $0° \le x \le 360°$ on the same set of axes. For how many values of x does $\cot \frac{1}{2}x = \tan 2x$? **5**

34. Sketch $y = 2 \tan \frac{1}{2}x$ and $y = \frac{1}{2} \cot 2x$ for $0° \le x \le 360°$ on the same set of axes. For how many values of x does $2 \tan \frac{1}{2}x = \frac{1}{2} \cot 2x$? **4**

Ⓒ **35.** Sketch $y = -\tan (-\frac{1}{2}x)$ and $y = -2 \cot x$ for $0° \le x \le 360°$ on the same set of axes. For how many values of x does $-2 \cot x = -\tan (-\frac{1}{2}x)$? **2**

36. Sketch $y = -\frac{1}{2} \tan (-2x)$ and $y = \cot (-2x)$ for $0° \le x \le 360°$ on the same set of axes. For how many values of x does $-\frac{1}{2} \tan (-2x) = \cot (-2x)$? **0**

37. Sketch $y = \tan 2x$ and $y = \cot \frac{1}{2}x$ for $0° \le x \le 360°$ on the same set of axes. Estimate the values of x for which $\tan 2x = \cot \frac{1}{2}x$. **36°, 108°, 180°, 252°, 324°**

38. Sketch $y = -\tan 2x$ and $y = \sin \frac{1}{2}x$ for $0° \le x \le 360°$ on the same set of axes. Estimate the values of x for which $-\tan 2x = \sin \frac{1}{2}x$. **75°, 160°, 250°, 0°, 360°**

➤ A Challenge To You

$S_n = 1 - 2 + 3 - 4 + 5 - 6 + \ldots + (-1)^{n-1}n$ as $n = 1, 2, 3, 4, \ldots$, find $S_{25} + S_{36} + S_{60}$. **−35**

18.6 Finding Logarithms of Trigonometric Functions

OBJECTIVES ▶ To find logarithms of the sin, cos, tan, and cot of any degree measure using a log-trig table
To find the degree measure when the log-trig value is given
To interpolate using a log-trig table

In an earlier chapter you learned how to do computations with logarithms. Recall the following:

$$\log \frac{a}{b} = \log a - \log b$$

$$\log a \cdot b = \log a + \log b$$
$$\log a^n = n \log a$$
$$\log \sqrt[n]{a} = \frac{1}{n} \log a$$

Thus, to find $N = \dfrac{\sqrt[4]{(34.5) \times (7.3)^3}}{186.4}$ using logs, write

$\log N = \dfrac{1}{4}\left[(\log (34.5) + 3 \log 7.3)\right] - \log 186.4$ and solve.

The following examples illustrate the use of log-trig tables.

Example 1 Find log tan 28° 10′ and log cos 27° 40′.

The log-trig functions at the top of the table must be used with degree measures in the left-hand column. A portion of a log-trig table is shown below.

Logarithms of Trigonometric Functions

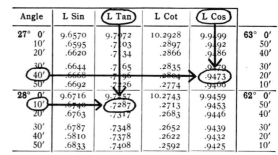

Angle	L Sin	L Tan	L Cot	L Cos	
27° 0′	9.6570	9.7072	10.2928	9.9499	**63° 0′**
10′	.6595	.7103	.2897	.9492	50′
20′	.6620	.7134	.2866	.9486	40′
30′	.6644	.7165	.2835	.9479	30′
40′	.6668	.7196	.2804	.9473	20′
50′	.6692	.7226	.2774	.9466	10′
28° 0′	9.6716	9.7257	10.2743	9.9459	**62° 0′**
10′	.6740	.7287	.2713	.9453	50′
20′	.6763	.7317	.2683	.9446	40′
30′	.6787	.7348	.2652	.9439	30′
40′	.6810	.7378	.2622	.9432	20′
50′	.6833	.7408	.2592	.9425	10′

* Subtract 10 from each entry in this table to obtain the proper logarithm of the indicated trigonometric function.

To find log tan 28° 10′ use the left-hand column and read across under L Tan (log tan) column. The log cos 27° 40′ can be found by reading across 27° 40′ under the L Cos (log cos) column. After reading the value from the table, subtract 10.

Thus, log tan 28° 10′ = 9.7287 − 10, and log cos 27° 40′ = 9.9473 − 10.

Example 2

Find log sin 46° 40′ and log cot 45° 50′.

Use the right column and the bottom column heads.

43° 0′	9.8338	9.9697	10.0303	9.8641	47° 0′
10′	.8351	.9722	.0278	.8629	50′
20′	.8365	.9747	.0253	.8618	40′
30′	.8378	.9772	.0228	.8606	30′
40′	.8391	.9798	.0202	.8594	20′
50′	.8405	.9823	.0177	.8582	10′
44° 0′	9.8418	9.9848	10.0152	9.8569	46° 0′
10′	.8431	.9874	.0126	.8557	50′
20′	.8444	.9899	.0101	.8545	40′
30′	.8457	.9924	.0076	.8532	30′
40′	.8469	.9949	.0051	.8520	20′
50′	.8482	9.9975	.0025	.8507	10′
45° 0′	9.8495	10.0000	10.0000	9.8495	45° 0′
	L Cos	L Cot	L Tan	L Sin	Angle

Thus, log sin 46° 40′ = 9.8618 − 10 and log cot 45° 50′ = 9.9874 − 10.

Example 3

Log sin u = 9.2251 − 10   Log tan u = .7320
Find u, $u <$ 90°.   Find u, $u <$ 90°.

Angle	L Sin	L Tan	L Cot	L Cos	
9° 0′	9.1943	9.1997	10.8003	9.9946	81° 0′
10′	.2022	.2078	.7922	.9944	50′
20′	.2100	.2158	.7842	.9942	40′
30′	.2176	.2236	.7764	.9940	30′
40′	.2251	.2313	.7687	.9938	20′
50′	.2324	.2389	.7611	.9936	10′
10° 0′	9.2397	9.2463	10.7537	9.9934	80° 0′
10′	.2468	.2536	.7464	.9931	50′
20′	.2538	.2609	.7391	.9929	40′
30′	.2606	.2680	.7320	.9927	30′
40′	.2674	.2750	.7250	.9924	20′
50′	.2740	.2819	.7181	.9922	10′
	L Cos	L Cot	L Tan	L Sin	Angle

Thus, when log sin u = 9.2251 − 10, u = 9° 40′. When log tan u = .7320, u = 79° 30′.

Example 4

Find log cos 36° 28′.

36° 28′ lies between the values 36° 20′ and 36° 30′. Make a table.

$$10 \left[8 \left[\begin{array}{ll} \text{Measure} & \text{log cosine} \\ 36°\,20′ & .9061 \\ 36°\,28′ & \\ 36°\,30′ & .9052 \end{array} \right] n \right] -.0009$$

$$\frac{8}{10} = \frac{n}{-.0009} \text{ or } 10n = -.0072$$
$$n = -.00072, \text{ or } n \doteq -.0007$$
$$.9061 + (-.0007) = .9054$$

Thus, log cos 36° 28′ = 9.9054 − 10.

You will now learn how to do computations with trig functions using logs.

Example 5 Find the value of $\dfrac{(39.6)^3 \sin 73° 10'}{\sqrt[3]{0.315}}$ to four significant digits.

Use logarithms.

Let $s = \dfrac{(39.6)^3 \sin 73° 10'}{\sqrt[3]{0.315}}$

$$\log s = 3 \log 39.6 + \log \sin 73° 10' - \tfrac{1}{3} \log 0.315$$
$$= 3(1.5977) + 9.9810 - 10 - \tfrac{1}{3}(9.4983 - 10)$$
$$= 4.7931 + 9.9810 - 10 - \tfrac{1}{3}(29.4983 - 30)$$
$$= 4.7741 - (9.8328 - 10)$$
$$\log s = 4.9413$$

Thus, $s = 87,360.$

Written Exercises

For Ex. 1–21, see TE Answer Section.

(A) **Find the value of each of the following.**

1. log sin 53° 40'
2. log cot 76° 50'
3. log cos 65° 20'
4. log tan 34° 10'
5. log cos 18° 30'
6. log sin 22° 36'
7. log tan 73° 44'
8. log cot 12° 58'
9. log tan 27° 25'
10. log cos 46° 17'
11. log sin 62° 33'
12. log cos 86° 42'

(B) **Find u, $0° < u < 90°$, for each of the following.**

13. log cos u = 9.9446 − 10
14. log tan u = 9.8797 − 10
15. log sin u = 9.7727 − 10
16. log tan u = .0076
17. log cot u = .1795
18. log cos u = 9.9684 − 10
19. log sin u = 9.8111 − 10
20. log cos u = 9.4775 − 10
21. log cot u = .4057

Find the value to four significant digits. Use logarithms.

22. $\dfrac{\cos 86° 10'}{(.437)^2}$ 0.3500

23. $\dfrac{(31.3)^3 \sqrt{0.736}}{\tan 43° 30'}$ 27,710

24. $\cot 75° 50' \sqrt{\dfrac{48.2}{5.64}}$ 0.7378

25. $\dfrac{\sqrt[3]{46.3} \sin 35° 30'}{(1.48)^2}$ 0.9520

26. $\dfrac{\cos 23° 36' (63.1)^3}{\sqrt{0.487}}$ 329,800

27. $\dfrac{(49.3)^3 \sqrt{107.3}}{\sin 73° 47'}$ 1,292,000

(C) 28. $\dfrac{\sin 43° 38' \cos 63° 42'}{(\tan 17° 14')^3}$ 10.22

29. $\dfrac{\sqrt[3]{\cos 33° 18'} \tan 16° 47'}{\sqrt[4]{187.6} \sin 10° 15'}$ 0.1182

30. $\dfrac{(12.3)^4 (\sin 73° 38')^3}{(\cos 15° 36')^2 \sqrt[3]{0.1487}}$ 41,130

31. $\dfrac{(38.6)^3 \tan 23° 18'}{\sqrt[3]{(\sin 46° 37')(\cos 70° 48')}}$ 39,910

18.7 Quadratic Trigonometric Equations

OBJECTIVE ▶ **To solve quadratic trigonometric equations**

Solving trigonometric equations is similar to solving algebraic equations. Each example that follows will be preceded by an algebraic example.

To solve $4x^2 - 5 = 0$, add 5 to both sides, divide each side by 4, and find the square root.

$$4x^2 = 5$$
$$x^2 = \frac{5}{4}$$
$$x = \pm\frac{1}{2}\sqrt{5}$$

Example 1 Determine the values of θ between 0° and 360° for which $4\sin^2\theta - 3 = 0$.

Think of $\sin\theta$ as x. Note that $\sin^2\theta$ is written $(\sin\theta)^2$. Add 3 to both sides, divide each side by 4, and find the square root.

$$4(\sin\theta)^2 = 3$$
$$(\sin\theta)^2 = \frac{3}{4}$$
$$\sin\theta = \pm\sqrt{\frac{3}{4}}, \text{ or } \pm\frac{\sqrt{3}}{2}$$

$$sin\ 60° = \frac{\sqrt{3}}{2} \blacktriangleright \quad \sin\theta = \frac{\sqrt{3}}{2} \qquad\qquad \sin\theta = \frac{-\sqrt{3}}{2}$$

1st quad.   2nd quad.   3rd quad.   4th quad.

Thus, $\theta = 60°, 120°, 240°$, and $300°$.

To solve the algebraic equation $2x^2 - x = 0$, factor, set each factor equal to zero, and solve.

$$x(2x - 1) = 0$$
$$x = 0 \quad \text{or} \quad 2x - 1 = 0$$
$$x = 0 \quad \text{or} \qquad x = \frac{1}{2}$$

Example 2 Determine the values of u, $0° \le u \le 360°$, for which $\tan^2 u - \sqrt{3}\tan u = 0$.

Factor. ▶ $\tan u(\tan u - \sqrt{3}) = 0$

Set each factor ▶ $\tan u = 0$ │ or $\tan u - \sqrt{3} = 0$
equal to 0.   │ $\tan u = \sqrt{3}$

$u = 0°, u = 180°$ │   Ref. angle 60°
                   │   1st quad. and 3rd quad.

Thus, $u = 0°, 180°, 60°$, and $240°$.

QUADRATIC TRIGONOMETRIC EQUATIONS

To solve the equation $3x^2 + 5x - 2 = 0$, factor, set each factor equal to zero.

$$(3x - 1)(x + 2) = 0$$
$$3x - 1 = 0 \quad \text{or} \quad x + 2 = 0$$
$$x = \frac{1}{3} \quad \text{or} \quad x = -2$$

Example 3

Determine values of u, $0° \le u \le 360°$, for which $2 \sin^2 u + 5 \sin u - 3 = 0$.

$$2 \sin^2 u + 5 \sin u - 3 = 0$$
$$(2 \sin u - 1)(\sin u + 3)$$
$$2 \sin u - 1 = 0 \quad \text{or} \quad \sin u + 3 = 0$$
$$\sin u = \frac{1}{2} \qquad\qquad \sin u = -3$$

Ref. $\angle$: 30°   No solution, since
$$\swarrow \quad \searrow \qquad -1 \le \sin u \le 1$$
1st quad.   2nd quad.

Thus, $u = 30°$ and $150°$.

To solve the equation $2x^2 - 5x + 1 = 0$, use the quadratic formula.

$$x = \frac{-b \pm \sqrt{b^2 - 4ac}}{2a} \qquad a = 2, b = -5, c = 1$$

$$x = \frac{-(-5) \pm \sqrt{(-5)^2 - 4(2)(1)}}{2(2)}$$

$$= \frac{5 + \sqrt{17}}{4} \text{ or } \frac{5 - \sqrt{17}}{4}$$

$$= \frac{5 + 4.123}{4} \text{ or } \frac{5 - 4.123}{4}$$

$$x = 2.281 \text{ or } .219$$

Example 4

Determine the values of u to the nearest degree between 0° and 360° for which $3 \cos^2 u - 4 \cos u - 2 = 0$.

Use the quadratic formula. $x = \dfrac{-b \pm \sqrt{b^2 - 4ac}}{2a}$, $a = 3, b = -4, c = -2$

$$\cos u = \frac{-(-4) \pm \sqrt{(-4)^2 - 4(3)(-2)}}{2(3)}$$

$$= \frac{4 \pm \sqrt{16 + 24}}{6}, \text{ or } \frac{4 \pm \sqrt{40}}{6}$$

$$\frac{4 + 6.32}{6} \qquad \frac{4 - 6.32}{6}$$

$$\cos u = \frac{10.32}{6} = 1.72 \quad \text{or} \quad \cos u = \frac{-2.32}{6} \doteq -.3867$$

                $\uparrow$ Ref. $\angle$: 67°

      No solution $\swarrow \quad \searrow$

                             2nd quad.   3rd quad.

Thus, $u = 113°$ and $247°$.

Oral Exercises

How many values of u, $0° \leq u \leq 360°$, are there for each of the following?

1. $\sin u = -.7632$ **2**
2. $\cos u = 2.6543$ **0**
3. $\tan u = -6.3214$ **2**
4. $\tan u = .4132$ **2**
5. $\sin u = -3.1249$ **0**
6. $\cos u = -.2987$ **2**

Written Exercises

For Ex. 1–33, see TE Answer Section.

Ⓐ Determine all values of θ, $0° \leq \theta \leq 360°$, to the nearest degree for which the equations are true.

1. $2 \cos^2 \theta - 5 = -4$
2. $10 \sin \theta - 5\sqrt{3} = 0$
3. $2 \cos \theta - \sqrt{3} = 0$
4. $\sin^2 \theta - 1 = 0$
5. $\cos^2 \theta = 0$
6. $\cot^2 \theta - 3 = 0$
7. $2 \sin \theta + \sqrt{3} = 0$
8. $\cot^2 \theta + \cot \theta = 0$
9. $2 \cos^2 \theta - \cos \theta = 0$
10. $2 \sin^2 \theta + \sqrt{3} \sin \theta = 0$
11. $\sqrt{3} \tan^2 \theta - \tan \theta = 0$
12. $2 \cos^2 \theta - \cos \theta - 1 = 0$
13. $\sin^2 \theta - 7 \sin \theta + 6 = 0$
14. $2 \cos^2 \theta + 3 \cos \theta + 1 = 0$
15. $\tan^2 \theta - 2 \tan \theta + 1 = 0$

Ⓑ **16.** $\tan^2 \theta - 5 \tan \theta - 2 = 0$
17. $3 \sin^2 \theta - 8 \sin \theta - 1 = 0$
18. $4 \cos^2 \theta + 5 \cos \theta - 2 = 0$
19. $5 \cos^2 \theta - 3 \cos \theta - 1 = 0$
20. $7 \cot^2 \theta + 4 \cot \theta - 3 = 0$
21. $7 \tan^2 \theta - 3 \tan \theta - 5 = 0$
22. $2 \sin^2 \theta - 5 \sin \theta = 1$
23. $\cot^2 \theta - 7 \cot \theta + 1 = 0$
24. $3 \cos^2 \theta + 6 \cos \theta + 1 = 0$

Ⓒ Determine all values of θ for which the equations are true.

25. $\sec^2 \theta - 4 = 0$
26. $4 \csc^2 \theta - 25 = 0$
27. $15 \csc^2 \theta + \csc \theta - 2 = 0$
28. $\csc^2 \theta - 7 \csc \theta + 12 = 0$
29. $2 \sec^2 \theta - \sec \theta - 15 = 0$
30. $3 \csc^2 \theta - 6 \csc \theta - 1 = 0$
31. $\sec^2 \theta - 5 \sec \theta - 3 = 0$
32. $5 \sec^2 \theta - 1 = 12$
33. $\sec^2 \theta + 7 \sec \theta - 3 = 0$

CALCULATOR ACTIVITY

You can use a calculator to solve quadratic trigonometric equations.

Example Solve $\sin^2 \theta - 7 \sin \theta + 5 = 0$ to the nearest ten minutes, $0 \leq \theta \leq 90°$.

1. Use the quadratic formula. $a = 1$, $b = -7$, $c = 5$.

2. Solve for $\sin \theta$: $\sin \theta = \dfrac{-(-7) \pm \sqrt{(-7)^2 - 4(1)(5)}}{2(1)}$

3. Compute $(-7)^2 - 4(5)$.
   Press ▶ $-7 \otimes \ominus$; $-4 \otimes 5 \ominus$; $49 \oplus -20 \ominus$
   Display ▶   49   ; -20 ;   29

4. Use the table to find $\sqrt{29} \doteq 5.39$.

5. Compute $\dfrac{7 + 5.39}{2}$ and $\dfrac{7 - 5.39}{2}$.

6. *Press* ▶ $7 \oplus 5.39 \oslash 2 \ominus$ and $7 \ominus 5.39 \oslash 2 \ominus$

7. *Display* ▶   6.195 and .805. Reject 6.195 since $-1 \leq \sin \theta \leq 1$.

8. Look in the table to find $\theta = 53° \, 40'$ to the nearest ten minutes.

QUADRATIC TRIGONOMETRIC EQUATIONS   **517**

18.8 Basic Trigonometric Identities

OBJECTIVE ▶ **To verify basic trigonometric identities using reciprocal, quotient, and Pythagorean identities**

Equations that are true for all permissible values of the variable are called identities. The equation $3 + x = x + 3$ is a statement of the commutative property for addition and is true for all real numbers. It is an example of an identity.

In this lesson you will learn how to verify certain trigonometric identities. The first two examples illustrate reciprocal identities.

Example 1

Show that $(\sin 45°)(\csc 45°) = 1$, $(\cos 60°)(\sec 60°) = 1$, and $(\tan 30°)(\cot 30°) = 1$.

$(\sin 45°)(\csc 45°)$	1	$(\cos 60°)(\sec 60°)$	1	$(\tan 30°)(\cot 30°)$	1
$\dfrac{\sqrt{2}}{2} \cdot \sqrt{2}$	1	$\dfrac{1}{2} \cdot \dfrac{2}{1}$	1	$\dfrac{\sqrt{3}}{3} \cdot \sqrt{3}$	1
$\dfrac{2}{2}$		1		$\dfrac{3}{3}$	
1				1	

Recall that $\sin A = \dfrac{y}{r}$, $\csc A = \dfrac{r}{y}$, $\cos A = \dfrac{x}{r}$, $\sec A = \dfrac{r}{x}$, $\tan A = \dfrac{y}{x}$, and $\cot A = \dfrac{x}{y}$. You will use these in Example 2.

Example 2

Show that for any degree measure A, $\sin A \cdot \csc A = 1$, $\cos A \cdot \sec A = 1$, and $\tan A \cdot \cot A = 1$.

$\sin A \cdot \csc A$	1	$\cos A \cdot \sec A$	1	$\tan A \cdot \cot A$	1
$\dfrac{y}{r} \cdot \dfrac{r}{y}$	1	$\dfrac{x}{r} \cdot \dfrac{r}{x}$	1	$\dfrac{y}{x} \cdot \dfrac{x}{y}$	1
1		1		1	

Reciprocal Identities

Sin and csc, cos and sec, and tan and cot are reciprocal functions.

$$\sin A \cdot \csc A = 1 \qquad\qquad \cos A \cdot \sec A = 1$$

$$\sin A = \frac{1}{\csc A} \text{ or } \csc A = \frac{1}{\sin A} \qquad \cos A = \frac{1}{\sec A} \text{ or } \sec A = \frac{1}{\cos A}$$

$$\tan A \cdot \cot A = 1$$

$$\tan A = \frac{1}{\cot A} \text{ or } \cot A = \frac{1}{\tan A}$$

Example 3 Show that for any degree measure A, $\tan A = \dfrac{\sin A}{\cos A}$ and $\cot A = \dfrac{\cos A}{\sin A}$.

Recall that $\sin A = \dfrac{y}{r}$, $\cos A = \dfrac{x}{r}$, $\tan A = \dfrac{y}{x}$, and $\cot A = \dfrac{x}{y}$.

$\tan A$	$\dfrac{\sin A}{\cos A}$
$\dfrac{y}{x}$	$\dfrac{\dfrac{y}{r}}{\dfrac{x}{r}}$
	$\dfrac{y}{r} \cdot \dfrac{r}{x} = \dfrac{y}{x}$

$\cot A$	$\dfrac{\cos A}{\sin A}$
$\dfrac{x}{y}$	$\dfrac{\dfrac{x}{r}}{\dfrac{y}{r}}$
	$\dfrac{x}{r} \cdot \dfrac{r}{y} = \dfrac{x}{y}$

Quotient Identities

$$\tan A = \frac{\sin A}{\cos A} \qquad \cot A = \frac{\cos A}{\sin A}$$

Example 4 Verify the quotient identities for $A = 210°$.

$\tan 210°$	$\dfrac{\sin 210°}{\cos 210°}$
$\dfrac{\sqrt{3}}{3}$	$\dfrac{-\dfrac{1}{2}}{-\dfrac{\sqrt{3}}{2}}$
	$-\dfrac{1}{2} \cdot \left(-\dfrac{2}{\sqrt{3}}\right)$
	$\dfrac{1}{\sqrt{3}}$, or $\dfrac{\sqrt{3}}{3}$

$\cot 210°$	$\dfrac{\cos 210°}{\sin 210°}$
$\sqrt{3}$	$\dfrac{-\dfrac{\sqrt{3}}{2}}{-\dfrac{1}{2}}$
	$\dfrac{-\sqrt{3}}{2}\left(-\dfrac{2}{1}\right)$
	$\sqrt{3}$

Example 5 Show that for any degree measure A, $\sin^2 A + \cos^2 A = 1$, $\tan^2 A + 1 = \sec^2 A$, and $\cot^2 A + 1 = \csc^2 A$.

$\sin^2 A + \cos^2 A$	1
$\left(\dfrac{y}{r}\right)^2 + \left(\dfrac{x}{r}\right)^2$	1
$\dfrac{y^2 + x^2}{r^2}$	
$x^2 + y^2 = r^2 \blacktriangleright \quad \dfrac{r^2}{r^2} = 1$	

$\tan^2 A + 1$	$\sec^2 A$
$\left(\dfrac{y}{x}\right)^2 + 1$	$\left(\dfrac{r}{x}\right)^2$
$\dfrac{y^2 + x^2}{x^2}$	$\dfrac{r^2}{x^2}$
$\dfrac{r^2}{x^2}$	

$\cot^2 A + 1$	$\csc^2 A$
$\left(\dfrac{x}{y}\right)^2 + 1$	$\left(\dfrac{r}{y}\right)^2$
$\dfrac{x^2 + y^2}{y^2}$	$\dfrac{r^2}{y^2}$
$\dfrac{r^2}{y^2}$	

BASIC TRIGONOMETERIC IDENTITIES

Pythagorean Identities

$$\sin^2 A + \cos^2 A = 1, \tan^2 A + 1 = \sec^2 A, \cot^2 A + 1 = \csc^2 A$$

Example 6 Verify the Pythagorean identities for $A = 120°$.

The terminal side is in the 2nd quadrant. Both sin and csc are positive, all others are negative. The reference angle is $60°$.

$\sin^2 120° + \cos^2 120°$	1	$\tan^2 120° + 1$	$\sec^2 120°$	$\cot^2 120° + 1$	$\csc^2 120°$
$\left(\dfrac{\sqrt{3}}{2}\right)^2 + \left(-\dfrac{1}{2}\right)^2$	1	$(-\sqrt{3})^2 + 1$	$(-2)^2$	$\left(-\dfrac{1}{\sqrt{3}}\right)^2 + 1$	$\left(\dfrac{2}{\sqrt{3}}\right)^2$
$\dfrac{3}{4} + \dfrac{1}{4} = 1$		$3 + 1$ 4	4	$\dfrac{1}{3} + 1 = \dfrac{4}{3}$	$\dfrac{4}{3}$

Written Exercises For complete solutions, see TE Answer Section.

(A) **Express as a function of sin, cos, or both.**

1. $\csc A$ $\dfrac{1}{\sin A}$
2. $\sec A$ $\dfrac{1}{\cos A}$
3. $\tan A$ $\dfrac{\sin A}{\cos A}$
4. $\cot A$ $\dfrac{\cos A}{\sin A}$

Verify each identity for $A = 30°$.

5. $\sin^2 A + \cos^2 A = 1$ 6. $\tan^2 A + 1 = \sec^2 A$ 7. $1 + \cot^2 A = \csc^2 A$ 8. $\cos A = \dfrac{1}{\sec A}$

Verify each identity for $\theta = 240°$.

9. $\sin^2 \theta = 1 - \cos^2 \theta$ 10. $\cot \theta = \dfrac{\cos \theta}{\sin \theta}$ 11. $\csc^2 \theta - 1 = \cot^2 \theta$ 12. $\sin \theta = \dfrac{1}{\csc \theta}$

Verify each identity for $x = 135°$.

13. $\cos^2 x = 1 - \sin^2 x$ 14. $\tan x = \dfrac{\sin x}{\cos x}$ 15. $\sec^2 x = 1 + \tan^2 x$ 16. $\csc^2 x = 1 + \cot^2 x$

Verify each identity for $B = 330°$.

17. $\sin B \cdot \csc B = 1$ 18. $\tan B \cdot \cot B = 1$ 19. $\cos B \cdot \sec B = 1$ 20. $\sin B = \dfrac{1}{\csc B}$

For Ex. 21–28, see TE Answer Section.

Write an equivalent expression using only sin x.

Hint: $\sin^2 x + \cos^2 x = 1$ so, $\cos x = \pm\sqrt{1 - \sin^2 x}$.

(B) 21. $\tan x$ 22. $\cot x$ 23. $\sec x$ 24. $\csc x$

Write an equivalent expression using only cos x.

25. $\cot x$ 26. $\sin x$ 27. $\csc x$ 28. $\sec x$

(C) **Prove each identity. Use the definitions of tan x, cot x, sec x, and csc x.**

29. $\tan^2 x + 1 = \sec^2 x$ 30. $1 + \cot^2 x = \csc^2 x$

Prove each identity. Use $\sin^2 A + \cos^2 A = 1$.

31. $\tan^2 A + 1 = \sec^2 A$ 32. $1 + \cot^2 A = \csc^2 A$

18.9 Proving Trigonometric Identities

OBJECTIVE ▶ To prove trigonometric identities

In the previous lesson you studied the reciprocal identities, the quotient identities, and the Pythagorean identities. You will now use these identities to prove other trigonometric identities.

Example 1 Prove the identity: $\tan x = \dfrac{\sec x}{\csc x}$.

Replace $\sec x$ with $\dfrac{1}{\cos x}$ and $\csc x$ with $\dfrac{1}{\sin x}$.

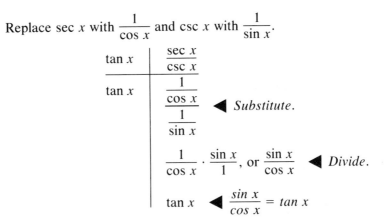

$$
\begin{array}{c|l}
\tan x & \dfrac{\sec x}{\csc x} \\[2ex]
\hline
\tan x & \dfrac{\dfrac{1}{\cos x}}{\dfrac{1}{\sin x}} \quad \blacktriangleleft \; Substitute. \\[3ex]
& \dfrac{1}{\cos x} \cdot \dfrac{\sin x}{1}, \text{ or } \dfrac{\sin x}{\cos x} \quad \blacktriangleleft \; Divide. \\[2ex]
& \tan x \quad \blacktriangleleft \; \dfrac{\sin x}{\cos x} = \tan x
\end{array}
$$

Example 2 Prove the identity: $\csc x = \sin x + \cot x \cos x$.

$$
\begin{array}{c|l}
\csc x & \sin x + \cot x \cos x \\[1ex]
\hline
\csc x & \sin x + \dfrac{\cos x}{\sin x} \cdot \cos x \quad \blacktriangleleft \; cot\, x = \dfrac{cos\, x}{sin\, x} \\[3ex]
& \dfrac{\sin^2 x + \cos^2 x}{\sin x} \\[3ex]
& \dfrac{1}{\sin x} \quad \blacktriangleleft \; sin^2\, x + cos^2\, x = 1 \\[3ex]
& \csc x \quad \blacktriangleleft \; \dfrac{1}{sin\, x} = csc\, x
\end{array}
$$

Summary	To prove a trigonometric identity: (1) Work with each side separately. (2) Substitute, using basic trigonometric identities, usually in terms of sin or cos. (3) Simplify by adding, subtracting, multiplying, or dividing. (4) When each side is the same expression, the identity has been proved.

Example 3 Prove the identity: $\csc x + \csc x \cdot \sec x = \dfrac{1 + \sec x}{\sin x}$.

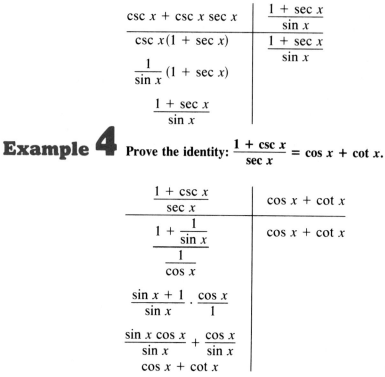

$$
\begin{array}{c|c}
\csc x + \csc x \sec x & \dfrac{1 + \sec x}{\sin x} \\[2ex]
\hline
\csc x(1 + \sec x) & \dfrac{1 + \sec x}{\sin x} \\[2ex]
\dfrac{1}{\sin x}(1 + \sec x) & \\[2ex]
\dfrac{1 + \sec x}{\sin x} &
\end{array}
$$

Example 4 Prove the identity: $\dfrac{1 + \csc x}{\sec x} = \cos x + \cot x$.

$$
\begin{array}{c|c}
\dfrac{1 + \csc x}{\sec x} & \cos x + \cot x \\[2ex]
\hline
\dfrac{1 + \dfrac{1}{\sin x}}{\dfrac{1}{\cos x}} & \cos x + \cot x \\[3ex]
\dfrac{\sin x + 1}{\sin x} \cdot \dfrac{\cos x}{1} & \\[2ex]
\dfrac{\sin x \cos x}{\sin x} + \dfrac{\cos x}{\sin x} & \\[2ex]
\cos x + \cot x &
\end{array}
$$

Written Exercises

For Ex. 1–18, see TE Answer Section.

(A) Prove each identity.

1. $\dfrac{\cot x}{\cos x} = \csc x$

2. $\sin x \cot x = \cos x$

3. $\sec x = \csc x \cdot \tan x$

4. $\cot x + \tan x = \csc x \sec x$

5. $\sec x = \cos x + \dfrac{\tan x}{\csc x}$

6. $\sin^2 x - \cos^2 x = 2 \sin^2 x - 1$

(B)

7. $\cot x - 1 = \cos x (\csc x - \sec x)$

8. $\sec x = \dfrac{\cos x}{1 + \sin x} + \tan x$

9. $\sin x + \dfrac{\cot x}{\sec x} = \csc x$

10. $\dfrac{\cot x + \cos x}{1 + \sin x} = \dfrac{\cos x}{\sin x}$

11. $\tan x - \cot x = \dfrac{1 - 2 \cos^2 x}{\sin x \cos x}$

12. $\dfrac{1 - \cos^2 x}{\cos x} \cdot \csc x = \tan x$

13. $2 \csc x = \dfrac{\sin x}{1 + \cos x} + \dfrac{\sin x}{1 - \cos x}$

14. $\cos x + \sin x = \dfrac{\sec x + \csc x}{\cot x + \tan x}$

(C)

15. $\dfrac{1 - \tan^2 x}{1 + \tan^2 x} = \dfrac{2 - \sec^2 x}{\sec^2 x}$

16. $\tan (180° + \theta) + \dfrac{1}{\cot (270° - \theta)} = \dfrac{\sec (180° - \theta)}{\sin (180° + \theta)}$

17. $\dfrac{\cot^2 \theta - 1}{\cot^2 \theta + 1} = \dfrac{2 - \sec^2 \theta}{\sec^2 \theta}$

18. $\sqrt{\dfrac{\sec \theta - \tan \theta}{\sec \theta + \tan \theta}} = \dfrac{1 - \sin \theta}{\cos \theta}$

18.10 Radian Measure

OBJECTIVES ▶ To express radian measure in degrees
To express degree measure in radians
To evaluate expressions involving radian measure

You have learned that an angle of rotation can be measured in degrees. An angle of rotation can also be measured using real numbers called *radians*. If an angle of rotation, which is the central angle of a given circle, intercepts an arc with the same length as a radius, then the angle is said to have a measure of 1 radian. When it intercepts an arc whose length is twice the radius, the angle is said to have a measure of 2 radians. See the figures below.

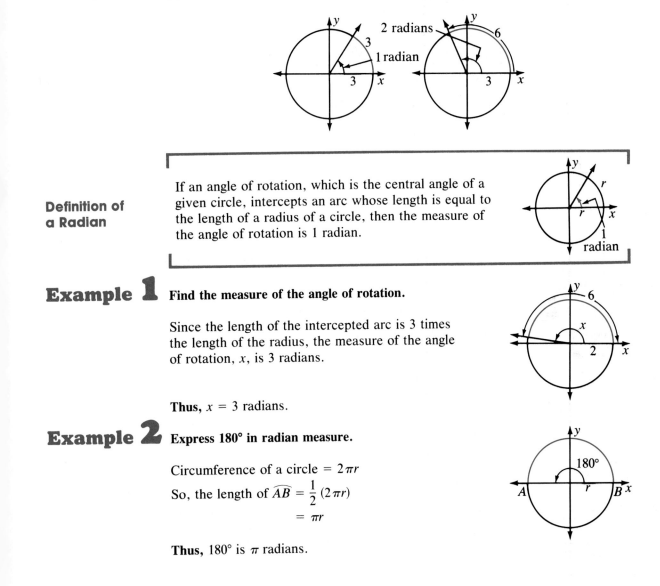

Definition of a Radian	If an angle of rotation, which is the central angle of a given circle, intercepts an arc whose length is equal to the length of a radius of a circle, then the measure of the angle of rotation is 1 radian.

Example 1 **Find the measure of the angle of rotation.**

Since the length of the intercepted arc is 3 times the length of the radius, the measure of the angle of rotation, x, is 3 radians.

Thus, $x = 3$ radians.

Example 2 **Express 180° in radian measure.**

Circumference of a circle $= 2\pi r$

So, the length of $\overarc{AB} = \dfrac{1}{2}(2\pi r)$

$\qquad\qquad\qquad = \pi r$

Thus, 180° is π radians.

In the preceding example you learned that 180° is π radians, or $180° = \pi$ (radians). Divide both sides by 180. The result is $1° = \dfrac{\pi \,(\text{rad})}{180}$. This formula will be used to change degree measure to radian measure.

Example 3 **Express each in radian measure.**

$$90° \qquad\qquad\qquad\qquad -210°$$

Multiply both sides by 90°. ▶

$$\text{use } 1° = \frac{\pi \ (\text{rad})}{180} \qquad\qquad \text{use } 1° = \frac{\pi \ (\text{rad})}{180}$$

$$90° = \frac{\pi}{180}\,(90°) \qquad\qquad -210° = \frac{\pi}{180}\,(-210°)$$

$$= \frac{\pi}{2} \qquad\qquad\qquad\qquad = -\frac{7\pi}{6}$$

Thus, $90°$ is $\dfrac{\pi}{2}$ radians and $-210°$ is $-\dfrac{7\pi}{6}$ radians.

Now, divide both sides of $180° = \pi$ (radians) by π. $1(\text{rad}) = \dfrac{180°}{\pi}$. This formula will be used to change from radian measure to degree measure.

Example 4 **Express in degree measure.**

$$\frac{3}{2}\pi \qquad\qquad\qquad\qquad \frac{7}{6}\pi$$

$$\text{use } 1(\text{rad}) = \frac{180°}{\pi} \qquad\qquad \text{use } 1(\text{rad}) = \frac{180°}{\pi}$$

$$\frac{3}{2}\pi = \frac{180°}{\pi}\left(\frac{3}{2}\pi\right) \qquad\qquad \frac{7}{6}\pi = \frac{180°}{\pi}\cdot\left(\frac{7}{6}\pi\right)$$

$$= 90(3), \text{ or } 270° \qquad\qquad = 30(7), \text{ or } 210°$$

Thus, $\dfrac{3}{2}\pi$ radians is $270°$ and $\dfrac{7}{6}\pi$ radians is $210°$.

Example 5 illustrates how to evaluate trigonometric expressions using radian measure.

Example 5 **Evaluate.**

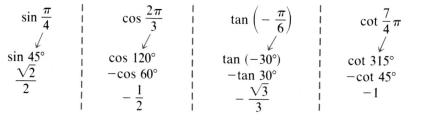

$$\sin\frac{\pi}{4} \qquad\qquad \cos\frac{2\pi}{3} \qquad\qquad \tan\left(-\frac{\pi}{6}\right) \qquad\qquad \cot\frac{7}{4}\pi$$

$$\downarrow \qquad\qquad\qquad \downarrow \qquad\qquad\qquad \downarrow \qquad\qquad\qquad \downarrow$$

$$\sin 45° \qquad\qquad \cos 120° \qquad\qquad \tan(-30°) \qquad\qquad \cot 315°$$

$$\frac{\sqrt{2}}{2} \qquad\qquad -\cos 60° \qquad\qquad -\tan 30° \qquad\qquad -\cot 45°$$

$$-\frac{1}{2} \qquad\qquad\qquad -\frac{\sqrt{3}}{3} \qquad\qquad\qquad -1$$

CHAPTER EIGHTEEN

Example 6 Evaluate $\dfrac{\sin \dfrac{5\pi}{6} - \cos \dfrac{3\pi}{4}}{\tan\left(-\dfrac{\pi}{4}\right)}$.

$$\frac{\sin \dfrac{5\pi}{6} - \cos \dfrac{3\pi}{4}}{\tan\left(-\dfrac{\pi}{4}\right)} = \frac{\sin 150° - \cos 135°}{\tan(-45°)} = \frac{\sin 30° - (-\cos 45°)}{-\tan 45°} = \frac{\dfrac{1}{2} - \left(\dfrac{-\sqrt{2}}{2}\right)}{-1} = -\frac{1 + \sqrt{2}}{2}$$

Reading in Algebra

Match each item at the right to one, and only one, item on the left.

1. Degrees to radians D
2. Radians to degrees E
3. 1 radian A
4. 360° B
5. real numbers C

A. Arc length is 8, radius is 8.
B. 2π
C. radians
D. $1° = \dfrac{\pi\,(\text{rad})}{180}$
E. $1\,(\text{rad}) = \dfrac{180°}{\pi}$

Written Exercises

Express each in radians.

(A)
1. 30° $\dfrac{\pi}{6}$
2. 120° $\dfrac{2\pi}{3}$
3. −200° $\dfrac{-10\pi}{9}$
4. 150° $\dfrac{5\pi}{6}$
5. 210° $\dfrac{7\pi}{6}$
6. 300° $\dfrac{5\pi}{3}$
7. −60° $\dfrac{-\pi}{3}$
8. −320° $\dfrac{-16\pi}{9}$
9. −270° $\dfrac{-3\pi}{2}$
10. 240° $\dfrac{4\pi}{3}$
11. −330° $\dfrac{-11\pi}{6}$
12. 225° $\dfrac{5\pi}{4}$
13. 450° $\dfrac{5\pi}{2}$
14. −360° -2π

Express each in degrees.

15. $\dfrac{\pi}{4}$ 45°
16. $\dfrac{3}{2}\pi$ 270°
17. $\dfrac{5\pi}{6}$ 150°
18. $\dfrac{7\pi}{6}$ 210°
19. $\dfrac{2}{3}\pi$ 120°
20. $-\pi$ −180°
21. $\dfrac{3}{4}\pi$ 135°

22. $-\dfrac{\pi}{8}$ −22.5°
23. $-\dfrac{3}{5}\pi$ −108°
24. $-\dfrac{2\pi}{9}$ −40°
25. -2π −360°
26. $\dfrac{9}{4}\pi$ 405°
27. $\dfrac{11\pi}{6}$ 330°
28. $-\dfrac{7\pi}{6}$ −210°

Evaluate each of the following.

(B)
29. $\sin \dfrac{\pi}{2}$ 1
30. $\cos \dfrac{5\pi}{2}$ 0
31. $\tan\left(-\dfrac{\pi}{4}\right)$ −1
32. $\cot \dfrac{7}{6}\pi$ $\sqrt{3}$
33. $\sin\left(-\dfrac{2}{3}\pi\right)$

34. $\dfrac{\tan \dfrac{5}{4}\pi - \cos \dfrac{5}{3}\pi}{\sin \dfrac{\pi}{6}}$ 1

35. $\dfrac{\cos \dfrac{5\pi}{4} + \tan \dfrac{7}{4}\pi}{\cot\left(\dfrac{5}{6}\pi\right)}$

36. $\dfrac{\sin \dfrac{\pi}{9} - \cos \dfrac{3}{2}\pi}{\tan\left(-\dfrac{3\pi}{4}\right)}$ 0.342

(C)
37. $\dfrac{\sec \dfrac{2\pi}{3} + \csc \dfrac{\pi}{6}}{\sec \dfrac{\pi}{4}}$ 0

38. $\dfrac{\csc \dfrac{2\pi}{5} - \sec\left(-\dfrac{1}{3}\pi\right) + \sin \dfrac{\pi}{3}}{\tan\left(-\dfrac{\pi}{4}\right)\cos\left(-\dfrac{\pi}{3}\right)}$ 0.17

39. $\dfrac{\cos \dfrac{11\pi}{6} - \sec\left(-\dfrac{\pi}{3}\right)}{\tan \dfrac{\pi}{6}\csc\left(-\dfrac{\pi}{4}\right)}$ $\dfrac{-3\sqrt{2} + 4\sqrt{6}}{4}$

40. $\dfrac{\sec\left(-\dfrac{\pi}{9}\right)\csc \dfrac{3\pi}{4} - \tan\left(-\dfrac{3\pi}{4}\right)}{\cos^2 \dfrac{\pi}{3} + \sin^2 \dfrac{\pi}{3}}$ 0.505

33. $\dfrac{-\sqrt{3}}{2}$
35. $\dfrac{\sqrt{6} + 2\sqrt{3}}{6}$

18.11 Applying Radian Measure

OBJECTIVES ▶ **To sketch graphs of trigonometric functions using radian measure**
To write the solutions of trigonometric equations in radians

The table below lists some special degree-radian relationships.

Degrees	0°	30°	45°	60°	90°	120°	135°	150°	180°
Radians	0	$\frac{\pi}{6}$	$\frac{\pi}{4}$	$\frac{\pi}{3}$	$\frac{\pi}{2}$	$\frac{2\pi}{3}$	$\frac{3\pi}{4}$	$\frac{5\pi}{6}$	π

Degrees	210°	225°	240°	270°	300°	315°	330°	360°
Radians	$\frac{7\pi}{6}$	$\frac{5\pi}{4}$	$\frac{4\pi}{3}$	$\frac{3\pi}{2}$	$\frac{5\pi}{3}$	$\frac{7\pi}{4}$	$\frac{11\pi}{6}$	2π

To graph the function $y = \sin x$ using radian measure, label the horizontal axis in radians and the vertical axis in real numbers. Make a table of values by choosing special radian measures and finding the corresponding values of y. The graph of $y = \sin x$, $0 \leq x \leq 2\pi$, is shown.

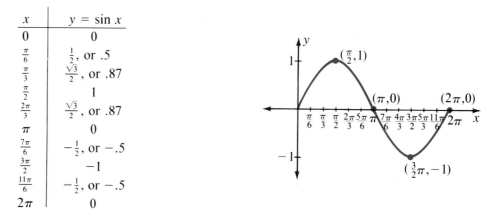

x	$y = \sin x$
0	0
$\frac{\pi}{6}$	$\frac{1}{2}$, or .5
$\frac{\pi}{3}$	$\frac{\sqrt{3}}{2}$, or .87
$\frac{\pi}{2}$	1
$\frac{2\pi}{3}$	$\frac{\sqrt{3}}{2}$, or .87
π	0
$\frac{7\pi}{6}$	$-\frac{1}{2}$, or $-.5$
$\frac{3\pi}{2}$	-1
$\frac{11\pi}{6}$	$-\frac{1}{2}$, or $-.5$
2π	0

Notice that the maximum value 1 occurs at $\frac{\pi}{2}$. The minimum value -1 occurs at $\frac{3\pi}{2}$. The period of $y = \sin x$ is 2π.

Example 1

Graph $y = 2 \cos x$ for $0 \leq x \leq 2\pi$. Determine the period and amplitude.

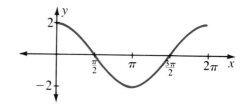

x	$\cos x$	$y = 2 \cos x$
0	1	2
$\frac{\pi}{2}$	0	0
π	-1	-2
$\frac{3\pi}{2}$	0	0
2π	1	2

Thus, period for $y = 2 \cos x$ is 2π.
Amplitude for $y = 2 \cos x$ is 2.

Example 2 Graph $y = \sin \frac{1}{2}x$ for $0 \le x \le 4\pi$. Determine the period and amplitude.

x	$\frac{1}{2}x$	$y = \sin \frac{1}{2}x$
0	0	0
π	π	1
2π	π	0
3π	$\frac{3\pi}{2}$	-1
4π	2π	0

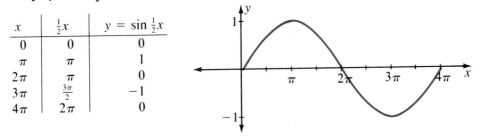

Thus, the period for $y = \sin \frac{1}{2}x$ is 4π and the amplitude is 1.

Example 3 Sketch $y = 2 \cos x$ and $y = \sin \frac{1}{2}x$ for $0 \le x \le 2\pi$ on the same set of axes. For how many values of x does $2 \cos x = \sin \frac{1}{2}x$?

Use Examples 1 and 2 to sketch the graphs.

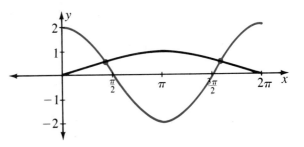

Thus, $2 \cos x = \sin \frac{1}{2}x$ for 2 values of x for $0 \le x \le 2\pi$.

Example 4 Solve $-3 \tan x - \sqrt{3} = 0$ if $0 \le x \le 2\pi$.

Solve for $\tan x$. Determine the reference angle.

$-3 \tan x = \sqrt{3}$

$\tan x = -\dfrac{\sqrt{3}}{3}$ Reference angle: $30°$ ◀ *Tan is negative in quadrants 2 and 4.*

     ↓   ↓
    2nd quad.   4th quad.
     150°   330°

Thus, the solutions are $\dfrac{5\pi}{6}$ and $\dfrac{11\pi}{6}$.

Example 5 Solve $2 \cos^2 x - 5 \cos x + 2 = 0$ if $0 \le x \le 2\pi$.

$(2 \cos x - 1)(\cos x - 2) = 0$ ◀ *Factor.*
$2 \cos x - 1 = 0$ or $\cos x - 2 = 0$ ◀ *Set each factor equal to 0.*
$\cos x = \frac{1}{2}$ $\cos x = 2$
Ref. $\angle$: $60°$ No solution, since $-1 \le \cos x \le 1$

  ↙   ↓
1st quad. 4th quad.
  60°   300°

Thus, the solutions are $\dfrac{\pi}{3}$ and $\dfrac{5\pi}{3}$.

Written Exercises _____

(A) **Graph $y = \sin 2x$ for $-2\pi \leq x \leq 2\pi$ to find each value below.**

   1. maximum and minimum   **2.** period π **3.** amplitude 1
      1, −1

Graph $y = 3 \cos x$ for $-\pi \leq x \leq \pi$ to find each value below.

   4. maximum and minimum   **5.** period 2π **6.** amplitude 3
      3, −3

Sketch each graph for $0 \leq x \leq 2\pi$. Determine the period and the amplitude.

   7. $y = \frac{1}{2} \sin x$ $2\pi, \frac{1}{2}$ **8.** $y = \cos 4x$ $\frac{\pi}{2}, 1$ **9.** $y = 3 \cos x$ $2\pi, 3$ **10.** $y = \sin 3x$ $\frac{2\pi}{3}, 1$

   11. $y = 2 \cos \frac{1}{2}x$ $4\pi, 2$ **12.** $y = \frac{1}{2} \sin 2x$ $\pi, \frac{1}{2}$ **13.** $y = \frac{1}{3} \cos 3x$ $\frac{2\pi}{3}, \frac{1}{3}$ **14.** $y = 4 \sin 2x$ $\pi, 4$

For Ex. 15–26, see TE Answer Section.
Solve each trigonometric equation if $0 \leq x \leq 2\pi$.

   15. $2 \sin x + 1 = 0$ **16.** $2 \cos x - \sqrt{3} = 0$ **17.** $\tan x = 1$

   18. $5 \sin^2 x = 0$ **19.** $2 \cos^2 x - 1 = 0$ **20.** $2 \sin x + \sqrt{3} = 0$

   21. $2 \cos^2 x + \cos x = 0$ **22.** $\sqrt{2} \sin^2 x - \sin x = 0$ **23.** $2 \cos^2 x - 7 \cos x - 4 = 0$

   24. $\sin^2 x - \frac{1}{4} = 0$ **25.** $6 \sin^2 x - 7 \sin x - 5 = 0$ **26.** $4 \cos^2 - 1 = 0$

(B) **27.** Sketch $y = 3 \sin x$ and $y = \cos 3x$ for $0 \leq x \leq 2\pi$ on the same set of axes. For how many values of x does $3 \sin x = \cos 3x$? **4**

                               28. Sketch $y = \cos \frac{1}{2}x$ and $y = \sin 3x$ for $0 \leq x \leq 2\pi$ on the same set of axes. For how many values of x does $\cos \frac{1}{2}x = \sin 3x$? **7**

Sketch each graph for $-\pi \leq x \leq 2\pi$. Determine the period and amplitude.

   29. $y = \tan x$ π, **none**   **30.** $y = 3 \tan x$ π, **none**   **31.** $y = \tan 3x$ $\frac{\pi}{3}$, **none**

   32. $y = -\cos x$ $2\pi, 1$ **33.** $y = 2 \sin (-2x)$ $\pi, 2$ **34.** $y = -\cos 2x$ $\pi, 1$

   35. $y = -2 \sin \frac{1}{2}x$ $4\pi, 2$ **36.** $y = -3 \cos (-x)$ $2\pi, 3$ **37.** $y = -3 \sin (-2x)$ $\pi, 3$

   38. $y = -\frac{1}{2} \sin 2x$ $\pi, \frac{1}{2}$ **39.** $y = \frac{1}{3} \cos 2x$ $\pi, \frac{1}{3}$ **40.** $y = -\frac{1}{2} \cos 3x$ $\frac{2\pi}{3}, \frac{1}{2}$

(C) **41.** $y = \sec x$ 2π, **none**   **42.** $y = \csc x$ 2π, **none**   **43.** $y = \cot x$ π, **none**

   44. $y = \sec 2x$ π, **none**   **45.** $y = -\frac{1}{2} \sec x$ 2π, **none** **46.** $y = \csc (-2x)$ π, **none**

Solve each trigonometric equation if $0 \leq x \leq 2\pi$.

   47. $\sec x = -\sqrt{2}$ $\frac{3\pi}{4}, \frac{5\pi}{4}$ **48.** $\csc x = -2$ $\frac{7\pi}{6}, \frac{11\pi}{6}$ **49.** $3 \sec x - 2\sqrt{3} = 0$ $\frac{\pi}{6}, \frac{11\pi}{6}$

   50. $2 \sec x + 1 = 0$ **No solution**   **51.** $2 \sec^2 x + 3 \sec x - 2 = 0$ **52.** $\csc^2 x - 4 = 0$ $\frac{\pi}{6}, \frac{5\pi}{6}, \frac{7\pi}{6}, \frac{11\pi}{6}$
                                                           $\frac{2\pi}{3}, \frac{4\pi}{3}$

   53. Sketch $y = \sin 2x$ and $y = 2 \cos x$ for $-\pi \leq x \leq \pi$ on the same set of axes. For what values of x does $\sin 2x = 2 \cos x$? $\frac{\pi}{2}, \frac{-\pi}{2}$

                               54. Sketch $y = 2 \sin x$ and $y = \sin \frac{1}{2}x$ for $-\pi \leq x \leq 2\pi$ on the same set of axes. For what values of x does $2 \sin x = \sin \frac{1}{2}x$? $0, \frac{5\pi}{6}$

   55. Sketch $y = -2 \sin \frac{1}{2}x$ and $y = -\frac{1}{2} \cos (-2x)$ for $0 \leq x \leq 2\pi$ on the same set of axes. For how many values of x does $-2 \sin \frac{1}{2}x = -\frac{1}{2} \cos (-2x)$? **2**

                               56. Sketch $y = \tan (-2x)$ and $y = -2 \cos \frac{1}{2}x$ for $0 \leq x \leq 2\pi$ on the same set of axes. For how many values of x does $\tan (-2x) = -2 \cos \frac{1}{2}x$? **5**

18.12 Inverses of Trigonometric Functions

OBJECTIVES ▶ To determine the inverse of a trigonometric function
To graph inverses of the sin, cos, and tan functions
To apply inverse function notation

Recall that the inverse of a function is formed by interchanging the elements of each ordered pair of the function. The inverse of a function is not necessarily a function. The *inverse function* is formed when the inverse of a given function is also a function.

Example 1 Find the inverse of $y = \cos x$.

Interchange x and y.

Thus, the inverse of $y = \cos x$ is $x = \cos y$.

After finding the inverse of a function, it is customary to solve for y. Cos $y = x$ can be written in two other ways: $y = \arccos x$, or $y = \cos^{-1} x$. Each is read "y is the angle whose cos is x." In $y = \cos^{-1} x$, -1 is *not* an exponent.

Example 2 Find u, if $u = \arcsin\left(-\frac{1}{2}\right)$, $0° \le u \le 360°$.

Read $u = \arcsin\left(-\frac{1}{2}\right)$ as u is the angle whose sin is $-\frac{1}{2}$.
Write $u = \arcsin\left(-\frac{1}{2}\right)$ as $\sin u = -\frac{1}{2}$.
$$\text{Ref. } \angle : 30°$$
$$\swarrow \qquad \searrow$$
$$\text{3rd quad.} \quad \text{4th quad.}$$
So, $\sin 210° = -\frac{1}{2}$ and $\sin 330° = -\frac{1}{2}$.
Thus, $u = 210°$ or $330°$.

Example 3 Find θ, if $\theta = \arccos \dfrac{\sqrt{2}}{2}$, $0 \le \theta \le 2\pi$.

Write $\theta = \arccos \dfrac{\sqrt{2}}{2}$ as $\cos \theta = \dfrac{\sqrt{2}}{2}$.
$$\text{Ref. } \angle : 45°$$
$$\swarrow \qquad \searrow$$
$$\text{1st quad.} \quad \text{4th quad.}$$
So, $\cos 45° = \dfrac{\sqrt{2}}{2}$ and $\cos 315° = \dfrac{\sqrt{2}}{2}$.
Thus, $\theta = \dfrac{\pi}{4}$ or $\dfrac{7\pi}{4}$.

In the next example you will learn how to graph the inverse of a trigonometric function.

Example 4

Sketch $y = $ arc sin x. Determine if the inverse is a function.

Make a table of values for $y = \sin x$ and interchange the elements of the ordered pairs.

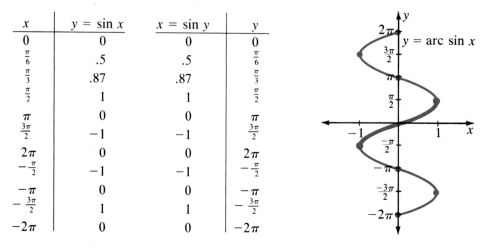

x	$y = \sin x$	$x = \sin y$	y
0	0	0	0
$\frac{\pi}{6}$	.5	.5	$\frac{\pi}{6}$
$\frac{\pi}{3}$	.87	.87	$\frac{\pi}{3}$
$\frac{\pi}{2}$	1	1	$\frac{\pi}{2}$
π	0	0	π
$\frac{3\pi}{2}$	-1	-1	$\frac{3\pi}{2}$
2π	0	0	2π
$-\frac{\pi}{2}$	-1	-1	$-\frac{\pi}{2}$
$-\pi$	0	0	$-\pi$
$-\frac{3\pi}{2}$	1	1	$-\frac{3\pi}{2}$
-2π	0	0	-2π

The graph does not pass the vertical line test, since there are many values of y for each x between -1 and 1.

Thus, the inverse of $y = \sin x$ is not a function.

The graphs of the inverses of $y = \cos x$ and $y = \tan x$ are shown below.

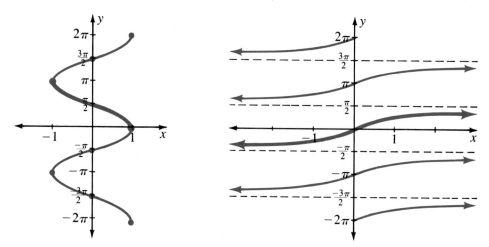

By restricting the interval of the graph of the inverse of a trig function, the inverse can be an inverse function in that interval. The shaded regions of the three graphs above are the graphs of the inverse functions.

To obtain inverse functions for $y = \sin x$, $y = \cos x$, and $y = \tan x$, restrict the range to values called *Principal Values*.

Inverse Trigonometric Functions

$$-\frac{\pi}{2} \leq \text{Arc sin} \leq \frac{\pi}{2}, \text{ or } -90° \leq \text{Arc sin} \leq 90°$$

$$0 \leq \text{Arc cos} \leq \pi, \text{ or } 0° \leq \text{Arc cos} \leq 180°$$

$$-\frac{\pi}{2} \leq \text{Arc tan} \leq \frac{\pi}{2}, \text{ or } -90° \leq \text{Arc tan} \leq 90°$$

In order to indicate principal value, capitalize the first letter of arc sin x as shown above.

The next three examples illustrate how to find a trig function given an inverse trig function.

Example 5 Find $\cos \theta$ if $\theta = \text{Arc sin}\left(-\frac{3}{5}\right)$.

Write $\theta = \text{Arc sin}\left(-\frac{3}{5}\right)$ as $\sin \theta = -\frac{3}{5}$.

The principal value of θ is

$$-\frac{\pi}{2} \leq \theta \leq \frac{\pi}{2} \quad \text{or} \quad -90° \leq \theta \leq 90°$$

$$\sin \theta = -\frac{3}{5}$$
$$\downarrow \qquad \downarrow$$
3rd quad.   4th quad.

There is no solution
in the 3rd quad. since
the Principal Values for
sin are in the 1st and 4th quad.

Find x.
$$x^2 + y^2 = r^2$$
$$x^2 + 9 = 25$$
$$x^2 = 16$$
$$x = 4$$

Thus, $\cos \theta = \frac{4}{5}$.

Example 6 Find $\sin\left(\text{Arc tan}\left(\frac{3}{4}\right)\right)$.

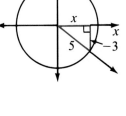

Let $A = \text{Arc tan}\frac{3}{4}$.

Write as $\tan A = \frac{3}{4}$ and $-90° \leq A \leq 90°$.
$$\swarrow \qquad \searrow$$
1st quad.   3rd quad.

Find r.   No solution since
$$x^2 + y^2 = r^2 \qquad -90° \leq A \leq 90°$$
$$9 + 16 = r^2$$
$$r = 5$$

Thus, $\sin A = \frac{3}{5}$, so $\sin\left(\text{Arc tan}\left(\frac{3}{4}\right)\right) = \frac{3}{5}$.

INVERSES OF TRIGONOMETRIC FUNCTIONS

Example 7 Find $\sin^{-1}\left(\tan\frac{5\pi}{6}\right)$.

$\text{Tan }\frac{5\pi}{6} = \tan 150° = -\tan 30°$, or $-\frac{\sqrt{3}}{3}$

Let $A = \sin^{-1}\left(-\frac{\sqrt{3}}{3}\right)$.   Write as $\sin A = -\frac{\sqrt{3}}{3} = -\frac{1.732}{3}$, or $-.5773$.

Look in the table.
Ref. $\angle$: 35° to the nearest degree.

3rd quad.   4th quad.   **Thus,** $\sin^{-1}\left(\tan\frac{5\pi}{6}\right) = -35°$ or $-\frac{7\pi}{36}$.
No solution $-35°$

Reading in **Algebra**

Write A if the statement is *always* true. Write S if the statement is *sometimes* true. Write N if the statement is *never* true.

1. Inverses of trig functions are functions. **S**
2. The inverse for $y = \sin x$ is $x = \sin y$. **A**
3. The inverse for a function is formed by interchanging the elements of each ordered pair of the function. **A**
4. If $\theta = \arc\tan(-2)$, then $\tan\theta = -2$. **A**
5. The inverse function for $y = \sin x$ is Arc sin x. **S**
6. The Principal Values for Arc tan x are $-\frac{\pi}{2} \le \text{Arc tan } x \le \frac{\pi}{2}$. **A**

Written **Exercises**

(A) **Find the inverse of each function.**

1. $y = \sin\frac{1}{2}x$ ↰
   $y = 2\sin^{-1}x$ ↲
2. $y = \cos x$ ↰
   $y = \cos^{-1}x$ ↲
3. $y = \tan x$ ↰
   $y = \tan^{-1}x$ ↲
4. $y = \cot x$ ↰
   $y = \cot^{-1}x$ ↲
5. $y = \frac{1}{2}\cos x$ ↰
   $y = \cos^{-1}(2x)$ ↲

Find θ for each of the following.

6. $\theta = \text{Arc sin } 0$ **0°**
7. $\theta = \text{Arc cos }\frac{1}{2}$ **60°**
8. $\theta = \text{Arc sin }\left(-\frac{1}{2}\right)$
9. $\theta = \text{Arc sin }\left(-\frac{\sqrt{3}}{2}\right)$
10. $\theta = \text{Arc cos }\frac{\sqrt{2}}{2}$ **45°**
11. $\theta = \text{Arc tan }(-1)$ ↰
    $-45°$ ↲
12. $\theta = \text{Arc tan }\left(-\frac{\sqrt{3}}{3}\right)$ ↰
    8. $-30°$ **$-30°$** ↲
13. $\theta = \text{Arc cos }(-1)$ ↰
    9. $-60°$ **180°** ↲

14. Find $\sin A$ if $A = \text{Arc cos }\left(-\frac{5}{13}\right)$. **$\frac{12}{13}$**
15. Find $\cos A$ if $A = \text{Arc sin }\frac{3}{5}$. **$\frac{4}{5}$**
16. Find $\tan A$ if $A = \text{Arc sin }\left(-\frac{12}{13}\right)$. **$-\frac{12}{5}$**
17. Find $\sin A$ if $A = \text{Arc tan }\left(-\frac{3}{4}\right)$. **$-\frac{3}{5}$**

(B) **Find the value of each of the following.**

18. $\cos\left(\text{Arc sin }\left(-\frac{\sqrt{2}}{2}\right)\right)$ **$\frac{\sqrt{2}}{2}$**
19. $\sin^{-1}\left(\tan\left(\frac{2}{3}\pi\right)\right)$ **None**
20. $\text{Arc sin }\left(\cos\left(-\frac{\pi}{4}\right)\right)$ **45°**
21. $\tan\left(\text{Arc cos }\left(\frac{\sqrt{3}}{3}\right)\right)$ **$\sqrt{2}$**
22. $\cos\left(\text{Arc tan }\left(-\frac{4}{3}\right)\right)$ **$\frac{3}{5}$**
23. $\tan\left(\text{Arc cos }\left(-\frac{5}{13}\right)\right)$ **$-\frac{12}{5}$**

(C) **Sketch each graph.** **For Ex. 24–35, see TE Answer Section.**

24. $y = \text{Arc sin } 2x$
25. $y = 2\text{ Arc cos }\frac{1}{2}x$
26. $y = -\frac{1}{2}\text{ Arc sin }(-2x)$
27. $y = -2\text{ Arc tan } x$
28. $y = -2\text{ Arc cos }\left(-\frac{1}{2}x\right)$
29. $y = \text{Arc cot } x$
30. $y = \text{Arc sin } x$
31. $y = \text{Arc cos } x$
32. $y = \text{Arc tan } x$
33. $y = 2\text{ Arc cot } x$
34. $y = \text{Arc sec } x$
35. $y = \text{Arc csc } x$

Applications

A sine graph can be generated from a unit circle.

First, construct a circle with a convenient measure for its radius.

Then, sketch a y-axis and a vertical measure bar. Graduate the measure bar in tenths so that 1 on the measure bar and y-axis correspond to the radius of the circle. Consult the figure below.

Now, sketch an x-axis, positioned as in the figure. Choose a point for π along the x-axis so that it corresponds to about 3.1 times the length of the radius of the circle. Select various points along the x-axis that can be easily identified by halving, quartering, and so on. For example, $\frac{\pi}{2}$ will be placed halfway from 0 to π. These points, including π, will be approximations.

In a similar way, choose points for $\pi, \frac{\pi}{2}, \frac{\pi}{3}$, and so on around the circle.

You can use a compass, a protractor, or triangles to help.

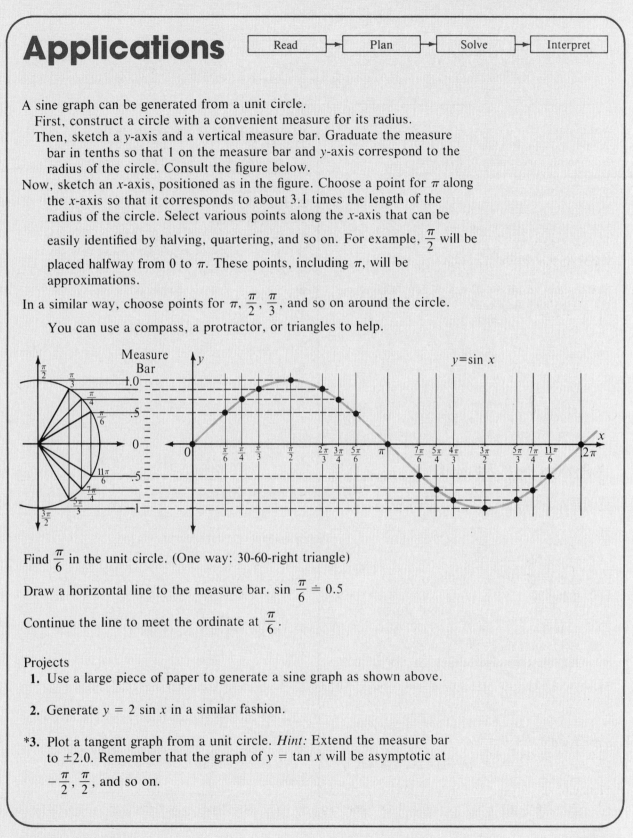

Find $\frac{\pi}{6}$ in the unit circle. (One way: 30-60-right triangle)

Draw a horizontal line to the measure bar. $\sin \frac{\pi}{6} \doteq 0.5$

Continue the line to meet the ordinate at $\frac{\pi}{6}$.

Projects

1. Use a large piece of paper to generate a sine graph as shown above.

2. Generate $y = 2 \sin x$ in a similar fashion.

*3. Plot a tangent graph from a unit circle. *Hint:* Extend the measure bar to ± 2.0. Remember that the graph of $y = \tan x$ will be asymptotic at $-\frac{\pi}{2}, \frac{\pi}{2}$, and so on.

Chapter Eighteen Review

Vocabulary
Amplitude of a function [18.1–18.3]
Inverse of a trig function [18.12]
Periodic function [18.1–18.3]
Principal Values [18.12]
Pythagorean identities [18.8]
Quotient identities [18.8]
Radian measure [18.10]
Reciprocal identities [18.8]

Sketch each graph for $0° \leq x \leq 360°$. Determine the period and amplitude. [18.1–18.5]

1. $y = 3 \cos x$ **360°, 3**   2. $y = \sin(-2x)$
3. $y = \frac{1}{2} \sin(\frac{1}{2} x)$ 4. $y = \tan 3x$ **60°, none**
5. $y = -\frac{1}{2} \cos(-2x)$ ★6. $y = -2 \sec x$

2. **180°, 1**   3. **720°, $\frac{1}{2}$**   5. **180°, $\frac{1}{2}$**   6. **360°, none**

7. Sketch $y = \sin 3x$ and $y = 2 \cos x$ for $-180° \leq x \leq 180°$ on the same set of axes. For how many values of x does $\sin 3x = 2 \cos x$? **2**   [18.4]

8. Find log sin 28° 33′. **9.6794 − 10**   [18.6]
9. Find log cot 48° 47′. **9.9425 − 10**   [18.6]
10. Find u, $0° \leq u \leq 90°$, if log cos u = 9.6348 − 10. **64° 27′**
11. Find u, $0° \leq u \leq 90°$, if log tan u = 9.8732 − 10. **36° 45′**   [18.6]

Find each value to four significant digits. Use logarithms. [18.6]

12. $\dfrac{(\cos 43°)^4}{\sqrt{38.7}}$ **0.1454**   13. $\dfrac{(498)^3 \sqrt{.038}}{\tan 57° 43′}$

14. **0°, 180°** 15. **0°, 180°, 360°, 45°, 135°** 13. **15,210,000**

Solve for θ to the nearest degree ($0° \leq \theta \leq 360°$).

14. $\cos^2 \theta - 1 = 0$ 15. $\sin^2 \theta - \dfrac{\sqrt{2}}{2} \sin \theta = 0$
16. $2 \sin^2 \theta + 5 \sin \theta - 6 = 0$ **62°, 118°**   [18.7]

Solve for θ if $0 \leq \theta \leq 2\pi$. [18.11]

17. $\cos \theta = -\dfrac{\sqrt{2}}{2}$ **$\frac{3\pi}{4}$**   18. $\tan^2 \theta + \tan \theta = 0$
19. $2 \sin^2 \theta - 3 \sin \theta + 1 = 0$ **$\frac{\pi}{6}, \frac{5\pi}{6}, \frac{\pi}{2}$**
★20. $16 \sec^2 \theta - 9 = 0$ **no solution**

18. **$0, \pi, 2\pi, \frac{3\pi}{4}, \frac{7\pi}{4}$**

Express in terms of sin, cos, or both. [18.8]

21. $\tan 23°$ $\frac{\sin 23°}{\cos 23°}$ 22. $\csc 38°$ $\frac{1}{\sin 38°}$
23. $\cot 74° 18′$ $\frac{\cos 74° 18′}{\sin 74° 18′}$ 24. $\sec(-305°)$ $\frac{1}{\cos(-305°)}$

Verify for $A = 240°$ [18.8]

25. $\sin^2 A + \cos^2 A = 1$
26. $\tan^2 A = \sec^2 A - 1$

For Ex. 25–26, 30–31, see TE Answer Section.

Write an equivalent expression using only cos x. [18.8]

27. $\cos x \cdot \dfrac{1}{\sec x}$ $\cos^2 x$ 28. $\tan x$ $\frac{\pm\sqrt{1 - \cos^2 x}}{\cos x}$
29. $\sin x \cdot \sec x$ $\frac{\pm\sqrt{1 - \cos^2 x}}{\cos x}$

Prove each identity. [18.9]

30. $\dfrac{1}{4} \csc \theta = \dfrac{\sin \theta}{3 \sin^2 \theta - \cos^2 \theta + 1}$
31. $\dfrac{\sin \theta}{\cot \theta} + \cos \theta = \sec \theta$

Express in radians. [18.10]
32. 60° $\frac{\pi}{3}$ 33. −45° $\frac{-\pi}{4}$ 34. 330° $\frac{11\pi}{6}$ 35. −140° $\frac{-7\pi}{9}$

Express in degrees. [18.10]
36. $\dfrac{\pi}{12}$ **15°**   37. $-\dfrac{4}{3}\pi$ 38. 6π 39. $-\dfrac{3}{2}\pi$

37. **−240°**   38. **1080°**   39. **−270°**

Evaluate. [18.10]

40. $\tan \dfrac{7\pi}{4}$ **−1**   41. $\cos\left(-\dfrac{\pi}{6}\right)$ $\frac{\sqrt{3}}{2}$

42. $\dfrac{\cos \frac{\pi}{3} - \sin \frac{\pi}{4}}{\tan\left(-\frac{\pi}{4}\right)}$ $\frac{\sqrt{2}-1}{2}$ 43. $\dfrac{\cot\left(-\frac{\pi}{3}\right) + \tan \frac{3\pi}{4}}{\sin \frac{11\pi}{6}}$ $\frac{2\sqrt{3}+6}{3}$

★44. $\sec\left(-\dfrac{\pi}{3}\right) + \csc \dfrac{3\pi}{4} - 3 \sec\left(-\dfrac{5\pi}{4}\right)$

$2 + 4\sqrt{2}$

Find the inverse of each function. Is the inverse a function? [18.12]

45. $y = \cos x$ ★46. $y = 3 \sin x$
  $y = \cos^{-1} x$, **no** $y = \sin^{-1} \frac{x}{3}$, **no**

Find each θ. [18.12]

47. $\theta = \text{Arc cos}\left(-\dfrac{\sqrt{3}}{2}\right)$ 48. $\theta = \text{Arc tan}\left(\dfrac{\sqrt{2}}{2}\right)$
  150°   **35°**

Chapter Eighteen Test

Sketch each graph for $0° \leq x \leq 360°$. Determine the period and amplitude.

1. $y = 2 \sin x$ **360°, 2**   **2.** $y = \cos \left(\frac{1}{2}x\right)$ **720°, 1**

3. $y = \frac{1}{2} \sin 2x$ **180°, $\frac{1}{2}$**   **4.** $y = \tan 2x$ **90°, none**

5. Sketch $y = \sin 2x$ and $y = 3 \cos x$ for $0° \leq x \leq 360°$ on the same set of axes. For how many values of x does $\sin 2x = 3 \cos x$?   **2**

6. Find $\log \cos 36° 45'$.   **9.9038 − 10**

7. Find u, $0° \leq u \leq 90°$, if $\log \tan u = 9.8685 − 10$.   **36° 27'**

Find the value to four significant digits. Use logarithms.

8. $\dfrac{(\sin 38°)^3}{\sqrt{.437}}$ **0.3529**   **9.** $\dfrac{(137)^4 \sqrt{.0867}}{\cos 43° 36'}$

                              143,240,000

Solve for θ to the nearest degree ($0° \leq \theta \leq 360°$).

10. $2 \sin^2 \theta - 1 = 0$ **45°, 135°, 225°, 315°**

11. $2 \cos^2 \theta - \cos \theta - 1 = 0$ **120°, 240°, 0°, 360°**

Solve for θ if $0 \leq \theta \leq 2\pi$.

12. $\tan^2 \theta = \tan \theta$ **13.** $\sin \theta = -\dfrac{\sqrt{3}}{2}$

   $0, \pi, 2\pi, \frac{\pi}{4}, \frac{5\pi}{4}$ $\frac{4\pi}{3}, \frac{5\pi}{3}$

Express in terms of sin, cos, or both.

14. $\tan (-230°)$ $\frac{\sin(-230°)}{\cos(-230°)}$ **15.** $\sec 43°$ $\frac{1}{\cos 43°}$

16. Verify for $A = 150°$. $\cos^2 A = 1 - \sin^2 A$

Write an equivalent expression using only cos x.

17. $\cot x$ $\frac{\pm \cos x}{\sqrt{1 - \cos^2 x}}$ **18.** $\tan x \cdot \csc x$ $\frac{1}{\cos x}$

Prove the identity.

19. $\sec \theta = \dfrac{\tan \theta}{\csc \theta} + \cos \theta$

Express in radians.

20. $45°$ $\frac{\pi}{4}$ **21.** $-330°$ $-\frac{11\pi}{6}$

Express in degrees.

22. $-\dfrac{5\pi}{6}$ **−150°**   **23.** $\dfrac{5}{3}\pi$ **300°**

Evaluate.

24. $\cos \left(-\dfrac{2\pi}{3}\right)$ $-\frac{1}{2}$ **25.** $\dfrac{\sin \frac{\pi}{6} + \cos \frac{7}{6}\pi}{\tan \left(-\frac{\pi}{3}\right)}$

                                       $\frac{-\sqrt{3}+3}{6}$

Find the inverse of each function. Is the inverse a function?

26. $y = \tan x$ **27.** $y = -2 \sin x$
     $y = \tan^{-1} x$, **no** $y = \sin^{-1} \left(-\frac{x}{2}\right)$, **no**

Find θ.

28. $\theta = $ Arc $\sin \left(-\dfrac{\sqrt{2}}{2}\right)$ $\frac{-\pi}{4}$

Find each value.

29. $\sin \left(\text{Arc} \tan \dfrac{5}{12}\right)$ $\frac{5}{13}$

30. $\tan \left(\text{Arc} \cos \dfrac{5}{6}\right)$ $\frac{\sqrt{11}}{5}$

31. Sketch $y = -\cos \left(\dfrac{1}{2}x\right)$ and $y = 3 \sin (2x)$ for $-\pi \leq x \leq 2\pi$ on the same set of axes. For how many values of x does $-\cos \frac{1}{2}x = 3 \sin 2x$?   **6**

Sketch each graph.

★**32.** $y = $ Arc $\cos x$

★**33.** $y = $ Arc $\tan x$

★**34.** $y = $ arc $\csc x$

Solve for θ if $0° \leq \theta \leq 360°$.

★**35.** $4 \csc^2 \theta - 9 = 0$ **41° 50', 138° 10', 221° 50', 318° 10'**

Prove the identity.

★**36.** $\dfrac{\sin \theta + \cos \theta}{\sec \theta + \csc \theta} = \dfrac{1}{\sec \theta \cdot \csc \theta}$

Evaluate.

★**37.** $\dfrac{\sec \left(-\frac{\pi}{4}\right) - \csc \frac{3}{2}\pi}{-6 \sec \frac{4\pi}{3}}$ $\frac{1 + \sqrt{2}}{12}$

For complete solutions, see TE Answer Section.

Computer Activities

A Sine of the Weather

Many natural occurrences are periodic in nature and can be represented by a sine function. Phenomena include sound waves, electrical currents, air pollution levels, business cycles, and temperature patterns. Temperature variation can be represented by the general form of the sine curve, $y = a \sin bx$, but with a shift in both the vertical and horizontal placement. To graph any trigonometric function you need a table of x, y values. You can use the computer to find these values.

PROGRAM

```
10 PRINT "PROGRAM PRINTS A CHART OF"
20 PRINT "VALUES FOR SIN FUNCTION GRAPH: Y = A * (SIN B * X)"
30 PRINT "ENTER A"
40 INPUT A
50 PRINT "ENTER B"
60 INPUT B
70 FOR X = 0 TO 360 STEP 45
80 LET R = Y * (3.14159/180)
90 LET Y = A * SIN (B * R)
100 PRINT "FOR ANGLE"; X; "A * SIN (B * X) = "; Y
110 NEXT X
120 END
```

Exercises

Run the above program for the following values of amplitude (a) and period (b).

1. $a = 1$ $b = 1$

2. $a = 2$ $b = 1$

3. $a = 1$ $b = 2$

4. $a = 1$ $b = \frac{1}{2}$ (Note: $b = \frac{1}{2}$ must be entered as .5.)

5. Write a program to compute the x and y values for the temperature variation curve using the sine function $y = 40 \sin ((2\pi/365)(x - 100)) + 25$, where a is 40, b is $2\pi/365$, 100 is the horizontal shift, and 25 is the vertical shift. Graph the x, y values, using days on the x-axis and degrees on the y-axis. (Contact your local weather service for the daily temperatures for a year to compare for the sine function generated.)

For solutions to Ex. 1–5, see TE Answer Section.

College Prep Test

In questions 1 and 2 use the information given. Right triangle ABC with right angle C

1. Quantity I $(AC)^2 + (BC)^2$ **C**
   Quantity II $(AB)^2$

2. Quantity I $2(AC)^2$ **D**
   Quantity II $(AB)^2$

3. Information: Triangle ABC

   Quantity I $AC + BC$ **A**
   Quantity II AB

4. Information: Triangle ABC with $m\angle C < 90°$. Triangle RST with $m\angle T > 90°$.

   Quantity I AB **D**
   Quantity II RS

5. Information: Right triangle ABC, C is a right angle and $m\angle B = 30°$.

   Quantity I AB **C**
   Quantity II $2AC$

6. Quantity I $\left(\dfrac{\pi}{2} + \dfrac{\pi}{6}\right)$ radians **C**
   Quantity II $30° + 90°$

7. Information: Right triangle ABC with right angle C. Right triangle RST with right angle T. The measure of angle S equals the measure of angle B.

   Quantity I $(AC)(RS)$ **C**
   Quantity II $(AB)(RT)$

8. Information: Right triangle ABC with right angle C and $m\angle A = 60°$. Right triangle RST with right angle T and $m\angle R = 45°$.

   Quantity I BC **D**
   Quantity II ST

9. Information: $m\angle A > m\angle B$
   $m\angle B > m\angle C$

   Quantity I $2\,m\angle A$
   Quantity II $m\angle B + m\angle C$ **A**

10. Information:

   Quantity I $d° + c°$
   Quantity II $a° + b° + c°$ **C**

19 TRIGONOMETRIC LAWS AND FORMULAS

Careers: Biological Sciences

A biologist may choose a career from among many different specialties. Three examples are entomology, icthyology, and microbiology.

An **entomologist** is concerned with reducing the harmful species of insects that destroy crops, buildings, and clothing, or cause disease in humans or wildlife. Efforts to increase and spread the many insects that are beneficial to the "balance of nature" are also important.

An **icthyologist** specializes in the study of fish: identifying, rearing, and hatching. These endeavors are important because fish are the chief source of protein for many groups of people around the world.

A **microbiologist** studies microorganisms such as bacteria and viruses. A career in microbiology may lead to important contributions in public health, industry, medicine, or agriculture.

19.1 Law of Cosines

OBJECTIVE ▶ **To find the length of a side of a triangle using the Law of Cosines**

If two sides and the included angle of any triangle are known, the length of the third side can be found. You will now learn how to derive formulas to do this and how to apply these formulas.

For the general triangle ABC, you can show that $a^2 = b^2 + c^2 - 2bc \cos A$.
In right $\triangle ABD$, $c^2 = h^2 + x^2$, or $h^2 = c^2 - x^2$.
In right $\triangle BDC$, $a^2 = h^2 + y^2$.

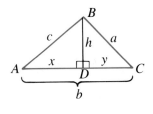

$$a^2 = h^2 + y^2$$

Since $h^2 = c^2 - x^2$ ▶ $= (c^2 - x^2) + y^2$
$= (y^2 - x^2) + c^2$

By factoring ▶ $= (y + x)(y - x) + c^2$

Since $b = x + y$, $y = b - x$ ▶ $= (b - x + x)(b - x - x) + c^2$
$= (b)(b - 2x) + c^2$

Since $\cos A = \frac{x}{c}$, $x = c \cos A$ ▶ $= b^2 - 2b(c \cos A) + c^2$
$= b^2 - 2bc \cos A + c^2$

So, $a^2 = b^2 + c^2 - 2bc \cos A$.

Law of Cosines

For any triangle ABC,
$a^2 = b^2 + c^2 - 2bc \cos A$
$b^2 = a^2 + c^2 - 2ac \cos B$
$c^2 = a^2 + b^2 - 2ab \cos C$.

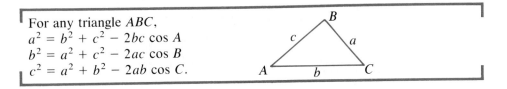

In general, the Law of Cosines states that the square of one side of a triangle equals the sum of the squares of the other two sides minus twice the product of these two sides and the cosine of the included angle.

Example 1 In $\triangle ABC$, $b = 8$, $c = 7$, and $m \angle A = 45°$. **Find a to the nearest unit.**

Use $a^2 = b^2 + c^2 - 2bc \cos A$.
$= 8^2 + 7^2 - 2(8)(7) \cos 45°$
$= 64 + 49 - 112\left(\dfrac{\sqrt{2}}{2}\right)$
$\doteq 64 + 49 - 56(1.414)$
$\doteq 33.8$

Thus $a \doteq \sqrt{33.8}$, or 6.

Example 2

In △ABC, a = 4, b = 6, and m∠c = 150°. Find c to the nearest unit.

Use $c^2 = a^2 + b^2 - 2ab \cos C$.

$$\begin{aligned}
&= 4^2 + 6^2 - 2(4)(6) \cos 150° \\
&= 16 + 36 - 48(-\cos 30°) \\
&= 52 - 48\left(-\frac{\sqrt{3}}{2}\right) \\
&= 52 + 24\sqrt{3} \\
&= 52 + 24(1.732) \\
c^2 &= 52 + 41.568 \\
c &= \sqrt{93.568} \doteq 9.673
\end{aligned}$$

Thus, $c = 10$ to the nearest unit.

For a right triangle, the Law of Cosines becomes the Pythagorean theorem. In right triangle ABC, m∠$c = 90°$. Use the Law of Cosines to find c.

$$\begin{aligned}
c^2 &= a^2 + b^2 - 2ab \cos C \\
&= a^2 + b^2 - 2ab \cos 90° \\
&= a^2 + b^2 - 2ab(0)
\end{aligned}$$

So, $c^2 = a^2 + b^2$.

The next example illustrates how the Law of Cosines can be used to solve problems.

Example 3

A surveyor at point R sights two points S and T on opposite sides of a lake. Point R is 120 meters from S and 180 meters from T, and the measure of angle R is 38°. Find the distance across the lake to the nearest meter.

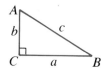

Use $r^2 = s^2 + t^2 - 2st \cos R$.

$$\begin{aligned}
&= (180)^2 + (120)^2 - 2(180)(120) \cos 38° \\
&= 32,400 + 14,400 - 43,200(.7880) \\
&= 46,800 - 34,041.6 \\
r^2 &= 12,758.4 \\
r &= \sqrt{12,758.4} \doteq 113
\end{aligned}$$

Thus, the distance across the lake $\doteq 113$ meters.

Reading in **Algebra**

Which one doesn't belong?

1. **a)** $c^2 = a^2 + b^2 - 2ab \cos 180°$ **b)** $c^2 = a^2 + b^2$ **c)** $c^2 = a^2 + b^2 - 2ab \cos 90°$ **a**
2. **a)** $r^2 = s^2 + t^2 - 2st \cos R$ **b)** $s^2 = r^2 + t^2 - 2rt \cos S$ **c)** $t^2 = r^2 + s^2 - 2rs \cos R$ **c**
3. **a)** $c = \sqrt{a^2 + b^2 - 2ab \cos C}$ **b)** $a = \sqrt{b^2 + c^2 - 2bc \cos A}$ **c)** $b = a + b - \sqrt{2ab \cos B}$ **c**

Oral Exercises

Give the form of the law of cosines needed to find x.

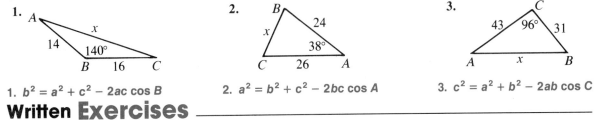

1. $b^2 = a^2 + c^2 - 2ac \cos B$

2. $a^2 = b^2 + c^2 - 2bc \cos A$

3. $c^2 = a^2 + b^2 - 2ab \cos C$

Written Exercises

(A) Each exercise refers to triangle ABC. Find the length of the indicated side to the nearest unit.

1. $a = 8, b = 9, m \angle C = 60°$. Find c. **9**
2. $a = 10, c = 18, m \angle B = 120°$. Find b. **25**
3. $b = 12, c = 15, m \angle A = 135°$. Find a. **25**
4. $a = 15, b = 14, m \angle C = 150°$. Find c. **28**
5. $a = 13, c = 18, m \angle B = 30°$. Find b. **9**
6. $b = 17, c = 12, m \angle A = 45°$. Find a. **12**
7. $b = 11.3, c = 13.1, m \angle A = 120°$. Find a. **21**
8. $a = 17.3, c = 19.7, m \angle B = 135°$. Find b. **34**
9. $a = 33.4, b = 22.7, m \angle C = 150°$. Find c. **54**
10. $b = 51.7, c = 73.2, m \angle A = 60°$. Find a. **65**

(B)
11. $b = 47.3, c = 72.9, m \angle A = 18°$. Find a. **32**
12. $a = 63.4, c = 27.6, m \angle B = 39°$. Find b. **45**
13. $a = 12.9, b = 16.3, m \angle C = 12° 30'$. Find c. **5**
14. $b = 19.6, c = 35.3, m \angle A = 45° 40'$. Find a. **26**
15. $b = 19.1, c = 34.6, m \angle A = 73° 18'$. Find a. **34**
16. $a = 41.3, b = 16.9, m \angle C = 81° 26'$. Find c. **42**
17. $a = 49.7, c = 43.1, m \angle B = 120° 33'$. Find b. **81**
18. $b = 123, c = 119, m \angle A = 105° 48'$. Find a. **193**

19. Two sides of a parallelogram form an angle of 72°. The lengths of two of the sides are 18 and 24 centimeters. How long is the shorter diagonal? **25**

20. A side and a base of an isosceles trapezoid form an angle of 54°. The length of the side is 14 centimeters and of the base is 34 centimeters. How long is a diagonal? **28**

21. Two ships left from the same port on paths that form an angle of 68°. Ship A traveled 400 km; ship B traveled 325 km. Find to the nearest kilometer the distance between them. **410 km**

22. Two airplanes left the same airport and formed a 65° angle in their flight paths. The first plane flew at 600 km/h, and the second flew at 800 km/h. How far apart were they after 2 hours? **1,541 km**

For Ex. 23–26, see TE Answer Section.

(C) 23. In $\triangle ABC$, $m \angle B < 90°$.
Prove that $b^2 = a^2 + c^2 - 2ac \cos B$.

24. In $\triangle ABC$, $m \angle C < 90°$.
Prove that $c^2 = a^2 + b^2 - 2ab \cos C$.

25. In $\triangle ABC$, $m \angle A > 90°$.
Prove that $a^2 = b^2 + c^2 - 2bc \cos A$.

26. In $\triangle ABC$, $m \angle B > 90°$.
Prove that $b^2 = a^2 + c^2 - 2ac \cos B$.

Cumulative Review

Use the Pythagorean relation to determine whether the following are measures of the sides of a right triangle.

1. 8, 15, 17 **Yes**
2. 5, 12, 13 **Yes**
3. $1, 2\sqrt{7}, 3\sqrt{3}$ **Yes**

LAW OF COSINES

19.2 Using the Law of Cosines to Find Angle Measures

OBJECTIVE ▶ **To use the Law of Cosines to find the degree measure of an angle**

You can apply the Law of Cosines to find the measure of an angle of any triangle if the lengths of the three sides are known.

Using the Law of Cosines involving cos A, solve for cos A as follows.

$$a^2 = b^2 + c^2 - 2bc \cos A$$
$$2bc \cos A = b^2 + c^2 - a^2$$

So, $\cos A = \dfrac{b^2 + c^2 - a^2}{2bc}$.

Finding an Angle Using the Law of Cosines

For any triangle ABC,

$$\cos A = \frac{b^2 + c^2 - a^2}{2bc}$$

$$\cos B = \frac{a^2 + c^2 - b^2}{2ac}$$

$$\cos C = \frac{a^2 + b^2 - c^2}{2ab}.$$

Example 1

In △ABC, $a = 6$, $b = 7$ and $c = 4$. Find m$\angle A$ and m$\angle B$ to the nearest degree.

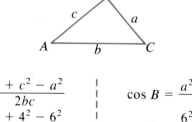

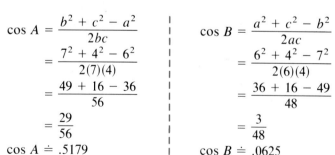

$$\cos A = \frac{b^2 + c^2 - a^2}{2bc}$$

$$= \frac{7^2 + 4^2 - 6^2}{2(7)(4)}$$

$$= \frac{49 + 16 - 36}{56}$$

$$= \frac{29}{56}$$

$$\cos A \doteq .5179$$

$$\cos B = \frac{a^2 + c^2 - b^2}{2ac}$$

$$= \frac{6^2 + 4^2 - 7^2}{2(6)(4)}$$

$$= \frac{36 + 16 - 49}{48}$$

$$= \frac{3}{48}$$

$$\cos B \doteq .0625$$

Thus, $m\angle A = 59°$ and $m\angle B = 86°$, to the nearest degree.

Example 2 In $\triangle ABC$, the length of the sides are 3, 4, and 6. Find the measure of the smallest angle to the nearest degree.

The angle opposite the shortest side has the least measure.

$$\cos B = \frac{a^2 + c^2 - b^2}{2ac}$$

$$= \frac{36 + 16 - 9}{2(6)(4)}$$

$$\cos B = \frac{43}{48}, \text{ or } .8958$$

$$m\angle B \doteq 26°$$

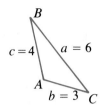

Thus, the measure of the smallest angle to the nearest degree is 26°.

Written Exercises

(A) **Find the measure of each angle to the nearest degree.**

1. $a = 3$, $b = 8$, $c = 7$. Find $m\angle A$. **22°**

2. $a = 9$, $b = 3$, $c = 9$. Find $m\angle B$. **19°**

3. $a = 13$, $b = 12$, $c = 5$. Find $m\angle B$. **67°**

4. $a = 2$, $b = 8$, $c = 7$. Find $m\angle C$. **54°**

5. $a = 7$, $b = 9$, $c = 3$. Find $m\angle A$. **41°**

6. $a = 6$, $b = 3$, $c = 4$. Find $m\angle C$. **36°**

7. $a = 10$, $b = 2$, $c = 9$. Find $m\angle C$. **55°**

8. $a = 10$, $b = 6$, $c = 9$. Find $m\angle A$. **81°**

(B) **9.** $a = 12.3$, $b = 9.6$, $c = 7.3$. Find $m\angle A$. **92°**

10. $a = 14.3$, $b = 19.5$, $c = 26.1$. Find $m\angle C$. **100°**

11. $a = 17.5$, $b = 16.4$, $c = 11.7$. Find $m\angle C$. **40°**

12. $a = 9.7$, $b = 23.4$, $c = 17.9$. Find $m\angle A$. **23°**

13. $a = 9.6$, $b = 17.5$, $c = 12.8$. Find $m\angle B$. **102°**

14. $a = 36.1$, $b = 44.7$, $c = 28.6$. Find $m\angle B$. **87°**

15. The measures of two sides of a parallelogram are 40 cm and 50 cm, and the length of one diagonal is 70 cm. Find the measures of the angles of the parallelogram. **102°, 78°**

16. Two straight roads $\overleftrightarrow{MN}$ and $\overrightarrow{PN}$ intersect at a town N. M is 62 km from N and P is 77 km from N. MP is 85 km. Find the angle that roads $\overleftrightarrow{MN}$ and $\overrightarrow{PN}$ make with each other. **75°**

In $\triangle ABC$, find the measure of the smallest angle to the nearest degree.

17. $a = 6$, $b = 8$, $c = 9$ **41°**

18. $a = 12$, $b = 13$, $c = 15$ **50°**

19. $a = 9$, $b = 3$, $c = 8$ **19°**

For Ex. 20–21, see TE Answer Section.

(C) **20.** Prove: For any $\triangle ABC$,
$$\cos B = \frac{a^2 + c^2 - b^2}{2ac}$$

21. Prove: For any $\triangle ABC$,
$$\cos C = \frac{a^2 + b^2 - c^2}{2ab}$$

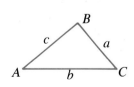

19.3 Area of a Triangle

OBJECTIVE ▶ **To apply formulas for the area of a triangle given the measures of two sides and the included angle**

If two sides and the included angle of any triangle are known, a formula for finding the area of the triangle can be derived as follows.

Recall that the area of a triangle is one half the product of the base and the height.

Area of $\triangle ABC = k = \frac{1}{2}bh$.

But $\sin A = \dfrac{h}{c}$, or $h = c \sin A$.

Now, substitute $c \sin A$ for h in the original formula.
$k = \frac{1}{2}b(c \sin A)$ or $\frac{1}{2}bc \sin A$

The area of a triangle is one half the product of the lengths of any two sides and the sine of the included angle measure.

Area of Any Triangle

For any triangle ABC,
$k = \frac{1}{2}bc \sin A$
$k = \frac{1}{2}ab \sin C$
$k = \frac{1}{2}ac \sin B$

Example 1 In $\triangle ABC$, $b = 10$, $c = 8$ and $m\angle A = 60°$. **Find the area in simplest radical form.**

$k = \frac{1}{2}bc \sin A$.
$\quad = \frac{1}{2}(10)(8) \sin 60°$
$\quad = 40 \cdot \dfrac{\sqrt{3}}{2}$, or $20\sqrt{3}$

Thus, the area of $\triangle ABC$ is $20\sqrt{3}$ square units.

Example 2 In $\triangle ABC$, $a = 8$, $b = 12$ and $m\angle C = 140°$. **Find the area to the nearest square unit.**

$k = \dfrac{1}{2} ab \sin C$.

$\quad = \dfrac{1}{2}(8)(12) \sin 140°$

$\quad = 48 \sin 40°$

$\quad \doteq 48(.6428)$

$\quad \doteq 30.8544$

Thus, the area of $\triangle ABC$ is 31 square units to the nearest square unit.

544

Example 3 In $\triangle PQR$, $q = 15$, $r = 60$. Find the measure of $\angle P$ to the nearest degree if the area is 240 square units.

Use an area formula for q, r, and $\angle P$.

$$k = \frac{1}{2} qr \sin P$$

$$240 = \frac{1}{2} (15)(60) \sin P$$

$$\sin P = \frac{240}{450} \doteq .5333$$

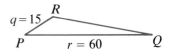

Thus, the measure of $\angle P$ is 32° to the nearest degree.

Oral **Exercises**

Give the form of the area formula needed to find the area of each triangle.

1. $a = 6$, $c = 8$, m$\angle B = 36°$
$k = \frac{1}{2} ac \sin B$

2. $b = 9$, $c = 7$, m$\angle A = 73°$
$k = \frac{1}{2} bc \sin A$

3. $a = 4$, $b = 8$, m$\angle C = 41°$
$k = \frac{1}{2} ab \sin C$

Written **Exercises**

Ⓐ In $\triangle ABC$, find the area to the nearest square unit.

1. $a = 12$, $b = 9$, m$\angle C = 43°$ **37** **2.** $b = 9$, $c = 7$, m$\angle A = 80°$ **31** **3.** $a = 6$, $c = 8$, m$\angle B = 70°$ **23**

4. $a = 7$, $b = 11$, m$\angle C = 34°$ **22** **5.** $a = 13$, $c = 12$, m$\angle B = 48°$ **58** **6.** $b = 12$, $c = 9$, m$\angle A = 38°$ **33**

In $\triangle PQR$, find the measure of $\angle P$ to the nearest degree.

7. $q = 8$, $r = 12$, $k = 38$ sq. units **52°**

8. $q = 14$, $r = 8$, $k = 54$ sq. units **75°**

9. $q = 16$, $r = 10$, $k = 74$ sq. units **68°**

10. $q = 6$, $r = 9$, $k = 22$ sq. units **55°**

Ⓑ In $\triangle ABC$, find the area to the nearest square unit.

11. $a = 6.2$, $b = 4.4$, m$\angle C = 150°$ **7**

12. $a = 9.7$, $c = 4.8$, m$\angle B = 135° 20'$ **16**

13. $a = 9.1$, $c = 7.6$, m$\angle B = 78°$ **34**

14. $b = 12.3$, $c = 13.7$, m$\angle A = 105° 30'$ **81**

15. The lengths of two sides of a parallelogram are 24 and 36 centimeters. Their included angle measures 50°. Find the area of the parallelogram. **662 cm²**

16. The lengths of two sides of a parallelogram are 30 and 45 centimeters. Their included angle measures 130°. Find the area of the parallelogram. **1034 cm²**

Ⓒ **17.** Prove: For any triangle ABC
$k = \frac{1}{2} ab \sin C$ and $k = \frac{1}{2} ac \sin B$.
For Ex. 17–18, see TE Answer Section.

18. Prove: The area of a parallelogram is equal to the product of the lengths of two adjacent sides and the sine of their included angle.

AREA OF A TRIANGLE

19.4 Law of Sines

OBJECTIVE ▶ **To apply the Law of Sines to find unknown measures in a triangle if two angles and a side of any triangle are known**

If two angles and a side of any triangle are known, the measure of the third angle and the lengths of the other two sides can be found.

Recall from the previous lesson three ways to write the area of a triangle, ABC.

$$\frac{1}{2}\, bc \sin A = \frac{1}{2}\, ab \sin C = \frac{1}{2}\, ac \sin B$$

Multiplying by 2. ▶ $\quad bc \sin A = ab \sin C = ac \sin B$

Dividing by abc. ▶ $\quad \dfrac{bc \sin A}{abc} = \dfrac{ab \sin C}{abc} = \dfrac{ac \sin B}{abc}$

So, $\dfrac{\sin A}{a} = \dfrac{\sin C}{c} = \dfrac{\sin B}{b}$.

Law of Sines

> For any triangle ABC,
> $$\frac{\sin A}{a} = \frac{\sin B}{b} = \frac{\sin C}{c}, \text{ or } \frac{a}{\sin A} = \frac{b}{\sin B} = \frac{c}{\sin C}.$$

In general, the Law of Sines states that the sides of a triangle are proportional to the sines of the angles opposite them.

Example 1 In $\triangle ABC$, $a = 16$, and $m \angle A = 40°$, $m \angle B = 58°$. Find b to the nearest unit.

Use $\quad \dfrac{a}{\sin A} = \dfrac{b}{\sin B}$ since a, $m \angle A$, and $m \angle B$ are given.

$\dfrac{16}{\sin 40°} = \dfrac{b}{\sin 58°}$

$\dfrac{16 \sin 58°}{\sin 40°} = b$

$\dfrac{16(.8480)}{.6428} = b$

$21.1076 \doteq b$

Thus, $b = 21$ to the nearest unit.

Example 2 In $\triangle ABC$, $a = 80$, $b = 60$, and m$\angle A = 52°$. Find the measure of $\angle B$ to the nearest degree.

Use $\dfrac{\sin A}{a} = \dfrac{\sin B}{b}$ since a, b, and m$\angle A$ are given.

$$\dfrac{\sin 52°}{80} = \dfrac{\sin B}{60}$$

$$\sin B = \dfrac{60(\sin 52°)}{80}$$

$$= \dfrac{60(.7880)}{80}$$

$$\sin B \doteq .5910$$

Thus, the measure of $\angle B$ is $36°$ to the nearest degree.

Example 3 In $\triangle ABC$, $b = 18$, m$\angle A = 64°$, m$\angle C = 55°$. Find c to the nearest unit.

First, find m$\angle B$.
m$\angle B + 55° + 64° = 180°$ so m$\angle B = 61°$

Use $\dfrac{b}{\sin B} = \dfrac{c}{\sin C}$.

$$\dfrac{18}{\sin 61°} = \dfrac{c}{\sin 55°}, \text{ or } c = \dfrac{18 \sin 55°}{\sin 61°}$$

$$c \doteq \dfrac{18(.8192)}{.8746}, \text{ or } 16.86$$

Thus, $c = 17$ to the nearest unit.

You can use logarithms to solve problems involving the Law of Sines.

Example 4 In $\triangle ABC$, m$\angle A = 42° \, 10'$, m$\angle B = 73° \, 18'$, $b = 36.14$. Find a to the nearest tenth.

Use $\dfrac{a}{\sin A} = \dfrac{b}{\sin B}$.

$$\dfrac{a}{\sin 42° \, 10'} = \dfrac{36.14}{\sin 73° \, 18'}, \text{ or } a = \dfrac{36.14 \sin 42° \, 10'}{\sin 73° \, 18'}$$

Take the log of each side. ▶ $\log a = \log 36.14 + \log \sin 42° \, 10' - \log \sin 73° \, 18'$
Interpolate. ▶ $ = 1.5580 \quad + \quad 9.8269 - 10 \quad - (9.9813 - 10)$
$$\log a = 1.4036$$

Thus, $a = 25.3$.

Oral Exercises

Give the form of the Law of Sines that is needed to find x.

1.

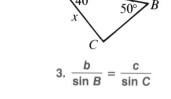

2.

3.

1. $\dfrac{a}{\sin A} = \dfrac{b}{\sin B}$

2. $\dfrac{\sin A}{a} = \dfrac{\sin C}{c}$

3. $\dfrac{b}{\sin B} = \dfrac{c}{\sin C}$

Written Exercises

(A)

1. For $\triangle ABC$, $a = 28$, $b = 59$, $m\angle B = 48°$. Find $m\angle A$ to the nearest degree. **21°**

2. For $\triangle ABC$, $a = 36$, $c = 18$, $m\angle A = 57°$. Find $m\angle C$ to the nearest degree. **25°**

3. For $\triangle PQR$, $p = 17$, $m\angle P = 75°$, $m\angle Q = 38°$. Find q to the nearest unit. **11**

4. For $\triangle PQR$, $r = 29$, $m\angle P = 37°$, $m\angle R = 71°$. Find p to the nearest unit. **19**

5. For $\triangle ABC$, $a = 14$, $c = 10$, $m\angle C = 30°$. Find $m\angle A$ to the nearest degree. **44°**

6. For $\triangle PQR$, $q = 5$, $r = 7$, $m\angle Q = 40°$. Find $m\angle R$ to the nearest degree. **64°**

7. For $\triangle PQR$, $p = 22$, $\sin P = \frac{1}{5}$, $\sin Q = \frac{4}{5}$. Find q to the nearest unit. **88**

8. For $\triangle ABC$, $\sin A = .40$, $\sin B = .65$, $a = 32$. Find b to the nearest unit. **52**

(B)

9. For $\triangle ABC$, $a = 16.3$, $m\angle B = 58°$, $m\angle C = 37°$. Find b, c, and $m\angle A$. **13.9, 9.8, 85°**

10. For $\triangle ABC$, $a = 12.3$, $b = 13.7$, $m\angle A = 18°\ 25'$. Find c, $m\angle B$, and $m\angle C$.
24.5, 20° 36′, 140° 59′

11. For $\triangle ABC$, $b = 14.8$, $c = 18.9$, $m\angle C = 42°\ 18'$. Find a, $m\angle A$, and $m\angle B$.
27, 105° 54′, 31° 48′

12. For $\triangle ABC$, $a = 15.1$, $c = 19.3$, $m\angle C = 37°\ 32'$. Find b, $m\angle A$, and $m\angle B$.
28.9, 28° 28′, 114°

13. The distance between town B and town A is 45 kilometers. The angle formed by the roads between towns A and B and between towns A and C measures 37°, and the angle formed by $\overline{AB}$ and $\overline{BC}$ measures 110°. Find the distance from town B to town C to the nearest kilometer. **50 km**

14. Two cars P and Q are parked on the same side of the street, 50 meters apart. Car R is not on the same road. The angle formed by $\overrightarrow{PQ}$ and $\overrightarrow{PR}$ is 112° 20′, and the angle formed by $\overrightarrow{QR}$ and $\overrightarrow{PR}$ is 28° 40′. Find the distance between P and R to the nearest meter. **66 m**

(C)

15. For $\triangle RST$, show that $\dfrac{\sin R}{r} = \dfrac{\sin T}{t} = \dfrac{\sin S}{s}$.

16. For $\triangle QRS$, show that $\dfrac{q}{\sin Q} = \dfrac{r}{\sin R} = \dfrac{s}{\sin S}$.

For Ex. 15–16, see TE Answer Section.

CALCULATOR ACTIVITIES

The calculator can be an aid in solving problems involving the Law of Sines.

From Example 3, $\dfrac{18}{\sin 61°} = \dfrac{c}{\sin 55°}$ or $c = \dfrac{18 \sin 55°}{\sin 61°} = \dfrac{18(.8192)}{.8746}$.

Compute ▶ $18 \otimes .8192 \div .8746 = 16.86$.

19.5 The Ambiguous Case

OBJECTIVE ▶ **To determine the number of triangles that can be constructed given certain data**

In this lesson, you will compare parts of a triangle to determine the number of triangles it is possible to construct.

Example 1 Given that $a = 18$, $b = 36$, and m$\angle A = 38°$, use the Law of Sines to find the measure of $\angle B$. How many triangles can be constructed using the given data?

Use $\dfrac{\sin A}{a} = \dfrac{\sin B}{b}$.

$\dfrac{\sin 38°}{18} = \dfrac{\sin B}{36}$, or $\sin B = \dfrac{36 \sin 38°}{18}$

$\sin B \doteq \dfrac{36(.6157)}{18}$, or 1.2314

Thus, there is no $\angle B$ for which $\sin B = 1.2314$ since $0 \leq \sin B \leq 1$ and no triangle can be constructed with the given data.

In general, $\dfrac{\sin A}{a} = \dfrac{\sin B}{b}$

$\sin B = \dfrac{b \sin A}{a}$,

but $\sin B = \dfrac{h}{a}$, so $h = b \sin A$.

Compare h and a. When $a < h$, ($a < b \sin A$), as in Example 1, no triangle can be constructed since $\sin B = \frac{h}{a}$ will be greater than 1. When $a = h$, $\sin B = 1$, one right $\triangle$ can be constructed.
When $a > h$, $\sin B < 1$, two $\triangle$'s can be constructed.
The following Summary is suggested.

Summary	A is an acute angle and $a < b$:
	1. If $a < h$, ($a < b \sin A$), no triangle can be constructed.
	2. If $a = h$, ($a = b \sin A$), one triangle can be constructed.
	3. If $a > h$, ($a > b \sin A$), two triangles can be constructed.

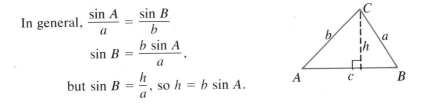

THE AMBIGUOUS CASE

Example 2 Given that m $\angle A = 34°$, $a = 21$, $b = 32$, and the height, h, is 25, can a triangle be constructed?

A is an acute angle, $a < b$ and $a < h$.

Thus, no triangle can be constructed.

In $\triangle ABC$, $\angle A$ is an acute angle. You will now determine how many triangles can be constructed if $a = b$ and if $a > b$.

$\angle A$ is an acute angle.

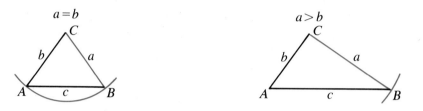

Summary	$\angle A$ is an acute angle:
	1. One triangle can be constructed if $a = b$.
	2. One triangle can be constructed if $a > b$.

Example 3 Given that m $\angle A = 130°$, $a = 12$, and $b = 13$, find the measure of $\angle C$ to the nearest degree. How many triangles can be constructed using the given data?

Use $\dfrac{\sin A}{a} = \dfrac{\sin B}{b}$.

$\dfrac{\sin 130°}{12} = \dfrac{\sin B}{13}$, or $\sin B = \dfrac{13 \sin 130°}{12}$

$\sin B \doteq \dfrac{13(.7660)}{12}$, or .8298

So, the measure of $\angle B$ is 56° to the nearest degree.
Find m $\angle C$. m $\angle A$ + m $\angle B$ + m $\angle C = 180°$
$130° + 56° + m \angle C = 180°$
$186° + m \angle C = 180°$
$m \angle C = 180° - 186°$, or $-6°$

Thus, no triangle can be constructed when angle A is obtuse and $a < b$.

Example 4 Given that m$\angle A$ = 130°, a = 12, b = 12, find the measure of $\angle C$ to the nearest degree. How many triangles can be constructed?

$$\sin B \doteq \frac{12(.7660)}{12}, \text{ or } .7660 \quad \blacktriangleleft \quad \sin B = \frac{b \sin A}{a}$$

So, the measure of $\angle B$ is 50°.

$$130° + 50° + m\angle C = 180°$$
$$m\angle C = 0°$$

Thus, no triangle can be constructed when angle A is obtuse and $a = b$.

Example 5 Given that m$\angle A$ = 130°, a = 12, b = 10, find the measure of $\angle C$ to the nearest degree. How many triangles can be constructed?

$$\sin B \doteq \frac{10(.7660)}{12}, \text{ or } .6383$$

So, the measure of $\angle B$ is 40° to the nearest degree.

$$130° + 40° + m\angle C = 180°$$
$$m\angle C = 10°$$

Thus, one triangle can be constructed when angle A is obtuse and $a > b$.

The last three examples suggest the following.

Summary	$\angle A$ is an obtuse angle or a right angle: 1. No triangle can be constructed if $a \leq b$. 2. One triangle can be constructed if $a > b$.

Example 6 How many triangles can be constructed if m$\angle A$ = 160°, a = 20, and b = 60?

$\angle A$ is an obtuse angle and $a < b$.

Thus, no triangle can be constructed when angle A is obtuse and $a < b$.

Written Exercises

How many triangles can be constructed?

1. m$\angle A$ = 36°, a = 12, b = 18 **2**
2. m$\angle A$ = 48°, a = 6, b = 7 **2**
3. m$\angle A$ = 40°, a = 50, b = 20 **1**
4. m$\angle A$ = 120°, a = 19, b = 21 **0**
5. m$\angle A$ = 90°, a = 96, b = 96 **0**
6. m$\angle A$ = 175°, a = 71, b = 58 **1**
7. m$\angle A$ = 15°, a = 100, b = 100 **1**
8. m$\angle A$ = 52°, a = 42, b = 38 **1**
9. m$\angle A$ = 133°, a = 16, b = 4 **1**
10. m$\angle A$ = 90°, a = 14, b = 14 **0**

THE AMBIGUOUS CASE

19.6 Sin (A ± B) and Sin 2A

OBJECTIVE ▶ **To apply the formulas for sin (A ± B) and sin 2A**

You can derive the formula for the sine of the sum of two angles in the following way.

Write the formulas for the areas of each of the three triangles shown at the right.
Area $\triangle ABC$ = area $\triangle ABD$ + area $\triangle BDC$

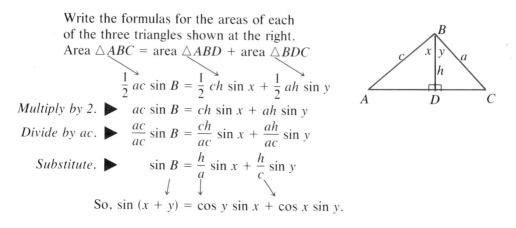

$$\frac{1}{2} ac \sin B = \frac{1}{2} ch \sin x + \frac{1}{2} ah \sin y$$

Multiply by 2. ▶ $ac \sin B = ch \sin x + ah \sin y$

Divide by ac. ▶ $\dfrac{ac}{ac} \sin B = \dfrac{ch}{ac} \sin x + \dfrac{ah}{ac} \sin y$

Substitute. ▶ $\sin B = \dfrac{h}{a} \sin x + \dfrac{h}{c} \sin y$

So, $\sin (x + y) = \cos y \sin x + \cos x \sin y$.

Sine of the Sum of Two Angles

$$\sin (A + B) = \sin A \cos B + \cos A \sin B$$

Example 1 Find sin 105° using special angle measures and the formula for sin (A + B). Answer may be left in simplest radical form.

$$\sin (A + B) = \sin A \cos B + \cos A \sin B$$

$105° = 60° + 45°$ ▶
$$\sin (60° + 45°) = \sin 60° \cos 45° + \cos 60° \sin 45°$$
$$= \frac{\sqrt{3}}{2} \cdot \frac{\sqrt{2}}{2} + \frac{1}{2} \cdot \frac{\sqrt{2}}{2}$$
$$= \frac{\sqrt{6}}{4} + \frac{\sqrt{2}}{4}$$

Thus, $\sin 105° = \dfrac{\sqrt{6} + \sqrt{2}}{4}$.

You can derive the formula for the sine of the difference of two angle measures using the formula for the sine of the sum of two angle measures. This derivation follows on the next page.

Rewrite the difference $x - y$ as the sum $x + (-y)$.

So, $\sin(x - y) = \sin[x + (-y)]$

$\qquad = \sin x \cos(-y) + \cos x \sin(-y)$

$\qquad = \sin x \cos y + \cos x(-\sin y)$, since $\begin{cases} \cos(-y) = \cos y \\ \sin(-y) = -\sin y \end{cases}$.

$\qquad = \sin x \cos y - \cos x \sin y$.

Sine of the Difference of Two Angles

$$\sin(A - B) = \sin A \cos B - \cos A \sin B$$

Example 2 Find $\sin 15°$. Use special angle measures and the formula for $\sin(A - B)$. Answer in simplest radical form.

$$\sin(A - B) = \sin A \cos B - \cos A \sin B$$
$$\sin(60° - 45°) = \sin 60° \cos 45° - \cos 60° \sin 45°$$
$$= \frac{\sqrt{3}}{2} \cdot \frac{\sqrt{2}}{2} - \frac{1}{2} \cdot \frac{\sqrt{2}}{2}, \text{ or } \frac{\sqrt{6}}{4} - \frac{\sqrt{2}}{4}$$

Thus, $\sin 15° = \dfrac{\sqrt{6} - \sqrt{2}}{4}$.

Example 3 If $\sin A = \frac{3}{5}$ and $\cos B = \frac{5}{13}$, where A and B are acute angles, find the value of $\sin(A + B)$.

$$\sin(A + B) = \sin A \cos B + \cos A \sin B$$
$$= \frac{3}{5} \cdot \frac{5}{13} + \frac{4}{5} \cdot \frac{12}{13}$$
$$= \frac{15}{65} + \frac{48}{65}$$
$$= \frac{63}{65}$$

Thus, $\sin(A + B) = \dfrac{63}{65}$.

Example 4 If $\sin A = \dfrac{15}{17}$ and $\angle A$ lies in the second quadrant, and if $\cos B = \dfrac{4}{5}$ and $\angle B$ lies in the first quadrant, find $\sin(A - B)$.

Using reference triangles, $\cos A = -\dfrac{8}{17}$ and $\sin B = \dfrac{3}{5}$.

$$\sin(A - B) = \sin A \cos B - \cos A \sin B$$
$$= \frac{15}{17}\left(\frac{4}{5}\right) - \left(\frac{-8}{17}\right) \cdot \frac{3}{5}$$
$$= \frac{60}{85} + \frac{24}{85}, \text{ or } \frac{84}{85}$$

Thus, $\sin(A - B) = \dfrac{84}{85}$.

SIN ($A \pm B$) AND SIN 2A

The sine of twice (double) an angle can also be derived using the formula for the sine of the sum of two angles.

Begin by rewriting $2x$ as the sum $(x + x)$.
$$\sin (2x) = \sin (x + x)$$
$$= \sin x \cos x + \cos x \sin x$$
$$= \sin x \cos x + \sin x \cos x$$
$$= 2 \sin x \cos x.$$

Sine of Twice an Angle

$$\sin 2A = 2 \sin A \cos A$$

Example 5 Find sin 120°. Use a special angle measure and the formula for sin 2A.

$$\sin 2A = 2 \sin A \cos A$$
$$\sin 2(60°) = 2 \sin 60° \cos 60°$$
$$= 2 \left(\frac{\sqrt{3}}{2} \right) \left(\frac{1}{2} \right), \text{ or } \frac{\sqrt{3}}{2}$$

Thus, $\sin 120° = \dfrac{\sqrt{3}}{2}.$

Example 6 If $\cos A = -\dfrac{5}{13}$ and $\angle A$ lies in the third quadrant, find sin 2A.

Use the reference triangle, $\sin A = -\dfrac{12}{13}.$

So, $\sin 2A = 2 \sin A \cos A.$
$$= 2 \left(-\frac{12}{13} \right) \left(-\frac{5}{13} \right)$$
$$= \frac{120}{169}$$

Thus, $\sin 2A = \dfrac{120}{169}.$

Oral Exercises

Write as a function of one angle.
1. sin 40° cos 30° + cos 40° sin 30° **sin 70°**
2. sin 50° cos 10° − cos 50° sin 10° **sin 40°**
3. 2 sin 15° cos 15° **sin 30°**
4. sin 125° cos 12° + cos 125° sin 12° **sin 137°**
5. cos 57° sin 33° − cos 33° sin 57° **−sin 24°**
6. 2 cos 25° sin 25° **sin 50°**
7. cos 70° sin 10° + cos 10° sin 70° **sin 80°**
8. sin 73° cos 62° − cos 73° sin 62° **sin 11°**

Written Exercises

Find the value of each. Use special angles and the formula for sin $(A + B)$ or   1. $\frac{\sqrt{6} + \sqrt{2}}{4}$
sin $(A - B)$. Answers may be left in simplest radical form.

(A)   **1.** sin 75°   **2.** sin 135° $\frac{\sqrt{2}}{2}$ **3.** sin 60° $\frac{\sqrt{3}}{2}$ **4.** sin 195°   **5.** sin 285°

     6. sin 165°   **7.** sin 150°   **8.** sin 255°   **9.** sin 435°   **10.** sin 375°

For Ex. 4–10, see TE Answer Section.

Find the value of each. Use special angles and the formula for sin 2A. Answers
may be left in simplest radical form.

11. sin 60° $\frac{\sqrt{3}}{2}$ **12.** sin 90° 1   **13.** sin 300° $\frac{-\sqrt{3}}{2}$ **14.** sin 270° -1 **15.** sin 450° 1

Find the value of sin $(A + B)$ and sin $(A - B)$.

16. sin $A = \frac{12}{13}$ and A lies in the 2nd quad.   **17.** cos $A = \frac{12}{13}$ and cos $B = \frac{4}{5}$, A and B are both

     cos $B = \frac{3}{5}$ and B lies in the 4th quad. $\frac{56}{65}, \frac{16}{65}$ acute angles. $\frac{56}{65}, \frac{-16}{65}$

18. sin $A = \frac{15}{17}$ and A lies in the 2nd quad.   **19.** sin $A = \frac{-8}{17}$ and A lies in the 4th quad.

     cos $B = \frac{-4}{5}$ and B lies in the 3rd quad.   cos $B = \frac{12}{13}$ and B lies in the 4th quad.

                 $\frac{-36}{85}, \frac{-84}{85}$ $\frac{-171}{221}, \frac{-21}{221}$

20. sin $A = \frac{7}{9}$ and A lies in the 1st quad.   **21.** cos $A = \frac{6}{13}$ and A lies in the 4th quad.

     cos $B = \frac{-4}{11}$ and B lies in the 2nd quad.   sin $B = \frac{4}{7}$ and B lies in the 1st quad.

         $\frac{-28 + 4\sqrt{210}}{99}, \frac{-28 - 4\sqrt{210}}{99}$ $\frac{-\sqrt{4389} + 24}{91}, \frac{-\sqrt{4389} - 24}{91}$

Find the value of sin 2A.

22. cos $A = \frac{-4}{5}$ and A lies in the 2nd quad. $\frac{-24}{25}$ **23.** cos $A = \frac{12}{13}$ and A is an acute angle. $\frac{120}{169}$

24. cos $A = \frac{15}{17}$ and A lies in the 4th quad. $\frac{-240}{289}$ **25.** sin $A = -\frac{8}{17}$ and A lies in the 3rd quad. $\frac{240}{289}$

Simplify each of the following for acute angle A.

(B)   **26.** $\frac{\sin^2 A}{\sin 2A}$ $\frac{\sin A}{2 \cos A}$ **27.** $\frac{\sin 2A}{\cos A}$ 2 sin A   **28.** $\frac{\tan A}{\sin 2A}$ $\frac{1}{2 \cos^2 A}$ **29.** cot A sin 2A

                                                                       2 cos^2 A

Find the value of each. Use special angles, the formula for sin $(A + B)$,
sin $(A - B)$, or sin 2A, and reciprocal relationships. Answers may be left in
simplest radical form.

30. csc 75°   **31.** csc 135° $\sqrt{2}$ **32.** csc 120° $\frac{2\sqrt{3}}{3}$ **33.** csc 15°   **34.** csc 90° 1

     $-\sqrt{2} + \sqrt{6}$ $\sqrt{6} + \sqrt{2}$

Prove each identity. Use the formula for sin $(A \pm B)$.

(C)   **35.** sin $(\pi + \theta) = -\sin \theta$ **36.** sin $(2\pi - \theta) = -\sin \theta$ **37.** sin $(\pi - \theta) = \sin \theta$

     38. sin $\left(\frac{\pi}{2} - \theta\right) = \cos \theta$ **39.** sin $\left(\frac{3\pi}{2} + \theta\right) = -\cos \theta$ **40.** sin $\left(\frac{\pi}{2} + \theta\right) = \cos \theta$

     41. sin $(180° + \theta) = -\sin \theta$ **42.** sin $(180° - \theta) = \sin \theta$ **43.** sin $(90° + \theta) = \cos \theta$

     44. sin $(90° - \theta) = \cos \theta$ **45.** sin $(360° - \theta) = -\sin \theta$ **46.** sin $(270° + \theta) = -\cos \theta$

For Ex. 35–46, see TE Answer Section.

SIN $(A \pm B)$ AND SIN 2A

19.7 Cos (*A* ± *B*) and Cos 2*A*

OBJECTIVE ▶ **To apply the formulas for cos (*A* ± *B*) and cos 2*A***

You can derive the formula for the cosine of the sum of two angles by using the formula for the sine of the difference of two angles and the cofunction relationship of sine and cosine.

In Chapter 17, you learned the cofunction relationship $\cos u = \sin (90 - u)$. If we let $u = x + y$, it follows that,

$$\cos (x + y) = \sin [90 - (x + y)]$$
$$= \sin [(90 - x) - y] \qquad \blacktriangleleft \quad 90 - (x + y) = (90 - x) - y$$
$$= \underbrace{\sin (90 - x)}\ \cos y - \underbrace{\cos (90 - x)}\ \sin y \qquad \blacktriangleleft \quad using\ formula\ for\ \sin (A - B),$$
$$A = 90 - x,\ B = y$$

So, $\cos (x + y) = \qquad \cos x \qquad \cos y - \qquad \sin x \qquad \sin y.$ ◀ $\sin (90 - x) = \cos x$
$$and\ \cos (90 - x) = \sin x$$

Cosine of the Sum of Two Angles

$$\cos (A + B) = \cos A \cos B - \sin A \sin B$$

Example 1

Find cos 75°. Use special angles and the formula for cos (*A* + *B*). Answer in simplest radical form.

$$\cos (A + B) = \cos A \cos B - \sin A \sin B$$
$75° = 45° + 30°$ ▶ $\cos (45° + 30°) = \cos 45° \cos 30° - \sin 45° \sin 30°$
$$= \frac{\sqrt{2}}{2} \cdot \frac{\sqrt{3}}{2} - \frac{\sqrt{2}}{2} \cdot \frac{1}{2}$$
$$= \frac{\sqrt{6}}{4} - \frac{\sqrt{2}}{4}$$

Thus, $\cos 75° = \dfrac{\sqrt{6} - \sqrt{2}}{4}$.

Example 2

If $\cos A = -\frac{4}{5}$ and $\angle A$ lies in the second quadrant and $\cos B = \frac{12}{13}$ and $\angle B$ lies in the fourth quadrant, find cos (*A* + *B*).

Using reference triangles, $\sin A = \frac{3}{5}$ and $\sin B = -\frac{5}{13}$.
$$\cos (A + B) = \cos A \cos B - \sin A \sin B$$
$$= -\frac{4}{5} \cdot \frac{12}{13} - \frac{3}{5} \cdot \left(-\frac{5}{13} \right)$$
$$= -\frac{48}{65} + \frac{15}{65},\ \text{or}\ -\frac{33}{65}$$

Thus, $\cos (A + B) = -\dfrac{33}{65}$.

You can derive the formula for the cos of the difference of two angles using the formula for the cosine of the sum of two angles.

Rewrite the difference $x - y$ as the sum $x + (-y)$.

$$\begin{aligned}
\cos (x - y) &= \cos [x + (-y)] \\
&= \cos x \cos (-y) - \sin x \sin (-y) \\
&= \cos x \cos y - \sin x (-\sin y) \\
&= \cos x \cos y + \sin x \sin y.
\end{aligned}$$

◀ $\begin{cases} \cos (-y) = \cos y \\ \sin (-y) = -\sin y \end{cases}$

Cosine of the Difference of Two Angles

$$\cos (A - B) = \cos A \cos B + \sin A \sin B$$

Example 3 If $\sin A = -\dfrac{15}{17}$ and $\angle A$ lies in the fourth quadrant and if $\tan B = -\dfrac{4}{3}$ and $\angle B$ lies in the second quadrant, find $\cos (A - B)$.

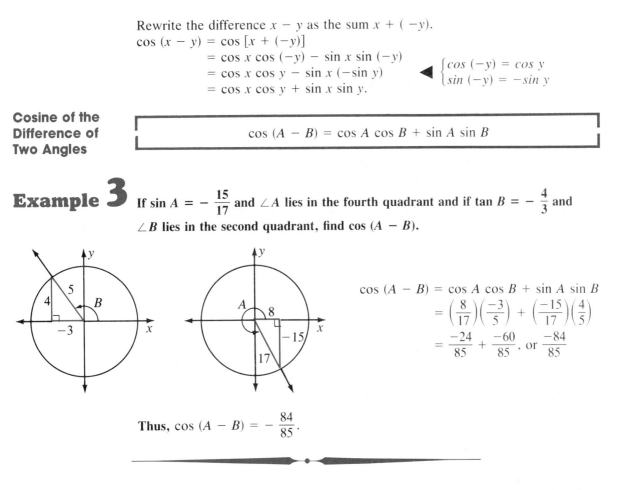

$$\begin{aligned}
\cos (A - B) &= \cos A \cos B + \sin A \sin B \\
&= \left(\frac{8}{17}\right)\left(\frac{-3}{5}\right) + \left(\frac{-15}{17}\right)\left(\frac{4}{5}\right) \\
&= \frac{-24}{85} + \frac{-60}{85}, \text{ or } \frac{-84}{85}
\end{aligned}$$

Thus, $\cos (A - B) = -\dfrac{84}{85}$.

You can derive the formula for the cosine of twice (double) an angle using the formula for the cosine of the sum of two angles.

Begin by rewriting $2x$ as the sum $(x + x)$.

$$\begin{aligned}
\text{So, } \cos 2x &= \cos (x + x) \\
&= \cos x \cos x - \sin x \sin x \\
&= \cos^2 x - \sin^2 x.
\end{aligned}$$

Cosine of Twice an Angle

$$\cos 2A = \cos^2 A - \sin^2 A$$

Observe that the formula for $\cos 2A$ is derived by using the formula for $\cos (A + B)$ and the formula for $\sin 2A$ is derived by using the formula for $\sin (A + B)$.

COS $(A \pm B)$ AND COS $2A$

Example 4 Find cos 120°. Use a special angle measure and the formula for cos 2A.

$$\cos 2A = \cos^2 A - \sin^2 A$$
$$\cos 120° = \cos 2(60°) = \cos^2 60° - \sin^2 60°$$
$$= \left(\frac{1}{2}\right)^2 - \left(\frac{\sqrt{3}}{2}\right)^2$$
$$= \frac{1}{4} - \frac{3}{4}, \text{ or } -\frac{1}{2}$$

Thus, $\cos 120° = -\frac{1}{2}$.

Example 5 If $\cos \theta = -\frac{15}{17}$ and θ lies in the third quadrant, find cos 2θ.

Using the reference triangle, $\cos \theta = \frac{-15}{17}$ and $\sin \theta = \frac{-8}{17}$.

$$\cos 2\theta = \cos^2 \theta - \sin^2 \theta$$
$$= \left(-\frac{15}{17}\right)^2 - \left(-\frac{8}{17}\right)^2$$
$$= \frac{225}{289} - \frac{64}{289}$$
$$= \frac{161}{289}$$

Thus, $\cos 2\theta = \frac{161}{289}$.

Recall from Chapter 18 that for any angle A, $\sin^2 A + \cos^2 A = 1$.
This identity can also be written as $\cos^2 A = 1 - \sin^2 A$ or $\sin^2 A = 1 - \cos^2 A$.
By using these identities, you can derive two additional formulas for cosine of twice an angle.
Begin with $\cos 2x = \cos^2 x - \sin^2 x$.

Replace $\cos^2 x$ with $1 - \sin^2 x$. | Replace $\sin^2 x$ with $1 - \cos^2 x$.

$\cos 2x = \cos^2 x - \sin^2 x$
$= (1 - \sin^2 x) - \sin^2 x$
$= 1 - 2 \sin^2 x$

$\cos 2x = \cos^2 x - \sin^2 x$
$= \cos^2 x - (1 - \cos^2 x)$
$= 2 \cos^2 x - 1$

Three Formulas for Cos 2A

$$\cos 2A = \cos^2 A - \sin^2 A$$
$$\cos 2A = 1 - 2 \sin^2 A$$
$$\cos 2A = 2 \cos^2 A - 1$$

558

Written Exercises

A Find the value of each. Use special angle measures and the formula for cos $(A + B)$ or cos $(A - B)$. Answers may be left in simplest radical form.

1. cos 105° **2.** cos 15° **3.** cos 135° **4.** cos 195° **5.** cos 285°

6. cos 165° **7.** cos 150° **8.** cos 255° **9.** cos 435° **10.** cos 375°

For Ex. 1–10, see TE Answer Section.

Find the value of each. Use special angles and the formula for cos $2A$. Answer in simplest radical form.

11. cos 90° 0 **12.** cos 60° $\frac{1}{2}$ **13.** cos 240° $-\frac{1}{2}$ **14.** cos 450° 0 **15.** cos 180° -1

Find the value of cos $(A + B)$ and cos $(A - B)$.

16. Cos $A = \frac{3}{5}$ and cos $B = \frac{12}{13}$. $\frac{16}{65}$, $\frac{56}{65}$
  A and B are both acute angles.

17. Cos $A = \frac{15}{17}$ and cos $B = \frac{5}{9}$. $\frac{75 - 16\sqrt{14}}{153}$,
  A and B are both acute angles. $\frac{75 + 16\sqrt{14}}{153}$

18. Cos $A = -\frac{5}{13}$ and A lies in the second quadrant. Cos $B = \frac{8}{17}$ and B lies in the fourth quadrant. $\frac{140}{221}$, $\frac{-220}{221}$

19. Cos $A = -\frac{6}{11}$ and A lies in the third quadrant. Cos $B = \frac{4}{5}$ and B lies in the first quadrant. $\frac{-24 + 3\sqrt{85}}{55}$, $\frac{-24 - 3\sqrt{85}}{55}$

Find the value of cos $2A$.

20. Cos $A = -\frac{4}{5}$ and A lies in the 3rd quad. $\frac{7}{25}$

21. Cos $A = \frac{12}{13}$ and A lies in the 1st quad. $\frac{119}{169}$

22. Cos $A = \frac{3}{7}$ and A lies in the 1st quad. $\frac{-31}{49}$

23. Cos $A = \frac{-7}{10}$ and A lies in the 2nd quad. $\frac{-1}{50}$

B Simplify.

24. $\dfrac{\cos 2A}{\sin^2 A - \cos^2 A}$ -1

25. $\dfrac{\cos^2 A - \sin^2 A}{2 \cos^2 A - 1}$ 1

26. $\dfrac{1 - 2 \sin^2 A}{\cos 2A}$ 1

C Find the value of each. Use special angle measures and the formula for cos $(A + B)$, cos $(A - B)$, or cos $2A$. Answer in simplest radical form.

27. sec 75° $\frac{?}{\sqrt{6} + \sqrt{2}}$ **28.** sec 135° $-\sqrt{2}$ **29.** sec 120° -2 **30.** sec 15° $\frac{?}{\sqrt{6} - \sqrt{2}}$ **31.** sec 90° undefined

Prove each identity. Use the formulas for cos $(A + B)$.

32. cos $(180° - \theta) = -\cos \theta$ **33.** cos $(360° - \theta) = \cos \theta$ **34.** cos $(180° + \theta) = -\cos \theta$

35. cos $(\pi + \theta) = -\cos \theta$ **36.** cos $(270° + \theta) = \sin \theta$ **37.** cos $(2\pi + \theta) = \cos \theta$

38. cos $(\frac{\pi}{2} + \theta) = -\sin \theta$ **39.** cos $(\pi - \theta) = -\cos \theta$ **40.** cos $(\frac{3}{2}\pi - \theta) = -\sin \theta$

For Ex. 32–40, see TE Answer Section.

Cumulative Review

1. A triangle's height and a rectangle's width are the same. The rectangle's length is three times its width. The triangle's base measures one half the rectangle's length. The rectangle's area minus the triangle's area is 9 square units. Find the height of the triangle to the nearest unit. **2**

2. A square and a rectangle have the same width. The rectangle's length is 8 cm more than three times its width. The sum of their areas is 192 square cm. Find the width of the square to the nearest centimeter. **6**

19.8 Tan (A ± B) and Tan 2A

OBJECTIVE ▶ To apply the formulas for tan (*A* ± *B*) and tan 2*A*

You can derive the formula for the tangent of the sum of two angles using the formulas for the sine and cosine of the sum of two angles.

Recall from Chapter 18 the identity $\tan A = \dfrac{\sin A}{\cos A}$.

$$\tan (x + y) = \frac{\sin (x + y)}{\cos (x + y)}$$

$$= \frac{\sin x \cos y + \cos x \sin y}{\cos x \cos y - \sin x \sin y}$$

◀ *Formula for sin (A + B)*
◀ *Formula for cos (A + B)*

Divide each term by cos *x* cos *y* and simplify.

$$\tan (x + y) = \frac{\dfrac{\sin x \ \cancel{\cos y}}{\cos x \ \cancel{\cos y}} + \dfrac{\cancel{\cos x} \sin y}{\cos x \cos y}}{\dfrac{\cancel{\cos x} \ \cancel{\cos y}}{\cancel{\cos x} \ \cancel{\cos y}} - \dfrac{\sin x \sin y}{\cos x \cos y}}$$

So, $\tan (x + y) = \dfrac{\tan x + \tan y}{1 - \tan x \tan y}$.

Tangent of the Sum of two Angles

$$\tan (A + B) = \frac{\tan A + \tan B}{1 - \tan A \tan B}$$

Example 1

Find tan 75°. Use special angle measures and the formula for tan (*A* + *B*). Answer in simplest radical form.

$$\tan (A + B) = \frac{\tan A + \tan B}{1 - \tan A \tan B}$$

$$\tan 75° = \tan (45° + 30°) = \frac{\tan 45° + \tan 30°}{1 - \tan 45° \tan 30°} = \frac{1 + \dfrac{\sqrt{3}}{3}}{1 - (1)\left(\dfrac{\sqrt{3}}{3}\right)}$$

$$= \frac{\dfrac{3 + \sqrt{3}}{3}}{\dfrac{3 - \sqrt{3}}{3}}, \text{ or } \frac{3 + \sqrt{3}}{3 - \sqrt{3}} \cdot \frac{3 + \sqrt{3}}{3 + \sqrt{3}} = \frac{9 + 6\sqrt{3} + 3}{9 - 3}$$

Thus, tan 75° = 2 + $\sqrt{3}$.

You can derive the formula for the tangent of the difference of two angles using the formula for the tan of the sum of two angles.

Rewrite the difference $x - y$ as the sum $x + (-y)$.

$$\tan (x - y) = \tan [x + (-y)]$$
$$= \frac{\tan x + \tan (-y)}{1 - \tan x \tan (-y)}$$
$$= \frac{\tan x - \tan y}{1 + \tan x \tan y}, \text{ since } \tan (-y) = -\tan y.$$

Tangent of the Difference of Two Angles

$$\tan (A - B) = \frac{\tan A - \tan B}{1 + \tan A \tan B}$$

Example 2 If $\tan A = \frac{4}{7}$ and $\tan B = \frac{13}{2}$, find $\tan (A - B)$.

$$\tan (A - B) = \frac{\tan A - \tan B}{1 + \tan A \tan B}$$
$$= \frac{\frac{4}{7} - \frac{13}{2}}{1 + \frac{4}{7}\left(\frac{13}{2}\right)}, \text{ or } \frac{-\frac{83}{14}}{\frac{66}{14}}$$

Thus, $\tan (A - B) = -\frac{83}{66}$.

You can derive the formula for the tangent of twice (double) an angle using the formula for the tan of the sum of two angles.

$$\tan 2x = \tan (x + x) = \frac{\tan x + \tan x}{1 - \tan x \tan x}, \text{ or } \frac{2 \tan x}{1 - \tan^2 x}$$

Tangent of Twice an Angle

$$\tan 2A = \frac{2 \tan A}{1 - \tan^2 A}$$

Example 3 Find $\tan 120°$. Use a special angle measure and the formula for $\tan 2x$. Answer in simplest radical form.

$$\tan 2A = \frac{2 \tan A}{1 - \tan^2 A}$$
$$\tan 120° = \tan 2(60°) = \frac{2 \tan 60°}{1 - \tan^2 60°} = \frac{2\sqrt{3}}{1 - (\sqrt{3})^2}, \text{ or } \frac{2\sqrt{3}}{-2}$$

Thus, $\tan 120° = -\sqrt{3}$.

TAN ($A \pm B$) AND TAN 2A

Example 4 If $\tan \theta = -\dfrac{7}{6}$, find $\tan 2\theta$.

$$\tan 2\theta = \frac{2\tan\theta}{1-\tan^2\theta} = \frac{2\left(-\dfrac{7}{6}\right)}{1-\left(-\dfrac{7}{6}\right)^2}$$

$$= \frac{\dfrac{-14}{6}}{1-\dfrac{49}{36}}, \text{ or } \frac{\dfrac{-14}{6}}{-\dfrac{13}{36}}, \text{ or } \frac{-14}{6}\cdot\frac{-36}{13}$$

Thus, $\tan 2\theta = \dfrac{84}{13}$.

Written Exercises

(A) Find the value of each. Use special angles and the formula for $\tan (A + B)$ or $\tan (A - B)$. Answer in simplest radical form.

1. $\tan 105°$ $\quad$ **2.** $\tan 15°$ $\quad$ **3.** $\tan 135°$ $\quad$ **4.** $\tan 120°$ $\quad$ **5.** $\tan 375°$
$-2 - \sqrt{3}$ $\qquad$ $2 - \sqrt{3}$ $\qquad$ -1 $\qquad$ $-\sqrt{3}$ $\qquad$ $2 - \sqrt{3}$

Find $\tan (A + B)$ for each of the following.

6. $\tan A = \frac{5}{3}$ and $\tan B = \frac{4}{7}$ **47** $\qquad\qquad$ **7.** $\tan A = -\sqrt{3}$ and $\tan B = \frac{\sqrt{2}}{2}$ $3\sqrt{3} - 4\sqrt{2}$

8. $\tan A = -\frac{3}{4}$ and $\tan B = \frac{5}{8}$ $\frac{-4}{47}$ $\qquad\quad$ **9.** $\tan A = \frac{-5}{12}$ and $\tan B = \frac{8}{7}$ $\frac{61}{124}$

Find $\tan (A - B)$ for each of the following.

10. $\tan A = -\frac{1}{3}$ and $\tan B = -\frac{\sqrt{2}}{2}$ $\frac{-9+10\sqrt{2}}{17}$ $\qquad$ **11.** $\tan A = \frac{7}{5}$ and $\tan B = -1$ -6

12. $\tan A = \sqrt{3}$ and $\tan B = \frac{\sqrt{2}}{2}$ $-3\sqrt{3} + 4\sqrt{2}$ $\qquad$ **13.** $\tan A = \frac{5}{12}$ and $\tan B = \frac{8}{17}$ $\frac{-11}{244}$

Find $\tan 2A$ for each of the following. $\qquad\qquad\qquad\qquad\qquad\qquad\qquad$ **undefined**

14. $\tan A = \frac{4}{5}$ $\frac{40}{9}$ $\qquad$ **15.** $\tan A = \frac{15}{17}$ $\frac{255}{32}$ $\qquad$ **16.** $\tan A = -\frac{5}{12}$ $\frac{-120}{119}$ $\qquad$ **17.** $\tan A = -1$

18. $\tan A = -\frac{3}{4}$ $\frac{-24}{7}$ $\qquad$ **19.** $\tan A = \frac{12}{11}$ $\frac{-264}{23}$ $\qquad$ **20.** $\tan A = \frac{4}{7}$ $\frac{56}{33}$ $\qquad\quad$ **21.** $\tan A = -\frac{3}{8}$ $\frac{-48}{55}$

(B) $\tan \theta = -\frac{5}{12}$, $\cos \beta = -\frac{3}{5}$, and β lies in the second quadrant.

22. Find $\tan (\theta + \beta)$. $\frac{-63}{16}$ $\qquad\qquad\qquad\qquad$ **23.** Find $\tan (\theta - \beta)$. $\frac{33}{56}$

24. Find $\tan 2\theta$. $\frac{-120}{119}$ $\qquad\qquad\qquad\qquad\quad$ **25.** Find $\tan 2\beta$. $\frac{24}{7}$

$\tan \theta = -\frac{7}{3}$, $\sin \beta = -\frac{5}{13}$, and β lies in the fourth quadrant.

26. Find $\tan (\theta + \beta)$. -99 $\qquad\qquad\qquad\qquad$ **27.** Find $\tan (\theta - \beta)$. $\frac{-69}{71}$

28. Find $\tan 2\theta$. $\frac{21}{20}$ $\qquad\qquad\qquad\qquad\qquad$ **29.** Find $\tan 2\beta$. $\frac{-120}{119}$

Find the value for each of the following.

30. $\dfrac{2\tan 15°}{1-\tan^2 15°}$ $\dfrac{\sqrt{3}}{3}$ $\qquad$ **31.** $\dfrac{2\tan 22.5°}{1-\tan^2 22.5°}$ 1 $\qquad$ **32.** $\dfrac{2\tan 67.5°}{1-\tan^2 67.5°}$ -1

(C) Prove each identity. Use the formulas for $\tan (A \pm B)$.

33. $\tan (180° + \theta) = \tan \theta$ $\qquad$ **34.** $\tan (180° - \theta) = -\tan \theta$ $\qquad$ **35.** $\tan (\pi + \theta) = \tan \theta$

36. $\tan (360° - \theta) = -\tan \theta$ $\qquad$ **37.** $\tan (2\pi + \theta) = \tan \theta$ $\qquad$ **38.** $\tan (\pi - \theta) = -\tan \theta$

For Ex. 33–38, see TE Answer Section.

19.9 Half-Angle Formulas

OBJECTIVE ▶ **To apply the formulas for $\sin \frac{A}{2}$, $\cos \frac{A}{2}$, and $\tan \frac{A}{2}$**

You can derive the formulas for the sine, cosine, and tangent of half an angle.
You will also learn how to apply these formulas.
One of the formulas for $\cos 2A$ is $\cos 2A = 1 - 2 \sin^2 A$.
If we replace A with $\frac{x}{2}$, the following equation is true.

$$\cos 2\left(\frac{x}{2}\right) = 1 - 2 \sin^2 \left(\frac{x}{2}\right)$$

$$\cos x = 1 - 2 \sin^2 \frac{x}{2}$$

$$2 \sin^2 \frac{x}{2} = 1 - \cos x$$

$$\sin^2 \frac{x}{2} = \frac{1 - \cos x}{2} \qquad \text{So, } \sin \frac{x}{2} = \pm \sqrt{\frac{1 - \cos x}{2}}.$$

Sine of Half an Angle

$$\sin \frac{A}{2} = \pm \sqrt{\frac{1 - \cos A}{2}}$$

Example 1 Find sin 30°. Use the formula for $\sin \frac{A}{2}$.

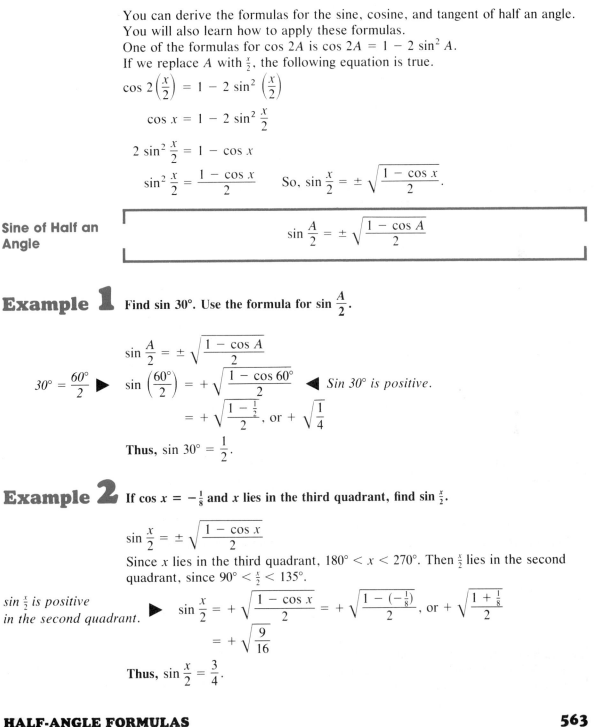

$$\sin \frac{A}{2} = \pm \sqrt{\frac{1 - \cos A}{2}}$$

$30° = \frac{60°}{2}$ ▶ $\sin \left(\frac{60°}{2}\right) = + \sqrt{\frac{1 - \cos 60°}{2}}$ ◀ *Sin 30° is positive.*

$$= + \sqrt{\frac{1 - \frac{1}{2}}{2}}, \text{ or } + \sqrt{\frac{1}{4}}$$

Thus, $\sin 30° = \frac{1}{2}$.

Example 2 If $\cos x = -\frac{1}{8}$ and x lies in the third quadrant, find $\sin \frac{x}{2}$.

$$\sin \frac{x}{2} = \pm \sqrt{\frac{1 - \cos x}{2}}$$

Since x lies in the third quadrant, $180° < x < 270°$. Then $\frac{x}{2}$ lies in the second quadrant, since $90° < \frac{x}{2} < 135°$.

$\sin \frac{x}{2}$ is positive in the second quadrant. ▶ $\sin \frac{x}{2} = + \sqrt{\frac{1 - \cos x}{2}} = + \sqrt{\frac{1 - (-\frac{1}{8})}{2}}, \text{ or } + \sqrt{\frac{1 + \frac{1}{8}}{2}}$

$$= + \sqrt{\frac{9}{16}}$$

Thus, $\sin \frac{x}{2} = \frac{3}{4}$.

To derive a formula for $\cos \frac{A}{2}$, use $\cos 2A = 2 \cos^2 A - 1$ and replace A with $\frac{x}{2}$.

$$\cos 2A = 2 \cos^2 A - 1$$

$$\cos 2 \left(\frac{x}{2} \right) = 2 \cos^2 \left(\frac{x}{2} \right) - 1 \qquad \cos x = 2 \cos^2 \left(\frac{x}{2} \right) - 1$$

$$2 \cos^2 \frac{x}{2} = 1 + \cos x \qquad \cos^2 \frac{x}{2} = \frac{1 + \cos x}{2}$$

So, $\cos \frac{x}{2} = \pm \sqrt{\dfrac{1 + \cos x}{2}}$

Cosine of Half an Angle

$$\cos \frac{A}{2} = \pm \sqrt{\frac{1 + \cos A}{2}}$$

Example 3

Find $\cos 75°$. Use the formula for $\cos \frac{A}{2}$. **Answer may be left in simplest radical form.**

$$\cos \frac{A}{2} = \pm \sqrt{\frac{1 + \cos A}{2}}. \text{ Write } 75° \text{ as } \frac{150°}{2}.$$

cos 75° is positive. ▶ $\cos \left(\dfrac{150°}{2} \right) = + \sqrt{\dfrac{1 + \cos 150°}{2}}$

$$\cos 150° = -\cos 30°$$
$$= -\frac{\sqrt{3}}{2}.$$

▶ $= \sqrt{\dfrac{1 + (-\frac{\sqrt{3}}{2})}{2}}$, or $\sqrt{\dfrac{2 - \sqrt{3}}{4}}$

Thus, $\cos 75° = \dfrac{\sqrt{2 - \sqrt{3}}}{2}$.

To derive a formula for $\tan \frac{x}{2}$, use $\tan A = \dfrac{\sin A}{\cos A}$ and replace A with $\frac{x}{2}$.

$$\tan \frac{x}{2} = \frac{\sin \frac{x}{2}}{\cos \frac{x}{2}} = \frac{\pm \sqrt{\dfrac{1 - \cos x}{2}}}{\pm \sqrt{\dfrac{1 + \cos x}{2}}} = \pm \sqrt{\frac{1 - \cos x}{1 + \cos x}}.$$

Tangent of Half an Angle

$$\tan \frac{A}{2} = \pm \sqrt{\frac{1 - \cos A}{1 + \cos A}}$$

Example 4

If $\cos x = \frac{1}{5}$ and x lies in the 1st quadrant, find $\tan \frac{x}{2}$.

$$\tan \frac{x}{2} = \pm \sqrt{\frac{1 - \cos x}{1 + \cos x}} = + \sqrt{\frac{1 - \frac{1}{5}}{1 + \frac{1}{5}}}, \text{ or } + \sqrt{\frac{\frac{4}{5}}{\frac{6}{5}}}$$

$$= + \sqrt{\frac{4}{6}} = \frac{2}{\sqrt{6}} = \frac{2\sqrt{6}}{6}$$

Thus, $\tan \dfrac{x}{2} = \dfrac{2\sqrt{6}}{6}$ or $\dfrac{\sqrt{6}}{3}$.

CHAPTER NINETEEN

Written Exercises _____

For Ex. 1–28, see TE Answer Section.

(A) Find the value of each. Use special angle measures and the formula for $\sin \frac{A}{2}$, $\cos \frac{A}{2}$, or $\tan \frac{A}{2}$. Answer in simplest radical form.

1. $\sin 15°$ 　　 2. $\cos 15°$ 　　 3. $\sin 22\frac{1}{2}°$ 　　 4. $\tan 22\frac{1}{2}°$ 　　 5. $\cos 22\frac{1}{2}°$

6. $\tan 15°$ 　　 7. $\tan 67\frac{1}{2}°$ 　　 8. $\cos 67\frac{1}{2}°$ 　　 9. $\sin 67\frac{1}{2}°$ 　　 10. $\sin 75°$

Find the value of $\sin \frac{A}{2}$ and $\cos \frac{A}{2}$ given the value of $\cos A$. Answer in simplest radical form.

11. $\cos A = \frac{3}{5}$ 　　 12. $\cos A = 0$ 　　 13. $\cos A = -\frac{5}{13}$ 　　 14. $\cos A = -\frac{1}{2}$

15. $\cos A = \frac{1}{4}$ 　　 16. $\cos A = -\frac{15}{17}$ 　　 17. $\cos A = -\frac{3}{4}$ 　　 18. $\cos A = -1$

Find the value of $\sin \frac{A}{2}$, $\cos \frac{A}{2}$, and $\tan \frac{A}{2}$. Answer in simplest radical form.

19. $\cos A = \frac{4}{5}$ and A is in the 4th quad.

20. $\cos A = \frac{-12}{13}$ and A is in the 2nd quad.

21. $\cos A = -\frac{\sqrt{3}}{2}$ and A is in the 3rd quad.

22. $\cos A = -\frac{1}{2}$ and A is in the 2nd quad.

(B) 23. $\cos A = \frac{1}{3}$ and A is in the 1st quad.

24. $\cos A = \frac{3}{4}$ and A is in the 4th quad.

25. $\cos A = -\frac{5}{12}$ and A is in the 2nd quad.

26. $\cos A = -\frac{4}{7}$ and A is in the 3rd quad.

27. $\cos A = a$ and A is in the 1st quad.

28. $\cos A = -b$ and A is in the 2nd quad.

(C) 29. Find $\tan \frac{A}{2}$ if $\sin A = -\frac{1}{2}$ and $\cos A = -\frac{\sqrt{3}}{2}$. $-\sqrt{7 + 4\sqrt{3}}$

30. Find $\tan \frac{\theta}{2}$ if $\cos \theta = -\frac{15}{17}$ and $90° < \theta < 180°$. **4**

31. Find $\tan \frac{\theta}{2}$ if $\sin \theta = \frac{4}{5}$ and $\cos \theta = -\frac{5}{13}$. **$\frac{3}{2}$**

32. Find $\tan \frac{B}{2}$ if $\cos B = -\frac{4}{5}$ and $180° < B < 270°$. **-3**

33. Prove: $\cot \frac{A}{2} = \pm \sqrt{\dfrac{1 + \cos A}{1 - \cos A}}$.

34. Prove: $\sec \frac{A}{2} = \pm \sqrt{\dfrac{2}{1 + \cos A}}$.

35. Prove: $\csc \frac{A}{2} = \pm \sqrt{\dfrac{2}{1 - \cos A}}$.

36. Find $\sec \frac{\theta}{2}$ If $\cos \theta = -\frac{1}{2}$ and $90° < \theta < 180°$. **2**

For Ex. 33–35, see TE Answer Section.

➤ A Challenge To You ━━━━━

Quadrilateral $ABCD$ is inscribed in a circle.
Find the measure of $\angle D$ to the nearest minute.
Hint: Draw $\overline{AC}$ and use the Law of Cosines twice, both involving AC. **49° 27′**

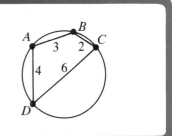

HALF-ANGLE FORMULAS 　　　　　　　　　　　　　　　　**565**

19.10 Double and Half-Angle Identities

OBJECTIVE ▶ **To prove identities using double and half-angle formulas**

You have derived and applied formulas for the sine, cosine and tangent of double and half angles. You will now use these formulas to prove some trigonometric identities.

Example 1 **Prove the identity** $\cos 2\theta = \dfrac{\csc^2 \theta - 2}{\csc^2 \theta}$.

Replace $\csc^2 \theta$ with $\dfrac{1}{\sin^2 \theta}$.

$$
\begin{array}{c|c}
\cos 2\theta & \dfrac{\csc^2 \theta - 2}{\csc^2 \theta} \\[2ex]
\hline
\cos 2\theta & \dfrac{\dfrac{1}{\sin^2 \theta} - 2}{\dfrac{1}{\sin^2 \theta}} \\[4ex]
& \dfrac{\dfrac{1 - 2\sin^2 \theta}{\sin^2 \theta}}{\dfrac{1}{\sin^2 \theta}} \\[4ex]
& 1 - 2\sin^2 \theta \\[2ex]
& \cos 2\theta
\end{array}
$$

Example 2 **Prove the identity** $\tan 2A = \dfrac{2 \tan A}{\sec^2 A - 2 \tan^2 A}$.

Replace $\tan 2A$ with $\dfrac{\sin 2A}{\cos 2A}$, $\sec^2 A$ with $\dfrac{1}{\cos^2 A}$, and $\tan A$ with $\dfrac{\sin A}{\cos A}$.

$$
\begin{array}{c|c}
\tan 2A & \dfrac{2 \tan A}{\sec^2 A - 2 \tan^2 A} \\[3ex]
\hline
\dfrac{\sin 2A}{\cos 2A} & \dfrac{2\,\dfrac{\sin A}{\cos A}}{\dfrac{1}{\cos^2 A} - 2\,\dfrac{\sin^2 A}{\cos^2 A}} \\[4ex]
\dfrac{2\sin A \cos A}{1 - 2\sin^2 A} & \dfrac{2\sin A}{\cos A} \cdot \dfrac{\cos^2 A}{1 - 2\sin^2 A} \\[4ex]
& \dfrac{2\sin A \cos A}{1 - 2\sin^2 A}
\end{array}
$$

The identity in Example 3 involves the formula for the sine of a half-angle.

Example 3 **Prove the identity** $\sin^2 \dfrac{\theta}{2} = \dfrac{\sec \theta - 1}{2 \sec \theta}$.

Replace $\sec \theta$ with $\dfrac{1}{\cos \theta}$ and $\sin \dfrac{\theta}{2}$ with $\pm \sqrt{\dfrac{1 - \cos \theta}{2}}$.

$$
\begin{array}{c|c}
\sin^2 \dfrac{\theta}{2} & \dfrac{\sec \theta - 1}{2 \sec \theta} \\[2ex]
\hline
\left(\pm \sqrt{\dfrac{1 - \cos \theta}{2}} \right)^2 & \dfrac{\dfrac{1}{\cos \theta} - 1}{2 \left(\dfrac{1}{\cos \theta} \right)} \\[3ex]
\dfrac{1 - \cos \theta}{2} & \dfrac{1 - \cos \theta}{\cos \theta} \cdot \dfrac{\cos \theta}{2} \\[3ex]
 & \dfrac{1 - \cos \theta}{2}
\end{array}
$$

Written Exercises

For Ex. 1–18, see TE Answer Section.

(A) **Prove each identity.**

1. $\tan \theta = \dfrac{\sin 2\theta}{1 + \cos 2\theta}$

2. $\sin^2 \theta = \dfrac{\tan \theta \sin 2\theta}{2}$

3. $\cot \theta = \dfrac{\sin 2\theta}{2 \sin^2 \theta}$

4. $\cos^2 \dfrac{\theta}{2} = \dfrac{\sec \theta + 1}{2 \sec \theta}$

5. $\tan \dfrac{\theta}{2} = \pm \dfrac{1 - \cos \theta}{\sin \theta}$

6. $\tan \dfrac{\theta}{2} = \pm \dfrac{\sin \theta}{1 + \cos \theta}$

(B) **7.** $2 \csc 2\theta = \dfrac{\cos \theta}{\sin \theta} + \dfrac{\sin \theta}{\cos \theta}$

8. $\sin^2 \theta - 2 \sin \theta \cos \theta + \cos^2 \theta = 1 - 2 \sin 2\theta$

9. $1 + \sin \theta = \left(\sin \dfrac{\theta}{2} + \cos \dfrac{\theta}{2} \right)^2$

10. $\cos \theta = \dfrac{\frac{1}{2} \sin^2 \theta}{\sin^2 \frac{1}{2} \theta} - 1$

11. $\dfrac{1 - \tan^2 \theta}{1 + \tan^2 \theta} = \cos 2\theta$

12. $\dfrac{\sin \theta + \cos \theta}{\cos \theta - \sin \theta} + \dfrac{\sin \theta - \cos \theta}{\sin \theta + \cos \theta} = 2 \tan 2\theta$

(C) **13.** $\tan 2\theta = \dfrac{\sin 4\theta}{1 + \cos 4\theta}$

14. $\cos 3\theta = 4 \cos^3 \theta - 3 \cos \theta$

15. $2 \csc 2\theta = \sec \theta \csc \theta$

16. $\sec 2\theta = \dfrac{\sec^2 \theta}{2 - \dfrac{1}{\cos^2 \theta}}$

17. $\dfrac{\sec^2 \theta}{2} + \tan \theta = \dfrac{1 + \sin 2\theta}{1 + \cos 2\theta}$

18. $\dfrac{\cos 3\theta}{\sin 3\theta} = (1 + \cos 6\theta)(\csc 6\theta)$

DOUBLE AND HALF-ANGLE IDENTITIES

Vocabulary

Ambiguous case [19.5]   Law of Cosines [19.1]
Area of a triangle [19.3] Law of Sines [19.4]

For triangle ABC, find the length of the indicated side to the nearest unit. [19.1]

1. $a = 8$, $c = 5$, m$\angle B = 42°$. Find b. **5**
2. $c = 10$, $b = 6$, m$\angle A = 130°$. Find a. **15**
3. $a = 17.3$, $b = 47.6$, m$\angle C = 67° 43'$. Find c. **44**
4. Two sides of a parallelogram form an angle of 63°. The lengths of two sides are 12 and 18 centimeters. How long is the shorter diagonal? **16 cm** [19.1]

For triangle ABC, find each angle to the nearest degree. [19.2]

5. $a = 6$, $b = 9$, $c = 4$. Find m$\angle A$. **32°**
6. $a = 4$, $b = 7$, $c = 10$. Find m$\angle B$. **33°**
7. $a = 12.7$, $b = 17.9$, $c = 23.6$. Find m$\angle C$. **100°**

For △ABC, find the area to the nearest square unit. [19.3]

8. $a = 6$, $b = 8$, m$\angle C = 48°$. **18**
9. $b = 8.3$, $c = 9.6$, m$\angle A = 63° 20'$ **36**

10. The lengths of two sides of a parallelogram are 30 and 34 centimeters. Their included angle measures 120°. Find the area of the parallelogram. **883 cm²** [19.3]

For △PQR, find m∠P to the nearest degree. [19.3]

11. $q = 9$, $r = 16$, area = 36 square units **30°**
12. $q = 11$, $r = 9$, area = 45 square units **65°**

13. For △ABC, $a = 60$, m$\angle A = 63°$, [19.4] m$\angle B = 47°$. Find b to the nearest unit. **49**
14. For △ABC, $a = 13.3$, $c = 18.5$, m$\angle A = 43° 40'$. Find m$\angle C$ to the nearest degree. **74°** [19.4]

How many triangles can be constructed? [19.5]

15. m$\angle A = 38°$, $a = 8$, $b = 12$ **2**
16. m$\angle A = 120°$, $a = 30$, $b = 10$ **1**

Find each. Use the formula for sin (A ± B) or sin $\frac{A}{2}$. Answer in simplest radical form. [19.6, 19.9]

17. sin 75° $\frac{\sqrt{6}+\sqrt{2}}{4}$
18. sin 15° $\frac{1}{2}\sqrt{2-\sqrt{3}}$
19. sin $22\frac{1}{2}°$ $\frac{1}{2}\sqrt{2-\sqrt{2}}$
20. If sin $A = -\frac{12}{13}$ and $\angle A$ lies in the third quadrant, find sin $2A$. $\frac{120}{169}$ [19.6]

Find each. Use the formula for cos(A ± B) or cos $\frac{A}{2}$. Answer in simplest radical form. [19.7, 19.9]

21. cos 15° $\frac{1}{2}\sqrt{2+\sqrt{3}}$
22. cos $67\frac{1}{2}°$ $\frac{1}{2}\sqrt{2-\sqrt{2}}$
23. cos $22\frac{1}{2}°$ $\frac{1}{2}\sqrt{2+\sqrt{2}}$

Find sin (A + B) and sin (A − B). [19.6]

24. sin $A = -\frac{4}{5}$ and $\angle A$ lies in the fourth quadrant. sin $B = \frac{5}{13}$ and $\angle B$ lies in the second quadrant. $\frac{63}{65}, \frac{33}{65}$

Find cos (A + B) and cos (A − B). [19.7]

25. cos $A = -\frac{12}{13}$ and $\angle A$ lies in the third quadrant. cos $B = \frac{3}{5}$ and $\angle B$ lies in the fourth quadrant. $-\frac{56}{65}, -\frac{16}{65}$

26. If cos $A = -\frac{1}{4}$ and $\angle A$ lies in the second quadrant, find cos $\frac{A}{2}$. $\frac{\sqrt{6}}{4}$ [19.9]

Prove the identity. Use formula for sin (A − B).

★27. sin $(\frac{3}{2}\pi - \theta) = -\cos \theta$. [19.6]

For Ex. 27, 32, and 34, see TE Answer Section.

28. Find tan $(A + B)$ if tan $A = -\frac{5}{12}$ and tan $B = -\frac{3}{5}$. $-\frac{61}{45}$ [19.8]

29. Find tan $2A$ if tan $A = \frac{4}{5}$. $\frac{40}{9}$ [19.8]

30. Find tan $(A − B)$ if tan $A = -\frac{8}{9}$ and tan $B = \frac{4}{7}$. $-\frac{92}{31}$ [19.8]

31. Find tan 105°. Use the formula for tan $(A + B)$. $-2 - \sqrt{3}$ [19.8]

32. Prove $\cos^2 \frac{\theta}{2} = \frac{\sin \theta + \tan \theta}{2 \tan \theta}$. [19.10]

★33. Find tan $\frac{A}{2}$ if sin $A = \frac{\sqrt{3}}{2}$ and cos $A = -\frac{1}{2}$. $\sqrt{3}$ [19.9]

★34. Prove: tan $(2\pi - \theta) = -\tan \theta$. [19.8]

Chapter Nineteen Test

For triangle *ABC*, find the length of the indicated side to the nearest unit.

1. $a = 5$, $b = 9$, $m\angle C = 50°$. Find c. **7**
2. $c = 12$, $b = 7$, $m\angle A = 140°$. Find a. **18**
3. $a = 23.4$, $c = 36.2$, $m\angle B = 73° 18'$. Find b. **37**

4. Two sides of a parallelogram form an angle of 48°. The lengths of the two sides are 14 and 16 centimeters. How long is the longer diagonal? **27**

For triangle *ABC*, find the angle measure to the nearest degree.

5. $a = 6$, $b = 5$, $c = 8$. Find $m\angle C$. **93°**
6. $a = 15$, $b = 7$, $c = 10$. Find $m\angle A$. **123°**
7. $a = 13.8$, $b = 24.6$, $c = 18.7$. Find $m\angle B$. **97°**

For △*ABC*, find the area to the nearest square unit.

8. $b = 14$, $c = 8$, $m\angle A = 73°$ **54**
9. $a = 6.3$, $b = 8.5$, $m\angle C = 30° 40'$ **14**

10. The lengths of two sides of a parallelogram are 64 and 82 centimeters. Their included angle measures 70°. Find the area of the parallelogram. **4,932 cm²**

For △*PQR*, find $m\angle P$ to the nearest degree.

11. $q = 7$, $r = 8$, area = 22 sq. units **52°**
12. $q = 14$, $r = 10$, area = 60 sq. units **59°**

13. For △*ABC*, $a = 32$, $m\angle A = 72°$, $m\angle C = 32°$. Find c to the nearest unit. **18**

14. For △*ABC*, $a = 16.4$, $c = 10.8$, $m\angle A = 38° 30'$. Find $m\angle C$ to the nearest degree. **24°**

How many triangles can be constructed?

15. $m\angle A = 28°$, $a = 7$, $b = 13$ **2**
16. $m\angle A = 130°$, $a = 16$, $b = 12$ **1**

Find each. Use the formula for sin $(A \pm B)$ or sin $\frac{A}{2}$. Answer in simplest radical form.

17. sin 15° $\frac{1}{2}\sqrt{2-\sqrt{3}}$
18. sin 75° $\frac{\sqrt{6}+\sqrt{2}}{4}$
19. sin $22\frac{1}{2}°$. $\frac{1}{2}\sqrt{2-\sqrt{2}}$

20. If $\sin A = -\frac{3}{5}$ and $\angle A$ lies in the third quadrant, find sin 2A. $\frac{24}{25}$

Find each. Use the formula for cos $(A \pm B)$ or cos $\frac{A}{2}$. Answer in simplest radical form.

21. cos 135° $\frac{-\sqrt{2}}{2}$
22. cos $22\frac{1}{2}°$ $\frac{1}{2}\sqrt{2+\sqrt{2}}$
23. cos 15° $\frac{1}{2}\sqrt{2+\sqrt{3}}$

Find sin $(A + B)$ and sin $(A - B)$.

24. $\sin A = \frac{5}{7}$ and $\angle A$ lies in the second quadrant. $\sin B = -\frac{4}{5}$ and $\angle B$ lies in the third quadrant. $\frac{-15+8\sqrt{6}}{35}$, $\frac{-15-8\sqrt{6}}{35}$

Find cos $(A + B)$ and cos $(A - B)$.

25. $\cos A = \frac{12}{13}$ and $\angle A$ lies in the first quadrant. $\cos B = -\frac{4}{5}$ and $\angle B$ lies in the second quadrant. $\frac{-63}{65}$, $\frac{-33}{65}$

26. If $\cos A = -\frac{5}{13}$ and $\angle A$ lies in the third quadrant, find cos $\frac{A}{2}$. $\frac{-2\sqrt{13}}{13}$

27. Find tan $(A + B)$ if $\tan A = \frac{4}{5}$ and $\tan B = -\frac{2}{3}$. $\frac{2}{23}$

28. Find tan 2A if $\tan A = \frac{3}{5}$. $\frac{15}{8}$

29. Find tan $(A - B)$ if $\tan A = -\frac{8}{9}$ and $\tan B = -\frac{3}{7}$. $-\frac{1}{3}$

30. Find tan 75°. Use the formula for tan $(A + B)$. $2 + \sqrt{3}$

For Ex. 31–34, see TE Answer Section.

31. Prove $\sin 2A = \dfrac{2 \cot A}{\csc^2 A}$.

32. Prove $2 \csc 2\theta = \tan \theta + \cot \theta$.

Prove the identity. Use the formula for sin $(A - B)$.

★ 33. $\sin\left(\frac{\pi}{2} + \theta\right) = \cos\theta$
★ 34. Prove $\tan(\pi - \theta) = -\tan\theta$.

★ 35. Find tan $\frac{A}{2}$ if $\sin A = -\frac{1}{2}$ and $\cos A = -\frac{\sqrt{3}}{2}$. $-\sqrt{7+4\sqrt{3}}$

Computer Activities

Surveying

To measure the distance between two points, A and B, a surveyor measures the distance to points A and B from a chosen point C. The surveyor could be measuring the distance across a pond, the distance from the top of one hill to another hill, or the distance of a road spanning a valley.

If the distance from C to A is 90 meters, the distance from C to B is 120 meters, and the measure of angle θ is 63, how far is it across the valley, the distance from A to B?

Using the computer, you can quickly and accurately solve this problem and other surveyor problems that are applications of the Law of Cosines.

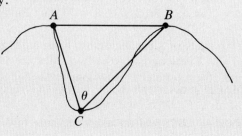

PROGRAM

```
10 PRINT "PROGRAM USES LAW OF COSINES"
20 PRINT "TO FIND DISTANCE BETWEEN A AND B"
30 REM C ↑ 2 = A ↑ 2 + B ↑ 2 - 2AB COS (THETA)
40 PRINT "ENTER LENGTH TO A AND B"
50 INPUT A, B
60 PRINT "ENTER MEASURE OF ANGLE ACB"
70 INPUT C1
80 REM CHANGE ANGLE TO RADIANS
90 LET R = C1 * (3.14159/180)
100 LET D = SQR (A ↑ 2 + B ↑ 2 - 2 * A * B * COS (R))
110 PRINT "THE DISTANCE FROM A TO B IS"; D; "METERS"
120 END
```

Exercises

Type in the above program and run it for the following values:

1. $A = 90$ m $B = 120$ m $m \angle \theta = 63$ **112.6667 m**

2. $A = 80$ m $B = 110$ m $m \angle \theta = 98$ **144.7391 m**

3. Given the measures of two angles of a triangle and a side opposite one of the angles, write a program to use the Law of Sines to find the remaining measures of the triangle. **For Ex. 3, see TE Answer Section.**

College Prep Test

DIRECTIONS: Choose the *one* best answer to each question or problem.

1.

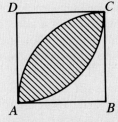

ABCD is a square. $AB = 4$. B is the center of arc AC. D is the center of arc AC. Find the area of the shaded region.
(A) $4(\pi - 2)$ **(B)** $16(\pi - 1)$ **(C)** $8(\pi - 1)$
(D) $8(\pi - 2)$ **(E)** $16\pi - 8$ **D**

2. A regular hexagon is inscribed in a circle. The radius of the circle is 6 cm.
Which is the area between the circle and the regular hexagon?
(A) $36\pi - 18$ **(B)** $54\sqrt{3} - 36\pi$
(C) $36\pi - 54\sqrt{3}$ **(D)** $54\sqrt{3} - 12\pi$
(E) None of these **C**

3.

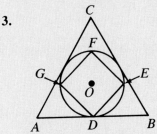

$\triangle ABC$ is equilateral with side of length s.
A circle is inscribed in the triangle.
A square is inscribed in the circle.
Which is the area of the square?
(A) $\frac{1}{6}s^2$ **(B)** s^2 **(C)** $\frac{1}{8}s^2$
(D) $\frac{1}{4}s^2$ **(E)** $\frac{1}{3}s^2$ **A**

4. For all real numbers a and b, define
$$a \star b = \frac{a + b}{ab}.$$
Find $(5 \star 5) \star 5$.

(A) 2 **(B)** 5 **(C)** $\frac{2}{5}$
(D) $\frac{27}{10}$ **(E)** $\frac{4}{25}$ **D**

5.

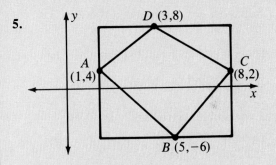

What is the area of $ABCD$?

(A) 49 **(B)** 98 **(C)** 56
(D) 43 **(E)** None of these **E**

6.

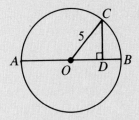

$\overline{AB}$ is a diameter of the circle with center O and radius 5.
If $\frac{BD}{DA} = \frac{1}{4}$, which is the value of OD?

(A) 4 **(B)** 12 **(C)** 13
(D) $\frac{5\sqrt{2}}{2}$ **(E)** 3 **E**

Cumulative Review (Chapters 17–19)

DIRECTIONS: Choose the *one* best answer to each question or problem. (Ex. 1–18)

1. Express sin 53° 18′ in terms of its cofunction. [17.8] **B**
   (A) csc 36° 42′ (B) cos 36° 42′
   (C) −cos 36° 42′ (D) −csc 36° 42′

2. In which quadrant is sin $u < 0$ and cot $u < 0$? [17.7] **D**
   (A) I (B) II (C) III (D) IV

3. Solve $\tan \theta = -\frac{\sqrt{3}}{3}$ for θ if $0 \le \theta \le 2\pi$. [18.11] **A**
   (A) $\frac{5}{6}\pi$ and $\frac{11}{6}\pi$ (B) $\frac{2}{3}\pi$ and $\frac{5}{3}\pi$
   (C) $\frac{2}{3}\pi$ and $\frac{4}{3}\pi$ (D) $\frac{5}{6}\pi$ and $\frac{7}{6}\pi$

4. Express 225° in radians. [18.10] **A**
   (A) $\frac{5}{4}\pi$ (B) $\frac{4}{3}\pi$ (C) $\frac{7}{6}\pi$ (D) $\frac{3}{4}\pi$

5. Express $\frac{2}{3}\pi$ radians in degrees. [18.10] **D**
   (A) 60° (B) 240° (C) 180° (D) 120°

6. Find the inverse of $y = -2 \sin x$. [18.12] **B**
   (A) $x = \arcsin(-\frac{y}{2})$ (B) $y = \arcsin(-\frac{x}{2})$
   (C) $x = -\arcsin(\frac{y}{2})$ (D) $y = -\arcsin(\frac{x}{2})$

7. Find θ, if $\theta = $ Arc sin $(-\frac{\sqrt{3}}{2})$. [18.12] **C**
   (A) 240° (B) 300° (C) −60° (D) 60°

8. Find cos (Arc tan $\frac{4}{3}$). [18.12] **A**
   (A) $\frac{3}{5}$ (B) $-\frac{3}{5}$
   (C) $\frac{3}{5}$ and $-\frac{3}{5}$ (D) None of these

9. Evaluate sec $(-\frac{\pi}{4})$ + csc $\frac{\pi}{2}$. [18.10] **C**
   (A) $\frac{\sqrt{2} + 2}{2}$ (B) $-\frac{\sqrt{2} + 2}{2}$
   (C) $\sqrt{2} + 1$ (D) $-\sqrt{2} + 1$

10. Write an equivalent expression for cot x using only sin x. [18.8] **D**
    (A) $\frac{1}{\sin^2 x}$ (B) $\sin^2 x$
    (C) $\pm \frac{\sin x}{\sqrt{1 - \sin^2 x}}$ (D) $\frac{\pm \sqrt{1 - \sin^2 x}}{\sin x}$

11. The lengths of two sides of a parallelogram are 20 and 30 centimeters. Their included angle measures 150°. Find the area of the parallelogram. [19.3] **B**
    (A) 150 cm² (B) 300 cm²
    (C) $150\sqrt{3}$ cm² (D) $150\sqrt{2}$ cm²

12. How many triangles can be constructed if m∠A = 46°, a = 16, and b = 14. [19.5] **B**
    (A) 0 (B) 1 (C) 2 (D) More than 2

13. Find cos 75°. [19.6] **B**
    (A) $\frac{\sqrt{6} + \sqrt{2}}{4}$ (B) $\frac{\sqrt{2}}{4}[\sqrt{3} - 1]$
    (C) $\frac{\sqrt{2}}{4}[1 - \sqrt{3}]$ (D) None of these

14. If sin $A = -\frac{5}{13}$ and ∠A lies in the third quadrant, find sin 2A. [19.6] **D**
    (A) $-\frac{120}{169}$ (B) $\frac{119}{169}$ (C) $-\frac{119}{169}$ (D) $\frac{120}{169}$

15. Find sin 15°. [19.7] **C**
    (A) $\frac{\sqrt{6} + \sqrt{2}}{4}$ (B) $\frac{\sqrt{2}}{2}[\sqrt{3} - 1]$
    (C) $\frac{\sqrt{6} - \sqrt{2}}{4}$ (D) $\frac{\sqrt{2} - \sqrt{6}}{4}$

16. If cos $A = -\frac{1}{5}$ and ∠A lies in the second quadrant, find cos $\frac{A}{2}$. [19.9] **D**
    (A) $\frac{1}{5}\sqrt{15}$ (B) $-\frac{1}{5}\sqrt{15}$
    (C) $-\frac{1}{5}\sqrt{10}$ (D) $\frac{1}{5}\sqrt{10}$

17. Find tan $(A - B)$ if tan $A = -\frac{5}{6}$ and tan $B = \frac{2}{3}$. [19.8] **A**
    (A) $-\frac{27}{8}$ (B) $\frac{3}{28}$ (C) $-\frac{27}{28}$ (D) $-\frac{3}{8}$

18. Find tan $\frac{A}{2}$ if cos $A = -\frac{1}{3}$ and ∠A is in the 4th quadrant. [19.9] **B**
    (A) $\sqrt{2}$ (B) $-\sqrt{2}$
    (C) $\pm\sqrt{2}$ (D) None of these

Determine the coordinates of point P and the radius r. [17.2]

19.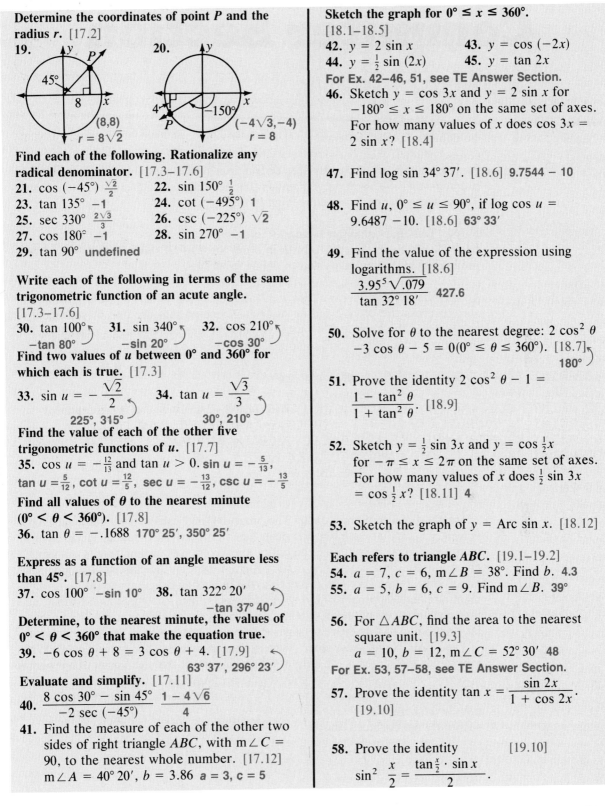

45°

8

(8,8)

$r = 8\sqrt{2}$

20.

4

−150°

$(-4\sqrt{3}, -4)$

$r = 8$

Find each of the following. Rationalize any radical denominator. [17.3–17.6]

21. cos $(-45°)$ $\frac{\sqrt{2}}{2}$ 22. sin 150° $\frac{1}{2}$

23. tan 135° -1 24. cot $(-495°)$ 1

25. sec 330° $\frac{2\sqrt{3}}{3}$ 26. csc $(-225°)$ $\sqrt{2}$

27. cos 180° -1 28. sin 270° -1

29. tan 90° **undefined**

Write each of the following in terms of the same trigonometric function of an acute angle. [17.3–17.6]

30. tan 100°   31. sin 340°   32. cos 210°

$-$tan 80° $-$sin 20° $-$cos 30°

Find two values of u between 0° and 360° for which each is true. [17.3]

33. sin $u = -\dfrac{\sqrt{2}}{2}$ 34. tan $u = \dfrac{\sqrt{3}}{3}$

225°, 315°   30°, 210°

Find the value of each of the other five trigonometric functions of u. [17.7]

35. cos $u = -\frac{12}{13}$ and tan $u > 0$. **sin $u = -\frac{5}{13}$,**

tan $u = \frac{5}{12}$, cot $u = \frac{12}{5}$, sec $u = -\frac{13}{12}$, csc $u = -\frac{13}{5}$

Find all values of θ to the nearest minute $(0° < \theta < 360°)$. [17.8]

36. tan $\theta = -.1688$ **170° 25′, 350° 25′**

Express as a function of an angle measure less than 45°. [17.8]

37. cos 100° $-$sin 10°   38. tan 322° 20′

$-$tan 37° 40′

Determine, to the nearest minute, the values of $0° < \theta < 360°$ that make the equation true.

39. $-6 \cos \theta + 8 = 3 \cos \theta + 4$. [17.9]

63° 37′, 296° 23′

Evaluate and simplify. [17.11]

40. $\dfrac{8 \cos 30° - \sin 45°}{-2 \sec (-45°)}$ $\dfrac{1 - 4\sqrt{6}}{4}$

41. Find the measure of each of the other two sides of right triangle ABC, with m$\angle C = 90$, to the nearest whole number. [17.12] m$\angle A = 40° 20′$, $b = 3.86$ $a = 3, c = 5$

Sketch the graph for $0° \le x \le 360°$. [18.1–18.5]

42. $y = 2 \sin x$ 43. $y = \cos(-2x)$

44. $y = \frac{1}{2} \sin(2x)$ 45. $y = \tan 2x$

For Ex. 42–46, 51, see TE Answer Section.

46. Sketch $y = \cos 3x$ and $y = 2 \sin x$ for $-180° \le x \le 180°$ on the same set of axes. For how many values of x does $\cos 3x = 2 \sin x$? [18.4]

47. Find log sin 34° 37′. [18.6] **9.7544 − 10**

48. Find u, $0° \le u \le 90°$, if log cos $u =$ 9.6487 −10. [18.6] **63° 33′**

49. Find the value of the expression using logarithms. [18.6]

$\dfrac{3.95^5 \sqrt{.079}}{\tan 32° 18′}$ **427.6**

50. Solve for θ to the nearest degree: $2 \cos^2 \theta$ $-3 \cos \theta - 5 = 0 (0° \le \theta \le 360°)$. [18.7]

180°

51. Prove the identity $2 \cos^2 \theta - 1 =$ $\dfrac{1 - \tan^2 \theta}{1 + \tan^2 \theta}$. [18.9]

52. Sketch $y = \frac{1}{2} \sin 3x$ and $y = \cos \frac{1}{2}x$ for $-\pi \le x \le 2\pi$ on the same set of axes. For how many values of x does $\frac{1}{2} \sin 3x = \cos \frac{1}{2}x$? [18.11] **4**

53. Sketch the graph of $y = $ Arc sin x. [18.12]

Each refers to triangle ABC. [19.1–19.2]

54. $a = 7$, $c = 6$, m$\angle B = 38°$. Find b. **4.3**

55. $a = 5$, $b = 6$, $c = 9$. Find m$\angle B$. **39°**

56. For $\triangle ABC$, find the area to the nearest square unit. [19.3]

$a = 10$, $b = 12$, m$\angle C = 52° 30′$ **48**

For Ex. 53, 57–58, see TE Answer Section.

57. Prove the identity tan $x = \dfrac{\sin 2x}{1 + \cos 2x}$. [19.10]

58. Prove the identity   [19.10]

$\sin^2 \dfrac{x}{2} = \dfrac{\tan \frac{x}{2} \cdot \sin x}{2}$.

Computer Section

OBJECTIVES: To run a BASIC program
To debug a BASIC program

A program is a set of step-by-step instructions to the computer. To run a BASIC program, there are certain commands that are referred to as *system commands*. These words have a special meaning to the computer.

RUN   Tells the computer to run the program
LIST   Tells the computer to print in order a list of all statements in the current program. This listing helps you to debug programs.

EXAMPLE: To run the program below, type in all the lines exactly as they are written. Be sure to press the correct button after each line so that the line or statement is entered into the computer's memory. Find the correct button by consulting the operator's manual for your computer. Enter will be used here.

```
10 PRINT "TYPE YOUR NAME"        ◄ Press enter.
20 INPUT N$
30 PRINT "WELCOME TO THE WORLD OF COMPUTERS,"; N$     ◄ Press enter.
40 PRINT "A COMPUTER REQUIRES A SPECIAL LANGUAGE"     ◄ Press enter.
50 PRINT "SOME LANGUAGES ARE BASIC, COBAL, AND PASCAL"    ◄ Press enter.
60 PRINT "BASIC IS THE LANGUAGE USED HERE"    ◄ Press enter.
70 PRINT "GOOD LUCK,"; N$        ◄ Press enter.
80 END
```

Type in LIST and press enter. The program you typed in should appear on the screen. Check that each line has been typed correctly. Correct a typing error or incorrect format by retyping the entire line. To remove a line that is causing an error and does not need to be in the program, type in the statement number and press enter. Some common errors to avoid in writing programs are missing statement numbers, improper ordering of statements, incorrect statement format, and unacceptable variable names. You can also debug or correct a BASIC program by responding to the error messages that may appear when running the program.

Type in RUN and press enter. Type in your name after the question mark. What you see on the screen is the output. Be sure to check that the output of a program is correct and reasonable. As you run the programs given in this book, you may find that reserved words or symbols for your computer may be different than the ones given here. If necessary, check the operator's manual for your computer and substitute the correct symbol.

PROBLEM SOLVING WITH THE COMPUTER

OBJECTIVE: To apply problem-solving steps in writing a computer program

You can use the computer to solve the same problem repeatedly once you have written the computer program. You will find that the computer is especially useful in solving problems that require a repeated process called *iteration*, logical comparison between numbers, or long computational procedures. There are several steps to follow when solving a problem with the aid of the computer.

ANALYZE the problem: This step requires that you state the problem clearly and completely. You make a flow chart in this step.

CODE the program: Translate your flow chart into a program language. In this book you will use BASIC (Beginners All Purpose Symbolic Instruction Code).

SIMULATE the program: Follow the program through with the aid of a flow chart. Use sample data that you can easily check by hand.

RUN the program: Enter the program into the computer at the terminal and run it with test data.

CORRECT the errors: Study the results of the program and determine if the output is accurate and reasonable. Sometimes you get output that looks correct but, because of an error in the program, it is really incorrect. Correct or "debug" the program and rerun it.

EXAMPLE 1: Apply the first three problem-solving steps for the following math problem: Find the sum of three numbers.

ANALYZE the problem: How many numbers are you going to add? *3*
What is the mathematical operation? *addition*
What will be the result of the problem? *the sum of 3 numbers*
What are the steps necessary to solve the problem? *Design a flow chart.*
Each shape in a flow chart has a special meaning.

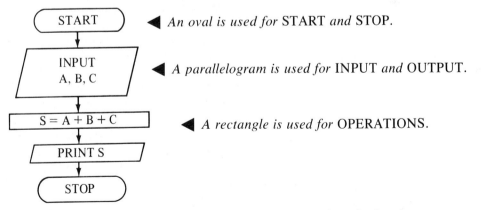

An oval is used for START and STOP.

A parallelogram is used for INPUT and OUTPUT.

A rectangle is used for OPERATIONS.

CODE the problem: You will learn BASIC statements to code this problem later in the chapter.

SIMULATE the program: Follow the steps on the flow chart with the numbers 4, 5, and 10. Add the three numbers 4, 5, and 10. Replace S with 19. Print S.

COMPUTER SECTION

EXAMPLE 2: Design a flow chart to compute the sum of the integers from 1 to 100. Print the sum.

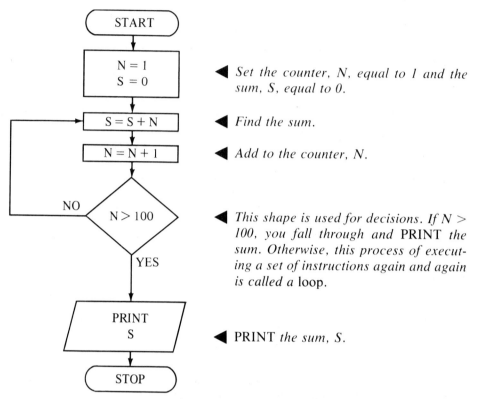

Set the counter, N, equal to 1 and the sum, S, equal to 0.

Find the sum.

Add to the counter, N.

This shape is used for decisions. If N > 100, you fall through and **PRINT** the sum. Otherwise, this process of executing a set of instructions again and again is called a loop.

PRINT the sum, S.

EXERCISES:

1. Problem: Change decimals to percents. State clearly the math involved in solving the problem. Design a flow chart to show the steps necessary to solve the problem.

2. Problem: Subtract two numbers. State clearly the math involved in solving the problem. If the result is negative, STOP. Print the answer where the answer is positive or zero. Design a flow chart to show the steps necessary to solve the problem.

3. Problem: Find the product of two numbers. Subtract 13. Add 3. Divide by 10. Print the answer. State clearly the math steps necessary to solve the problem. Design a flow chart to show the steps necessary to solve the problem.

4. Problem: Find the rate of speed, given the distance and time. State clearly the math steps necessary to solve the problem. Design a flow chart to show the steps necessary to solve the problem.
For answers to all exercises, see TE Answer Section.

NUMERICAL EXPRESSIONS IN BASIC

OBJECTIVES:
To write numbers in BASIC
To write numerical expressions using BASIC symbols
To evaluate BASIC numerical expressions

To use the five steps in problem solving on the computer and to write other programs, you need to be able to communicate with the computer. BASIC is one of many programming languages you can use. Two other popular languages used today are FORTRAN and COBOL.

You write numbers in BASIC as decimals or decimal approximations.

EXAMPLE 1:
Write the following numbers in BASIC form.

Numeric form	BASIC form
3	3
-71	-71
$\dfrac{7}{8}$	.875
$\sqrt{3}$	1.732051
π	3.141593
$3\dfrac{1}{4}$	3.25

For mathematical calculations, BASIC has five operations. The five arithmetic symbols are: addition (+), subtraction (−), multiplication (∗), division (/), and raise to a power (↑). A numerical expression in BASIC can be a single number or a phrase.

EXAMPLE 2:
Write each of the following numerical expressions using BASIC arithmetic symbols.

Numerical expression	BASIC arithmetic symbol
$88 + 6$	$88 + 6$
$10 - 7$	$10 - 7$
6×8	$6 * 8$
$12 \div 4$	$12 \ / \ 4$
3^2	$3 \uparrow 2$

BASIC performs operations in this order.

1. Raising a number to a power.
2. Multiplication and division from left to right.
3. Addition and subtraction from left to right.
4. When parentheses are present, do the operations within the parentheses first, following the above order.

BASIC
SYMBOLS

EXAMPLE 3:   Evaluate each BASIC numerical expression.

BASIC expression	Value
(4 + 2) + 5	11
8 − 7	1
7 − 8	−1
(10 − 7) + 4	7
16 / 4 ∗ 3	12
35 / (2 + 3)	7
4 + 2 ↑ 3 − 5	4 + 8 − 5 or 7
(4 + 2) ↑ 3 − 5	216 − 5 or 211

EXAMPLE 4:   Evaluate the BASIC numerical expression.
$$(35 * 4) + (6 + 9)/3$$

Think ▶   First perform operations in parentheses.
$$35 * 4 = 140$$
$$6 + 9 = 15$$
New problem: $140 + 15/3$

Think ▶   Perform division before addition.
$$15/3 = 5$$
New problem: $140 + 5 = 145$

EXERCISES: Write the following numbers in BASIC form.

1. $2\frac{1}{2}$ *2.5*   **2.** 9,832 *9832*   **3.** $\frac{3}{16}$ *0.1875*

4. $\frac{1}{3}$ *0.3333*   **5.** $-16\frac{7}{8}$ *−16.875*   **6.** 21.37 *21.37*

Write each expression using BASIC arithmetic symbols.

7. $\frac{(7 \cdot 3)}{8}$ *(7 ∗ 3)/8*   **8.** 6^2 *6 ↑ 2*

9. $\frac{64 + 4}{16} \cdot \frac{4}{12}$ *((64 + 4)/16) ∗ (4/12)*   **10.** $110 - 5^2$ *110 −5 ↑ 2*

11. 3/4 + 8 *.75 + 8 or ((3/4) + 8)*   **12.** $\frac{6 \cdot 2 + (7 - 11)}{5^3 + 4/12}$

((6 ∗ 2) + (7 − 11))/((5 ↑ 3) + (4/12))

Evaluate each BASIC numerical expression.

13. 6 − 32 + 5 *−21*   **14.** (3 ∗ 12)/6 *6*

15. 12 − 5 ∗ 3 + 27/9 *−6*   **16.** 3 ↑ 2 ∗ 8 + 7 *79*

17. 48/6 ∗ 2 + 3 ↑ (2 + 1) *43*   **18.** 4 ↑ 2/8 ∗ 6 ↑ 2 − 12 *60*

VARIABLE EXPRESSION IN BASIC

OBJECTIVES: To write BASIC variables
To write variable expressions using BASIC variables
To write equations and inequalities in BASIC form

A variable in BASIC is a quantity whose value can be assigned and changed during a computer program. The variable can be referred to by name. Each program variable is stored in the computer's memory.

A BASIC variable is a single letter or a letter followed by a single digit.

EXAMPLE 1:   Tell if each of the following is an acceptable BASIC variable:
A, X, 3, Y, 4A, A1, XYZ, NEW, A2, X9, NEW1, A344.

Acceptable BASIC Variables	Unacceptable BASIC Variables
A	3
X	4A
Y	XYZ
A1	NEW
A2	NEW1
X9	A344

A variable expression in BASIC can be a single variable or an expression.

EXAMPLE 2:   Write the following algebraic expressions in BASIC and indicate the variable.

	BASIC Expression	Variable
6 increased by Y	$6 + Y$	Y
10 more than 3 times A	$3 * A + 10$	A
M decreased by 7	$M - 7$	M
One-third of the sum of X, Y, and Z	$(X + Y + Z)/3$	X, Y, Z
B raised to the power of 2	$B \uparrow 2$	2

You can use variables in equations.

EXAMPLE 3:   Write a BASIC equation for the area of a rectangle.

$$A = L * W$$

where A = area
L = length
W = width

Write a BASIC equation for a line.

$$Y = M * X + B$$

where (X, Y) is a point on a line, M is the slope of the line, and B is the y-intercept.

You can write variables when comparing quantities.

EXAMPLE 4: Write the given algebraic expression in BASIC form.

Variable Expression	BASIC Expression
$x - 2x > 20 + 3x$	$X - 2 * X > 20 + 3 * X$
$y \geq 2x + 3$	$Y > = 2 * X + 3$
$x^2 + 6 < y^2 - 3$	$X \uparrow 2 + 6 < Y \uparrow 2 - 3$
$(x + y)^2 \neq x^2 + y^2$	$(X + Y) \uparrow 2 <> X \uparrow 2 + Y \uparrow 2$
$x + y < 3$	$X + Y < = 3$

EXERCISES: Write BASIC variables for the following: *(Answers may vary.)*

1. number of teachers in the school T
2. length of altitude of triangle A
3. coefficients in quadratic equation $Y = AX^2 + BX + C$ A, B, C
4. probability of tossing heads H
5. percentage of water in solution W
6. degree of polynomial D
7. coordinates of turning point in parabola X, Y

Tell if each of these BASIC expressions has acceptable variables.

8. $Y = X \uparrow 2 - 3X + 1$ *yes*
9. $A = 2 * \pi * R$ *no $A = 2 * P * R$*
10. $PRIN = PRIN + INTER$ *no $P = P + I$*
11. $(Z * 3) \uparrow 2 = F$ *yes*
12. $T = DIST/RA$ *no $T = D/RI$*
13. $N = A * R \uparrow (N - 1)$ *yes*

Write in BASIC form.

14. $S = \dfrac{A(R^N - 1)}{R - 1}$ $S = (A * (R \uparrow N - 1))/(R - 1)$

15. $X > \dfrac{(6 - 3X)}{8}$ $X > = ((6 - 3 * X))/8$

16. $Y < 3Y^2 + 16Y - 12$ $Y < 3 * Y \uparrow 2 + 16 * Y - 12$

17. $C \neq \pi R^2$ (use 3.14 for π) $C <> 3.14 * (R \uparrow 2)$

18. $Z > 3XY^2(XY + 3)$ $Z > (3 * X * Y \uparrow 2) * (X * Y + 3)$

19. $(X + 5) \cdot \dfrac{X}{X - 4} = \dfrac{X + 5}{1} \cdot \dfrac{X}{X - 4}$ $((X + 5) * X)/(X - 4) = ((X + 5 * X)/(X - 4)$

*Write a BASIC equation or inequality for the following problems. Indicate variables used.

20. The average of 5 test scores $A = (T1 + T2 + T3 + T4 + T5)/5$
21. Y raised to the 4th power is not equal to Z $Z <> (Y \uparrow 4)$
22. T is less than or equal to 8 minus 3 times U $(T < = 8 - 3 * U)$

SIMPLE BASIC STATEMENTS

OBJECTIVES: To number statements in a BASIC program
To write LET statements
To write PRINT statements
To write END statements

A program is a set of instructions to the computer. Each instruction contains a BASIC command and is numbered so that the computer will execute each statement in the correct order. The last statement is always the END statement. The END statement tells the computer the program is finished.

EXAMPLE 1: Indicate possible numbers for the following BASIC program.

```
10 LET A = 6
20 PRINT A
30 END
```

◀ *Lines are not numbered consecutively so that instructions may be added later, if needed.*

The LET command assigns a value or expression to a variable.

EXAMPLE 2: What is the value of the variable in each statement?

```
LET X = 8
LET Y = -7
```
Assigns the value of 8 to the variable X.
Assigns the value of -7 to Y.

```
LET A = 3
LET B = 5
LET C = A + B
```
The computer performs A + B and stores the result, 8, in memory at a place called C.

You can also use the LET statement to increase the value of a variable.

EXAMPLE 3: What is the effect on C of the following statement?

```
LET C = C + 1
```
This instruction increases the value of C by 1.

The PRINT statement causes the computer to print what follows the PRINT word. You can use the print statement to print numerical constants and expressions.

EXAMPLE 4: What will the computer print after each statement?

Numeric Constants and Expressions	Computer PRINTS
`PRINT 16`	16
`PRINT (3 + 2) * 6`	30
`PRINT 7, 8, 8 - 7, 8 + 7`	7, 8, 1, 15

You can use the PRINT statement to print characters or strings of characters. To do this write the PRINT statement and enclose the character or string of characters inside quotation marks. You can vary the spacing on each line of output, too. If you use a comma, you will get wide spacing. If you use a semicolon, you will get close spacing. To skip a line in the output, use a PRINT statement by itself.

COMPUTER SECTION

EXAMPLE 6:   What is the output of the following PRINT statements?

```
                                              OUTPUT
10 PRINT "THE ANSWER IS NO"        THE ANSWER IS NO
20 PRINT                          (one line of space)
30 LET X = 3
40 LET Y = 2
50 PRINT "SUM ="; X + Y            SUM = 5
60 PRINT "6/12"                   6/12
70 PRINT "X ="; X; "Y ="; Y       X = 3 Y = 2
```

EXERCISES: What is the value of the variable Y in each statement? The phrases in the boxes give information needed to find X. They are not part of the program statement.

1. Let Y = 13 *13*
2. Let Y = 3 + 4 * X (if X = 2) *11*
3. Let Y = (4 * 18)/6 $\uparrow$ 2 + 1 *3*
4. Let Y = (S1 * S2 * S3) / 3 (Where S1 − 5, S2 = 6, S3 = −3) *−30*
5. Let Y = Y + 3 (where Y = 2 before this instruction) *5*
6. Let Y = 7
   Let Y = Y $\uparrow$ 3 *y^3 or 343*

What will the computer print after each of the following PRINT statements?

7. PRINT −7 *−7*
8. PRINT "THE PRODUCT IS"; Y (*where Y = 21*) *THE PRODUCT IS 21*
9. PRINT "(8 $\uparrow$ 2)/16" *(8 $\uparrow$ 2)/16*
10. PRINT X $\uparrow$ Y (*where X = 2 and Y = 3*) *8*
11. PRINT "M + N", M + N (*where M = 5, N = −5*) *M + N $\varnothing$*
12. PRINT "TODAY IS THANKSGIVING" *TODAY IS THANKSGIVING*
13. PRINT 18, 33 / 11, "THE ANSWER IS"; X (*where X = 1376*)
    18   3   THE ANSWER IS 1376

What will the computer print at the end of each program?

14.
```
10 LET N1 = 12
20 LET N2 = 4
30 LET N3 = N1 * N2 + N1 ↑ 2 +
   N2 ↑ 2
40 PRINT "THE ANSWER IS", N3
50 END
```
THE ANSWER IS 208

15.
```
10 LET N = 35
20 LET A = 12
30 LET L = 114
40 LET S = (N/2) * (A + L)
50 PRINT "THE SUM OF THE
   FIRST"; N; "TERMS IS"; S
60 END
```
THE SUM OF THE FIRST 35 TERMS IS 2205

COMPUTER SECTION

BASIC STATEMENTS FOR INPUTTING DATA

OBJECTIVES: To use INPUT statements
To use READ/DATA statements

The INPUT command is used to enter data into the computer. This instruction prompts the computer to type a "?" and to wait for you to enter a number for each variable in the command. The numbers and variables are separated by commas.

EXAMPLE 1:

```
10 INPUT A
 ? 3
```
A is assigned the value 3.

```
10 INPUT X, Y, Z
 ? 5, 10, 15
```
X is assigned the value 5.
Y is assigned the value 10.
Z is assigned the value 15.

EXAMPLE 2:

What is the output if you assign B, the value of 7 and H, the value of 4?

```
10 INPUT B, H
20 LET A = .5 * B * H
30 PRINT "THE AREA OF THE TRIANGLE IS"; A
40 END
```

OUTPUT
Computer prints: ?
You enter two numbers separated by a comma: ? 7, 4
Computer prints:

```
THE AREA OF THE TRIANGLE IS 14
```

The READ and DATA statements are used to enter data into the program. They are used together as a pair.

EXAMPLE 3:

What values are assigned to A, B, and C with the following statements?

```
20 READ A, B, C
40 DATA 4, 6, 8
```
When the READ command is read by the computer, the variable A is assigned 4, the variable B is assigned 6, and the variable C is assigned 8. Some computers will then print OUT OF DATA IN LINE 20.

EXAMPLE 4:

What is the computer output for the following program?

```
10 READ L, B
20 LET T = L + 2 * B
30 PRINT "THE TOTAL AREA OF A CYLINDER IS"; T
40 DATA 7, 8
50 END
OUTPUT
THE TOTAL AREA OF A CYLINDER IS 23
```

The DATA statement can be located anywhere in the program before the END statement.

EXAMPLE 5:   What is the computer output for the following program?

```
10 READ M, R
20 LET L = {M / 360} * {2 * 3, 14 * R}
30 PRINT "THE LENGTH OF THE ARC IS"; L
40 DATA 90, 4
50 END
OUTPUT
THE LENGTH OF THE ARC IS 6.28
```

The next lesson gives examples of the DATA statement used with IF THEN and GO TO statements.

EXERCISES: What is the computer output for each program?

1.
```
10 LET P = 15
20 LET Q = -2
30 LET R = P * Q
40 PRINT R
50 END  -30
```

2.
```
10 LET X1 = 12
20 LET X2 = 4
30 PRINT X1/X2
40 END  3
```

3.
```
10 INPUT M, X, B
20 LET Y = M * X + B
30 PRINT Y
40 END
? 2, 1, -3  -1
```

4.
```
 5 INPUT M, N, X
10 LET P1 = X ↑ M * X ↑ N
15 LET P2 = X ↑ (M + N)
20 PRINT "PRODUCT OF
   POWERS EQUALS"
25 PRINT "P1 ="; P1
30 PRINT "P2 ="; P2
40 END
? 2, 3, 2
```
PRODUCT OF POWERS EQUAL P1 = 32 P2 = 32

5.
```
10 READ M1, M2, M3
20 LET A = (M1 + M2 + M3) /3
30 PRINT "THE AVERAGE MEASURE
   IS"; A
40 DATA 7, 6, 8
50 END  THE AVERAGE MEASURE IS 7
```

6.
```
2 READ D, T
4 PRINT D, T, D/T
6 DATA 360, 6
8 END
```
360   6   60

7. Write a program to find the power of a number, X. Use an INPUT statement to enter the number, X, and the power, P. Use a PRINT statement to print "X RAISED TO THE"; P; "POWER IS"; Y *10 INPUT X, P   20 LET Y = X ↑ P   30 PRINT "X RAISED TO THE"; P; "POWER IS"; Y   40 END*

8. Write a program to find the change from $10.00 for a list of 5 grocery item costs. Use a DATA statement to enter the item costs. Use a READ statement to assign the costs to the five variables. Use a PRINT statement to print "THE CHANGE IS" followed by the amount. *10 READ P1, P2, P3, P4, P5   20 LET T = P1 + P2 + P3 + P4 + P5   30 LET C = 10.00 − T   40 PRINT "THE CHANGE IS"; C   50 DATA $1.89, $1.62, $.59, $2.01, $.89   60 END*

BASIC CONDITIONALS

OBJECTIVES: To use GO TO statements
To use IF THEN statements

The GO TO statement causes the computer to go to a new statement and continue the program from there.

EXAMPLE 1: What statement is executed after statement 40?

```
10 READ A, B
20 LET C = A + B
30 PRINT "C="; C
40 GO TO 10          ◀ The computer goes back to line 10.
50 DATA 2, 4, 6, 8, 10,  ◀ Assigns 2 to A and 4 to B first time.
   12                      Assigns 6 to A and 8 to B second time.
60 END                    Assigns 10 to A and 12 to B third time.
```

The IF THEN statement is a conditional command. If the given condition is true, the computer will branch to the given statement. If it is false the computer will execute the next statement.

EXAMPLE 2: Write a program to compute the square of numbers less than or equal to 10.

```
10 INPUT X           ◀ If the variable is greater than 10,
20 IF X>10 THEN 50     the program ends; otherwise it
30 LET C = X ↑ 2       continues.
40 PRINT C
50 END
```

EXAMPLE 3: Tell which path the computer would take for the given set of data. This program will print only positive numbers from a given set of data.

```
10 READ X
20 IF X < 0 THEN 10
30 PRINT X
40 GO TO 10
50 DATA 2, -2, -3, 3,
   -1, 7, -7, 8
60 END
```

$$\underset{\downarrow \text{false? Yes}}{\overset{\text{IF } 2 < 0 \text{ THEN } 10}{\longrightarrow}} \text{True? No.} \qquad \underset{\downarrow \quad \text{false? No}}{\overset{\text{IF } -2 < 0 \text{ THEN } 10}{\longrightarrow}} \text{True? Yes.}$$

Program goes to 10 and continues until all numbers have been read.

EXERCISES: Write the IF . . . THEN statements for the following conditions.

1. If the value of N1 equals N2 then go to line 150 *20 IF N1 = N2 THEN 150*

2. If the value of 25 multiplied by T is less than 30 multiplied by U, then go to line 295. *20 IF 25 * T < 30 * U THEN 295*

3. If the value of A is greater than or equal to 0, then go back to line 50. Let this statement number be after line 50. *120 IF A > = 0 THEN 50*

4. If the value of T1 is not equal to T2 then go to line 1000. (Use <> for not equal.) *20 IF T1 <> T2 THEN 1000*

Give the output for each program.

5.
```
10 READ S, T
20 DATA 6, -42, 18, 36, 30, 24
30 IF S ↑ 2 < T ↑ 2 THEN 10
40 PRINT S, T
50 GO TO 10
60 END
```
6	*-42*
18	*36*

OUT OF DATA LINE 20

6.
```
3 INPUT U, V, W
6 LET X = ((3 * U + W)/V ↑ 2
9 IF U > 25 THEN 15
12 PRINT U
15 END
?5, 2, 3
```
4.5

7.
```
10 LET X = 5
20 PRINT X/5;
30 LET X = X + 5
40 IF X > 45 THEN 60
50 GO TO 20
60 END
```
(Semicolon in line 20 causes all output on same line.)

1 2 3 4 5 6 7 8 9

8.
```
5 READ A, B, C, D
10 LET S1 = A ↑ 2 + 2 * A * B +
   B ↑ 2
15 LET S2 = (C + D) * (C + D)
20 IF S1 <> S2 THEN 5
25 PRINT "THE SQUARE OF SUM
   FOR"; C, D
30 GO TO 5
35 DATA 3, 5, 5, 3, 2, 7, 3, 1
40 END
```
OUT OF DATA LINE 35

9. Write a program to tell whether a number is positive or negative using an INPUT statement.

10. Write a program to test for which whole number values of X between −2 and 2 the two equations are equal. Print values of X for which the two equations are equal.

$$Y1 = 3X + 2 \qquad Y2 = 2X + 3$$

11. Write a program to find the greatest number of three given numbers. Print the answer.

For Ex. 9–11, see TE Answer Section.

ITERATION IN BASIC

OBJECTIVE: To use the FOR NEXT loop

The FOR and NEXT statements go together. The same variable is used in both the FOR command and NEXT command. Use the FOR NEXT loop to repeat a group of instructions.

EXAMPLE 1:   What values are assigned to N in the program below?

N is assigned values of 1, 2, 3, 4, 5.

```
10 FOR N = 1 TO 5
```
◀ *Any number of instructions*

After N has been assigned 5, the program will drop out of the loop to line 55 and continue.

```
50 NEXT N
55 INSTRUCTION
```

EXAMPLE 2:   Write a program to find the cube of numbers from 1 to 4.

```
10 FOR X = 1 TO 4              OUTPUT
20 LET Y = X ↑ 3          CUBE IS 1
30 PRINT "CUBE IS"; Y     CUBE IS 8
40 NEXT X                 CUBE IS 27
50 END                    CUBE IS 64
```

Sometimes, you will have a set of instructions that you want to repeat again and again. Each pass through the loop is called an *iteration*. Recall that there are several statements in BASIC which you can use for loops. You can use the IF THEN and GO TO statements, or you can use the FOR NEXT statements.

EXAMPLE 3:   Write programs to find the value of the expression $\dfrac{2 * X + X \uparrow 2}{X - 5}$ for values of X from 1 to 4. Use the IF THEN statement in Program A and the FOR NEXT statement in Program B.

Program A (IF THEN)   Program B (FOR NEXT)

```
10 LET X = 1                  10 FOR X = 1 TO 4
20 PRINT (2 * X + X ↑ 2)/(X - 5)   20 PRINT (2 * X + X ↑ 2)/(X - 5)
30 LET X = X + 1              30 NEXT X
40 IF X > 4 THEN 60          40 END
50 GO TO 20
60 END
```

OUTPUT From Both A and B
```
        -.75
        -2.6666666
        -7.5
        -24
```

The FOR . . . NEXT loop can be incremented by numbers other than one with the step option: FOR X = 1 to N STEP N where N is any number.

EXAMPLE 4: Give the output for the following program.

```
10 FOR X = 2 TO 10 STEP 2
20 PRINT X
30 NEXT X
40 END
```

Output
2
4
6
8
10

EXERCISES:

Give the output for each program.

1.
```
10 FOR B = 0 TO 50 STEP 10
20 LET S = B + 1          0    1
30 PRINT B, S            10   11
40 NEXT B                20   21
50 END                   30   31
                         40   41
                         50   51
```

3.
```
2 LET C = 1
4 FOR Y = 1 TO 4
6 LET T = C ↑ Y
8 LET C = C + 1
10 PRINT T;
12 NEXT Y
14 END  1  4  9  16
```

2.
```
5 FOR R = 12 TO 3 STEP -3
10 PRINT (2 * R) + (R/3);
15 NEXT R
20 END   Semicolon puts answer on same line.
              28   24   14   7
```

4.
```
5 PRINT "FAHRENHEIT CENTIGRADE"
10 FOR F = 32 TO 102 STEP 10
20 LET C = 5/9 * (F - 32)
30 PRINT F, C
40 NEXT F
50 END
```

*5.
```
10 FOR X = 1 TO 12
20 FOR Y = 1 TO 12
30 PRINT X * Y;
40 NEXT Y
50 PRINT
60 NEXT X
70 END    generates multiplication table
```

6. Write a program to find the sum of the cubes from 1 to 10 with a FOR . . . NEXT loop. Print the sum with an appropriate message.

7. Write a program to find the multiples of 8 between 9 and 96 with a FOR . . . NEXT loop. Print the multiples with an appropriate message. (Start the loop with the first value that is a multiple of 8.)
For Ex. 4, 6, 7, see TE Answer Section.

ADVANCED BASIC STATEMENTS *(Optional)*

OBJECTIVES: To use REM statements
To use BASIC functions
To use character strings
To use arrays and dimension statements

The REM statement allows the programmer to enter comments into the program listing that do not effect the output but provide documentation about what is happening in the program.

EXAMPLE 1:   Use a REM statement to indicate what the variables are and what the program does.

```
 5 REM INPUT THE STOPPING POINT, A; THE NUMBER B,
   FOR FINDING
 7 REM MULTIPLES OF 4
10 INPUT A, B
20 REM THIS LOOP WILL PRINT THE MULTIPLES OF A NUMBER
30 FOR X = 1 TO A
40 LET Y = B * X
50 PRINT Y
60 NEXT X
70 END
? 4, 3
```

OUTPUT   3 6 9 12

These REM statements give information but do not change the output. It is very important to document your program for finding errors later on.

BASIC functions are computer programs that are already written and stored in the computer for use within BASIC programs.

Some BASIC functions you may want to use are:

1. SQR(X)   ◀ *finds square root of X.*

2. INT(X)   ◀ *gives the greatest integer less than or equal to X.*

3. SIN(X)   ◀ *gives the sine, cosine, or tangent of X where X is in radian*
COS(X)   *measure.*
TAN(X)

4. RND(X)   ◀ *finds a random number between 0 and 1.*

EXAMPLE 2: Write a program to find the square root of X using a BASIC function.

```
10 INPUT X
20 LET Y = SQR{X}          ◀  SQR is BASIC function name and call to
30 PRINT Y                     square root program.
40 END
 ? 4          OUTPUT: 2
 ? 11         OUTPUT: 3.317
```

> *Note: This is correct, but the computer actually gives the answer 3.31663.*

A character string variable allows you to use alphabetic characters for a variable in BASIC. A character variable is represented by a letter followed by a dollar sign.

$$A\$$$
$$R\$$$

You can use a character string variable to ask a question, make a choice, or represent a name.

Use a character string variable to answer "YES" or "NO."

```
50 PRINT "DO YOU WANT TO CONTINUE?"
60 PRINT "ANSWER YES OR NO"
70 INPUT A$                    Quotation marks are
80 IF A$ = "YES" THEN 10   ◀  needed for computer to
90 END                         process characters.
```

BASIC also provides a means for storing a list of items in the computer's memory. This is done with an *array* and a *dimension statement*.
DIM A(5) creates an array with 5 spaces. Each space is given a subscript from 1 to 5.

EXAMPLE 3:
```
10 DIM A{5}
20 FOR X = 1 TO 5
30 LET A{X} = X ↑ 2     ◀  Sets each array position equal to the
40 PRINT A{X}              square of X.
50 NEXT X               ◀  Prints the value of the array position.
60 END
```

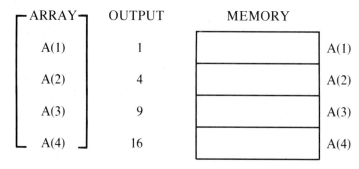

⌈ ARRAY ⌉	OUTPUT		MEMORY	
A(1)	1			A(1)
A(2)	4			A(2)
A(3)	9			A(3)
⌊ A(4) ⌋	16			A(4)

EXERCISES: Write a BASIC program to evaluate and print the following expressions for INPUT A and B. *For Ex. 1–5, see TE Answer Section.*

1. $\dfrac{(a + b)}{(a^2 + b^2)}$

2. $\sqrt{\dfrac{\dfrac{a + b}{a - b}}{a^2 - b^2}}$

3. $\sqrt{(a + b)^3}$

4. $\text{INT } \dfrac{ab}{a + b}$

5. Write a BASIC program to compute the area of a rectangle given its two sides. Print the answers as the greatest integer less than or equal to the calculated answers.

Give the OUTPUT for each program.

6.
```
10 INPUT X
20 LET Y = INT (X)
30 PRINT Y
40 IF Y = INT(X) THEN 60
50 GO TO 70
60 PRINT "INTEGER VALUE
   EQUALS INPUT"
70 END
 ? 3.82
```

7.1	1
2	1.41421
3	1.73205
4	2
5	2.23607
6	2.44949
7	2.64575
8	2.82842
9	3

3

7.
```
10 FOR X = 1 TO 9
20 PRINT X, SQR(X)
30 NEXT X
40 END
```

8.
```
10 DIM L(10)
20 REM THIS LOOP PLUS THE LIST L
30 FOR X = 1 TO 10
40 LET L(X) = RND
50 NEXT X
60 REM THIS LOOP PRINTS OUT
   ARRAY IN REVERSE
70 FOR X = 10 TO 1 STEP -1
80 PRINT L(S);
90 NEXT X
100 END
```
10 9 8 7 6 5 4 3 2 1

9.
```
10 LET A$= "WRONG"
20 LET B$= "RIGHT"
30 PRINT "WHAT IS 3 * 7?"
40 INPUT X
50 IF X = 21 THEN 80
60 PRINT A$
70 GO TO 90
80 PRINT B$
90 END
 ? 30
```
WRONG

10.
```
10 PRINT "A SET IS A COLLECTION"
20 PRINT "OF OBJECTS TYPE IN TRUE OR FALSE"
30 INPUT A$
40 IF A$ = "TRUE" THEN 70
50 PRINT "NO THE DEFINITION IS TRUE"
60 GO TO 99
70 PRINT "VERY GOOD, YOU ARE RIGHT"
99 END
 ? TRUE
```
VERY GOOD, YOU ARE RIGHT

Squares and Square Roots

No.	Sq.	Sq. Root		No.	Sq.	Sq. Root
1	1	1.000		51	2,601	7.141
2	4	1.414		52	2,704	7.211
3	9	1.732		53	2,809	7.280
4	16	2.000		54	2,916	7.348
5	25	2.236		55	3,025	7.416
6	36	2.449		56	3,136	7.483
7	49	2.646		57	3,249	7.550
8	64	2.828		58	3,364	7.616
9	81	3.000		59	3,481	7.681
10	100	3.162		60	3,600	7.746
11	121	3.317		61	3,721	7.810
12	144	3.464		62	3,844	7.874
13	169	3.606		63	3,969	7.937
14	196	3.742		64	4,096	8.000
15	225	3.873		65	4,225	8.062
16	256	4.000		66	4,356	8.124
17	289	4.123		67	4,489	8.185
18	324	4.243		68	4,624	8.246
19	361	4.359		69	4,761	8.307
20	400	4.472		70	4,900	8.357
21	441	4.583		71	5,041	8.426
22	484	4.690		72	5,184	8.485
23	529	4.796		73	5,329	8.544
24	576	4.899		74	5,476	8.602
25	625	5.000		75	5,625	8.660
26	676	5.099		76	5,776	8.718
27	729	5.196		77	5,929	8.775
28	784	5.292		78	6,084	8.832
29	841	5.385		79	6,241	8.888
30	900	5.477		80	6,400	8.944
31	961	5.568		81	6,561	9.000
32	1,024	5.657		82	6,724	9.055
33	1,089	5.745		83	6,889	9.110
34	1,156	5.831		84	7,056	9.165
35	1,225	5.916		85	7,225	9.220
36	1,296	6.000		86	7,396	9.274
37	1,369	6.083		87	7,569	9.327
38	1,444	6.164		88	7,744	9.381
39	1,521	6.245		89	7,921	9.434
40	1,600	6.325		90	8,100	9.487
41	1,681	6.403		91	8,281	9.539
42	1,764	6.481		92	8,464	9.592
43	1,849	6.557		93	8,649	9.644
44	1,936	6.633		94	8,836	9.695
45	2,025	6.708		95	9,025	9.747
46	2,116	6.782		96	9,216	9.798
47	2,209	6.856		97	9,409	9.849
48	2,304	6.928		98	9,604	9.899
49	2,401	7.000		99	9,801	9.950
50	2,500	7.071		100	10,000	10.000

* Logarithms of Trigonometric Functions

* Subtract 10 from each entry in this table to obtain the proper logarithm of the indicated trigonometric function.

Angle	L Sin	L Tan	L Cot	L Cos	Angle
0° 0'				10.0000	90° 0'
10'	7.4637	7.4637	12.5363	.0000	50'
20'	.7648	.7648	.2352	.0000	40'
30'	7.9408	7.9409	12.0591	.0000	30'
40'	8.0658	8.0658	11.9342	.0000	20'
50'	.1627	.1627	.8373	10.0000	10'
1° 0'	8.2419	8.2419	11.7581	9.9999	89° 0'
10'	.3088	.3089	.6911	.9999	50'
20'	.3668	.3669	.6331	.9999	40'
30'	.4179	.4181	.5819	.9999	30'
40'	.4637	.4638	.5362	.9998	20'
50'	.5050	.5053	.4947	.9998	10'
2° 0'	8.5428	8.5431	11.4569	9.9997	88° 0'
10'	.5776	.5779	.4221	.9997	50'
20'	.6097	.6101	.3899	.9996	40'
30'	.6397	.6401	.3599	.9996	30'
40'	.6677	.6682	.3318	.9995	20'
50'	.6940	.6945	.3055	.9995	10'
3° 0'	8.7188	8.7194	11.2806	9.9994	87° 0'
10'	.7423	.7429	.2571	.9993	50'
20'	.7645	.7652	.2348	.9993	40'
30'	.7857	.7865	.2135	.9992	30'
40'	.8059	.8067	.1933	.9991	20'
50'	.8251	.8261	.1739	.9990	10'
4° 0'	8.8436	8.8446	11.1554	9.9989	86° 0'
10'	.8613	.8624	.1376	.9989	50'
20'	.8783	.8795	.1205	.9988	40'
30'	.8946	.8960	.1040	.9987	30'
40'	.9104	.9118	.0882	.9986	20'
50'	.9256	.9272	.0728	.9985	10'
5° 0'	8.9403	8.9420	11.0580	9.9983	85° 0'
10'	.9545	.9563	.0437	.9982	50'
20'	.9682	.9701	.0299	.9981	40'
30'	.9816	.9836	.0164	.9980	30'
40'	.9945	.9966	11.0034	.9979	20'
50'	9.0070	9.0093	10.9907	.9977	10'
6° 0'	9.0192	9.0216	10.9784	9.9976	84° 0'
10'	.0311	.0336	.9664	.9975	50'
20'	.0426	.0453	.9547	.9973	40'
30'	.0539	.0567	.9433	.9972	30'
40'	.0648	.0678	.9322	.9971	20'
50'	.0755	.0786	.9214	.9969	10'
7° 0'	9.0859	9.0891	10.9109	9.9968	83° 0'
10'	.0961	.0995	.9005	.9966	50'
20'	.1060	.1096	.8904	.9964	40'
30'	.1157	.1194	.8806	.9963	30'
40'	.1252	.1291	.8709	.9961	20'
50'	.1345	.1385	.8615	.9959	10'
8° 0'	9.1436	9.1478	10.8522	9.9958	82° 0'
10'	.1525	.1569	.8431	.9956	50'
20'	.1612	.1658	.8342	.9954	40'
30'	.1697	.1745	.8255	.9952	30'
40'	.1781	.1831	.8169	.9950	20'
50'	.1863	.1915	.8085	.9948	10'
9° 0'	9.1943	9.1997	10.8003	9.9946	81° 0'
	L Cos	L Cot	L Tan	L Sin	Angle

Logarithms of Trigonometric Functions

Angle	L Sin	L Tan	L Cot	L Cos	Angle
9° 0'	9.1943	9.1997	10.8003	9.9946	81° 0'
10'	.2022	.2078	.7922	.9944	50'
20'	.2100	.2158	.7842	.9942	40'
30'	.2176	.2236	.7764	.9940	30'
40'	.2251	.2313	.7687	.9938	20'
50'	.2324	.2389	.7611	.9936	10'
10° 0'	9.2397	9.2463	10.7537	9.9934	80° 0'
10'	.2468	.2536	.7464	.9931	50'
20'	.2538	.2609	.7391	.9929	40'
30'	.2606	.2680	.7320	.9927	30'
40'	.2674	.2750	.7250	.9924	20'
50'	.2740	.2819	.7181	.9922	10'
11° 0'	9.2806	9.2887	10.7113	9.9919	79° 0'
10'	.2870	.2953	.7047	.9917	50'
20'	.2934	.3020	.6980	.9914	40'
30'	.2997	.3085	.6915	.9912	30'
40'	.3058	.3149	.6851	.9909	20'
50'	.3119	.3212	.6788	.9907	10'
12° 0'	9.3179	9.3275	10.6725	9.9904	78° 0'
10'	.3238	.3336	.6664	.9901	50'
20'	.3296	.3397	.6603	.9899	40'
30'	.3353	.3458	.6542	.9896	30'
40'	.3410	.3517	.6483	.9893	20'
50'	.3466	.3576	.6424	.9890	10'
13° 0'	9.3521	9.3634	10.6366	9.9887	77° 0'
10'	.3575	.3691	.6309	.9884	50'
20'	.3629	.3748	.6252	.9881	40'
30'	.3682	.3804	.6196	.9878	30'
40'	.3734	.3859	.6141	.9875	20'
50'	.3786	.3914	.6086	.9872	10'
14° 0'	9.3837	9.3968	10.6032	9.9869	76° 0'
10'	.3887	.4021	.5979	.9866	50'
20'	.3937	.4074	.5926	.9863	40'
30'	.3986	.4127	.5873	.9859	30'
40'	.4035	.4178	.5822	.9856	20'
50'	.4083	.4230	.5770	.9853	10'
15° 0'	9.4130	9.4281	10.5719	9.9849	75° 0'
10'	.4177	.4331	.5669	.9846	50'
20'	.4223	.4381	.5619	.9843	40'
30'	.4269	.4430	.5570	.9839	30'
40'	.4314	.4479	.5521	.9836	20'
50'	.4359	.4527	.5473	.9832	10'
16° 0'	9.4403	9.4575	10.5425	9.9828	74° 0'
10'	.4447	.4622	.5378	.9825	50'
20'	.4491	.4669	.5331	.9821	40'
30'	.4533	.4716	.5284	.9817	30'
40'	.4576	.4762	.5238	.9814	20'
50'	.4618	.4808	.5192	.9810	10'
17° 0'	9.4659	9.4853	10.5147	9.9806	73° 0'
10'	.4700	.4898	.5102	.9802	50'
20'	.4741	.4943	.5057	.9798	40'
30'	.4781	.4987	.5013	.9794	30'
40'	.4821	.5031	.4969	.9790	20'
50'	.4861	.5075	.4925	.9786	10'
18° 0'	9.4900	9.5118	10.4882	9.9782	72° 0'
	L Cos	L Cot	L Tan	L Sin	Angle

Logarithms of Trigonometric Functions

Angle	L Sin	L Tan	L Cot	L Cos	Angle
18° 0'	9.4900	9.5118	10.4882	9.9782	72° 0'
10'	.4939	.5161	.4839	.9778	50'
20'	.4977	.5203	.4797	.9774	40'
30'	.5015	.5245	.4755	.9770	30'
40'	.5052	.5287	.4713	.9765	20'
50'	.5090	.5329	.4671	.9761	10'
19° 0'	9.5126	9.5370	10.4630	9.9757	71° 0'
10'	.5163	.5411	.4589	.9752	50'
20'	.5199	.5451	.4549	.9748	40'
30'	.5235	.5491	.4509	.9743	30'
40'	.5270	.5531	.4469	.9739	20'
50'	.5306	.5571	.4429	.9734	10'
20° 0'	9.5341	9.5611	10.4389	9.9730	70° 0'
10'	.5375	.5650	.4350	.9725	50'
20'	.5409	.5689	.4311	.9721	40'
30'	.5443	.5727	.4273	.9716	30'
40'	.5477	.5766	.4234	.9711	20'
50'	.5510	.5804	.4196	.9706	10'
21° 0'	9.5543	9.5842	10.4158	9.9702	69° 0'
10'	.5576	.5879	.4121	.9697	50'
20'	.5609	.5917	.4083	.9692	40'
30'	.5641	.5954	.4046	.9687	30'
40'	.5673	.5991	.4009	.9682	20'
50'	.5704	.6028	.3972	.9677	10'
22° 0'	9.5736	9.6064	10.3936	9.9672	68° 0'
10'	.5767	.6100	.3900	.9667	50'
20'	.5798	.6136	.3864	.9661	40'
30'	.5828	.6172	.3828	.9656	30'
40'	.5859	.6208	.3792	.9651	20'
50'	.5889	.6243	.3757	.9646	10'
23° 0'	9.5919	9.6279	10.3721	9.9640	67° 0'
10'	.5948	.6314	.3686	.9635	50'
20'	.5978	.6348	.3652	.9629	40'
30'	.6007	.6383	.3617	.9624	30'
40'	.6036	.6417	.3583	.9618	20'
50'	.6065	.6452	.3548	.9613	10'
24° 0'	9.6093	9.6486	10.3514	9.9607	66° 0'
10'	.6121	.6520	.3480	.9602	50'
20'	.6149	.6553	.3447	.9596	40'
30'	.6177	.6587	.3413	.9590	30'
40'	.6205	.6620	.3380	.9584	20'
50'	.6232	.6654	.3346	.9579	10'
25° 0'	9.6259	9.6687	10.3313	9.9573	65° 0'
10'	.6286	.6720	.3280	.9567	50'
20'	.6313	.6752	.3248	.9561	40'
30'	.6340	.6785	.3215	.9555	30'
40'	.6366	.6817	.3183	.9549	20'
50'	.6392	.6850	.3150	.9543	10'
26° 0'	9.6418	9.6882	10.3118	9.9537	64° 0'
10'	.6444	.6914	.3086	.9530	50'
20'	.6470	.6946	.3054	.9524	40'
30'	.6495	.6977	.3023	.9518	30'
40'	.6521	.7009	.2991	.9512	20'
50'	.6546	.7040	.2960	.9505	10'
27° 0'	9.6570	9.7072	10.2928	9.9499	63° 0'
	L Cos	L Cot	L Tan	L Sin	Angle

Logarithms of Trigonometric Functions

Angle	L Cos	L Cot	L Tan	L Sin	Angle
36° 0'	9.9080	10.1387	9.8613	9.7692	**54°** 0'
10'	.9070	.1361	.8639	.7710	50'
20'	.9061	.1334	.8666	.7727	40'
30'	.9052	.1308	.8692	.7744	30'
40'	.9042	.1282	.8718	.7761	20'
50'	.9033	.1255	.8745	.7778	10'
37° 0'	9.9023	10.1229	9.8771	9.7795	**53°** 0'
10'	.9014	.1203	.8797	.7811	50'
20'	.9004	.1176	.8824	.7828	40'
30'	.8995	.1150	.8850	.7844	30'
40'	.8985	.1124	.8876	.7861	20'
50'	.8975	.1098	.8902	.7877	10'
38° 0'	9.8965	10.1072	9.8928	9.7893	**52°** 0'
10'	.8955	.1046	.8954	.7910	50'
20'	.8945	.1020	.8980	.7926	40'
30'	.8935	.0994	.9006	.7941	30'
40'	.8925	.0968	.9032	.7957	20'
50'	.8915	.0942	.9058	.7973	10'
39° 0'	9.8905	10.0916	9.9084	9.7989	**51°** 0'
10'	.8895	.0890	.9110	.8004	50'
20'	.8884	.0865	.9135	.8020	40'
30'	.8874	.0839	.9161	.8035	30'
40'	.8864	.0813	.9187	.8050	20'
50'	.8853	.0788	.9212	.8066	10'
40° 0'	9.8843	10.0762	9.9238	9.8081	**50°** 0'
10'	.8832	.0736	.9264	.8096	50'
20'	.8821	.0711	.9289	.8111	40'
30'	.8810	.0685	.9315	.8125	30'
40'	.8800	.0659	.9341	.8140	20'
50'	.8789	.0634	.9366	.8155	10'
41° 0'	9.8778	10.0608	9.9392	9.8169	**49°** 0'
10'	.8767	.0583	.9417	.8184	50'
20'	.8756	.0557	.9443	.8198	40'
30'	.8745	.0532	.9468	.8213	30'
40'	.8733	.0506	.9494	.8227	20'
50'	.8722	.0481	.9519	.8241	10'
42° 0'	9.8711	10.0456	9.9544	9.8255	**48°** 0'
10'	.8699	.0430	.9570	.8269	50'
20'	.8688	.0405	.9595	.8283	40'
30'	.8676	.0379	.9621	.8297	30'
40'	.8665	.0354	.9646	.8311	20'
50'	.8653	.0329	.9671	.8324	10'
43° 0'	9.8641	10.0303	9.9697	9.8338	**47°** 0'
10'	.8629	.0278	.9722	.8351	50'
20'	.8618	.0253	.9747	.8365	40'
30'	.8606	.0228	.9772	.8378	30'
40'	.8594	.0202	.9798	.8391	20'
50'	.8582	.0177	.9823	.8405	10'
44° 0'	9.8569	10.0152	9.9848	9.8418	**46°** 0'
10'	.8557	.0126	.9874	.8431	50'
20'	.8545	.0101	.9899	.8444	40'
30'	.8532	.0076	.9924	.8457	30'
40'	.8520	.0051	.9949	.8469	20'
50'	.8507	.0025	.9975	.8482	10'
45° 0'	9.8495	10.0000	10.0000	9.8495	**45°** 0'
	L Sin	L Tan	L Cot	L Cos	Angle

Logarithms of Trigonometric Functions

Angle	L Sin	L Tan	L Cot	L Cos	Angle
27° 0'	9.6570	9.7072	10.2928	9.9499	**63°** 0'
10'	.6595	.7103	.2897	.9492	50'
20'	.6620	.7134	.2866	.9486	40'
30'	.6644	.7165	.2835	.9479	30'
40'	.6668	.7196	.2804	.9473	20'
50'	.6692	.7226	.2774	.9466	10'
28° 0'	9.6716	9.7257	10.2743	9.9459	**62°** 0'
10'	.6740	.7287	.2713	.9453	50'
20'	.6763	.7317	.2683	.9446	40'
30'	.6787	.7348	.2652	.9439	30'
40'	.6810	.7378	.2622	.9432	20'
50'	.6833	.7408	.2592	.9425	10'
29° 0'	9.6856	9.7438	10.2562	9.9418	**61°** 0'
10'	.6878	.7467	.2533	.9411	50'
20'	.6901	.7497	.2503	.9404	40'
30'	.6923	.7526	.2474	.9397	30'
40'	.6946	.7556	.2444	.9390	20'
50'	.6968	.7585	.2415	.9383	10'
30° 0'	9.6990	9.7614	10.2386	9.9375	**60°** 0'
10'	.7012	.7644	.2356	.9368	50'
20'	.7033	.7673	.2327	.9361	40'
30'	.7055	.7701	.2299	.9353	30'
40'	.7076	.7730	.2270	.9346	20'
50'	.7097	.7759	.2241	.9338	10'
31° 0'	9.7118	9.7788	10.2212	9.9331	**59°** 0'
10'	.7139	.7816	.2184	.9323	50'
20'	.7160	.7845	.2155	.9315	40'
30'	.7181	.7873	.2127	.9308	30'
40'	.7201	.7902	.2098	.9300	20'
50'	.7222	.7930	.2070	.9292	10'
32° 0'	9.7242	9.7958	10.2042	9.9284	**58°** 0'
10'	.7262	.7986	.2014	.9276	50'
20'	.7282	.8014	.1986	.9268	40'
30'	.7302	.8042	.1958	.9260	30'
40'	.7322	.8070	.1930	.9252	20'
50'	.7342	.8097	.1903	.9244	10'
33° 0'	9.7361	9.8125	10.1875	9.9236	**57°** 0'
10'	.7380	.8153	.1847	.9228	50'
20'	.7400	.8180	.1820	.9219	40'
30'	.7419	.8208	.1792	.9211	30'
40'	.7438	.8235	.1765	.9203	20'
50'	.7457	.8263	.1737	.9194	10'
34° 0'	9.7476	9.8290	10.1710	9.9186	**56°** 0'
10'	.7494	.8317	.1683	.9177	50'
20'	.7513	.8344	.1656	.9169	40'
30'	.7531	.8371	.1629	.9160	30'
40'	.7550	.8398	.1602	.9151	20'
50'	.7568	.8425	.1575	.9142	10'
35° 0'	9.7586	9.8452	10.1548	9.9134	**55°** 0'
10'	.7604	.8479	.1521	.9125	50'
20'	.7622	.8506	.1494	.9116	40'
30'	.7640	.8533	.1467	.9107	30'
40'	.7657	.8559	.1441	.9098	20'
50'	.7675	.8586	.1414	.9089	10'
36° 0'	9.7692	9.8613	10.1387	9.9080	**54°** 0'
	L Cos	L Tan	L Cot	L Sin	Angle

n	0	1	2	3	4	5	6	7	8	9
55	7404	7412	7419	7427	7435	7443	7451	7459	7466	7474
56	7482	7490	7497	7505	7513	7520	7528	7536	7543	7551
57	7559	7566	7574	7582	7589	7597	7604	7612	7619	7627
58	7634	7642	7649	7657	7664	7672	7679	7686	7694	7701
59	7709	7716	7723	7731	7738	7745	7752	7760	7767	7774
60	7782	7789	7796	7803	7810	7818	7825	7832	7839	7846
61	7853	7860	7868	7875	7882	7889	7896	7903	7910	7917
62	7924	7931	7938	7945	7952	7959	7966	7973	7980	7987
63	7993	8000	8007	8014	8021	8028	8035	8041	8048	8055
64	8062	8069	8075	8082	8089	8096	8102	8109	8116	8122
65	8129	8136	8142	8149	8156	8162	8169	8176	8182	8189
66	8195	8202	8209	8215	8222	8228	8235	8241	8248	8254
67	8261	8267	8274	8280	8287	8293	8299	8306	8312	8319
68	8325	8331	8338	8344	8351	8357	8363	8370	8376	8382
69	8388	8395	8401	8407	8414	8420	8426	8432	8439	8445
70	8451	8457	8463	8470	8476	8482	8488	8494	8500	8506
71	8513	8519	8525	8531	8537	8543	8549	8555	8561	8567
72	8573	8579	8585	8591	8597	8603	8609	8615	8621	8627
73	8633	8639	8645	8651	8657	8663	8669	8675	8681	8686
74	8692	8698	8704	8710	8716	8722	8727	8733	8739	8745
75	8751	8756	8762	8768	8774	8779	8785	8791	8797	8802
76	8808	8814	8820	8825	8831	8837	8842	8848	8854	8859
77	8865	8871	8876	8882	8887	8893	8899	8904	8910	8915
78	8921	8927	8932	8938	8943	8949	8954	8960	8965	8971
79	8976	8982	8987	8993	8998	9004	9009	9015	9020	9025
80	9031	9036	9042	9047	9053	9058	9063	9069	9074	9079
81	9085	9090	9096	9101	9106	9112	9117	9122	9128	9133
82	9138	9143	9149	9154	9159	9165	9170	9175	9180	9186
83	9191	9196	9201	9206	9212	9217	9222	9227	9232	9238
84	9243	9248	9253	9258	9263	9269	9274	9279	9284	9289
85	9294	9299	9304	9309	9315	9320	9325	9330	9335	9340
86	9345	9350	9355	9360	9365	9370	9375	9380	9385	9390
87	9395	9400	9405	9410	9415	9420	9425	9430	9435	9440
88	9445	9450	9455	9460	9465	9469	9474	9479	9484	9489
89	9494	9499	9504	9509	9513	9518	9523	9528	9533	9538
90	9542	9547	9552	9557	9562	9566	9571	9576	9581	9586
91	9590	9595	9600	9605	9609	9614	9619	9624	9628	9633
92	9638	9643	9647	9652	9657	9661	9666	9671	9675	9680
93	9685	9689	9694	9699	9703	9708	9713	9717	9722	9727
94	9731	9736	9741	9745	9750	9754	9759	9763	9768	9773
95	9777	9782	9786	9791	9795	9800	9805	9809	9814	9818
96	9823	9827	9832	9836	9841	9845	9850	9854	9859	9863
97	9868	9872	9877	9881	9886	9890	9894	9899	9903	9908
98	9912	9917	9921	9926	9930	9934	9939	9943	9948	9952
99	9956	9961	9965	9969	9974	9978	9983	9987	9991	9996

Common Logarithms of Numbers

n	0	1	2	3	4	5	6	7	8	9
10	0000	0043	0086	0128	0170	0212	0253	0294	0334	0374
11	0414	0453	0492	0531	0569	0607	0645	0682	0719	0755
12	0792	0828	0864	0899	0934	0969	1004	1038	1072	1106
13	1139	1173	1206	1239	1271	1303	1335	1367	1399	1430
14	1461	1492	1523	1553	1584	1614	1644	1673	1703	1732
15	1761	1790	1818	1847	1875	1903	1931	1959	1987	2014
16	2041	2068	2095	2122	2148	2175	2201	2227	2253	2279
17	2304	2330	2355	2380	2405	2430	2455	2480	2504	2529
18	2553	2577	2601	2625	2648	2672	2695	2718	2742	2765
19	2788	2810	2833	2856	2878	2900	2923	2945	2967	2989
20	3010	3032	3054	3075	3096	3118	3139	3160	3181	3201
21	3222	3243	3263	3284	3304	3324	3345	3365	3385	3404
22	3424	3444	3464	3483	3502	3522	3541	3560	3579	3598
23	3617	3636	3655	3674	3692	3711	3729	3747	3766	3784
24	3802	3820	3838	3856	3874	3892	3909	3927	3945	3962
25	3979	3997	4014	4031	4048	4065	4082	4099	4116	4133
26	4150	4166	4183	4200	4216	4232	4249	4265	4281	4298
27	4314	4330	4346	4362	4378	4393	4409	4425	4440	4456
28	4472	4487	4502	4518	4533	4548	4564	4579	4594	4609
29	4624	4639	4654	4669	4683	4698	4713	4728	4742	4757
30	4771	4786	4800	4814	4829	4843	4857	4871	4886	4900
31	4914	4928	4942	4955	4969	4983	4997	5011	5024	5038
32	5051	5065	5079	5092	5105	5119	5132	5145	5159	5172
33	5185	5198	5211	5224	5237	5250	5263	5276	5289	5302
34	5315	5328	5340	5353	5366	5378	5391	5403	5416	5428
35	5441	5453	5465	5478	5490	5502	5514	5527	5539	5551
36	5563	5575	5587	5599	5611	5623	5635	5647	5658	5670
37	5682	5694	5705	5717	5729	5740	5752	5763	5775	5786
38	5798	5809	5821	5832	5843	5855	5866	5877	5888	5899
39	5911	5922	5933	5944	5955	5966	5977	5988	5999	6010
40	6021	6031	6042	6053	6064	6075	6085	6096	6107	6117
41	6128	6138	6149	6160	6170	6180	6191	6201	6212	6222
42	6232	6243	6253	6263	6274	6284	6294	6304	6314	6325
43	6335	6345	6355	6365	6375	6385	6395	6405	6415	6425
44	6435	6444	6454	6464	6474	6484	6493	6503	6513	6522
45	6532	6542	6551	6561	6571	6580	6590	6599	6609	6618
46	6628	6637	6646	6656	6665	6675	6684	6693	6702	6712
47	6721	6730	6739	6749	6758	6767	6776	6785	6794	6803
48	6812	6821	6830	6839	6848	6857	6866	6875	6884	6893
49	6902	6911	6920	6928	6937	6946	6955	6964	6972	6981
50	6990	6998	7007	7016	7024	7033	7042	7050	7059	7067
51	7076	7084	7093	7101	7110	7118	7126	7135	7143	7152
52	7160	7168	7177	7185	7193	7202	7210	7218	7226	7235
53	7243	7251	7259	7267	7275	7284	7292	7300	7308	7316
54	7324	7332	7340	7348	7356	7364	7372	7380	7388	7396

Trigonometric Functions

x	csc x	sec x	cot x	tan x	cos x	sin x	x
30'	7.6613	1.0086	7.5958	.1317	.9914	.1305	30'
40'	7.4957	1.0090	7.4287	.1346	.9911	.1334	20'
50'	7.3372	1.0094	7.2687	.1376	.9907	.1363	10'
8° 0'	7.1853	1.0098	7.1154	.1405	.9903	.1392	82° 0'
10'	7.0396	1.0102	6.9682	.1435	.9899	.1421	50'
20'	6.8998	1.0107	6.8269	.1465	.9894	.1449	40'
30'	6.7655	1.0111	6.6912	.1495	.9890	.1478	30'
40'	6.6363	1.0116	6.5606	.1524	.9886	.1507	20'
50'	6.5121	1.0120	6.4348	.1554	.9881	.1536	10'
9° 0'	6.3925	1.0125	6.3138	.1584	.9877	.1564	81° 0'
10'	6.2772	1.0129	6.1970	.1614	.9872	.1593	50'
20'	6.1661	1.0134	6.0844	.1644	.9868	.1622	40'
30'	6.0589	1.0139	5.9758	.1673	.9863	.1650	30'
40'	5.9554	1.0144	5.8708	.1703	.9858	.1679	20'
50'	5.8554	1.0149	5.7694	.1733	.9853	.1708	10'
10° 0'	5.7588	1.0154	5.6713	.1763	.9848	.1736	80° 0'
10'	5.6653	1.0160	5.5764	.1793	.9843	.1765	50'
20'	5.5749	1.0165	5.4845	.1823	.9838	.1794	40'
30'	5.4874	1.0170	5.3955	.1853	.9833	.1822	30'
40'	5.4026	1.0176	5.3093	.1883	.9827	.1851	20'
50'	5.3205	1.0182	5.2257	.1914	.9822	.1880	10'
11° 0'	5.2408	1.0187	5.1446	.1944	.9816	.1908	79° 0'
10'	5.1636	1.0193	5.0658	.1974	.9811	.1937	50'
20'	5.0886	1.0199	4.9894	.2004	.9805	.1965	40'
30'	5.0159	1.0205	4.9152	.2035	.9799	.1994	30'
40'	4.9452	1.0211	4.8430	.2065	.9793	.2022	20'
50'	4.8765	1.0217	4.7729	.2095	.9787	.2051	10'
12° 0'	4.8097	1.0223	4.7046	.2126	.9781	.2079	78° 0'
10'	4.7448	1.0230	4.6382	.2156	.9775	.2108	50'
20'	4.6817	1.0236	4.5736	.2186	.9769	.2136	40'
30'	4.6202	1.0243	4.5107	.2217	.9763	.2164	30'
40'	4.5604	1.0249	4.4494	.2247	.9757	.2193	20'
50'	4.5022	1.0256	4.3897	.2278	.9750	.2221	10'
13° 0'	4.4454	1.0263	4.3315	.2309	.9744	.2250	77° 0'
10'	4.3901	1.0270	4.2747	.2339	.9737	.2278	50'
20'	4.3362	1.0277	4.2193	.2370	.9730	.2306	40'
30'	4.2837	1.0284	4.1653	.2401	.9724	.2334	30'
40'	4.2324	1.0291	4.1126	.2432	.9717	.2363	20'
50'	4.1824	1.0299	4.0611	.2462	.9710	.2391	10'
14° 0'	4.1336	1.0306	4.0108	.2493	.9703	.2419	76° 0'
10'	4.0859	1.0314	3.9617	.2524	.9696	.2447	50'
20'	4.0394	1.0321	3.9136	.2555	.9689	.2476	40'
30'	3.9939	1.0329	3.8667	.2586	.9681	.2504	30'
40'	3.9495	1.0337	3.8208	.2617	.9674	.2532	20'
50'	3.9061	1.0345	3.7760	.2648	.9667	.2560	10'
15° 0'	3.8637	1.0353	3.7321	.2679	.9659	.2588	75° 0'
x	sec x	csc x	tan x	cot x	sin x	cos x	x

Trigonometric Functions

x	sin x	cos x	tan x	cot x	sec x	csc x	x
0° 0'	.00000	1.0000	.00000		1.0000		90° 0'
10'	.00291	1.0000	.00291	343.77	1.0000	343.78	50'
20'	.00582	1.0000	.00582	171.88	1.0000	171.89	40'
30'	.00873	1.0000	.00873	114.59	1.0000	114.59	30'
40'	.01164	.9999	.01164	85.940	1.0001	85.946	20'
50'	.01454	.9999	.01455	68.750	1.0001	68.757	10'
1° 0'	.01745	.9998	.01746	57.290	1.0002	57.299	89° 0'
10'	.02036	.9998	.02036	49.104	1.0002	49.114	50'
20'	.02327	.9997	.02328	42.964	1.0003	42.976	40'
30'	.02618	.9997	.02619	38.188	1.0003	38.202	30'
40'	.02908	.9996	.02910	34.368	1.0004	34.382	20'
50'	.03199	.9995	.03201	31.242	1.0005	31.258	10'
2° 0'	.03490	.9994	.03492	28.6363	1.0006	28.654	88° 0'
10'	.03781	.9993	.03783	26.4316	1.0007	26.451	50'
20'	.04071	.9992	.04075	24.5418	1.0008	24.562	40'
30'	.04362	.9990	.04366	22.9038	1.0010	22.926	30'
40'	.04653	.9989	.04658	21.4704	1.0011	21.494	20'
50'	.04943	.9988	.04949	20.2056	1.0012	20.230	10'
3° 0'	.05234	.9986	.05241	19.0811	1.0014	19.107	87° 0'
10'	.05524	.9985	.05533	18.0750	1.0015	18.103	50'
20'	.05814	.9983	.05824	17.1693	1.0017	17.198	40'
30'	.06105	.9981	.06116	16.3499	1.0019	16.380	30'
40'	.06395	.9980	.06408	15.6048	1.0021	15.637	20'
50'	.06685	.9978	.06700	14.9244	1.0022	14.958	10'
4° 0'	.06976	.9976	.06993	14.3007	1.0024	14.336	86° 0'
10'	.07266	.9974	.07285	13.7267	1.0027	13.763	50'
20'	.07556	.9971	.07578	13.1969	1.0029	13.235	40'
30'	.07846	.9969	.07870	12.7062	1.0031	12.746	30'
40'	.08136	.9967	.08163	12.2505	1.0033	12.291	20'
50'	.08426	.9964	.08456	11.8262	1.0036	11.868	10'
5° 0'	.08716	.9962	.08749	11.4301	1.0038	11.474	85° 0'
10'	.09005	.9959	.09042	11.0594	1.0041	11.105	50'
20'	.09295	.9957	.09335	10.7119	1.0044	10.758	40'
30'	.09585	.9954	.09629	10.3854	1.0046	10.433	30'
40'	.09874	.9951	.09923	10.0780	1.0049	10.128	20'
50'	.10164	.9948	.10216	9.7882	1.0052	9.839	10'
6° 0'	.10453	.9945	.10510	9.5144	1.0055	9.5668	84° 0'
10'	.10742	.9942	.10805	9.2553	1.0058	9.3092	50'
20'	.11031	.9939	.11099	9.0098	1.0061	9.0652	40'
30'	.11320	.9936	.11394	8.7769	1.0065	8.8337	30'
40'	.11609	.9932	.11688	8.5555	1.0068	8.6138	20'
50'	.11898	.9929	.11983	8.3450	1.0072	8.4647	10'
7° 0'	.12187	.9925	.12278	8.1443	1.0075	8.2055	83° 0'
10'	.12476	.9922	.12574	7.9530	1.0079	8.0157	50'
20'	.12764	.9918	.12869	7.7704	1.0083	7.8344	40'
30'	.13053	.9914	.13165	7.5958	1.0086	7.6613	30'
x	cos x	sin x	cot x	tan x	csc x	sec x	x

Trigonometric Functions

x	csc x	sec x	cot x	tan x	cos x	sin x	x
30'	2.6131	1.0824	2.4142	.4142	.9239	.3827	30'
20'	2.5949	1.0837	2.3945	.4176	.9228	.3854	40'
10'	2.5770	1.0850	2.3750	.4210	.9216	.3881	50'
67° 0'	2.5593	1.0864	2.3559	.4245	.9205	.3907	23° 0'
50'	2.5419	1.0877	2.3369	.4279	.9194	.3934	10'
40'	2.5247	1.0891	2.3183	.4314	.9182	.3961	20'
30'	2.5078	1.0904	2.2998	.4348	.9171	.3987	30'
20'	2.4912	1.0918	2.2817	.4383	.9159	.4014	40'
10'	2.4748	1.0932	2.2637	.4417	.9147	.4041	50'
66° 0'	2.4586	1.0946	2.2460	.4452	.9135	.4067	24° 0'
50'	2.4426	1.0961	2.2286	.4487	.9124	.4094	10'
40'	2.4269	1.0975	2.2113	.4522	.9112	.4120	20'
30'	2.4114	1.0990	2.1943	.4557	.9100	.4147	30'
20'	2.3961	1.1004	2.1775	.4592	.9088	.4173	40'
10'	2.3811	1.1019	2.1609	.4628	.9075	.4200	50'
65° 0'	2.3662	1.1034	2.1445	.4663	.9063	.4226	25° 0'
50'	2.3515	1.1049	2.1283	.4699	.9051	.4253	10'
40'	2.3371	1.1064	2.1123	.4734	.9038	.4279	20'
30'	2.3228	1.1079	2.0965	.4770	.9026	.4305	30'
20'	2.3088	1.1095	2.0809	.4806	.9013	.4331	40'
10'	2.2949	1.1110	2.0655	.4841	.9001	.4358	50'
64° 0'	2.2812	1.1126	2.0503	.4877	.8988	.4384	26° 0'
50'	2.2677	1.1142	2.0353	.4913	.8975	.4410	10'
40'	2.2543	1.1158	2.0204	.4950	.8962	.4436	20'
30'	2.2412	1.1174	2.0057	.4986	.8949	.4462	30'
20'	2.2282	1.1190	1.9912	.5022	.8936	.4488	40'
10'	2.2154	1.1207	1.9768	.5059	.8923	.4514	50'
63° 0'	2.2027	1.1223	1.9626	.5095	.8910	.4540	27° 0'
50'	2.1902	1.1240	1.9486	.5132	.8897	.4566	10'
40'	2.1779	1.1257	1.9347	.5169	.8884	.4592	20'
30'	2.1657	1.1274	1.9210	.5206	.8870	.4617	30'
20'	2.1537	1.1291	1.9074	.5243	.8857	.4643	40'
10'	2.1418	1.1308	1.8940	.5280	.8843	.4669	50'
62° 0'	2.1301	1.1326	1.8807	.5317	.8829	.4695	28° 0'
50'	2.1185	1.1343	1.8676	.5354	.8816	.4720	10'
40'	2.1070	1.1361	1.8546	.5392	.8802	.4746	20'
30'	2.0957	1.1379	1.8418	.5430	.8788	.4772	30'
20'	2.0846	1.1397	1.8291	.5467	.8774	.4797	40'
10'	2.0736	1.1415	1.8165	.5505	.8760	.4823	50'
61° 0'	2.0627	1.1434	1.8040	.5543	.8746	.4848	29° 0'
50'	2.0519	1.1452	1.7917	.5581	.8732	.4874	10'
40'	2.0413	1.1471	1.7796	.5619	.8718	.4899	20'
30'	2.0308	1.1490	1.7675	.5658	.8704	.4924	30'
20'	2.0204	1.1509	1.7556	.5696	.8689	.4950	40'
10'	2.0101	1.1528	1.7437	.5735	.8675	.4975	50'
60° 0'	2.0000	1.1547	1.7321	.5774	.8660	.5000	30° 0'
x	sec x	csc x	tan x	cot x	sin x	cos x	x

Trigonometric Functions

x	csc x	sec x	cot x	tan x	cos x	sin x	x
75° 0'	3.8637	1.0353	3.7321	.2679	.9659	.2588	15° 0'
50'	3.8222	1.0361	3.6891	.2711	.9652	.2616	10'
40'	3.7817	1.0369	3.6470	.2742	.9644	.2644	20'
30'	3.7420	1.0377	3.6059	.2773	.9636	.2672	30'
20'	3.7032	1.0386	3.5656	.2805	.9628	.2700	40'
10'	3.6652	1.0394	3.5261	.2836	.9621	.2728	50'
74° 0'	3.6280	1.0403	3.4874	.2867	.9613	.2756	16° 0'
50'	3.5915	1.0412	3.4495	.2899	.9605	.2784	10'
40'	3.5559	1.0421	3.4124	.2931	.9596	.2812	20'
30'	3.5209	1.0430	3.3759	.2962	.9588	.2840	30'
20'	3.4867	1.0439	3.3402	.2994	.9580	.2868	40'
10'	3.4532	1.0448	3.3052	.3026	.9572	.2896	50'
73° 0'	3.4203	1.0457	3.2709	.3057	.9563	.2924	17° 0'
50'	3.3881	1.0466	3.2371	.3089	.9555	.2952	10'
40'	3.3565	1.0476	3.2041	.3121	.9546	.2979	20'
30'	3.3255	1.0485	3.1716	.3153	.9537	.3007	30'
20'	3.2951	1.0495	3.1397	.3185	.9528	.3035	40'
10'	3.2653	1.0505	3.1084	.3217	.9520	.3062	50'
72° 0'	3.2361	1.0515	3.0777	.3249	.9511	.3090	18° 0'
50'	3.2074	1.0525	3.0475	.3281	.9502	.3118	10'
40'	3.1792	1.0535	3.0178	.3314	.9492	.3145	20'
30'	3.1516	1.0545	2.9887	.3346	.9483	.3173	30'
20'	3.1244	1.0555	2.9600	.3378	.9474	.3201	40'
10'	3.0977	1.0566	2.9319	.3411	.9465	.3228	50'
71° 0'	3.0716	1.0576	2.9042	.3443	.9455	.3256	19° 0'
50'	3.0458	1.0587	2.8770	.3476	.9446	.3283	10'
40'	3.0206	1.0598	2.8502	.3508	.9436	.3311	20'
30'	2.9957	1.0609	2.8239	.3541	.9426	.3338	30'
20'	2.9714	1.0620	2.7980	.3574	.9417	.3365	40'
10'	2.9474	1.0631	2.7725	.3607	.9407	.3393	50'
70° 0'	2.9238	1.0642	2.7475	.3640	.9397	.3420	20° 0'
50'	2.9006	1.0653	2.7228	.3673	.9387	.3448	10'
40'	2.8779	1.0665	2.6985	.3706	.9377	.3475	20'
30'	2.8555	1.0676	2.6746	.3739	.9367	.3502	30'
20'	2.8334	1.0688	2.6511	.3772	.9356	.3529	40'
10'	2.8118	1.0700	2.6279	.3805	.9346	.3557	50'
69° 0'	2.7904	1.0712	2.6051	.3839	.9336	.3584	21° 0'
50'	2.7695	1.0724	2.5826	.3872	.9325	.3611	10'
40'	2.7488	1.0736	2.5605	.3906	.9315	.3638	20'
30'	2.7285	1.0748	2.5386	.3939	.9304	.3665	30'
20'	2.7085	1.0760	2.5172	.3973	.9293	.3692	40'
10'	2.6888	1.0773	2.4960	.4006	.9283	.3719	50'
68° 0'	2.6695	1.0785	2.4751	.4040	.9272	.3746	22° 0'
50'	2.6504	1.0798	2.4545	.4074	.9261	.3773	10'
40'	2.6316	1.0811	2.4342	.4108	.9250	.3800	20'
30'	2.6131	1.0824	2.4142	.4142	.9239	.3827	30'
x	sec x	csc x	tan x	cot x	sin x	cos x	x

x	csc x	sec x	cot x	tan x	cos x	sin x	x
	sec x	csc x	tan x	cot x	sin x	cos x	
30'	1.6427	1.2605	1.3032	.7673	.7034	.6088	30'
20'	1.6365	1.2623	1.2964	.7720	.7916	.6111	40'
10'	1.6304	1.2662	1.2876	.7766	.7898	.6134	50'
52° 0'	1.6243	1.2690	1.2799	.7813	.7880	.6157	38° 0'
50'	1.6183	1.2719	1.2723	.7860	.7862	.6180	10'
40'	1.6123	1.2748	1.2647	.7907	.7844	.6202	20'
30'	1.6064	1.2779	1.2572	.7954	.7826	.6225	30'
20'	1.6005	1.2808	1.2497	.8002	.7808	.6248	40'
10'	1.5948	1.2837	1.2423	.8050	.7790	.6271	50'
51° 0'	1.5890	1.2868	1.2349	.8098	.7771	.6293	39° 0'
50'	1.5833	1.2898	1.2276	.8146	.7753	.6316	10'
40'	1.5777	1.2929	1.2203	.8195	.7735	.6338	20'
30'	1.5721	1.2960	1.2131	.8243	.7716	.6361	30'
20'	1.5666	1.2991	1.2059	.8292	.7698	.6383	40'
10'	1.5611	1.3022	1.1988	.8342	.7679	.6406	50'
50° 0'	1.5557	1.3054	1.1918	.8391	.7660	.6428	40° 0'
50'	1.5504	1.3086	1.1847	.8441	.7642	.6450	10'
40'	1.5450	1.3118	1.1778	.8491	.7623	.6472	20'
30'	1.5398	1.3151	1.1708	.8541	.7604	.6494	30'
20'	1.5346	1.3184	1.1640	.8591	.7585	.6517	40'
10'	1.5294	1.3217	1.1571	.8642	.7566	.6539	50'
49° 0'	1.5243	1.3250	1.1504	.8693	.7547	.6561	41° 0'
50'	1.5192	1.3284	1.1436	.8744	.7528	.6583	10'
40'	1.5142	1.3318	1.1369	.8796	.7509	.6604	20'
30'	1.5092	1.3352	1.1303	.8847	.7490	.6626	30'
20'	1.5042	1.3386	1.1237	.8899	.7470	.6648	40'
10'	1.4993	1.3421	1.1171	.8952	.7451	.6670	50'
48° 0'	1.4945	1.3456	1.1106	.9004	.7431	.6691	42° 0'
50'	1.4897	1.3492	1.1041	.9057	.7412	.6713	10'
40'	1.4849	1.3527	1.0977	.9110	.7392	.6734	20'
30'	1.4802	1.3563	1.0913	.9163	.7373	.6756	30'
20'	1.4755	1.3600	1.0850	.9217	.7353	.6777	40'
10'	1.4709	1.3636	1.0786	.9271	.7333	.6799	50'
47° 0'	1.4663	1.3673	1.0724	.9325	.7314	.6820	43° 0'
50'	1.4617	1.3711	1.0661	.9380	.7294	.6841	10'
40'	1.4572	1.3748	1.0599	.9435	.7274	.6862	20'
30'	1.4527	1.3786	1.0538	.9490	.7254	.6884	30'
20'	1.4483	1.3824	1.0477	.9545	.7234	.6905	40'
10'	1.4439	1.3863	1.0416	.9601	.7214	.6926	50'
46° 0'	1.4396	1.3902	1.0355	.9657	.7193	.6947	44° 0'
50'	1.4352	1.3941	1.0295	.9713	.7173	.6967	10'
40'	1.4310	1.3980	1.0235	.9770	.7153	.6988	20'
30'	1.4267	1.4020	1.0176	.9827	.7133	.7009	30'
20'	1.4225	1.4061	1.0117	.9884	.7112	.7030	40'
10'	1.4184	1.4101	1.0058	.9942	.7092	.7050	50'
45° 0'	1.4142	1.4142	1.0000	1.0000	.7071	.7071	45° 0'

x	sin x	cos x	tan x	cot x	sec x	csc x	x
	cos x	sin x	cot x	tan x	csc x	sec x	
30° 0'	.5000	.8660	.5774	1.7321	1.1547	2.0000	60° 0'
10'	.5025	.8646	.5812	1.7205	1.1567	1.9900	50'
20'	.5050	.8631	.5851	1.7090	1.1586	1.9801	40'
30'	.5075	.8616	.5890	1.6977	1.1606	1.9703	30'
40'	.5100	.8601	.5930	1.6864	1.1626	1.9606	20'
50'	.5125	.8587	.5969	1.6753	1.1646	1.9511	10'
31° 0'	.5150	.8572	.6009	1.6643	1.1666	1.9416	59° 0'
10'	.5175	.8557	.6048	1.6534	1.1687	1.9323	50'
20'	.5200	.8542	.6088	1.6426	1.1708	1.9230	40'
30'	.5225	.8526	.6128	1.6319	1.1728	1.9139	30'
40'	.5250	.8511	.6168	1.6212	1.1749	1.9049	20'
50'	.5275	.8496	.6208	1.6107	1.1770	1.8959	10'
32° 0'	.5299	.8480	.6249	1.6003	1.1792	1.8871	58° 0'
10'	.5324	.8465	.6289	1.5900	1.1813	1.8783	50'
20'	.5348	.8450	.6330	1.5798	1.1835	1.8699	40'
30'	.5373	.8434	.6371	1.5697	1.1857	1.8612	30'
40'	.5398	.8418	.6412	1.5597	1.1879	1.8527	20'
50'	.5422	.8403	.6453	1.5497	1.1901	1.8444	10'
33° 0'	.5446	.8387	.6494	1.5399	1.1924	1.8361	57° 0'
10'	.5471	.8371	.6536	1.5301	1.1946	1.8279	50'
20'	.5495	.8355	.6577	1.5204	1.1969	1.8198	40'
30'	.5519	.8339	.6619	1.5108	1.1992	1.8118	30'
40'	.5544	.8323	.6661	1.5013	1.2015	1.8039	20'
50'	.5568	.8307	.6703	1.4919	1.2039	1.7960	10'
34° 0'	.5592	.8290	.6745	1.4826	1.2062	1.7883	56° 0'
10'	.5616	.8274	.6787	1.4733	1.2086	1.7806	50'
20'	.5640	.8258	.6830	1.4641	1.2110	1.7730	40'
30'	.5664	.8241	.6873	1.4550	1.2134	1.7655	30'
40'	.5688	.8225	.6916	1.4460	1.2158	1.7581	20'
50'	.5712	.8208	.6959	1.4370	1.2183	1.7507	10'
35° 0'	.5736	.8192	.7002	1.4281	1.2208	1.7435	55° 0'
10'	.5760	.8175	.7046	1.4193	1.2233	1.7362	50'
20'	.5783	.8158	.7089	1.4106	1.2258	1.7291	40'
30'	.5807	.8141	.7133	1.4019	1.2283	1.7221	30'
40'	.5831	.8124	.7177	1.3934	1.2309	1.7151	20'
50'	.5854	.8107	.7221	1.3848	1.2335	1.7082	10'
36° 0'	.5878	.8090	.7265	1.3764	1.2361	1.7013	54° 0'
10'	.5901	.8073	.7310	1.3680	1.2387	1.6945	50'
20'	.5925	.8056	.7355	1.3597	1.2413	1.6878	40'
30'	.5948	.8039	.7400	1.3514	1.2440	1.6812	30'
40'	.5972	.8021	.7445	1.3432	1.2467	1.6746	20'
50'	.5995	.8004	.7490	1.3351	1.2494	1.6681	10'
37° 0'	.6018	.7986	.7536	1.3270	1.2521	1.6616	53° 0'
10'	.6041	.7969	.7581	1.3190	1.2549	1.6553	50'
20'	.6065	.7951	.7627	1.3111	1.2577	1.6489	40'
30'	.6088	.7934	.7673	1.3032	1.2605	1.6427	30'

Glossary

The explanations given in this glossary are intended to be brief descriptions of the terms listed. They are not necessarily definitions.

abscissa *(p. 209)* The first number of an ordered pair, which indicates the direction and distance to move horizontally from the origin. The x-coordinate of the ordered pair (x, y) is the abscissa.

absolute value (of a real number) *(p. 8)* The absolute value of the real number x is written as $|x|$. $|x| = -x$ if x is a negative number and $|x| = x$ if x is a positive number or zero.

additive identity matrix *(p. 257)* I is called the additive identity matrix for any matrix A if A and I have the same dimensions and $A + I = A$.

additive inverse matrix *(p. 257)* $-A$ is called the additive inverse matrix of any matrix A if A and $-A$ have the same dimensions and $A + (-A) = I$.

amplitude *(p. 496)* The amplitude of a trig function is its maximum value.

angle of rotation *(p. 454)* An angle of rotation is formed by rotating a ray about its end point, or vertex.

antilogarithm (base-n) *(p. 404)* For each real number x and each positive number $n \neq 1$, $\operatorname{antilog}_n x = n^x$. For example, $\operatorname{antilog}_5 3 = 5^3 = 125$.

arithmetic mean *(p. 361)* The arithmetic mean of x and y is their average $\dfrac{x + y}{2}$.

arithmetic means *(p. 361)* The terms between two given terms of an arithmetic progression are called the arithmetic means between the given terms.

arithmetic progression (A.P.) *(p. 357)* A progression formed by adding the same number to any term to obtain the next term.

arithmetic series *(p. 364)* The indicated sum of the terms of an arithmetic progression. $3, 6, 9, \cdots$ is an arithmetic progression and $3 + 6 + 9 + \cdots$ is an arithmetic series.

binomial expansion *(p. 382)* The indicated sum of the terms of the nth power of a binomial. For example, $(a + b)^3$ is $a^3 + 3a^2b + 3ab^2 + b^3$.

characteristic *(p. 392)* The integer part of a base-10 logarithm. $\log 54{,}600 = 4.7372$ and $\log 0.0546 = 8.7372 - 10$. The characteristic of $\log 54{,}600$ is 4 and the characteristic of $\log 0.0546$ is $8 - 10$, or -2.

combination *(p. 435)* A selection of objects without regard to order.

combined variation *(p. 295)* A combined variation is a function defined by an equation of the form $y = \dfrac{kxz}{w}$, or $\dfrac{yw}{xz} = k$, where k is a nonzero constant.

complex number *(p. 187)* A number that can be written in the form $a + bi$ where a and b are real numbers and $i = \sqrt{-1}$.

cosecant function *(p. 469)* For any angle of rotation u, the cosecant (csc) of u is $\dfrac{r}{y}$; $\csc u = \dfrac{r}{y}$.

cosine function *(p. 461)* For any angle of rotation u, the cosine (cos) of u is $\dfrac{x}{r}$; $\cos u = \dfrac{x}{r}$.

consistent system *(p. 240)* When a system of linear equations has at least one solution, the system is called a consistent system.

constant function *(p. 282)* A constant function is a linear function whose graph is a horizontal line, ray, or segment.

cotangent function *(p. 465)* For any angle of rotation u, the cotangent (cot) of $u = \dfrac{x}{y}$; $\cot u = \dfrac{x}{y}$.

dependent events *(p. 443)* Events in which one event depends upon the other are called dependent events.

dependent system *(p. 241)* When a system of

linear equations has all solutions in common, the system is called a dependent system.

determinant *(p. 250)* A real number assigned to a matrix.

discriminant *(p. 195)* The radicand, $b^2 - 4ac$, in the quadratic formula is called the discriminant of the quadratic equation. The discriminant determines the nature of the solutions of the equation.

distance formula *(p. 224)* The distance, d, between any two points whose coordinates are (x_1, y_1) and (x_2, y_2) is determined by the formula $d = \sqrt{(x_2 - x_1)^2 + (y_2 - y_1)^2}$ called the distance formula.

domain *(p. 276)* The set of all first coordinates of the ordered pairs of a relation.

ellipse *(p. 314)* The set of all points in a plane such that for each point of the set, the sum of its distances from two fixed points is constant.

exponential equation *(pp. 33, 158, 406)* Equations such as $2^x = 16$ and $5^{4x+1} = 125$ where the variable appears in the exponent.

factorial notation $(n!)$ *(p. 426)* $0! = 1$ and for each positive integer n, $n! = 1 \cdot 2 \cdot 3 \cdots n$.

fractional equation *(p. 116)* An equation such as $\frac{2n - 9}{n - 7} + \frac{n}{2} = \frac{5}{n - 7}$ in which a variable appears in a denominator.

function *(p. 276)* A function is a relation, a set of ordered pairs, in which different ordered pairs have different first coordinates.

fundamental counting principle *(p. 424)* This principle is used to find the number of permutations of n objects taken r at a time.

geometric mean *(p. 372)* The geometric mean (mean proportional) of x and y is $\sqrt{xy}$ or $-\sqrt{xy}$.

geometric means *(p. 372)* The terms between two given terms of a geometric progression.

geometric progression (G.P.) *(p. 368)* A progression formed by multiplying any term by the same nonzero number to obtain the next term.

geometric series *(p. 375)* The indicated sum of the terms of a geometric progression. $3 + 6 + 12 + \cdots$ is a geometric series since $3, 6, 12, \cdots$ is a geometric progression.

hyperbola *(p. 317)* A hyperbola is the set of all points in a plane such that for each point of the set, the difference of its distances from two fixed points is constant.

imaginary number *(p. 188)* Any complex number $a + bi$, where $b \neq 0$, like $5 - 2i$ and $4i$.

inclusive events *(p. 442)* Events that can both occur at the same time.

inconsistent system *(p. 241)* A system of linear equations that has no solution.

independent events *(p. 443)* Events where neither event depends upon the other.

independent system *(p. 240)* A system of linear equations that has exactly one solution.

inverse functions *(p. 285)* When both a relation and its inverse are functions, they are called inverse functions.

inverse relations *(p. 295)* The inverse of a relation is formed by reversing the order of the elements of each ordered pair.

inverse variation *(p. 291)* A function that is defined by an equation of the form $xy = k$ or $y = \frac{k}{x}$, where k is a nonzero constant.

irrational number *(p. 140)* A real number whose decimal numeral is nonterminating and nonrepeating.

joint variation *(p. 294)* A function that is defined by an equation of the form $y = kxz$ or $\frac{y}{xz} = k$, where k is a nonzero constant.

law of cosines *(p. 538)* The law of cosines is used to find the length of a side of a triangle when the measures of the two other sides and included angle are known. In general, $a^2 = b^2 + c^2 - 2bc \cos A$ $b^2 = a^2 + c^2 - 2ac \cos B$ $c^2 = a^2 + b^2 - 2ab \cos C$

law of sines *(p. 545)* The law of sines is used to find the measure of an angle and length of a side of a triangle when the measures of two angles and a side are known. In general, $\frac{\sin A}{a} = \frac{\sin B}{b} = \frac{\sin C}{c}$.

linear function *(p. 282)* A function whose graph

is a nonvertical line, ray, or segment. The equation $y = mx + b$ describes a linear function.

logarithm (base-n) *(p. 404)* For each positive number y and each positive number $n \neq 1$, if $y = n^x$, then $\log_n y = \log_n n^x = x$. For example, $125 = 5^3$ and $\log_5 125 = \log_5 5^3 = 3$.

logarithm (common; base-10) *(p. 390)* For each real number $y > 0$, the base-10 logarithm of y, or $\log y$, is defined as follows: If $y = 10^x$, then $\log y = \log 10^x = x$. Base-10 logarithms are also called common logarithms.

mantissa *(p. 392)* The decimal part of a base-10 logarithm. $\log 54{,}600 = 4.7372$ and the mantissa of $\log 54{,}600$ is 0.7372.

matrix *(p. 250)* An array of numbers or other elements arranged in rows and columns.

multiplicative identity matrix *(p. 260)* I is called the multiplicative identity matrix for any square matrix A if $A \cdot I = A$.

multiplicative inverse matrix *(p. 260)* A^{-1} is called the multiplicative inverse matrix of any square matrix A if $A \cdot A^{-1} = I$.

mutually exclusive events *(p. 442)* Events that cannot both occur at the same time.

parabola *(p. 306)* A set of points in a plane that are equidistant from a fixed point and a fixed line.

periodic function *(p. 496)* A function that repeats itself. If $f(x) = f(x + p)$, then f is a periodic function with a period of p.

permutation (linear) *(p. 425)* A linear arrangement of objects in a definite order.

permutation (circular) *(p. 433)* The number of circular permutations of n distinct objects is $(n - 1)!$.

point-slope form of an equation of a line *(p. 216)* An equation of a nonvertical line in the form $y - y_1 = m(x - x_1)$, where m is the slope of the line and $P(x_1, y_1)$ is any point on the line.

principal values *(p. 530)* To obtain an inverse function of a trigonometric function, restrict the range of the inverse. The restricted values are called principal values.

probability *(p. 438)* The probability of a simple event is the number of favorable outcomes divided by the total number of all possible outcomes.

progression *(p. 357)* An ordered list of numbers formed according to some pattern; a sequence.

pure imaginary number *(p. 188)* Any complex number $a + bi$, where $a = 0$, like $4i$.

Pythagorean relation *(p. 78)* For each right triangle ABC with right angle C, $a^2 + b^2 = c^2$. And, if $a^2 + b^2 = c^2$, then triangle ABC is a right triangle with right angle C.

quadrants *(p. 209)* The two axes in a coordinate plane separate the plane into four sections called quadrants.

quadratic equation (in one variable) *(p. 68)* The standard form of a quadratic equation in one variable is $ax^2 + bx + c = 0$ where a, b, and c are numbers and $a \neq 0$.

quadratic formula *(p. 169)* The solutions of the general quadratic equation, $ax^2 + bx + c = 0$, are given by the quadratic formula, $x = \dfrac{-b \pm \sqrt{b^2 - 4ac}}{2a}$.

quadratic inequality (in one variable) *(p. 71)* The standard form of a quadratic inequality in one variable is either $ax^2 + bx + c < 0$ or $ax^2 + bx + c > 0$ where a, b, and c are numbers and $a \neq 0$.

radian *(p. 522)* If an angle of rotation, which is the central angle of a given circle, cuts off an arc whose length is equal to the length of a radius of a circle, then the measure of the angle of rotation is 1 radian.

radical equation *(p. 178)* An equation like $\sqrt[3]{6x + 10} = -2$ in which a radicand contains a variable.

range *(p. 276)* The set of all second coordinates of the ordered pairs of a relation.

rational expression *(p. 91)* A rational expression is either a polynomial P or a quotient $\dfrac{P}{Q}$ of polynomials P and Q.

rational number *(p. 89)* A rational number is one that can be written in the form $\frac{a}{b}$ where a and b are integers, $b \neq 0$. Examples of rational numbers are -8, 0, 7, $2\frac{3}{4}$, 9.62, $\sqrt{25}$, $\frac{22}{7}$, and $3.43434\cdots$.

real numbers *(p. 141)* All the rational numbers together with all the irrational numbers.

GLOSSARY

rectangular hyperbola *(p. 319)* A hyperbola whose equation is $xy = k$, where k is a nonzero real number.

reference angle *(p. 455)* The positive acute angle formed between the terminal side and the x-axis.

repeating decimal *(p. 89)* A nonterminating decimal in which one block of digits continues to repeat in consecutive blocks. The numeral $3.7242424\cdots$, or $3.72\overline{24}$, is a repeating decimal.

secant function *(p. 469)* For any angle of rotation u, the secant (sec) of u is $\frac{r}{x}$; $\sec u = \frac{r}{x}$.

sequence *(p. 357)* An ordered list of numbers formed according to some pattern; a progression.

sine function *(p. 461)* For any angle of rotation u, the sine (sin) of u is $\frac{y}{r}$; $\sin u = \frac{y}{r}$.

slope and *parallel lines* *(p. 228)* If two or more different nonvertical lines have the same slope, then the lines are parallel.

slope and *perpendicular lines* *(p. 229)* If two lines have negative reciprocal slopes, the lines are perpendicular.

square matrix *(p. 250)* A matrix that has the same number of rows as columns.

square root *(pp. 139, 187)* For $k > 0$, the positive (principal) square root of k is $\sqrt{k}$ and has the property that $(\sqrt{k})^2 = k$.

standard form of a linear equation *(p. 216)* A linear equation in two variables written in the form $ax + by = c$.

synthetic division *(p. 130)* A short method of dividing a polynomial in x by a binomial of the form $x - a$ where a is a rational number.

tangent function *(p. 465)* For any angle of rotation u, the tangent (tan) of $u = \frac{y}{x}$; $\tan u = \frac{y}{x}$.

terminating decimal *(p. 89)* A decimal in which there is a last digit as in 5.372. Every terminating decimal is a rational number.

trigonometric identities *(p. 517)* Trigonometric equations that are true for all permissible values of the variables.

value of a function *(p. 279)* For any ordered pair (x, y), of a function, y is the value of the function at x. For any given element of the domain of a function there is a corresponding element in the range which is called the value of the function.

Symbol List

$=$	is equal to
$<$	is less than
$>$	is greater than
$\{x \mid x > 5\}$	the set of all numbers x such that x is greater than 5
$\lvert x \rvert$	the absolute value of x
$\sqrt{a}$	the principal square root of a
$\varnothing$	the empty set
$\doteq$	is approximately equal to
$\sqrt[n]{x}$	the nth root of x
$a \pm \sqrt{b}$	$a + \sqrt{b}, \; a - \sqrt{b}$
i	$\sqrt{-1}$

(x, y)	the ordered pair of numbers x, y
$\overline{AB}$	segment AB
$\overleftrightarrow{AB}$	line AB
AB	the distance from A to B
$\parallel$	is parallel to
$\perp$	is perpendicular to
$f(x)$	f at x (the value of function f at x)
f^{-1}	the inverse of function f
$\log x$	the base-10 logarithm of x
$\log_n x$	the base-n logarithm of x
$\sin^{-1}$	arc sine

Index

ANNOTATED ANSWERS

This section contains those answers that do not appear on the TE text page.

Page 22

24. $R(r_1 + r_2) = r_1 r_2$; $R = \dfrac{r_1 r_2}{r_1 + r_2}$; $\dfrac{1}{R} = \dfrac{r_1 + r_2}{r_1 r_2} =$
$\dfrac{r_1}{r_1 r_2} + \dfrac{r_2}{r_1 r_2}$; $\dfrac{1}{R} = \dfrac{1}{r_2} + \dfrac{1}{r_1} = \dfrac{1}{r_1} + \dfrac{1}{r_2}$

Page 43

55. $(a + b + c)(a + b + c) = a^2 + ab + ac$
$+ ab + b^2 + bc + ac + bc + c^2 = a^2 + b^2$
$+ c^2 + 2ab + 2ac + 2bc$

Page 59

34. $(2x + 3)(5x + 4)$ **35.** $(4n - 3)(3n - 2)$
36. $(2y - 3)(6y + 5)$ **37.** $(9a - 4)(2a - 3)$
38. $(2x - 5)(12x + 7)$ **39.** $(8n - 7)(2n + 3)$
40. $(2c - 3)(10c - 9)$ **41.** $(8a + 9)(3a - 4)$
42. $(3y - 4z)(2y + 3z)$ **43.** $(5x - 6y)(x + 2y)$
44. $(9m + 5n)(4m - 3n)$ **45.** $(8c - 5d)(3c + 4d)$
46. $(5x^2 - 6)(3x^2 + 2)$ **47.** $(4x^2 - 5)(3x^2 - 2)$
48. $(3y^2 + 4)(6y^2 - 5)$ **49.** $(3y^2 + 2)(2y^2 - 9)$
50. $(2n^2 - 3)(5n^2 - 8)$
51. $(3a^2 + 10)(3a^2 - 2)$
52. $(2x^2 y^2 - 3)(x^2 y^2 - 2)$
53. $(3a^2 b^2 + 5)(a^2 b^2 - 2)$
54. $(5m^2 n^2 - 6)(m^2 n^2 + 2)$
55. $(3c^2 d^2 + 4)(2c^2 d^2 + 5)$
56. $(5x^2 + 8y^2)(x^2 + 3y^2)$
57. $(7c^2 + 6d^2)(2c^2 - 3d^2)$
58. cannot be factored **59.** $(x^3 - 6y^2)(x^3 - y^2)$
60. $(5m^2 + n^3)(m^2 - n^3)$

Page 67

53. Ex. 51 and 52 both contain $(x + y)(x - y)$ as a factor.
$x^4 + x^2 y^2 + y^4 = (x^4 + 2x^2 y^2 + y^4) - x^2 y^2 =$
$(x^2 + y^2)^2 - (xy)^2 = (x^2 + y^2 + xy)(x^2 + y^2 - xy) =$
$(x^2 + xy + y^2)(x^2 - xy + y^2)$.

Page 84

3. $(5a^2 b^2 + 4)(5a^2 b^2 - 3)$
4. $(2x^{n+1} - 1)(x^{n+1} - 5)$
5. $(3a + 4)(3a - 4)$
6. $(n + 4)(n^2 - 4n + 16)$
13. $16n^2 - 36$ **14.** $9a^2 - 30a + 25$
19. $3x(3x - 1)(2x - 1)$ **20.** $-1(2a - 7)(a + 2)$
21. $3(2y + 3)(2y - 3)$ **22.** $-1(y - 5)^2$
23. $(2n^2 + 3)(n + 3)(n - 3)$
24. $(2c + 3)(2c - 3)(c + 2)(c - 2)$
25. $2ab(a - 5)(a + 3)$
26. $3(x - 2y)(x^2 + 2xy + 4y^2)$ **27.** $(x^2 + 5)(x + 4)$
28. $(3c - 4d)(5a - 2b)$ **29.** $2x^{3n}(x^{2n} + 3)(x^{2n} - 3)$

Page 86

2.
```
10 REM "PROGRAM FINDS BOTH
   TRIANGULAR AND SQUARE"
20 REM "NUMBERS FOR VALUES OF A
   FROM 1 TO 50"
```

```
30 PRINT "TRIANGULAR AND
   SQUARE NUMBERS"
40 FOR A = 1 TO 1200
50 LET T = (A * (A + 1))/2
60 LET S1 = SQR (T)
70 LET R = INT (S1)
80 IF R < > S1 THEN 100
90 PRINT T
100 NEXT A
110 END
```

Page 101

6. $\dfrac{9b^2 c^5 d - 10ad}{24a^3 b^4 c^6}$ **14.** $\dfrac{6n - 25}{(n + 5)(n - 5)}$

22. $\dfrac{8x - 1}{(x + 3)(x - 3)}$ **23.** $\dfrac{-5c - 24}{(c + 5)(c - 5)}$

24. $\dfrac{3x - 7}{(x + 2)(x - 2)}$ **27.** $\dfrac{11y - 9}{6(y + 3)(y - 1)}$

28. $\dfrac{x - 60}{3(x - 4)(x - 5)}$ **29.** $\dfrac{40am + 10an + 4m^2 - 4mn}{5a(m - n)(m - n)}$

30. $\dfrac{2ac - 5bc - 9ab + 6b^2}{2c(3a + 2b)(3a - 2b)}$

Page 110

2.
```
25 PRINT "ENTER PRINCIPAL"
30 INPUT P
32 PRINT "ENTER NO. OF YEARS"
34 INPUT S
36 PRINT "ENTER INTEREST RATE
   AS A DECIMAL"
38 INPUT R
40 FOR Y = 1 TO S
50 FOR Q = 1 TO 4
60 LET I = R * P / 4
70 NEXT Q
80 NEXT Y
90 PRINT "AFTER"; S; "YEARS THE
   AMOUNT SAVED IS $"; I
100 END
```

3.
```
10 PRINT "PROGRAM COMPARES
   INTEREST RATES"
20 PRINT "ON 3000, COMPOUNDED
   QUARTERLY AND"
30 PRINT "INVESTED FOR 3 YEARS"
40 DIM I(5), P(5), R(5)
50 FOR K = 1 TO 5
60 LET P(K) = 3000
70 NEXT K
80 LET R(1) = .08
90 LET R(2) = .0825
100 LET R(3) = .085
110 LET R(4) = .0875
120 LET R(5) = .09
130 FOR Y = 1 TO 3
140 FOR Q = 1 TO 4
150 FOR K = 1 TO 5
```

```
160  LET I(K) = P(K) * R(K) / 4
180  LET P(K) = P(K) + I(K)
190  NEXT K
200  NEXT Q
210  NEXT Y
220  FOR K = 1 TO 5
230  PRINT "AFTER 3 YEARS THE SAVED
     AMOUNT"
240  PRINT "IS $"; P(K); "AT"; R(K)
250  NEXT K
260  END
```

Page 136

Statements 10, 30, 40, 50, 120, 160, 190, and 200 are different.

```
 10  PRINT "PROGRAM DIVIDES A 5TH
     DEGREE"
 20  PRINT "POLYNOMIAL BY A
     BINOMIAL"
 30  DIM C(6), A(6)
 40  PRINT "ENTER 6 COEFFICIENTS OF
     POLYNOMIAL"
 50  FOR I = 1 TO 6
 60  INPUT C(I)
 70  NEXT I
 80  PRINT "ENTER 2ND TERM OF
     BINOMIAL"
 90  INPUT D
100  LET D = -D
110  LET A(1) = C(1)
120  FOR I = 2 TO 6
130  LET A(I) = A(I-1) * D + C(I)
140  NEXT I
150  PRINT "COEFFICIENTS OF
     QUOTIENT ARE"
160  FOR I = 1 TO 5
170  PRINT A(I),
180  NEXT I
190  PRINT "REMAINDER IS"; A(6)
200  IF A(6) < > 0 THEN 230
210  PRINT "THE BINOMIAL IS A
     FACTOR"
220  GO TO 240
230  PRINT "THE BINOMIAL IS
     NOT A FACTOR"
240  END
```

Page 177 (Challenge)

$$10\left(\frac{25 + 5\sqrt{37}}{2} - 20\right)\left(4 \cdot \frac{25 + 5\sqrt{37}}{2} - 20\right)$$

$$= [5(25 + 5\sqrt{37}) - 200] \quad [2(25 + 5\sqrt{37}) - 20]$$

$$= (125 + 25\sqrt{37} - 200)(50 + 10\sqrt{37} - 20)$$

$$= (25\sqrt{37} - 75)(10\sqrt{37} + 30) = 250 \cdot 37 + 750\sqrt{37}$$

$$- 750\sqrt{37} - 2{,}250 = 9{,}250 - 2{,}250 = 7{,}000$$

Page 184

```
4.   4  DIM S(4)
     5  FOR I = 1 TO 4
    10  PRINT "ENTER LENGTH OF BOX,
        WIDTH OF BOX, AND LENGTH OF
        KITE"
    20  INPUT X, Y, K
    30  LET D = SQR(X ↑ 2 + Y ↑ 2)
```

```
 40  IF D > = K THEN 70
 50  PRINT "KITE STICKS WON'T FIT"
 60  GO TO 80
 70  PRINT "KITE STICKS WILL FIT.
     DIAGONAL IS"; D
 80  REM SAVE ALL DIAGONALS IN S
 90  LET S(I) = D
100  NEXT I
110  REM THE MINIMUM DIAGONAL
     NEEDED IS
120  REM THE MAXIMUM DIAGONAL
     OF GIVEN SAMPLE
130  LET M = S(1)
140  FOR I = 2 TO 4
150  IF S(I) < M THEN 170
160  LET M = S(I)
170  NEXT I
180  PRINT "DIAGONAL NEEDED FOR
     GIVEN SAMPLE IS"; M
190  END
```

```
5.  10  PRINT "PROGRAM FINDS BOX
        WITH LEAST PERIMETER"
    20  PRINT "FOR A GIVEN KITE STICK"
    30  DIM L(4), W(4), P(4)
    40  PRINT "ENTER LENGTH OF KITE"
    50  INPUT K
    60  FOR I = 1 TO 4
    70  PRINT "ENTER LENGTH AND
        WIDTH OF BOX"
    80  INPUT L(I), W(I)
    90  LET P(I) = 2 * (L(I) + W(I))
   100  NEXT I
   110  REM FIND BOX WITH LEAST
        PERIMETER FOR KITE
   120  FOR I = 1 TO 4
   130  IF K < = SQR(L(I) ↑ 2
        + W(I) ↑ 2) THEN 160
   140  NEXT I
   150  GO TO 250
   160  LET S = P(I)
   170  LET N = I
   180  FOR I = 1 TO 4
   190  IF P(I) > S THEN 230
   200  IF K > SQR(L(I) ↑ 2
        + W(I) ↑ 2) THEN 230
   210  LET S = P(I)
   220  LET N = I
   230  NEXT I
   240  IF N < > 0 THEN 270
   250  PRINT "KITE WON'T FIT IN
        ANY OF THESE BOXES"
   260  GO TO 290
   270  PRINT "THE BOX WITH THE
        LEAST PERIMETER"
   280  PRINT "IS BOX"; N;
        "WITH PERIMETER"; S
   290  END
```

```
6.  10  REM PROGRAM SOLVES
        QUADRATIC EQUATION
    20  PRINT "ENTER COEFFICIENTS
        A, B, C"
```

```
30 INPUT A, B, C
35 LET D1 = B ↑ 2 - 4 * A * C
36 IF D1 = 0 THEN 80
37 IF D1 < 0 THEN 110
40 LET D = SQR(D1)
50 LET X1 = (-B + D) / (2 * A)
60 LET X2 = (-B - D) / (2 * A)
70 PRINT "THE TWO SOLUTIONS
   ARE"; X1; "AND"; X2
75 GO TO 120
80 LET X1 = -B / (2 * A)
90 PRINT "THE ONE SOLUTION
   IS"; X1
100 GO TO 120
110 PRINT "THERE IS NO REAL
    SOLUTION"
120 END
```

Page 200

37. $r + s = \dfrac{-b + \sqrt{b^2 - 4ac}}{2a} + \dfrac{-b - \sqrt{b^2 - 4ac}}{2a}$

$= \dfrac{-2b}{2a} = \dfrac{-b}{a}; rs = \dfrac{-b + \sqrt{b^2 - 4ac}}{2a} \cdot$

$\dfrac{-b - \sqrt{b^2 - 4ac}}{2a} = \dfrac{(-b)^2 - (\sqrt{b^2 - 4ac})^2}{4a^2}$

$= \dfrac{b^2 - (b^2 - 4ac)}{4a^2} = \dfrac{4ac}{4a^2} = \dfrac{c}{a}$

40. If x is even, $ax^2 + bx$ is even. Therefore, if $ax^2 + bx + c$ were 0, c would have to be even. If x is odd, ax^2 and bx are odd and $ax^2 + bx$ is even. Again, if $ax^2 + bx + c$ were 0, c would have to be even. Since c is odd, x is neither an even number nor an odd number.

Page 204

```
4. 10 PRINT "PROGRAM FINDS THE
      DIFFERENCE OF TWO"
   20 PRINT "COMPLEX NUMBERS"
   30 PRINT "ENTER THE
      COEFFICIENT A AND B"
   40 PRINT "OF THE MINUEND"
   50 INPUT A, B
   60 PRINT "ENTER THE
      COEFFICIENTS C AND D"
   70 PRINT "OF THE SUBTRAHEND"
   80 INPUT C, D
   90 LET A1 = A - C
  100 LET B1 = B - D
  110 PRINT "THE COEFFICIENTS OF
      THE REMAINDER ARE"
  120 PRINT "A IS"; A1, "B IS"; B1
  130 END
5. 10 PRINT "PROGRAM FINDS THE
      PRODUCT OF PAIRS OF"
   20 PRINT "CONJUGATE COMPLEX
      NUMBERS"
   30 READ A, B
   40 REM PRODUCT IS A↑2 + B↑2
   50 LET P = A↑2 + B↑2
   60 PRINT "PRODUCT IS"; P
   70 GO TO 30
   80 DATA 5, -2, 6, 3, 2, -4
   90 END
```

Page 211

For Exercises 14–47, the coordinates of two points are given. **14.** $(0, -1), (2, -7)$ **15.** $(0, 3), (3, 3)$ **16.** $(0, 2), (1, 5)$ **17.** $(0, -2), (2, 6)$ **18.** $(0, 3), (1, 7)$ **19.** $(0, 4), (1, 6)$ **20.** $(0, -3), (1, 5)$ **21.** $(0, -5), (5, 0)$ **22.** $(0, 3), (3, 0)$ **23.** $(0, -5), (1, -3)$ **24.** $(0, -5), (1, -7)$ **25.** $(0, -3)(1, -1)$ **26.** $(0, 0), (3, 3)$ **27.** $(0, 3), (1, 1)$ **28.** $(0, -5), (1, -3)$ **29.** $(0, 4), (1, 2)$ **30.** $(0, -3), (2, -2)$ **31.** $(0, 6), (4, 0)$ **32.** $(0, -5), (1, -8)$ **33.** $(0, 3), (3, -2)$ **34.** $(1, 3), (3, 4)$ **35.** $(1, 2), (3, 3)$ **36.** $(0, -3), (3, -7)$ **37.** $(2, 0), (5, 4)$ **38.** $(0, 24), (6, 0)$ **39.** $(-10, 0), \left(0, 6\frac{2}{3}\right)$ **40.** $(5, -3), (-5, 0)$ **41.** $(-3, 3), (-12, 4)$ **42.** $(1, 1), (4, 2)$ **43.** $(0, 4), (3, 2)$ **44.** $(0, -3), (1, 3)$ **45.** $(0, 3), (1, 2.5)$ **46.** $(10, 0), (0, -5.2)$ **47.** $(0, -1.4), (1, -2.6)$

Page 219

52. $y - y_1 = m(x - x_1); y - 0 = \dfrac{b}{-a}(x - a);$

$y = \dfrac{-b}{a}(x - a); ay = -bx + ab; bx + ay = ab;$

$\dfrac{bx}{ab} + \dfrac{ay}{ab} = \dfrac{ab}{ab}; \dfrac{x}{a} + \dfrac{y}{b} = 1$

Page 222

For Exercises 1–20 and 33–38, the coordinates of two points are given. **1.** $(0, 3), (3, 5)$ **2.** $(0, -2), (3, -4)$ **3.** $(0, 1), (3, 2)$ **4.** $(0, 4), (2, 3)$ **5.** $(0, -1), (1, -3)$ **6.** $(0, 1), (1, -1)$ **7.** $(0, -2), (-1, 1)$ **8.** $(0, 3), (1, 8)$ **9.** $(0, 4), (1, 2)$ **10.** $(0, -1), (1, -4)$ **11.** $(0, -3), (1, 1)$ **12.** $(0, 5), (1, 4)$ **13.** $(0, 2), (2, -1)$ **14.** $(9, 0), (0, -3)$ **15.** $(0, 5), (3, 5)$ **16.** $(0, -3), (4, 0)$ **17.** $(0, 4), (1, 3)$ **18.** $(4, 0), (4, 4)$ **19.** $(-4, 0), (-4, 4)$ **20.** $(0, -3), (5, -5)$ **33.** $(1, 3), (-3, 4)$ **34.** $\left(0, \dfrac{11}{3}\right), \left(\dfrac{11}{3}, 0\right)$ **35.** $\left(0, -\dfrac{1}{2}\right), \left(1, -\dfrac{7}{6}\right)$ **36.** $(0, 1), (5, -3)$ **37.** $(2, 2), (5, -5)$ **38.** $(0, -10), (1, -7)$

Page 225

7. $2\sqrt{5}$ **8.** $\sqrt{89}$ **9.** $\sqrt{97}$ **10.** 15 **11.** $3\sqrt{13}$ **12.** $\sqrt{58}$ **13.** $\sqrt{149}$ **14.** 5 **15.** $\sqrt{41}$ **16.** $5\sqrt{5}$ **17.** $2\sqrt{5}$ **18.** $\sqrt{146}$ **19.** $\sqrt{10}$ **20.** $\sqrt{85}$ **21.** $2\sqrt{2}$ **22.** $\sqrt{433}$ **23.** $\dfrac{\sqrt{229}}{6}$ **24.** $\dfrac{7}{4}\sqrt{5}$ **25.** $\dfrac{\sqrt{221}}{6}$ **26.** $\dfrac{\sqrt{5}}{2}$ **27.** $\dfrac{17}{20}$ **28.** $\dfrac{\sqrt{2}}{3}$ **29.** $\sqrt{b^2 + 4a^2}$ **30.** $\sqrt{4x^2 + 12x + 9 + 4y^2}$ **31.** $\sqrt{9p^2 + 16s^2}$ **32.** a **33.** a **34.** $\dfrac{a - b + 2}{2}$ **35.** $\dfrac{\sqrt{b^2 + 16a^2}}{12}$ **36.** $\dfrac{\sqrt{625d^2 + 16c^2}}{30}$ **37.** $\dfrac{\sqrt{25b^2 + 16a^2}}{8}$ **53.** $c + b + \sqrt{d^2 + e^2} + \sqrt{(c - d + b)^2 + e^2}$ **55.** $\dfrac{\sqrt{6481}}{30} + \dfrac{7}{30}\sqrt{349} + \dfrac{3}{2}\sqrt{10}$ **56.** $\sqrt{(e - a)^2 + (f - b)^2} + \sqrt{(h - d)^2 + (g - c)^2}$

Page 227

41. Midpoint $M(-1, 2)$; $AM = MC = 5$; $BM = MD = 10$

Page 233

1. $m(\overline{AB}) = \dfrac{5-2}{2-1} = 3$; $m(\overline{BC}) = \dfrac{6-5}{-1-2} = -\dfrac{1}{3}$; $\overline{AB} \perp \overline{BC}$ **2.** $m(\overline{AB}) = \dfrac{1+2}{5+1} = \dfrac{1}{2}$; $m(\overline{BC}) = \dfrac{5-1}{3-5} = -2$; $\overline{AB} \perp \overline{BC}$

3. $m(\overline{AB}) = \dfrac{3+5}{7-5} = 4$; $m(\overline{BC}) = \dfrac{5-3}{-1-7} = -\dfrac{1}{4}$; $\overline{AB} \perp \overline{BC}$ **4.** $m(\overline{AB}) = \dfrac{-1-3}{4-2} = -2$; $m(\overline{BC}) = \dfrac{1+1}{8-4} = \dfrac{1}{2}$; $\overline{AB} \perp \overline{BC}$

5. $m(\overline{AB}) = \dfrac{-8-2}{-1-1} = 5$; $m(\overline{BC}) = \dfrac{-3+8}{0+1} = 5$; $m(\overline{AB}) = m(\overline{BC})$ **6.** $m(\overline{AB}) = \dfrac{2-0}{1-0} = 2$; $m(\overline{DC}) = \dfrac{5-3}{6-5} = 2$; $\overline{AB} \parallel \overline{DC}$; $m(\overline{AD}) = \dfrac{3-0}{5-0} = \dfrac{3}{5}$; $m(\overline{BC}) = \dfrac{5-2}{6-1} = \dfrac{3}{5}$; $\overline{AD} \parallel \overline{BC}$

7. $AC = \sqrt{(5-1)^2 + (4-2)^2} = \sqrt{16+4} = 2\sqrt{5}$; midpoint D of $\overline{AB} = (5, 2)$; midpoint E of $\overline{BC} = (6, 4)$; $DE = \sqrt{(4-2)^2 + (6-5)^2} = \sqrt{4+1} = \sqrt{5}$; $DE = \dfrac{1}{2} AC$

8. $AB = \sqrt{(4-1)^2 + (7-2)^2} = \sqrt{9+25} = \sqrt{34}$; $BC = \sqrt{(4-7)^2 + (7-2)^2} = \sqrt{9+25} = \sqrt{34}$; $AB = BC$ **9.** $m(\overline{AB}) = 0$, $m(\overline{BC}) = \dfrac{b}{0}$, undefined, $\overline{AB} \perp \overline{BC}$; $m(\overline{AD}) = \dfrac{b}{0}$, undefined, $\overline{AB} \perp \overline{AD}$; $m(\overline{CD}) = 0$, $\overline{CD} \perp \overline{AD}$; $\overline{CD} \perp \overline{BC}$

11. $M(\overline{AC}) = \left(\dfrac{a+c}{2}, \dfrac{b+d}{2}\right)$; $M(\overline{BD}) = \left(\dfrac{a+c}{2}, \dfrac{b+d}{2}\right)$ **13.** $m(\overline{SU}) = \dfrac{b}{a + \sqrt{a^2 - b^2}}$; $m(\overline{TV}) = \dfrac{-b}{a - \sqrt{a^2 - b^2}}$; $\dfrac{b}{a + \sqrt{a^2 - b^2}}$.

$\dfrac{-b}{a - \sqrt{a^2 - b^2}} = \dfrac{-b^2}{a^2 - (\sqrt{a^2 - b^2})^2} = \dfrac{-b^2}{a^2 - (a^2 - b^2)} = \dfrac{-b^2}{b^2} = -1$; $\dfrac{b}{a + \sqrt{a^2 - b^2}}$

is the negative reciprocal of $\dfrac{-b}{a - \sqrt{a^2 - b^2}}$; $\overline{TV} \perp \overline{SU}$

Page 235

4.
```
10 PRINT "ENTER MEASURES OF
   SIDES OF TRIANGLE WITH
   LARGEST SIDE LAST"
20 INPUT A, B, C
30 LET X = A↑2 + B↑2
40 LET Y = C↑2
50 IF X = Y THEN 80
60 PRINT "NOT A RIGHT TRIANGLE"
70 GO TO 90
```

```
80 PRINT "IS A RIGHT TRIANGLE"
90 END
```

5.
```
10 PRINT "ENTER LENGTH OF
   DIAGONAL AND ONE SIDE"
20 INPUT D, S
30 LET X = SQR (D↑2 - S↑2)
40 LET A = X * S
50 PRINT "AREA IS"; A
60 PRINT "FOR SIDES OF
   LENGTHS"; X; "AND"; S
70 END
```

Page 236

40. Since opposite sides have equal slopes $\left(3 \text{ and } -\dfrac{1}{3}\right)$, they are parallel. Therefore, $ABCD$ is a parallelogram.

Page 237

5. Passes through $(0, 5)$, $(1, 3)$ **6.** Passes through $(0, 3)$, $(1, 1)$ **22.** Since opposite sides have equal slopes $\left(\dfrac{2}{3} \text{ and } \dfrac{-5}{3}\right)$, they are parallel. Therefore, $ABCD$ is a parallelogram.   **24.** Let the coordinates be $A(-a, 0)$, $B(a, 0)$, $C(0, b)$; midpoint of $\overline{AC}$ is $N\left(-\dfrac{a}{2}, \dfrac{b}{2}\right)$; midpoint of $\overline{BC}$ is $M\left(\dfrac{a}{2}, \dfrac{b}{2}\right)$; midpoint of $\overline{AB}$ is $O(0, 0)$; use the distance formula to show than $AN = NC = CM = MB = OM = ON$. $\triangle ABC$ contains 4 smaller isosceles triangles.

Page 242

18. Any two equations with $m_1 = m_2$, $b_1 \neq b_2$

Page 255 (Challenge)

$Q = aM + bN + cP = ax^2 - ax + a + bx^2 + bx + b - cx^2 + cx + c$
$Q = (a + b - c)x^2 + (-a + b + c)x + (a + b + c)$
$Q = -1x^2 + -1x + 1$
$a + b - c = -1$; $-a + b + c = -1$; $a + b + c = 1$;
$2b = -2$; $b = -1$; $2b + 2c = 0$; $-2 + 2c = 0$; $c = 1$;
$a - 1 - 1 = -1$; $a - 2 = -1$; $a = 1$

Page 255 (Review)

1. points left of $-7\dfrac{1}{2}$ **2.** points left of, and including, 6   **3.** points between -2 and 6

Page 258

11. $\begin{bmatrix} 8 & -3 \\ -7 & -6 \end{bmatrix} + \begin{bmatrix} 0 & 0 \\ 0 & 0 \end{bmatrix} = \begin{bmatrix} 8 & -3 \\ -7 & -6 \end{bmatrix}$

12. $\begin{bmatrix} 8 & -3 \\ -7 & -6 \end{bmatrix} + \begin{bmatrix} 1 & -2 \\ 7 & -9 \end{bmatrix} = \begin{bmatrix} 9 & -5 \\ 0 & -15 \end{bmatrix}$; $\begin{bmatrix} 1 & -2 \\ 7 & -9 \end{bmatrix} + \begin{bmatrix} 8 & -3 \\ -7 & -6 \end{bmatrix} = \begin{bmatrix} 9 & -5 \\ 0 & -15 \end{bmatrix}$

13. $\left[\begin{bmatrix} 8 & -3 \\ -7 & -6 \end{bmatrix} + \begin{bmatrix} 1 & -2 \\ 7 & -9 \end{bmatrix}\right] + \begin{bmatrix} 3 & 5 \\ -2 & -6 \end{bmatrix} = \begin{bmatrix} 9 & -5 \\ 0 & -15 \end{bmatrix} + \begin{bmatrix} 3 & 5 \\ -2 & -6 \end{bmatrix} = \begin{bmatrix} 12 & 0 \\ -2 & -21 \end{bmatrix}$;

$$\begin{bmatrix} 8 & -3 \\ -7 & -6 \end{bmatrix} + \left[\begin{bmatrix} 1 & -2 \\ 7 & -9 \end{bmatrix} + \begin{bmatrix} 3 & 5 \\ -2 & -6 \end{bmatrix} \right] =$$

$$\begin{bmatrix} 8 & -3 \\ -7 & -6 \end{bmatrix} + \begin{bmatrix} 4 & 3 \\ 5 & -15 \end{bmatrix} = \begin{bmatrix} 12 & 0 \\ -2 & -21 \end{bmatrix}$$

14. $\begin{bmatrix} 1 & -2 \\ 7 & -9 \end{bmatrix} + \begin{bmatrix} 3 & 5 \\ -2 & -6 \end{bmatrix} = \begin{bmatrix} 4 & 3 \\ 5 & -15 \end{bmatrix};$

$$\begin{bmatrix} 3 & 5 \\ -2 & -6 \end{bmatrix} + \begin{bmatrix} 1 & -2 \\ 7 & -9 \end{bmatrix} = \begin{bmatrix} 4 & 3 \\ 5 & -15 \end{bmatrix}$$

15. $\left[\begin{bmatrix} 1 & -2 \\ 7 & -9 \end{bmatrix} + \begin{bmatrix} 3 & 5 \\ -2 & -6 \end{bmatrix} \right] + \begin{bmatrix} 8 & -3 \\ -7 & -6 \end{bmatrix} =$

$$\begin{bmatrix} 4 & 3 \\ 5 & -15 \end{bmatrix} + \begin{bmatrix} 8 & -3 \\ -7 & -6 \end{bmatrix} = \begin{bmatrix} 12 & 0 \\ -2 & -21 \end{bmatrix};$$

$$\begin{bmatrix} 1 & -2 \\ 7 & -9 \end{bmatrix} + \left[\begin{bmatrix} 3 & 5 \\ -2 & -6 \end{bmatrix} + \begin{bmatrix} 8 & -3 \\ -7 & -6 \end{bmatrix} \right] =$$

$$\begin{bmatrix} 1 & -2 \\ 7 & -9 \end{bmatrix} + \begin{bmatrix} 11 & 2 \\ -9 & -12 \end{bmatrix} = \begin{bmatrix} 12 & 0 \\ -2 & -21 \end{bmatrix}$$

16. $\left[\begin{bmatrix} 3 & 5 \\ -2 & -6 \end{bmatrix} + \begin{bmatrix} 1 & -2 \\ 7 & -9 \end{bmatrix} \right] + \begin{bmatrix} 8 & -3 \\ -7 & -6 \end{bmatrix} =$

$$\begin{bmatrix} 4 & 3 \\ 5 & -15 \end{bmatrix} + \begin{bmatrix} 8 & -3 \\ -7 & -6 \end{bmatrix} = \begin{bmatrix} 12 & 0 \\ -2 & -21 \end{bmatrix};$$

$$\begin{bmatrix} 3 & 5 \\ -2 & -6 \end{bmatrix} + \left[\begin{bmatrix} 1 & -2 \\ 7 & -9 \end{bmatrix} + \begin{bmatrix} 8 & -3 \\ -7 & -6 \end{bmatrix} \right] =$$

$$\begin{bmatrix} 3 & 5 \\ -2 & -6 \end{bmatrix} + \begin{bmatrix} 9 & -5 \\ 0 & -15 \end{bmatrix} = \begin{bmatrix} 12 & 0 \\ -2 & -21 \end{bmatrix}$$

Page 262

1. Yes **2.** Yes **3.** No **4.** Yes

5. $\begin{bmatrix} 6 & -9 & -15 \\ 18 & -30 & -18 \\ -24 & -36 & 12 \end{bmatrix}$ **6.** $\begin{bmatrix} -72 & -18 \\ 45 & -9 \\ 81 & 27 \end{bmatrix}$

7. $\begin{bmatrix} -7 & -6 & -9 \\ -8 & 1 & 5 \end{bmatrix}$ **8.** $\begin{bmatrix} -9 & 12 \\ 19 & -26 \end{bmatrix}$

9. $\begin{bmatrix} 5 & 1 & 8 \\ 11 & 20 & 0 \end{bmatrix}$ **10.** not possible **11.** $\begin{bmatrix} 8 & -8 & 0 \\ -4 & 6 & -2 \end{bmatrix}$

12. Identity $= \begin{bmatrix} 1 & 0 \\ 0 & 1 \end{bmatrix}$; Inverse $= \begin{bmatrix} \dfrac{5}{2} & \dfrac{7}{2} \\ 2 & 3 \end{bmatrix}$

13. Identity $= \begin{bmatrix} 1 & 0 \\ 0 & 1 \end{bmatrix}$; Inverse $= \begin{bmatrix} -\dfrac{1}{20} & -\dfrac{1}{10} \\ \dfrac{3}{10} & -\dfrac{2}{5} \end{bmatrix}$

14. not possible **15.** Identity $= \begin{bmatrix} 1 & 0 & 0 \\ 0 & 1 & 0 \\ 0 & 0 & 1 \end{bmatrix}$;

Inverse $= \begin{bmatrix} -\dfrac{2}{27} & -\dfrac{8}{27} & \dfrac{11}{54} \\ -\dfrac{19}{27} & -\dfrac{22}{27} & \dfrac{37}{54} \\ -\dfrac{8}{27} & -\dfrac{5}{27} & \dfrac{17}{54} \end{bmatrix}$

16. $\left[\begin{bmatrix} -3 & 1 \\ -2 & -4 \end{bmatrix} \cdot \begin{bmatrix} 1 & -6 \\ 3 & -2 \end{bmatrix} \right] \cdot \begin{bmatrix} 7 & -3 \\ 2 & 5 \end{bmatrix} =$

$$\begin{bmatrix} 0 & 16 \\ -14 & 20 \end{bmatrix} \begin{bmatrix} 7 & -3 \\ 2 & 5 \end{bmatrix} = \begin{bmatrix} 32 & 80 \\ -58 & 142 \end{bmatrix};$$

$$\begin{bmatrix} -3 & 1 \\ -2 & -4 \end{bmatrix} \left[\begin{bmatrix} 1 & -6 \\ 3 & -2 \end{bmatrix} \cdot \begin{bmatrix} 7 & -3 \\ 2 & 5 \end{bmatrix} \right] =$$

$$\begin{bmatrix} -3 & 1 \\ -2 & -4 \end{bmatrix} \begin{bmatrix} -5 & -33 \\ 17 & -19 \end{bmatrix} = \begin{bmatrix} 32 & 80 \\ -58 & 142 \end{bmatrix}$$

17. $\begin{bmatrix} 1 & -6 \\ 3 & -2 \end{bmatrix} \cdot \begin{bmatrix} 7 & -3 \\ 2 & 5 \end{bmatrix} = \begin{bmatrix} -5 & -33 \\ 17 & -19 \end{bmatrix};$

$$\begin{bmatrix} 7 & -3 \\ 2 & 5 \end{bmatrix} \cdot \begin{bmatrix} 1 & -6 \\ 3 & -2 \end{bmatrix} = \begin{bmatrix} -2 & -36 \\ 17 & -22 \end{bmatrix};$$

$\therefore B \cdot C \neq C \cdot B$

18. $\begin{bmatrix} -3 & 1 \\ -2 & -4 \end{bmatrix} \cdot \begin{bmatrix} 1 & -6 \\ 3 & -2 \end{bmatrix} =$

$$\begin{bmatrix} 0 & 16 \\ -14 & 20 \end{bmatrix}; \quad \begin{bmatrix} 1 & -6 \\ 3 & -2 \end{bmatrix} \cdot \begin{bmatrix} -3 & 1 \\ -2 & -4 \end{bmatrix} =$$

$$\begin{bmatrix} 9 & 25 \\ -5 & 11 \end{bmatrix}; \quad \therefore A \cdot B \neq B \cdot A$$

19. $\begin{bmatrix} -3 & 1 \\ -2 & -4 \end{bmatrix} \cdot$

$$\left[\begin{bmatrix} 1 & -6 \\ 3 & -2 \end{bmatrix} + \begin{bmatrix} 7 & -3 \\ 2 & 5 \end{bmatrix} \right] = \begin{bmatrix} -3 & 1 \\ -2 & -4 \end{bmatrix} \cdot$$

$$\begin{bmatrix} 8 & -9 \\ 5 & 3 \end{bmatrix} = \begin{bmatrix} -19 & 30 \\ -36 & 6 \end{bmatrix}; \quad \begin{bmatrix} -3 & 1 \\ -2 & -4 \end{bmatrix} \cdot$$

$$\begin{bmatrix} 1 & -6 \\ 3 & -2 \end{bmatrix} + \begin{bmatrix} -3 & 1 \\ -2 & -4 \end{bmatrix} \begin{bmatrix} 7 & -3 \\ 2 & 5 \end{bmatrix} =$$

$$\begin{bmatrix} 0 & 16 \\ -14 & 20 \end{bmatrix} + \begin{bmatrix} -19 & 14 \\ -22 & -14 \end{bmatrix} = \begin{bmatrix} -19 & 30 \\ -36 & 6 \end{bmatrix}$$

$\therefore A \cdot (B + C) = A \cdot B + A \cdot C$

20. $\begin{bmatrix} -3 & 1 \\ -2 & -4 \end{bmatrix} \begin{bmatrix} 1 & 0 \\ 0 & 1 \end{bmatrix} = \begin{bmatrix} -3 & 1 \\ -2 & -4 \end{bmatrix};$

$$\begin{bmatrix} 1 & 0 \\ 0 & 1 \end{bmatrix} \begin{bmatrix} -3 & 1 \\ -2 & -4 \end{bmatrix} = \begin{bmatrix} -3 & 1 \\ -2 & -4 \end{bmatrix};$$

$\therefore A \cdot I = I \cdot A$

21. $\begin{bmatrix} 1 & -6 \\ 3 & -2 \end{bmatrix} \cdot \begin{bmatrix} -\dfrac{1}{8} & \dfrac{3}{8} \\ -\dfrac{3}{16} & \dfrac{1}{16} \end{bmatrix} = \begin{bmatrix} 1 & 0 \\ 0 & 1 \end{bmatrix}$

Page 271

```
TOTAL MILES        MILES PER GALLON
    578                38.53333
    218                18.16666
    353                17.64999
CENTS PER MILE
  2.984428E-02
  8.256882E-02
  9.915012E-02
```

Page 272

10. $x = \dfrac{e_1 d_2 - e_2 d_1}{c_2 d_2 - c_2 d_1}; \quad y = \dfrac{e_1 c_2 - c_1 e_2}{c_2 d_1 - c_1 d_2}$

22. $\begin{bmatrix} 5 & 1 & 5 \\ -1 & 7 & 4 \\ 6 & -3 & 2 \end{bmatrix}$ **23.** $\begin{bmatrix} -9 & 12 & 2 \\ 11 & -12 & 13 \end{bmatrix}$

24. $\begin{bmatrix} 1 & 0 \\ 0 & 1 \end{bmatrix}$; $\begin{bmatrix} -7 & 3 \\ -2 & -1 \end{bmatrix}$; $\begin{bmatrix} \dfrac{1}{13} & \dfrac{3}{13} \\ -\dfrac{2}{13} & \dfrac{7}{13} \end{bmatrix}$

25. $\begin{bmatrix} 1 & 0 & 0 \\ 0 & 1 & 0 \\ 0 & 0 & 1 \end{bmatrix}$; $\begin{bmatrix} -3 & 1 & -2 \\ -2 & -1 & -2 \\ 3 & -2 & 1 \end{bmatrix}$;

$\begin{bmatrix} -\dfrac{5}{3} & 1 & -\dfrac{4}{3} \\ -\dfrac{4}{3} & 1 & -\dfrac{2}{3} \\ \dfrac{7}{3} & -1 & \dfrac{5}{3} \end{bmatrix}$

Page 278

1. $D = \{3, 2, -1, -2, 0\}$; $R = \{1, -3, 5, -2, 2\}$; yes
2. $D = \{8, 7, -7, -8, 5\}$; $R = \{7, 8, -2\}$; yes
3. $D = \{0, 8, -3, 4, 5\}$; $R = \{0, 7, 6, -1\}$; yes
4. $D = \{3, 4, 5, -3, -4\}$; $R = \{-3, -4, -5, 3, 4\}$; yes
5. $D = \{3, 4, -4, -3, 2\}$; $R = \{2, -2, -3\}$; yes
6. $D = \{0, 3, 1, 2\}$; $R = \{1, 4, -3\}$; No
7. $D = \{1, -1, 2, -2, 3\}$; $R = \{-2, 0, -4, 3\}$; yes
8. $D = \{9, 7, 8, -9, -8\}$; $R = \{7, 8, 9\}$; yes
9. $D = \{4, -1, -3\}$; $R = \{-1, 4, 3, -3, 0\}$; No
10. $D = \{6, -3, -6\}$; $R = \{-3, 3, 5, 6\}$; No
11. $D = \{-3, -1, 2, 3\}$; $R = \{2, -2, -1, 1\}$;
    12. $D = \{-2, 0, 2, 4\}$; $R = \{2, -2, 0, 1\}$;
13. $D = \{-3, -2, -1, 0, 1, 2, 3\}$; $R = \{-3, -2, -1, 0\}$
    14. $D = \{x \mid x \text{ is a real number}\}$; $R = \{y \mid 1 \leq y\}$;
yes **15.** $D = \{x \mid x \leq 3\}$; $R = \{y \mid y \text{ is real}\}$; no
16. $D = \{x \mid -3 \leq x \leq 3\}$; $R = \{y \mid -3 \leq y \leq 3\}$; No
17. $D = \{x \mid -3 \leq x < 2\}$; $R = \{y \mid -2 \leq y < 2\}$; yes
18. $D = \{x \mid x \text{ is real}\}$; $R = \{y \mid y \text{ is real}\}$; yes
19. $D = \{x \mid 0 \leq x \leq 4\}$; $R = \{y \mid -2 \leq y \leq 2\}$; No
20. $D = \{x \mid -4 \leq x < 4\}$; $R = \{y \mid y \text{ is an integer and } -2 \leq y \leq 2\}$; yes **21.** $D = \{x \mid 0 \leq x\}$; $R = \{y \mid y \text{ is real}\}$; No **22.** $D = \{x \mid x \text{ is any real number except } -2\}$; $R = \{y \mid y \text{ is real and not equal to } f(-2) \text{ and not equal to } 0\}$; yes **23.** $D = \{\text{all even integers}\}$; $R = \{\text{all integers}\}$; yes **24.** $D = \{\text{all natural numbers} > 1\}$; $R = \{\text{squares of all natural numbers} > 1\}$ **25.** $\{\text{squares of all natural numbers} > 1\}$; $R = \{\text{all natural numbers} > 1\}$; yes **26.** $D = \{\text{all integers}\}$; $R = \{y \mid y = 2x + 3\}$; yes

Page 284

25. darkened circle at $(0, 0)$ and all points to the left; open circle at $(0, -1)$ and all points to the right
26. darkened circle at $(0, 0)$; a line from $(0, 0)$ to the right with slope -1; a line from $(0, 0)$ to the left with slope 1 **27.** all points right of and including $x = 2$, 2 units above x axis; all points including origin and between origin and $x = 2$, 1 unit above x axis; all points left of origin, 1 unit below x axis. **28.** include pts: $(3, 3)$, $(2, 2)$, $(1, 1)$, $(0, 0)$, $(-1, -1)$, $(-2, -2)$, $(-3, -3)$; move horizontally 1 unit to the right of all these

points except $(3, 3)$ **29.** include pts: $(-3, 3)$, $(-2, 2)$, $(-1, 1)$, $(0, 0)$, $(1, -1)$, $(2, -2)$, $(3, -3)$; move horizontally one unit to right of all these points except $(3, -3)$ **30.** include pts: $(4, 6)$, $(3, 5)$, $(2, 4)$, $(1, 3)$, $(0, 2)$, $(-1, 1)$, $(-2, 0)$, $(-3, -1)$, $(-4, -2)$; move horizontally 1 unit to the right of all these points except $(4, 6)$ **31.** include points: $(-4, -6)$, $(-3, -5)$, $(-2, -4)$, $(-1, -3)$, $(0, -2)$, $(1, -1)$, $(2, 0)$, $(3, 1)$, $(4, 2)$; move horizontally one unit to the right of all these points except $(4, 2)$ **33.** discontinuous x-axis, open only where irrationals would appear; discontinuous horizontal line at $y < 1$, open only where rationals would appear.

Page 287

28. The segment $\overline{PQ}$ has slope $\dfrac{y - x}{x - y} = -1$ and is thus $\perp$ to the line $y = x$, which has slope 1. The midpoint of $\overline{PQ}$ is $\left(\dfrac{x + y}{2}, \dfrac{x + y}{2} \right)$; this lies on the line $y = x$, so $y = x$ is the $\perp$ bisector of $\overline{PQ}$.

Challenge

Let $(x, f(x))$, $(x + 1, f(x + 1))$, and $(x + 2, f(x + 2))$ be points on the graph of the linear function; slopes of segments joining any two of these points are the same; $\dfrac{f(x + 2) - f(x + 1)}{(x + 2) - (x + 1)} = \dfrac{f(x + 1) - f(x)}{x + 1 - x}$; $f(x + 2) - f(x + 1) = f(x + 1) - f(x)$

Page 300

4. Only altered steps are given.

```
10 PRINT "PROGRAM FINDS RADIUS
   OF CURVE"
60 PRINT "ENTER FORCE ON CAR"
70 INPUT F
80 LET R = (M * (V↑2)) / F
90 PRINT "THE RADIUS REQUIRED
   IS"; R
100 PRINT "METERS"
```

Page 309

32. The vertex lies on the axis of symmetry, so its x-coordinate is $-\dfrac{b}{2a}$; substitute $-\dfrac{b}{2a}$ for x to find y:
$y = a\left(-\dfrac{b}{2a} \right)^2 + b\left(-\dfrac{b}{2a} \right) + c$; $y = \dfrac{ab^2}{4a^2} - \dfrac{b^2}{2a} + c$;
$y = -\dfrac{b^2}{4a} + c$; $y = \dfrac{4ac - b^2}{4a}$

Page 313

The graphs in Ex. 29–36 are circles centered at the origin. The radius is given. **29.** 5 **30.** 4 **31.** 9 **32.** 10 **33.** 6 **34.** $\sqrt{3} \doteq 1.73$ **35.** $2\sqrt{3} \doteq 3.46$ **36.** $\sqrt{6} \doteq 2.45$

Page 320

The graphs in Ex. 1–15 are hyperbolas with asymptotes given on TE page 320. Some points through which each graph passes are given here. **1.** $(4, 0)$, $(-4, 0)$ **2.** $(5, 0)$, $(-5, 0)$ **3.** $(2, 0)$, $(-2, 0)$ **4.** $(6, 0)$, $(-6, 0)$ **5.** $(3, 0)$, $(-3, 0)$ **6.** $(7, 0)$, $(-7, 0)$

7. $(7, 0)$, $(-7, 0)$ **8.** $(10, 0)$, $(-10, 0)$ **9.** $(2, 0)$, $(-2, 0)$ **10.** $(9, 0)$, $(-9, 0)$ **11.** $(10, 0)$, $(-10, 0)$ **12.** $(11, 0)$, $(-11, 0)$ **13.** $(4, 1)$, $(1, 4)$, $(-4, -1)$, $(-1, -4)$ **14.** $(1, 1)$, $\left(\frac{1}{2}, 2\right)$, $(-1, -1)$, $\left(-\frac{1}{2}, -2\right)$ **15.** $(7, 1)$, $(1, 7)$, $(-7, -1)$, $(-1, -7)$ **16.** $(4, 1)$, $(2, 2)$, $(-4, -1)$, $(-2, -2)$ The graphs in Ex. 17–32 and 37–40 are hyperbolas. For each graph the equations of the asymptotes and some points through which the graph passes are given. **17.** $y = \pm \frac{4}{3} x$; $(0, 4)$, $(0, -4)$ **18.** $y = \pm \frac{5}{4} x$; $(0, 5)$, $(0, -5)$ **19.** $y = \pm \frac{9}{5} x$; $(0, 9)$, $(0, -9)$ **20.** $y = \pm 3x$; $(0, 6)$, $(0, -6)$ **21.** $x = 0$, $y = 0$; $(-1, 6)$, $(-6, 1)$, $(6, -1)$, $(1, -6)$ **22.** $x = 0$, $y = 0$; $(-1, 9)$, $(-9, 1)$, $(1, -9)$, $(9, -1)$ **23.** $x = 0$, $y = 0$; $(-1, 12)$, $(-12, 1)$, $(1, -12)$, $(12, -1)$ **24.** $x = 0$, $y = 0$; $(-1, 4)$, $(-4, 1)$, $(1, -4)$, $(4, -1)$ **25.** $y = \pm 2x$; $(3, 0)$, $(-3, 0)$ **26.** $y = \pm \frac{2}{3} x$; $(3, 0)$, $(-3, 0)$ **27.** $y = \pm \frac{4}{3} x$; $(3, 0)$, $(-3, 0)$ **28.** $y = \pm 2x$; $(2, 0)$, $(-2, 0)$ **29.** $y = \pm 2x$; $(0, 4)$, $(0, -4)$ **30.** $y = \pm \frac{3\sqrt{5}}{5} x$; $(0, 3)$, $(0, -3)$ **31.** $y = \pm \frac{1}{2} x$; $(0, 2)$, $(0, -2)$ **32.** $y = \pm \frac{\sqrt{5}}{2} x$; $(0, 5)$, $(0, -5)$ **37.** $y = \pm \frac{2}{3} x$; $(-6, 5)$, $(0, 5)$ **38.** $y = \pm \frac{3}{5} x$; $(9, -1)$, $(-1, -1)$ **39.** $y = \pm \frac{5}{8} x$; $(9, 7)$, $(-7, 7)$ **40.** $y = \pm \frac{4}{5} x$; $(2, -2)$, $(-18, -2)$

Page 326

1. move $y = x^2$, 1 unit to the left   **2.** move $y = x^2$ 3 units to the right   **3.** move $y = x^2$ 1 unit to the right   **4.** move $y = x^2$ 3 units to the left   **5.** move $y = x^2$ 1 unit up   **6.** move $y = x^2$ 2 units down.   **7.** move $y = x^2$ 4 units down.   **8.** move $y = x^2$ 3 units up.   **9.** move $y = x^2$ 2 units to the right, 1 unit up.   **10.** move $y = x^2$ 2 units to the left, 1 unit down.   **11.** move $y = x^2$ 1 unit right, 2 units down   **12.** move $y = x^2$ 1 unit right, 2 up.   **13.** move $y = |x|$ 3 units left   **14.** move $y = |x|$ 3 units right   **15.** move $y = |x|$ 1 unit up   **16.** move $y = |x|$ 1 unit down.   **17.** move $y = |x|$ 1 unit right, 2 units up.   **18.** move $y = |x|$ 2 units left, 3 units down.   **19.** move $y = |x|$, 3 units right, 1 unit down   **20.** move $y = |x|$ 3 units left, 2 units up.   **21.** $y = x^2 - 2x + 1$; $y = (x - 1)^2$; move $y = x^2$ 1 unit right.   **22.** $y = (x + 2)^2$; move $y = x^2$ 2 units left   **23.** $y = (x - 2)^2$; move $y = x^2$ 2 units right   **24.** $y = (x + 3)^2$; move $y = x^2$ 3 units left   **25.** $y = (x + 5)^2 - 25 + 5$; $y = (x + 5)^2 - 20$; move $y = x^2$ 5 units left, 20 down.   **26.** $y = (x - 3)^2 - 9 + 4$; $y = (x - 3)^2 - 5$; move $y = x^2$ 3 units right, 5 units down.   **27.** move $y = x^2$ 3 units left, 4 down   **28.** $y = (x - 4)^2 - 16 - 4$; $y = (x - 4)^2 - 20$; move $y = x^2$ right 4 units, down 20 units   **29.** move circle $x^2 + y^2 = 16$ 1 unit right, 2 units down.   **30.** move $x^2 + y^2 = 4$ 1 unit left, 3 units down.   **31.** move $x^2 + y^2 = 25$ 2 units left, 1 unit down.   **32.** move $\frac{x^2}{16} + \frac{y^2}{4} = 1$ 2 units left, 1 unit up.

33. move $\frac{x^2}{25} - \frac{y^2}{4} = 1$ 1 unit left, 2 units down.   **34.** move $x^2 + y^2 = 4$ 3 units right, 2 down.   **35.** move $\frac{x^2}{25} - \frac{y^2}{9} = 1$ 4 units right, 3 units up   **36.** move $\frac{x^2}{9} - \frac{y^2}{25} = 1$ 3 units right, 2 units down   **37.** move $\frac{x^2}{100} + \frac{y^2}{81} = 1$ 3 units right, 4 units up   **38.** $(x + 4)^2 + (y + 2)^2 = 39$; move $x^2 + y^2 = 39$ 4 units left, 2 units down.   **39.** move $\frac{x^2}{16} + \frac{y^2}{32} = 1$ 1 unit left, 2 units down.   **40.** move $\frac{x^2}{16} + \frac{y^2}{24} = 1$ 2 units left, 1 unit up.   **41.** move $\frac{x^2}{4} + \frac{y^2}{9} = 1$ 3 units right, 2 units down.   **42.** move $\frac{x^2}{14} - \frac{y^2}{21} = 1$ 2 units left, 1 unit up.   **43.** move $\frac{x^2}{4} + \frac{y^2}{36} = 1$ 3 units right, 2 units up.   **44.** move $\frac{y^2}{9} - \frac{x^2}{4} = 1$ 2 units right, 1 unit down.

Page 330

Ex. 9–16. The graphs are parabolas with vertex at the origin. Two other points are given.   **9.** $(2, -1)$, $(-2, -1)$ **10.** $(-3, 3)$, $(-3, -3)$ **11.** $(4, 4)$, $(-4, 4)$ **12.** $(10, 10)$, $(-10, 10)$ **13.** $(20, 20)$, $(20, -20)$ **14.** $(6, 6)$, $(-6, 6)$ **15.** $(3, -3)$, $(-3, -3)$ **16.** $(-2, 2)$, $(-2, -2)$ **31.** The chord through any point $(0, x)$ on the major axis has length

$$2y = 2 \frac{b\sqrt{a^2 - x^2}}{a}. \text{ When } x = c, y = 2 \frac{b\sqrt{a^2 - c^2}}{a}$$

$$= 2\frac{b\sqrt{b^2}}{a} = \frac{2b^2}{a}$$ **32.** $\sqrt{(x + c)^2 + y^2}$

$- \sqrt{(x - c)^2 + y^2} = 2a$; $x^2 + 2xc + c^2 + y^2 = 4a^2$

$+ 4a\sqrt{(x - c)^2 + y^2} + x^2 - 2xc + c^2 + y^2$;

$4xc - 4a^2 = 4a\sqrt{(x - c)^2 + y^2}$; $x^2 c^2 - 2xca^2 + a^4 = a^2(x^2 - 2cx + c^2 + y^2)$; $x^2 c^2 - a^2 x^2 - a^2 y^2 = a^2 c^2 - a^4$; $x^2(c^2 - a^2) - a^2 y^2 = a^2(c^2 - a^2)$;

$\frac{x^2}{a^2} - \frac{y^2}{c^2 - a^2} = 1$; let $b^2 = c^2 - a^2$; $\frac{x^2}{a^2} - \frac{y^2}{b^2} = 1$

Page 331

```
4.   10  PRINT "PROGRAM FINDS
         EQUATION OF AXIS OF SYMMETRY"
     20  PRINT "ENTER THE COEFFICIENTS
         A, B, C"
     30  INPUT A, B, C
     40  PRINT "EQUATION OF AXIS OF
         SYMMETRY"
     50  PRINT "X="; -1 * B; "/"; 2 * A
     60  PRINT "COORDINATES OF TURNING
         POINT" TO LET X = (-1 * B)/
         (2 * A)
     80  LET Y = A * (X↑2) = B * X + C
     90  PRINT X; ","; Y
    100  END
```

9. (m, n); $(-m, -n)$; $(-m, n)$ **10.** $(-r, s)$; (r, s)
(r, s) **13.** $(0, 12)$, $(3, 3)$, $(6, 12)$; $x = 3$; $(3, 3)$
14. $(0, 3)$, $(2, 11)$, $(4, 3)$; $x = 2$, $(2, 11)$ **15.** $(0, 0)$,
$(3, -3)$, $(-3, -3)$; $x = 0$; $(0, 0)$ **16.** $(0, 9)$
$\left(-\frac{3}{2}, \frac{9}{2}\right)$, $(-3, 9)$; $x = -\frac{3}{2}$, $\left(-\frac{3}{2}, \frac{9}{2}\right)$ **17.** $(0, -3)$,
$(-2, -7)$, $(-4, -3)$; $x = -2$; $(-2, -7)$; -4.6, 0.6
18. $(0, 1)$, $\left(\frac{7}{4}, \frac{57}{8}\right)$, $\left(\frac{7}{2}, 1\right)$; $x = \frac{7}{4}$; $\left(\frac{7}{4}, \frac{57}{8}\right)$; -0.1,
3.6 **27.** circle, center at $(0, 0)$, radius 7   **28.** circle,
center at $(0, 0)$ radius $3\sqrt{3}$ **30.** $a = \pm 6$, $b = \pm 2$;
$(6, 0)$, $(-6, 0)$, $(0, 2)$, $(0, -2)$ **31.** $a = \pm 4$, $b = \pm 7$;
$(4, 0)$, $(-4, 0)$, $(0, 7)$, $(0, -7)$ **32.** $a = \pm 2$,
$b = \pm 6$; $(2, 0)$, $(-2, 0)$, $(0, 6)$, $(0, -6)$
33. $a = \pm\sqrt{6}$, $b = \pm\sqrt{10}$; $(\sqrt{6}, 0)$, $(-\sqrt{6}, 0)$,
$(0, \sqrt{10})$, $(0, -\sqrt{10})$ **34.** asymptotes; $y = \pm\frac{2}{3}x$,
passes through $(3, 0)$ and $(-3, 0)$ **35.** asymptotes:
$x = 0$ and $y = 0$, passes through $(-1, 6)$, $(-6, 1)$ and
$(1, -6)$, $(6, -1)$ **40.** move $y = |x|$ down 4 units
41. move $y = x^2$ 2 units right, 3 units down.
42. move $y = |x|$ 3 units left, 2 units down   **43.** move
$y = x^2$ 4 units up.   **44.** $y = (x + 3)^2 - 9 + 4$;
$y = (x + 3)^2 - 5$; move $y = x^2$ 3 units left, 5 units
down.   **45.** move circle $x^2 + y^2 = 16$ 1 unit right,
2 units down.   **46.** move ellipse $\frac{x^2}{16} + \frac{y^2}{4} = 1$ 3 units

right, 5 units down   **47.** move ellipse $\frac{x^2}{9} + \frac{y^2}{16} = 1$
5 units right, 1 unit up.   **48.** $y^2 = -16x$; $(0, 0)$,
$(-1, 4)$, $(-1, -4)$

6. $(0, 3)$, $(-4, -13)$, $(-8, 3)$ **7.** $(0, 0)$, $(3, -6)$,
$(-3, -6)$ **8.** $(0, 2)$, $(-3, -7)$, $(-6, 2)$; $(-3, -7)$,
$x = -3$; -5.6, -0.4 **9.** $(0, 3)$, $\left(\frac{3}{2}, \frac{15}{2}\right)$, $(3, 3)$;
$\left(\frac{3}{2}, \frac{15}{2}\right)$, $x = \frac{3}{2}$; -0.4, 3.4
16. $a = \pm 4$, $b = \pm 2$; $(4, 0)$, $(-4, 0)$, $(0, 2)$, $(0, -2)$
17. $a = \pm 2$, $b = \pm 6$; $(2, 0)$, $(-2, 0)$, $(0, 6)$, $(0, -6)$
18. $a = \pm 2$, $b = \pm 3$; $(2, 0)$, $(-2, 0)$, $(0, 3)$, $(0, -3)$
19. asymptotes: $y = \pm\frac{1}{2}x$; $(4, 0)$, $(-4, 0)$
20. asymptotes: $x = 0$ and $y = 0$, passing through
$(1, -2)$, $(2, -1)$ and $(-1, 2)$, $(-2, 1)$ **25.** move
$y = |x|$ 3 units up   **26.** move $y = |x|$ 1 unit right,
2 units up   **27.** move $y = x^2$ 3 units left, 2 units down
28. $y = (x + 2)^2 - 5$; move $y = x^2$ 2 units left, 5 units
down.   **29.** move circle $x^2 + y^2 = 16$ 3 units right,
1 unit down   **30.** move ellipse $\frac{x^2}{16} + \frac{y^2}{4} = 1$ 5 units left,
2 units up.

30. $(0, -4)$, $(2, -1)$, $(-2, -7)$ **31.** $(0, 6)$, $(4, 9)$,

$(-4, 3)$ **35.** Midpt of $\overline{AB}$: $\left(\frac{2 + 5}{2}, \frac{-3 + 6}{2}\right)$;
$M\left(\frac{7}{2}, \frac{3}{2}\right)$; Midpt of $\overline{BC}$: $\left(\frac{5 + 3}{2}, \frac{6 + 2}{2}\right)$; $N(4, 4)$;
Midpt of $\overline{CD}$: $\left(\frac{3 - 2}{2}, \frac{2 - 1}{2}\right)$; $R\left(\frac{1}{2}, \frac{1}{2}\right)$; Midpt of
$\overline{AD}$: $\left(\frac{2 - 2}{2}, \frac{-3 - 1}{2}\right)$; $S(0, -2)$; m of $\overline{MN}$:

$\dfrac{4 - \frac{3}{2}}{4 - \frac{7}{2}} = \dfrac{\frac{5}{2}}{\frac{1}{2}} = 5$; m of $\overline{NR}$: $\dfrac{4 - \frac{1}{2}}{4 - \frac{1}{2}} = 1$; m of $\overline{RS}$:

$\dfrac{-2 - \frac{1}{2}}{0 - \frac{1}{2}} = \dfrac{-\frac{5}{2}}{-\frac{1}{2}} = 5$; m of $\overline{MS}$: $\dfrac{-2 - \frac{3}{2}}{0 - \frac{7}{2}}$; $\dfrac{-\frac{7}{2}}{-\frac{7}{2}} = 1$;

$ABCD$ is a parallelogram since the opposite sides have the
same slopes.   **44.** $y = 2\left(x + \frac{3}{2}\right)^2 - \frac{11}{2}$; move
$y = 2x^2$ $\frac{3}{2}$ units left, $\frac{11}{2}$ down   **46.** move $y = |x|$ down
3 units   **47.** move $y = x^2$ 2 units left, 3 units down
48. move ellipse $\frac{x^2}{9} + \frac{y^2}{4} = 1$ 1 unit right and 2 units
down.   **49.** move circle $x^2 + y^2 = 9$ 2 units left, 2 units
up.

17. $\left(\dfrac{13 \pm 2\sqrt{46}}{3}, \dfrac{-5 \mp \sqrt{46}}{3}\right)$
24. $\left(\dfrac{16 + 12\sqrt{6}}{19}, \dfrac{-3 + 12\sqrt{6}}{19}\right)$,
$\left(\dfrac{16 - 12\sqrt{6}}{19}, \dfrac{-3 - 12\sqrt{6}}{19}\right)$
26. $\left(\dfrac{-2 + \sqrt{46}}{2}, \dfrac{8 - \sqrt{46}}{2}\right)$,
$\left(\dfrac{-2 - \sqrt{46}}{2}, \dfrac{8 + \sqrt{46}}{2}\right)$

2. above, including the line containing $(0, -2)$, $(2, 1)$
4. below the line containing $(0, -5)$, $(3, 0)$ **6.** below the
line containing $(0, -5)$, $(7, -3)$ **8.** above, including the
line containing $(0, -6)$, $(2, -11)$ **10.** below the line
containing $(0, -2)$, $(4, -7)$ **12.** below the line
containing $(0, -7)$, $(1, -5)$ **14.** above, including the line
containing $(0, 4)$, $(6, 4)$ **16.** left of the line containing
$(5, 1)$, $(5, 5)$

(For Ex. 18–36, the coordinates of two points of each line
are given. The points of a given line may or may not be
part of the graph.)   **18.** below, including the line
containing $(0, -1)$, $(1, 2)$ *and* above the line containing
$(0, 4)$, $(1, 2)$ **20.** above, including the line containing
$(0, 6)$, $(2, 1)$ *and* below, including the line containing
$(0, 2)$, $(4, -1)$ **22.** below the line containing $(0, 5)$,
$(6, 0)$ *and* above, including the line containing $(0, 3)$,
$(3, -1)$ **24.** above, including the line containing
$(0, -3)$, $(3, -5)$ *and* above, including the line containing

(0, 2), (3, −2)   **26.** below the line containing (0, −8), (2, −7) *and* below, including the line containing (0, 2), (2, 1)   **28.** below, including the line containing (0, −6), (−1, −3) *and* above the line containing (0, 1), (1, 3)   **30.** below, including the line containing (0, 2), (4, 2) *and* left, including the line containing (4, 0), (4, 5)   **32.** above, including the line containing (0, 5), (5, 5) *and* right, including the line containing (−3, 0), (−3, 6)   **34.** below, including the line containing (0, −8), (1, −6) *and* below the line containing (0, 2), (3, 1) *and* above, including the line containing (0, 2), (2, 1)   **36.** above, including the line containing (0, −1), (1, 1) *and* above, including the line containing (0, 1), (1, 5) *and* above, including the line containing (0, 3), (1, 5)

Page 351

2. outside, including the circle containing (2, 0), (0, 2)
4. outside the circle containing (4, 0), (0, 4)   **6.** outside the two branches of the hyperbola containing (8, 1), (−8, −1), asymptotes: $x = 0, y = 0$ **8.** outside, including the two branches of the hyperbola containing (−1, 2), (1, −2), asymptotes: $x = 0, y = 0$ **10.** outside, including the ellipse containing (6, 0), (0, 4)   **12.** outside the ellipse containing (4, 0), (0, 1)   **14.** inside, including the two branches of the hyperbola containing (5, 0), (−5, 0), asymptotes: $y = \dfrac{\pm 2\sqrt{2}}{5}x$ **16.** inside the two branches of the hyperbola containing (5, 0), (−5, 0), asymptotes: $y = \pm \dfrac{9}{5}x$ **18.** inside, including the ellipse containing (3, 0), (0, 1.7)   **20.** inside, including the two branches of the hyperbola containing (2, 0), (−2, 0), asymptotes: $y = \pm \sqrt{2}x$ **22.** inside the two branches of the hyperbola containing (2, 0), (−2, 0), asymptotes: $y = \pm \dfrac{5}{2}x$ **24.** inside the ellipse containing (2, 0), (0, 5)
(For Ex. 26–40, the coordinates of two points of each line or curve are given. The points of a given line or curve may or may not be part of the graph.)   **26.** outside the circle containing (5, 0), (0, 5) *and* above the line containing (0, 3), (4, 6)   **28.** outside the two branches of the hyperbola containing (1, −5), (−1, 5), asymptotes: $x = 0$, $y = 0$ *and* above, including the line containing (0, −2), (3, −4)   **30.** outside, including the two branches of the hyperbola containing (2.8, 0), (−2.8, 0), asymptotes: $y = \pm \dfrac{\sqrt{2}}{2}x$ *and* below the line containing (0, −2), (1, 1)
32. inside, including the two branches of the hyperbola containing (5.1, 0), (−5.1, 0), asymptotes: $y = \pm \dfrac{4}{3}x$ *and* below, including the line containing (−1, 1), (−5, 2)
34. outside the two branches of the hyperbola containing (3.4, 0), (−3.4, 0), asymptotes: $y = \pm x$ *and* inside, including the circle containing (6, 0), (0, 6)
36. outside the two branches of the hyperbola containing (5.1, 0), (−5.1, 0), asymptotes: $y = \pm \dfrac{1}{3}x$ *and* inside, including the ellipse containing (2, 0), (0, 5)

38. outside, including the two branches of the hyperbola containing (0, 3), (0, −3), asymptotes: $y = \pm \dfrac{\sqrt{3}}{2}x$ *and* outside, including the ellipse containing (5, 0), (0, 2.2)
40. inside, including the ellipse containing (2.4, 0), (0, 1.7), *and* inside, including the two branches of the hyperbola containing (2.2, 0), (−2.2, 0), asymptotes: $y = \pm \dfrac{\sqrt{15}}{5}x$

Page 352

14. below the line containing (0, 5), (1, 2)   **16.** above the line containing (0, −3), (5, −3)   **18.** inside the two branches of the hyperbola containing (4, 1), (−4, −1), asymptotes: $x = 0, y = 0$ **20.** outside, including the ellipse containing (2.4, 0), (0, 1.7)   **22.** outside the ellipse containing (2, 0), (0, 3)   **24.** above the line containing (0, −2), (2, 3) *and* below, including the line containing (1, 1), (5, 5)   **26.** above the line containing $\left(0, \dfrac{7}{3}\right)$, $\left(2, \dfrac{1}{3}\right)$ *and* above, including the line containing (0, −5), (2, −10)   **28.** inside, including the circle containing (5, 0), (0, 5) *and* above the line containing (0, 3), (2, 4)   **30.** outside, including the ellipse containing (9, 0), (0, 2) *and* below, including the line containing (0, 4), (2, 7)   **32.** outside, including the ellipse containing (3.9, 0), (0, 3.4) *and* outside, including the two branches of the hyperbola containing (3, 0), (−3, 0), asymptotes: $y = \pm \dfrac{\sqrt{6}}{3}x$

Page 353

10. below, including the line containing (0, −3), (3, −1)
12. inside, including the two branches of the hyperbola containing (2.4, 0), (−2.4, 0), asymptotes: $y = \pm x$
14. inside, including the ellipse containing (6, 0), (0, 2)
16. above, including the line containing (0, 2), (4, 5) *and* below, including the line containing (0, 2), (1, 3)
18. inside, including the two branches of the hyperbola containing (2, 0), (−2, 0), asymptotes: $y = \pm x$ *and* above, including the line containing (0, −2), (3, 0)   **20.** outside, including the two branches of the hyperbola containing (4, 1), (−4, −1), asymptotes: $x = 0, y = 0$ *and* above, including the line containing (1, −1), (2, −2)   **22.** above, including the line containing (0, 4), (1, 1) *and* above, including the line containing (0, −3), (2, −2) *and* below the line containing (0, 3), (3, 5)

Page 360

48. A.P. with common difference d: $a, a + d, a + 2d, a + 3d, a + 4d, \ldots$; odd numbered terms: $a, a + 2d, a + 4d, \ldots$, which is an A.P. with common difference $2d$ **49.** First A.P.: $a, a + d, a + 2d, \ldots, a + (n − 3)d, a + (n − 2)d, a + (n − 1)d$; Second A.P.: $a + (n − 1)d, a + (n − 2)d, a + (n − 3)d, \ldots, a + 2d, a + d, a$, which is an A.P. with common difference $−1d$.

Page 363

32. $\underline{x}, \underline{\quad}, \underline{y}$ is an A.P.; $l = a + (n - 1)d$;

$y = x + 2d$; $d = \dfrac{y - x}{2}$; $x + \dfrac{y - x}{2} = \dfrac{x + y}{2}$

33. $2x - 1$ and $2x + 1$ are consecutive odd integers if

x is an integer; $\dfrac{(2x - 1) + (2x + 1)}{2} = \dfrac{4x}{2} = 2x$;

$2x$ is an even integer if x is an integer.

Page 367

33. $\displaystyle\sum_{k=1}^{50} 10kx = 10x + 20x + 30x + \cdots + 500x$

$= 10x(1 + 2 + 3 + \cdots + 50) = 10x \cdot \displaystyle\sum_{k=1}^{50} k$

34. $\displaystyle\sum_{j=1}^{20} (jx + jy) = (x + 2x + 3x + \cdots + 20x) + \cdots$

$+ (y + 2y + 3y + \cdots + 20y) = \displaystyle\sum_{j=1}^{20} jx + \displaystyle\sum_{j=1}^{20} jy$

35. $\displaystyle\sum_{c=1}^{30} (c + t) = (1 + t) + (2 + t) + (3 + t) + \cdots$

$+ (30 + t) = 30t + (1 + 2 + 3 + \cdots + 30)$

$= 30t + \displaystyle\sum_{c=1}^{30} c$ **36.** $(4x - 3) + (5x - 3)$

$+ (6x - 3) + (7x - 3) = 32$; $22x = 44$; 2

37. $\displaystyle\sum_{n=1}^{k} (2n - 1) = 1 + 3 + 5 + 7 + \cdots + (2k - 1)$

$= \dfrac{k}{2}[1 + (2k - 1)] = \dfrac{k}{2} \cdot 2k = k^2$;

The sum of the first k positive odd integers is k^2.

38. $\displaystyle\sum_{n=1}^{k} 2n = 2 + 4 + 6 + 8 + \cdots + 2k$

$= \dfrac{k}{2}(2 + 2k) = \dfrac{k}{2} \cdot 2(k + 1) = k(k + 1)$;

The sum of the first k positive even integers is $k(k + 1)$.

Page 374

45. $\underline{x}, \underline{\quad}, \underline{y}$ is a G.P.; $l = a \cdot r^{n-1}$;

$y = x \cdot r^2$; $r^2 = \dfrac{y}{x}$; $r = \pm\dfrac{\sqrt{xy}}{x}$; $x \cdot \left(\pm\dfrac{\sqrt{xy}}{x}\right)$

$= \pm\sqrt{xy}$ **46.** $a + bi, \underline{\quad}, a - bi$ is a G.P.;

$l = a \cdot r^{n-1}$; $a - bi = (a + bi) \cdot r^2$;

$r^2 = \dfrac{a - bi}{a + bi}$; $r = \pm\sqrt{\dfrac{a - bi}{a + bi}}$;

Multiply $a + bi$ by r to get $\pm\sqrt{a^2 + b^2}$

Page 378

45. $\displaystyle\sum_{k=1}^{4} ax^{k-1} = ax^0 + ax^1 + ax^2 + ax^3$

$= a \cdot 1 + a(x^1 + x^2 + x^3) = a + a \cdot \displaystyle\sum_{k=1}^{3} x^k$

46. $(x^3 + 3) + (x^4 + 3) + (x^5 + 3) = 9$;

$x^3 + x^4 + x^5 = 0$; $x^3(1 + x + x^2) = 0$;

$x^3 = 0$ or $x^2 + x + 1 = 0$; $x = 0$ or

$x = \dfrac{-1 \pm \sqrt{1 - 4}}{2}$; 0, $\dfrac{-1 \pm i\sqrt{3}}{2}$

T–138

Page 384

1. $a^8 + 8a^7b + 28a^6b^2 + 56a^5b^3 + 70a^4b^4 + 56a^3b^5 + 28a^2b^6 + 8ab^7 + b^8$ **2.** $a^9 - 9a^8b + 36a^7b^2 - 84a^6b^3 + 126a^5b^4 - 126a^4b^5 + 84a^3b^6 - 36a^2b^7 + 9ab^8 - b^9$ **3.** $x^6 + 12x^5 + 60x^4 + 160x^3 + 240x^2 + 192x + 64$ **4.** $32c^5 - 240c^4 + 720c^3 - 1080c^2 + 810c - 243$ **5.** $x^{16} + 8x^{14}y + 28x^{12}y^2 + 56x^{10}y^3 + 70x^8y^4 + 56x^6y^5 + 28x^4y^6 + 8x^2y^7 + y^8$

6. $m^{10} - 10m^8n + 40m^6n^2 - 80m^4n^3 + 80m^2n^4 - 32n^5$ **7.** $16r^4 + 160r^3t + 600r^2t^2 + 1,000rt^3 + 625t^4$

8. $y^4 - 0.8y^3 + 0.24y^2 - 0.032y + 0.0016$

9. $64x^6 + 19.2x^5 + 2.4x^4 + 0.16x^3 + 0.006x^2 + 0.00012x + 0.000001$ **16.** $x^{12} - 8x^9y + 24x^6y^2 - 32x^3y^3 + 16y^4$ **17.** $32c^{15} + 240c^{12}d^2 + 720c^9d^4 + 1080c^6d^6 + 810c^3d^8 + 243d^{10}$ **18.** $x^6 + 6x^5\sqrt{2} + 30x^4 + 40x^3\sqrt{2} + 60x^2 + 24x\sqrt{2} + 8$

19. $16x^4 - 32x^3\sqrt{y} + 24x^2y - 8xy\sqrt{y} + y^2$

20. $16r^8 + 16r^6t + 6r^4t^2 + r^2t + \dfrac{1}{16}t^4$

21. $\dfrac{1}{x^5} + \dfrac{5}{x^4y} + \dfrac{10}{x^3y^2} + \dfrac{10}{x^2y^3} + \dfrac{5}{xy^4} + \dfrac{1}{y^5}$

22. $x^{12} + 12x^{11}y + 66x^{10}y^2 + 220x^9y^3$

23. $x^{11} - 22x^{10}y + 220x^9y^2 - 1,320x^8y^3$

24. $x^{20} + 30x^{18}y^3 + 405x^{16}y^6 + 3,240x^{14}y^9$

25. $1 + 0.07 + 0.0021 + 0.000035$ **26.** $1 + 0.16 + 0.0112 + 0.000448$ **27.** $1 + 0.18 + 0.0135 + 0.00054$

28. $\sqrt{x} + \dfrac{2\sqrt{x}}{x} - \dfrac{2\sqrt{x}}{x^2} + \dfrac{4x}{x^3}$

29. $\sqrt[3]{x^2} + \dfrac{6\sqrt[3]{x^2}}{x} - \dfrac{9\sqrt[3]{x^2}}{x^2} + \dfrac{36\sqrt[3]{x^2}}{x^3}$

30. $\dfrac{\sqrt[3]{x^2}}{x} + \dfrac{3\sqrt[3]{x^2}}{x^2} + \dfrac{18\sqrt[3]{x^2}}{x^3} + \dfrac{126\sqrt[3]{x^2}}{x^4}$

Page 385

3.
```
10 PRINT "DIVINE PROPORTION"
20 DIM S(21), D (20)
30 LET S(1) = 1
40 LET S(2) = 1
50 FOR T = 1 TO 19
60 LET S(T + 2) = S(T + 1) + S(T)
70 NEXT T
80 REM COMPUTE DIVINE PROPORTION
90 FOR I = 1 TO 20
100 LET D(I) = S(I + 1)/S(I)
110 PRINT D(I),
120 NEXT I
130 END
```

Page 386

29. $x^4 + 12x^3y + 54x^2y^2 + 108xy^3 + 81y^4$

30. $32x^{15} - 80x^{12}y + 80x^9y^2 - 40x^6y^3 + 10x^3y^4 - y^5$

31. $\dfrac{1}{m^4} + \dfrac{4}{m^3n} + \dfrac{6}{m^2n^2} + \dfrac{4}{mn^3} + \dfrac{1}{n^4}$

Page 396

32. $\log((a \cdot b) \cdot c) = \log(a \cdot b) + \log c = \log a + \log b + \log c$ **33.** $\log(x^2 - y^2) - \log(x + y)^2 = \log\dfrac{x^2 - y^2}{(x + y)^2} = \log\dfrac{(x - y)(x + y)}{(x + y)(x + y)} = \log\dfrac{(x - y)}{(x + y)}$

$= \log (x - y) - \log (x + y)$ **34.** $\log \dfrac{a \cdot b}{c} = \log (a \cdot b)$
$- \log c = \log a + \log b - \log c$ **35.** $\log \dfrac{a}{b \cdot c} = \log a$
$- \log (b \cdot c) = \log a - [\log b + \log c] = \log a -$
$\log b - \log c$

Page 399

29. $\log \left(\dfrac{a^2}{bc}\right)^r = \log \dfrac{(a^2)^r}{(bc)^r} = \log (a^2)^r - \log (bc)^r$
$= r \log a^2 - r \log bc = 2r \cdot \log a - r \cdot \log b - r \cdot$
$\log c$ **30.** $\log \sqrt[n]{\dfrac{ab}{c}} = \log \left(\dfrac{ab}{c}\right)^{\frac{1}{n}} = \dfrac{1}{n} \cdot \log \left(\dfrac{ab}{c}\right) =$
$\dfrac{1}{n} [\log ab - \log c] = \dfrac{1}{n} [\log a + \log b - \log c] =$
$\dfrac{\log a + \log b - \log c}{n}$

Page 403

1. $\log 6 + \log l + \log w$ **2.** $2 \log m + \log n$
3. $\log 3 + 3 \log t + 2 \log v$ **4.** $\log 8 + \log f - \log g$
5. $2 \log v - \log 2 - \log h$ **6.** $\log 5 + \log d - 2 \log t$
7. $3(\log m + \log n - \log p)$ **8.** $4(2 \log t + \log v)$
9. $3(2 \log a - \log b - 4 \log c)$
10. $\dfrac{1}{2} (\log 2 + \log g + \log h)$

11. $\dfrac{1}{3} (\log \pi + 2 \log d)$ **12.** $\dfrac{1}{4} (\log 5 + \log d -$
$3 \log g)$ **13.** $\log 2 + \log \pi + \log r + \log h$
14. $\log \pi + 2 \log r$ **15.** $\log b + \log h - \log 2$
16. $\log i - \log p - \log r$ **17.** $\log V + \log 3 - \log h$
18. $\log d + \log 2 - 2 \log t$ **19.** $\dfrac{1}{2} (\log 2 +$

$\log g + \log h)$ **20.** $\dfrac{1}{3} \log V$ **21.** $\dfrac{1}{2} (\log E - \log m)$
30. $\log P + 12 \log 1.09$ **31.** $\log 4 - \log 3 + \log \pi +$
$3 \log r$ **32.** $\dfrac{1}{2} (\log A - \log 4 - \log \pi)$ **33.** $\dfrac{1}{2} (\log V$
$+ \log 3 - \log \pi - \log h)$ **36.** $\log y^{\frac{2}{3}} - \log y^{\frac{3}{4}} +$
$\log y^{\frac{4}{3}} - \log y^{\frac{5}{4}} = \log \dfrac{y^{\frac{2}{3}} y^{\frac{4}{3}}}{y^{\frac{3}{4}} y^{\frac{5}{4}}} = \log \dfrac{y^2}{y^2} = \log 1 = 0$
37. $\log 3^{\frac{2}{5}} - \log 2^{\frac{1}{5}} - \log (2^2)^{\frac{2}{5}} + \log (3^3)^{\frac{1}{5}} =$
$\log 3^{\frac{2}{5}} - \log 2^{\frac{1}{5}} - \log 2^{\frac{4}{5}} + \log 3^{\frac{3}{5}} = \log 3^{\frac{5}{5}} - \log 2^{\frac{5}{5}}$
$= \log 3 - \log 2$

Page 407

22. Let $x = \log_a y$; Then $a^x = y$; $\log a^x = \log y$;
$x \log a = \log y$; $x = \dfrac{\log y}{\log a}$; $\log_a y = \dfrac{\log y}{\log a}$
23. Let $\log_a y = b$; then $a^b = y$; $\log_b a^b = \log_b y$;
$b \log_b a = \log_b y$; $b = \dfrac{\log_b y}{\log_b a}$; $\log_a y = \dfrac{\log_b y}{\log_b a}$
24. Let $\log_a y = x$; then $a^x = y$; $\log_y a^x = \log_y y$;
$x \log_y a = \log_y y$; $x \log_y a = 1$; $x = \dfrac{1}{\log_y a}$; $\log_a y = \dfrac{1}{\log_y a}$

1. $\left(-3, \dfrac{1}{27}\right), \left(-2, \dfrac{1}{9}\right), \left(-1, \dfrac{1}{3}\right), (0, 1), (1, 3), (2, 9),$
$(3, 27)$; $D = \{$all real numbers$\}$; $R = \{y \mid y > 0\}$; $(0, 1)$
belongs to function; increasing **2.** $(-3, 27), (-2, 9),$
$(-1, 3), (0, 1), \left(1, \dfrac{1}{3}\right), \left(2, \dfrac{1}{9}\right), \left(3, \dfrac{1}{27}\right)$; $D = \{$all real
numbers$\}$; $R = \{y \mid y > 0\}$; $(0, 1)$ belongs to function;
decreasing **3.** $\left(\dfrac{1}{27}, -3\right), \left(\dfrac{1}{9}, -2\right), \left(\dfrac{1}{3}, -1\right), (1, 0),$
$(3, 1), (9, 2), (27, 3)$; $D = \{x \mid x > 0\}$; $R = \{$all real
numbers$\}$; $(1, 0)$ belongs to function; increasing

4. $(27, -3), (9, -2), (3, -1), (1, 0), \left(\dfrac{1}{3}, 1\right), \left(\dfrac{1}{9}, 2\right),$
$\left(\dfrac{1}{27}, 3\right)$; $D = \{x \mid x > 0\}$; $R = \{$all real numbers$\}$;
$(1, 0)$ belongs to function; decreasing **5.** $\left(-3, \dfrac{1}{1000}\right),$
$\left(-2, \dfrac{1}{100}\right), \left(-1, \dfrac{1}{10}\right), (0, 1), (1, 10), (2, 100),$
$(3, 1000)$; $D = \{$all real numbers$\}$; $R = \{y \mid y > 0\}$;
$(0, 1)$ belongs to function; increasing **6.** $\left(\dfrac{1}{1000}, -3\right),$
$\left(\dfrac{1}{100}, -2\right), \left(\dfrac{1}{10}, -1\right), (1, 0), (10, 1), (100, 2),$
$(1000, 3)$; $D = \{x \mid x > 0\}$; $R = \{$all real numbers$\}$;
$(1, 0)$ belongs to function; increasing **7.** $y = \log_4 x$:
$\left(\dfrac{1}{64}, -3\right), \left(\dfrac{1}{16}, -2\right), \left(\dfrac{1}{4}, -1\right), (1, 0), (4, 1),$
$(16, 2), (64, 3)$; $y = 4^x$: $\left(-3, \dfrac{1}{64}\right), \left(-2, \dfrac{1}{16}\right),$
$\left(-1, \dfrac{1}{4}\right), (0, 1), (1, 4), (2, 16), (3, 64)$.
8. $y = \log_{\frac{1}{5}} x$: $(125, -3), (25, -2), (5, -1), (1, 0),$
$\left(\dfrac{1}{5}, 1\right), \left(\dfrac{1}{25}, 2\right), \left(\dfrac{1}{125}, 3\right)$; $y = \left(\dfrac{1}{5}\right)^x$: $(-3, 125),$
$(-2, 25), (-1, 5), (0, 1), \left(1, \dfrac{1}{5}\right), \left(2, \dfrac{1}{25}\right), \left(3, \dfrac{1}{125}\right)$
9. $\left(-3, \dfrac{3}{8}\right), \left(-2, \dfrac{3}{4}\right), \left(-1, \dfrac{3}{2}\right), (0, 3),$
$(1, 6), (2, 12), (3, 24)$; $D = \{$all real numbers$\}$;
$R = \{y \mid y > 0\}$; $(0, 3)$ belongs to function; increasing
10. $(-3, 54), (-2, 18), (-1, 6), (0, 2), \left(1, \dfrac{2}{3}\right), \left(2, \dfrac{2}{9}\right),$
$\left(3, \dfrac{2}{27}\right)$; $D = \{$all real numbers$\}$; $R = \{y \mid y > 0\}$;
$(0, 2)$ belongs to function; decreasing **11.** $(1, 0),$
$(2, 5.0), \left(\dfrac{1}{2}, -5\right), (4, 10)$; $D = \{x \mid x > 0\}$; $R = \{$all real
numbers$\}$; $(1, 0)$ belongs to function; increasing
12. $(1, 0), (9, 6), \left(\dfrac{1}{3}, -3\right), (3, 3)$; $D = \{x \mid x > 0\}$;
$R = \{$all real numbers$\}$; $(1, 0)$ belongs to function;
increasing **13.** $\left(-3, 2\dfrac{1}{27}\right), \left(-2, 2\dfrac{1}{9}\right), \left(-1, 2\dfrac{1}{3}\right),$
$(0, 3), (1, 5), (2, 11), (3, 29)$; $D = \{$all real numbers$\}$;
$R = \{y \mid y > 2\}$; $(0, 3)$ belongs to function; increasing
14. $(-3, 4), (-2, 0), (-1, -2), (0, -3), (1, -3.5),$
$(2, -3.75), (3, -3.87)$; $D = \{$all real numbers$\}$; decreasing
$R = \{y \mid y > -4\}$; $(0, -3)$ belongs to function **23.** If f is
described by $f(x) = \log_5 x$, or $y = \log_5 x$, then the inverse

of f is described by $x = \log_5 y$, or $y = 5^x$, or $g(x) = 5^x$.
24. If f is described by $y = \log_n x$, or $x = n^y$, then the inverse of f is described by $y = n^x$.   **25.** $\left(-3, \frac{1}{64}\right)$,
$\left(-2, \frac{1}{32}\right)$, $\left(-1, \frac{1}{16}\right)$, $\left(0, \frac{1}{8}\right)$, $\left(1, \frac{1}{4}\right)$, $\left(2, \frac{1}{2}\right)$, $(3, 1)$
26. $(2.13, -3)$, $(2.25, -2)$, $(2.5, -1)$, $(3, 0)$, $(4, 1)$, $(6, 2)$, $(10, 3)$

Page 419

5.
```
10  PRINT "PROGRAM COMPUTES
    TABLE OF LOGS FOR GIVEN
    RANGE"
20  PRINT "ENTER THE LOGS
    BETWEEN WHICH THE LOG YOU"
30  PRINT "WANT ARE FOUND,
    ENTER SMALLEST FIRST"
40  INPUT X, Y
50  PRINT "ENTER THE MANTISSA
    OF X AS .XXXX"
60  INPUT X1
70  PRINT "ENTER THE MANTISSA
    OF Y AS .XXXX"
80  INPUT Y1
90  LET V = X
100 IF V > Y THEN 160
110 LET V1 = ((V - X) *
    (Y1 - X1))/(Y - X)
120 LET V1 = X1 + V1
130 PRINT V1,
140 LET V = V + 1
150 GO TO 100
160 END
```
6.
```
10  PRINT "PROGRAM INTERPOLATES
    ANTILOGS"
20  PRINT "ENTER THE MANTISSAS
    BETWEEN"
30  PRINT "WHICH THE ANTILOG
    YOU WANT ARE FOUND"
40  PRINT "ENTER SMALLEST
    FIRST"
50  INPUT X1, Y1
60  PRINT "ENTER THE NUMBER WHOSE
    ANTILOG YOU WANT"
70  INPUT V1
80  PRINT "ENTER ANTILOG OF X1"
90  INPUT X
100 PRINT "ENTER ANTILOG OF Y1"
110 INPUT Y
120 LET V = ((V1 - X1) *
    (Y - X))/(Y1 - X1)
130 LET V = V + X
140 PRINT "ANTILOG OF "; V1;
    "IS "; V
150 END
```

Page 420

25. $\frac{1}{3}(\log 3 + 2 \log v - \log 4 - \log k)$
26. $\log V + \log 3 - \log \pi - 2 \log r$
27. $\log \left(\frac{xy^2}{z^3}\right)^3$ **33.** $(-2, 36)$, $(-1, 6)$, $(0, 1)$, $\left(1, \frac{1}{6}\right)$,

$\left(2, \frac{1}{36}\right)$ **34.** $\left(\frac{1}{36}, -2\right)$, $\left(\frac{1}{6}, -1\right)$, $(1, 0)$, $(6, 1)$, $(36, 2)$,

39. $\frac{2}{5} \log 2^2 - \frac{1}{5} \log 2 = \log 2^{\frac{4}{5}} - \log 2^{\frac{1}{5}} =$

$\log \dfrac{2^{\frac{4}{5}}}{2^{\frac{1}{5}}} = \log 2^{\frac{3}{5}} = \frac{1}{5} \log 2^3 = \frac{1}{5} \log 8$

40. Let $\log_n 69 = x$. Then $n^x = 69$; $\log n^x = \log 69$; $x \log n = \log 69$; $x = \dfrac{\log 69}{\log n}$; $\log_n 69 = \dfrac{\log 69}{\log n}$

41. $y = \log_4 x$; $x = 4^y$; The inverse of $x = 4^y$ is $y = 4^x$.

Page 421

19. $(-2, 16)$, $(-1, 4)$, $(0, 1)$, $\left(1, \frac{1}{4}\right)$, $\left(2, \frac{1}{16}\right)$
20. $\left(\frac{1}{25}, -2\right)$, $\left(\frac{1}{5}, -1\right)$, $(1, 0)$, $(5, 1)$, $(25, 2)$
24. $2 \log xy - \log xy^4 = \log (xy)^2 - \log xy^4 =$

$\log x^2 y^2 - \log xy^4 = \log \dfrac{x^2 y^2}{xy^4} = \log \dfrac{x}{y^2} = \log x -$

$\log y^2 = \log x - 2 \log y$ **25.** $\frac{3}{4} \log 9 - \frac{1}{2} \log 3 =$

$\log 9^{\frac{3}{4}} - \log 3^{\frac{1}{2}} = \log (3^2)^{\frac{3}{4}} - \log 3^{\frac{1}{2}} = \log 3^{\frac{3}{2}} -$

$\log 3^{\frac{1}{2}} = \log \dfrac{3^{\frac{3}{2}}}{3^{\frac{1}{2}}} = \log 3^1 = \log (3^3)^{\frac{1}{3}} = \frac{1}{3} \log 3^3 =$

$\frac{1}{3} \log 27$ **26.** Let $x = \log_8 59$; then $8^x = 59$; $x \log 8 =$

$\log 59$; $x = \dfrac{\log 59}{\log 8}$ **27.** $y = \log_6 x$; $x = 6^y$; the inverse of $x = 6^y$ is $y = 6^x$.

Page 437

21. a. Prove: $\binom{n}{r} = \binom{n}{n-r}$.

$\binom{n}{r} = \dfrac{n!}{r! (n-r)!} = \dfrac{n!}{(n-r)! \, r!}$; and

$\binom{n}{n-r} = \dfrac{n!}{(n-r)! [n-(n-r)]!} = \dfrac{n!}{(n-r)! \, r!}$.

So, $\binom{n}{r} = \binom{n}{n-r}$.

b. Prove: $\binom{n}{r} + \binom{n}{r+1} = \binom{n+1}{r+1}$.

$\binom{n}{r} + \binom{n}{r+1} = \dfrac{n!}{r! (n-r)!} + \dfrac{n!}{(r+1)! (n-r-1)!} =$

$\dfrac{(r+1) \, n!}{(r+1) r! (n-r)!} + \dfrac{n! (n-r)}{(r+1)! (n-r)(n-r-1)!} =$

$\dfrac{n! (r+1+n-r)}{(r+1)! (n-r)!} = \dfrac{(n+1)!}{(r+1)! (n-r)!}$; and

$\binom{n+1}{r+1} = \dfrac{(n+1)!}{(r+1)! (n+1-r-1)!}$

$= \dfrac{(n+1)!}{(r+1)! (n-r)!}$.

So, $\binom{n}{r} + \binom{n}{r+1} = \binom{n+1}{r+1}$.

3. READY

```
10 PRINT "PICK A CARD GAME"
20 DIM D(52)
30 REM STORE DECK OF CARDS
40 REM ACE = 1 BUT SCORES HIGHEST
50 LET J = 1
55 FOR K = 1 TO 4
60 FOR N = 1 TO 13
70 D(J) = N
80 NEXT N
90 NEXT K
100 FOR K = 1 TO 26
110 REM FIND RANDOM NUMBERS
    BETWEEN 1 AND 52
120 LET N = INT(100 * RND(0) + 1)
126 IF N <= 52 THEN 130
127 LET N = N - 52
130 IF D(N) = 0 THEN 120
140 LET Y = D(N)
150 LET D(N) = 0
160 PRINT "YOUR CARD IS"; Y
170 LET N = INT(100 * RND(0) + 1)
176 IF N <= 52 THEN 180
177 LET N = N - 52
180 IF D(N) = 0 THEN 170
190 LET C = D(N)
200 LET D(N) = 0
210 PRINT "COMPUTER CARD IS"; C
215 PRINT
220 REM WAS AN ACE DRAWN?
230 IF Y = 1 THEN 260
240 IF C = 1 THEN 290
250 IF C > Y THEN 290
260 REM YOU SCORE A POINT
270 LET Y1 = Y1 + 1
280 GO TO 310
290 REM COMPUTER SCORES A POINT
300 LET C1 = C1 + 1
310 NEXT K
320 IF C1 > Y1 THEN 350
330 PRINT "YOU ARE THE WINNER"
340 GO TO 360
350 PRINT "COMPUTER IS THE
    WINNER"
360 PRINT "YOUR SCORE IS"; Y1
370 PRINT "COMPUTER SCORE IS"; C1
380 END
```

Page 453

27. $(0, -2), (-3, 0), (3, -4)$
34. axis of symmetry: $x = -3$; turning point: $(-3, 11)$;
$(0, 2), (-6, 2), (-3, 11)$
36. the circle $(x^2 + y^2 = 36)$ and all its interior points with
the exception of the interior points of the ellipse
$\left(\dfrac{x^2}{9} + \dfrac{y^2}{4} = 1\right)$

Page 461

32. $c^2 = a^2 + b^2$; $c^2 = x^2 + x^2$; $c^2 = 2x^2$; $c = x\sqrt{2}$
33. Assume $\triangle ABC$ is an equilateral $\triangle$, with

$m \angle A = m \angle B = m \angle C = 60$.
$c^2 = a^2 + b^2$; $c^2 = x^2 + x^2$; $c^2 = 2x^2$; $c = x\sqrt{2}$
Draw altitude $\overline{AD}$; $\overline{AD}$ bisects $\angle A$; $m \angle BAD = 30$;

$$\overline{BD} \cong \overline{DC}; \quad \boxed{BD = \frac{1}{2} AB \text{ or } AB = 2BD}$$

$(AB)^2 = (BD)^2 + (AD)^2 = \left(\dfrac{AB}{2}\right)^2 + (AD)^2$;

$(AB)^2 = \dfrac{(AB)^2}{4} + (AD)^2$; $4(AB)^2 - (AB)^2 = 4(AD)^2$;

$3(AB)^2 = 4(AD)^2$; $(AD)^2 = \dfrac{3}{4}(AB)^2$; $AD = \dfrac{1}{2}\sqrt{3}(AB)$

Page 465

1. $\dfrac{\sqrt{3}}{2}$ **2.** $\dfrac{1}{2}$ **3.** $\dfrac{\sqrt{2}}{2}$ **4.** $\dfrac{\sqrt{2}}{2}$ **5.** $\dfrac{1}{2}$ **6.** $\dfrac{\sqrt{3}}{2}$

7. 0 **8.** 1 **9.** 0 **10.** 0 **11.** 0 **12.** -1 **13.** $\dfrac{\sqrt{2}}{2}$

14. $-\dfrac{\sqrt{3}}{2}$ **15.** $\dfrac{-\sqrt{3}}{2}$ **16.** $\dfrac{1}{2}$ **17.** -1 **18.** $\dfrac{-\sqrt{2}}{2}$

19. $\dfrac{-\sqrt{2}}{2}$ **20.** $\dfrac{\sqrt{3}}{2}$ **21.** $\dfrac{\sqrt{3}}{2}$ **22.** $-\dfrac{1}{2}$

23. $\dfrac{1}{2}$ **24.** $-\dfrac{1}{2}$ **25.** $-\cos 45°$ **26.** $-\sin 30°$
27. $-\cos 30°$ **28.** $-\sin 45°$ **29.** $\sin 45°$
30. $-\sin 60°$ **31.** $\sin 30°$ **32.** $-\sin 30°$ **33.** $-\sin 45°$
34. $\cos 60°$ **35.** $-\cos 30°$ **36.** $\cos 30°$

Page 469

25. $-\cot 70°$ **26.** $-\tan 50°$ **27.** $\cot 50°$ **28.** $\tan 30°$
29. $-\tan 20°$ **30.** $-\cot 85°$ **31.** $\tan 70°$
32. $-\cot 60°$ **33.** $-\tan 30°$ **34.** $-\cot 60°$
35. $\cot 70°$ **36.** $-\tan 80°$

Page 472

19. $-\sec 60°$ **20.** $\csc 30°$ **21.** $-\csc 60°$
22. $-\sec 30°$ **23.** $-\sec 60°$ **24.** $-\csc 45°$
25. $\csc 60°$ **26.** $-\csc 30°$ **27.** $-\sec 10°$
28. $\sec 20°$ **29.** $\csc 10°$ **30.** $-\csc 35°$

Page 474

Use the diagram on page 473 of the text.

44. $\tan u = \dfrac{b}{-a} = -\dfrac{b}{a}$; $\tan(-u) = \dfrac{b}{a}$; $\tan(-u) = -\tan u$

45. $\cot u = \dfrac{-a}{b} = -\dfrac{a}{b}$; $\cot(-u) = \dfrac{a}{b}$; $\cot(-u) = -\cot u$

46. $\sec u = \dfrac{r}{-a} = -\dfrac{r}{a}$; $\sec(-u) = \dfrac{r}{-a} = -\dfrac{r}{a}$;

$\sec(-u) = \sec u$ **47.** $\csc u = \dfrac{r}{b}$; $\csc(-u) = \dfrac{r}{-b} =$

$-\dfrac{r}{b}$; $\csc(-u) = -\csc u$

Page 476 Written Exercises

1. $x = -5$, $y = 12$, $r = 13$; $\sin u = \dfrac{12}{13}$, $\cos u = -\dfrac{5}{13}$,

$\cot u = -\dfrac{5}{12}$, $\sec u = -\dfrac{13}{5}$, $\csc u = \dfrac{13}{12}$ **2.** $x = -5$,

$y = 12$, $r = 13$; $\cos u = -\dfrac{5}{13}$, $\tan u = -\dfrac{12}{5}$, $\cot u =$

$-\dfrac{5}{12}$, $\sec u = -\dfrac{13}{5}$; $\csc u = \dfrac{13}{12}$ **3.** $x = -5$, $y = -12$,

$r = 13$; $\sin u = -\frac{12}{13}$, $\tan u = \frac{12}{5}$, $\cot u = \frac{5}{12}$, $\sec u = -\frac{13}{5}$, $\csc u = -\frac{13}{12}$ **4.** $x = 4$, $y = -3$, $r = 5$; $\cos u = \frac{4}{5}$, $\tan u = -\frac{3}{4}$, $\cot u = -\frac{4}{3}$, $\sec u = \frac{5}{4}$, $\csc u = -\frac{5}{3}$ **5.** $x = 3$, $y = -4$, $r = 5$; $\sin u = -\frac{4}{5}$, $\cos u = \frac{3}{5}$, $\tan u = -\frac{4}{3}$, $\sec u = \frac{5}{3}$, $\csc u = -\frac{5}{4}$

6. $x = -5$, $y = 12$, $r = 13$; $\sin u = \frac{12}{13}$, $\cos u = -\frac{5}{13}$, $\tan u = -\frac{12}{5}$, $\cot u = -\frac{5}{12}$, $\csc u = \frac{13}{12}$ **7.** $x = -12$, $y = 5$, $r = 13$; $\sin u = \frac{5}{13}$, $\tan u = -\frac{5}{12}$; $\cot u = -\frac{12}{5}$, $\sec u = -\frac{13}{12}$, $\csc u = \frac{13}{5}$ **8.** $x = 12$, $y = 5$, $r = 13$; $\sin u = \frac{5}{13}$, $\cos u = \frac{12}{13}$, $\tan u = \frac{5}{12}$, $\cot u = \frac{12}{5}$, $\sec u = \frac{13}{12}$ **9.** $x = -3$, $y = -4$, $r = 5$; $\sin u = -\frac{4}{5}$, $\cos u = -\frac{3}{5}$, $\cot u = \frac{3}{4}$, $\sec u = -\frac{5}{3}$, $\csc u = -\frac{5}{4}$

10. $x = 12$, $y = -5$, $r = 13$; $\sin u = -\frac{5}{13}$, $\cos u = \frac{12}{13}$, $\tan u = -\frac{5}{12}$, $\cot u = -\frac{12}{5}$, $\csc u = -\frac{13}{5}$

11. $x = -1$, $y = 1$, $r = \sqrt{2}$; $\sin u = \frac{\sqrt{2}}{2}$, $\cos u = -\frac{\sqrt{2}}{2}$, $\cot u = -1$, $\sec u = -\sqrt{2}$, $\csc u = \sqrt{2}$

12. $x = \sqrt{3}$, $y = -1$, $r = 2$; $\sin u = \frac{1}{2}$, $\cos u = \frac{\sqrt{3}}{2}$, $\tan u = -\frac{\sqrt{3}}{3}$, $\sec u = \frac{2\sqrt{3}}{3}$, $\csc u = -2$

13. $x = 12$, $y = 5$, $r = 13$; $\cos u = \frac{12}{13}$, $\tan u = \frac{5}{12}$, $\cot u = \frac{12}{5}$, $\sec u = \frac{13}{12}$, $\csc u = \frac{13}{5}$ **14.** $x = -3$, $y = 4$, $r = 5$; $\sin u = \frac{4}{5}$, $\tan u = -\frac{4}{3}$, $\cot u = -\frac{3}{4}$, $\sec u = -\frac{5}{3}$, $\csc u = \frac{5}{4}$ **15.** $x = 1$, $y = 1$, $r = \sqrt{2}$; $\sin u = \frac{\sqrt{2}}{2}$, $\cos u = \frac{\sqrt{2}}{2}$, $\tan u = 1$, $\sec u = \sqrt{2}$, $\csc u = \sqrt{2}$ **16.** $x = -4$, $y = 3$, $r = 5$; $\sin u = \frac{3}{5}$, $\cos u = -\frac{4}{5}$, $\cot u = -\frac{4}{3}$, $\sec u = -\frac{5}{4}$, $\csc u = \frac{5}{3}$

17. $x = \sqrt{3}$, $y = 1$, $r = 2$; $\sin u = \frac{1}{2}$, $\cos u = \frac{\sqrt{3}}{2}$, $\cot u = \sqrt{3}$, $\sec u = \frac{2\sqrt{3}}{3}$, $\csc u = 2$ **18.** $x = 1$, $y = -1$, $r = \sqrt{2}$; $\sin u = -\frac{\sqrt{2}}{2}$, $\tan u = -1$, $\cot u = -1$, $\sec u = \sqrt{2}$, $\csc u = -\sqrt{2}$

19. $x = -\sqrt{3}$, $y = 1$, $r = 2$; $\sin u = \frac{1}{2}$, $\cos u = -\frac{\sqrt{3}}{2}$, $\tan u = -\frac{\sqrt{3}}{3}$, $\cot u = -\sqrt{3}$, $\csc u = 2$ **20.** $x = 1$, $y = -1$, $r = \sqrt{2}$; $\sin u = -\frac{\sqrt{2}}{2}$, $\cos u = \frac{\sqrt{2}}{2}$, $\tan u = -1$, $\cot u = -1$. $\sec u = \sqrt{2}$

21. $\cos u = -\frac{1}{2}$, $\cot u = -\frac{\sqrt{3}}{3}$, $\sec u = -2$,

$\csc u = \frac{2\sqrt{3}}{3}$ **22.** $\sin u = -\frac{\sqrt{3}}{2}$, $\tan u = \sqrt{3}$, $\sec u = -2$, $\csc u = -\frac{2\sqrt{3}}{3}$ **23.** $\tan u = -1$, $\cot u = -1$, $\sec u = \sqrt{2}$, $\csc u = -\sqrt{2}$

24. $\sin u = \frac{\sqrt{2}}{2}$, $\cos u = -\frac{\sqrt{2}}{2}$, $\cot u = -1$, $\csc u = \sqrt{2}$ **25.** $\sin u = -\frac{12}{13}$, $\cos u = -\frac{5}{13}$, $\cot u = \frac{5}{12}$, $\csc u = -\frac{13}{12}$ **26.** 1st quadrant: $\cos u = \frac{5}{13}$, $\tan u = \frac{12}{5}$, $\cot u = \frac{5}{12}$, $\sec u = \frac{13}{5}$; 2nd quadrant: $\cos u = -\frac{5}{13}$, $\tan u = -\frac{12}{5}$, $\cot u = -\frac{5}{12}$, $\sec u = -\frac{13}{5}$

27. $\sin u = -\frac{5\sqrt{41}}{41}$, $\cot u = -\frac{4}{5}$, $\sec u = \frac{\sqrt{41}}{4}$, $\csc u = -\frac{\sqrt{41}}{5}$ **28.** $\sin u = \frac{1}{2}$, $\tan u = -\frac{\sqrt{3}}{3}$, $\sec u = -\frac{2\sqrt{3}}{3}$, $\csc u = 2$ **29.** 3rd quadrant: $\cos u = -\frac{24}{25}$, $\tan u = \frac{7}{24}$, $\cot u = \frac{24}{7}$, $\sec u = -\frac{25}{24}$; 4th quadrant: $\cos u = \frac{24}{25}$, $\tan u = -\frac{7}{24}$, $\cot u = -\frac{24}{7}$, $\sec u = \frac{25}{24}$

30. $\sin u = \frac{3}{5}$, $\cos u = -\frac{4}{5}$, $\cot u = -\frac{4}{3}$, $\csc u = \frac{5}{3}$

Page 480

48. 15° 30′, 344° 30′ **49.** 109° 50′, 289° 50′
50. 38° 10′, 218° 10′ **51.** 104° 50′, 284° 50′
52. 119° 10′, 240° 50′ **53.** 248° 10′, 291° 50′
54. 54° 20′, 125° 40′ **55.** 9° 30′, 170° 30′
56. 38° 40′, 321° 20′ **57.** $-\tan 60° = -\cot 30°$
58. $\cot 20°$ **59.** $-\sin 44°$ **60.** $-\cos 70° = -\sin 20°$
61. $-\sin 44°$ **62.** $-\sin 35° 40′$ **63.** $-\cos 54° 50′ = -\sin 35° 10′$ **64.** $\tan 32° 40′$ **65.** $-\cot 28° 10′$
66. $-\tan 45° 20′ = -\cot 44° 40′$ **67.** $-\cos 68° = -\sin 22° = -\dfrac{1}{\csc 22°}$ **68.** $\dfrac{1}{\csc 39° 50′}$ **69.** $\sin 3° 20′ = \dfrac{1}{\csc 3° 20′}$ **70.** $\tan 10° 40′ = \dfrac{1}{\cot 10° 40′}$
71. $-\tan 55° 40′ = -\cot 34° 20′ = -\dfrac{1}{\tan 34° 20′}$
72. $-\cot 56° 20′ = -\tan 33° 40′ = -\dfrac{1}{\cot 33° 40′}$
73. $\cos 19° 30′ = \dfrac{1}{\sec 19° 30′}$ **74.** $-\cot 50° 40′ = -\tan 39° 20′ = -\dfrac{1}{\cot 39° 20′}$ **75.** 1.2258 **76.** 2.0204
77. 1.2929 **78.** -1.0176 **79.** 1° 20′ **80.** 69°
81. 30° 20′ **82.** 62° 30′ **83.** 33° 20′, 326° 40′
84. 188° 20′, 351° 40′ **85.** 146° 20′, 213° 40′
86. 38° 20′, 141° 40′ **87.** 69°, 291°
88. 202° 50′, 337° 10′

T–142

Page 482

19. $\cos \theta = -\frac{\sqrt{3}}{2}$; $\theta = 150°, 210°, 510°, 570°$

20. $\tan \theta = -1$; $\theta = 135°, 315°, 495°, 675°$

21. $\cot \theta = \sqrt{3}$; $\theta = 30°, 210°, 390°, 570°$

22. $2 \sin \theta = -1$; $\sin \theta = -\frac{1}{2}$; $\theta = 210°, 330°, 570°, 690°$ **23.** $-3 \cos \theta - 5 = -6 \cos \theta$;

$3 \cos \theta = 5$; $\cos \theta = \frac{5}{3}$; no solution   **24.** $\sin \theta = 1$; $\theta = 90°, 450°$ **25.** $\tan \theta = \frac{3}{\sqrt{3}} = \sqrt{3}$;

$\theta = 60°, 240°, 420°, 600°$ **26.** $5 \sin \theta = 4$; $\sin \theta = \frac{4}{5} = 0.8000$; $\theta = 53° 10', 126° 50', 413° 10',$

$486° 50'$ **27.** $5 \cot \theta = -7$; $\cot \theta = -\frac{7}{5} = -1.4000$;

$\theta = 144° 30', 324° 30', 504° 30', 684° 30'$

28. $\sec \theta = -\frac{8}{3} = -2.6667$; $\theta = 112°, 248°, 472°,$

$608°$ **29.** $\csc \theta = 5$; $\theta = 11° 30', 168° 30',$

$371° 30', 528° 30'$ **30.** $5 \sec \theta = -12$; $\sec \theta = -\frac{12}{5}$

$= -2.4000$; $\theta = 114° 40', 245° 20', 474° 40', 605° 20'$

31. $\csc \theta = -1$; $\theta = 270°, 630°$ **32.** $\sec \theta = \frac{8.4}{2}$

$= 4.2000$; $\theta = 76° 10', 283° 50', 436° 10', 643° 50'$

33. $\sec \theta = \frac{1}{3} = 0.3333$; no values   **34.** $3 \sec \theta - 36 = 10 \sec \theta$; $7 \sec \theta = -36$; $\sec \theta = -\frac{36}{7}$

$= -5.1429$; $\theta = 101° 10', 258° 50', 461° 10',$

$618° 50'$ **35.** $\frac{1}{3} \csc \theta = \frac{8}{5}$; $\csc \theta = \frac{24}{5}$

$= 4.8000$; $\theta = 12°, 168°, 372°, 528°$ **36.** $4 \csc \theta - 24 = 9 \csc \theta + 12$; $5 \csc \theta = -36$; $\csc \theta = -\frac{36}{5}$

$= -7.2000$; $\theta = 188°, 352°, 548°, 712°$

Page 488 Oral Exercises

1. adjacent $\angle A$: b; opposite $\angle A$: a **2.** adjacent $\angle B$: a; opposite $\angle B$: b **3.** adjacent $\angle H$: i; opposite $\angle H$: h
4. adjacent $\angle I$: h; opposite $\angle I$: i **5.** adjacent $\angle D$: l; opposite $\angle D$: d **6.** adjacent $\angle E$: d; opposite $\angle E$: e

Page 488 Written Exercises

1. $\sin G = \frac{g}{i}$; $\cos G = \frac{h}{i}$; $\tan G = \frac{g}{h}$; $\cot G = \frac{h}{g}$

2. $\sin H = \frac{h}{i}$; $\cos H = \frac{g}{i}$; $\tan H = \frac{h}{g}$; $\cot H = \frac{g}{h}$

3. $\sin A = \frac{a}{c}$; $\cos A = \frac{b}{c}$; $\tan A = \frac{a}{b}$; $\cot A = \frac{b}{a}$

4. $\sin B = \frac{b}{c}$; $\cos B = \frac{a}{c}$; $\tan B = \frac{b}{a}$; $\cot B = \frac{a}{b}$

5. $\sin D = \frac{d}{f}$; $\cos D = \frac{e}{f}$; $\tan D = \frac{d}{e}$; $\cot D = \frac{e}{d}$

6. $\sin E = \frac{e}{f}$; $\cos E = \frac{d}{f}$; $\tan E = \frac{e}{d}$; $\cot E = \frac{d}{e}$

Page 490

1. sin   **2.** tan   **3.** tan   **4.** cot   **5.** sin   **6.** cos
7. cot   **8.** sin   [Also, reciprocal fcns]

Page 491

20. $\tan 13° 23' = \frac{9.6}{b}$; $b = \frac{9.6}{.2379} = 40.4$; $\sin 13° 23' = \frac{9.6}{c}$; $c = \frac{9.6}{.2314} = 41.5$; $B = 90° - 13° 23' = 76° 37'$

21. $\sin 49° 18' = \frac{b}{13.3}$; $b = 13.3(.7581) = 10.1$;

$\cos 49° 18' = \frac{a}{13.3}$; $a = 13.3(.6521) = 8.7$;

$A = 90° - 49° 18' = 40° 42'$ **22.** $\tan 63° 38' = \frac{a}{9.1}$; $a = 9.1(2.0174) = 18.4$; $\cos 63° 38' = \frac{9.1}{c}$;

$c = \frac{9.1}{.4441} = 20.5$; $B = 90° - 63° 38' = 26° 22'$

23. $\sin 74° 46' = \frac{12.3}{c}$; $c = \frac{12.3}{.9649} = 12.7$, $\tan 74° 46'$

$= \frac{12.3}{a}$; $a = \frac{12.3}{3.6723} = 3.3$, $A = 90° - 74° 46' = 15° 14'$ **24.** $\tan 11° 12' = \frac{a}{7.8}$; $a = 7.8(.1980) = 1.5$;

$\cos 11° 12' = \frac{7.8}{c}$; $c = \frac{7.8}{.9810} = 7.95$ or 8.0;

$B = 90° - 11° 12' = 78° 48'$ **25.** $\cos 16° 56' = \frac{a}{11.8}$; $a = 11.8(.9567) = 11.3$; $\sin 16° 56' = \frac{b}{11.8}$;

$b = 11.8(.2913) = 3.4$; $A = 90° - 16° 56' = 73° 4'$

26. $\sin 33° 11' = \frac{a}{16.5}$; $a = 16.5(.5473) = 9.0$;

$\cos 33° 11' = \frac{b}{16.5}$; $b = 16.5(.8369) = 13.8$;

$B = 90° - 33° 11' = 56° 49'$ **27.** $\cos 73° 33' = \frac{6.3}{c}$; $c = \frac{6.3}{.2832} = 22.2$; $\tan 73° 33' = \frac{b}{6.3}$;

$b = 6.3(3.3770) = 21.3$; $A = 90° - 73° 33' = 16° 27'$

28. $\sin 38° 37' = \frac{12.5}{c}$; $c = 20.0$; $b = 15.6$; $B = 51° 23'$

Page 492

1. I, 45°   **2.** III, 30°   **3.** III, 45°   **4.** II, 60°
5. I, 30°   **6.** 90°   **7.** I, 60°   **8.** IV, 60°   **9.** III, 80°
10. 90°   **11.** I, 40°   **12.** 0°   **17.** $\frac{1}{2}$ **18.** $-\frac{\sqrt{3}}{3}$
19. $-\frac{2\sqrt{3}}{3}$ **20.** $-\frac{\sqrt{3}}{2}$ **21.** 0   **22.** undefined
23. undefined   **24.** 0   **36.** $\sin u = \frac{5}{13}$,

$\cos u = \frac{12}{13}$, $\cot u = \frac{12}{5}$, $\sec u = \frac{13}{12}$,

$\csc u = \frac{13}{5}$ **37.** $\sin u = \frac{4}{5}$, $\tan u = -\frac{4}{3}$,

$\cot u = -\frac{3}{4}$, $\sec u = -\frac{5}{3}$, $\csc u = \frac{5}{4}$

38. $\cos u = -\frac{24}{25}$, $\tan u = -\frac{7}{24}$, $\cot u = -\frac{24}{7}$,

$\csc u = \frac{25}{7}$

Page 493

1. II, 70°   **2.** III, 50°   **3.** III, 70°   **4.** I, 20°
24. 4th quadrant: $\cos u = \frac{12}{13}$, $\tan u = -\frac{5}{12}$,

$\cot u = -\frac{12}{5}$, $\sec u = \frac{13}{12}$, $\csc u = -\frac{13}{5}$

T–143

25. 2nd quadrant; $\sin u = \frac{4}{5}$, $\tan m = -\frac{4}{3}$, $\cot u = -\frac{3}{4}$, $\sec u = -\frac{5}{3}$, $\csc u = \frac{5}{4}$

Page 494

4.
```
10 REM PROGRAM FINDS LENGTH
   OF WIRE GIVEN DISTANCE
   FROM MAST
15 REM TO POINT WHERE WIRE
   JOINS THE BOAT
20 PRINT "ENTER DISTANCE"
30 INPUT B
40 PRINT "ENTER MEASURE OF
   ANGLE A IN DEGREES"
50 INPUT A
60 REM MEASURE IN DEGREES
   CHANGED TO RADIANS
70 LET R = A * (3.14159/180)
80 LET L = B/COS(R)
90 PRINT "LENGTH OF WIRE IS"; L
100 END
```

Page 499

(For Ex. 21–28, the coordinates of four points of each curve are given.) **21.** (0°, 1), (90°, 0), (180°, 1), (270°, 0) **22.** (0°, 0), (90°, −1), (180°, 0), (270°, 1) **23.** (0°, 0), (90°, −1), (180°, 0), (270°, 1) **24.** (0°, 1), (90°, 0), (180°, −1), (270°, 0) **25.** (0°, 1), (90°, undefined), (180°, −1), (270°, undefined) **26.** (0, −1), (90°, undefined), (180°, 1), (270°, undefined) **27.** (0, undefined), (90°, 1), (180°, undefined), (270°, −1) **28.** (0, undefined), (90°, −1), (180°, undefined), (270°, 1)

Page 505

23. 180°, none **24.** 120°, none **25.** 720°, none **26.** 360°, none

Page 514

1. 9.9061 − 10 **2.** 9.3691 − 10 **3.** 9.6205 − 10 **4.** 9.8317 − 10 **5.** 9.9770 − 10 **6.** 9.5847 − 10 **7.** 10.5350 − 10 **8.** 10.6378 − 10 **9.** 9.7150 − 10 **10.** 9.8395 − 10 **11.** 9.9481 − 10 **12.** 8.7601 − 10 **13.** 28° 20′ **14.** 37° 10′ **15.** 36° 20′ **16.** 45° 30′ **17.** 33° 29′ **18.** 21° 36′ **19.** 40° 20′ **20.** 72° 32′ **21.** 21° 27′

Page 517

1. 45°, 135°, 225°, 315° **2.** 60°, 120° **3.** 30°, 330° **4.** 90°, 270° **5.** 90°, 270° **6.** 30°, 150°, 210°, 330° **7.** 240°, 300° **8.** 90°, 270°, 135°, 315° **9.** 90°, 270°, 60°, 300° **10.** 0°, 180°, 240°, 300° **11.** 0°, 180°, 30°, 210° **12.** 120°, 240°, 0°, 360° **13.** 90° **14.** 120°, 240°, 180° **15.** 45°, 225° **16.** 79°, 259°, 160°, 340° **17.** 187°, 353° **18.** 71°, 289° **19.** 33°, 327°, 104°, 256° **20.** 67°, 247°, 135°, 315° **21.** 47°, 227°, 147°, 327° **22.** 191°, 349° **23.** 8°, 188°, 82°, 262° **24.** 101°, 259° **25.** 60°, 120°, 240°, 300° **26.** 24°, 156°, 204°, 336° **27.** no solution **28.** 14°, 166°, 19°, 161° **29.** 114°, 246°, 71°, 289° **30.** 28°, 152° **31.** 80°, 280° **32.** 52°, 128°, 232°, 308° **33.** 98°, 262°

Page 520

21. $\dfrac{\sin x}{\cos x} = \dfrac{\sin x}{\pm\sqrt{1-\sin^2 x}}$ **22.** $\dfrac{\cos x}{\sin x} = \dfrac{\pm\sqrt{1-\sin^2 x}}{\sin x}$

23. $\dfrac{1}{\cos x} = \dfrac{1}{\pm\sqrt{1-\sin^2 x}}$ **24.** $\dfrac{1}{\sin x}$

25. $\dfrac{\cos x}{\sin x}$; $\dfrac{\cos x}{\pm\sqrt{1-\cos^2 x}}$ **26.** $\pm\sqrt{1-\cos^2 x}$

27. $\dfrac{1}{\sin x}$; $\dfrac{1}{\pm\sqrt{1-\cos^2 x}}$ **28.** $\dfrac{1}{\cos x}$

29. $\tan^2 x + 1 = \sec^2 x$; $\left(\dfrac{\sin x}{\cos x}\right)^2 + 1 = \sec^2 x$;

$\dfrac{\sin^2 x}{\cos^2 x} + 1 = \sec^2 x$; $\dfrac{\sin^2 x + \cos^2 x}{\cos^2 x} = \sec^2 x$; $\dfrac{1}{\cos^2 x} = \sec^2 x$; $\sec^2 x = \sec^2 x$ **30.** $1 + \cot^2 x = \csc^2 x$;

$1 + \left(\dfrac{\cos x}{\sin x}\right)^2 = \csc^2 x$; $\dfrac{\sin^2 x}{\sin^2 x} + \dfrac{\cos^2 x}{\sin^2 x} = \csc^2 x$;

$\dfrac{\sin^2 x + \cos^2 x}{\sin^2 x} = \csc^2 x$; $\dfrac{1}{\sin^2 x} = \csc^2 x$; $\csc^2 x = \csc^2 x$

31. $\tan^2 A + 1 = \sec^2 A$; $\left(\dfrac{\sin A}{\cos A}\right)^2 + 1 = \sec^2 A$; $\dfrac{\sin^2 A}{\cos^2 A}$

$+ 1, = \sec^2 A$; $\dfrac{\sin^2 A}{\cos^2 A} + \dfrac{\cos^2 A}{\cos^2 A} = \sec^2 A$; $\dfrac{\sin^2 A + \cos^2 A}{\cos^2 A}$

$= \sec^2 A$; $\dfrac{1}{\cos^2 A} = \sec^2 A$; $\sec^2 A = \sec^2 A$

32. $1 + \cot^2 A = \csc^2 A$; $1 + \dfrac{\cos^2 A}{\sin^2 A} = \csc^2 A$; $\dfrac{\sin^2 A}{\sin^2 A}$

$+ \dfrac{\cos^2 A}{\sin^2 A} = \csc^2 A$; $\dfrac{\sin^2 A + \cos^2 A}{\sin^2 A} = \csc^2 A$; $\dfrac{1}{\sin^2 A}$

$= \csc^2 A$; $\csc^2 A = \csc^2 A$

Page 522 Written Exercises

1. $\dfrac{\cot x}{\cos x} = \csc x$; $\dfrac{\cos x}{\sin x} \div \cos x = \csc x$; $\dfrac{\cos x}{\sin x \cos x}$

$= \csc x$; $\dfrac{1}{\sin x} = \csc x$; $\csc x = \csc x$

2. $\sin x \cdot \cot x = \cos x$; $\sin x \cdot \dfrac{\cos x}{\sin x} = \cos x$; $\cos x$

$= \cos x$ **3.** $\sec x = \csc x \cdot \tan x$; $\sec x = \dfrac{1}{\sin x} \cdot \dfrac{\sin x}{\cos x}$;

$\sec x = \dfrac{1}{\cos x}$; $\sec x = \sec x$ **4.** $\cot x + \tan x$

$= \csc x \cdot \sec x$; $\dfrac{\cos x}{\sin x} + \dfrac{\sin x}{\cos x} = \csc x \cdot \sec x$;

$\dfrac{\sin^2 x + \cos^2 x}{\sin x \cdot \cos x} = \csc x \cdot \sec x$; $\dfrac{1}{\sin x \cdot \cos x}$

$= \csc x \cdot \sec x$; $\dfrac{1}{\sin x} \cdot \dfrac{1}{\cos x} = \csc x \cdot \sec x$; $\csc x \cdot \sec x$

$= \csc x \cdot \sec x$ **5.** $\sec x = \cos x + \dfrac{\tan x}{\csc x}$;

$\sec x = \cos x + \dfrac{\sin x}{\cos x} \div \dfrac{1}{\sin x}$; $\sec x = \cos x + \dfrac{\sin^2 x}{\cos x}$;

$\sec x = \dfrac{\cos^2 x}{\cos x} + \dfrac{\sin^2 x}{\cos x}$; $\sec x = \dfrac{\cos^2 x + \sin^2 x}{\cos x}$;

$\sec x = \dfrac{1}{\cos x}$; $\sec x = \sec x$ **6.** $\sin^2 x - \cos^2 x$

$= 2\sin^2 x - 1$; $\sin^2 x - \cos^2 x = 2\sin^2 x - 1$;

$2\sin^2 x - (\sin^2 x + \cos^2 x)$; $2\sin^2 x - \sin^2 x - \cos^2 x$;

$\sin^2 x - \cos^2 x$ **7.** $\cot x - 1 = \cos x(\csc x - \sec x)$;

$\cot x - 1 = \cos x \left(\dfrac{1}{\sin x} - \dfrac{1}{\cos x}\right)$; $\cot x - 1 = \dfrac{\cos x}{\sin x}$

$-\dfrac{\cos x}{\cos x}$; $\cot x - 1 = \cot x - 1$ **8.** $\sec x = \dfrac{\cos x}{1 + \sin x}$

$+ \tan x$; $\sec x = \dfrac{\cos x}{1 + \sin x} + \dfrac{\sin x}{\cos x}$;

$\sec x = \dfrac{\cos^2 x + \sin x + \sin^2 x}{\cos x(1 + \sin x)}$; $\sec x = \dfrac{1 + \sin x}{\cos x(1 + \sin x)}$;

$\sec x = \dfrac{1}{\cos x}$; $\sec x = \sec x$ **9.** $\sin x + \dfrac{\cot x}{\sec x}$

$= \csc x$; $\sin x + \dfrac{\cos x}{\sin x} \div \dfrac{1}{\cos x} = \csc x$; $\sin x + \dfrac{\cos^2 x}{\sin x}$

$= \csc x$; $\dfrac{\sin^2 x + \cos^2 x}{\sin x} = \csc x$; $\dfrac{1}{\sin x} = \csc x$;

$\csc x = \csc x$ **10.** $\dfrac{\cot x + \cos x}{1 + \sin x} = \dfrac{\dfrac{\cos x}{\sin x} + \cos x}{1 + \sin x}$;

$\dfrac{\dfrac{\cos x + \sin x \cos x}{\sin x}}{1 + \sin x}$; $\dfrac{\cos x(1 + \sin x)}{\sin x} \cdot \dfrac{1}{1 + \sin x}$; $\dfrac{\cos x}{\sin x}$

11. $\tan x - \cot x = \dfrac{1 - 2\cos^2 x}{\sin x \cos x}$; $\dfrac{1}{\sin x \cos x} - \dfrac{2\cos^2 x}{\sin x \cos x}$;

$\dfrac{\sin^2 x + \cos^2 x}{\sin x \cos x} - \dfrac{2\cos^2 x}{\sin x \cos x}$; $\dfrac{\sin^2 x + \cos^2 x - 2\cos^2 x}{\sin x \cos x}$;

$\dfrac{\sin^2 x - \cos^2 x}{\sin x \cos x}$; $\dfrac{\sin^2 x}{\sin x \cos x} - \dfrac{\cos^2 x}{\sin x \cos x}$; $\dfrac{\sin x}{\cos x} - \dfrac{\cos x}{\sin x}$;

$\tan x - \cot x$ **12.** $\dfrac{1 - \cos^2 x}{\cos x} \cdot \csc x = \tan x$; $\dfrac{\sin^2 x}{\cos x}$

$\cdot \dfrac{1}{\sin x} = \tan x$; $\dfrac{\sin x}{\cos x} = \tan x$; $\tan x = \tan x$

13. $2 \csc x = \dfrac{\sin x}{1 + \cos x} + \dfrac{\sin x}{1 - \cos x}$;

$2 \csc x = \dfrac{\sin x - \sin x \cos x + \sin x + \sin x \cos x}{1 - \cos^2 x}$;

$2 \csc x = \dfrac{2 \sin x}{\sin^2 x}$; $2\left(\dfrac{1}{\sin x}\right)$;

$2 \csc x$ **14.** $\cos x + \sin x = \dfrac{\sec x + \csc x}{\cot x + \tan x}$;

$\cos x + \sin x = \left(\dfrac{1}{\cos x} + \dfrac{1}{\sin x}\right) \div \left(\dfrac{\cos x}{\sin x} + \dfrac{\sin x}{\cos x}\right)$;

$\cos x + \sin x = \left(\dfrac{\sin x + \cos x}{\cos x \sin x}\right) \div \left(\dfrac{\cos^2 x + \sin^2 x}{\sin x \cos x}\right)$;

$\cos x + \sin x = \dfrac{\sin x + \cos x}{\cos^2 x + \sin^2 x}$;

$\cos x + \sin x = \sin x + \cos x$ **15.** $\dfrac{1 - \tan^2 x}{1 + \tan^2 x}$

$= \dfrac{2 - \sec^2 x}{\sec^2 x}$; $\dfrac{2 - (1 + \tan^2 x)}{1 + \tan^2 x}$; $\dfrac{1 - \tan^2 x}{1 + \tan^2 x}$

16. $\tan(180 + \theta) + \dfrac{1}{\cot(270 - \theta)}$; $\tan \theta + \tan(270 - \theta)$;

$\tan \theta + \tan(90 - \theta)$; $\tan \theta + \cot \theta$; $\dfrac{\sin \theta}{\cos \theta} + \dfrac{\cos \theta}{\sin \theta}$;

$\dfrac{\sin^2 \theta + \cos^2 \theta}{\cos \theta \sin \theta}$; $\dfrac{1}{\cos \theta \sin \theta}$; $\dfrac{1}{\cos \theta} \cdot \dfrac{1}{\sin \theta}$; $\dfrac{\sec \theta}{\sin \theta}$;

$\dfrac{-\sec \theta}{-\sin \theta}$; $\dfrac{\sec(180 - \theta)}{\sin(180 + \theta)}$ **17.** $\dfrac{\cot^2 \theta - 1}{\cot^2 \theta + 1} = \dfrac{2 - \sec^2 \theta}{\sec^2 \theta}$;

$\dfrac{2 - (1 + \tan^2 \theta)}{1 + \tan^2 \theta}$; $\dfrac{1 - \tan^2 \theta}{1 + \tan^2 \theta}$; $\dfrac{\dfrac{1 - \tan^2 \theta}{\tan^2 \theta}}{\dfrac{1 + \tan^2 \theta}{\tan^2 \theta}}$; $\dfrac{\dfrac{1}{\tan^2 \theta} - 1}{\dfrac{1}{\tan^2 \theta} + 1}$;

$\dfrac{\cot^2 \theta - 1}{\cot^2 \theta + 1}$ **18.** $\sqrt{\dfrac{\sec \theta - \tan \theta}{\sec \theta + \tan \theta}} = \dfrac{1 - \sin \theta}{\cos \theta}$;

$\sqrt{\left(\dfrac{1}{\cos \theta} - \dfrac{\sin \theta}{\cos \theta}\right) \div \left(\dfrac{1}{\cos \theta} + \dfrac{\sin \theta}{\cos \theta}\right)} = \dfrac{1 - \sin \theta}{\cos \theta}$;

$\sqrt{\left(\dfrac{1 - \sin \theta}{\cos \theta}\right) \div \left(\dfrac{1 + \sin \theta}{\cos \theta}\right)} = \dfrac{1 - \sin \theta}{\cos \theta}$;

$\sqrt{\dfrac{1 - \sin \theta}{1 + \sin \theta} \cdot \dfrac{1 - \sin \theta}{1 - \sin \theta}} = \dfrac{1 - \sin \theta}{\cos \theta}$;

$\sqrt{\dfrac{(1 - \sin \theta)^2}{1 - \sin^2 \theta}} = \dfrac{1 - \sin \theta}{\cos \theta}$; $\sqrt{\dfrac{(1 - \sin \theta)^2}{\cos^2 \theta}}$

$= \dfrac{1 - \sin \theta}{\cos \theta}$; $\dfrac{1 - \sin \theta}{\cos \theta} = \dfrac{1 - \sin \theta}{\cos \theta}$

Page 528

15. $\sin x = -\dfrac{1}{2}$; $x = \dfrac{7\pi}{6}, \dfrac{11\pi}{6}$ **16.** $\cos x = \dfrac{\sqrt{3}}{2}$;

$x = \dfrac{\pi}{6}, \dfrac{11\pi}{6}$ **17.** $\dfrac{\pi}{4}, \dfrac{5\pi}{4}$ **18.** $\sin x = 0$; $x = 0$,

$\pi, 2\pi$ **19.** $\cos^2 x = \dfrac{1}{2}$; $\cos x = \pm\dfrac{1}{\sqrt{2}} = \pm\dfrac{\sqrt{2}}{2}$;

$x = \dfrac{\pi}{4}, \dfrac{7\pi}{4}, \dfrac{3\pi}{4}, \dfrac{5\pi}{4}$ **20.** $2 \sin x = -\sqrt{3}$;

$\sin x = \dfrac{-\sqrt{3}}{2}$; $x = \dfrac{4\pi}{3}, \dfrac{5\pi}{3}$ **21.** $\cos x(2 \cos x + 1)$

$= 0$; $\cos x = 0$; $\cos x = -\dfrac{1}{2}$; $x = \dfrac{\pi}{2}, \dfrac{3\pi}{2}, \dfrac{2\pi}{3}, \dfrac{4\pi}{3}$

22. $\sin x(\sqrt{2} \sin x - 1) = 0$; $\sin x = 0$; $\sin x = \dfrac{\sqrt{2}}{2}$;

$x = 0, \pi, 2\pi, \dfrac{\pi}{4}, \dfrac{3\pi}{4}$ **23.** $(2 \cos x + 1)(\cos x - 4)$

$= 0$; $\cos x = -\dfrac{1}{2}$; $\cos x = 4\,(\text{reject})$; $x = \dfrac{2\pi}{3}, \dfrac{4\pi}{3}$

24. $\sin^2 x = \dfrac{1}{4}$; $\sin x = \pm\dfrac{1}{2}$; $x = \dfrac{\pi}{6}, \dfrac{5\pi}{6}, \dfrac{7\pi}{6}, \dfrac{11\pi}{6}$

25. $(3 \sin x - 5)(2 \sin x + 1) = 0$; $\sin x = \dfrac{5}{3}$

(reject); $\sin x = -\dfrac{1}{2}$; $x = \dfrac{7\pi}{6}, \dfrac{11\pi}{6}$

26. $4 \cos^2 x = 1$; $\cos^2 x = \dfrac{1}{4}$; $\cos x = \pm\dfrac{1}{2}$;

$x = \dfrac{\pi}{3}, \dfrac{2\pi}{3}, \dfrac{4\pi}{3}, \dfrac{5\pi}{3}$

Page 532

For Exercises 24–35, points on the curve are given.

24. $(0, 0)$, $\left(\dfrac{\sqrt{2}}{2}, \dfrac{\pi}{2}\right)$, $(1, \pi)$, $(0, 2\pi)$

25. $(2, 0)$, $\left(1, \dfrac{\pi}{6}\right)$, $\left(0, \dfrac{\pi}{4}\right)$, $\left(-1, \dfrac{\pi}{3}\right)$

26. $\left(\dfrac{1}{2}, \pi\right)$, $\left(\dfrac{\sqrt{3}}{4}, \dfrac{2\pi}{3}\right)$, $\left(\dfrac{\sqrt{2}}{4}, \dfrac{\pi}{2}\right)$, $(0, 0)$

27. $\left(2\sqrt{3}, -\dfrac{\pi}{3}\right)$, $\left(2, -\dfrac{\pi}{4}\right)$, $(0, 0)$, $\left(-2, \dfrac{\pi}{4}\right)$

28. $(-2, 0)$, $\left(0, -\dfrac{\pi}{4}\right)$, $\left(1, -\dfrac{\pi}{3}\right)$, $\left(2, -\dfrac{\pi}{2}\right)$

29. $(0, 0)$, $\left(1, \dfrac{\pi}{4}\right)$, $\left(-\dfrac{\sqrt{3}}{3}, -\dfrac{\pi}{3}\right)$, $\left(-1, -\dfrac{\pi}{4}\right)$

30. $\left(-1, -\dfrac{\pi}{2}\right)$, $\left(-\dfrac{\sqrt{3}}{2}, -\dfrac{\pi}{3}\right)$, $(0, 0)$, $\left(1, \dfrac{\pi}{2}\right)$

31. $(1, 0)$, $\left(\dfrac{\sqrt{2}}{2}, 4\right)$, $\left(\dfrac{1}{2}, \dfrac{\pi}{3}\right)$, $\left(0, \dfrac{\pi}{2}\right)$

32. $(0, 0)$, $\left(-1, -\dfrac{\pi}{4}\right)$, $\left(1, \dfrac{\pi}{4}\right)$, $\left(\sqrt{3}, \dfrac{\pi}{3}\right)$

33. $(0, 0)$, $\left(1, \dfrac{\pi}{2}\right)$, $\left(-1, -\dfrac{\pi}{2}\right)$, $\left(\dfrac{\sqrt{3}}{3}, \dfrac{2\pi}{3}\right)$

34. $(1, 0)$, $\left(\sqrt{2}, \dfrac{\pi}{4}\right)$, $\left(2, \dfrac{\pi}{3}\right)$, $(-1, \pi)$

35. $\left(-1, -\dfrac{\pi}{2}\right)$, $\left(-\sqrt{2}, -\dfrac{\pi}{4}\right)$, $(0, 0)$, $\left(1, \dfrac{\pi}{2}\right)$

Page 534

25. $\sin^2 240° + \cos^2 240°$; $\left(\dfrac{-\sqrt{3}}{2}\right)^2 + \left(-\dfrac{1}{2}\right)^2$

$= \dfrac{3}{4} + \dfrac{1}{4} = 1$ **26.** $\left(\dfrac{\sqrt{3}}{3}\right)^2 = \left(\dfrac{2\sqrt{3}}{3}\right)^2 - 1$;

$\dfrac{3}{9} = \dfrac{12}{9} - \dfrac{9}{9}$; $\dfrac{1}{3} = \dfrac{1}{3}$ **30.** $\dfrac{\sin\theta}{3\sin^2\theta + (1 - \cos^2\theta)}$

$= \dfrac{1}{4}\csc\theta$; $\dfrac{\sin\theta}{3\sin^2\theta + \sin^2\theta} = \dfrac{1}{4}\csc\theta$; $\dfrac{\sin\theta}{4\sin^2\theta}$

$= \dfrac{1}{4}\csc\theta$; $\dfrac{1}{4\sin\theta} = \dfrac{1}{4}\csc\theta$; $\dfrac{1}{4}\csc\theta = \dfrac{1}{4}\csc\theta$

31. $\sin\theta \div \dfrac{\cos\theta}{\sin\theta} + \cos\theta = \sec\theta$; $\dfrac{\sin^2\theta}{\cos\theta} + \dfrac{\cos\theta}{1}$

$= \sec\theta$; $\dfrac{\sin^2\theta + \cos^2\theta}{\cos\theta} = \sec\theta$; $\dfrac{1}{\cos\theta} = \sec\theta$;

$\sec\theta = \sec\theta$

Page 535

16. $\cos^2 150° = 1 - \sin^2 150°$; $\left(-\dfrac{\sqrt{3}}{2}\right)^2$

$= 1 - \left(\dfrac{1}{2}\right)^2$; $\dfrac{3}{4} = 1 - \dfrac{1}{4}$; $\dfrac{3}{4} = \dfrac{3}{4}$

19. $\sec\theta = \left(\dfrac{\sin\theta}{\cos\theta} \div \dfrac{1}{\sin\theta}\right) + \cos\theta$; $\sec\theta =$

$\dfrac{\sin^2\theta}{\cos\theta} + \dfrac{\cos\theta}{1}$; $\sec\theta = \dfrac{\sin^2\theta + \cos^2\theta}{\cos\theta}$;

$\sec\theta = \dfrac{1}{\cos\theta}$; $\sec\theta = \sec\theta$

32. $(1, 0)$, $\left(\dfrac{\sqrt{2}}{2}, \dfrac{\pi}{4}\right)$, $\left(0, \dfrac{\pi}{2}\right)$, $(-1, \pi)$

33. $\left(-1, -\dfrac{\pi}{4}\right)$, $(0, 0)$, $\left(1, \dfrac{\pi}{4}\right)$, $\left(\text{undef.}, \dfrac{\pi}{2}\right)$

34. $\left(-1, -\dfrac{\pi}{2}\right)$, $\left(-\sqrt{2}, -\dfrac{\pi}{4}\right)$, $(\text{undef.}, 0)$, $\left(1, \dfrac{\pi}{2}\right)$

36. $(\sin\theta + \cos\theta) \div \left(\dfrac{1}{\cos\theta} + \dfrac{1}{\sin\theta}\right) = \dfrac{1}{\sec\theta\csc\theta}$;

$(\sin\theta + \cos\theta) \div \left(\dfrac{\sin\theta + \cos\theta}{\sin\theta\cos\theta}\right) = \dfrac{1}{\sec\theta\csc\theta}$;

$\dfrac{(\sin\theta + \cos\theta)(\sin\theta\cos\theta)}{(\sin\theta + \cos\theta)} = \dfrac{1}{\sec\theta\csc\theta}$;

$\sin\theta\cos\theta = \dfrac{1}{\sec\theta\csc\theta}$; $\dfrac{1}{\csc\theta\sec\theta} = \dfrac{1}{\sec\theta\csc\theta}$

37. $\dfrac{\sqrt{2} + y}{-6(-2)} = \dfrac{\sqrt{2} + 1}{12}$

Page 536

```
1. FOR ANGLE 0 A*SIN(B*X) = 0
   FOR ANGLE 45 A*SIN(B*X) = .7071062
   FOR ANGLE 90 A*SIN(B*X) = 1
   FOR ANGLE 135 A*SIN(B*X) = .7071088
   FOR ANGLE 180 A*SIN(B*X) =
```

```
   3.511003E-06
   FOR ANGLE 225 A*SIN(B*X) =
   -.7071038
   FOR ANGLE 270 A*SIN(B*X) = -1
   FOR ANGLE 315 A*SIN(B*X) =
   -.7071106
   FOR ANGLE 360 A*SIN(B*X) =
   -7.022007E-06

2. FOR ANGLE 0 A*SIN(B*X) = 0
   FOR ANGLE 45 A*SIN(B*X) = 1.414212
   FOR ANGLE 90 A*SIN(B*X) = 2
   FOR ANGLE 135 A*SIN(B*X) = 1.414217
   FOR ANGLE 180 A*SIN(B*X) =
   7.022007E-06
   FOR ANGLE 225 A*SIN(B*X) =
   -1.414207
   FOR ANGLE 270 A*SIN(B*X) = -2
   FOR ANGLE 315 A*SIN(B*X) = 1.414221
   FOR ANGLE 360 A*SIN(B*X) =
   -1.404401E-05

3. FOR ANGLE 0 A*SIN(B*X) = 0
   FOR ANGLE 45 A*SIN(B*X) = 1
   FOR ANGLE 90 A*SIN(B*X) =
   4.447271E-06
   FOR ANGLE 135 A*SIN(B*X) = -1
   FOR ANGLE 180 A*SIN(B*X) =
   -7.022007E-06
   FOR ANGLE 225 A*SIN(B*X) = 1
   FOR ANGLE 270 A*SIN(B*X) =
   9.549929E-06
   FOR ANGLE 315 A*SIN(B*X) = -1
   FOR ANGLE 360 A*SIN(B*X) =
   -1.399720E-05

4. FOR ANGLE 0 A*SIN(B*X) = 0
   FOR ANGLE 45 A*SIN(B*X) = .382683
   FOR ANGLE 90 A*SIN(B*X) = .707106
   FOR ANGLE 135 A*SIN(B*X) = .923879
   FOR ANGLE 180 A*SIN(B*X) = 1
   FOR ANGLE 225 A*SIN(B*X) = .9238804
   FOR ANGLE 270 A*SIN(B*X) = .7071088
   FOR ANGLE 315 A*SIN(B*X) = .3826859
   FOR ANGLE 360 A*SIN(B*X) =
   -3.511003E-06

5.  10 REM PROGRAM COMPUTES X
       AND Y VALUES
    20 REM FOR THE TEMPERATURE
       VARIATION CURVE
    30 REM VALUE FOR A
    40 LET A = 40
    50 REM VALUE FOR B
    60 LET B = (2 * 3.14159/365)
    70 FOR X = 0 TO 365 STEP 30
    80 LET R = (X * B) - (100 * B)
    90 LET Y = A*SIN (R) + 25
   100 PRINT "FOR ANGLE"; X;
       "A SIN(BX) = "; Y
   110 NEXT X
   120 END
```

Page 541

23. $b^2 = h^2 + y^2$, but $h^2 = c^2 - x^2$
$b^2 = c^2 - x^2 + y^2$
$b^2 = (y^2 - x^2) + c^2$
$b^2 = (y + x)(y - x) + c^2$
$b^2 = (a - x + x)(a - x - x) + c^2$
$b^2 = a(a - 2x) + c^2 \quad \begin{cases} a = x + y \\ y = a - x \end{cases}$
$b^2 = a^2 - 2ax + c^2$
$b^2 = a^2 - 2a(c \cos B) + c^2 \quad \begin{cases} \cos B = \frac{x}{c} \\ x = c \cos B \end{cases}$
$b^2 = a^2 + c^2 - 2ac \cos B$

24. $c^2 = h^2 + y^2$, but $h^2 = b^2 - x^2$
$c^2 = b^2 - x^2 + y^2$
$c^2 = (y^2 - x^2) + b^2$
$c^2 = (y + x)(y - x) + b^2$
$c^2 = (a - x + x)(a - x - x) + b^2 \quad \begin{cases} a = x + y \\ y = a - x \end{cases}$
$c^2 = a(a - 2x) + b^2$
$c^2 = a^2 - 2ax + b^2$
$c^2 = a^2 + b^2 - 2a(b \cos C) \quad \begin{cases} \cos C = \frac{x}{b} \\ x = b \cos C \end{cases}$
$c^2 = a^2 + b^2 - 2ab \cos C$

25. $c^2 = h^2 + x^2$ or $h^2 = c^2 - x^2$
$a^2 = (b + x)^2 + h^2$
$a^2 = (b + x)^2 + (c^2 - x^2)$
$a^2 = b^2 + 2bx + x^2 + c^2 - x^2$
$a^2 = b^2 + c^2 + 2bx \quad \begin{cases} \cos A = -\frac{x}{c} \\ x = -c \cos A \end{cases}$
$a^2 = b^2 + c^2 - 2bc \cos A$

26. $c^2 = h^2 + x^2$ or $h^2 = c^2 - x^2$
$b^2 = h^2 + (a + x)^2$
$b^2 = c^2 - x^2 + a^2 + 2ax + x^2$
$b^2 = a^2 + c^2 + 2ax \quad \begin{cases} \cos B = -\frac{x}{c} \\ x = -c \cos B \end{cases}$
$b^2 = a^2 + c^2 - 2ac \cos A$

Page 543

20. For any $\triangle ABC$, $b^2 = a^2 + c^2 - 2ac \cos B$;
$2ac \cos B + b^2 = a^2 + c^2$; $2ac \cos B = a^2 + c^2 - b^2$;
$\cos B = \dfrac{a^2 + c^2 - b^2}{2ac}$ **21.** For any $\triangle ABC$,
$c^2 = a^2 + b^2 - 2ab \cos C$; $2ab \cos C = 2ab \cos C$;
$c^2 + 2ab \cos C = a^2 + b^2$; $2ab \cos C = a^2 + b^2 - c^2$;
$\cos C = \dfrac{a^2 + b^2 - c^2}{2ab}$

Page 545

17. $\sin C = \dfrac{h}{a}$; $h = a \cdot \sin C$; but $k = \frac{1}{2} bh$;
$k = \frac{1}{2} b(a \cdot \sin C)$; $k = \frac{1}{2} ab \sin C$

18. Area of $\triangle ABD = \frac{1}{2} m \cdot n \cdot \sin A$; Area of
parallelogram $= 2 \cdot$ Area of $\triangle ABD =$
$2\left(\frac{1}{2} m \cdot n \cdot \sin A\right)$; Area of parallelogram $= m \cdot n \cdot \sin A$

Page 548

15. $\frac{1}{2} st \sin R = \frac{1}{2} tr \sin S = \frac{1}{2} sr \sin t$;
$\dfrac{st \sin R}{str} = \dfrac{tr \sin S}{str} = \dfrac{sr \sin t}{str}$; $\dfrac{\sin R}{r} = \dfrac{\sin S}{s} = \dfrac{\sin T}{t}$;

16. $\frac{1}{2} rq \sin S = \frac{1}{2} rs \sin Q = \frac{1}{2} qs \sin R$;

$\dfrac{rq \sin S}{rqs} = \dfrac{rs \sin Q}{rsq} = \dfrac{qs \sin R}{rsq}$; $\dfrac{\sin S}{s} = \dfrac{\sin Q}{q} = \dfrac{\sin R}{r}$;
$\dfrac{s}{\sin S} = \dfrac{q}{\sin Q} = \dfrac{r}{\sin R}$

Page 555

4. $\sin 195° = \sin (135° + 60°)$; $\sin (135° + 60°) =$
$\sin 135° \cos 60° + \cos 135° \sin 60° = \dfrac{\sqrt{2}}{2} \cdot \dfrac{1}{2} + \left(\dfrac{-\sqrt{2}}{2}\right) \cdot$
$\dfrac{\sqrt{3}}{2} = \dfrac{\sqrt{2}}{4} - \dfrac{\sqrt{6}}{4} = \dfrac{\sqrt{2} - \sqrt{6}}{4}$ **5.** $\sin 285° =$
$\sin (225° + 60°) = \sin 225° \cos 60° + \cos 225° \sin 60° =$
$\left(\dfrac{-\sqrt{2}}{2}\right)\left(\dfrac{1}{2}\right) + \left(\dfrac{-\sqrt{2}}{2}\right)\left(\dfrac{\sqrt{3}}{2}\right) = \dfrac{-\sqrt{2}}{4} - \dfrac{\sqrt{6}}{4} =$
$-\left(\dfrac{\sqrt{2} + \sqrt{6}}{4}\right)$ **6.** $\sin 165° = \sin (135° + 30°) =$
$\sin 135° \cos 30° + \cos 135° \sin 30° =$
$\dfrac{\sqrt{2}}{2} \cdot \dfrac{\sqrt{3}}{2} + \left(\dfrac{-\sqrt{2}}{2}\right) \cdot \dfrac{1}{2} = \dfrac{\sqrt{6}}{4} - \dfrac{\sqrt{2}}{4} = \dfrac{\sqrt{6} - \sqrt{2}}{4}$
7. $\sin 150° = \sin (90° + 60°) = \sin 90° \cos 60° +$
$\cos 90° \sin 60° = 1 \cdot \dfrac{1}{2} + 0 = \dfrac{1}{2}$ **8.** $\sin 255° =$
$\sin (225° + 30°) = \sin 225° \cos 30° + \cos 225° \sin 30° =$
$\left(\dfrac{-\sqrt{2}}{2}\right)\left(\dfrac{\sqrt{3}}{2}\right) + \left(\dfrac{-\sqrt{2}}{2}\right)\left(\dfrac{1}{2}\right) = \dfrac{-\sqrt{6}}{4} - \dfrac{\sqrt{2}}{4} =$
$-\left(\dfrac{\sqrt{6} + \sqrt{2}}{4}\right)$ **9.** $\sin 435° = \sin (405° + 30°) =$
$\sin 405° \cos 30° + \cos 405° \sin 30° = \dfrac{\sqrt{2}}{2} \cdot \dfrac{\sqrt{3}}{2} +$
$\dfrac{\sqrt{2}}{2} \cdot \dfrac{1}{2} = \dfrac{\sqrt{6}}{4} + \dfrac{\sqrt{2}}{4} = \dfrac{\sqrt{6} + \sqrt{2}}{4}$ **10.** $\sin 375° =$
$\sin (315° + 60°) = \sin 315° \cos 60° + \cos 315° \sin 60° =$
$-\left(\dfrac{\sqrt{2}}{2}\right)\left(\dfrac{1}{2}\right) + \dfrac{\sqrt{2}}{2} \cdot \dfrac{\sqrt{3}}{2} = \dfrac{-\sqrt{2}}{4} + \dfrac{\sqrt{6}}{4} = \dfrac{\sqrt{6} - \sqrt{2}}{4}$
35. $\sin (\pi + \theta) = -\sin \theta$; $\sin \pi \cos \theta + \cos \pi \sin \theta =$
$-\sin \theta$; $0 + (-1) \sin \theta = -\sin \theta$; $-\sin \theta = -\sin \theta$
36. $\sin (2\pi - \theta) = -\sin \theta$; $\sin 2\pi \cos \theta -$
$\cos 2\pi \sin \theta = -\sin \theta$; $0 - \sin \theta = -\sin \theta$
37. $\sin (\pi - \theta) = \sin \theta$; $\sin \pi \cos \theta - \cos \pi \sin \theta =$
$\sin \theta$; $0 - (-1) \sin \theta = \sin \theta$; $\sin \theta = \sin \theta$
38. $\sin \left(\dfrac{\pi}{2} - \theta\right) = \cos \theta$; $\sin \dfrac{\pi}{2} \cos \theta - \cos \dfrac{\pi}{2} \sin \theta =$
$\cos \theta$; $1 \cdot \cos \theta - 0 = \cos \theta$; $\cos \theta = \cos \theta$
39. $\sin \left(\dfrac{3\pi}{2} + \theta\right) = -\cos \theta$; $\sin \dfrac{3\pi}{2} \cos \theta +$
$\cos \dfrac{3\pi}{2} \sin \theta = -\cos \theta$; $(-1) \cos \theta + 0 = -\cos \theta$;
$-\cos \theta = -\cos \theta$ **40.** $\sin \left(\dfrac{\pi}{2} + \theta\right) = \cos \theta$;
$\sin \dfrac{\pi}{2} \cos \theta + \cos \dfrac{\pi}{2} \sin \theta = \cos \theta$; $1 \cdot \cos \theta + 0 =$
$\cos \theta$; $\cos \theta = \cos \theta$ **41.** $\sin (180° + \theta) = -\sin \theta$;
$\sin 180° \cos \theta + \cos 180° \sin \theta = -\sin \theta$;
$0 + (-1) \sin \theta = -\sin \theta$; $-\sin \theta = -\sin \theta$
42. $\sin (180° - \theta) = \sin \theta$; $\sin 180° \cos \theta -$
$\cos 180° \sin \theta = \sin \theta$; $0 - (-1) \sin \theta = \sin \theta$;
$\sin \theta = \sin \theta$ **43.** $\sin (90° + \theta) = \cos \theta$;
$\sin 90° \cos \theta + \cos 90° \sin \theta = \cos \theta$; $1 \cdot \cos \theta + 0 =$
$\cos \theta$; $\cos \theta = \cos \theta$ **44.** $\sin (90° - \theta) = \cos \theta$;
$\sin 90° \cos \theta - \cos 90° \sin \theta = \cos \theta$; $\cos \theta - 0 =$
$\cos \theta$; $\cos \theta = \cos \theta$ **45.** $\sin (360° - \theta) = -\sin \theta$;

T–147

$\sin 360° \cos \theta - \cos 360° \sin \theta = -\sin \theta$;
$0 - (1) \sin \theta = -\sin \theta$; $-\sin \theta = -\sin \theta$

46. $\sin (270° + \theta) = -\cos \theta$; $\sin 270° \cos \theta + \cos 270° \sin \theta = -\cos \theta$; $-1 \cdot \cos \theta + 0 = -\cos \theta$; $-\cos \theta = -\cos \theta$

Page 559

1. $\dfrac{\sqrt{2} - \sqrt{6}}{4}$ **2.** $\dfrac{\sqrt{2} + \sqrt{6}}{4}$ **3.** $\dfrac{-\sqrt{2}}{2}$

4. $\dfrac{-\sqrt{2} - \sqrt{6}}{4}$ **5.** $\dfrac{-\sqrt{2} + \sqrt{6}}{4}$ **6.** $\dfrac{-\sqrt{2} - \sqrt{6}}{4}$

7. $\dfrac{-\sqrt{3}}{2}$ **8.** $\dfrac{-\sqrt{2} - \sqrt{6}}{4}$ **9.** $\dfrac{-\sqrt{2} + \sqrt{6}}{4}$

10. $\dfrac{\sqrt{2} + \sqrt{6}}{4}$ **32.** $\cos (180° - \theta) = -\cos \theta$;

$\cos 180° \cos \theta + \sin 180° \sin \theta = -\cos \theta$; $-1 \cdot \cos \theta + 0 = -\cos \theta$; $-\cos \theta = -\cos \theta$ **33.** $\cos (360° - \theta) = \cos \theta$; $\cos 360° \cos \theta + \sin 360° \sin \theta = \cos \theta$; $1 \cdot \cos \theta + 0 = \cos \theta$; $\cos \theta = \cos \theta$ **34.** $\cos (180° + \theta) = -\cos \theta$; $\cos 180° \cos \theta - \sin 180° \sin \theta = -\cos \theta$; $-1 \cdot \cos \theta - 0 = -\cos \theta$; $-\cos \theta = -\cos \theta$ **35.** $\cos (\pi + \theta) = -\cos \theta$; $\cos \pi \cos \theta - \sin \pi \sin \theta = -\cos \theta$; $-1 \cdot \cos \theta - 0 = -\cos \theta$; $-\cos \theta = -\cos \theta$ **36.** $\cos (270° + \theta) = \sin \theta$; $\cos 270° \cos \theta - \sin 270° \sin \theta = \sin \theta$; $0 - (-1)(\sin \theta) = \sin \theta$; $\sin \theta = \sin \theta$ **37.** $\cos (2\pi + \theta) = \cos \theta$; $\cos 2\pi \cos \theta - \sin 2\pi \sin \theta = \cos \theta$; $1 \cdot \cos \theta - 0 = \cos \theta$; $\cos \theta = \cos \theta$ **38.** $\cos \left(\dfrac{\pi}{2} + \theta\right) = -\sin \theta$; $\cos \dfrac{\pi}{2} \cos \theta - \sin \dfrac{\pi}{2} \sin \theta = -\sin \theta$; $0 - 1 \cdot \sin \theta = -\sin \theta$; $-\sin \theta = -\sin \theta$ **39.** $\cos (\pi - \theta) = -\cos \theta$; $\cos \pi \cos \theta + \sin \pi \sin \theta = -\cos \theta$; $-1 \cdot \cos \theta + 0 = -\cos \theta$; $-\cos \theta = -\cos \theta$ **40.** $\cos \left(\dfrac{3\pi}{2} - \theta\right) = -\sin \theta$; $\cos \dfrac{3\pi}{2} \cos \theta + \sin \dfrac{3\pi}{2} \sin \theta = -\sin \theta$; $0 + (-1) \sin \theta = -\sin \theta$; $-\sin \theta = -\sin \theta$

Page 562

33. $\tan (180° + \theta) = \dfrac{\tan 180° + \tan \theta}{1 - \tan 180° \tan \theta} = \dfrac{0 + \tan \theta}{1 - 0}$

$= \tan \theta$ **34.** $\tan (180° - \theta) = \dfrac{\tan 180° - \tan \theta}{1 + \tan 180° \tan \theta} =$

$\dfrac{0 - \tan \theta}{1 + 0} = -\tan \theta$ **35.** $\tan (\pi + \theta) =$

$\dfrac{\tan \pi + \tan \theta}{1 - \tan \pi \tan \theta} = \dfrac{0 + \tan \theta}{1 - 0} = \tan \theta$ **36.** $\tan$

$(360° - \theta) = \dfrac{\tan 360° - \tan \theta}{1 + \tan 360° \tan \theta} = \dfrac{0 - \tan \theta}{1 + 0} = -\tan \theta$

37. $\tan (2\pi + \theta) = \dfrac{\tan 2\pi + \tan \theta}{1 - \tan 2\pi \tan \theta} = \dfrac{0 + \tan \theta}{1 - 0}$

$= \tan \theta$ **38.** $\tan (\pi - \theta) = \dfrac{\tan \pi - \tan \theta}{1 + \tan \pi \tan \theta} =$

$\dfrac{0 - \tan \theta}{1 + 0} = -\tan \theta$

Page 565

1. $\frac{1}{2}\sqrt{2 - \sqrt{3}}$ **2.** $\frac{1}{2}\sqrt{2 + \sqrt{3}}$ **3.** $\frac{1}{2}\sqrt{2 - \sqrt{2}}$

4. $\sqrt{3 - 2\sqrt{2}}$ **5.** $\frac{1}{2}\sqrt{2 + \sqrt{2}}$ **6.** $\sqrt{7 - 4\sqrt{3}}$

7. $\sqrt{3 + 2\sqrt{2}}$ **8.** $\frac{1}{2}\sqrt{2 - \sqrt{2}}$ **9.** $\frac{1}{2}\sqrt{2 + \sqrt{2}}$

10. $\frac{1}{2}\sqrt{2 + \sqrt{3}}$ **11.** $\pm\frac{1}{5}\sqrt{5}, \pm\frac{2}{5}\sqrt{5}$

12. $\pm\frac{1}{2}\sqrt{2}, \pm\frac{1}{2}\sqrt{2}$ **13.** $\pm\frac{3}{13}\sqrt{13}, \pm\frac{2}{13}\sqrt{13}$

14. $\pm\frac{1}{2}\sqrt{3}, \pm\frac{1}{2}$ **15.** $\pm\frac{1}{4}\sqrt{6}, \pm\frac{1}{4}\sqrt{10}$

16. $\pm\frac{4}{17}\sqrt{17}, \pm\frac{\sqrt{17}}{17}$ **17.** $\pm\frac{1}{4}\sqrt{14}, \pm\frac{1}{4}\sqrt{2}$

18. $\pm 1, 0$ **19.** $\frac{1}{10}\sqrt{10}, -\frac{3}{10}\sqrt{10}, -\frac{1}{3}$

20. $\frac{5}{26}\sqrt{26}, \frac{1}{26}\sqrt{26}, 5$ **21.** $\frac{1}{2}\sqrt{2 + \sqrt{3}},$

$\frac{1}{2}\sqrt{2 - \sqrt{3}}, -\sqrt{7 + 4\sqrt{3}}$ **22.** $\frac{1}{2}\sqrt{3}, \frac{1}{2}, \sqrt{3}$

23. $\frac{1}{3}\sqrt{3}, \frac{1}{3}\sqrt{6}, \frac{1}{2}\sqrt{2}$ **24.** $\frac{1}{4}\sqrt{2}, -\frac{1}{4}\sqrt{14},$

$-\frac{1}{7}\sqrt{7}$ **25.** $\frac{1}{12}\sqrt{102}, \frac{1}{12}\sqrt{42}, \frac{1}{7}\sqrt{119}$

26. $\frac{1}{14}\sqrt{154}, -\frac{1}{14}\sqrt{142}, -\frac{1}{3}\sqrt{33}$ **27.** $\frac{1}{2}\sqrt{2(1 - a)},$

$\frac{1}{2}\sqrt{2(1 + a)}, \ \frac{1}{1 + a}\sqrt{1 - a^2}$ **28.** $\frac{1}{2}\sqrt{2 + 2b}$

$\frac{1}{2}\sqrt{2 - 2b}, \dfrac{\sqrt{1 - b^2}}{1 - b}$ **33.** $\cot \dfrac{A}{2} = \left(\cos \dfrac{A}{2}\right) \div$

$\left(\sin \dfrac{A}{2}\right) = \left(\pm\sqrt{\dfrac{1 + \cos A}{2}}\right) \div \left(\pm\sqrt{\dfrac{1 - \cos A}{2}}\right)$

$= \pm\sqrt{\dfrac{1 + \cos A}{1 - \cos A}}$ **34.** $\sec \dfrac{A}{2} = \dfrac{1}{\cos \dfrac{A}{2}}$

$= 1 \div \pm\sqrt{\dfrac{1 + \cos A}{2}} = \pm\sqrt{\dfrac{2}{1 + \cos A}}$ **35.** $\csc \dfrac{A}{2}$

$= \dfrac{1}{\sin \dfrac{A}{2}} = 1 \div \pm\sqrt{\dfrac{1 - \cos A}{2}} = \pm\sqrt{\dfrac{2}{1 - \cos A}}$

Page 567

1. $\tan \theta = \dfrac{2 \sin \theta \cos \theta}{1 + 2 \cos^2 \theta - 1}$; $\tan \theta = \dfrac{2 \sin \theta \cos \theta}{2 \cos^2 \theta}$;

$\tan \theta = \dfrac{\sin \theta}{\cos \theta}$; $\tan \theta = \tan \theta$ **2.** $\sin^2 \theta = \dfrac{\sin \theta}{\cos \theta} \cdot$

$\dfrac{2 \sin \theta \cos \theta}{2}$; $\sin^2 \theta = \dfrac{2 \sin^2 \theta}{2}$; $\sin^2 \theta = \sin^2 \theta$

3. $\cot \theta = \dfrac{2 \sin \theta \cos \theta}{2 \sin^2 \theta}$; $\cot \theta = \dfrac{\cos \theta}{\sin \theta}$; $\cot \theta = \cot \theta$

4. $\cos^2 \dfrac{\theta}{2} = \left(\dfrac{1}{\cos \theta} + 1\right) \div \left(2 \cdot \dfrac{1}{\cos \theta}\right)$;

$\cos^2 \dfrac{\theta}{2} = \dfrac{1 + \cos \theta}{\cos \theta} \cdot \dfrac{\cos \theta}{2}$; $\cos^2 \dfrac{\theta}{2} = \dfrac{1 + \cos \theta}{2}$;

$\cos^2 \dfrac{\theta}{2} = \cos^2 \dfrac{\theta}{2}$ **5.** $\tan \dfrac{\theta}{2} = \pm\sqrt{\dfrac{1 - \cos \theta}{\sin \theta}}$;

$\pm\sqrt{\dfrac{1 - \cos \theta}{1 + \cos \theta} \cdot \dfrac{1 - \cos \theta}{1 - \cos \theta}} = \dfrac{1 - \cos \theta}{\sin \theta}$;

$\pm\sqrt{\dfrac{(1 - \cos \theta)^2}{1 - \cos^2 \theta}} = \dfrac{1 - \cos \theta}{\sin \theta}$; $\pm\sqrt{\dfrac{(1 - \cos \theta)^2}{\sin^2 \theta}} =$

$\dfrac{1 - \cos \theta}{\sin \theta}$; $\pm\dfrac{1 - \cos \theta}{\sin \theta} = \pm\dfrac{1 - \cos \theta}{\sin \theta}$ **6.** $\tan \dfrac{\theta}{2} =$

$\pm\dfrac{\sin \theta}{1 + \cos \theta}$; $\pm\sqrt{\dfrac{1 - \cos \theta}{1 + \cos \theta} \cdot \dfrac{1 + \cos \theta}{1 + \cos \theta}} =$

$\pm\dfrac{\sin \theta}{1 + \cos \theta}$; $\pm\sqrt{\dfrac{1 - \cos^2 \theta}{(1 + \cos \theta)^2}} = \pm\dfrac{\sin \theta}{1 + \cos \theta}$;

$\pm \sqrt{\dfrac{\sin^2 \theta}{(1 + \cos \theta)^2}} = \pm \dfrac{\sin \theta}{1 + \cos \theta}$; $\pm \dfrac{\sin \theta}{1 + \cos \theta} =$

$\pm \dfrac{\sin \theta}{1 + \cos \theta}$ **7.** $2 \csc 2\theta = \dfrac{\cos^2 \theta + \sin^2 \theta}{\sin \theta \cos \theta}$;

$2 \csc 2\theta = \dfrac{1}{\sin \theta \cos \theta}$; $2 \csc 2\theta = 1 \div \dfrac{\sin 2\theta}{2}$;

$2 \csc 2\theta = \dfrac{2}{\sin 2\theta}$; $2 \csc 2\theta = 2 \csc 2\theta$ **8.** $\sin^2 \theta -$

$2 \sin \theta \cos \theta + \cos^2 \theta = 1 - 2 \sin 2\theta$;

$\sin^2 \theta + \cos^2 \theta - 2 \sin \theta \cos \theta = 1 - 2 \sin 2\theta$;

$1 - 2 \sin \theta \cos \theta = 1 - 2 \sin 2\theta$; $1 - \sin 2\theta =$

$1 - \sin 2\theta$ **9.** $1 + \sin \theta = \sin^2 \dfrac{\theta}{2} + 2 \sin \dfrac{\theta}{2}$

$\cos \dfrac{\theta}{2} + \cos^2 \dfrac{\theta}{2}$; $1 + \sin \theta = 1 + 2 \sin \dfrac{\theta}{2} \cos \dfrac{\theta}{2}$;

$1 + \sin \theta = 1 + 2 \sqrt{\dfrac{1 - \cos \theta}{2}} \cdot \sqrt{\dfrac{1 + \cos \theta}{2}}$;

$1 + \sin \theta = 1 + \dfrac{2}{2} \sqrt{1 - \cos^2 \theta}$; $1 + \sin \theta =$

$1 + \sqrt{\sin^2 \theta}$; $1 + \sin \theta = 1 + \sin \theta$ **10.** $\cos \theta =$

$\left(\dfrac{1}{2} \sin^2 \theta - \sin^2 \dfrac{1}{2} \theta \right) \div \sin^2 \dfrac{1}{2} \theta$; $\cos \theta =$

$\left(\dfrac{1}{2} \sin^2 \theta - \left(\dfrac{1 - \cos \theta}{2} \right) \right) \div \dfrac{1 - \cos \theta}{2}$; $\cos \theta =$

$\dfrac{\sin^2 \theta - 1 + \cos \theta}{1 - \cos \theta}$; $\cos \theta = \dfrac{1 - \cos^2 \theta - 1 + \cos \theta}{1 - \cos \theta}$;

$\cos \theta = \dfrac{\cos \theta (1 - \cos \theta)}{1 - \cos \theta}$; $\cos \theta = \cos \theta$

11. $\left(1 - \dfrac{\sin^2 \theta}{\cos^2 \theta} \right) \div \left(1 + \dfrac{\sin^2 \theta}{\cos^2 \theta} \right) = \cos 2\theta$;

$\left(\dfrac{\cos^2 \theta - \sin^2 \theta}{\cos^2 \theta} \right) \div \left(\dfrac{\cos^2 \theta + \sin^2 \theta}{\cos^2 \theta} \right) = \cos 2\theta$;

$\cos^2 \theta - \sin^2 \theta = \cos 2\theta$; $\cos 2\theta = \cos 2\theta$

12. $\dfrac{-(\sin \theta + \cos \theta)^2 + (\sin \theta - \cos \theta)^2}{\sin^2 \theta - \cos^2 \theta} = 2 \tan 2\theta$;

$\dfrac{-\sin^2 \theta - 4 \sin \theta \cos \theta - \cos^2 \theta + \sin^2 \theta + \cos^2 \theta}{\sin^2 \theta - \cos^2 \theta} =$

$2 \left(\dfrac{2 \tan \theta}{1 - \tan^2 \theta} \right)$; $\dfrac{-4 \sin \theta \cos \theta}{\sin^2 \theta - \cos^2 \theta} = \left(4 \cdot \dfrac{\sin \theta}{\cos \theta} \right) \div$

$\left(1 - \dfrac{\sin^2 \theta}{\cos^2 \theta} \right)$; $\dfrac{4 \sin \theta \cos \theta}{\cos^2 \theta - \sin^2 \theta} = \left(4 \cdot \dfrac{\sin \theta}{\cos \theta} \right) \div$

$\left(\dfrac{\cos^2 \theta - \sin^2 \theta}{\cos^2 \theta} \right)$; $\dfrac{4 \sin \theta \cos \theta}{\cos^2 \theta - \sin^2 \theta} =$

$\dfrac{4 \sin \theta \cos \theta}{\cos^2 \theta - \sin^2 \theta}$ **13.** $\tan 2\theta = \dfrac{\sin 2 (2\theta)}{1 + \cos 2 (2\theta)}$;

$\tan 2\theta = \dfrac{2 \sin 2\theta \cos 2\theta}{1 + 2 \cos^2 2\theta - 1}$; $\tan 2\theta =$

$\dfrac{2 \sin (2\theta) \cos (2\theta)}{2 \cos^2 (2\theta)}$; $\tan 2\theta = \dfrac{\sin 2\theta}{\cos 2\theta}$; $\tan 2\theta = \tan 2\theta$

14. $\cos 3\theta = 4 \cos^2 \theta - 3 \cos \theta$; $\cos (\theta + 2\theta) =$

$4 \cos^2 \theta - 3 \cos \theta$; $\cos \theta \cos 2\theta - \sin \theta \sin 2\theta =$

$4 \cos^2 \theta - 3 \cos \theta$; $\cos \theta [2 \cos^2 \theta - 1] - \sin \theta$

$[2 \sin \theta \cos \theta] = 4 \cos^2 \theta - 3 \cos \theta$; $2 \cos^3 \theta -$

$\cos \theta - 2 \sin^2 \theta \cos \theta = 4 \cos^2 \theta - 3 \cos \theta$;

$2 \cos^2 \theta - \cos \theta - 2 [1 - \cos^2 \theta] \cos \theta = 4 \cos^2 \theta -$

$3 \cos \theta$; $2 \cos^2 \theta - \cos \theta - 2 \cos \theta + 2 \cos^2 \theta =$

$4 \cos^2 \theta - 3 \cos \theta$; $4 \cos^2 \theta - 3 \cos \theta = 4 \cos^2 \theta -$

$3 \cos \theta$ **15.** $\dfrac{2}{\sin 2\theta} = \sec \theta \csc \theta$; $\dfrac{2}{2 \sin \theta \cos \theta} =$

$\sec \theta \csc \theta$; $\dfrac{1}{\sin \theta \cos \theta} = \sec \theta \csc \theta$; $\dfrac{1}{\cos \theta} \cdot \dfrac{1}{\cos \theta} =$

$\sec \theta \csc \theta$; $\sec \theta \csc \theta = \sec \theta \csc \theta$ **16.** $\sec 2\theta =$

$\left(\dfrac{1}{\cos^2 \theta} \right) \div \left(\dfrac{2 \cos^2 \theta - 1}{\cos^2 \theta} \right)$; $\sec 2\theta = \dfrac{1}{\cos^2 \theta} \cdot$

$\dfrac{\cos^2 \theta}{2 \cos^2 \theta - 1}$; $\sec 2\theta = \dfrac{1}{2 \cos^2 \theta - 1}$; $\sec 2\theta = \sec 2\theta$

17. $\dfrac{1}{2 \cos^2 \theta} + \dfrac{\sin \theta}{\cos \theta} = \dfrac{1 + \sin 2\theta}{1 + \cos 2\theta}$; $\dfrac{1 + 2 \sin \theta \cos \theta}{2 \cos^2 \theta}$

$= \dfrac{1 + \sin 2\theta}{1 + \cos 2\theta}$; $\dfrac{1 + \sin 2\theta}{\cos 2\theta + 1} = \dfrac{1 + \sin 2\theta}{1 + \cos 2\theta}$; $\dfrac{1 + \sin 2\theta}{1 + \cos 2\theta} =$

$\dfrac{1 + \sin 2\theta}{1 + \cos 2\theta}$ **18.** $\dfrac{\cos 3\theta}{\sin 3\theta} = \dfrac{1 + \cos 6\theta}{\sin 6\theta}$; $\dfrac{\cos 3\theta}{\sin 3\theta} =$

$\dfrac{1 + \cos 2 (3\theta)}{\sin 2 (3\theta)}$; $\dfrac{\cos 3\theta}{\sin 3\theta} = \dfrac{1 + (2 \cos^2 3\theta - 1)}{2 \sin 3\theta \cos 3\theta}$; $\dfrac{\cos 3\theta}{\sin 3\theta} =$

$\dfrac{1 + 2 \cos^2 3\theta - 1}{2 \cos 3\theta \sin 3\theta}$; $\dfrac{\cos 3\theta}{\sin 3\theta} = \dfrac{2 \cos^2 3\theta}{2 \sin 3\theta \cos 3\theta}$; $\dfrac{\cos 3\theta}{\sin 3\theta} =$

$\dfrac{\cos 3\theta}{\sin 3\theta}$

Page 568

27. $\sin \dfrac{3\pi}{2} \cos \theta - \sin \theta \cos \dfrac{3\pi}{2} = -1 \cos \theta -$

$\sin \theta (0) = -\cos \theta$ **32.** $\cos^2 \theta = \left(\sin \theta + \dfrac{\sin \theta}{\cos \theta} \right) \div$

$\dfrac{2 \sin \theta}{\cos \theta}$; $\cos^2 \theta = \dfrac{\sin \theta \cos \theta + \sin \theta}{2 \cos \theta} \cdot \dfrac{\cos \theta}{\sin \theta}$; $\cos^2 \theta =$

$\dfrac{(\cos \theta + 1)}{2}$; $\cos^2 \theta = \dfrac{1 + \cos \theta}{2}$; $\cos^2 \theta = \cos^2 \theta$

34. $\tan (2\pi - \theta) = \dfrac{\tan 2\pi - \tan \theta}{1 + \tan 2\pi \tan \theta} = \dfrac{0 - \tan \theta}{1 - 0 (\tan \theta)} =$

$-\tan \theta$

Page 569

31. $\sin 2A = \dfrac{2 \cos A}{\sin A} \div \dfrac{1}{\sin^2 A}$; $\sin 2A = \dfrac{2 \cos A}{\sin A} \cdot$

$\dfrac{\sin^2 A}{1}$; $\sin 2A = 2 \cos A \sin A$; $\sin 2A = 2 \sin A \cos A$;

$\sin 2A = \sin 2A$ **32.** $2 \csc 2\theta = \tan \theta + \cot \theta$;

$2 \csc 2\theta = \dfrac{\sin \theta}{\cos \theta} + \dfrac{\cos \theta}{\sin \theta}$; $2 \csc 2\theta = \dfrac{\sin^2 \theta + \cos^2 \theta}{\cos \theta \sin \theta}$;

$2 \csc 2\theta = \dfrac{1}{\sin \theta \cos \theta}$; $2 \csc 2 = \dfrac{2}{2 \sin \theta \cos \theta}$;

$2 \csc 2\theta = \dfrac{2}{\sin 2\theta}$; $2 \csc 2\theta = 2 \csc 2\theta$

33. $\sin \dfrac{\pi}{2} \cos \theta + \cos \dfrac{\pi}{2} \sin \theta = 1 \cos \theta + 0 \sin \theta =$

$\cos \theta$ **34.** $\tan (\pi - \theta) = \dfrac{\tan \pi - \tan \theta}{1 + \tan \pi \tan \theta} =$

$\dfrac{0 - \tan \theta}{1 + 0 \cdot \tan \theta} = -\tan \theta$

Page 570

```
10 REM PROGRAM USES THE LAW OF
   SINES TO FIND
20 REM REMAINING MEASURES OF A
   TRIANGLE
30 PRINT "ENTER MEASURE OF ANGLE A"
40 INPUT A
50 PRINT "ENTER MEASURE OF ANGLE B"
```

```
 60 INPUT B
 70 PRINT "ENTER MEASURE OF SIDE A"
 80 INPUT A1
 90 REM FIND MEASURE OF ANGLE C
100 LET C = 180 - (A + B)
110 REM CHANGE ANGLES TO RADIANS
120 LET R1 = A * (3.14159/180)
130 LET R2 = B * (3.14159/180)
140 LET R3 = C * (3.14159/180)
150 REM SIN (A)/A = SIN (B)/B = SIN (C)/C
160 LET B1 = (A1 * SIN (R2))/SIN (R1)
170 LET C1 = (A1 * SIN (R3))/SIN (R1)
180 PRINT "THE REMAINING SIDES OF
    THE TRIANGLE"
190 PRINT "ARE: SIDE B = "; B1;
    "SIDE C = "; C1
200 PRINT "THE MEASURE OF ANGLE
    C IS "; C
210 END
```

Page 573

42. $(0, 0)$, $(45°, \sqrt{2})$, $(90°, 2)$, $(360°, 0)$ **43.** $(0°, 1)$,
$(45°, 0)$, $(90°, -1)$, $(135°, 0)$ **44.** $(0, 0)$, $\left(45°, \frac{1}{2}\right)$,
$(90°, 0)$, $(180°, 0)$ **45.** $(0°, 0)$, $\left(22\frac{1}{2}°, 1\right)$, $\left(67\frac{1}{2}°, -1\right)$,
$(90°, 0)$ **46.** 2 values **57.** $\tan x = \dfrac{2 \sin x \cos x}{1 + 2\cos^2 x - 1}$;
$\tan x = \dfrac{2 \sin x \cos x}{2 \cos^2 x}$; $\tan x = \dfrac{\sin x}{\cos x}$; $\tan x = \tan x$

58. $\pm\sin^2 \dfrac{x}{2} = \left(\pm\sqrt{\dfrac{1 - \cos x}{1 + \cos x}} \cdot \sin x\right) \div 2$;
$\pm\left(\dfrac{1 - \cos x}{2}\right) = \left(\pm\sqrt{\dfrac{(1 - \cos x)^2}{1 - \cos^2 x}} \cdot \sin x\right) \div 2$;
$\pm\left(\dfrac{1 - \cos x}{2}\right) = \pm\dfrac{(1 - \cos x)}{2 \sin^2 x} \cdot \sin x$; $\pm\left(\dfrac{1 - \cos x}{2}\right) = \pm\left(\dfrac{1 - \cos x}{2}\right)$

Page 586

```
 9. 10 INPUT X
    20 IF X<0 THEN 50
    30 PRINT "X IS POSITIVE OR ZERO"
    40 GO TO 60
    50 PRINT "X IS NEGATIVE"
    60 END

10. 10 READ X
    20 LET Y1=3*X+2
    30 LET Y2=2*X+3
    40 IF Y1<>Y2 THEN 60
    50 PRINT "FOR X="; X; "THE
       EQUATIONS ARE EQUAL"
    60 GO TO 10
    70 DATA -2, -1,0,1,2
    80 END

11. 10 READ X1,X2,X3
    20 IF X1>=X2 THEN 50
    30 IF X2>X3 THEN 80
    40 GO TO 70
```

```
    50 IF X1>=X3 THEN 100
    60 PRINT "GREATEST IS"; X1
    70 GO TO 120
    80 PRINT "GREATEST IS"; X2
    90 GO TO 120
   100 PRINT "GREATEST IS"; X3
   120 DATA 326,236,623
   130 END
```

Page 588

4.

FAHRENHEIT	CENTIGRADE
32	0
42	5.555556
52	11.11111
62	16.66667
72	22.22222
82	27.77778
92	33.33333
102	38.88889

```
 6. 10 LET S = 0
    20 FOR X = 1 TO 10
    30 LET S=S+X↑3
    40 NEXT X
    50 PRINT "SUM OF CUBES";S
    60 END

 7. 10 FOR M=16 TO 96 STEP 8
    20 PRINT M;"IS A MULTIPLE"
    30 NEXT M
    40 END
```

Page 591

```
 1. 10 PRINT "ENTER A&B"
    20 INPUT A,B
    30 LET S=(A+B)/(A↑2+B↑2)
    40 PRINT "S=";S
    50 END

 2. 10 PRINT "ENTER A&B"
    20 INPUT A,B
    30 LET S=SQR((A+B)/((A-B)/(A↑2-B↑2)))
    40 PRINT "S=";S
    50 END

 3. 10 PRINT "ENTER A&B"
    20 INPUT A,B
    30 LET S=SQR((A+B)↑3)
    40 PRINT "S=";S
    50 END

 4. 10 PRINT "ENTER A&B"
    20 INPUT A,B
    30 LET S=INT((A*B)/(A+B))
    40 PRINT "S=";S
    50 END

 5. 10 PRINT "ENTER LENGTH & WIDTH OF
       RECTANGLE"
    20 INPUT L,W
    30 LET A=L*W
    40 LET A=INT(A)
    50 PRINT A
    60 END
```